GW00656311

MusicMaster

MUSICMASTER
METAL CATALOGUE
2nd EDITION

Edited by

Neil Jeffries

Retail Entertainment Data

Retail Entertainment Data Publishing Ltd,
Paulton House, 8 Shepherdess Walk, London N1 7LB

2nd edition published by Retail Entertainment Data Publishing Ltd. 1994.

1st edition published 1990.

Editorial and advertising enquiries: 0171 490 0049. Fax: 0171 253 1308.

Book trade and record trade enquiries: Music Sales, Newmarket Road, Bury St Edmunds, Suffolk, IP33 3YB. Tel: 01284 702600. Fax: 01284 768301.

Private book orders: MusicMaster, Bournehall House, Bournehall Road, Bushey, Herts WD2 3YG. Tel: 0181 421 8123. Fax: 0181 421 8155.

Database Typeset by BPC Whitefriars, Tunbridge Wells.

Printed and bound in Great Britain by BPC Wheatons Ltd, Exeter, Devon.

Cover artwork and design by IIIIi, London.

Publisher: Brenda Daly. **Editor:** Matthew Garbutt.
Editorial Assistant: Gary Ford. **Editorial Team:** Jane Scarratt, Bruno MacDonald.
Sales Manager: Marie-Clare Murray. **Product Manager:** Chris Spalding.
Senior Sales Executive: Anna Sperni. **Sales Executive:** Adrian Pope.

ISBN 0 904520 86 2

© **Retail Entertainment Data Publishing Ltd. 1994**

MUSICMASTER
METAL CATALOGUE
2ND EDITION

CONTENTS

HOW TO USE THE METAL CATALOGUE

Welcome to MusicMaster's 2nd edition of the Metal Catalogue.

The **Main Section** contains the majority of the recording information. It is divided into 26 separate chapters from A through to Z. The 'black strip' headings are the key to finding the artist you want, and are listed alphabetically by name. Recordings under each 'black strip' heading are listed in alphabetical order. Where a recording has a sub-title, this appears in brackets after the recording title. Tracks are listed, where available, after the recording title. Format and catalogue numbers are shown in bold on the same line to make them easier to read and are sorted chronologically where appropriate. This is followed by the record label, release date and the distributor. Deleted recordings are marked with a solid black square.

The **Compilation Section** has been re-organised to make searching easier and quicker. Recordings are listed alphabetically by title (shown in upper case) and thereafter the format and layout are as for the Main Section of the catalogue.

There is a **Useful Address Section** at the back of the catalogue which contains information on record companies, dealers, magazines and relevant organisations.

RECORDING TITLE

BLACK STRIP HEADING

Black Sabbath

HEADLESS CROSS.
Tracks / Headless cross / Cloak and dagger / Headless cross (edit).
- ■ **7"** . . . . **EIRSCB 107**
- ■ **12"** . . . . **EIRST 107**
- ■ **12"** . . . . **EIRSPB 107**

I.R.S. (Illegal) / Apr '89

TRACK LISTING

HEADLESS CROSS.
Tracks / Gates of hell / Headless cross / Devil and daughter / When death calls / Kill in the spirit world / Call of the wild / Black moon / Nightwing.
- **CD** . . . . **EIRSACD 1002**

I.R.S. (Illegal) / May '94 / EMI
- ■ **LP** . . . . **EIRSA 1002**
- **MC** . . . . **EIRSAC 1002**

I.R.S. (Illegal) / Apr '89 / EMI

FORMAT

CATALOGUE NUMBER

HEAVEN AND HELL.
Tracks / Neon knights / Children of the sea / Lady evil / Heaven and hell / Wishing well / Die young / Walk away / Lonely is the word.
- ■ **CD** **830 171-2**

Vertigo / '87
- ■ **LP** . . . . **PRICE 10**

Vertigo / May '83
- ■ **MC** . . . . **PRIMC 10**

Vertigo / May '83
- ■ **LP** **9102 752**

Vertigo / Apr '80
- **CD** **550 0592**
- **MC** **550 0594**

Spectrum (1) / Jun '93 / PolyGram

DELETED

RECORD LABEL

RELEASE DATE

DISTRIBUTOR

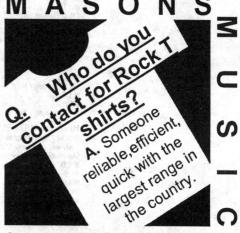

INTRODUCTION

Since the first edition of this catalogue was published back in 1990 the great musical beast known as Heavy Metal has seen changes no-one was predicting four years ago. A few sceptics were praying for them, the wiser bands were working on them, but if anyone had actually seen the light they weren't going out of their way to hold it up so we could all see the way ahead.

Forgive me now if I pick on just one band who might have been among the few with their hands on the torch . . .

As I sit here writing this, I am listening to Soundgarden's magnificent 'Superunknown' album for inspiration and general edification. Four years ago this would have been unthinkable (also technically impossible, since the album was not released until this year-but let's not quibble at this early stage). I say 'unthinkable' meaning 'of virtually no relevance' - Soundgarden were listed in that first volume (so were Nirvana) but was anyone really sure why? If searching for the right mood, I would probably have flicked past Soundgarden's then year-old second album, 'Louder Than Love', and doubtless let my finger run a little further back down the alphabet to pluck out something by The Scorpions (or perhaps even Saxon) . . . Oh yes!

These days, let's face it, people like me only pluck out albums by The Scorpions (or even Saxon) when we are alone and quite sure all the windows are closed. Oh sure, we still talk about both acts with great affection and will be sure to flick to their entries and measure our own collections of those two bands against the listings in this catalogue . . . but something has changed. It's not just that for these bands visits to the trichologist are more frequent than the hairdressers, and the old legs can't get them to the top of the drum-riser (never mind jump off) quite so quickly, or that spray-on stripy Spandex is so hard to find these days (God knows how we've tried). No, Metal music has turned a corner, and it's the younger acts that are leading the way . . .

Back in 1989, Soundgarden's singer Chris Cornell had the vision to declare in Kerrang!, the UK weekly Metal 'bible', "Obviously, we're not gonna come out with all the Metal clichés that have been put on the radio for the past eight years. If the suburban Metal guy likes it, and the college guy who buys Red Hot Chili Peppers or The Sugarcubes, so be it . . .".

What he was talking about was the burgeoning 'Alternative Metal' scene and the fact that it was possible to play no-nonsense, hard-hitting rock without recourse to re-writing the same old recipe or re-working the torn and frayed template that had seen Metal through the late '70s and early '80s (very nicely thank-you), but that the same effect could be achieved in a new and fresher way . . .

Cornell was also talking about opening doors, not just to new and uncharted areas (which the Metal fan in 1994 now accepts without pause for thought), but also to people such as 'the college guy' he referred to, or to any of the Slacker or Surf-bum generation who wouldn't have given old style Metal a second glance - let alone a listen. And the beauty of it is, at a time when old-style Metal was in real danger of running out of steam, most old-style Metal fans became aware of this, and were

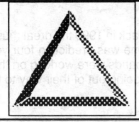

poised, ready to look beyond their normal territories. The result is that in 1994 Metal fans are just as likely to appreciate Soundgarden as The Scorpions (or even Saxon). The choice has never been broader, Metal never healthier.

This didn't make the choice of entries for this second edition any easier, but it has made the catalogue that much richer. The boundaries have come down and now there is so much more to list, as well as to listen to. Much of it was there all along, hidden behind walls of misconception and misapprehension, but a lot more has sprung up since. And whilst it is true to say that time can be a cruel yardstick, generally what is around today is no better or worse than what has gone before - only different. It is equally true to say that the future has rarely looked as bright . . .

Alongside all the old, more familiar Metal mutants - Thrash, Speed, Black, Glam, Death, Trad, White, Trash, Soft, Doom (take your pick, you've plenty of choice!) - variants like AOR, Prog Rock, Pomp and Blues Rock remain, but now it's common to find Metal fans also collecting Hardcore, Hip-Hop, Punk, Rap, Techno, Industrial and Garage. Moreover, the 'Alternative Metal' scene continues to grow at its own pace, much of it mixing any number of the above sub-genres in cocktails whose flavours we may only fully appreciate in another four years from now . . .

Four years in which today's Metal superstars like Metallica, Guns N' Roses, Bon Jovi, Def Leppard, not to mention hardy perennials like AC/DC and Aerosmith, as well as new generation heroes like Pearl Jam, Alice In Chains, Sepultura, The Red Hot Chili Peppers, Skid Row, Pantera, Soundgarden et al, may have gone nova, gone bust or (and let's all close our eyes reverently and cross our fingers fervently), gone the way of that elusive spray-on stripy Spandex . . .

Neil Jeffries, Kerrang!

THE EDITOR

Neil Jeffries survived a normal '60s childhood, cruel North Sea breezes and then left his home town of Lowestoft with only an abnormally large collection of Heavy Metal records and an unfashionably naff haircut to hint at his chosen means of avoiding debtors' prison.

In 1981, after completing a Geography degree in the Yorkshire mecca of Leeds (a venue he chose almost entirely out of his love for Leeds United), he was suitably qualified to find his way back down the M1 to London where he began working for Kerrang! magazine on a freelance basis.

After a brief sojourn as a proper journalist on a sensible magazine, the lure of Heavy Metal got the better of him and he returned to Kerrang! as Deputy Editor, in 1988. In 1992 he became Editor of the magazine's Special Projects division and also began contributing to RAW magazine.

As befits this new found maturity, he is now as likely to be caught headbanging to a Therapy? record as playing air guitar to Deep Purple's 'In Rock'. When not indulging in either of the above, or yet another curry at the New Arjun, Mr Jeffries is happiest at home in Wood Green, curled up with his girlfriend and their cat, admiring his abnormally large collection of Heavy Metal records and regretting the passing of that naff haircut.

THE OFFICIAL MUSIC MASTER CD CATALOGUE
14th EDITION

The 14th Edition of Music Master's best selling CD Catalogue is our most comprehensive listing of recordings released on CD in the UK. This fully revised and updated publication supplies track listings, catalogue numbers, label and distributor details as well as release and deletion dates. It is a must for all CD fans, and those who want to find favourite recordings or complete collections.

£14.95

DIRECTORY OF POPULAR MUSIC
Compiled and edited by Leslie Lowe

Who wrote that song? This catalogue identifies the composer, publisher and recording artist for over 9,000 of the most popular songs this century.

£14.95

PRICE GUIDE FOR RECORD COLLECTORS
2nd EDITION.
Compiled and edited by Nick Hamlyn

This catalogue prices 42,000 collectable LPs, EPs, singles and picture discs. It includes a 16 page colour section of photographs of classic covers and extensive notes from the editor Nick Hamlyn.

£12.95

OFFICIAL MUSIC MASTER COUNTRY MUSIC CATALOGUE
2nd EDITION.
Edited by Tony Byworth.

This catalogue lists more than 12,000 country music albums, singles and videos, and is the definitive reference work on country music recordings. The second edition also includes biographies for over 600 of the most popular and influential artists, and a colour section of album covers. The book is the ideal companion for anyone keen to hear more country music.

£14.95

OFFICIAL MUSIC MASTER JAZZ & BLUES CATALOGUE
2nd EDITION.
Edited by Graham Langley.

Fully revised and updated, the 2nd Edition of the Official Music Master Jazz & Blues Catalogue lists over 34,000 jazz and blues recordings, along with label information, catalogue numbers, track listings, and a colour section of classic album sleeves. The catalogue also includes more than 700 up-to-date biographies covering artists from the early pioneers through to contemporary jazz and blues stars such as Snowboy, Philip Bent and Zakiya Hooker.

£14.95

TO ORDER:

Please send payment (cheques made payable to R.E.D. Publishing Ltd) plus postage per catalogue as follows: UK: £1.75, Europe: £4.00, Outside Europe: £6.00. All books are sent registered delivery in the UK, and by Airspeeded service elsewhere.

Retail Entertainment Data

Paulton House, 8 Shepherdess Walk, London, N1 7LB.
Tel: +44-(0)71-490-0049 Fax: +44-(0)71-253-1308

A

A II Z

I'M THE ONE WHO LOVES YOU.
Tracks: I'm the one who love you / Ringside seat.
■ 7" . . . . POSP 314
Polydor / Oct '81.

NO SUN AFTER MIDNIGHT.
Tracks: No sun after midnight / Treason / Valhalla force (12" only).
■ 12" . . . . POSPX 243
■ 7" . . . . POSP 243
Polydor / Oct '81.

WITCH OF BERKELEY, THE.
Tracks: No fun after midnight / Lay down / Walking the distance / Glastonbury massacre / Danger UXB / Witch of Berkeley / Last stand / Romp / King is dead.
■ MC. .3170 587
Polydor / Oct '80.

A.C.

EVERYONE SHOULD BE KILLED.
Tracks: Some songs / Some more songs / Blur including new H.C. song / Even more songs / Tim / Judge / Spin cycle / Song / Pavarotti / Unbelievable / Music sucks / Newest H.C. song / Chiffon & chips / Guy Smiley / Seth / I'm not allowed to like A.C. anymore / EX.A Blur / G.M.O.T.R. / I'm wicked underground / Blur including G / Shut up Mike / Abomination of unnecessarily augmented.. / Radio hit / Loser / When I think of the true punk rock bands / Eddy Grant / MTV is my source for new music / Song titles are fucking stupid / Having to make up song titles sucks / Well you know, mean Gene / Song / Iron funeral / Chapel of gristle / Hellbent for leatherman / Alcoholic / Chump change / Slow song for split 7" / Des Bink's hairstyle / Newest H.C. song / Greatful dead / Aging disgracefully / Brutally morbid axe of Satan / Surfer / You must be wicked underground if you own this / Choke edge / Otis Sistrunk / Russty, knoife / Fred Bash / Guess which 10 of these are actual song titles / Our band is wicked sick (we have flu) / Guy le Fleur / Song / Empire sandwich shop / Morrisey / Selling out by having song titles / Grindcore is very terrifying / Song / Guy Lombardo.
CD .MOSH 101CD
LP . . . . MOSH 101
■ MC. . . . . .MOSH 101MC
Earache / Nov '93.

Aaron, Lee

BARELY HOLDING ON.
Tracks: Barely holding on / Dangerous zone.
■ 12" . . . . RR 125488
■ 7" . . . . .RR 5488
■ 12" P.Disc. . . . . RRP 65488
Road Runner / Jul '85.

CALL OF THE WILD.
Tracks: Rock me all over / Running from the fire / Champion / Barely holding on / Burning love / Beat 'em up / Paradise / Evil game / Danger zone / Hot to be rocked / Line of fire.
MC. RR 49780
Road Runner / Oct '85 / Pinnacle.
■ MC. . . . . CDIX 46
■ LP . . . . DIX 46
10 / Aug '86.
■ LP . . . . XID 24
10 / '89.

DANGER ZONE.
Tracks: Not Advised.
■ VHS . . . . HEN 2058
Hendring Video / Aug '87.

LEE AARON.
Tracks: Powerline / Hands are tied / Only human / Empty heart / Number one / Don't rain on my parade / Going off the deep end / If this is love / Eye for an eye / Heartbeat of the world / Dream with me.
CD . . . . DIXCD 49
■ LP . . . . DIX 49
■ MC. . . . . CDIX 49
10 / Apr '87.

LEE AARON PROJECT, THE.

Tracks: Not Advised.
■ LP . . . . RR 9842
Road Runner / Jul '84.

METAL QUEEN.
Tracks: Metal Queen / Lady of the darkest night / Head above water / Got to be the one / Shake it up / Deceiver / Steal away your love / Hold out / Breakdown / We will be rockin'.
■ LP . . . . RR 9861
Road Runner / Jul '84.
■ MC. . . . . CDIX 47
■ LP . . . . DIX 47
10 / Aug '86.
■ LP . . . . XID 25
10 / '89.

METAL QUEEN.
Tracks: Metal queen.
■ 12" . . . . RR 12 5507
Road Runner / Sep '84.

METAL QUEEN.
Tracks: Not Advised.
■ VHS . . . . HEN 2333
Hendring Video / Apr '91.

ONLY HUMAN.
Tracks: Only human / Empty heart / Call of the wild.
■ 12" . . . . TENT 155
■ 7" . . . . TEN 155
10 / '87.

ROCK ME ALL OVER.
Tracks: Rock me all over / Line of fire / Evil game.
■ 12" . . . . RR 12 5495
Road Runner / Jun '85.

Aaronsrod

ILLUSIONS KILL.
Tracks: Do me in / I wanna take you higher / She say..no way / Never cry wolf / Russian roulette. / Hard as stone / Deceiving eyes / Mirage / Roll the dice / Khoram's blade.
■ LP . . . . RR 9690
Road Runner / '87.

Abattoir

ONLY SAFE PLACE, THE.
Tracks: Not Advised.
■ LP . . . . .N 0045
Noise / '88.

VICIOUS ATTACK.
Tracks: Not Advised.
■ LP . . . . RR 9788
Road Runner / Jul '85.

ABC Diablo

LAST INTOXICATION OF THE SENSES.
Tracks: Not Advised.
CD .CC 001CD
LP .CC 001LP
Common Cause / Jun '93 / Plastic Head.

Abomination

ABOMINATION.
Tracks: Not Advised.
LP . . . . NB 028
Nuclear Blast / '92 / Plastic Head.

TRAGEDY STRIKES.
Tracks: Not Advised.
LP . . . . NB 050
■ CD . . . . .NB 050CD
Nuclear Blast / Jul '91.

Abruptum

IN UMBRA MALFTJAE.
Tracks: Not Advised.
CD . . . . ANTI-MOSH 009CD
Voices Of Wonder / Apr '94 / Plastic Head.

AC/DC

Formed in Australia by Angus and Malcolm Young, AC/DC enjoyed moderate success with first two albums, before *Dirty Deeds Done Dirt Cheap* album attracted attention in UK and US. By 1979, band were poised to lead resurgence of heavy metal, but were forced to replace singer Bon Scott, who died in April 1980. Band recruited Brian Johnson (ex-Geordie) for platinum-selling *Back In Black*, which rejuvenated sales of previous albums, notably Scott's swansong *Highway To Hell*. Band have endured many of the misfortunes that dog superstar metal acts: unstable line-ups, critical disdain and accusations of Satanism and sexism. They remain one of most popular acts in genre, with hit singles and albums, sold-out tours and two headlining appearances at Castle Donington to their credit.

74 JAILBREAK.
Tracks: Not Advised.
CD 756792449-2
Atlantic / Sep '94 / WEA.

AC/DC: INTERVIEW PICTURE DISC.
Tracks: Not Advised.
LP P.Disc . . . . BAK 2030
Baktabak / Apr '87 / Arabesque Ltd.
■ LP P.Disc . . . . CT 1016
Music & Media / Feb '88.

ARE YOU READY.
Tracks: Are you ready.
■ 12" . . . . B 8830 T
■ 7" .B 8830
Atco / Apr '91.

BACK IN BLACK.
Tracks: Back in black / Hell's bells / Shoot to thrill / Give the dog a bone / What do you do for money honey / Rock 'n' roll ain't noise pollution / Let me put my love into you / You shook me all night long / Shake a leg / Have a drink on me.
■ MC. K4 50735
Atlantic / '87.
■ CD . . . . K 250735
Atlantic / Feb '87.
■ LP . . . . K 50735
Atlantic / '88.
CD 756792418-2
MC. 756792418-4
Atlantic / Aug '94 / WEA.

BIG GUN.
Tracks: Big gun / Back in black / For those about to rock (we salute you).
■ 12" . . . . B 8396T
■ 7" .B 8396
■ CD Single . . . . B 8396CD
■ MC Single. . . . . B 8396C
East West / Jun '93.

BLOW UP YOUR VIDEO.
Tracks: Heatseeker / That's the way I wanna rock 'n' roll / Meanstreak / Go zone / Kissin' dynamite / Nick of time / Some sin for nuthin' / Ruff stuff / Two's up / This means war.
CD 781 828-2
■ LP . . . . WX 144
MC. . . . . WX 144C
Atlantic / Feb '88 / WEA.

BOX SET, 1.
Tracks: Not Advised.
■ LP Set. . . . . .AC/DC 1
EMI (Australia) / Sep '87.

BOX SET: AC/DC 2.
Tracks: Not Advised.
■ LP Set. . . . . .AC/DC 2
EMI (Australia) / Nov '87.

CLIPPED.
Tracks: Not Advised.
VHS 8536502343
Warner Music Video / Oct '92 / WEA.

DANGER.
Tracks: Danger / Back in business.
■ 12" . . . . A 9532 T

■ 7" . . . . .A 9532
Atlantic / Jul '85.

DIRTY DEEDS DONE DIRT CHEAP.
Tracks: Dirty deeds done dirt cheap / Love at first feel / Big balls / Rocker / Problem child / There's gonna be some rockin' / Ain't no fun waiting round to be a millionaire / Ride on / Squealer.
■ LP . . . . K 50323
■ MC. K4 50323
Atlantic / '87.
■ CD K2 50323
Atlantic / Aug '87.
CD. 756792414-2
MC. 756792414-4
Atlantic / Jul '94 / WEA.

DIRTY DEEDS DONE DIRT CHEAP.
Tracks: Dirty deeds done dirt cheap / Jack.
■ 7" . . . . K 10899
Atlantic / Feb '77.
■ 7" . . . . HM 2
Atlantic / Jun '80.

DIRTY DEEDS DONE DIRT CHEAP (LIVE).
Tracks: Dirty deeds done dirt cheap (live) / Shoot to thrill.
■ 12" . . . . B 6073T
■ CD Single . . . . B 6073CD
Atco / Feb '93.

FLICK OF THE SWITCH.
Tracks: Rising power / Badlands / Brain shake / Flick of the switch / Deep in the hole / Landslide / Guns for hire / Bedlam in Belgium.
■ MC. . . . . .K 7801004
East West / Aug '83.
■ LP 780 100-1
■ MC. 780 100-4
Atlantic / Jul '87.
■ CD 780 100-2
Atlantic / '89.
CD. 756792448-2
MC. 756792448-4
Atlantic / Sep '94 / WEA.

FLY ON THE WALL.
Tracks: Fly on the wall / Shake your foundations / First blood / Danger / Sink in pink / Playing with the girls / Stand up / Hell or high water / Back in business / Send for the man.
CD. 781 263-2
■ LP 781 263-1
MC. 781 263-4
Atlantic / Jul '85 / WEA.

FLY ON THE WALL.
Tracks: Not Advised.
VHS 750 102-3
Atlantic / Jun '86 / WEA.

FOR THOSE ABOUT TO ROCK (WE SALUTE YOU).
Tracks: For those about to rock (we salute you) / Put the finger on you / Let's get it up / Inject the venom / Snowballed / Evil walk / C.O.D. / Breaking the rules / Night of the long knives / Spellbound.
■ MC. . . . . K 450851
East West / Nov '81.
■ CD 250 851
Atlantic / Feb '87.
■ LP . . . . K 50851
■ MC. K4 50851
Atlantic / Jul '87.
CD. 756792412-2
MC. 756792412-4
Atlantic / Jul '94 / WEA.

FOR THOSE ABOUT TO ROCK (WE SALUTE YOU).
Tracks: For those about to rock (we salute you) / Let there be rock.
■ 7" . . . . K 11721
Atlantic / Jul '82.

GIRLS GOT RHYTHM.
Tracks: Girls got rhythm / Get it hot.
■ 7" . . . . K 11406
Atlantic / Nov '79.

GUNS FOR HIRE.
Tracks: Guns for hire / Landslide.
■ 7" . . . . .A 9774
Atlantic / Oct '83.

HEAT SEEKER.
Tracks: Heat seeker / Go zone / Snake high.
■ 12" . . . . A 9136 T
■ 7" . . . . .A 9136
Atlantic / Dec '87.

HIGH VOLTAGE.
Tracks: It's a long way to the top / Rock and roll singer / Jack / T.N.T / Can I sit next to you girl / Little lover / She's got balls / High voltage / Live wire.
■ MC. . . . . K 450257
East West / Feb '80.
■ CD 2502572
WEA / Oct '87.
■ LP . . . . K 50257
Atlantic / Oct '87.
■ MC. K4 50257
WEA / Oct '87.
CD. 756792413-2
MC. 756792413-4
Atlantic / Jul '94 / WEA.

HIGH VOLTAGE.
Tracks: High voltage.
■ 7" . . . . HM 1
Atlantic / Jun '80.

HIGH VOLTAGE.
Tracks: Not Advised.
VHS . . . . .VVC 452
Virgin Vision / '88 / Gold & Sons / TBD.

HIGHWAY TO HELL.
Tracks: Highway to Hell / Girls got rhythm / Touch too much / Beating around the bush / Shot down in flames / Get it hot / If you want blood (you've got it) / Love hungry / Night prowler.
■ MC. K4 50628
Atlantic / Aug '79.
■ CD . . . . K 250628
East West / Feb '87.
■ CD 250 628 2
Atlantic / Jul '87.
■ LP . . . . K 50628
Atlantic / '88.
CD. 756792419-2
MC. 756792419-4
Atlantic / Aug '94 / WEA.

HIGHWAY TO HELL.
Tracks: Highway to Hell / If you want blood you've got it.
■ 7" . . . . K 11321
Atlantic / Jul '87.
■ 12" . . . . B 8479T
■ 7" .B 8479
■ CD Single . . . . B 8479CDX
■ CD Single . . . . B 8479CD
Atco / Oct '92.

IF YOU WANT BLOOD YOU'VE GOT IT.
Tracks: Riff raff / Hell ain't a bad place to be / Bad boy boogie / Jack / Problem child / Whole lotta Rosie / Rock 'n' roll damnation / High voltage / Let there be rock / Rocker.
■ LP . . . . K 50532
■ MC. K4 50532
Atlantic / '78.
■ MC. . . . . K 450532
Elektra / Oct '78.
■ CD . . . . K 781 553 2
Atlantic / Jun '89.
CD. 756792447-2
MC. 756792447-4
Atlantic / Sep '94 / WEA.

IT'S A LONG WAY TO THE TOP.
Tracks: It's a long way to the top.
■ 7" . . . . HM 3
Atlantic / '87.

LET THERE BE ROCK.
Tracks: Go down / Dog eat dog / Let there be rock / Bad boy boogie / Overdose / Crapsody in blue / Hell ain't a bad place to be / Whole lotta Rosie.
■ MC. . . . . K 450366
MC / Oct '77.
■ LP . . . . K 50366
■ MC. K4 50366
Atlantic / Sep '77.
■ CD . . . . K 250366
Atlantic / Jun '89.
CD. 756792445-2
MC. 756792445-4
Atlantic / Sep '94 / WEA.

LET THERE BE ROCK.
Tracks: Let there be rock / Problem child.
■ 7" . . . . K 11018
WEA / '78.

LET THERE BE ROCK.
Tracks: Not Advised.
■ VHS . . . . PEV 34073
Warner Home Video / Jan '86.
VHS . . . . PES 34073
Warner Home Video / Aug '94 / WEA / Hollywood Nites / Gold & Sons / TBD.

LET'S GET IT UP.
Tracks: Let's get it up / Back in black.
■ 7" . . . . K 11706
Atlantic / Feb '82.

LIVE.
Tracks: Thunderstruck / Shoot to thrill / Back in black / Sin city / Who made who / Heatseeker / Fire your guns / Jailbreak / Jack / Razor's edge / Dirty deeds done cheap / Money talks / Hell's bells / Are you ready / That's the way I wanna rock 'n' roll / High voltage / You shook me all night long / Whole lotta Rosie / Let there be rock / Bonny / Highway to hell / T.N.T. / For those about to rock (we salute you).
CD. 7567922152
■ LP . . . . WX 493
MC. . . . . WX 493C
Atco / Nov '92 / WEA.

LIVE AT DONNINGTON.
Tracks: Not Advised.
VHS 8536503466
WEA / Nov '92 / WEA.

MONEY TALKS.
Tracks: Money talks / Mistress for Christmas / Borrowed time (Not on 7".).
■ CD Single . . . . B 8886CD
■ MC Single. . . . . B 8886C
■ 12" . . . . B 8886T
■ 7" .B 8886
East West / Nov '90.

MUSIC AND MEDIA INTERVIEW PICTURE DISC.
Tracks: Not Advised.
■ LP P.Disc . . . . AC 1001
■ LP P.Disc . . . . MM 1210
Music & Media / Feb '88.

NERVOUS SHAKEDOWN.
Tracks: Nervous shakedown / Rock 'n' roll ain't noise pollution.
■ 12" . . . . A 9651 T
■ 7" .A 9651
Atlantic / Jul '84.

POWER AGE.
Tracks: Gimme a bullet / Down payment blues / Gone shootin' / Riff raff / Sin City / Up to my neck in you / What's next to the Moon / Cold hearted man / Kicked in the teeth.
■ LP . . . . K 50483
■ MC. K4 50483
Atlantic / May '78.
■ CD . . . . K 781 548 2
Atlantic / Jun '89.
CD. 756792446-2
MC. 756792446-4
Atlantic / Sep '94 / WEA.

RAZOR'S EDGE, THE.
Tracks: Thunderstruck / Fire your guns / Money talks / Razor's edge / Mistress for Christmas / Rock your heart out / Are you ready / Got you by the balls / Shot of love / Let's make it / Goodbye and good riddance to bad luck / If you dare.
CD 756 791 413 2
■ LP . . . . WX 364
MC. . . . . WX 364C
Atco / Sep '90 / WEA.
DCC 7567 914135
WEA / Jan '93 / WEA.

ROCK 'N' ROLL AIN'T NOISE POLLUTION.
Tracks: Rock 'n' roll ain't noise pollution / Hell's bells.
■ 7" . . . . K 11630
Atlantic / Nov '80.

ROCK 'N' ROLL DAMNATION.
Tracks: Rock 'n' roll damnation / Sin City.
■ 7" . . . . K 11142
Atlantic / Jun '78.

SHAKE YOUR FOUNDATIONS.
Tracks: Shake your foundations / Stand up / Jailbreak (On 12" only.).
■ CD Single . . . . A 9474 T
Atlantic.
■ 7" .A 9474
■ 12" . . . . A 9474 T
Atlantic / Jan '86.
■ 12" 786837 0
Atlantic (Import) / May '88.

THAT'S THE WAY I WANNA ROCK 'N' ROLL EP.
Tracks: That's the way I wanna rock'n'roll / Kissin' dynamite / Shoot to thrill (live) / Whole lotta Rosie (live).
■ 12" . . . . A 9098 T

■ DELETED

■ CD Single. . . . . A 9098 CD
■ EP .A 9098
Atlantic / Mar '88.

THAT'S THE WAY I WANNA ROCK 'N' ROLL EP (IMPORT).
Tracks: That's the way I wanna rock'n'roll / Whole lotta Rosie.
■ CD Single. 786 586-2
Atlantic (Import) / Aug '88.

THUNDERSTRUCK.
Tracks: Thunderstruck / Fire your guns / Chase the ace (Not on 7" single.).
■ MC Single. . . . . B 8907 C
■ 12". . . . . B 8907 T
■ 7" . . . . .B 8907
■ CD Single . . . . B 8907 CD
Atco / Sep '90.

TOUCH TOO MUCH.
Tracks: Touch too much / Live wire / Shot down in flames.
■ 7" . . . . K 11435
Atlantic / Jan '80.

WHO MADE WHO (Film Soundtrack for Maximum Overdrive).
Tracks: Who made who / You shook me all night long / D.T. / Sink the pink / Ride on / Hell's bells / Shake your foundations / Chase the ace / For those about to rock (we salute you).
MC. . . . . .WX 57 C
Atlantic / May '86 / WEA.
CD 781 650-2
■ LP . . . . WX 57
Atlantic / '88.

WHO MADE WHO.
Tracks: Who made who / Guns for hire (live).
■ 7" . . . . .A 9425
■ CD Single . . . . A 9425 CD
■ 12". . . . . A 9425 T
Atlantic / May '85.

WHO MADE WHO.
Tracks: Not Advised.
VHS 7567501143
Warner Music Video / Oct '91 / WEA.

WHOLE LOTTA ROSIE.
Tracks: Whole lotta Rosie / Hell ain't a bad place to be.
■ 7" . . . . K 11207
Atlantic / '78.
■ 7" . . . . HM 4
Atlantic / Jun '80.

YOU SHOOK ME ALL NIGHT LONG.
Tracks: You shook me all night long / Have a drink on me.
■ 7" . . . . K 11600
Atlantic / Sep '80.

YOU SHOOK ME ALL NIGHT LONG (LIVE).
Tracks: She's got balls (version) / You shook me all night long (live) / She's got balls (live).
■ 7" . . . . .A 9377
■ 7" P.Disc . . . . A 9377 P
■ 12". . . . . A 9377 T
Atlantic / Sep '86.
■ 12". 786 792 0
Atlantic (Import) / May '88.

Accept

German five-piece hard rock group formed 1977 - influenced many of the thrash bands of the late 1980's. Initially signed to Metronome, supported Judas Priest in 1981. Third album Restless & Wild, widely regarded as their best work. Accept split in line-up changes since 1985's Metal Heart. Accept split in 1989, reformed again in 1991, and recorded Objection Overruled in 1993.

ACCEPT.
Tracks: Lady Lou / Tired of me / Seawinds / Take him in my heart / Sounds of war / Free me now / Glad to be alone / That's rock'n'roll / Hell driver / Street fighter.
■ LP . . . . METAL 103
Brain (Germany) / Jul '83.
■ LP 0060 188
Brain (Germany) / Sep '83.
■ LP P.Disc . . . . METALP 103
Razor / Mar '85.

BALLS TO THE WALL.
Tracks: Balls to the wall / London leatherboys / Fight it back / Head over heels / Losing more than you've

ever had / Love child / Turn me on / Losers and winners / Guardian of the night / Winter dreams.
■ LP . . . . PRT 25791
■ MC. 40 25791
Portrait / Jan '84.

BALLS TO THE WALL.
Tracks: Balls to the wall / Losing more than you've ever had.
■ 12". . . . . TA 4211
■ 7" . . . . .A 4311
CBS / Apr '84.

BALLS TO THE WALL/ METAL HEART.
Tracks: Not Advised.
■ Double LP. . . . . PRT A 241
Portrait / Aug '87.

BEST OF ACCEPT.
Tracks: Burning / Restless and wild / Son of a bitch / Breaker / Do it / I'm rebel / No time to lose / Princess of the dawn / Lady Lou.
■ LP 811 994 1
Metronome (Polygram) / Dec '83.
■ MC. 811 994 4
Metronome (Polygram) / Oct '87.
CD 811 994 2
Metronome (Polygram) / '88 / PolyGram.

BREAKER.
Tracks: Starlight / Breaker / Run if you can / Can't stand the night / Son of a bitch / Burning / Feelings / Midnight highway / Breaking up again / Down and out.
■ LP 1060 390
Polydor (Germany) / Dec '81.
CD . . . . CLACD 245
Castle Classics / Apr '92 / BMG / Castle Communications.

BREAKER/I'M A REBEL.
Tracks: Not Advised.
■ Double LP . . . . TFOLP 23
■ CD Set. . . . . TFOCD 23
■ MC. . . . . TFOMC 23
That's Original / Oct '89.

COLLECTION: ACCEPT.
Tracks: Lady Lou / I'm a rebel / Thunder and lightning / Breaker / Burning / Son of a bitch / Fast as a shark / Restless and wild / Princess of the dawn / Ball to the wall / London leather boys / Love child / Metal heart / Up to the limit / Screaming for a love bite / Monster man / TV War / King.
■ CD. . . . . CCSCD 311
■ MC. . . . . CCSMC 311
Castle / Oct '91.

EAT THE HEAT.
Tracks: X-T-C / Love sensation / Stand 4 what U R / Generation clash / Hellhammer / Prisoner / Chain reaction / D-train / Turn the wheel / Mistreated.
■ LP 4652291
■ CD 4652292
■ MC. 4652294
Epic / Aug '89.

HUNGRY YEARS.
Tracks: Fast as a shark / Burning / Son of a bitch / Princess of the dawn / I'm a rebel / Breaker / Restless and wild / King / Midnight highway.
MC. . . . . METAMC 119
■ CD . . . . METACD 119
■ LP . . . . METALP 119
Razor / Jul '91.

I'M A REBEL.
Tracks: I'm a rebel / Save us / No time to lose / Thunder and lightning / China lady / I wanna be no hero / King / Do it.
■ LP 1025
Logo / Aug '80.
■ LP 0060 060
Brain (Germany) / Jul '83.

I'M A REBEL.
Tracks: I'm a rebel.
■ 7" . . . . GO 389
Logo / Jul '80.

KAISOKU-BAN.
Tracks: Metal heart / Screaming for a love bite / Up to the limit / Head over heels / Love child / Living for tonight.
■ LP . . . . PRT 54916
■ MC. 40 54916
Portrait / Feb '86.

LIVE IN JAPAN.
Tracks: Not Advised.
■ CD 290876
Ariola Express / Nov '92.

METAL HEART.
Tracks: Metal heart / Midnight mover / Up to the limit / Wrong is right / Screaming for a love bite / Too high to get it right / Dogs on leads / Teach us to survive / Living for tonight / Bound to fail.
■ LP . . . . PRT 26358
■ MC. 40 26358
Portrait / Mar '85.

METAL MASTERS.
Tracks: Not Advised.
■ LP . . . . RAZD 11
■ MC. . . . . .RAZDK 11
Razor / Jun '84.
CD . . . . .RAZCD 11
Razor / '87 / Grapevine Distribution.

MIDNIGHT MOVER.
Tracks: Midnight mover / Balls to the wall / London leatherboys (on 12" only) / Wrong is right.
■ 12". . . . . TX 6130
■ 7" . . . . .A 6100
Portrait / Mar '85.

OBJECTION OVERRULED.
Tracks: Bullet proof / I don't wanna be like you / Slaves to metal / Objection overruled / This one's for you / Sick, dirty and mean / Projectors of terror / All or nothing / Rich and famous / Anamos la vida / Instrumental.
CD 7432112466-2
LP 7432112466-1
MC. 7432112466-4
RCA / Feb '93 / BMG.

RESTLESS AND WILD.
Tracks: Fast as a shark / Restless and wild / Demons night / Ahead of the pack / Shake your hands / Neon nights / Get ready / Flash rockin' man / Don't go stealing my soul away / Princess of the dawn.
■ LP P.Disc. . . . . HMIPD 6
Heavy Metal / Mar '83.
■ LP . . . . PRT 32804
MC. 40 32804
Portrait / Aug '86 / Sony.
■ CD . . . . HMIXD 6
■ LP . . . . .HMILP 6
■ MC. . . . . HMIMC 6
Heavy Metal / Apr '87.

RESTLESS AND WILD.
Tracks: Restless and wild / Fast as a shark.
■ 12". 12HIGH 3
Heavy Metal / Feb '84.

RUSSIAN ROULETTE.
Tracks: T.V. war / Monsterman / Russian roulette / It's hard to find a way / Aiming high / Heaven is hell / Another second to be / Walking in the shadow / Man enough to cry / Stand tight.
■ LP . . . . PRT 26893
■ MC. 40 26893
Portrait / Apr '86.

Accused

GRINNING LIKE AN UNDERTAKER.
Tracks: Not Advised.
CD. . . . . CDJUST 17
LP . . . . JUST 17
Music For Nations / Dec '90 / Pinnacle.

MARTHA SPLATTERHEAD'S MADDEST STORIES EVER TOLD.
Tracks: Not Advised.
CD . . . . WEBITE 43 CD
■ LP . . . . WEBITE 43
We Bite / Feb '89.

MORE FUN THAN AN OPEN CASKET FUNERAL.
Tracks: Halo of flies / W.C.A.L.T. / Rape / Lifeless zone / Scotty / Devil woman / Bethany home / Mechanized death / Take no prisoners / Splatter rock / Septi-child / I'll be glad when you're dead, you rascal you.
■ LP . . . . .JUST 11
Rough Justice / Jan '88.

RETURN OF MARTHA SPLATTERHEAD, THE.
Tracks: Not Advised.
■ LP 88561-8197-1
Combat Core (USA) / Nov '86.
■ LP . . . . .GURT 017
COR / Feb '89.
■ LP . . . . .MOSH 1
Earache / Feb '89.

SPLATTER ROCK.
Tracks: Not Advised.
CD . . . . NMR 7103CD
LP . . . . NMR 7103

■ DELETED

MC. . . . . .NMR 7103MC
Nasty Mix / Jun '92 / RTM / Pinnacle / Koch International / ACD Trading Ltd.

Accuser

CONVICTION, THE.
Tracks: Not Advised.
■ LP . . . . .ATOMH 003
Atom / '89.

EXPERIMENTAL ERRORS.
Tracks: Not Advised.
■ LP . . . . .ATOMH 006
Atom / '89.

REPENT.
Tracks: Not Advised.
CD. . . . . RTD 15181393
LP . . . . .RTD 1581393LP
Rough Trade (Germany) / Nov '92 / Pinnacle.

WHO DOMINATES WHO.
Tracks: Not Advised.
CD. . . . . ATOMH 008CD
■ LP . . . . .ATOMH 008
Atom / '89.

Acheron

RITES OF THE BLACK MASS.
Tracks: Not Advised.
CD. . . . . TURBO 007CD
LP . . . . TURBO 007LP
MC. . . . . TURBO 007MC
Turbo Music / Nov '92 / Plastic Head.

Acid

DON'T LOSE YOUR DREAMS.
Tracks: Drivin' / All through the night / Draw the line / Memories / Die by order / Up to the neck / Fine / Don't lose your dreams / To the edge of the world / Dark voices.
■ LP .080604
S.P.V. / Aug '89.

HELL ON WHEELS.
Tracks: Hell on wheels / Hooked on metal.
■ 7" 841 691
Road Runner / Jul '82.

MANIAC.
Tracks: Not Advised.
■ LP . . . . MEGATON 007
Megaton / Jan '84.

Acid Drinkers

ARE YOU A REBEL.
Tracks: Del Rocca / I mean acid (do you like it) / L.O.V.E. machine / I am the mystic / Megalopolis / Moshin' in the nite / Barmy army / Waitin' for the hair / F**k the violence (I'm sure I'm right) / Women with the dirty feet / Nagasaki baby / Mike Cwel.
LP .FLAG 45
MC . . . . .TFLAG 45
■ CD . . . . CDFLAG 45
Music For Nations / Sep '90.

DIRTY MONEY - DIRTY TRICKS.
Tracks: Not Advised.
CD . . . . .CDFLAG 59
LP .FLAG 59
MC . . . . .TFLAG 59
Music For Nations / Jun '91 / Pinnacle.

STRIP TEASE.
Tracks: Strip tease / King kong bless you / Seek and destroy / Rock 'n' roll beast / Rats/Feeling naity / Poplin twist / Masterhood of hearts devouring / You are lost my dear / Menel song/Always look on the bright side of life / Blood is boiling / My caddish promise / Mentally deficient / Hell it is a place on earth / Ronnie and the brotherspider / I'm a rocker.
CD . . . . .CDFLAG 76
Music For Nations / Nov '92 / Pinnacle.

Acid Horse

NO NAME, NO SLOGAN.
Tracks: No name, no slogan.
■ 12" 12DVN 103
■ CD Single. . . . . .CDDVN 103
Devotion / Feb '92.

Acid Reign

Formed in 1985, this British thrash band was formed in Yorkshire by vocalist 'H'. Joined by Ramsey, Kev, Adam and Mac, their first release, the mini LP *Moshkinstein* (1988) was followed by 1989's *The Fear* on Under One Flag. After many line-up changes, Acid Reign toured with Exodus and Nuclear Assault. Recorded *Obnoxious*, in 1990 and disbanded.

FEAR, THE.
Tracks: You never know / Insane ecstasy / Blind agression / Lost in solitude / Reflection of truths / Humanoia / Life in forms.
CD. . . . . .CDFLAG 31
■ LP . . . . .FLAG 31
MC. . . . . .TFLAG 31
Under One Flag / Mar '89 / Pinnacle.

HANGIN' ON THE TELEPHONE.
Tracks: Hangin' on the telephone / Motherly love / Warriors of Genghis Khan.
■ 12" . . . . 12 FLAG 109
■ 7" . . . . .FLAG 109
■ MC Single. . . . . .TFLAG 109
Under One Flag / Jan '90.

HUMANOIA.
Tracks: Humanoia.
■ 10" 10FLAG 106
Music For Nations / Jun '89.

MOSHKINSTEIN.
Tracks: Not Advised.
■ LP . . . . MFLAG 20
Under One Flag / Aug '89.

OBNOXIOUS.
Tracks: Not Advised.
LP .FLAG 39
Under One Flag / Apr '90 / Pinnacle.
CD. . . . . .CDFLAG 39
MC. . . . . .TFLAG 39
Under One Flag / Jul '92 / Pinnacle.

WORST OF ACID RAIN, THE.
Tracks: Not Advised.
CD. . . . . .CDFLAG 60
LP .FLAG 60
MC. . . . . .TFLAG 60
Music For Nations / Sep '91 / Pinnacle.

Acrophet

CORRUPT MINDS.
Tracks: Intro to corruption / Lifeless image / Crime for loving / Holy spirit / Ceremonial slaughter / Forgotten faith / Corrupt minds / Slaves of sin / From the depths / Living in today / Warped illusions / Victims of the holocaust.
CD. . . . . .RR 9523 2
Road Runner / Nov '88 / Pinnacle.
■ LP . . . . RR 9523 1
Road Runner / Oct '88.

Adam Bomb

PURE SEX.
Tracks: Not Advised.
■ CD . . . . .WKFMCD 140
■ LP . . . . .WKFMLP 140
■ MC . . . . .WKFMMC 140
FM Records / Mar '90.

PURE SEX.
Tracks: Pure sex.
■ 12" . . . . .12 VHF 54
FM Records / Mar '90.

Adams, Bryan

Canadian star whose early songwriting credits appear on albums by likes of Kiss and Bachman-Turner Overdrive. 1983's *Cuts Like A Knife* album was U.S. breakthrough; U.K. success followed in 1985 when *Reckless* album exploded on both sides of Atlantic, spawning clutch of hit singles. Profile raised even further by *Everything I Do* single's record-breaking spell atop U.K. charts and huge-selling *Waking Up The Neighbours* and *So Far, So Good* albums. Adams is now stadium-filling international attraction.

(EVERYTHING I DO) I DO IT FOR YOU.
Tracks: (Everything I do) I do it for you.
■ 12" . . . . .AMY 789
■ 7" . . . . AM 789
■ MC Single. . . . . .AMMC 789

CD Single. . . . . .AMCD 789
A&M / Jun '91.

ALL FOR LOVE (Adams, Bryan & Rod Stewart/Sting).
Tracks: All for love.
■ 7" 580477-7
■ CD Single. 580477-2
■ MC Single. 580477-4
A&M / Jan '94.

ALL I WANT IS YOU.
Tracks: All I want is you.
■ 7" . . . . AM 879
■ CD Single. . . . . .AMCD 879
■ MC Single. . . . . .AMMC 879
A&M / Jul '92.

BRYAN ADAMS.
Tracks: Hidin' from love / Win some lose some / Wait and see / Give me your love / Wastin' time / Don't ya say it / Remember / State of mind / Try to see it my way.
■ LP . . . . AMLH 64800
A&M / '80.
■ CD . . . . CDA 3100
A&M / Aug '89.
CD. . . . . CDMID 100
MC. . . . . CMID 100
A&M / Oct '92 / PolyGram.

BRYAN ADAMS - GREATEST HITS.
Tracks: Not Advised.
VHS 895403
Polygram Music Video / Nov '93 / PolyGram.

CAN'T STOP THIS THING WE STARTED.
Tracks: Can't stop this thing we started.
■ 12" . . . . AMY 812
■ 7" . . . . AM 812
■ CD Single. . . . . .AMCD 812
■ MC Single. . . . . .AMMC 812
A&M / Oct '91.

CHRISTMAS TIME.
Tracks: Christmas time / Reggae Christmas.
■ 12" . . . . AMY 297
■ 7" . . . . AM 297
A&M / Dec '85.

CUTS LIKE A KNIFE.
Tracks: Only one / Take me back / This time / Straight from the heart / Cuts like a knife / I'm ready / What's it gonna be / Don't leave me lonely / Best was yet to come.
■ CD . . . . CDA 4919
A&M.
■ MC . . . . CAM 64919
■ LP . . . . AMLH 64919
A&M / Mar '86.
CD. . . . . CDMID 102
A&M / Aug '91 / PolyGram.
MC. . . . . CMID 102
A&M / Oct '92 / PolyGram.

CUTS LIKE A KNIFE.
Tracks: Cuts like a knife / Fits ya good.
■ 7" . . . . AM 129
A&M / Sep '83.

CUTS LIKE A KNIFE/RECKLESS.
Tracks: Only one / Take me back / This time / Straight from the heart / Cuts like a knife / I'm ready / What's it gonna be / Don't leave me lonely / Best was yet to come / One night love affair / She's only happy when she's dancin' / Run to you / Heaven / Somebody / Summer of '69 / Kids wanna rock / It's only love / Long gone / Ain't gonna cry.
■ MC . . . . AMC 24101
A&M / Jun '89.

DIANA.
Tracks: Diana.
■ 12" . . . . SP 23030
A&M (import) / May '88.

HEARTS ON FIRE.
Tracks: Hearts on fire / Run to you / Native sun (on 12" only).
■ 12" . . . . ADAM 312
■ 7" . . . . ADAM 3
■ MC Single. . . . . .ADAMC 312
A&M / May '87.

HEAT OF THE NIGHT.
Tracks: Heat of the night / Another day.
■ 12" . . . . ADAM 12
■ 7" . . . . ADAM 2
A&M / Mar '87.

HEAVEN.
Tracks: Heaven / Diana.
■ 12" . . . . AMY 256

■ 7" . . . . **AM 256**
A&M / May '85.

HIDIN' FROM LOVE.
Tracks: Hidin' from love / Wait and see.
■ 7" . . . . **AMS 7520**
A&M / Apr '80.

INTO THE FIRE.
Tracks: Heat of the night / Into the fire / Victim of love / Another day / Native son / Only the strong survive / Rebel / Remembrance day / Hearts on fire / Home again.
■ LP . . . . **AMA 3907**
■ CD . . . . **CDA 3907**
■ MC. . . . . **AMC 3907**
A&M / Apr '87.

IT'S ONLY LOVE (Adams, Bryan & Tina Turner).
Tracks: It's only love / Best is yet to come.
■ 12" . . . . **AMY 285**
■ 7" . . . . **AM 285**
A&M / Oct '85.

LET ME TAKE YOU DANCING.
Tracks: Let me take you dancing / Don't turn me away.
■ 7" . . . . **AMS 7460**
A&M / Nov '79.

LIVE LIVE LIVE.
Tracks: Not Advised.
CD **3970942**
MC. **3970944**
A&M / Aug '94 / PolyGram.

LONELY NIGHTS.
Tracks: Lonely nights / Don't look now.
■ 7" . . . . **AMS 8183**
A&M / Nov '81.

ONE GOOD REASON.
Tracks: One good reason.
■ 7" . . . . **AM 170**
A&M / Jan '84.

PLEASE FORGIVE ME.
Tracks: Please forgive me / Can't stop this thing we started / There will never be another tonight / C'mon everybody.
■ 7" **580422-7**
■ CD Single **580422-2**
■ MC Single. **580422-4**
A&M / Oct '93.

RECKLESS.
Tracks: One night love affair / She's only happy when she's dancin' / Run to you / Heaven / Somebody / Summer of '69 / Kids wanna rock / It's only love / Long gone / Ain't gonna cry.
CD . . . . **CDA 5013**
■ LP . . . . **AMA 5013**
MC. . . . . **AMC 5013**
A&M / Feb '85 / PolyGram.

RECKLESS.
Tracks: Run to you / Summer of '69 / Somebody / Heaven / Kids wanna rock / This time.
VHS . . . . **AMV 848**
A&M Sound Pictures / '84 / Gold & Sons / PolyGram Music Video / TBD.
VHS . . . . **AMV 827**
A&M Sound Pictures / '88 / Gold & Sons / PolyGram Music Video / TBD.

RUN TO YOU.
Tracks: Run to you / I'm ready / Cuts like a knife.
■ 12" . . . . **AMY 224**
■ 7" . . . . **AM 224**
A&M / Dec '84.

SO FAR SO GOOD (Collection Of The Best Of Bryan Adams).
Tracks: Not Advised.
CD **540157-2**
DCC **540157-5**
LP **540157-1**
MC. **540157-4**
A&M / Nov '93 / PolyGram.

SOMEBODY.
Tracks: Somebody / Long gone.
■ 12" . . . . **AMY 236**
■ 7" . . . . **AM 236**
■ 7" P.Disc . . . . **AMP 236**
A&M / Mar '85.

STRAIGHT FROM THE HEART.
Tracks: Straight from the heart / Fits you good / Straight from the heart (live) (On 12" only) / Run too close (In doublepack only) / Somebody (In doublepack only) / One good reason.
■ 7" . . . . **AM 103**

A&M / Mar '83.
■ 12" . . . . **AMY 322**
■ 7" . . . . **AM 322**
■ 7" Set . . . . **AMS 322**
A&M / Jun '86.

SUMMER OF '69.
Tracks: Summer of '69 / Kids wanna rock.
■ 12" . . . . **AMY 267**
■ 7" . . . . **AM 267**
A&M / Jul '85.

THERE WILL NEVER BE ANOTHER TONIGHT.
Tracks: There will never be another tonight.
■ 12" . . . . **AMY 838**
■ CD Single . . . . **AMCD 838**
■ MC Single . . . . **AMMC 838**
■ 7" . . . . **AM 838**
A&M / Nov '91.

THIS TIME.
Tracks: This time / I'm ready / Lonely nights (On 12" only).
■ 12" . . . . **AMY 295**
■ 7" . . . . **AM 295**
A&M / Feb '86.

THOUGHT I'D DIED AND GONE TO HEAVEN.
Tracks: Thought I'd died and gone to heaven.
■ 12" . . . . **AMY 848**
■ 7" . . . . **AM 848**
■ CD Single . . . . **AMCD 848**
■ MC Single . . . . **AMMC 848**
A&M / Feb '92.

VICTIM OF LOVE.
Tracks: Victim of love / Heat of the night (live).
■ 7" . . . . **AM 407**
■ 12" . . . . **AMY 407**
■ MC Single . . . . **AMF 407**
A&M / Oct '87.

WAKING UP THE NEIGHBOURS.
Tracks: Not Advised.
CD **3971642**
LP **3971641**
MC. **3971644**
A&M / Oct '91 / PolyGram.
DCC **397 164-5**
A&M / Jan '93 / PolyGram.

WAKING UP THE NEIGHBOURS.
Tracks: Can't stop this thing we started / (Everything I do) I do it for you (Previously unseen black & white version.) / Thought I'd died and gone to heaven / Do I have to say the words / All I want is you / There will never be another tonight / Touch the hand.
VHS **089 514-3**
Polygram Music Video / Jan '93 / PolyGram.

YOU WANT IT, YOU GOT IT.
Tracks: Lonely nights / One good reason / Don't look now / Coming home / Fits ya good / Tonight / Jealousy / You want it you got it / Last chance / No one makes it right.
■ CD . . . . **CDA 3154**
■ MC. . . . . **CAM 64864**
■ LP . . . . **AMLH 64864**
A&M / '86.
CD . . . . **CDMID 101**
MC. . . . . **CMID 101**
A&M / Oct '92 / PolyGram.

KICK 'EM HARD.
Tracks: Distemper / Waiting for yesterday / Kick 'em hard / You're perfect / You never know / Man made act of God / Serves you right / Bitch.
■ CD . . . . **FOR 302CD**
Forge Europe / Jun '93.

PITY OF MAN.
Tracks: Not Advised.
CD . . . . **RAT 508CD**
LP . . . . **RAT 508**
Rattlesnake / Feb '91.

CRUISING WITH ELVIS IN BIGFOOTS' UFO.
Tracks: If this is Tuesday / Swindel / My mother can't drive / Second to none / Imaginary midget western, Theme from / Flip side unclassified / Bulimic food fight / Stew / Something about... Amy Carter / Baby elephant walk.
■ LP . . . . **JUST 12M**
Rough Justice / Oct '88.

HUMONGOUSFUNGUSAMONGUS.
Tracks: AOD VS son of Godzilla / Office building / Yuppe / Answer / Pope - on a rope / Fishin' musician / Pizza 'n' beer / Bugs / Youth blimp / Commercial cuts / Survive / Masterpiece / Crowd control / Velvet Elvis / F**k the neighbours / Surfin' Jew / Bruces lament / Nice song.
■ LP . . . . **JUST 5**
Rough Justice / Jan '87.

IMAGINARY MIDGET WESTERN, THEME FROM.
Tracks: Imaginary midget western, Theme from / Detroit rock city / Coffin cruiser.
■ 10" . . . . **10 KORE 105**
Rough Justice / Oct '88.

WACKY HI JINKS OF.
Tracks: Not Advised.
■ LP . . . . **BOR 12002**
Buy Our (USA) / Sep '87.

LOST IT ALL.
Tracks: Wasted life / Jester / Destinized / Religions for sale / No more wars / Smash the odds / Lost it all / Total extremes / Metaphysics / Fight back / Angel of bread.
■ LP . . . . **ACHE 13**
Manic Ears / Jun '88.

REM's Peter Buck summarised Aerosmith's U.S. career with: "If you grew up in the '70s, you liked Aerosmith." Classic albums *Toys In The Attic* and *Rocks* were basis of band's stadium-filling appeal, but drug addiction tore band apart at turn of decade. Rejuvenation began with collaboration with Run DMC on *Walk This Way* single in 1986; continuing with albums *Permanent Vacation* and *Pump*. Latter was band's commercial breakthrough in UK, heralded by single *Love In An Elevator*. Initially derided as Stones clones, Aerosmith inspired many in turn; their influence is evident on Guns N' Roses. They continue to be valid and contemporary: 1993's *Get A Grip* album yielded several hit singles, innovative videos, and a headlining appearance at the Castle Donington 'Monsters of Rock' festival.

AEROSMITH.
Tracks: Make it / Somebody / Dream on / One way street / Mama Kin / Write me a letter / Movin' out / Walking the dog.
■ CD **4666662**
■ MC **4666664**
Columbia / Mar '92.
CD **474962 2**
Columbia / Nov '93 / Sony.

AEROSMITH: INTERVIEW PICTURE DISC.
Tracks: Not Advised.
LP P.Disc . . . . **BAK 2091**
Baktabak / Apr '88 / Arabesque Ltd.
CD P.Disc . . . . **CBAK 4032**
Baktabak / Apr '91 / Arabesque Ltd.

AMAZING.
Tracks: Amazing.
■ 12" . . . . **GFST 63**
■ CD Single . . . . **GFSTD 63**
■ MC Single. . . . . **GFSC 63**
Geffen / Dec '93.

ANGEL.
Tracks: Angel / Girl keeps comin' apart.
■ 7" . . . . **GEF 34**
■ CD Single . . . . **GEF 34CD**
■ 12" . . . . **GEF 34T**
■ 12" P.Disc. . . . . **GEF 34TP**
Geffen / Apr '88.

ANTHOLOGY - AEROSMITH.
Tracks: Toys in the attic / Sweet emotion / Walk this way (live) / No more no more / You see me crying / Bright light fright / Lord of the thighs / Back in the saddle (live) / Sick as a dog / Critical mass / Bite the hand that feeds / Sight for sore eyes / Mother popcorn / Train kept a rollin' / S.O.S. / Rock in a hard place / Jailbait / Push comes to shove / Rats in the cellar / Bone to bone / Dream on.
MC. . . . . **RAWTC 037**
■ LP . . . . **RAWLP 037**
■ CD . . . . **RAWCD 037**
Raw Power / Jun '88.

■ **DELETED**

A 5

CLASSICS LIVE.
Tracks: Train kept a rollin' / Kings and Queens / Sweet emotion / Dream on.
■ LP . . . . CBS 26901
MC. 40 26901
CBS / Sep '86 / Sony.
CD. .474971 2
Columbia / Nov '93 / Sony.

CLASSICS LIVE II.
Tracks: Back in the saddle / Walk this way / Movin' out / Draw the line / Same old song and dance / Last child / Let the music do the talking / Toys in the attic.
■ CD 4600372
■ LP 4600371
MC. 4600374
CBS / Nov '89.
CD. .474972 2
Columbia / Nov '93 / Sony.

COME TOGETHER.
Tracks: Come together / Kings and queens.
■ 7" . . . . CBS 6584
CBS / Sep '78.

CRYIN'.
Tracks: Cryin'.
■ 12" . . . . .GFST 56
■ CD Single. . . . . .GFSTD 56
■ MC Single. . . . . GFSC 56
Geffen / Oct '93.

DONE WITH MIRRORS.
Tracks: Let the music do the talking / My fist, your face / Woman on you / Reason a dog / Shela / Gypsy boots / She's on fire / Hop / Darkness (Extra track on cassette only.).
■ LP . . . . GEF 26695
■ MC. 4026695
Geffen / Dec '85.
■ CD 924091 2
■ LP 924091 1
■ MC. 924091 4
Geffen / Jun '89.
■ CD . . . . .GEFD 24091
■ MC. . . . . .GEFC 24091
Geffen / Apr '91.
CD. . . . . .GFLD 19052
MC. . . . . .GFLC 19052
Geffen / May '94 / BMG.

DRAW THE LINE.
Tracks: Draw the line / Kings and queens / Sight for sore eyes / Milk cow blues.
CD. .474966 2
Columbia / Nov '93 / Sony.

DRAW THE LINE/TOYS IN THE ATTIC/ROCKS.
Tracks: Not Advised.
CD Set 4673852
CBS / Dec '90 / Sony.

DUDE (LOOKS LIKE A LADY).
Tracks: Dude (looks like a lady) / Simoriah / Once is enough (Available on 12" only.).
■ 7" . . . . GEF 29
■ 12" P.Disc. . . . . GEF 29TP
■ 12". . . . . .GEF 29T
Geffen / Oct '87.

DUDE (LOOKS LIKE A LADY).
Tracks: Dude (looks like a lady) / Monkey on my back / Love in an elevator / Walk this way.
■ 12". . . . . .GEF 72T
■ 12". . . . . .GEF 72TW
■ 7" . . . . GEF 72
■ CD Single . . . . .GEF 72CD
Geffen / Feb '90.

EAT THE RICH.
Tracks: Eat the rich.
■ 12". . . . . .GFSV 46
■ CD Single . . . . .GFSTD 46
■ MC Single. . . . . GFSC 46
Geffen / Jun '93.

GEMS.
Tracks: Rats in the cellar / Lick and a promise / Chip away the stone / No surprize / Mama kin / Adam's apple / Nobody's fault / round and 'round / Critical mass / Lord of the Thighs / Jailbait / Train kept a rollin'.
■ LP 4632241
Columbia / Nov '89.
CD. 4632242
MC. 4632244
Columbia / Nov '89 / Sony.
CD. 474973 2
Columbia / Nov '93 / Sony.

GET A GRIP.
Tracks: Intro / Eat the rich / Get a grip / Fever / Livin' on the edge / Flesh / Walk on down / Shut up and dance / Cryin' / Gotta love it / Crazy / Line up / Can't stop messin' / Amazing / Boogie man.
CD. . . . . GED 24444
LP . . . . GEF 24444
MC. . . . . GEC 24444
Geffen / Apr '93 / BMG.

GET YOUR WINGS.
Tracks: Same old song and dance / Lord of the thighs / Woman of the world / Train kept a rollin' / Spaced / SOS (too bad) / Season's of wither / Pandora's box.
■ CD 4667322
■ MC. 4667324
Columbia / Mar '92.
CD. 474963 2
Columbia / Nov '93 / Sony.

GREATEST HITS: AEROSMITH.
Tracks: Dream on / Same old song and dance / Sweet emotion / Walk this way / Remember (walkin' in the sand) / Back in the saddle / Draw the line / Kings and queens / Come together / Last child.
■ LP . . . . CBS 84704
CBS / Feb '81.
MC. 4607034
■ LP 4607031
CBS / Feb '88.
■ CD 4607032
■ LP P.Disc. 4607038
CBS / Oct '89.
CD. 474969 2
Columbia / Nov '93 / Sony.

JANIE'S GOT A GUN.
Tracks: Janie's got a gun / Voodoo medicine man.
■ 12". . . . . .GEF 68T
■ 7" . . . . GEF 68
Geffen / Nov '89.

LIVE BOOTLEG.
Tracks: Back in the saddle / Sweet emotion / Lord of the thighs / Toys in the attack / Last child / Come together / Walk this way / Sick as a dog / Dream on / Mama kin / S.O.S. / Train kept a rollin' / Sight for sore eyes / Chip away the stone / I ain't got you / Mother popcorn.
■ Double LP. . . . . CBS 88325
CBS / Jan '79.
■ Double LP. . . . . CG 35564
MC. . . . . CGT 35564
CBS / Dec '87 / Sony.
CD. 474967 2
Columbia / Nov '93 / Sony.

LIVE TEXAS JAM '78.
Tracks: Rats in the cellar / Seasons of wither / I wanna know why / Walking the dog / Walk this way / Lick and a promise / Get the lead out / Draw the line / Sweet emotion / Same old song and dance / Milk cow blues / toys inthe attic.
VHS 490132
Sony Music Video / Mar '94 / Sony.

LIVIN' ON THE EDGE.
Tracks: Livin' on the edge.
■ 12". . . . . .GFSTP 35
■ CD Single. . . . . GFSTD 35
■ MC Single. . . . . GFSC 35
Geffen / Mar '93.

LOVE IN AN ELEVATOR.
Tracks: Love in an elevator / Young lust / Ain't enough (Available on CD single only).
■ 12". . . . . .GEF 63T
■ 7" . . . . GEF 63
■ CD Single . . . . .GEF 63CD
Geffen / Aug '89.
■ 12" P.Disc. . . . . GEF 63TP
■ MC Single. . . . . GEF 63C
Geffen / Sep '89.

NIGHT IN THE RUTS.
Tracks: No surprize / Chiquitita / Remember walking in the sand / Cheese cake / Three mile smile / Reefer head woman / Bone to bone (Coney Island white fish boy) / Mia / Think about it.
■ LP 83681
CBS / Feb '80.
■ CD 4667202
Columbia / Dec '90.
■ MC. 4667204
Columbia / Mar '92.
CD. 474968 2
Columbia / Nov '93 / Sony.

OTHER SIDE, THE.
Tracks: Other side.
■ 12". . . . . .GEF 79T
■ 12" P.Disc. . . . . .GEF 79TP
■ 7" . . . . GEF 79

CD Single. . . . . .GEF 79CD
■ MC Single. . . . . GEF 79C
Geffen / Aug '90.

PANDORA'S BOX.
Tracks: When I needed you / Make it / Movin' out / One way street / On the road again / Mama kin / Same old song and dance / Train kept a rollin' / Seasons of wither / Write me a letter / Dream on / Pandora's box / Rattlesnake shake / Walking the dog / Lord of the Thighs / Toys in the attic / round and 'round / Krawhitham / You see me crying sweet emotion / No more no more / Walk this way / I wanna know why / Big ten-inch record / Rats in the cellar / Last child / All your love / Soul saver / Nobody's fault / Lick and a promise / Adam's apple / Draw the line / Critical mass / Kings and Queens / Milkcow blues / I live in Connecticut / Three mile smile / Let it slide / Cheese cake / Bone to bone (Coney Island white fish boy) / No surpise / Come together / Downtown Charlie / Sharpshooter / Shithouse shuffle / South station blues / Riff and roll / Jailbait / Major Barbara / Chip away the stone / Helter skelter / Back in the saddle / Circle jerk.
CD Set 4692932
■ MC Set 4692934
Columbia / Dec '91.

PANDORA'S TOYS.
Tracks: Sweet emotion / Draw the line / Walk this way / Dream on / Train keep a rollin' / Mama kin / Seasons of wither / Big ten inch / All your love / Helter skelter / Chip away / Rattle snake shake / Rockin' pneumonia.
MiniDisc. 476956 8
Columbia / Jul '94 / Sony.
CD. 476956 2
MC. 476956 4
Columbia / Jun '94 / Sony.

PERMANENT VACATION.
Tracks: Hearts done time / Magic touch / Rag doll / Simoriah / Dude (looks like a lady) / St. John / Hangman jury / Girl keeps comin' apart / Angel / Permanent vacation / I'm down / Movie.
■ CD 9241622
■ LP . . . . WX 126
■ MC. . . . . WX 126C
Geffen / Aug '87.
■ CD . . . . .GEFD 24162
■ MC. . . . . .GEFC 24162
Geffen / Apr '91.
LP . . . . GEF 24162
Geffen / Jun '94 / BMG.
CD. . . . . .GFLD 19254
MC. . . . . .GFLC 19254
Geffen / May '94 / BMG.

PUMP.
Tracks: Young lust / F.I.N.E / Love in an elevator / Monkey on my back / Janie's got a gun / Other side / My girl / Don't get mad, get even / Voodoo medicine man / What it takes.
■ CD 9242542
■ LP . . . . WX 304
■ MC. . . . . WX 304C
Geffen / Sep '89.
■ LP . . . . GEF 24254
■ CD . . . . .GEFD 24254
■ MC. . . . . .GEFC 24254
Geffen / Jan '91.
CD. . . . . .GFLD 19255
MC. . . . . .GFLC 19255
Geffen / May '94 / BMG.

RAG DOLL.
Tracks: Rag doll / Simoriah.
■ 12". . . . . .GEF 76T
■ 7" . . . . GEF 76
Geffen / Apr '90.

REMEMBER (WALKING IN THE SAND).
Tracks: Remember (walkin' in the sand) / Bone to bone.
■ 7" . . . . CBS 8220
CBS / Feb '80.

ROCK IN A HARD PLACE.
Tracks: Jailbait / Bitches brew / Cry me a river / Jig is up / Push comes to shove / Lightning strikes / Bolivian ragamuffin / Prelude to Joanie / Joanie's butterfly / Rock in a hard place.
CD. 474970 2
Columbia / Nov '93 / Sony.

ROCKS.
Tracks: Back in the saddle / Last child / Rats in the cellar / Combination / Sick as a dog / Nobody's fault / Get the lead out / Lick and a promise / Home tonight.
■ CD . . . . CD 32517
CBS / Jul '89.
■ LP 32360
CBS / Nov '89.

■ CD . . . . CD 32360
MC 40-32360
CBS / '91 / Sony.
CD 474965 2
Columbia / Nov '93 / Sony.

SHUT UP AND DANCE.
Tracks: Shut up and dance.
■ 7" . . . . GFS 75
■ CD Single . . . . .GFSXD 75
■ CD Single . . . . .GFSTD 75
■ MC Single. . . . . GFSC 75
Geffen / Jun '94.

THINGS THAT GO PUMP IN THE NIGHT.
Tracks: Not Advised.
■ VHS 7599 83172 3
Warner Music Video / Oct '90.
VHS . . . . .GEFV 38172
Geffen Video / May '94 / BMG.

TOYS IN THE ATTIC.
Tracks: Toys in the attic / Uncle Salty / Adam's apple
/ Walk this way / Big ten inch record / Sweet emotion
/ No more no more / round and 'round / You see me
crying.
■ LP . . . . CLALP 135X
■ MC. . . . . CLAMC 135X
■ CD . . . . CLACD 135X
Castle Classics / '87.
■ CD 4606982
MC. 4606984
Columbia / Apr '91 / Sony.
CD 474964 2
Columbia / Nov '93 / Sony.

VIDEO SCRAPBOOK.
Tracks: Not Advised.
■ VHS . . . . HEN 2105
Hendring Video / Aug '88.

Afflicted

PRODIGAL SUN.
Tracks: Not Advised.
CD . . . . .NB 063CD
LP . . . . .NB 063LP
Nuclear Blast / Nov '92 / Plastic Head.

After Hours

AFTER HOURS.
Tracks: Not Advised.
MC. . . . . .AFT 001
After Hours / Aug '89 / Sony / Backs Distribution.

TAKE OFF.
Tracks: Love attack / Better late than never / Stay by
my side / Take off / Game / Another lonely night /
Paint it black / Without you.
■ LP P.Disc . . . . WKFMPD 89
■ CD . . . . .WKFMXD 89
■ LP . . . . .WKFMLP 89
■ MC. . . . . WKFMMC 89
FM Records / Aug '88.

Aftermath

DON'T CHEER ME UP.
Tracks: Not Advised.
■ LP 20001
Mushroom (Australia) / Feb '89.

Agent Steel

MAD LOCUST RISING.
Tracks: Swarm is on us / Mad locust rising / Ripper /
Let it be done / Day at Guyana.
■ 12" . . . . 12 KUT 124
Music For Nations / Aug '86.

MAD LOCUST RISING.
Tracks: Nothing left / Unexpected / Day at Guyana /
Never surrender / Mad locust rising / Ripper / Evil
eye / Bleed / Rager.
VHS . . . . .JE 186
Jettisoundz / '89 / TBD / Visionary Communications.

SKEPTICS APOCALYPSE.
Tracks: Calling / Taken by force / Bleen for the Godz
/ 144.000 gone / Back to reign / Agents of steel / Evil
eye / Children of the sun / Guilty as charged.
■ LP . . . . .RR 9759
Road Runner / Sep '85.
CD . . . . RO 97592
Roadracer / Apr '89 / Pinnacle.

UNSTOPPABLE FORCE.
Tracks: Not Advised.
CD . . . . CDMFN 66
MC . . . . TMFN 66
■ LP . . . . MFN 66
Music For Nations / Aug '89.

Agnostic Front

CAUSE FOR ALARM.
Tracks: Not Advised.
■ LP . . . . JUST 3
Rough Justice / May '86.
CD . . . . .CDJUST 3
Rough Justice / Aug '87 / Pinnacle.

LAST WARNING.
Tracks: Not Advised.
CD . . . . RR 90782
■ LP . . . . RR 90781
Road Runner / May '93.

LIBERTY AND JUSTICE (FOR ALL).
Tracks: Not Advised.
CD . . . . .CDJUST 8
Rough Justice / Oct '87 / Pinnacle.
■ LP . . . . JUST 8
Rough Justice / '89.

ONE VOICE.
Tracks: Not Advised.
CD . . . . RO 92222
LP . . . . RO 92221
Road Runner / Jan '92 / Pinnacle.

VERY BEST OF AGNOSTIC FRONT.
Tracks: Not Advised.
CD . . . . CDJUST 20M
LP . . . . .JUST 20M
MC. . . . . TJUST 20M
Music For Nations / Jul '92 / Pinnacle.

VICTIM IN PAIN.
Tracks: Not Advised.
■ LP 88561-8181-1
Combat Core (USA) / Aug '87.

Agony

FIRST DEFIANCE, THE.
Tracks: Hey Suze / Falling rain / Discipline / Chasing
dreams / Ah-ha / Sailors on the sea / Dream girl /
Dream girl / Strung out on you / Country girl /
Goodnight darling.
CD . . . . .CDFLAG 19
■ LP . . . . .FLAG 19
Under One Flag / Apr '88.

Agothocles

BLACK CLOUDS DETERMINATE.
Tracks: Not Advised.
CD . . . . .CYBER 10
Cyber / Aug '94 / Plastic Head.

THEATRICAL SYMBOLIZATION.
Tracks: Not Advised.
CD . . . . .CYBERCD 2
Plastic Head / Jun '92 / Plastic Head.

Agressor

DESTINY.
Tracks: Not Advised.
■ CD . . . . CDNUK 154
■ LP . . . . .NUK 154
■ MC. . . . . ZCNUK 154
Noise / Aug '90.

SATAN'S SODOMY.
Tracks: Not Advised.
CD . . . . BMCD 36
Black Mark / Jun '94 / Plastic Head.

TOWARDS BEYOND.
Tracks: Intro / Forteress / Positonic showering /
Antediluvian / Epileptic aura / Hyaloid / Crypt /
Future past/Eldest things / Turkish march (CD only).
■ CD . . . . BMCD 023
MC. . . . . .BMCT 023
Black Mark / Sep '92 / Plastic Head.

Airdash

BOTH ENDS OF THE PATH.
Tracks: Not Advised.
CD . . . . BMCD 14
LP . . . . BMLP 14
Black Mark / '92 / Plastic Head.

Airrace

I DON'T CARE.
Tracks: I don't care / Caught in the game.
■ 7" . . . . .B 9702
Atco / Dec '84.

SHAFT OF LIGHT.
Tracks: I don't care / Promise to call / First one over
the line / Open your eyes / Not really me / Brief
encounter / Caught in the game / Do you want my
love again / Didn't want to lose ya / All I'm asking.
■ LP 790 219-1
Atco / Dec '84.

Alaska

ALASKA: ALIVE.
Tracks: Not Advised.
VHS . . . . .VVD 096
Virgin Vision / Gold & Sons / TBD.

HEADLINES.
Tracks: Headlines / Sorcerer.
■ 7" . . . . .KUT 130
Music For Nations / Sep '88.

HEART OF THE STORM.
Tracks: Not Advised.
■ LP . . . . MFN 23
Music For Nations / May '84.

I DON'T KNOW WHY.
Tracks: I don't know why / Out on a limb.
■ 7" . . . . K 16640
WEA / Jul '74.

MISS YOU TONIGHT.
Tracks: Miss you tonight / Voi.
■ 12" . . . . 12 KUT 116
■ 7" . . . . .KUT 116
Music For Nations / May '85.

NEED YOUR LOVE.
Tracks: Need your love / Susie blue.
■ 12" . . . . 12 KUT 108
■ 7" . . . . .KUT 108
Music For Nations / '84.

PACK, THE.
Tracks: Not Advised.
■ LP . . . . MFN 41
Music For Nations / Mar '85.
CD 845 089
Intercord / Oct '88 / Pinnacle / C.M. Distribution.

SHOW SOME EMOTION.
Tracks: Show some emotion / You don't have to
worry.
■ 12" . . . . .BROX 196
■ 7" . . . . BRO 196
Bronze / Oct '85.

Alcatrazz

DISTURBING THE PEACE.
Tracks: God blessed video / Mercy / Will you be
home tonight / Wire and wood / Desert diamond /
Stripper / Painted lover / Lighter shade of green /
Sons and lovers / Sky fire / Breaking the heart of the
city.
■ MC. . . . . EJ 2402994
■ LP . . . . EJ 2402991
Capitol / Aug '85.

GOD BLESSED VIDEO.
Tracks: God blessed video / Wire and wood.
■ 7" . . . . .CL 366
Capitol / Aug '85.

ISLAND IN THE SUN.
Tracks: Island in the sun / General hospital.
■ 12" . . . . .RCAT 434
■ 7" . . . . .RCA 434
Rocshire / Aug '84.

■ DELETED

LIVE SENTENCE.
Tracks: Not Advised.
CD. .CDMFN 134
Music For Nations / Jun '92 / Pinnacle.

LIVE SENTENCE - NO PAROLE FROM ROCK'N'ROLL.
Tracks: Island in the sun / General hospital / Jet to jet / Hiroshima mon amour / Kree nakoorie / Incubus / Too young to die, too drunk to live / Big foot / Starcarr Lane / Suffer me.
■ LP . . . . PL 83263
■ MC. PK 83263
RCA / Aug '84.
■ LP . . . . SLAM 11
Grand Slam (USA) / '88.

NO PAROLE FROM ROCK'N'ROLL.
Tracks: Not Advised.
CD. .CDMFN 133
Music For Nations / Jul '92 / Pinnacle.

RADIO 5.
Tracks: Blinded / Blame it on the night / Long time no love / Halfway there / Short change / Think it over / Communication / Save my heart / So hard / Miles away.
■ LP . . . . RCALP 3066
■ MC. RCAK 3066
RCA / May '82.

ROCKIN' HIGH.
Tracks: Rockin' high / Run wild.
■ 7" . . . . RCA 29
RCA / Jan '81.

THINK IT OVER.
Tracks: Think it over / Halfway there.
■ 7" .RCA 183
RCA / Feb '82.

YOU AND THE NIGHT.
Tracks: You and the night / Run wild.
■ 7" . . . . RCA 81
RCA / May '81.

YOUNG BLOOD.
Tracks: Rockin' high / Young blood / Maybe tomorrow / Late news / Deadline / Crazy dancer / Give it all away / Live fast, die hard / You and the night / Run wild.
MC. . . . . RCAK 5023
RCA / May '81 / BMG.
■ LP . . . . RCALP 5023
RCA / Sep '81.

Alice In Chains

Quartet from Seattle whose Stateside popularity exploded with the release of a single called Would which became a hit after featuring in the soundtrack to the movie Singles. The Alice In Chains album it later featured on, Dirt, and its predecessor Face-lift showed them as masters of bottom heavy metal - with vocalist Layne Staley's tortured tones and guitarist Jerry Cantrell's inspired riffing and fluid lead work. Staley's much publicised (and documented, lyrically) battle with heroin has more than once threatened to overpower the band but any group that can step sideways and make much lighter jammy material as on the two EP's Sap and, especially, Jar Of Flies ought to survive and go on to greatness.

ANGRY CHAIR.
Tracks: Angry chair / I know somethin' ('bout you) / Bleed the freak (live) (On CD Single & 12" only) / Hate to feel (live) (On CD Single & 12" only).
■ CD Single 659365-2
■ 12". 659365-6
■ 7" P.Disc 659365-7
Columbia / Jun '93.

DIRT.
Tracks: Them bones / Dam that river / Rain when I die / Down in a hole / Sick man / Rooster / Junkhead / Dirt / God smack / Hate to feel / Angry chair / Would.
CD. .472330-2
■ LP 472330-1
MC. .472330-4
Columbia / Oct '92 / Sony.
MiniDisc. 472330-8
Columbia / May '94 / Sony.

DOWN IN A HOLE.
Tracks: Down in a hole (Radio edit) / Rooster / Love, hate, love (Available on 12" only.) / Down in a hole (LP version) / Little bitter (Available on 12" only.) / What the hell have I (Available on CDS only.).
■ 12". 659751 6

■ 7". 659751 7
■ CD Single. 659751 2
Columbia / Oct '93.

FACE LIFT, A.
Tracks: We die young / Man in the box / Sea of sorrow / Bleed the freak / I can't remember / Love, hate, love / It ain't like that / Sunshine / Put you down / Confusion / I know somethin' ('bout you) / Real thing.
CD. .4672012
■ LP 4672011
MC. .4672014
Sony Music / '91 / Sony.
CD. .4672002
■ LP 4672001
MC. .4672004
CBS / Oct '92 / Sony.

JAR OF FLIES/SAP.
Tracks: Rotten apple / Nutshell / I stay away / No excuses / Whale & wasp / Don't follow / Swing on this / Brother / Got me wrong / Right turn / Am I inside / Love story.
CD Set 475713 2
LP Set 475713 1
MC Set 475713 4
Columbia / Jan '94 / Sony.

THEM BONES.
Tracks: Them bones / We die young / Got me wrong (Not available on 7" format.) / Am I inside (Not available on 7" format.).
■ 12". 659090 6
■ 7". 659090 7
■ CD Single. 659090 2
Columbia / Mar '93.

WOULD.
Tracks: Would / Man in the box / Brother (On 12" / CDs only) / Right turn (On 12"/CDs only).
■ 12". 658888-6
■ 7". 658888-7
■ CD Single. 658888-2
Columbia / Jan '93.

Alloy

ALLOY.
Tracks: Not Advised.
CD. .VROOM 4
LP .VROOM 4.1
Engine / Aug '93 / Plastic Head.

Almighty

Formed in 1988 by ex-New Model Army guitarist Ricky Warwick, The Almighty quickly emerged as one of the leading lights of the British rock revival of the 80's. Their albums have sold in increasing numbers and the most recent album Powertrippin' even breached the Top 5 in 1993. Sadly, a recent tour of the U.S. proved that British bands, no matter how succesful at home, find it difficult to repeat this success in the States.

BLOOD, FIRE AND LIVE.
Tracks: Full force lovin' machine / Lay down the law / Destroyed / Resurrection mutha / You've gone wild / Blood, fire and love / Wild and wonderful / You ain't seen nothin' yet.
CD. 847 107-2
MC. 847 107-4
■ LP 847 107-1
Polydor / Oct '89.

BLOOD, FIRE AND LOVE.
Tracks: Not Advised.
CD. 841 347-2
MC. 841 347-4
■ LP 841 347-1
Polydor / Sep '89.

CRANK.
Tracks: Not Advised.
CD. .CDCHR 6086
MC. .TCCHR 6086
EMI / Sep '94 / EMI.

DESTROYED.
Tracks: Destroyed / Blood, fire and love.
■ 12". . . . . PZ 60
■ 7". . . . . PO 60
Polydor / Oct '89.

DEVIL'S TOY.
Tracks: Devil's toy.
■ 12". . . . . .PZ 144
■ 7". . . . . PO 144
■ MC Single. . . . . .POCS 144
Polydor / Apr '91.

FREE AND EASY.
Tracks: Free and easy / Hell to pay.
■ 12". . . . . .PZ 127
■ 7". . . . . PO 127
■ MC Single. . . . . .POCS 127
Polydor / Feb '91.

JESUS LOVES YOU, BUT I DON'T.
Tracks: Jesus loves you, but I don't / Wing and a prayer (On 12" & cassette only) / Power and the glory (On CD only) / F.O.A.D. (On CD only).
12". . . . . .PZ 321
CD Single. . . . . .PZCD 321
MC Single . . . . .POCS 321
Polydor / Jul '94 / PolyGram.

LITTLE LOST SOMETIMES.
Tracks: Little lost sometimes / Wild road to satisfaction / Crucify (live) (12" only) / Detroit (live) (CD single only).
■ 12". . . . . .PZ 151
■ 7". . . . . PO 151
■ CD Single . . . . .PZCD 151
Polydor / Jun '91.

OVER THE EDGE.
Tracks: Over the edge / Lifeblood (live) / Takin' hold (live) / Jesus loves you..but I don't (live) (CDS only) / Blind (CDS only).
■ 7". . . . . PO 298
■ CD Single. . . . . .PZCD 298
■ MC Single. . . . . .POCS 298
Polydor / Oct '93.

POWER.
Tracks: Power / Detroit / Wild and wonderful (live) / Lay down the law.
■ 12". . . . . .PZF 66
■ 12" P.Disc. . . . . .PZP 66
■ 7". . . . . PO 66
■ CD Single . . . . .PZCD 66
■ MC Single. . . . . .POCS 66
Polydor / Jan '90.

POWERTRIPPIN'.
Tracks: Not Advised.
CD. 519 226-2
MC. 519 226-4
Polydor / Mar '93 / PolyGram.
CD. 519 104-2
■ LP 519 104-1
■ MC. 519 104-4
Polydor / Oct '93.

SOUL DESTRUCTION.
Tracks: Not Advised.
CD. 847 961-2
MC. 847 961-4
■ LP 847 961-1
Polydor / Apr '91.

SOUL DESTRUCTION LIVE.
Tracks: Destroyed / Full force loving machine / Love religion / What more do you want / Loaded / Praying to the red light / Power / Little lost sometimes / Bandaged knees / Sin against the light / Devil's toy / Cruchy / Free 'n' easy / Lay down the law / Hell to pay / Wild and wonderful.
VHS 0833083
Polygram Music Video / '91 / PolyGram.

WILD AND WONDERFUL.
Tracks: Wild and wonderful / Thunderbird.
■ 12". . . . . .PZ 75
■ 7". . . . . PO 75
■ MC Single. . . . . .POCS 75
Polydor / Jun '90.

Amayon

PURULENCE SPLIT.
Tracks: Not Advised.
CD. .CDAR 016
Adipocre / Feb '94 / Plastic Head.

Amboy Dukes

ALL I NEED.
Tracks: All I need / Doing the best I can.
■ 7". 56172
Polydor / Jul '67.

JOURNEY TO THE CENTRE OF THE MIND.
Tracks: Not Advised.
CD. .MDCD 0911
Mainstream / Jul '92 / Discovery.

TURN BACK TO ME.
Tracks: Turn back to me / I never complain about you.
■ 7". 56149
Polydor / Feb '67.

■ DELETED

Amebix

ARISE.
Tracks: Not Advised.
■ LP . . . . VIRUS 46
Alternative Tentacles / Jul '85.
CD . . . . VIRUS 46CD
Alternative Tentacles / Jul '94 / RTM / Pinnacle.

ENEMY, THE.
Tracks: Enemy.
■ 7" . . . . SDL 6
Spiderleg / Sep '82.

MONOLITH.
Tracks: Monolith / Nobody's driving / Power remains / Time bomb / Last will and testament / I.C.B.M. / Chain reaction / Fallen from grace / Coming home.
■ LP . . . . HMRLP 99
■ MC. . . . . HMRMC 99
Heavy Metal / Aug '87.
■ CD . . . . HMRXD 99
Heavy Metal / Jul '89.
■ LP . . . . HMR LP 99
FM Records / Oct '92.

NO SANCTUARY.
Tracks: Not Advised.
■ LP . . . . SDL 14
Spiderleg / Oct '83.

WINTER.
Tracks: Winter.
■ 7" . . . . SDL 10
Spiderleg / Feb '83.

Anacrusis

MANIC IMPRESSIONS.
Tracks: Not Advised.
CD . . . . CDZORRO 23
LP . . . . ZORRO 23
Music For Nations / Jul '91 / Pinnacle.

REASON.
Tracks: Stop me / Not forgotten / Silent crime / Afraid to feel / Vital / Terrified / Wrong / Misshapen intent / Child inside / Quick to doubt.
CD . . . . CDATV 9
LP . . . . ATV 9
Active / Feb '90 / Pinnacle.

SCREAMS & WHISPERS.
Tracks: Sound the alarm / Sense of will / Too many prophets / Release / Division / Tool of seperation / Grateful / Screaming breath / My soul's affliction / Driven / Brotherhood / Release (Remix).
CD . . . . CDZORR 059
Metal Blade / May '93 / Pinnacle.

SUFFERING HOUR.
Tracks: Not Advised.
■ LP . . . . AXISLP 4
Axis / Jun '88.

Anathema

CRESTFALLEN E.P.
Tracks: ..And I lust / Sweet suffering / Everwake / Crestfallen / They die (CDonly).
■ 12" . . . . VILE 036T
■ CD Single . . . . VILE 036TCD
Peaceville / Nov '92.

SERENADES.
Tracks: Lovelorn rhapsody / Sweet tears / J'ai fait une prommesse / They (will always) die / Sleepless / Sleep in sanity / Scars of the old scream / Under a veil (of black lace) / Where shadows dance / Dreaming: The romance (CD only.)
CD . . . . VILE 034CD
LP . . . . VILE 034
Peaceville / Sep '92 / Vital Distribution / Pinnacle.

Anderson, Angry

BEATS FROM A SINGLE DRUM.
Tracks: Not Advised.
CD . . . . CD 53217
Pacific (USA) / Jul '87 / Pinnacle.
CD . . . . CDGRUB 11
■ LP . . . . GRUB 11
MC. . . . . TGRUB 11
Food For Thought / Apr '89 / Pinnacle.

BLOOD FROM STONE. •
Tracks: Not Advised.
CD . . . . MFNCD 121
LP . . . . MFN 121
MC. . . . . TMFN 121
Music For Nations / Sep '91 / Pinnacle.

CALLING.
Tracks: Calling.
■ 12" . . . . 12 YUM 116
■ 7" . . . . YUM 116
■ CD Single . . . . CDYUM 116
Music For Nations / Feb '89.

SUDDENLY.
Tracks: Suddenly.
■ 7" . . . . YUM 113
Food For Thought / Nov '88.

Anesthesy

EXALTATION OF THE ECLIPSE.
Tracks: Not Advised.
CD . . . . BMCD 54
Black Mark / May '94 / Plastic Head.

Angel

20TH CENTURY FOXES.
Tracks: 20th century foxes / Can you feel it.
■ 7" . . . . CAN 193
Casablanca / Jun '80.

ON AND ON.
Tracks: On and on / Angel.
■ 7" . . . . CBX 514
Casablanca / Feb '76.

SINFUL.
Tracks: Don't take your love / L.A. lady / Just can't take it / You can't buy love / Bad time / Waited a long time / I'll bring the whole world to your door / I'll never fall in love again / Wild and hot / Lovers live on.
■ LP . . . . CAL 2046
Casablanca / '79.

THAT MAGIC TOUCH.
Tracks: That magic touch / Big boy (let's do it again).
■ 7" . . . . CAN 104
Casablanca / May '77.

WINTER SONG.
Tracks: Winter song / Can you feel it.
■ 7" . . . . CAN 113
Casablanca / Nov '78.

Angel Witch

Satan fixated NWOBHM band's moment of chart glory was in 1980 when their *Sweet Danger* single spent a week at number 75. Angel Witch split after recording their eponymous debut LP on the Bronze label and reformed in the late 1980's.

ANGEL WITCH.
Tracks: Angel Witch / Gorgon / Atlantis / White witch / Confused / Sorceress / Sweet danger / Free man / Angel of death / Devil's tower.
■ LP . . . . BRON 532
MC. . . . . BRONC 532
Bronze / Dec '80 / WEA.
CD . . . . CLACD 239
■ MC. . . . . CLAMC 239
■ LP . . . . CLALP 239
Castle Classics / May '91.

ANGEL WITCH.
Tracks: Angel Witch / Gorgon.
■ 7" . . . . BRO 108
Bronze / Oct '82.

DOCTOR PHIBES.
Tracks: Angel Witch / Atlantis / White Witch / Confused / Sorceress / Loser / Dr. Phibes / Gorgon / Sweet danger / Free man / Angel of death / Devil's tower / Suffer.
■ LP . . . . RAWLP 025
Raw Power / Sep '86.

FRONTAL ASSAULT.
Tracks: Frontal assault / Dream world / Rendezvous with the blade / Religion (born again) / Straight from hell / She don't lie / Take to the wing / Something wrong / Undergods.
■ LP . . . . KILP 4003
Killerwatt / May '86.

GOODBYE.
Tracks: Goodbye / Reawakening.
■ 7" . . . . KIL 3001
Killerwatt / Jul '85.

LIVE.
Tracks: Angel of death / Confused / Gorgon / Extermination day / Flight 19 / White Witch / Sweet danger / Sorceress / Baphamet / Atlantis / Angel Witch.
CD . . . . CDZORRO 1

MC. . . . . TZORRO 1
■ LP . . . . ZORRO 1
Music For Nations / May '90.

LOSER.
Tracks: Loser / Suffer / Dr. Phibes.
■ EP . . . . BRO 121
Bronze / May '81.

SCREAMIN' 'N' BLEEDING'.
Tracks: Who's to blame / Child of the night / Evil games / Afraid of the dark / Screamin' n' bleedin' / Reawakening / Waltz the night / Goodbye / Fatal kiss / UXV.
■ LP . . . . KILP 4001
Killerwatt / Jul '85.

SCREAMIN' ASSAULT.
Tracks: She don't lie / Frontal assault / Something wrong / Straight from hell / Reawakening / Screamin' n' bleedin' / Waltz the night / Rendezvous with the blade / Goodbye / Take to the wing / Fatal kiss / Undergods / UXV.
CD . . . . KILCD 1001
Killerwatt / Dec '88 / Kingdom Records.

SWEET DANGER.
Tracks: Sweet danger / Hades paradise / Flight nineteen.
■ 7" . . . . EMI 5064
■ 12" 12EMI 5064
EMI / May '80.

Angels

BEYOND SALVATION.
Tracks: Not Advised.
■ LP . . . . CHR 1677
■ CD . . . . CCD 1677
■ MC. . . . . ZCHR 1677
Chrysalis / Mar '90.

LIVE FROM ANGEL CITY.
Tracks: Not Advised.
■ LP . . . . ACE 001
Telegram (USA) / Dec '88.

Angkor Wat

CORPUS CHRISTI.
Tracks: Not Advised.
CD . . . . CDZORRO 5
LP . . . . ZORRO 5
Music For Nations / May '90 / Pinnacle.

WHEN OBSCENITY BECOMES THE NORM..AWAKE.
Tracks: Not Advised.
■ LP . . . . RO 94571
Roadracer / May '89.

Angus

PAPA DON'T FREAK.
Tracks: Papa don't freak.
■ 12" . . . . MEGATON 2.19
Megaton / Jul '87.

TRACK OF DOOM.
Tracks: Not Advised.
■ LP . . . . MEGATON 0017
Megaton / Jul '86.

WARRIOR OF THE WORLD.
Tracks: Warriors of the world / Moving fast / Leather and lace / Money satisfies / Black despair / 2086 / Freedom fighter / I'm in love with love / If God's in heaven.
■ LP . . . . MEGATON 020
Megaton / Nov '87.

Annihilated

PATH TO DESTRUCTION.
Tracks: Path to destruction.
■ 12" . . . . BREW 1
Annihilated / Oct '86.

Annihilator

Canadian Thrash band formed in 1985 by guitarist/songwriter Jeff Waters, Roy Harmann, Wayne Darley, Dave Scott Davis and Randy Rampage - ex D.O.A. Their debut album, *Alice In Hell* (Roadrunner) was released in 1989 and was considered one of the best thrash albums of the year. Recorded *Never Never Land* in 1990.

ALICE IN HELL.
Tracks: Crystal Ann / W.T.Y.D. / Burns like a buzzsaw blade / Schizos (are never alone) (parts 1 & 2) /

Human insecticide / Alison Hell / Wicked mystic / Word salad / Ligeia.

CD	RR 9488 2
MC	RR 9488 4
■ LP	RR 9488 1

Road Runner / Apr '89.

ANNIHILATOR.
Tracks: Not Advised.

LP	WRR 006

Wild Rags / Nov '88 / Plastic Head.

BAG OF TRICKS.
Tracks: Alison Hell / Phantasmagoria / Back to the crypt / Gallery / Human insecticide / Fun Palace / W.T.Y.D. / Word salad / Live wire / Knight jumps Queen / Fantastic things / Bats in the belfry / Evil appetite / Gallery '86 / Alison Hell '86 / Phantasmagoria '86.

CD	RR 8997-2
MC	RR 8997-4

Road Runner / Jul '94 / Pinnacle.

CREATED IN HATE.
Tracks: Not Advised.

■ LP	VOV 668
MC	VOV 668C

Metalworks / Apr '88.

KING OF THE KILL.
Tracks: Box / King of the kill / Hell is a war / Bliss / Second to none / Annihilator / 21 / In the blood / Fiasco (slate) / Fiasco / Catch the wind / Speed / Bad child.

CD	CDMFN 171

Music For Nations / Oct '94 / Pinnacle.

NEVER NEVER LAND.
Tracks: Not Advised.

CD	RR 93742
LP	RR 93741
MC	RR 93744

Road Runner / Jul '90 / Pinnacle.

SET THE WORLD ON FIRE.
Tracks: Set the world on fire.

■ 12"	RR 23856
■ CD Single	RR 23853

Road Runner / Apr '93.

SET THE WORLD ON FIRE.
Tracks: Not Advised.

CD	RR 92002
MC	RR 92004
■ CD	RR 92005
■ LP	RR 92001

Road Runner / May '93.

STONEWALL.
Tracks: Stonewall / W.T.Y.D. (live) / Word salad (live).

■ 12"	RR 24256
■ CD Single	RR 24253
■ MC Single	RR 24254

Road Runner / Feb '91.

ULTIMATE DESECRATION, THE.
Tracks: Not Advised.

■ LP	VOV 675

Metalworks / May '89.

Anthem

GYPSY WAYS.
Tracks: Gypsy ways (win, lose or draw) / Bad habits die hard / Cryin' heart / Midnight sun / Final risk / Love in vain / Legal killing / Silent child / Shout it out / Night stalker.

CD	CDMFN 103
LP	MFN 103

Music For Nations / Aug '90 / Pinnacle.

HUNTING TIME.
Tracks: Juggler / Evil touch / Sleepless night / Let your heart beat / Hunting time / Tears for the lovers / Jailbreak / Bottle bottom.

CD	CDMFN 104
LP	MFN 104

Music For Nations / Aug '90 / Pinnacle.

NO SMOKE WITHOUT FIRE.
Tracks: Shadow walk / Blinded pain / Love on the edge / Power and blood / Night we stand / Hungry soul / Do you understand / Voice of thunderstorm / Fever eyes.

CD	CDMFN 101
LP	MFN 101
MC	TMFN 101

Music For Nations / Aug '90 / Pinnacle.

Anthrax

New York band formed in 1981. Undistinguished 1984 debut was followed by introduction into line-up of Joey Belladonna, one of thrash's few genuine singers. Group's success exploded in 1987; *I am the law* single made Top 40 and *Among the living* was first of group's five U.K. Top 20 albums. Equally important was collaboration with rap superstars Public Enemy for 1991 *Bring the noize* single and tour. Belladonna was replaced by Armored Saint's John Bush shortly afterwards, but band retain their niche in metal market.

AMONG THE LIVING.
Tracks: Among the living / Caught in a mosh / I am the law / Eflinkufsin (N.F.L.) / Skeleton in the closet / Indians / One world / A.D.I. Horror of it all / Imitation of life.

■ CD	CID 9865
■ LP	ILPS 9865
■ MC	ICT 9865
■ LP P.Disc	PILPS 9865

Island / Apr '87.

CD	IMCD 186

Island / Mar '94 / PolyGram.

AMONG THE LIVING/ PERSISTENCE OF TIME.
Tracks: Not Advised.

CD Set	ITSCD 6

Island / Nov '92 / PolyGram.

ANTHRAX LIVE NOIZE.
Tracks: Not Advised.

VHS	82838-3

Polygram Music Video / Apr '94 / PolyGram.

ANTHRAX: INTERVIEW COLLECTION.
Tracks: Not Advised.

7" Set	BAKPAK 1017

Baktabak / Nov '89 / Arabesque Ltd.

ANTHRAX: INTERVIEW PICTURE DISC.
Tracks: Not Advised.

■ LP P.Disc	CT 1021

Music & Media / Feb '88.

ANTHRAX: INTERVIEW PICTURE DISC (BAKTABAK).
Tracks: Not Advised.

LP P.Disc	BAK 2134

Baktabak / Jun '89 / Arabesque Ltd.

ANTI-SOCIAL.
Tracks: Anti-social / Parasite / Le-sect.

■ 12" Remix	12ISR 409
■ 12"	12 IS 409
■ 7"	IS 409
■ CD Single	CIDX 409
■ MC Single	CIS 409

Island / Mar '89.

ARMED AND DANGEROUS.
Tracks: Not Advised.

■ LP	MRS 05
■ LP P.Disc	MRS 05P

Megaforce (USA) / Aug '87.

CD	CDMFN 123
LP	MFN 123
MC	TMFN 123

Music For Nations / Nov '91 / Pinnacle.

ATTACK OF THE KILLER B'S.
Tracks: Milk (Ode to Billy) / Bring the noise / Keep it in the family (Live) / Startin' up a posse / Protest and survive / Chromatic death / I'm the man '91 / Parasite / Pipeline / Sects / Belly of the beast (Live) / N.F.B.

■ CD	CID 9980
■ MC	ICT 9980
■ LP	ILPS 9980

Island / Jun '91.

CD	IMCD 180
MC	ICM 9980

Island / Mar '94 / PolyGram.

BLACK LODGE.
Tracks: Black lodge.

■ 12"	EKR 171T
■ 7"	EKR 171
■ CD Single	EKR 171CD

Elektra / Sep '93.

BRING THE NOISE (Anthrax & Chuck D).
Tracks: Bring the noise / Keep it in the family / I am the law '91.

■ 12"	12IS 490
■ 7"	IS 490
■ CD Single	CID 490

Island / Jul '91.

■ 10"	10 IS 490

Island / Jun '91.

FISTFUL OF METAL.
Tracks: Deathrider / I'm eighteen / Subjagator / Howling furies (American remix) / Death from above / Across the river / Metal thrashing mad / Panic / Soldiers of metal (American remix) / Soldiers of metal / Anthrax / Howling furies.

CD	CDMFN 14
■ LP	MFN 14
■ Double LP	MFN 14DM
■ LP P.Disc	MFN 14P
MC	TMFN 14

Music For Nations / Apr '87 / Pinnacle.

GOT THE TIME.
Tracks: Got the time.

■ 12"	12 IS 475
■ 7"	IS 475
■ CD Single	CID 476
■ MC Single	CIS 476

Island / Oct '90.

I AM THE LAW.
Tracks: Bud. E. Luvbomb and Satan's lounge band / I am the law.

■ 7"	LAW 1
■ 12"	12IS 316

Island / Feb '87.

I'M THE MAN.
Tracks: I'm the man / Caught in the mosh / I am the law (live).

■ 12"	12IS 338
■ 7"	IS 338
■ 7" P.Disc	ISP 338

Island / Jul '87.

IN MY WORLD.
Tracks: In my world / Keep it in the family.

■ 10"	10 IS 470
■ 12" P.Disc	12 ISP 470
■ CD Single	CID 470
■ 7"	IS 470
■ MC Single	CIS 470

Island / Jul '90.

INDIANS.
Tracks: Indians / Sabbath bloody sabbath / Taint.

■ 12"	12IS 325
■ 7" P.Disc	ISP 325
■ 7"	IS 325
■ MC Single	CIS 325

Island / Jun '87.

LIVE - THE ISLAND YEARS.
Tracks: (Efilnikufesin) N.F.L. / A.I.R. / Parasite / Keep it in the family / Caught in a mosh / Indians / Antisocial / Bring the noise / I am the law / Metal thrashing mad / In my world / Not it's dark.

CD	CID 8027
LP	ILPS 8027
MC	ICT 8027

Island / Apr '94 / PolyGram.

MAD HOUSE.
Tracks: Mad house / A.I.R. / God save the Queen.

■ 12"	12IS 285

Island / Sep '86.

■ 12"	12ISB 285

Island / May '86.

■ 12" P.Disc	12ISP 285

Island / Sep '86.

MAKE ME LAUGH.
Tracks: Make me laugh / Anti social (live) / Friggin' in the riggin' (Available on 12" only.).

■ 12"	12IS 379
■ 7"	IS 379
■ CD P.Disc	CIDP 379

Island / Jul '88.

MUSIC AND MEDIA INTERVIEW PICTURE DISCS.
Tracks: Not Advised.

■ LP P.Disc	MM 1254

Music & Media / Feb '88.

N.F.V.
Tracks: Not Advised.

VHS	0822743

Polygram Music Video / '91 / PolyGram.

OIDIVNIKUFESIN (N.F.V.).
Tracks: Among the living / Caught in the mosh / Metal thrashing mad / I am the law / Mad house / Indians / Medusa / NFL / Armed and dangerous / Air/I'm the man/ / Gung ho.

VHS	IVA 006

Island Visual Arts / Oct '88 / PolyGram / TBD.

ONLY.
Tracks: Only / Cowboy song (On CD1 only) / Auf wiedersehen (On CD2 only).
- 7" .... EKR 166
- CD Single .... EKR 166CD2
- CD Single .... EKR 166CD1
- MC Single .... EKR 166C
Elektra / Apr '93.

PERSISTENCE OF TIME.
Tracks: Time / Blood / Keep it in the family / In my world / Gridlock / Intro to reality / Belly of the beast / Got the time / H8 red / One man stands / Discharge.
- CD .... CID 9967
- MC .... ICT 9967
- LP .... ILPS 9967
Island / Aug '90.
- LP P.Disc .... ILPSP 9967
Island / May '91.
CD .... IMCD 178
MC .... ICM 9967
Island / Mar '94 / PolyGram.

PERSISTENCE THROUGH TIME.
Tracks: Not Advised.
VHS .... IVA 056
Island Visual Arts / Oct '90 / PolyGram / TBD.

SOUND OF WHITE NOISE, THE.
Tracks: Potters field / Only / Room for one more / Packaged rebellion / Hy pro glo / Invisible / 1000 points of hate / Black lodge / C11 H17.. / Burst / This is not an exit.
CD 755961430-2
LP 755961430-1
MC 755961430-4
Elektra / May '93 / WEA.

SPREADING THE DISEASE.
Tracks: Gung-ho / Armed and dangerous / Afters / Enemy / S.S.C. / Stand or fall / Madhouse / Lone justice / A.I.R.
- LP .... MFN 62
Music For Nations / Feb '86.
MC .... TMFN 62
Music For Nations / Feb '86 / Pinnacle.
- CD .... CID 9806
Island / May '88.
CD .... IMCD 136
MC .... ICM 9806
Island / Aug '91 / PolyGram.

STATE OF EUPHORIA.
Tracks: Be all, end all / Out of sight out of mind / Make me laugh / Antisocial / Who cares wins / Now it's dark / Schism / Misery loves company / 13 / Finale.
- CD .... CID 9916
- LP .... ILPS 9916
- MC .... ICT 9916
Island / Sep '88.
- LP P.Disc .... PILPS 9916
Island / Mar '89.
CD .... IMCD 187
Island / Mar '94 / PolyGram.

THROUGH TIME.
Tracks: Metal thrashing mad / Madhouse / Indians / I'm the man / I am the law / Antisocial / Who cares wins / In my world / Got the time.
VHS 0828343
Polygram Music Video / '91 / PolyGram.

Anti Nowhere League

British punk band, the Anti-Nowhere League - Animal, Magoo, P.J. and Winston - spent most of 1981 touring the London area. Their debut single, a version of Ralph McTell's *Streets Of London*, was a hit in early '82. 10,000 copies were seized by the Obscene Publications Squad because of the 'offensive' B-side *So What* - a song which was later covered by Metallica. The Anti Nowhere League had further minor hit singles including *I Hate People* and *Woman* and disbanded in 1987. They were still playing live dates in 1994.

BEST OF THE ANTI NOWHERE LEAGUE.
Tracks: Streets of London / I hate people / We are the league / Let's break the law / Animal / Woman / Rocker / For you / Ballad of JJ Decay / Out on the wasteland / We will survive / Queen and country / On the waterfront / Let the country feed you (Live) / Going down (Live) / Snowman (Live) / So what (Live).
- CD .... STR CD 013
Street Link / Oct '92.
CD .... DOJOCD 128
Dojo / Mar '93 / Castle Communications / BMG.
CD .... CLEO 07279CD
Cleopatra / Jan '94 / Plastic Head / Pinnacle.

FOR YOU.
Tracks: For you.
- 7" .... ABCD 6
WXYZ / Jul '87.

I HATE PEOPLE.
Tracks: I hate people.
- 7" .... ABCD 2
WXYZ / Jul '87.

LIVE AND LOUD.
Tracks: For you / Queen and country / Johannesburg / Wreck a nowhere / Streets of London / Crime / We will survive / Branded / Woman / Can't stand rock 'n' roll / We are the league / Something else / Let the country feed you / Let's break the law / I hate people / Snowman / On the waterfront / Going down.
LP .... LINKLP 120
Link / Mar '90 / ACD Trading Ltd.
CD .... LINKCD 120
Link / Oct '90 / ACD Trading Ltd.

LONG LIVE THE LEAGUE.
Tracks: For you / We will survive / Out on the wasteland / On the waterfront / Queen and country / We're the league / Streets of London / So what / Let's break the law / Ballad of JJ Decay / Woman / Snowman / Wreck a nowhere / Let the country feed you / Going down / I hate people.
- LP .... DOJOLP 15
Dojo / Apr '86.
- CD .... DOJOCD 15
Dojo / '87.

OUT ON THE WASTELAND.
Tracks: Out on the wasteland / We will survive / Queen and country.
- 12" .... ABCS 004T
- 7" .... ABCS 004
- 7" P.Disc .... ABCS 004P
ABC (Indie) / Dec '84.

PERFECT CRIME, THE.
Tracks: Crime / On the waterfront / Branded / I don't believe this is my England / Johannesburg / Shining / Working for the company / System / Curtain.
- LP .... GWLP 12
- MC .... GWTC 12
GWR / May '87.

PERFECT CRIME, THE/ LIVE IN YUGOSLAVIA.
Tracks: Crime / Atomic harvest / On the waterfront / Branded / (I don't believe) This is my England / Johannesburg / Shining / Working for the company / System / Curtain / Let's break the law / Streets of London / We will survive / I hate people / For you / Woman / Can't stand rock 'n' roll / Wreck a nowhere / Paint it black / We are the league.
CD .... LOMACD 9
Castle / Nov '92 / BMG.

STREETS OF LONDON.
Tracks: Streets of London.
- 7" .... ABCD 1
WXYZ / Nov '88.

WE ARE THE LEAGUE.
Tracks: We're the league / Animal / Woman / Can't stand rock 'n' roll / (We will not) Rememeber you / Snowman / Streets of London / I hate people (Remix) / Reck-a-nowhere / World war III / Nowhere man / Let's break the law (Remix) / Rocker / So what.
CD .... DOJOCD 128
Dojo / Apr '93 / Castle Communications / BMG.

WE ARE..THE LEAGUE.
Tracks: We are the league / Animal / Woman / Can't stand rock 'n' roll / (We will not) Rememeber you / Snowman / Streets of London / I hate..people (Remix) / Reck-a-nowhere / World war III / Nowhere man / Let's break the law (Remix) / Rocker / So what.
CD .... STR CD 028
Street Link / Oct '92 / BMG.

WE ARE..THE LEAGUE.
Tracks: Roll on world war three / So what / Wreck a nowhere / Let's break the law / Woman / Streets of London / For you.
- LP .... LMNOP 1
WXYZ / Apr '82.
- LP .... LMNOPC 1
WXYZ / Jun '82.
- LP .... NOSE 6
I.D. / Nov '85.

WE ARE..THE LEAGUE (LIVE IN YUGOSLAVIA).
Tracks: Not Advised.
- LP .... NOSE 3
I.D. / Oct '83.
- LP .... NOSE 36

I.D. / Jan '89.
CD .... CDOSE 36
I.D. / Jan '90.

WOMAN.
Tracks: Woman / Rocker.
- 7" .... ABCD 4
- 7" P.Disc .... ABCDP 4
WXYZ / Jun '82.

Antiseen

BLOOD OF FREAKS.
Tracks: Blood of freaks.
- 7" .... AJAX 003
Ajax / Apr '92.

TWO HEADED DOG.
Tracks: Two headed dog.
- 7" .... AJAX 007
Ajax / Apr '92.

Antix

GET UP GET HAPPY.
Tracks: Not Advised.
- LP .... HMASP 42
Heavy Metal America / Oct '85.

Anvil

BACKWAXED.
Tracks: Not Advised.
- LP .... RR 9776
Road Runner / Jun '85.

FORGED IN FIRE.
Tracks: Not Advised.
- LP .... LAT 1170
- MC .... CAT 1170
Noir / May '83 / Pinnacle / Jetstar.
CD .... RR 349927
- LP .... RR 9927
Road Runner / '88.

HARD AND HEAVY.
Tracks: Not Advised.
- LP .... LAT 1100
- MC .... CAT 1100
Noir / Jan '82 / Pinnacle / Jetstar.

MAKE IT UP TO YOU.
Tracks: Make it up to you / Metal on metal.
- 12" .... MET 12 002
- 7" .... MET 002
Noir / Jun '83.

METAL ON METAL.
Tracks: Not Advised.
MC .... CAT 1130
Noir / Jul '82 / Pinnacle / Jetstar.
- LP .... LAT 1130
Noir / May '82.
CD .... RR 349917
Road Runner / Jun '89 / Pinnacle.

PAST AND PRESENT LIVE.
Tracks: Concrete jungle / Toe jam / Motorneount / Forged in fire / Blood on the ice / March of the crabs / Jack hammer / Metal on metal / Winged assassins / 666 / Mothra.
CD .... RO 94532
- LP .... RO 94531
Roadracer / Aug '89.

STEAMIN'.
Tracks: Steamin'.
- 12" .... MET 12 001
- 7" .... MET 001
Noir / Aug '82.

STRENGTH OF STEEL.
Tracks: Strength of steel / Concrete jungle / 9-2-5 / I dreamed it was the end of the world / Flight of the bumble beast / Cut loose / Mad dog / Straight between the eyes / Wild eyes / Kiss of death / Paper general.
- LP .... RR 9618
Road Runner / Jun '87.

Apocalypse

APOCALYPSE.
Tracks: Not Advised.
CD .... CDFLAG 23
- LP .... FLAG 23
Under One Flag / Aug '89.
MC .... TFLAG 23
Under One Flag / Aug '89 / Pinnacle.

- DELETED

A 11

Apochrypha

AREA 54.
Tracks: Terrors holding on to you / Night in the fog / Instrubation [8]X3 (instrumental) / Tian'anmen Square / Refuse the offer that you can't refuse / Catch 22 / Power elite / Area 54 / Detriment of man / Born to this world.
CD . . . . RR 93452
Road Runner / Nov '90 / Pinnacle.

EYES OF TIME.
Tracks: Not Advised.
CD . . . . .RR 9507 2
■ LP . . . . .RR 9507 1
Road Runner / Dec '88.

FORGOTTEN SCROLL, THE.
Tracks: Penance / Lost children of hope / Holy wars (only lock the doors) / Fall of the crest / Tablet of destiny / Look to the sun / Riding in the night / Distorted reflections / Broken dreams.
■ LP . . . . RR 95681
Road Runner / Feb '88.

April Sixteenth

SLEEP WALKING.
Tracks: Not Advised.
■ LP . . . . HD 032
High Dragon / Jun '88.

April Wine

ALL OVER TOWN.
Tracks: All over town / Crash and burn.
■ 7" . . . . CL 16181
Capitol / Jan '81.

ANIMAL GRACE.
Tracks: This could be the right one / Sons of the pioneers / Without your love / Rock tonite / Hard rock kid / Money talks / Gimme that thing called love / Last time I'll ever sing the blues.
MC . . . . TC EST 2400834
■ LP . . . . EST 2400831
Capitol / Apr '84.

APRIL WINE.
Tracks: Not Advised.
CD . . . . REP 4212-WY
Repertoire (Germany) / Aug '91 / Pinnacle.

CHILD'S GARDEN.
Tracks: Child's garden / Whole world's goin' crazy.
■ 7" . . . . HLU 10544
London / Oct '76.

ELECTRIC JEWELS.
Tracks: Not Advised.
CD . . . . .RR 4212
Repertoire (Germany) / Jul '93 / Pinnacle.

HARDER FASTER.
Tracks: I like to rock / Say hello / Tonight / Ladies man / Before the dawn / Babes in arms / Better do it well / 21st century schizoid man.
■ LP .EST 12013
Capitol / Nov '79.

I LIKE TO ROCK.
Tracks: I like to rock / Rock 'n' roll is a vicious game / Before the dawn / Roller.
■ 7" . . . . CL 16121
Capitol / Feb '80.

JUST BETWEEN YOU AND ME.
Tracks: Just between you and me / Big city girls.
■ 7" . . . . CL 16184
Capitol / Feb '81.

LADIES MAN.
Tracks: Ladies man / Oowatanite / Get ready for love (Only available on 12" single.) / I like to rock (Only available on 12" single.).
■ 12" 12CL 16164
■ 7" . . . . CL 16164
Capitol / Aug '80.

LIVE IN LONDON.
Tracks: Not Advised.
■ VHS . . . . MVP 99 1017 2
PMI / Jun '86.
■ VHS . . . . HEN 2171
Hendring Video / Mar '89.

NATURE OF THE BEAST.
Tracks: All over town / Tellin' me lies / Sign of the gypsy queen / Just between you and me / Wanna rock / Caught in the crossfire / Future tense / Big city girls / Crash and burn / Bad boys / One more time.
■ LP .EST 12125
Capitol / Jan '81.

ON RECORD.
Tracks: Not Advised.
CD . . . . .REP 4213-WY
Repertoire (Germany) / Aug '91 / Pinnacle.
CD . . . . RR 4213
Repertoire (Germany) / Jul '93 / Pinnacle.

POWER PLAY.
Tracks: Anything you want you get it / Enough is enough / If you see Kay / What if we fall in love / Waiting on a miracle / Doin' it right / Ain't got your love / Blood money / Tell me why / Runners in the night.
■ LP .EST 12218
Capitol / Aug '82.

ROLLER.
Tracks: Roller / Right down to it.
■ 7" . . . . CL 16075
Capitol / Apr '79.

SIGN OF THE GYPSY QUEEN.
Tracks: Sign of the gypsy queen / Crash and burn.
■ 7" .CL 205
Capitol / May '81.

THIS COULD BE THE RIGHT ONE.
Tracks: This could be the right one / Really don't want your love.
■ 7" .CL 328
Capitol / '84.

YOU WON'T DANCE WITH ME.
Tracks: You won't dance with me / Shot down.
■ 7" . . . . HLU 10549
London-American / Jul '77.

Aragorn

BLACK ICE.
Tracks: Black ice / Noonday.
■ 7" .NEAT 07
Neat / Feb '81.

Arcane

DESTINATION UNKNOWN.
Tracks: Not Advised.
CD .WRE 906CD
LP . . . . WRE 906
Wild Rags / Jan '91 / Plastic Head.

Arcwelder

PULL.
Tracks: Not Advised.
CD .TG 108CD
LP . . . . TG 108
Touch & Go / Feb '93 / SRD.

RALEIGH.
Tracks: Raleigh.
■ 7" . . . . TG 105
Touch & Go / Oct '92.

XERXES.
Tracks: Not Advised.
CD .TG 126CD
LP . . . . TG 126
Touch & Go / Apr '94 / SRD.

Ardkore

NAPALM STIX TO KIDZ.
Tracks: Not Advised.
■ LP .VOV 671
Metalworks / Nov '88.

Ark

COVER ME WITH RAIN.
Tracks: Not Advised.
■ CD . . . . AMA 1003CD
■ MC . . . . AMA 1003MC
Ama Productions / Nov '92.

SPIRITUAL PHYSICS.
Tracks: Not Advised.
CD . . . . MC 301CD
LP . . . . MC 301
Mutilation Corps. / Jun '93 / Plastic Head.

Armageddon

ARMAGEDDON.
Tracks: Not Advised.
CD .REP 4235-WP
Repertoire (Germany) / Aug '91 / Pinnacle.

INVISIBLE CIRCLE.
Tracks: Not Advised.
CD . . . . DEAF 013CD

LP . . . . DEAF 013
Peaceville / '93 / Vital Distribution / Pinnacle.

Armed Force

ARMED FORCE.
Tracks: Not Advised.
■ LP . . . . IW 1009
Iron Works (USA) / Jan '87.

Armed Forces

TAKE ON THE NATION.
Tracks: Not Advised.
CD . . . . .CDMFN 136
MC . . . . .TMFN 136
Music For Nations / Jun '92 / Pinnacle.

Armored Saint

DELIRIOUS NOMAD.
Tracks: Long before I die / Nervous man / Over the edge / Laugh / Conqueror / For the sake / Aftermath / In the hole / You're never alone / Released.
MC . . . . ZCHR 1516
■ LP . . . . CHR 1516
Chrysalis / Jan '86.

MARCH OF THE SAINTS.
Tracks: March of the saint / Can U deliver / Mad house / Take a turn / Seducer / Mutiny on the world / Glory hunter / Stricken by fate / Envy / False alarm.
■ LP . . . . CHR 1479
■ MC . . . . ZCHR 1479
Chrysalis / Oct '84.

RAISING FEAR.
Tracks: Raising fear / Saturday night special / Out on a limb / Isolation / Chemical euphoria / Frozen will / Human vulture / Book of blood / Terror / Underdogs / Legacy.
■ LP . . . . CHR 1610
■ MC . . . . ZCHR 1610
Chrysalis / Oct '87.

SAINTS WILL CONQUER.
Tracks: Raising fear / Nervous man / Book of blood / Can U deliver / Mad house / No reason to live.
CD . . . . .RR 9520 2
■ LP . . . . .RR 9520 1
Road Runner / Sep '88.
CD . . . . .CDZORRO 28
LP . . . . ZORRO 28
MC . . . . .TZORRO 28
Music For Nations / Aug '91 / Pinnacle.

SYMBOL OF SALVATION.
Tracks: Not Advised.
CD . . . . .CDZORRO 20
LP . . . . ZORRO 20
MC . . . . .TZORRO 20
Metal Blade / Mar '91 / Pinnacle.

TRIP THRU RED TIMES, A.
Tracks: Not Advised.
VHS . . . . VFN 2
Video For Nations / '89 / Pinnacle.

Artch

ANOTHER RETURN.
Tracks: Not Advised.
CD . . . . ACTCD 5
LP . . . . ACTLP 5
Active / Jul '91 / Pinnacle.

Artificial Peace

ASSAULT & BATTERY.
Tracks: Assault & battery.
■ 7" .LF 008
Lemon Flower / Sep '92.

ASSUALT AND BATTERY.
Tracks: Assualt and battery.
■ 7" .LF 008
Plastic Head / Jun '92.

DISCOGRAPH.
Tracks: Not Advised.
CD . . . . .LF 038
Plastic Head / Jun '92 / Plastic Head.

OUTSIDE LOOKING.
Tracks: Not Advised.
LP . . . . .LF 009
Lost & Found / Apr '92 / Plastic Head.

Artillery

Danish thrash band, formed in 1982 by Jorgen Sandau and Carstan Nielsen. They were joined by Michael Stutzer, Flemming Ronsdorf and Morten Stutzer. Their first album, *Fear Of Tomorrow*, was released in 1985 on Neat. A follow up album, *Terror Squad*, was released in 1987.

ARTILLERY 3.
Tracks: Not Advised.
■ LP . . . . NEAT 1046
Neat / Aug '88.
CD . . . . NEATCD 1046
Neat / Aug '88 / Grapevine Distribution.

BY INHERITANCE.
Tracks: 7-00 from Tashkent / Beneath the clay / Bombfood / Life in bondage / Razamanaz / Khomaniac / By inheritance / Don't believe / Equal at first / Back in the trash.
CD . . . . RO 93972
LP . . . . RO 93971
MC . . . . RO 93974
Road Runner / May '90 / Pinnacle.

FEAR OF TOMORROW.
Tracks: Time has come / Almighty / Show you hate / King thy name is slayer / Out of the sky / Into the universe / Eternal war / Deed of darkness.
■ LP . . . . NEAT 1030
Neat / Nov '86.
MC . . . . NEATC 1030
Neat / Nov '86 / Grapevine Distribution.

TERROR SQUAD.
Tracks: Challenge / In the trash / Terror squad / Let there be sin / Hunger and greed / Therapy / At war with science / Decapitation of deviants.
■ LP . . . . NEAT 1038
Neat / Apr '87.
MC . . . . NEATC 1038
Neat / Apr '87 / Grapevine Distribution.

As Serenity Fades

EARTHBORN.
Tracks: Not Advised.
CD .CDAR 018
Adipocre / May '94 / Plastic Head.

Asap

DOWN THE WIRE.
Tracks: Down the wire (long distance mix) (12" & CD single only.) / Down the wire (crossed line mix) (Only on MC and 7" single.) / When she's gone / School days (12" & CD single only.).
■ 12" 12EM 131
■ 12" 12EMP 131
■ 7" . . . . EM 131
■ 7" . . . . EMS 131
■ 7" P.Disc . . . . .EMPD 131
■ CD Single . . . . .CDEM 131
■ MC Single . . . . TCEM 131
EMI / Jan '90.

SILVER AND GOLD.
Tracks: Silver & gold (7" only.) / Blood brothers (7" only.) / Silver and gold (12" remix) (Not on 7".) / Blood brothers (alt. version) (Not on 7".) / Fighting man (Not on 7".).
■ 12" 12EMP 107
■ 12" 12EM 107
■ 12" P.Disc. 12EMPD 107
■ 7" . . . . EMG 107
■ 7" . . . . EM 107
■ CD Single . . . . .CDEM 107
EMI / Oct '89.

SILVER AND GOLD.
Tracks: Lion / Silver & gold / Down the wire / You could be a King / After the storm / Misunderstood / Kid gone astray / Fallen heroes / Wishing your life away / Blood on the ocean.
■ LP . . . . EMC 3566
■ CD . . . . .CDEMC 3566
■ LP . . . . .EMCG 3566
■ MC . . . . TCEMC 3566
EMI / Oct '89.

Asia

Asia represent one of the most carefully contrived projects in the history of rock. In 1980, following the disintergration of Yes, Steve Howe and Geoff Downes teamed up with ex-Family, King Crimson, Roxy Music and Uriah Heep bassist John Wetton and in 1981 by Carl Palmer (of E.L.P.). A supergroup had been assembled and with

unashamed calculation, Asia recorded an eponymous debut LP in 1982 that was ideally suited for AOR radio stations in U.S.A. hiring a professional radio consultant to advise them. *Asia*, was America's biggest selling album in 1982. It's first two tracks, *Heat Of The Night*, and *Only Time Will Tell*, were also hit singles. The group was less well received in their native country, the album a steady but unspectacular seller. 1983's follow-up *Alpha*, was a weaker version of the same formula. Shortly after its release, Wetton departed and was replaced another former E.L.P. member, Greg Lake. Asia have continued to record into the 1990's with less success.

ALPHA.
Tracks: Don't cry / Smile has left your eyes / Never in a million years / My own time (I'll do what I want) / Heat goes on / Eye to eye / Last to know / True colours / Midnight sun / Open your eyes.
■ LP . . . . GEF 25508
Geffen / Aug '83.
■ LP 9040081
■ MC 9040084
Geffen / Sep '86.
■ CD 9040082
Geffen / Jun '89.
■ CD . . . . .GEFD 04008
■ MC . . . . .GEFC 04008
Geffen / Apr '91.
■ MC . . . . .GFLC 19053
Geffen / Apr '92.
CD . . . . .GFLD 19053
Geffen / Apr '92 / BMG.

AQUA.
Tracks: Not Advised.
CD . . . . .WKFMXD 180
■ LP . . . . .WKFMLP 180
MC . . . . .WKFMMC 180
FM Coast To Coast / Feb '92 / FM Revolver / Sony.
LP 109281
MC 109284
Musidisc / Jun '92 / Vital Distribution / Discovery / A.D.A. Distribution / Harmonia Mundi (UK).

ARIA.
Tracks: Not Advised.
CD . . . . .CDVEST 8
LP . . . . VEST 8
MC . . . . .TVEST 8
Bulletproof / May '94 / Pinnacle.

ASIA.
Tracks: Go / Voice of America / Hard on me / Wishing / Rock and roll dream / Countdown to zero / Love now till eternity / Too late / Suspicion / After the war / Heat of the moment / Only time will tell / Sole survivor / Time again / One step closer / Wildest dreams / Without you / Cutting it fine / Here comes the feeling.
■ LP . . . . GEF 85577
Geffen / May '82.
■ LP 9020081
■ MC 9020084
Geffen / Sep '86.
CD . . . . .GFLD 19054
Geffen / Nov '90 / BMG.
■ MC . . . . .GFLC 19054
Geffen / Nov '90.
■ CD . . . . .GEFD 02008
■ MC . . . . .GEFC 02008
Geffen / Apr '91.

ASIA (LIVE).
Tracks: Not Advised.
VHS . . . . .VVD 959
Virgin Vision / Oct '91 / Gold & Sons / TBD.

ASIA IN ASIA.
Tracks: Not Advised.
VHS . . . . MA 11009
Vestron Music Video / Sep '84 / Sony / Gold & Sons / TBD.

ASTRA.
Tracks: Go / Voice of America / Hard on me / Wishing / Rock and roll dream / Countdown to zero / Love now till eternity / Too late / Suspicion / After the war.
■ LP . . . . GEF 26413
■ CD 9240722
■ MC 4026413
Geffen / Dec '85.
■ CD . . . . .CDGEF 26413
Geffen / Oct '86.

DON'T CRY.
Tracks: Don't cry / True colours.
■ 12" . . . . TA 3580
■ 7" . . . . .A 3580
Geffen / Aug '83.

GO.
Tracks: Go / After the war.
■ 12" . . . . TA 6737
■ 7" . . . . .A 6737
Geffen / Dec '85.

HEAT OF THE MOMENT.
Tracks: Heat of the moment / Time again.
■ 7" . . . . GEFA 2494
Geffen / Jul '82.

LIVE IN MOSCOW.
Tracks: Not Advised.
CD . . . . .ESSCD 174
MC . . . . .ESSMC 174
Essential / Jun '92 / Total / BMG.

ONLY TIME WILL TELL.
Tracks: Only time will tell / Ride easy.
■ 7" . . . . GEFA 2228
Geffen / Aug '82.

SMILE HAS LEFT YOUR EYES.
Tracks: Smile has left your eyes / Lying to yourself / Midnight sun.
■ 12" . . . . TA 3866
■ 7" . . . . .A 3836
Geffen / Oct '83.

SOLE SURVIVOR.
Tracks: Sole survivor / Here comes the feeling.
■ 7" . . . . GEFA 2884
Geffen / Oct '82.

THEN AND NOW.
Tracks: Only time will tell / Wildest dreams / Smile has left your eyes / Prayin' 4 a miracle / Summer / Heat of the moment / Don't cry / Days like these / Am I in love / Voice of America.
CD 7599242982
■ LP 7599242981
MC 7599242984
WEA / Aug '90 / WEA.
■ CD . . . . .GEFD 24298
■ MC . . . . .GEFC 24298
Geffen / Aug '91.

WHO WILL STOP THE RAIN.
Tracks: Who will stop the rain / Aqua part 1 / Heart of gold / Obsession (Only available on CD Single.).
■ 10" 109521
■ 12" 109526
■ 7" 109527
■ CD Single 109522
Musidisc / Aug '92.

Asphyx

ASPHYX.
Tracks: Not Advised.
CD . . . . CM 77063-2
MC . . . . CM 77063-4
Century Media / May '94 / Plastic Head.

LAST ONE ON EARTH.
Tracks: Not Advised.
CD 8497342
LP 0897341
MC 0897344
Century Media / Nov '92 / Plastic Head.

Assassin

INTERSTELLAR EXPERIENCE.
Tracks: Not Advised.
CD .087521
■ LP 087519
MC .087520
Steamhammer (Germany) / '89 / Pinnacle.

UPCOMING TERROR.
Tracks: Not Advised.
CD .087530
■ LP 081895
Steamhammer (Germany) / '89.

Assuck

ANTICAPITAL.
Tracks: Not Advised.
CD . . . . .CC 005CD
LP . . . . CC 005
Common Cause / Jun '94 / Plastic Head.

Asylum

BASS, THE FINAL FRONT.
Tracks: Bass, the final front.
■ 12".................... FEFT 002
Feet First / Mar '92.

LEOPARDS.
Tracks: Leopards.
■ 7"..................... DAMP 057
Waterfront / Jan '88.

SYSTEM OVERLOAD.
Tracks: System Overload.
■ 7"..................... EFA 06182
Houses In Motion / Oct '92.

WE WILL BE FREE (Asylum/ Stalag 17/ Toxic Waste).
Tracks: Not Advised.
■ LP.................... WARZONE 1
Warzone / Mar '87.

At The Gates

GARDENS OF GRIEF.
Tracks: Not Advised.
LP.................... DOL 005MLP
Dolores / Nov '92 / Plastic Head.

RED IN THE SKY IS OURS, THE.
Tracks: Not Advised.
CD.................... DEAF 010CD
LP..................... DEAF 010
Deaf / Nov '92 / Vital Distribution.

TERMINAL SPIRIT DISEASE.
Tracks: Swarm / Terminal spirit disease / World returned / Forever blind / Fevered circle / Beautiful wound / All life ends (Live) / Burning darkness (Live) / Kingdom gone (Live).
CD.................... VILE 047CD
LP..................... VILE 047
Peaceville / Jun '94 / Vital Distribution / Pinnacle.

WITH FEAR I KISS THE BURNING DARKNESS.
Tracks: Beyond good and evil / Raped by the light of Christ / Break of Autumn / Non-divine / Primal breath / Stardrowned / Blood of the sunsets / Burning darkness / Ever opening flower / Through the red.
CD.................... DEAF 014CD
LP..................... DEAF 014
Deaf / Aug '93 / Vital Distribution.

At War

ORDERED TO KILL.
Tracks: Not Advised.
■ LP.................... GWD 90550
MC..................... GWC 90550
New Renaissance(USA) / Nov '87 / Pinnacle.

Atheist

ELEMENTS.
Tracks: Not Advised.
CD.................... CDMFN 150
LP..................... MFN 150
Music For Nations / Jul '93 / Pinnacle.

PIECE OF TIME.
Tracks: Piece of time / Unholy war / Room with a view / On they slay / Beyond / I deny / Why brother / Life / No truth.
CD.................... CDATV 8
LP..................... ATV 8
Active / Jan '90 / Pinnacle.

UNQUESTIONABLE PRESENCE.
Tracks: Not Advised.
CD.................... CDATV 20
LP..................... ATV 20
MC..................... TATV 20
Music For Nations / Oct '91 / Pinnacle.

Atlain

LIVING IN THE DARK.
Tracks: Not Advised.
■ LP.................... SKULL 8365
Mausoleum / Mar '85.

Atlantic

POWER.
Tracks: It's only love / Power / War / Bad blood / Can't hold on / Hands of fate / Every beat of my heart / Dangerous games / Nothing to lose / Hard to believe.

CD.................... CDMFN 168
Music For Nations / Oct '94 / Pinnacle.

Atlantis

ATLANTIS.
Tracks: Not Advised.
LP..................... REP 2145
MC..................... REP 2145-TS
Repertoire (Germany) / Aug '91 / Pinnacle.
CD.................... REP 4145
Repertoire (Germany) / Jul '93 / Pinnacle.

IT'S GETTING BETTER.
Tracks: Not Advised.
CD.................... REP 4232-WP
Repertoire (Germany) / Aug '91 / Pinnacle.

RISING.
Tracks: Not Advised.
LP..................... RR 93431
MC..................... RR 93434
■ CD.................... RR 93432
Road Runner / Apr '91.

Atom Gods

WOW.
Tracks: Not Advised.
■ LP.................... GWLP 30
GWR / Aug '89.

Atom Heart Mother

MR INDESTRUCTABLE.
Tracks: Mr. Indestructable.
■ 7"..................... ABS 100
Abstract / Oct '93.

SKIN 'EM UP, CHOP 'EM OUT RAWHIDE.
Tracks: Not Advised.
CD.................... ABT 095 CD
Abstract / Oct '92 / Pinnacle.

Atom Kraft

CONDUCTORS OF NOIZE.
Tracks: Requiem / Total metal / Queen of death / Vision of Belshazzar / Foliage / Rich bitch / Tutonic pain / Demolition.
■ LP.................... NEAT 1041
Neat / Jul '87.

CONDUCTORS OF NOIZE (Filmed Live at Hammersmith Odeon).
Tracks: Requiem / Total metal / Queen of death / Vision of Belshazzar / Foliage / Rich bitch / Tutonic pain / Demolition.
VHS.................... JE 167
Jettisoundz / Aug '88 / TBD / Visionary Communications.

FUTURE WARRIORS.
Tracks: Future warriors / Starchild / Dead man's hand / Total metal / Pour the metal in / Death valley / Warzones / Burn in hell / Heat and pain / This planet's burning.
■ LP.................... NEAT 1028
Neat / Sep '85.

QUEEN OF DEATH.
Tracks: Queen of death / Protector / Demolition / Funeral pyre / Mode III.
■ 12".................... NEAT 55 12
Neat / Oct '86.

Atom Seed

GET IN LINE.
Tracks: Get in line / Castles in the sky / What you say (live) (Only on 12" and CD single) / Burn (live) (Only on 12" and CD single).
■ 12".................... LONX 307
■ 12" P.Disc.................... LONXP 307
■ 7"..................... LON 307
■ CD Single.................... LONCD 307
London / Aug '91.

GET IN LINE.
Tracks: Not Advised.
CD.................... HMRXD 163
FM Records / Nov '92 / FM Revolver / Sony.
■ LP.................... HMRLP 163
MC..................... HMRMC 163
Heavy Metal / Nov '92 / Sony / FM Revolver.

I DON'T WANT TO TALK ABOUT IT.

Tracks: I don't want to talk about it / Doghouse sexbeat / Shake that thing what.
■ 12".................... ORGAN 001
Heavy Metal / Apr '90.
■ 12".................... ORGAN001
FM Records / Oct '92.

REBEL.
Tracks: Rebel / Everybody / Fools to fall / Rebel (adrenalin mix) (Only on 12" Single) / Forget it Joe (Only on 12" and CD Single).
■ 12".................... LONX 299
■ 12" Remix.................... LONXR 299
■ 7"..................... LON 299
■ CD Single.................... LONCD 299
FFRR / May '91.

Atrocity

ART OF DEATH, THE.
Tracks: Not Advised.
CD.................... CORE 10CD
LP..................... CORE 10
Metalcore / Feb '92 / Pinnacle.

BLUT.
Tracks: Not Advised.
CD.................... MASSCD 033
LP..................... MASSLP 033
Massacre / Jun '94 / Plastic Head.

HALLUCINATIONS.
Tracks: Not Advised.
CD.................... NB 038CD
LP..................... NB 038
Nuclear Blast / Jan '91 / Plastic Head.

INFECTED.
Tracks: Not Advised.
CD.................... CORE 3CD
LP..................... CORE 3
Metalcore / Oct '90 / Pinnacle.

TODESSEHNSUCHT.
Tracks: Not Advised.
LP..................... RR 91281
MC..................... RR 91284
Road Runner / Aug '92 / Pinnacle.
CD.................... RR 91282
Road Runner / Jan '94 / Pinnacle.

Atrophy

SOCIALIZED HATE.
Tracks: Not Advised.
CD.................... RR 9518 2
■ LP.................... RR 9518 1
Road Runner / Oct '88.

VIOLENT BY NATURE.
Tracks: Puppies and friends / Violent by nature / In their eyes / Too late to change / Slipped through the cracks / Forgotten but not gone / Process of elimination / Right to die / Things change.
CD.................... RO 9450 2
LP..................... RO 9450 1
MC..................... RO 9450 4
Roadracer / Mar '90 / Pinnacle.

Attacker

BATTLE AT HELMS DEEP.
Tracks: Not Advised.
■ LP.................... RR 9750
Road Runner / Sep '85.

Attention

HEARTS OF STONE.
Tracks: Not Advised.
LP..................... XM 011
X-Mist Records / Apr '92 / Plastic Head.

Attika

WHEN HEROES FALL.
Tracks: Not Advised.
CD.................... MASSCD 023
Massacre / Feb '94 / Plastic Head.

Attitude

GOOD, THE BAD AND THE OBNOXIOUS, THE.
Tracks: Not Advised.
■ LP.................... WEBITE 28
We Bite / Apr '88.

■ DELETED

KEIN SCHLAF BIS DEUTSHLAND.
Tracks: Not Advised.
■ LP . . . . WEBITE 21
We Bite / Nov '87.

Attitude Adjustment

AMERICAN PARANOIA.
Tracks: Grey world / Dope friend / Hunger and poverty / Fu*k Chuck / Dead serious / Johnny / Attitude adjustment / DSFA / American paranoia / Warfear / Streetwise / Working class pride / In the centre / Bombs / Rambo / Incredible end.
■ LP . . . . PUS 0012-11
Pusmort / Jan '87.
CD . . . . BC 1683
CD . . . . BCCD 1683
Bitzcore / Nov '89 / Plastic Head.

NO MORE MR. NICE GUY.
Tracks: Not Advised.
LP . . . . .FACE 12
In Your Face / Jan '91.

OUT OF HAND.
Tracks: Not Advised.
LP . . . . FACE 020
In Your Face / Sep '92.

OUT OF HAND/NO MORE.
Tracks: Not Advised.
CD . . . . BC 1680CD
Bitzcore / Jul '93 / Plastic Head.

Autograph

SIGN IN PLEASE.
Tracks: Send her to me / Turn up the radio / Nineteen and non-stop / Cloud 10 / Deep end / My girlfriend's boyfriend isn't me / Thrill of love / Friday in the night / All I'm gonna take.
MC . . . . PK 89495
■ LP . . . . PL 89495
RCA / Mar '85.

TURN UP THE RADIO.
Tracks: Turn up the radio / Thrill of love / Fever line.
■ 12" .RCAT 483
■ 7" . . . . .RCA 483
RCA / Mar '85.

Autopsy

ACTS OF THE...
Tracks: Not Advised.
CD . . . . VILE 033 CD
LP . . . . VILE 033
MC . . . . VILE 033 MC
Peaceville / Oct '92 / Vital Distribution / Pinnacle.

FIEND FOR BLOOD.
Tracks: Fiend for blood.
■ 12" . . . . .VILE 029T
■ CD Single . . . . VILE 029TCD
MC Single . . . . .VILE 029MC
Peaceville / Mar '92 / Vital Distribution / Pinnacle.

MENTAL FUNERAL.
Tracks: Not Advised.
CD .VILE 025CD
LP . . . . .VILE 025P
LP . . . . VILE 025
MC .VILE 025MC
Peaceville / Apr '91 / Vital Distribution / Pinnacle.

RETRIBUTION FOR THE DEAD.
Tracks: Retribution for the dead / Destined to fester / In the grip of winter.
■ 12" . . . . VILE 24T
■ CD Single . . . . .VILE 24TCD
■ MC Single . . . . .VILE 24TMC
Peaceville / Feb '91.

SEVERED SURVIVAL.
Tracks: Not Advised.
CD .VILECD 012
■ LP . . . . VILE 012
■ MC . . . . .VILEC 012
Peaceville / Apr '89.
■ LP P.Disc . . . . .VILE 012P
Peaceville / Jan '92.

Avenger

BLOOD SPORTS.
Tracks: Enforcer / You'll never make me (alive) / Matriarch / Warfare / On the rocks / Rough ride / Victims of force / Death race 2000 / Night of the jackal.
■ LP . . . . NEAT 1018
Neat / '85.

KILLER ELITE.
Tracks: Revenge attack / Run for your life / Brand of torture / Steel on steel / Right to rock / Hard times / Under the hammer / Face to the ground / Dangerous games / Yesterday's hero / M.M.85 / Saw mill.
■ LP . . . . NEAT 1026
Neat / '85.

TOO WILD TO TAME.
Tracks: Too wild to tame / On the rocks.
■ 7" .NEAT 31
Neat / Oct '88.

Aviary

ANTHEM FOR THE USA.
Tracks: Anthem for the USA / Puddles.
■ 7" . . . . EPC 7391
Epic / Jun '79.

SOARING.
Tracks: Soaring / Feel the heart.
■ 7" . . . . EPC 7780
Epic / Aug '79.

Aviator

ALL YOUR LOVE IS GONE.
Tracks: All your love is gone / Wood wharf gumbo.
■ 7" . . . . HAR 5208
Harvest / Jul '80.

AVIATOR.
Tracks: Front line / Back on the street / Don't turn away / Wrong place, wrong time / Never let the rock stop / Comeback / Magic / Can't stop / Too young / Every schoolboy knows / Through the night.
■ LP . . . . PL 89934
■ MC . . . . PK 89934
RCA / Jan '87.

LAY DOWN YOUR WEARY TUNE.
Tracks: Lay down your weary tune / Greed.
■ 7" . . . . HAR 5171
Harvest / Oct '78.

TIME TRAVELLER.
Tracks: Time traveller / Rocking chair.
■ 7" . . . . HAR 5180
Harvest / Feb '79.

TURBULENCE.
Tracks: Way of the world / American / Turbulence / Ovation / Fallen star / Track eleven / Get your rocks off / Strange worlds.
■ LP . . . . SHSP 4107
Harvest / Apr '80.

Awful Truth

AWFUL TRUTH.
Tracks: It takes so long / I should have known all along / Ghost of heaven / Drowning man / Circle of pain / Higher / No good reason / Mary.
CD . . . . CDZORRO 3
LP . . . . ZORRO 3
MC . . . . TZORRO 3
Metal Blade / Aug '90 / Pinnacle.

Axe

HEAT IN THE STREET.
Tracks: Heat in the street / Midnight drives me mad.
■ 7" .B 9850
Atco / Nov '83.

I CAN'T HELP MYSELF.
Tracks: I can't help myself / Let me know.
■ 7" . . . . MCA 611
MCA / Jun '80.

NEMESIS.
Tracks: Heat in the street / Young hearts / All through the night / I'll think you'll remember tonight / She's had the power / Girls, girls, girls / Eagle flies alone / Keep playing that rock 'n' roll / Foolin' your mama again / Let the music come back / Masquerade.
■ LP 790 099-1
Atco / '84.

OFFERING.
Tracks: Rock 'n' roll party in the streets / Video inspiration / Steal another fantasy / Jennifer / I got the fire / Burn the city down / Now or never / Holdin' on / Silent soldiers.
■ LP . . . . K 50895
Atlantic / '84.

Axe Attack

NIGHTMARE.
Tracks: Not Advised.
■ LP . . . . AXE 7024
Axe Killer / Jul '86.

Axe Victims

ANOTHER VICTIM.
Tracks: Not Advised.
■ LP .SKULL 8334
MC .TAPE 78334
Mausoleum / Jun '84 / Pinnacle.

Axegrinder

RISE OF THE SERPENT MEN, THE.
Tracks: Never ending winter / Life chain / Evilution / Final war / Hellstorm / War machine / Rise of the serpent men.
■ LP . . . . VILE 007
Peaceville / Oct '88.
CD . . . . DEAF 0102 CD
MC . . . . DEAF 0102 MC
Deaf / Aug '90 / Vital Distribution.

Axemaster

BLESSING IN THE SKIES.
Tracks: Not Advised.
■ LP . . . . A 33
Azra (USA) / Sep '87.

Axewitch

LORD OF THE FLIES.
Tracks: Not Advised.
■ LP .FINGLP 101
Neon / Jan '84.

VISIONS OF THE PAST.
Tracks: Visions of the past / Give them hell / Tonight / Hot lady / Stand up / Heading for a storm / Born in hell / Time to live.
■ LP . . . . NEAT 1025
Neat / May '85.

Axxis

KINGDOM OF THE NIGHT.
Tracks: Living in a world / Kingdom of the night / Never say never / Fire and ice / Young souls / Singing for a song / Love is like an ocean / Moon / Tears of the trees / Just one night / Kings made of steel / Living in a world (Ext. version) (CD only.)
■ CD . . . . CDPCS 7334
■ LP . . . . PCS 7334
■ MC . . . . TCPCS 7334
Parlophone / Sep '89.

KINGDOM OF THE NIGHT.
Tracks: Kingdom of the night / Young souls / Kings made of steel (12" & CD only.).
■ 12" 12R 6225
■ 7" . . . . .R 6225
■ 7" P.Disc . . . . RPD 6225
■ CD Single . . . . CDR 6225
Parlophone / Aug '89.

B

B.S.G.

WARM INSIDE.
Tracks: Not Advised.
CD . . . . .XM 031CD
LP . . . . XM 031
X-Mist Records / Apr '92 / Plastic Head.

Babes In Toyland

U.S. trio, formed in late '80s by guitarist/
singer Kat Bjelland. Despite debut on Sub
Pop label and success of 1992's *Fontanelle*,
they were eclipsed by female hardcore acts
who followed in their wake, notably L7 and
Hole. Ironically, both feature musicians
from Bjelland's pre-Babes bands: she and
Hole's Courtney Love contrived feud for benefit of press. Babes drummer Lori Barbero
is major metal fan, who has "hung out" with
Metallica, beaten Lemmy at pool and declined advances of Gene Simmons.

PAINKILLERS.
Tracks: Not Advised.
CD 185122
LP 185121
MC 185124
Southern / Jun '93 / SRD.

PEEL SESSIONS: BABES IN TOYLAND.
Tracks: Catatonic / Ripe / Primus / Spit to see the
shine / Pearl / Dogg / Laugh my head off / Mad pilot.
CD . . . . SFMCD 211
MC . . . . SFMAC 211
■ Mini LP . . . . SFPMA 211
Strange Fruit / Mar '92.

SPANKING MACHINE.
Tracks: Not Advised.
LP 891831
Twin Tone / Jul '90 / Pinnacle.

Baby Animals

BABY ANIMALS.
Tracks: Rush you / Early warning / Painless / Make it
end / Big time friends / Working for the enemy / One
word / Break my heart / Waste of time / One too
many / Ain't gonna get.
■ CD . . . . PD 90580
■ LP . . . . PL 90580
■ MC . . . . PK 90580
Imago / Feb '92.

EARLY WARNING.
Tracks: Early warning / Baby animals / Ain't gonna
get (Only on 12" and CD Single.) / Rush you (Only on
12" and CD Single.).
■ 12" . . . . PT 49156
■ 7" . . . . PB 49155
■ CD Single . . . . PD 49156
Imago / Nov '91.

ONE WORD.
Tracks: One word / Waste of time (live).
■ MC Single . . . . PK 49155
■ 12" . . . . PT 49136
■ 7" . . . . PB 49135
■ CD Single . . . . PD 49156
RCA / Feb '92.

PAINLESS.
Tracks: Painless / Dedicate / Early warning (live)
(CD single only).
■ 12" . . . . PK 49117
■ 7" . . . . PB 49117
■ CD Single . . . . PD 49118
Imago / Mar '92.

SHAVED AND DANGEROUS.
Tracks: Don't tell me what to do / Bupata / Life from
a distance / Be my friend / Lovin' lies / Lights out at
eleven / Backbone / Nervous at night / Because I can
/ Stoopid / At the end of the day.
CD 2787210 192
MC 2787210 194
Imago / Aug '93 / BMG.

Baby Tuckoo

FIRSTBORN.
Tracks: Hot wheels / Things aren't always what they
seem / Holdin' on / Mony mony / A.W.O.L. / Baby's
rocking tonight / Broken heart / Sweet rock'n'roll.
■ LP . . . . ULTRA 2
Albion / Mar '84.
■ LP . . . . CLALP 115
■ MC . . . . .CLAMC 115
Castle Classics / Jul '86.

FORCE MAJEURE.
Tracks: Not Advised.
■ LP . . . . MFN 56
MC . . . . TMFN 56
Music For Nations / Feb '86 / Pinnacle.

MONY MONY.
Tracks: Mony mony / Baby's rocking tonight.
■ 7" .TUCK 001
Albion / Mar '84.

ROCK ROCK.
Tracks: Rock rock.
■ 12" . . . . .12 KUT 120
Music For Nations / May '86.

TEARS OF A CLOWN, THE.
Tracks: Tears of a clown / Over you / Lights go down
(Available on 12" only).
■ 12" . . . . .12 FAA 105
■ 7" .FAA 105
Fun After All / Aug '86.

Babylon A.D.

BABYLON A.D.
Tracks: Bang go the bells / Hammer swings down /
Caught up in the crossfire / Desperate / Kid goes
wild / Shot o'love / Maryanne / Back in Babylon /
Sweet temptation / Sally danced.
■ CD .260313
■ LP .210313
■ MC .410313
Arista / Jun '90.

KID GOES WILD.
Tracks: Kid goes wild / Shot o'love / Kid goes wild
(think it over mix) (Available on 12" single).
■ 12" .613521
■ 7" 113521
■ MC Single 411051
Arista / Sep '90.

NOTHING SACRED.
Tracks: Take the dog off the chain / Bad blood / So
savage the heart / Sacrifice your love / Redemption /
Down the river of no return / Psychedelic sex reac-
tion / Dream train / Blind ambition / Slave your body
/ Of the rose / Pray for the wicked.
■ CD 07822187022
■ MC 07822187024
Arista / Jun '92.

Babys

BABY'S ANTHOLOGY, THE.
Tracks: Head first / Isn't it time / Midnight rendez-
vous / Money / Back on my feet again / Give me your
love / Turn and walk away / Everytime I think of you /
If you've got the time / Sweet 17.
■ LP . . . . CHR 1351
MC . . . . ZCHR 1351
Chrysalis / Oct '81 / EMI.

BABYS.
Tracks: Looking for love / If you've got the time / I
believe in love / Wild man / Laura / I love how you
love me / Rodeo / Over and over / Read my stars /
Dying man.
■ LP . . . . CHR 1129
■ MC . . . . ZCHR 1129
Chrysalis / '83.

BROKEN HEART.
Tracks: Wrong or right / Give me your love / Isn't it
time / And if you could see me fly / Golden mile /
Broken heart / I'm falling / Rescue me / Silver dream
/ Piece of the action.
■ LP . . . . CHR 1150

■ MC . . . . ZCHR 1150
Chrysalis / '83.

HEAD FIRST.
Tracks: Love don't prove I'm right / Everytime I think
of you / I was one / White lightning / Run to Mexico /
Head first / You (got it) / Please don't leave me here
/ California.
■ LP . . . . CHR 1195
■ MC . . . . ZCHR 1195
Chrysalis / '82.

ISN'T IT TIME.
Tracks: Isn't it time.
■ 7" . . . . CHS 2173
Chrysalis / Jan '78.

ON THE EDGE.
Tracks: Turn and walk away / Sweet 17 / She's my
girl / Darker side of town / Rock'n'roll is / Downtown
/ Postcard / Too far gone / Gonna be somebody /
Love won't wait.
■ LP . . . . CHR 1305
Chrysalis / Dec '80.

TRUE LOVE TRUE CONFESSIONS.
Tracks: True love true confessions / Broken heart /
Money.
■ 7" . . . . CHS 2398
Chrysalis / Jan '80.

UNION JACKS.
Tracks: Back on my feet again / True love true
confession / Union jacks / In your eyes / Anytime /
Jesus are you there / Turn around in Tokyo / Love is
just a mystery.
■ LP . . . . CHR 1267
Chrysalis / Feb '80.

Babysitters

BABYSITTERS, THE.
Tracks: Can you hear it / American toys / No parti-
cular place / Beard song / I wanna be on the T.V. /
Pickin' the blues / Old L.A. / Give us a loan /
Everybody loves you when you're dead / Tel Aviv /
Rock 'n' roll chicken / Alright O.K.
■ LP . . . . HMRLP 35
MC . . . . HMRMC 35
Heavy Metal / Jun '85 / Sony / FM Revolver.

I WANNA BE ON THE TV.
Tracks: I wanna be on the TV / Everybody loves you
when you're dead.
■ 7" . . . . VHF 11
FM Records / Jun '85.

LIVE AT THE MARQUEE.
Tracks: Picking up the blues / Can you hear it /
Overkill / Big girls / Frank Bough.
■ 12" . . . . KIL 122
Killerwatt / Nov '86.

Bachman-Turner Overdrive

This Canadian rock group initially featuring
Randy and Robbie Bachman, Fred Turner
and Blair Thornton, were formed in 1972.
They released their debut LP in 1973 and
after extensive touring enjoyed US chart
hits in 1974 with the singles *Let It Ride* and
Takin' Care Of Business. BTO's third album,
Not Fragile, featured the classic single, *You
Ain't Seen Nothing Yet*. The single was a
huge international seller and a fine
example of their accessible hard rock style,
particularly popular recently with DJ's Mike
Smash and Dave Nice adopting the song as
their tune. Although the band were a big
live attraction, sales since were disappointing and Bachman Turner Overdrive disbanded in 1979.

B T O.
Tracks: For the weekend / Just look at me now / My
sugaree / City's still growin' / Another fool / Lost in a
fantasy / Toledo / Service with a smile.
■ LP . . . . CLTLP 353
■ MC . . . . ZCCLT 353
Compleat (USA) / Nov '84.

■ DELETED

B 1

BEST OF (SO FAR).
Tracks: Blue collar / Gimme your money please / Hey you / Let it ride / Lookin' out for no.1 / Roll on down the highway / Stayed awake all night / Take it like a man / Takin' care of business / You ain't seen nothin' yet.
■ LP 9100 026
Mercury / Jan '77.

FOR THE WEEKEND.
Tracks: For the weekend / Just look at me now.
■ 7" . . . . CLT 6
Compleat (USA) / Sep '84.

GREATEST HITS: BACHMAN TURNER OVERDRIVE.
Tracks: Lookin' out for no. 1 / Hey you / Taking care of business / You ain't seen nothin' yet / Flat broke love / Rock and roll nights / Roll on down the highway / Freeways / Down down / Let it ride / Can we all come together / Jamaica.
■ ' ▷ 6430 151
MC. 7420 043
Mercury / Aug '81 / PolyGram.
CD. 830 039-2
Mercury / '86 / PolyGram.

HEARTACHES.
Tracks: Heartaches / Rock'n'roll nights.
■ 7" 6167759
Mercury / Apr '79.

LIVE FOR LIFE.
Tracks: Not Advised.
■ LP . . . . IMCA 5760
■ MC. . . . . IMCAC 5760
MCA / Aug '86.

MY WHEELS WON'T TURN.
Tracks: My wheels won't turn / Life still goes on.
■ 7" .6167 520
Mercury / May '77.

NIGHTRIDING: BACHMAN-TURNER OVERDRIVE.
Tracks: Roll on down the highway / Hey you / Freeway / Takin' care of business / Down down / You ain't seen nothin' yet / Let it ride / Flat broke love / Can we all come together / Rock and roll nights / Jamaica / Looking after no. 1.
■ LP . . . . .KNLP 10008
■ MC. . . . . KNMC 10008
Nightriding / Jul '88.

NOT FRAGILE.
Tracks: Not Advised.
■ LP 9100 007
Mercury / Dec '74.

ROLL ON DOWN THE HIGHWAY.
Tracks: Roll on down the highway.
■ 7" 6167 071
Mercury / Feb '75.

ROLL ON DOWN THE HIGHWAY.
Tracks: Not Advised.
CD 550 4212
MC 550 4214
Spectrum (1) / Aug '94 / PolyGram.

SHOTGUN RIDER.
Tracks: Shotgun rider / Just for you.
■ 7" 6167 567
Mercury / Sep '77.

STAYED AWAKE ALL NIGHT.
Tracks: Stayed awake all night / Down and out man.
■ 7" 6052 357
Mercury / Jan '77.

STREET ACTION.
Tracks: Not Advised.
■ LP 9100 051
Mercury / Apr '78.

YOU AIN'T SEEN NOTHING YET.
Tracks: Four wheel drive / She's a devil / You ain't seen nothin' yet / Gimme your money please / Free wheelin' / Not fragile / Roll on down the highway / My wheels won't turn / Take it like a man.
■ MC. . . . . .PRIMC 46
Mercury / Oct '83.
■ LP . . . . PRICE 46
N/A / Oct '83.

YOU AIN'T SEEN NOTHING YET.
Tracks: You ain't seen nothin' yet / Roll on down the highway.
■ 7" 6167 025
Mercury / Nov '74.
■ 7" .CUT 109
Mercury / Oct '84.

Backsliders

NATIONAL NIGHTMARE.
Tracks: National nightmare / Gotta be right / Undertaker / Hear me howlin / Did you no wrong / Do it again / I blow my head away / I just wanna play / Snakeskin cowboys / Fighting, riding, having fun.
■ LP . . . . HMILP 103
MC. . . . . .HMIMC 103
Heavy Metal / Nov '87 / Sony / FM Revolver.

Bad Beach

CORNUCOPIA.
Tracks: Morgan Le Fey / Armageddon son / Bad beach / Septa salina / Beach patrol / Dionysus / Bad trip / Blind fate / Purple indian / Level 45 / It's always better / Victim of society / All systems go / Zero is born / Puppy killer / End of the day.
■ LP . . . . ACHE 04
Manic Ears / May '87.

CUT IT OFF.
Tracks: Cut it off / Widey's County / You are in me / Big whole / Self destruct / Cut me up / Inside / Fat American / Slagheap / Skull rise / Push and pull.
■ LP . . . . K 044/122
Konkurrel / Sep '88.

Bad Brains

American Rastafarian hardcore act, formed in 1981 whose sets also included liberal doses of rootsy reggae numbers. Popular with 'skatepunk' types - 1983's *Rock For Light* (Abstract) was well received. Furious live set well documented on the *The Youth Are Getting Restless* in 1990. Vocalist 'HR' replaced by ex-Faith No More's Chuck Mosley but band split soon afterwards.

BAD BRAINS.
Tracks: Not Advised.
LP . . . . DEI 2001-1
MC. A 106
Reach Out International / Mar '93 / Reach Out Int.
Records / Windsong International Ltd.

BAD BRAINS LIVE.
Tracks: Not Advised.
■ LP . . . . SST 160 LP
SST / '88.

I AGAINST I.
Tracks: Not Advised.
■ LP . . . . .SST 065
SST / Nov '86.
CD . . . . .SST 065 CD
SST / Feb '88 / Pinnacle.
CD . . . . LICD 900231
Line / Nov '89 / C.M. Distribution / Grapevine Distribution / A.D.A. Distribution / Conifer Records.
MC. . . . . .SST 065 C
SST / May '93 / Pinnacle.

I AND I SURVIVE.
Tracks: I and I survive / Destroy Babylon.
■ 12". . . . . .YUMT 101
Food For Thought / Mar '83.

I LOVE JAH.
Tracks: Bad brains / Sailin' on / Big takeover.
■ 12" . . . . VIRUS 13
Alternative Tentacles / Jun '82.

LIVE.
Tracks: Not Advised.
CD . . . . .SST 160 CD
LP .SST 160
MC. . . . . .SST 160 C
SST / May '93 / Pinnacle.

QUICKNESS.
Tracks: Soul craft / Voyage into infinity / Messengers / With the quickness / Gene machine / Don't bother me / Don't blow bubbles / Sheba / Yout juice / No conditions / Silent tears / Prophets eye / Endtro.
CD . . . . CARCD 4
■ LP . . . . CARLP 4
■ MC. . . . . CARC 4
Caroline / Jul '89.

RISE.
Tracks: Rise / Miss Freedom / Unidentified / Love is the answer / Free / Hair / Coming in numbers / Yes Jah / Take your time / Peace of mind / Without you / Outro.
CD 474265 2
LP 474265 1
MC. 474265 4
Epic / Sep '93 / Sony.

ROCK FOR LIGHT.
Tracks: Big takeover / Attitude / Right brigade / Joshua's song / I and I survive / Banned in DC / Supertouch / Destroy Babylon / FVK / Meek / I / Coptic times / Sailin' on / Rock for light / Rally round jah throne / At the movies / Riot squad / How low can a punk get / We will not / Jam.
■ CD . . . . PVCCD 8933
■ LP . . . . PVC 8933
■ MC. . . . . PVCC 8933
PVC (USA) / '87.
CD . . . . CARCD 12
■ LP . . . . .CARLP 12
■ MC. . . . . CARC 12
Caroline / Feb '91.

ROCK FOR LIGHT/I AGAINST I.
Tracks: Coptic times / Attitude / We will not / Sailin' on / Rally 'round jah throne / Right brigade / F V K / Riot squad / Meek shall inherit the earth / Joshua's song / Banned in D C / How low can a punk get / Big takeover / I and I survive / Destroy Babylon / Rock for light / At the movies / Intro / I against I / House of suffering / Re-ignition / Secret 77 / Let me help / She's calling you / Sacred love / Hired gun / Return to heaven.
CD Set . . . . LICD 921176
Line / May '92 / C.M. Distribution / Grapevine Distribution / A.D.A. Distribution / Conifer Records.

SPIRIT ELECTRICITY.
Tracks: Not Advised.
■ 10". . . . . .SST 228
■ CD Single . . . . .SST 228 CD
■ MC Single. . . . . .SST 228 C
SST / May '93.

YOUTH ARE GETTING RESTLESS, THE (Live at the Paradiso, Amsterdam 1987).
Tracks: I / Rock for light / Right brigade / House of suffering / Day tripper / She's a rainbow / Coptic times / Sacred love / Re-ignition / Let me help / Youth are getting restless / Banned in DC / Sailin' on / Fearless vampire killer / At the movies / Revolution (dub) / Pay to cum / Big takeover.
LP . . . . CARLP 8
■ MC . . . . CARC 8
■ CD . . . . CARCD 8
Caroline / May '90.

Bad Company

Originally a quartet put together by Free singer Paul Rodgers and ex-Mott The Hoople guitarist Mick Ralphs. Older fans of Free felt cheated that Rodgers' stunning blues voice was being used to deliver mainstream rock - but Bad Company found legions of new fans anyway. On their first two albums they practically invented AOR rock as was later to dominate American FM airwaves and became a blueprint adapted by later bands like Foreigner, Boston, Journey et al. But Bad Company began to sound like the bands who were copying them after the first four albums. When Rodgers left and the line-up fluctuated. These days, however, as a five-piece without him, they still make better-than-average records and sell huge amounts of concert tickets in the USA.

10 FROM 6.
Tracks: Can't get enough / Feel like makin' love / Run with the pack / Shooting star / Movin' on / Bad Company / Rock 'n' roll fantasy / Electric land / Ready for love / Live for the music.
CD 781 625-2
MC. . . . . .WX 31 C
■ LP . . . . WX 31
Atlantic / Jan '86.

BAD COMPANY.
Tracks: Not Advised.
■ LP . . . . ILPS 9279
Island / Jan '78.
■ MC. . . . . ICT 9279
Island / Jun '81.
CD. 756792441-2
Warner Bros. / Sep '94 / WEA.

BURNIN' SKY.
Tracks: Not Advised.
■ LP . . . . ILPS 9441
Island / Mar '77.
CD 756792450-2
Atlantic / Sep '94 / WEA.

CAN'T GET ENOUGH.
Tracks: Can't get enough / Bad company / No smoke without fire (Available on 12" format only.) / Shake it up (Available on 12" format only.)
■ 7" . . . . WIP 6191
Island / Jun '74.

■ DELETED

■ 12″. . . . . A 7954T
■ 7″. . . . . A 7954
■ CD Single. . . . . A 7954CD
■ MC Single. . . . . A 7954MC
Atlantic / Mar '90.

DANGEROUS AGE.
Tracks: One night / Shake it up / No smoke without fire / Bad man / Dangerous age / Dirty boy / Rock of America / Something about you / Way it goes / Love attack.
CD. . . . . K 781 884 2
■ MC. . . . . K 781 884 4
■ LP . . . . K 781 884 1
Atlantic / Aug '88.

DESOLATION ANGELS.
Tracks: Rock 'n' roll fantasy / Crazy circles / Gone, gone, gone / Evil wind / Early in the morning / Lonely for your love / Oh, Atlanta / Take the time / Rhythm machine / She brings me love.
■ MC. SK4 59408
■ LP . . . . SSK 59408
Swansong / Mar '79.
CD. 756792451-2
Atlantic / Sep '94 / WEA.

FAME AND FORTUNE.
Tracks: Burning up / This love / Fame and fortune / Long walk / Valerie / Hold on my heart / That girl / When we made love / If I'm sleeping / Tell it like it is.
■ CD 781 684-2
■ LP . . . . WX 69
■ MC. . . . . .WX 69 C
Atlantic / Oct '86.

FAME AND FORTUNE.
Tracks: Fame and fortune.
■ 7″. . . . . .A 9296
Atlantic / Feb '87.

FEEL LIKE MAKIN' LOVE.
Tracks: Feel like makin' love.
■ 7″ . . . . WIP 6242
Island / Aug '75.

GOOD LOVIN' GONE BAD.
Tracks: Good lovin' gone bad / Whisky bottle.
■ 7″ . . . . WIP 6223
Island / Mar '75.

HERE COMES TROUBLE.
Tracks: How about that / Stranger than fiction / Here comes the trouble / This could be the one / Both feet in the water / Take this town / What about you / Little angel / Hold on to my heart / Brokenhearted / My only one.
CD. 7567917592
MC. 7567917594
Atco / Oct '92 / WEA.

HOLY WATER.
Tracks: Not Advised.
CD. 7567 91371 2
■ LP 7567 91371 1
MC. 7567 91371 4
Atco / Jun '90 / WEA.

ROCK 'N' ROLL FANTASY.
Tracks: Rock 'n' roll fantasy / Crazy circles.
■ 7″ . . . . SSK 19416
Swansong / '79.

ROUGH DIAMONDS.
Tracks: Electric land / Untie the knot / Nuthin' on the TV / Painted face / Kickdown / Ballad of the band / Cross country boy / Old Mexico / Downhill ryder / Racetrack.
■ LP . . . . SSK 59419
Swansong / '84.
CD. 756792452-2
Atlantic / Sep '94 / WEA.

RUN WITH THE PACK.
Tracks: Live for the music / Simple man / Honeychild / Love me somebody / Run with the pack / Silver blue and gold / Young blood / Do right by your woman / Sweet lil' sister / Fade away.
■ LP . . . . .ILPS 9346
Island / Jan '78.
MC. . . . . .ICT 9346
Island / Jun '81 / PolyGram.
■ CD . . . . SS 8503-2
Swansong / Oct '88.
CD. 756792435-2
WEA / Jul '94 / WEA.

STRAIGHT SHOOTER.
Tracks: Good lovin' gone bad / Feel like makin' love / Weep no more / Shooting star / Deal with the preacher / Wild fire women / Anna / Call on me.
■ LP . . . . .ILPS 9304
Island / Jan '78.
■ MC. . . . . .ICT 9304

Island / Jun '81.
■ CD . . . . SS 8502-2
Swansong / Oct '88.
CD. 756782637-2
Warner Bros. / Jun '94 / WEA.

THIS LOVE.
Tracks: This love / Tell it like it is / Burning up (Extra track on 12″ only) / Fame and fortune (on 12″ only).
■ 12″. . . . . A 9355 T
■ 7″. . . . . .A 9355
Atlantic / Nov '86.

WHAT YOU HEAR IS WHAT YOU GET (The Best Of Bad Company - Live).
Tracks: How about that / Holy water / Rock 'n' roll fantasy / If you needed somebody / Here comes trouble / Ready for love / Shooting star / No smoke without a fire / Feel like makin' love / Take this town / Movin' on / Good lovin' gone bad / Fist full of blisters / Can't get enough / Bad company.
CD. 756792307-2
MC. 756792307-4
Atco / Dec '93 / WEA.

Bad English

Predictably short-lived agglomeration of ex-Babys/Journey personnel - notably singer John Waite and guitarist Neil Schon. Band split in 1991 after two albums and one U.S. chart-topper, When I See You Smile.

BACKLASH.
Tracks: So this is Eden / Straight to your heart / Time stood still / Time alone with you / Dancing off the edge of the world / Rebel say a prayer / Savage face / Pray for rain / Make love last / Life at the top.
■ CD 4685692
■ LP 4685691
■ MC. 4685694
Epic / Oct '91.
MiniDisc. 468569-3
Epic / Apr '93 / Sony.

BAD ENGLISH.
Tracks: Best of what I got / Heaven is a 4 letter word / Possession / Forget me not / When I see you smile / Tough times don't last / Ghost in your heart / Price of love / Ready when you are / Lay down / Restless ones / Rockin' horse / Don't walk away.
MC. 4634474
■ LP 4634471
■ CD 4634472
Epic / Sep '89.

BAD ENGLISH.
Tracks: Best of what I got / When I see you smile / Heaven is a 4 letter word / Price of love / Forget me not.
■ VHS 490442
CMV Enterprises (Video) / Jul '90.

DON'T WALK AWAY.
Tracks: Don't walk away / Tough times don't last / Price of love.
■ 12″. 6561136
■ 7″. 6561137
■ CD Single. 6561132
■ MC Single. 6561134
Epic / Sep '90.

FORGET ME NOT.
Tracks: Forget me not / Lay down / Rockin' horse (Only on CD and 12″ single.).
■ 12″. 6550896
■ 7″. 6550897
■ CD Single. 6550892
Epic / Aug '89.

PRICE OF LOVE.
Tracks: Price of love (remix) / Restless ones / Ready when you are.
■ CD Single. 6556763
■ 12″. 6556766
■ 7″ P.Disc 6556760
■ 7″ P.Disc 6556767
Epic / Feb '90.

STRAIGHT TO YOUR HEART.
Tracks: Straight to your heart / Make love last / Forget me not (Only on CD and 12″ Single.) / When I see you smile (Only on 12″ and CD Single.).
■ 12″. 6574208
■ 7″. 6574207
■ CD Single. 6574209
■ MC Single. 6574204
Epic / Oct '91.

WHEN I SEE YOU SMILE.
Tracks: When I see you smile / Rockin' horses / Tough times don't last.
■ 12″. 6553478

■ 12″. 6553446
■ 7″ P.Disc 6553470
■ CD Single 6552942
■ MC Single. 6553474
Epic / Nov '89.
■ 7″ 6553477
Epic / Nov '89.

Bad Lizard

POWER OF DESTRUCTION.
Tracks: Not Advised.
■ LP . . . . .RR 9728
Road Runner / Jan '86.

Bad Moon Rising

BAD MOON RISING.
Tracks: Hands on / If it ain't dirty / Without your love / Full moon / Lie down / Old flames / Built for speed / Dark side of babylon / Sunset after midnight / Way ward son.
CD. . . . . .CDFLAG 78
Under One Flag / Jan '93 / Pinnacle.

BLOOD.
Tracks: Dangerous game / Servants of the sun / Devil's son (Where our children die) / Blood on the streets / Tears in the dark / Heart of darkness / Chains / Til the morning comes / Time will tell / Remember me.
CD. . . . . .CDFLAG 79
Under One Flag / Apr '93 / Pinnacle.

Bad News

Spoof metal act created for TV by the Comic Strip team. Operating in same vein as Spinal Tap, Bad News were incredibly successful and even managed to secure a support slot with rock Gods, Iron Maiden. However their astute observations on all things metal was not warmly received in all quarters - they were bottled off stage during their set at 1986's Donnington festival.

BAD NEWS.
Tracks: Hey hey Bad News / Warriors of Ghengis Khan / Bohemian rhapsody / Bad News / Masturbike / Drink till I die.
MC. . . . . TCEMC 3535
■ CD . . . . CDP 748 310 2
■ LP . . . . .EMC 3535
EMI / Oct '87.

BAD NEWS TOUR AND A FISTFUL OF TRAVELLERS CHEQUES.
Tracks: Not Advised.
VHS . . . . .VVD 230
Virgin Vision / Gold & Sons / TBD.

BOHEMIAN RHAPSODY.
Tracks: Bohemian rhapsody / Life with Brian.
■ 7″ . . . . EMX 24
■ 7″ P.Disc . . . . EMP 24
EMI / Sep '87.
■ 7″ . . . . EM 24
EMI / Sep '87.

BOHEMIAN RHAPSODY (VIDEO SINGLE).
Tracks: Bohemian rhapsody / Every mistake imaginable.
■ VHS . . . . .MVW 99 0071 2
PMI / Oct '87.

BOOTLEG.
Tracks: Bad dreams / AGM / Double entendre / Locked in / Aids / O levels / Wedding / H.M. farmer / Masturbike / Cashing in on Christmas (dub).
■ LP . . . . .EMC 3542
■ MC. . . . . TCEMC 3542
EMI / Feb '88.

CASH IN COMPILATION, THE.
Tracks: Hey hey bad news / Bad dreams / Warriors of Ghengis Khan / A.G.M. / Bohemian rhapsody / Pretty woman / O levels / Life with Brian / Bad news / Masturbike / Double entendre / Drink till I die / Cashing in on Christmas (Dub).
CD. . . . . .DOJOCD 152
Dojo / Sep '93 / Castle Communications / BMG.

CASHING IN ON CHRISTMAS.
Tracks: Cashing in on Christmas (version) / Cashing in on Christmas (let's bank mix) (On 12″ single only) / Bad News.
■ 12″. 12EM 36
■ 7″ . . . . .EMG 36
■ 7″ . . . . EM 36
EMI / Nov '87.

MORE BAD NEWS.
Tracks: Not Advised.
VHS . . . . .VVD 295
Virgin Vision / Gold & Sons / TBD.

Bad Religion

AGAINST THE GRAIN.
Tracks: Not Advised.
CD. E 864092
MC. E 864094
Epitaph / Dec '90 / Plastic Head.
LP . . . . E 864091
Epitaph / Dec '90 / Plastic Head.

ALONG THE WAY.
Tracks: Not Advised.
VHS . . . . .BRVID 1
Nuclear Blast / Apr '94 / Plastic Head.

AMERICAN JESUS.
Tracks: American Jesus.
7" .SFTRI 232
Sympathy For The Record Industry / Aug '94 / Plastic Head.

ATOMIC.
Tracks: Atomic.
7" .SFTRI 158
Sympathy For The Record Industry / Aug '94 / Plastic Head.

BAD RELIGION 1980-85.
Tracks: Not Advised.
CD. E 864072 X
Epitaph / Nov '91 / Plastic Head.

BIG BANG LIVE.
Tracks: Not Advised.
VHS . . . . .BRVID 2
Nuclear Blast / Apr '94 / Plastic Head.

GENERATOR.
Tracks: Not Advised.
CD. E 864162
LP . . . . E 864161
MC. E 864164
Epitaph / Mar '92 / Plastic Head.

HOW COULD HE.
Tracks: Not Advised.
CD. E 86407CD
LP . . . . E 86407
MC. E 86407MC
Epitaph / Jul '93 / Plastic Head.

NO CONTROL.
Tracks: Not Advised.
CD. E 864062
LP . . . . E 864061
MC. E 864064
Epitaph / Jun '93 / Plastic Head.

RECIPE FOR HATE.
Tracks: Not Advised.
CD. E 864202
LP . . . . E 864201
MC. E 864204
Epitaph / Jun '93 / Plastic Head.

STRANGER THAN FICTION.
Tracks: Stranger than fiction.
7" .SFTR 1326
Sympathy For The Record Industry / Aug '94 / Plastic Head.

STRANGER THAN FICTION.
Tracks: Incomplete / Leave mine to me / Stranger than fiction / Tiny voices / Handshake / Better off dead / Infected / Television / Individual / Hooray for me / Slumber / Marked / Inner logic / What it is / 21st Century (digital boy).
CD .477343-2
LP 477343-1
MC. .477343-4
Columbia / Sep '94 / Sony.

SUFFER.
Tracks: Not Advised.
LP . . . . E 864041
MC. E 864044
MC. E 864042
Epitaph / Jun '93 / Plastic Head.

Bad Steve

KILLING THE NIGHT.
Tracks: Not Advised.
■ LP . . . . .SKULL 8370
Mausoleum / May '85.

Badlands

BADLANDS.
Tracks: Not Advised.
CD. 781 966-2
■ LP 781 966-1
MC. 781 966-4
Titanium/Atlantic / Jun '89 / WEA.

DAG THE GIBLETS.
Tracks: Not Advised.
VHS 8536502513
Warner Music Video / Oct '92 / WEA.

VOODOO HIGHWAY.
Tracks: Last time / Show me the way / Shine on / Whiskey dust / Joe's blues / Soul stealer / 3 Day funk / Silver horses / Love don't mean a thing / Voodoo highway / Fire and rain / Heaven's train / In a dream.
CD. 7567822514
MC. 7567822512
■ LP 7567822511
Atlantic / Jun '91.

Baird, Dan

I LOVE YOU PERIOD.
Tracks: Not Advised.
■ 7" . . . . .DEFA 22
■ CD Single . . . . .DEFCD 22
■ MC Single. . . . . DEFMC 22
American Recordings / Feb '93.

Balaam

DAY AND NIGHT (Balaam & The Angel).
Tracks: Day and night.
■ 12" . . . . 12 CHAP 3
■ 7" . . . . CHAP 3
Chapter 22 / Sep '85.

DAYS OF MADNESS (Balaam & The Angel).
Tracks: Don't want your love / I took a little / She really gets to me / Body & soul / Heartbreaker / Tender loin / Two days of madness / Did he fall / Goodbye forever / I am the only one / Stop messin' around.
■ LP . . . . .V 2598
MC. TCV 2598
■ CD . . . . CDV 2598
Virgin / Nov '89.

GREATEST STORY EVER TOLD, THE (Balaam & The Angel).
Tracks: New kind of love / Don't look down / She knows / Burn me down / Light of the world / Slow down / Wave / Warm again / Her end / Nothing there at all / Walk away (CD only) / Day and night (CD only).
■ LP . . . . .V 2377
■ MC . . . . TCV 2377
Virgin / Aug '86.
■ CD . . . . CDV 2377
Virgin / Aug '86.
MC. OVEDC 250
■ LP . . . . OVED 250
Virgin / '89.

I LOVE THE THINGS YOU DO TO ME (Balaam & The Angel).
Tracks: I love the things you do to me / You're in the way of my dreams / Things you know (on 12" only) / As tears go by (Extra track on 12" only.)
■ 12" . . . . VS 993-12
■ 7" . . . . .VS 993
Virgin / Sep '87.

I TOOK A LITTLE (Balaam & The Angel).
Tracks: I took a little / Long time lovin' you / Big city fun time girl (Available on 12" only.) / Would I die for .. (Available on 12" only.)
■ 12" . . . . VST 1213
■ 12" . . . . VSP 1213
■ 12" . . . . VSTX 1213
■ 7" . . . . .VS 1213
■ CD Single . . . . .VSCD 1213
Virgin / Sep '89.

LIGHT OF THE WORLD (Balaam & The Angel).
Tracks: Light of the world / Day and night / She knows (Extra track on 12" only) / Love (Extra track on 12" only) / Family and friends.
■ 12" . . . . VS 890-12
■ 7" . . . . .VS 890
Virgin / Aug '86.

LITTLE BIT OF LOVE (Balaam & The Angel).
Tracks: Little bit of love / Did you fall (or were you pushed) / She really gets to me (acoustic version) (Only on 12" and CD single.).
■ 12" . . . . VST 1229
■ CD Single . . . . VSCD 1229
■ 7" . . . . .VS 1229
Virgin / Mar '90.

LIVE FREE OR DIE (Balaam & The Angel).
Tracks: I'll show you something special / I love the things you do to me / Big city fun time girl / On the run / It goes on / Live free or die / Long time loving you / Would I die for you / I won't be afraid / Running out of time / You took my soul (CD only) / Let it happen (CD only) / You're in the way of my dreams (CD only) / As tears go by (CD only) / I feel love (CD & cassette only).
■ MC . . . . TCV 2476
■ LP . . . . .V 2476
■ CD . . . . CDV 2476
Virgin / Jul '88.

LIVE FREE OR DIE (Balaam & The Angel).
Tracks: Live free or die (7" only) / Eagle (On 12" only) / Complete control (On 12" only).
■ 12" . . . . VST 1124
■ 7" . . . . .VS 1124
Virgin / Aug '88.

LOVE ME (Balaam & The Angel).
Tracks: Love me.
■ 12" 220022
Chapter 22 / Apr '85.

NO MORE INNOCENCE.
Tracks: Not Advised.
LP . . . . TENS 001
MC. TENS 001MC
■ CD . . . . TENS 001CD
Intense / Oct '91.

PRIME TIME.
Tracks: Shame on you / Prime time / Next to me / What love is / Gathering dust / Eagle / She's not you / Mr. Business / Like a train / Burnin' / Just no good.
CD. . . . . .CDBLEED 1
Bleeding Hearts / Apr '93 / Pinnacle.

SHE KNOWS (Balaam & The Angel).
Tracks: She knows / Dreams wide awake / Sister moon (extra track on double-pack only) / Warm again (extra track on double-pack only) / 2 into 1 (extra track on 12" only) / Darklands (extra track on 12" only).
■ 12" . . . . VS 842-12
■ 7" Set . . . . .VSD 842
■ 7" . . . . .VS 842
Virgin / Mar '86.

SLOW DOWN (Balaam & The Angel).
Tracks: Slow down / Walk away / Travel on (Extra track on 12" only) / In the morning.
■ 7" . . . . .VS 864
■ 12" . . . . VS 864-12
Virgin / Jun '86.

SOMETHING SPECIAL (Balaam & The Angel).
Tracks: Something special / I feel love / Let it happen (Extra track on 12") / You took my soul (Extra track on 12").
■ 12" . . . . VS 970-12
■ 7" . . . . .VS 970
Virgin / Jun '87.

SUN FAMILY (Balaam & The Angel).
Tracks: Not Advised.
■ LP . . . . .CHAPLP 4
Chapter 22 / Nov '86.

WORLD OF LIGHT (Balaam & The Angel).
Tracks: World of light.
■ 7" 22 001
Chapter 22 / Nov '84.

Bang Tango

AIN'T NO JIVE, LIVE.
Tracks: Dancin' on coals / Twentieth century boy / Someone like you / Midnight struck / Attack of life.
■ CD . . . . MCAD 10531
■ LP . . . . MCA 10531
■ MC . . . . MCAC 10531
MCA / Jun '92.

DANCIN' ON COALS.
Tracks: Not Advised.
■ CD . . . . MCAD 10196
■ LP . . . . MCA 10196
■ MC . . . . MCAC 10196
MCA / May '91.

PSYCHO CAFE.
Tracks: Not Advised.
■ CD . . . . DMCG 6048
■ LP . . . . MCG 6048
■ MC . . . . MCGC 6048
MCA / May '89.

Bangalore Choir

ON TARGET.
Tracks: Angel in black / Loaded gun / If the good die young (we'll live forever) / Doin' the dance / Hold on to you / All or nothin' / Slippin' away / She can't stop / Freight train rollin' / Just one night
CD 7599244332
MC 7599244334
Giant / Apr '92 / BMG.

Banished

DELIVER US UNTO PAIN.
Tracks: Diseased chaos / Deliver me unto pain / Cast out the flesh / Skinned / Inherit his soul / Valley of the dead / Succumb to the fear / Altered minds / Scars / Anointing of the sick / Enter the confines / Through deviant eyes.
■ CD . . . . DEAF 013CD
Deaf / Jan '94.
■ LP . . . . DEAF 013
Deaf / Jan '94.

Banshee

CRY IN THE NIGHT.
Tracks: Not Advised.
■ LP . . . . RR 9525 1
Road Runner / Dec '88.

Baphomet

DEAD SHALL INHERIT, THE.
Tracks: Not Advised.
CD . . . . VILE 031CD
LP . . . . VILE 031
MC . . . . VILE 031MC
Peaceville / May '92 / Vital Distribution / Pinnacle.

TRUST.
Tracks: Not Advised.
CD . . . . MASSCD 027
Massacre / Apr '94 / Plastic Head.

Barnes, Jimmy

Raw-throated frontman for Australian band Cold Chisel launched solo career in '82. Despite initial participation of rock luminaries (including hitmakers Desmond Child and Jim Vallance, and Journey-men Neil Schon and Jonathon Cain), Barnes' brand of AOR has yet to reap rewards outside Australia.

BARNESTORMING.
Tracks: Not Advised.
CD . . . . D 245212
Mushroom (Australia) / May '94 / Total / BMG.

BODYSWERVE.
Tracks: Not Advised.
■ LP . . . . RML 53138
Mushroom (Australia) / May '88.

FLESH & WOOD/THE HEAT.
Tracks: Not Advised.
CD Set . . . . D 45045
MC Set . . . . C 45045
Mushroom (Australia) / Feb '94 / Total / BMG.

FOR THE WORKING CLASS MAN.
Tracks: Not Advised.
■ Double LP . . . . RML 53196/7
Mushroom (Australia) / May '88.

FREIGHT TRAIN HEART.
Tracks: Driving wheels / Seven days / Too much ain't enough love / Lessons in love / Waitin' for the heartache / Last frontier / I'm still on your side / Do or die / I wanna get started with you / Walk on.
■ LP 9241461
■ CD 9241462
■ MC 9241464
Geffen / '88.

HEAT.
Tracks: Not Advised.
CD . . . . TVD 93372
MC . . . . TVC 93372
Mushroom (Australia) / Jun '93 / Total / BMG.
LP . . . . TVL 93372
Mushroom (Australia) / Nov '93 / Total / BMG.

JIMMY BARNES.
Tracks: No second prize / I'd die to be with you tonight / Working class man / Promise me you'll call / Boys cry out for war / Paradise / Without your love / American heartbeat / Thick skinned / Ride the night away / Daylight.
■ LP 9240891
■ MC 9240894
Geffen / May '86.

SOUL DEEP.
Tracks: Not Advised.
CD . . . . TVD 93344
Mushroom (Australia) / Aug '94 / Total / BMG.

STAND UP E.P.
Tracks: Not Advised.
■ 12" . . . . T 12094
■ CD Single . . . . D 12094
■ MC Single . . . . C 12094
Mushroom (Australia) / Nov '93.

STONE COLD.
Tracks: Stone cold.
■ CD Single . . . . D 11504
Mushroom (Australia) / Feb '94.

TOO MUCH AIN'T ENOUGH LOVE.
Tracks: Too much ain't enough love / Do or die / Working class man (12" only) / Resurrection shuffle (Available on 12" only).
■ 12" . . . . GEF 38T
■ 7" . . . . GEF 38
Geffen / May '88.

TWO FIRES.
Tracks: Lay down your guns / Let's make it last all night / Little darlin' / Love is enough / Hardline / One of a kind / Sister mercy / When your love is gone / Between two fires / Fade to black / Hold on.
CD 7567821412
East West / Sep '90 / WEA.
■ LP 756 782 141 1
■ MC 756 782 141 4
Atlantic / Sep '90.
CD . . . . TVD 93318
Mushroom (Australia) / May '94 / Total / BMG.

WORKING CLASS MAN.
Tracks: Working class man (remix) / Boys cry out for war.
■ 12" . . . . GEF 3T
■ 7" . . . . GEF 3
Geffen / May '86.

Baron Rojo

BARON AL ROJO VIVI.
Tracks: Not Advised.
■ LP . . . . BALLS 83454
Mausoleum / '84.

BRUTAL VOLUME.
Tracks: Not Advised.
■ LP . . . . SKULL 8327
Mausoleum / '84.

LARGA VIDA AL ROCK AND ROLL.
Tracks: Not Advised.
■ LP . . . . SKULL 8328
Mausoleum / '84.

METAL MORFOSIS.
Tracks: Not Advised.
■ LP . . . . SKULL 8322
Mausoleum / '84.

VOLUMEN ROJO (SPANISH VERSION).
Tracks: Not Advised.
■ LP . . . . SKULL 8326
Mausoleum / '84.

Barren Cross

ATOMIC ARENA.
Tracks: Not Advised.
■ LP . . . . MFN 84
Music For Nations / Aug '89.

HOTTER THAN HELL.
Tracks: Imaginary music / Killers of the unborn / Going nowhere / Opus to the third heaven / In the eye of the fire / Light the flame / King Jesus and

blues jam / Dying day / Close to the edge / Dead lock / King of Kings / Rock for the king / Terrorist child / Give your life.
CD . . . . MD 93832
LP . . . . MD 93831
Medusa (USA) / Jul '90.

ROCK FOR THE KING.
Tracks: Not Advised.
CD . . . . SSD 8064
Myrrh / '88 / Word Records (UK) / Sony.

STATE OF CONTROL.
Tracks: Not Advised.
CD . . . . CDENV 530
■ LP . . . . ENVLP 530
■ MC . . . . TCENV 530
Enigma (EMI) / Jun '89.

Barth, Bobby

DON'T COME TO ME.
Tracks: Don't come to me / Sara.
■ 7" . . . . .B 9549
Atco / May '86.

TWO HEARTS-ONE BEAT.
Tracks: Stop in the name of love / Sara / Knifes edge / I don't want to be alone tonight / Burn me once, burn me twice / Once in a lifetime / Dangerous games / Don't come to me.
MC 790 502-4
■ LP 790 502-1
Atco / May '86.

Bastard Kestrel

BASTARD.
Tracks: Tharn / Semtex sandwich / Motofry / Ten / Surf pink baby / Love story / Ulrich / (Born) brain stupid / Sheep dip / Skitzersister / Bruising / Slob / Dooby bloody do.
■ LP . . . . KESTREL LP
Kestrel / Sep '89.

CHOR TRANCE.
Tracks: Chor trance.
■ EP . . . . GLUM 002
Glum / Mar '88.

OH SPLENDID MUSHROOM.
Tracks: Not Advised.
■ LP . . . . WIIIJLP 2
Wiiija / Sep '89.

RASERA.
Tracks: Rasera.
■ 12" . . . . WIIIKIT 2
Wiiija / Aug '88.

STENCH.
Tracks: Stench.
■ 7" . . . . SLUM 003
Goldhanger / Feb '93.

Bathory

BATHORY.
Tracks: Not Advised.
■ LP . . . . FLAG 8
Under One Flag / Mar '87.

BLOOD FIRE DEATH.
Tracks: Odens ride over wordland / Golden wall of heaven / Pace 'til death / Dies irae / Fine day to die / Holocaust / For all those who died / Blood fire death.
CD . . . . CDFLAG 26
■ LP . . . . FLAG 26
■ MC . . . . TFLAG 26
Under One Flag / Oct '88.
■ LP P.Disc . . . . FLAG 26P
Under One Flag / Apr '89.

HAMMERHEART.
Tracks: Not Advised.
■ CD . . . . CDNUK 153
■ LP . . . . NUK 153
■ MC . . . . ZCNUK 153
Noise / Apr '90.

JUBILEUM VOLUME 1.
Tracks: Rider at the gate of dawn / Crawl to your cross / Sacrifice / Dies irae / Through blood by thunder / You don't move me (I don't give a fuck) / Odens ride over Nordland / Fine day to die / War / Enter the eternal fire / Song to hall up high / Under the runes / Equimanthorn / Blood fire death.
CD . . . . BMCD 666-7
MC . . . . BMCT 666-7
Black Mark / Nov '92 / Plastic Head.

RETURN, THE.
Tracks: Total destruction / Born for burning / Wind of mayhem / Bestial lust / Possessed / Rite of darkness / Reap of evil / Son of the dammed / Sadist / Return of the darkness and evil.
■ LP . . . . FLAG 9
Under One Flag / Mar '87.

RETURN.. THE.
Tracks: Revelation of doom / Total destruction / Born for burning / Wind of mayhem / Bestial lust / Possessed / Rite of darkness / Reap of evil / Son of the damned / Sadist / Return of the darkness and evil.
CD . . . . BMCD 666-2
Black Mark / May '92 / Plastic Head.

TWILIGHT OF THE GODS.
Tracks: Not Advised.
CD . . . . BMCD 666-6
LP .BMLP 666-6
MC. . . . . .BMCT 666-6
Black Mark / '92 / Plastic Head.

UNDER THE SIGN OF THE BLACK MARK.
Tracks: Nocturnal obeisance / Massacre / Woman of dark desires / Call from the grave / Equimanthorn / Enter the eternal fire / Chariots of fire / 13 candles / Of doom.
■ LP .FLAG 11
MC. .TFLAG 11
Under One Flag / Jun '87 / Pinnacle.

Batlord

BLOOD SURE DEATH.
Tracks: Leprosy / Forgotten past / Pull the plug / Primitive ways / Born dead / Left to die / Open casket / Choke on it.
■ LP P.Disc . . . . FLAG 24P
Under One Flag / May '89.

Battery

ONLY THE DIEHARD REMAIN.
Tracks: Not Advised.
CD . . . . LF 089CD
Lost & Found / May '94 / Plastic Head.

WE WON'T FALL.
Tracks: Not Advised.
CD . . . . .LF 055
Lost & Found / Aug '93 / Plastic Head.

Battle Bratt

BATTLE BRATT.
Tracks: Not Advised.
CD . . . . US 015 CD
U.S. Metal / Jun '89 / Vital Distribution.
■ LP . . . . US 015
U.S. Metal / Jun '89.

Battleaxe

BURN THIS TOWN.
Tracks: Not Advised.
■ LP . . . . .MFN 8
Music For Nations / Jul '83.

POWER FROM THE UNIVERSE.
Tracks: Not Advised.
■ LP . . . . MFN 25
Music For Nations / Jul '84.

Be-Bop Deluxe

British band centering around guitarist Bill Nelson. Be-Bop Deluxe were a diverse fusion of 1970's rock, heavy metal and glitter pop. Formed in Wakefield, Yorkshire in 1972, secured a deal with Harvest after winning support of John Peel. Their debut LP *Axe Victim* (1974) reached the album charts. After many personnel changes, Nelson released *Futurama* in 1975. The following year the band had two hit albums; *Sunburst Finish* and *Modern Music*, and two hit singles; *Ships In The Night* and the *Hot Valves* EP. Be-Bop Deluxe were voted NME's Best New Band in 1976. Released the top 10 LP *Live! In The Air Age* in 1977. The group disbanded in 1979 with Nelson forming Red Noise, before going solo in 1980. *Quit Dreaming And Get On The Beam* was released on Nelson's Cocteau label in 1981 and is his most successful LP to date. Has recorded prolifically since but has kept a low profile.

AXE VICTIM.
Tracks: Axe victim / Love is swift arrows / Jet silver and the dolls of venus / Third floor heaven / Night creature / Rocket cathedrals / Adventures in a Yorkshire landscape / Jets at dawn / No trains to heaven / Darkness (L'immoraliste) / Piece of mine (live) / Mill Street junction (live) / Adventures in a Yorkshire landscape (live).
CD . . . . CZ 327
EMI / Feb '91 / EMI.

AXE VICTIM/FUTURAMA.
Tracks: Axe victim / Love is swift arrows / Jet silver and the dolls of Venus / Third floor heaven / Night creatures / Rocket cathedrals / Adventures in a Yorkshire landscape / Jets at dawn / No trains to heaven / Darkness / Stage whispers / Love with the madman / Maid in heaven / Sister seagull / Sound track / Music in dreamland / Jean Cocteau / Between the worlds / Swan song.
■ Double CD . . . . .EDP 154 6793
Harvest / Sep '83.

BE BOP DELUXE SINGLES A'S & B'S.
Tracks: Jet silver and the dolls of Venus / Between the worlds / Maid in heaven / Ships in the night / Kiss of light / Japan / Panic in the world / Electrical language / Third floor heaven / Lights / Crying to the sky / Shine / Futurist manifesto / Blue as a jewel / Surreal / Estate.
■ LP . . . . SHSM 2034
MC. . . . . TCSHSM 2034
Harvest / May '81 / EMI.

BETWEEN THE WORLDS.
Tracks: Between the worlds / Lights.
■ 7" . . . . HAR 5091
Harvest / Feb '75.

BOP TO THE RED NOISE.
Tracks: Ships in the night (1976) / Life in the air age (1976) / Maid in heaven (1975) / Jean Cocteau (1975) / 3rd floor heaven (1974) / Rocket cathedrals (1974) / No trains to heaven (1974) / Orphans of Babylon (1976) / Modern music (1976) / New precision (1978) / Don't touch me (1979) / For young moderns (1979).
■ LP . . . . DOJOLP 42
Dojo / Aug '86.

DRASTIC PLASTIC.
Tracks: Electrical language / New precision / New mysteries / Surreal estate / Love in flames / Panic in the world / Dangerous stranger / Superenigmatix / Visions of endless hopes / Possession / Islands of the dead / Blimps / Lovers are mortal / Lights.
■ LP . . . . SHSP 4091
Harvest / Feb '78.
■ CD . . . . CDP 794 733 2
EMI / Feb '91.

ELECTRICAL LANGUAGE.
Tracks: Electrical language / Surreal estate.
■ 7" . . . . HAR 5158
Harvest / May '78.

FUTURAMA.
Tracks: Stage whispers / Love with the madman / Maid in heaven / Sister seagull / Sound track / Music in dreamland / Jean Cocteau / Between the worlds / Swan song / Between the worlds (single version) / Maid in heaven (live) / Speed of the wind.
■ CD . . . . CZ 328
EMI / Feb '91.

HOT VALVES EP.
Tracks: Maid in heaven / Blazing apostles / Jet silver and the dolls of Venus / Bring back the spark.
■ EP . . . . HAR 5117
Harvest / Nov '76.

JAPAN.
Tracks: Japan / Futuristic manifesto.
■ 7" . . . . HAR 5135
Harvest / Sep '77.

JET SILVER.
Tracks: Jet silver / Third floor heaven.

LIVE - IN THE AIR-AGE.
Tracks: Life in the air age / Ships in the night / Piece of mind / Fair exchange / Mill Street junction / Adventures in a Yorkshire landscape / Blazing apostles / Shine / Sister seagull / Maid in heaven.
■ Double LP . . . . SHVL 816
Harvest / Aug '77.
CD . . . . CZ 331
EMI / Feb '91 / EMI.

MAID IN HEAVEN.
Tracks: Maid in heaven / Lights.
■ 7" . . . . HAR 5098
Harvest / Jun '75.

MODERN MUSIC.
Tracks: Orphans of Babylon / Twilight capers / Kiss of light / Bird charmer's destiny / Gold at the end of my rainbow / Bring back the spark / Modern music / Dancing in the moonlight (all alone) / Honeymoon on Mars / Lost in the neon world / Dance of the Uncle Sam humanoids / Modern music (reprise) / Forbidden lovers / Down on terminal street / Make the music magic / Futurist manifesto / Quest for the harvest of the stars / Autosexual.
■ LP . . . . SHSP 4058
Harvest / Sep '76.
■ CD . . . . CZ 330
EMI / Feb '91.

PANIC IN THE WORLD.
Tracks: Panic in the world / Maid in Heaven / Electrical language / Blue as a jewel.
■ 7" . . . . HAR 5147
Harvest / Jan '78.
■ 7" . . . . .COQ 7
Cocteau / Aug '83.

RADIOLAND.
Tracks: Life in the air age / Sister seagull / Third floor heaven / Blazing apostles / Maid in heaven / Kiss of light / Adventures in a Yorkshire landscape / Fair exchange / Ships in the night / Modern music / Dancing in the moonlight / Honeymoon on Mars / Lost in the neon world / New precision / Superenigmatix / Possession / Dangerous stranger / Islands of the dead / Panic in the world.
CD . . . . WINCD 065
Windsong / Aug '94 / Pinnacle / A.D.A. Distribution.

RAIDING THE DIVINE ARCHIVES (Best of Be Bop Deluxe).
Tracks: Jet silver and the Dolls of Venus / Adventures in a Yorkshire landscape / Maid in Heaven / Ships in the night / Life in the air age / Kiss of light / Sister Seagull / Modern music / Japan / Panic in the world / Bring back the spark / Forbidden lovers / Electrical Language / Fair exchange (CD only.) / Sleep that burns (CD only.) / Between the worlds (CD only.) / Music in dreamland (CD only.).
■ LP . . . . EMS 1130
■ MC . . . . TCEMS 1130
Harvest / Feb '87.
CD . . . . CZ 296
EMI / Apr '90 / EMI.

SHIPS IN THE NIGHT.
Tracks: Ships in the night / Maid in heaven.
■ 7" . . . . HAR 5104
Harvest / Feb '76.
■ 7" .G45 21
EMI Golden 45's / Apr '84.

SINGLES A'S & B'S.
Tracks: Jet silver and the dolls of Venus / Maid in heaven / Kiss of light / Panic in the world / Third floor heaven / Crying to the sky / Futurist manifesto / Surreal estate / Between the worlds / Ships in the night / Japan / Electrical language / Lights / Shine / Blue as a jewel.
CD . . . . SEECD 336
See For Miles / Feb '92 / Pinnacle.

SUNBURST FINISH.
Tracks: Fair exchange / Heavenly homes / Ships in the night / Crying to the sky / Sleep that burns / Beauty secrets / Life in the air age / Like an old blues / Crystal gazing / Blazing apostles / Shine (CD only.) / Speed of the wind (CD only.) / Blue as a jewel (CD only.).
■ LP . . . . SHSP 4053
Harvest / Jan '76.
■ LP . . . . FA 3004
Fame / Jun '82.
■ LP . . . . REV LP 71
MC. . . . . REV MC 71
Revolver / Jun '86 / FM Revolver / Sony.
CD . . . . CZ 329
EMI / Feb '91 / EMI.

Beastialit

DEHYDRATED SPLIT.
Tracks: Not Advised.
CD . . . . METALAGE 1CD
Clay / Apr '94 / Plastic Head.

Beauvoir, Jean

DRUMS ALONG THE MOHAWK.
Tracks: Feel the heat / Never went down / Missing the young days / Rockin' in the street / Sorry I missed your wedding day / Drive you home / Sam's songs play on and on / This is our house / If I was me / Nina.
■ LP . . . . V 2370
■ MC . . . . TCV 2370

Virgin / '86.
CD . . . . CDV 2370
Virgin / '87 / EMI.
■ **MC** . . . . OVEDC 222
■ **LP** . . . . OVED 222
Virgin / '88.

FEEL THE HEAT.
Tracks: Feel the heat / Standing in the line of fire.
■ **12"** . . . . VS 834-12
■ **7"** . . . . .VS 834
Virgin / Aug '86.

GAMBLIN' MAN.
Tracks: Gamblin' man (Not on 12') / Gamblin' man (go-go mix) (CD & 12" only) / Dangerously (On all versions) / Gamblin' man (African thang mix) (12" only) / Feel the heat (CD only).
■ **CD Single** . . . . VSCD 1056
Virgin / Aug '88.
■ **12"** . . . . VST 1056
■ **7"** . . . . VS 1056
Virgin / Mar '88.

JACKNIFED.
Tracks: Jacknifed / Standing on my own feet / Gamblin' man / Alone again / Searching for a light / Dyin' at your door / Spend your life with me / Find my way home / If love could only / Jimmy.
■ **LP** . . . . .V 2511
■ **MC** . . . . TCV 2511
■ **CD** . . . . CDV 2511
Virgin / May '88.

MISSING THE YOUNG DAYS.
Tracks: Crazy / Missing the young days.
■ **12"** . . . . VS 874-12
■ **7"** . . . . .VS 874
Virgin / Jan '87.

Beck, Jeff

Jeff Beck was born in Surrey in 1944. After replacing Eric Clapton in the Yardbirds, Beck left the group in December 1966 and teamed up with pop maestro Mickie Most to record the perennial party favourite and huge hit *Hi-Ho Silver Lining*. Jeff Beck then formed his own group, which included future stars Rod Stewart and Ron Wood. Recorded *Cosa Nostra Beck-Ola* LP - a blues/ rock offering that lay the groundwork for heavy metal. After many personnel changes, Beck was joined by Tim Bogert and Carmine Appice. The trio's self-titled album hit the Top Thirty in '73 but Beck's real return to form came in the mid-70's: the albums *Blow By Blow* & *Wired*, featured some of his best guitar work. *There And Back* was released in 1980, this was followed by another period of inactivity that typified Beck's erratic and fragmented career, although this has not altered his status as one of rock's most influential guitarists. Beck's most notable recent recording was 1989's *Guitar Shop*.

AMBITIOUS.
Tracks: Ambitious / Escape.
■ **12"** . . . . TA 6981
■ **7"** . . . . .A 6981
Epic / Mar '86.

ANTHOLOGY.
Tracks: Not Advised.
■ **LP** . . . . MA 14185
MC . . . . MAMC 914185
Masters (Holland) / '88.

BECK, BOGERT, APPICE (Beck, Bogert, Appice).
Tracks: Black cat moan / Lady / Oh to love you / Superstition / Sweet sweet surrender / Why should I care about you / Lose myself with love / Livin' alone / I'm so proud.
■ **LP** . . . . EPC 65455
Epic / Apr '73.
■ **LP** . . . . EPC 32491
MC .40 32491
Epic / Sep '84 / Sony.
■ **LP** . . . . ESSLP 011
■ **MC** . . . . ESSMC 011
■ **CD** . . . . ESSCD 011
Essential / Nov '89.

BECKOLOGY.
Tracks: Trouble in mind / Nursery rhyme (live) / Wandering man blues / Steeled blues / Heart full of soul / I'm not talking / I ain't done wrong / I'm a man / Shape of things / Over, under, sideways, down / Happenings ten years time ago / Hot house of Omagararshid / Lost women / Rack myh mind / Nazz are blue / Psycho daisies / Jeff's boogie / Too much monkey business (live) / Sun is shining (live) /

You're a better man than I (live) / Love me like I love you (live) / Hi ho silver lining / Tallyman / Beck's bolero / I ain't superstitious / Rock my plimsoul / Jail house rock / Plynth (water down the drain) / I've been drinking / Definitely maybe / New ways/train train / Going down / I can't give back the love I feel for you / Superstition / Black cat moan (live) / Blues deluxe BBA boogie (live) / Jizz whizz / Cause we've ended as lovers / Goodbye pork pie hat / Love is green / Diamond dust / Freeway jam (live) / Pump / People get ready / Escape / Gets us all in the end / Back on the street / Wild thing / Train kept a-rollin' / Sleepwalk / Stumble / Big block / Where were you.
CD Set 4692602
MC Set 4692624
Epic / May '94 / Sony.

BEST OF BECKOLOGY.
Tracks: Heart full of soul / Shapes of things / Over, under, sideways, down / Hi ho silver lining / Tallyman / Jailhouse rock / I've been drinking / I ain't superstitious / Superstition / Cause we've ended as lovers / Pump / People get ready / Wild thing / Where were you / Trouble in mind / Star cycle (Cassette & CD only).
■ **LP** 4713481
■ **CD** 4713482
■ **MC** 4713484
Epic / Mar '92.

BEST OF JEFF BECK (1967-69) (Featuring Rod Stewart).
Tracks: Shapes of things / Morning dew / You shook me / I ain't superstitious / All shook up / Jailhouse rock / Tallyman / Love is blue / I've been drinking / Rock my plimsoul / Beck's bolero / Rice pudding.
■ **LP** . . . . FA 41 3125 1
MC . . . . FA 41 3125 4
Fame / May '85 / EMI.

BLOW BY BLOW.
Tracks: It doesn't really matter / She's a woman / Constipated duck / Air blower / Scatterbrain / Cause we've ended as lovers / Thelonious / Freeway jam / Diamond dust.
■ **LP** . . . . EPC 32367
■ **MC** 40 32367
Epic / Sep '83.
■ **CD** . . . . CD 69117
Epic / '88.
■ **CD** . . . . CD 32367
CBS / Jul '89.
CD 4690122
MC 4690124
Epic / Apr '94 / Sony.

COSA NOSTRA BECK-OLA.
Tracks: All shook up / Spanish boots / Girl from Mill Valley / Jailhouse rock / Plynth (water down the drain) / Hangman's knee / Rice pudding.
■ **LP** . . . . SCX 6351
Columbia (EMI) / Sep '69.
■ **MC** . . . . ED 2606004
■ **LP** . . . . ED 2606001
Capitol / Jul '85.

CRAZY LEGS (Beck, Jeff & Big Town Playboys).
Tracks: Race with the devil / Cruisin' / Crazy legs/ Double talkin' baby / Woman love / Lotta lovin' / Catman / Pink Thunderbird / Baby blue / You better believe / Who slapped John / Say Mama / Red blue jeans & a ponytail / Five feet of lovin' / B-I-Bickey-Bi-Bo-Bo-Go / Blues stay away / Pretty pretty baby / Hold me, hug me, rock me.
CD 473597-2
LP 473597-1
MC 473597-4
Sony Music / Jun '93 / Sony.

FINAL PEACE.
Tracks: Final peace / Scatterbrain / Too much to lose / Led boots.
■ **EP** . . . . EPCA 1009
Epic / Feb '81.

FLASH.
Tracks: Ambitious / Gets us all in the end / Escape / People get ready / Stop, look and listen / Get workin' / Ecstacy / Night after night / You know, we know / Get us all in the end / Ecstasy.
■ **LP** . . . . EPC 26112
■ **MC** 40 26112
Epic / Jul '85.
CD . . . . CD 26112
Epic / Jan '89 / Sony.
CD 982838 2
MC 982838 4
Pickwick/Sony Collector's Choice / Mar '94 / Pickwick / Pinnacle.

FLASH / BLOW BY BLOW / THERE AND BACK.
Tracks: Ambitious / Gets us all in the end / Escape / People get ready / Stop look & listen / Get workin' / Ecstasy / Night after night / You know, we know / Nighthamks / Back on the streets / You know what I mean / She's a woman / Constipated duck / Air blower / Scatterbrain / Cause we've ended as lovers / Thelonius / Freeway jam / Diamond dust / Star cycle / Too much to lose / You never know / Pump / El Becko / Golden road / Space boogie / Final peace.
CD Set 468802 2
Epic / Feb '93 / Sony.

GUITAR SHOP.
Tracks: Guitar shop / People get ready / Cause we've ended as lovers / Blue wind.
■ **12"** . . . . BECK T1
■ **7"** . . . . BECK 1
■ **CD Single** . . . . CDBECK 1
Epic / Oct '89.

HI HO SILVER LINING.
Tracks: Hi ho silver lining / Beck's bolero / Rock my plimsoul.
■ **7"** . . . . .DB 8151
Columbia (EMI) / Mar '67.
■ **12"** . . . . 12 RR 3
■ **7"** .RR 3
RAK Replay / Sep '82.
■ **7" P.Disc** . . . . RRP 3
RAK Replay / Sep '82.

I'VE BEEN DRINKING (Beck, Jeff & Rod Stewart).
Tracks: I've been drinking.
■ **7"** .RR 4
RAK Replay / May '73.

JEFF BECK GROUP (Beck, Jeff Group).
Tracks: Ice cream cakes / Glad all over / Tonight I'll be staying here with you / Sugar cane / I can't give back the love I feel for you / Going down / I gotta have a song / High ways / Highways / Definitely maybe.
■ **LP** . . . . EPC 64899
Epic / Jul '72.

JEFF BECK'S GUITAR SHOP.
Tracks: Guitar shop / Behind the veil / Where were you / Day in the house / Sling shot / Savoy / Big block / Stand on it / Two rivers.
CD 4634722
■ **LP** 4634721
■ **MC** 4634724
Epic / Oct '89.

LATE 60'S WITH ROD STEWART.
Tracks: Hi ho silver lining / Tallyman / Love is blue / Beck's bolero / Rock my plimsoul / I've been drinking / Shapes of things / Let me love you / Morning dew / You shook me / All shook up / Spanish boots / Jailhouse rock / Plynth (water down the drain) / Hangman's knee / Rice pudding / Ol' man river / Greensleeves / I ain't superstitious.
■ **CD** . . . . CZ 130
EMI / Sep '88.

LEGENDS IN MUSIC - JEFF BECK.
Tracks: Not Advised.
CD . . . . .LECD 080
Wisepack / Jul '94 / TBD / Conifer Records.

LIVE: JEFF BECK (Beck, Jeff with Jan Hammer Group).
Tracks: Freeway jam / Earth (still our only home) / She's a woman / Full moon boogie / Darkness earth in search of a sun / Scatterbrain / Blue wind.
■ **LP** . . . . EPC 32297
■ **MC** 40 32297
Epic / Jun '85.

LOVE IS BLUE.
Tracks: Love is blue.
■ **7"** . . . . .DB 8359
Columbia (EMI) / Feb '68.

MUSTANG SALLY (Beck, Jeff & Buddy Guy).
Tracks: Mustang Sally.
■ **7"** . . . . ORE 30
■ **CD Single** . . . . ORECD 30
Silvertone / Sep '91.

PEOPLE GET READY.
Tracks: People get ready / Back on the street / You know, we know (Only on 12" single).
■ **12"** . . . . TA 6387
■ **7"** . . . . .A 6387
Epic / Jul '85.

■ DELETED

PEOPLE GET READY (Beck, Jeff & Rod Stewart).
Tracks: People get ready / Train kept a-rollin' (Not on CD single) / Cause we've ended as lovers (CD single only) / Where were you (CD single only) / Train train (CD 2 only.) / New ways (CD 2 only.).
- 7".................................6577567
- CD Single........................6577565
- CD Single........................6577562
- MC Single........................6577564

Epic / Feb '92.

ROUGH AND READY.
Tracks: Got the feeling / Situation / Short business / Max's tune / I've been used / New ways / Train train / Jody.
- LP.............................EQ 30973

Epic / Jul '72.
- MC................................40 32037

CBS / Aug '84 / Sony.
- LP.................................32037

CBS / Aug '84.

ROUGH AND READY/JEFF BECK GROUP.
Tracks: Ice cream cakes / Glad all over / Tonight I'll be staying here with you / Sugar cane / I can't give back the love I feel for you / Going down / I gotta have a song / Highways / Definitely maybe / Got the feeling / Situation / Max's tune / I've been used / New ways / Short business / Jody.
- Double LP....................TFOLP 19
- CD Set.......................TFOCD 19
- MC...........................TFOMC 19

That's Original / May '89.

STOP, LOOK AND LISTEN.
Tracks: Stop, look and listen / You know, we know.
- 12"..............................TX 6507
- 7"................................A 6587

Epic / Sep '85.

TALLYMAN.
Tracks: Tallyman.
- 7"..............................DB 8227

Columbia (EMI) / Aug '67.

THERE AND BACK.
Tracks: Star cycle / Too much to lose / You never knew / Pump / El Becko / Golden road / Space boogie / Final peace.
- LP...........................EPC 83288
- CD............................CD 83288

Epic / Jul '80.
- LP...........................EPC 32197
- MC..............................40 32197

Epic / Aug '84.

TRUTH.
Tracks: Shapes of things / Let me love you / Morning dew / You shook me / Ol' man river / Greensleeves / Rock my plimsoul / Beck's bolero / Blues de luxe / I ain't superstitious.
- LP.............................ATAK 42
- MC...........................TC ATAK 42

Columbia (EMI) / '85 / EMI.
- MC...........................TCFA 3155
- LP..............................FA 3155

Fame / Jun '86.

TRUTH/BECKOLA (Beck, Jeff Group).
Tracks: Shapes of things / Let me love you / Morning dew / You shook me / Ol' man river / Greensleeves / Rock my plimsoul / Beck's bolero / Blues deluxe / I ain't superstitious / All shook up / Spanish boots / Girl from Mill Valley / Jailhouse rock / Plynth (water down the drain) / Hangman's knee / Rice pudding.
- CD.............................CZ 374
- MC..........................TCEMS 1379

EMI / Feb '91.

WILD THING.
Tracks: Wild thing / Get us all in the end / Night hawk.
- 12"..............................TA 7271
- 7"...............................A 7271

Epic / Jul '86.

WIRED.
Tracks: Led boots / Come dancing / Goodbye pork pie hat / Head for backstage pass / Blue wind / Sophie / Play with me / Love is green.
- LP................................86012

CBS / Jul '76.
- LP...........................EPC 32067
- MC..............................40 32067

Epic / Mar '82 / Sony.
- CD...........................CD 86012

Epic / '88.

Becker, Jason

PERPETUAL BURN.
Tracks: Altitudes / Perpetual blues / Mabel's fatal fable / Temple of the absurd / Eleven blue Egyptians / Dweller in the cellar / Opus pocus.
- CD..............................RR 9528 2
- LP..............................RR 9528 1
- MC.............................RR 9528 4

Road Runner / Sep '88.

Bedlem

BEDLEM.
Tracks: I believe in you (fire in my body) / Hot lips / Sarah / Sweet sister Mary / Seven long years / Beast / Whiskey and wine / Lookin' through love's eyes / Putting on the flesh / Set me free.
- LP...........................METALP 104

Razor / Jun '85.

Beggars & Thieves

BEGGARS AND THIEVES.
Tracks: No more broken dreams / Billy knows better / Waitin' for the man / Your love is in vain / Isn't it easy / Let's get lost / Heaven and hell / Love junkie / Kill me / Love's a bitch / Beggars & Thieves.
- CD.............................7567821132
- LP.............................7567821131
- MC.............................7567821134

WEA / Aug '90 / WEA.

Behemoth

DEATHWINGS.
Tracks: Deathwings / Vengence.
- 7"...............................CONT 1

Bullet Continental / Apr '84.

Beherit

DEATH YELL.
Tracks: Death yell.
- 7"............................TURBO 010

Turbo Music / Nov '92.

H4180V21C.
Tracks: Not Advised.
- CD............................SP 119CD

Spinefarm / Jun '94 / Plastic Head.

Belial

NEVER AGAIN.
Tracks: Not Advised.
- CD................................LRC 666

Lethal / Feb '94 / Plastic Head.

Believer

DIMENSIONS.
Tracks: Not Advised.
- CD..............................RR 91012
- LP..............................RR 91011

Road Runner / Sep '93 / Pinnacle.

SANITY OBSCURE.
Tracks: Not Advised.
- LP..............................RC 93121
- MC..............................RC 93124

Road Runner / Jun '91 / Pinnacle.
- CD..............................RC 93122

Road Runner / Jan '94 / Pinnacle.

Benatar, Pat

Classically trained Pat Benatar started recording at the beginning of the 1980's. Benatar had three big selling 'soft-rock' LP's. The 1982 album *Get Nervous*, featured the big seller *Shadows Of The Night*. Her biggest single was *Love Is A Battlefield*, co-written by Mike Chapman from the *Live From Earth* LP. Her brand of dramatic pop/ rock is staple diet on US rock radio but, like the music of so many of her peers, finds little acceptance in the UK.

ALL FIRED UP.
Tracks: All fired up.
- 12".............................PATX 5
- 7"..............................PAT 5

Chrysalis / Jun '88.

BENATAR.
Tracks: Not Advised.
- VHS..............................RVT 20282

RCA/Columbia (video) / '88 / Gold & Sons / TBD / Sony.

BEST SHOTS.
Tracks: Hit me with your best shot / Love is a battlefield / We belong / We live for love / Sex as a weapon / Invincible / Shadows of the night / Heartbreaker / Fire and ice / Treat me right / If you think you know how to love me / You better run.
- LP.............................TAT V 1
- MC............................ZTAT V 1

Chrysalis / Nov '87 / EMI.
- CD.............................CCD 1538
- MC............................ZPATV 1

Chrysalis / Oct '87 / EMI.
- LP.............................PATV 1

Chrysalis / '88.

BEST SHOTS.
Tracks: You better run / I'm gonna follow you / Fire and ice / Promises in the dark / Shadows of the night / Anxiety (get nervous) / Little too late / Love is a batlefield / We belong / Painted desert / Sex as a weapon / Le bel age.
- VHS............................CVHS 5015

Chrysalis Music Video / Feb '88 / EMI.

CRIMES OF PASSION.
Tracks: Treat me right / You better run / Never wanna leave you / Hit me with your best shot / Hell is for children / Prisoner of love / Out a touch / Little paradise / I'm gonna follow you / Wuthering heights / It's a lovely life / Eastern shadows / Joanna / Stretch / Poiliceman's ball / Stax / Taken in hand / Paradise lost / Box / Web of love / Dangerous woman.
- LP.............................CHR 1275
- MC............................ZCHR 1275

Chrysalis / Sep '80.
- CD.............................ACCD 1275

Chrysalis / Jun '85 / EMI.

DON'T WALK AWAY.
Tracks: Don't walk away / Lift 'em on up / Hell is for children (live) (12" & CD single only.) / We live for love (special mix) (12" & Cd single).
- CD Single.....................PAT CD 6
- 12"............................PATX 6
- 7"..............................PAT 6

Chrysalis / Sep '88.

FIRE AND ICE.
Tracks: Fire and ice / Hard to believe.
- 7" P.Disc.....................CHSP 2529

Chrysalis / Jul '81.

GET NERVOUS.
Tracks: Shadows of the night / I want out / Looking for a stranger / Anxiety (get nervous) / Fight it out / Victim / Little too late / I'll do it / Tell it to her / Silent partners.
- LP P.Disc.....................PCHR 1396
- CD.............................ACCD 1396
- LP.............................CHR 1396
- MC............................ZCHR 1396

Chrysalis / Nov '82.

GRAVITY'S RAINBOW.
Tracks: Pictures of a gone world / Everybody lay down / Somebody's baby / Ties that bind / You and I / Disconnected / Crazy / Everytime I fall back / Sanctuary / Rise (part 1) / Kingdom key / Tradin' down.
- CD...........................CDCHR 6054
- MC..........................TCCHR 6054

Chrysalis / Oct '93 / EMI.

HEARTBREAKER.
Tracks: Heartbreaker / My clone sleeps alone.
- 7".............................CHS 2395

Chrysalis / '83.

HIT ME WITH YOUR BEST SHOT.
Tracks: Promises in the dark / Fire and ice / Just like me / Precious / Hit me with your best shot.
- 7".............................CHS 2474

Chrysalis / '82.

HIT VIDEOS.
Tracks: Not Advised.
- VHS...........................RVT 20790

RCA/Columbia (video) / '88 / Gold & Sons / TBD / Sony.

IN THE HEAT OF THE NIGHT.
Tracks: Heartbreaker / I need a lover / If you think you know how to love me / In the heat of the night / My clone sleeps alone / We live for love / Rated X / Don't let it show / No you don't / So sincere.
- LP.............................CHR 1236

Chrysalis / Jun '85.
- CD...........................CDFA 3286

■ DELETED

■ MC. . . . . TCFA 3286
Fame / Dec '92.
CD. . . . . ACCD 1236
MC. . . . . ZCHR 1236
Chrysalis / Jul '94 / EMI.

IN THE HEAT OF THE NIGHT/CRIMES OF PASSION.
Tracks: Heartbreaker / I need a lover / If you think you know how to love me / In the heat of the night / My clone sleeps alone / We live for love / Rated X / Don't let it show / No you don't / So sincere / Treat me right / You better run / Never wanna leave you / Hit me with your best shot / Hell is for children / Prisoner of love / Outa touch / Little paradise / I'm gonna follow you / Wuthering heights.
■ MC Set . . . . ZCDP 108
Chrysalis / Dec '82.

INVINCIBLE.
Tracks: Invincible / Invincible (instrumental).
■ 7" . . . . PAT 3
Chrysalis / Oct '85.
■ 12". PATX 3
Chrysalis / '86.

LIVE FROM EARTH.
Tracks: Looking for a stranger / I want out / We live for love / Hell is for children / Hit me with your best shot / Promises in the dark / Heartbreaker / Love is a battlefield / Lipstick lies / Fire and ice.
■ LP P.Disc. . . . . CHRP 1451
■ CD. . . . . ACCD 1451
■ LP. . . . . CHR 1451
■ MC. . . . . ZCHR 1451
Chrysalis / Oct '83.

LOVE IS A BATTLEFIELD.
Tracks: Love is a battlefield / Here's my heart.
■ 12". . . . . .CHS 122747
■ 7". . . . . CHS 2747
Chrysalis / Jan '84.
■ 12". PATX 1
■ 7". PAT 1
Chrysalis / Feb '85.

ONE LOVE.
Tracks: One love / Wide awake in dreamland / Sex as a weapon (12" only as extra track) / Love is a battlefield (Extra track on CD only).
■ 12". PATX 7
■ 7". PAT 7
■ CD Single. . . . . PATCD 7
Chrysalis / Dec '88.
■ 12" P.Disc. . . . . PATXP 7
Chrysalis / Jan '89.

PAT BENATAR: INTERVIEW PICTURE DISC.
Tracks: Not Advised.
LP P.Disc. . . . . BAK 2111
Baktabak / Jan '89 / Arabesque Ltd.

PRECIOUS TIME.
Tracks: Promises in the dark / Fire and ice / Just like me / Precious time / It's a tuff life / Take it any way you want it / Hard to believe / Helter skelter / Evil genius.
■ LP. . . . . CHR 1346
■ MC. . . . . ZCHR 1346
Chrysalis / Jul '81.
■ CD. . . . . ACCD 1346
Chrysalis / '86.

SEVEN THE HARD WAY.
Tracks: Sex as a weapon / Le bel age / Walking in the underground / Big life / Red version / 7 rooms of gloom / Run between the raindrops / Invincible / Art of letting go.
■ LP. . . . . CHR 1507
■ MC. . . . . ZCHR 1507
Chrysalis / Nov '85.
■ CD. . . . . ACCD 1507
Chrysalis / Apr '86.

SEX AS A WEAPON.
Tracks: Sex as a weapon / Red version.
■ 12". PATX 4
■ 7". PAT 4
Chrysalis / Feb '86.

SHADOWS OF THE NIGHT.
Tracks: Shadows of the night / Victim.
■ 12". . . . . .CHS 122662
■ 7". . . . . CHS 2662
Chrysalis / Apr '82.
■ 7". PAT 2
Chrysalis / Jun '85.
■ 12". PATX 2
Chrysalis / '86.

SOMEBODY'S BABY.
Tracks: Somebody's baby / Temptation / Promises in the dark (Features on TCCHS 5001 only).

■ CD Single. . . . . CDCHSS 5001
■ MC Single. . . . . TCCHS 5001
Chrysalis / Oct '93.

TREAT ME RIGHT.
Tracks: Treat me right / Hell is for children.
■ 7". . . . . CHS 2511
Chrysalis / Apr '81.

TROPICO.
Tracks: Diamond field / We belong / Painted desert / Temporary heroes / Love in the ice age / Ooh ooh song / Outlaw blues / Suburban king / Crazy world like this / Takin' it back.
■ CD. . . . . ACCD 1471
■ LP. . . . . CHR 1471
■ MC. . . . . ZCHR 1471
Chrysalis / Nov '84.

TRUE LOVE.
Tracks: Bloodshot eyes / Payin' the cost to be the boss / So long / I've got papers on you / I feel lucky / True love / Good life / Evening / I get evil / Don't happen no more / Please come home for Christmas.
■ LP. . . . . CHR 1805
Chrysalis / Nov '91.
CD. . . . . CCD 1805
MC. . . . . ZCHR 1805
Chrysalis / Feb '94 / EMI.

TRUE LOVE.
Tracks: True love / Payin' the cost to be the boss / Evening.
■ 12". PATX 8
■ 7". PAT 8
■ CD Single. . . . . PATCD 8
■ MC Single. . . . . PATMC 8
Chrysalis / Jun '91.

VERY BEST OF PAT BENATAR.
Tracks: Heartbreaker / We live for love / Promises in the dark / Fire and ice / Ooh ooh song / Hit me with your best shot / Shadows of the night / Anxiety (get nervous) / I want out / Lipstick lies / Love is a battlefield / We belong / All fired up / Hell is for children / Invincible / Somebody's baby / Everybody lay down / True love.
CD. . . . . CDCHR 6070
MC. . . . . TCCCHR 6070
Chrysalis / Apr '94 / EMI.

WE BELONG.
Tracks: We belong / Suburban king / We live for love (Extra track on 12" version only).
■ 12". . . . . .CHS 122821
■ 7". . . . . CHS 2821
Chrysalis / Dec '84.

WE LIVE FOR LOVE.
Tracks: We live for love / I need a lover / If you think you know how to love me.
■ 7". . . . . CHS 2403
Chrysalis / '80.
■ 12". . . . . .CHS 122403
Chrysalis / '82.

WIDE AWAKE IN DREAMLAND.
Tracks: All fired up / One love / Let's stay together / Don't walk away / Too long a soldier / Cool soldier / Cerebral man / Lift 'em on up / Suffer the little children / Wide awake in dreamland.
■ LP. . . . . CDL 1628
■ MC. . . . . ZCDL 1628
■ CD. . . . . CCD 1628
Chrysalis / Jun '88.
CD. CD25CR 19
Chrysalis / Mar '94 / EMI.

Benediction

DARK IS THE SEA.
Tracks: Not Advised.
CD. . . . . .NB 059CD
Mini LP . . . . NB 059
Nuclear Blast / Apr '92 / Plastic Head.

GRAND LEVELLER.
Tracks: Not Advised.
CD. . . . . .NB 048CD
■ LP. . . . . NB 048
■ LP P.Disc. . . . . .NB 048PD
Revolver / Sep '91.

SUBCONCIOUS TERROR.
Tracks: Not Advised.
CD. 842971
LP .082971
Nuclear Blast / Aug '90 / Plastic Head.
■ LP P.Disc. . . . . NB 033PD
MC. . . . . NB 033MC
Revolver / Jul '91 / FM Revolver / Sony.

TRANSCEND THE RUBICON.
Tracks: Not Advised.
CD. . . . . .NB 073CD
LP. . . . . NB 073
MC. . . . . NB 073MC
Nuclear Blast / Jun '93 / Plastic Head.

WRONG SIDE OF THE GRAVE.
Tracks: Wrong side of the grave.
■ 7". . . . . NB 073PDS
Nuclear Blast / Jul '93.

Bengal Tigers

METAL FETISH.
Tracks: Not Advised.
■ LP. . . . . HMILP 19
Heavy Metal / Sep '84.

Benidiction

GROTESQUE ASHEN EPITAPH, THE.
Tracks: Not Advised.
CD. . . . . NB 088-2
Nuclear Blast / May '94 / Plastic Head.

Bestial Warlust

VENGEANCE WAR.
Tracks: Not Advised.
CD. . . . . MIN 7316-2D
Modern Invasion / Jul '94 / Plastic Head.

Bethlehem

DARK METAL.
Tracks: Not Advised.
CD. . . . . .CDAR 022
Adipocre / Jul '94 / Plastic Head.

Beyond

CHASM.
Tracks: Not Advised.
CD. . . . . .CDMFN 147
LP. . . . . MFN 147
Music For Nations / Jul '93 / Pinnacle.

CRAWL.
Tracks: Sacred garden / Empire / Sick / Day before tomorrow / One step too far / Second sight / Great indifference / Eve of my release / No more happy ever afters / Lead the blind / Dominoes.
MC. . . . . .TCSHSP 4128
■ CD. . . . . .CDSHSP 4128
■ LP. . . . . SHSP 4128
Harvest / Jun '91.

EMPIRE.
Tracks: Empire / Everybody wins / Empire (radiation cocktail mix) (12" posterbag only) / One step too far (Brain surgery mix) (CD single only).
■ 12". 12HARP 5300
■ 7". . . . . HAR 5300
■ CD Single. . . . . CDHAR 5300
Harvest / Jun '91.

EPISCENE.
Tracks: Not Advised.
■ LP. . . . . CHIME 25
Midnight Music / May '87.

GOB.
Tracks: Melt / Frog scab / Working man / Throb.
■ 12". . . . . 12 HAR 5302
CD. . . . . .CDHAR 5302
EMI / Oct '92 / EMI.

MANIC SOUND PANIC.
Tracks: Manic sound panic.
■ 12". . . . . ABB 15T
Big Cat / Apr '90.

NO EXCUSE.
Tracks: No excuse / Portrait (live) / California uber alles (live).
■ 12". . . . . ABB 22 T
■ CD Single. . . . . ABB 22 CD
Big Cat / Jul '90.

ONE STEP TOO FAR.
Tracks: One step too far (12" only.) / One step too far (edit) (7" only.) / Break on through / Touch me I'm sick.
■ 12". 12EM 191
■ CD Single. . . . . .CDEM 191
EMI / May '91.

RAGING EP.
Tracks: Great indifference / Nail / Eve of my release / Empire (live) (Only on 12" PD and CD Single.) / Day before tomorrow (live) (Only on 12"PD Single.).
■ 12" P.Disc. 12HARPD 5301
■ 7" . . . . HARS 5301
■ CD Single . . . . CDHAR 5301
Harvest / Oct '91.

WISH.
Tracks: Wish / Live to love another day.
■ 7" . . . . .RAD 102
Radioactive / Jul '81.

Beyond Dawn

LONGING FOR SCARLET DAYS.
Tracks: Not Advised.
CD . . . . .CDAR 019
Adipocre / May '94 / Plastic Head.

Biafra, Jello

Former Dead Kennedy, Biafra became unwitting rock spokesman after lengthy court case, relating to alleged "distribution of harmful matter to minors" (a poster with Kennedys' album *Frankenchrist*). Became entangled in more wide-ranging anti-censorship debate; while continuing to record, including work with Ministry and others. Collaborated with Ice-T on latter's *Freedom of Speech*: title track samples Black Sabbath and was used as intro tape at Slayer shows.

HIGH PRIEST OF HARMFUL MATTER.
Tracks: Not Advised.
■ Double LP. . . . . VIRUS 66
Alternative Tentacles / Jul '89.
CD . . . . VIRUS 66CD
Alternative Tentacles / Mar '93 / RTM / Pinnacle.

LAST SCREAM OF THE MISSING NEIGHBORS (Biafra, Jello & DOA).
Tracks: Not Advised.
CD . . . . VIRUS 78 CD
LP . . . . VIRUS 78
Alternative Tentacles / Feb '90 / RTM / Pinnacle.

NO MORE COCOONS.
Tracks: Not Advised.
■ LP . . . . VIRUS 59
Alternative Tentacles / Nov '87.
CD . . . . VIRUS 59CD
Alternative Tentacles / Mar '93 / RTM / Pinnacle.

PRAIRIE HOME INVASION.
Tracks: Not Advised.
CD . . . . .VIRUS 137CD
LP . . . . VIRUS 137
Alternative Tentacles / Mar '94 / RTM / Pinnacle.

PRAISE THE LARD.
Tracks: Praise the lard.
■ 7" . . . . UNKNOWN
Alternative Tentacles / Mar '89.

SKY IS FALLING, THE (Biafra, Jello & No Means No).
Tracks: Not Advised.
CD . . . . .VIRUS 085CD
LP . . . . VIRUS 085
MC. . . . . .VIRUS 085C
Alternative Tentacles / Jun '91 / RTM / Pinnacle.

WILL THE FETUS BE ABORTED.
Tracks: Will the fetus be aborted.
■ 7" . . . . VIRUS 136
■ CD Single . . . . .VIRUS 136CD
Alternative Tentacles / Oct '93.

Big Black

Ferociously independent, Chicago based three piece led by cult figure Steve Albini. Their unique sound, dominated by drum machine and abrasive guitar, has been enormously influential on bands like Therapy, Ministry and Nine Inch Nails. Coming to prominence alongside Sonic Youth and Husker Du, their final album *Songs About Fucking* is now regarded as a masterpiece of the U.S. independent scene. After splitting Big Black, Albini went on to form Rapeman, provoking a storm of controversy which still has not completely abated even though they split up after only one album. Disillusioned and embittered by the response to Rapeman, Albini turned his talents to production, working with The Pixies,

P.J. Harvey and Nirvana amongst others. He has recently emerged with a new outfit, Shellac, who display the same uncompromising air that he has always shown.

ATOMISER.
Tracks: Not Advised.
■ LP . . . . .BFFP 11
Blast First / Nov '86.
■ LP . . . . HMS 043
Homestead / Sep '86.

BIG BLACK: LIVE.
Tracks: Not Advised.
CD . . . . BFFP 49CD
■ LP . . . . .BFFP 49
MC. . . . . BFFP 49C
Blast First / Oct '89 / RTM / Pinnacle.

HAMMER PARTY.
Tracks: Not Advised.
■ LP . . . . HMS 044
Homestead / Dec '86.
CD . . . . HMS 044 CD
Homestead / Jul '89 / SRD.

HEADACHE.
Tracks: Not Advised.
■ LP . . . . .BFFP 14
MC. . . . . .BFFP 14C
Blast First / Jun '87 / RTM / Pinnacle.

IL DUCE.
Tracks: Il duce.
■ 7" . . . . HMS 042
Homestead / Sep '86.

MODEL, THE.
Tracks: Model / Whore.
■ 7" . . . . .BFFP 24
Blast First / Sep '87.

PIGPILE.
Tracks: Not Advised.
CD . . . . TG 81CD
LP . . . . TG 81
MC. . . . . TG 81C
VHS . . . . TG 81V
Touch & Go / Nov '92 / SRD.

RACER X.
Tracks: Not Advised.
■ LP . . . . HMS 007
Homestead / May '85.

RICH MANS' TRACK.
Tracks: Not Advised.
CD . . . . BFFP 23CD
Blast First / RTM / Pinnacle.

SONGS ABOUT FUCKING.
Tracks: Not Advised.
CD . . . . BFFP 19CD
MC. . . . . .BFFP 19C
Blast First / RTM / Pinnacle.
■ LP . . . . .BFFP 19
Blast First / Sep '87.

SOUND OF IMPACT.
Tracks: Not Advised.
■ LP . . . . NOT 2
Blast First / Jul '87.

Big Chill

HALFWAY TO HEAVEN.
Tracks: Not Advised.
CD . . . . .CDMFN 142
LP . . . . MFN 142
MC. . . . . TMFN 142
Music For Nations / Sep '92 / Pinnacle.

Big F

BIG F, THE.
Tracks: Killing time / Why / Dr. Vine / Monkey boy 2 kill / Biz about brains / What the cowboy / Here's to the good life / Power pig / Alpert tango / Good God (shot dead at Honk King).
■ LP . . . . EKT 70
Elektra / Apr '90.

Big House

ALL NITE.
Tracks: All nite.
■ 7" 74321107331
■ 12" 74321107332
RCA / Jul '92.

BIG HOUSE.
Tracks: Dollar in my pocket (pretty things) / All nite / Refuse 2 run / baby doll / Can't cry anymore / Devil's

road / Nothing comes 4 free / Happiness / L.A. / Angel on my arm.
CD. . . . . PD 83094
■ LP . . . . PL 83094
■ MC. . . . . PK 83094
Boom Town / May '92.

Biohazard

New York quartet formed 1988, Biohazard released their eponymous debut in late 1990. Graduated through Road Runner label to WEA; debut for latter - *State Of The World Address* - was among 1994's highest-acclaimed metal albums. Band fuse hardcore riffing with rap, epitomised by collaboration with Cypress Hill on *Judgement Night* soundtrack.

BIOHAZARD.
Tracks: Not Advised.
CD. 844650
LP 084650
Maze / Dec '90.

HOW IT IS.
Tracks: How it is.
10" . . . . .W 0259TE
CD Single . . . . W 0259CDX
CD Single . . . . .W 0259CD
MC Single . . . . .W 0259C
Warner Bros. / Aug '94 / WEA.

STATE OF THE WORLD ADDRESS.
Tracks: Not Advised.
CD 936245595-2
LP 936245595-1
MC. 936245595-4
WEA / May '94 / WEA.

URBAN DISCIPLINE.
Tracks: Chamber spins three / Punishment / Shades of grey / Business / Black and white and red all over / Man with a promise / Disease / Hold my own (Available on CD only.) / Urban disciple / Loss / Wrong side of the tracks / Mistaken identity / We're only gonna die (From our own arrogance) / Tears of blood / Shades of grey (live) (Only on CD Digi-pack) / Punishment (live) (Only on CD Digi-pack).
CD . . . . RR 91122
LP . . . . RR 91121
MC. . . . . RR 91124
Road Runner / Oct '92 / Pinnacle.

Bitch

BITCH IS BACK.
Tracks: Do you wanna rock / Hot and heavy / Me and the boys / Storm raging up / Bitch is back / Head banger / Fist to face / Turns me on / Skullcrusher.
■ LP . . . . RR 9627
Metal Blade / Jun '87.

Bitch

FIRST BITE.
Tracks: First bite / Maggie.
■ 7" . . . . RX 101
Pinnacle / Jul '81.

Bitches Brue

LEATHER LOVE.
Tracks: Leather love / Ready for love.
■ 12" . . . . .12 VHF 46
FM Records / Mar '88.

WE MIGHT NOT BE AMERICAN BUT STILL WE FK.**
Tracks: Not Advised.
■ LP . . . . HMRLP 131
■ CD . . . . .HMRXD 131
■ MC. . . . . .HMRMC 131
Heavy Metal / Aug '89.

Bitches Sin

ALWAYS READY (FOR LOVE).
Tracks: Always ready (for love) / Sign of the times.
■ 7" . . . . .NEAT 09
Neat / Apr '81.

INVADERS.
Tracks: Not Advised.
■ LP . . . . OTH 14
Metalother / May '89.

NO MORE CHANCES.
Tracks: No more chances / Overnight / Ice angels.
■ 12" . . . . .QT 001 12

■ DELETED

■ 7″ . . . . QT 001
QT / Dec '83.

OUT OF MY MIND.
Tracks: Out of my mind.
■ 7″ . . . . .TCAS 21
Terminal / Aug '83.

PREDATOR.
Tracks: Not Advised.
■ LP . . . . HMRLP 4
Heavy Metal / Jun '82.

Bitter End

HARSH REALITIES.
Tracks: Not Advised.
CD . . . . .CDZORRO 10
LP . . . . ZORRO 10
MC . . . . .TZORRO 10
Metal Blade / Jul '89 / Pinnacle.

Black Crowes

Atlanta, Georgia six-piece formed by Robinson brothers Chris (vocals) and guitarist Rich (guitars). Play old-fashioned '60's influenced rock 'n' roll often compared to The Rolling Stones and The Faces but owing much more to the likes of Humble Pie and Leon Wilkinson. Live they like to jam, on record they are more concise but just as spontaneous; thanks to one of the best rhythm sections in the business - Johnny Colt (bass) and Steve Gorman (drums). Much of their first album Shake Your Money Maker was recorded as live, whilst basic tracks for the second The Southern Harmony And Musical Companion (again produced by Brendan O'Brien and featuring new guitarist Marc Ford) were completed in just eight days!

HARD TO HANDLE.
Tracks: Hard to handle / Jealous again / Twice as hard / Stare it cold.
■ 12″ . . . . DEFA 612
■ 7″ . . . . DEFA 6
■ CD Single . . . . DEFAC 6
■ MC Single. . . . . DEFAM 6
American Recordings / Aug '90.
■ 7″ . . . . .DEFA 10
■ MC Single. . . . . .DEFAC 10
American Recordings / Aug '91.

HOTEL ILLNESS.
Tracks: Hotel illness.
■ 12″ . . . . .DEFX 23
■ 7″ . . . . .DEFA 23
■ CD Single . . . . .DEFCD 23
American Recordings / Nov '92.

JEALOUS AGAIN.
Tracks: Jealous again / Thick 'n' thin / She talks to angels (Not on DEFAP 812 & CD single) / Waitin' guilty (Only on 12″ and CD single.) / She talks to angels (live) (CD single only) / Could I've been so blind (CD single only) / Jealous again (acoustic) (DEFAP 812 only) / She talks to angels (acoustic) (DEFAP 812 only) / Struttin' blues (DEFAP 812 only).
■ 12″ P.Disc. . . . . DEFAP 412
■ 12″ . . . . DEFA 412
■ 7″ . . . . DEFA 4
■ CD Single . . . . DEFAC 4
American Recordings / Jun '90.
■ 12″ . . . . DEFA 812
■ 12″ . . . . DEFAP 812
■ 7″ . . . . DEFA 8
■ CD P.Disc. . . . . DEFAC 8
American Recordings / Jun '91.
■ CD Single . . . . .SST 003 CD
■ MC Single. . . . . .SST 003 C
SST / May '93.

REMEDY.
Tracks: Remedy (Available on 12″ and CD single only) / Darling of the underground press / Time will tell.
■ 12″ . . . . DEFA 1612
■ 7″ . . . . .DEFA 16
■ CD Single . . . . .DEFCD 16
■ MC Single. . . . . DEFMC 16
American Recordings / Apr '92.

SEEING THINGS.
Tracks: Could I have been so blind (Not on 12″ & CD single.) / She talks to angels / Sister luck / Hard to handle / Twice as hard (Only on 12″ & CD single.) / Jealous again (Only on 12″ & CD single.)
■ MC Single. . . . . .DEFAC 13
American Recordings / Oct '91.
■ 12″ . . . . .DEFAG 13

■ 7″ . . . . .DEFA 13
American Recordings / Sep '91.

SHAKE YOUR MONEY MAKER.
Tracks: Twice as hard / Jealous again / Sister luck / Could I've been so blind / Seeing things / Hard to handle / Thick 'n' thin / She talks to angels / Struttin' blues / Stare it cold.
CD 842 515 2
LP 842 515 1
MC 842 515 4
Vertigo / Mar '90 / PolyGram.

SOUTHERN HARMONY AND MUSICAL COMPANION, THE.
Tracks: Sting me / Remedy / Thorn in my pride / Bad luck blue eyes goodbye / Sometimes salvation / Hotel illness / Black moon creepin' / No speak, no slave / My morning song / Time will tell.
CD 5122632
MC 5122634
■ LP 5122631
American Recordings / May '92.
DCC 512 263-5
American Recordings / Jan '93 / PolyGram.

TWICE AS HARD.
Tracks: Twice as hard / Jealous again (live) / Jealous guy (live) (Only on 12″ and CD single).
■ 12″ . . . . .DEFA 712
■ 12″ P.Disc. . . . . .DEFAP 712
■ 7″ . . . . DEFA 7
■ CD Single . . . . DEFAC 7
■ MC Single. . . . . DEFAM 7
American Recordings / Jan '91.

WHO KILLED THAT BIRD WAY OUT ON YOUR WINDOW SILL.
Tracks: Not Advised.
VHS 874763
Polygram Music Video / Jul '93 / PolyGram.

Black Crucifixion

PROMEATHEAN GIFT.
Tracks: Not Advised.
CD . . . . .LMCD 222
Lethal / Nov '93 / Plastic Head.

Black Flag

ANNIHILATE THIS WEEK.
Tracks: Annihilate this week.
■ CD Single . . . . .SST 081 CD
SST / Dec '88.
■ 7″ . . . . SST 081
■ MC Single. . . . . .SST 081 C
SST / May '93.

BLACK FLAG LIVE.
Tracks: Can't decide / Slip it in / Black coffee / Six pack / My war / I love you / Rats eyes.
■ VHS . . . . JE 131
Jettisoundz / Aug '93.

DAMAGED.
Tracks: Not Advised.
CD . . . . .SST 007 CD
LP . . . . SST 007
MC . . . . .SST 007 C
SST / May '93 / Pinnacle.

EVERYTHING WENT BLACK.
Tracks: Not Advised.
CD . . . . .SST 015 CD
LP . . . . SST 015
MC . . . . .SST 015 C
SST / May '93 / Pinnacle.

FAMILY MAN.
Tracks: Not Advised.
■ LP . . . . SST 026
SST / Sep '84.
CD . . . . .SST 026 CD
MC . . . . .SST 026 C
SST / May '93 / Pinnacle.

FIRST FOUR YEARS, THE.
Tracks: Not Advised.
■ LP . . . . SST 021
SST / Apr '89.
CD . . . . .SST 021 CD
MC . . . . .SST 021 C
SST / May '93 / Pinnacle.

I CAN SEE YOU.
Tracks: I can see you.
■ 12″ . . . . SST 226
■ CD Single . . . . .SST 226 CD
■ MC Single. . . . . .SST 226 C
SST / Jun '90.

IN MY HEAD.
Tracks: Not Advised.
■ LP . . . . SST 045
SST / Sep '85.
CD . . . . .SST 045 CD
MC . . . . .SST 045 C
SST / May '93 / Pinnacle.

JEALOUS AGAIN.
Tracks: Jealous again / Revenge / White minority / No values / You bet..
■ 12″ . . . . SST 3
SST / Mar '83.
■ 10″ . . . . SST 907
SST / May '93.

LIVE 84.
Tracks: Process of weeding out / My ghetto / Jealous again / I love you / Swinging man / Three nights / Nothing left inside / Black coffee.
MC . . . . .SST 030
SST / Dec '84 / Pinnacle.

LOOSE NUT.
Tracks: Not Advised.
■ LP . . . . SST 035
SST / Jun '85.
CD . . . . .SST 035 CD
SST / Feb '88 / Pinnacle.
MC . . . . .SST 035 C
SST / May '93 / Pinnacle.

LOUIE LOUIE.
Tracks: Not Advised.
■ 10″ . . . . SST 922
■ 7″ . . . . SST 175
■ CD Single . . . . .SST 175 CD
SST / May '93.

MY WAR.
Tracks: Not Advised.
■ LP . . . . SST 023
SST / Mar '84.
CD . . . . .SST 023 CD
MC . . . . .SST 023 C
SST / May '93 / Pinnacle.

NERVOUS BREAKDOWN.
Tracks: Nervous breakdown.
■ 7″ . . . . SST 001
SST / Jul '89.
■ 10″ . . . . SST 916
■ CD Single . . . . .SST 001 CD
■ MC Single. . . . . .SST 001 C
SST / May '93.

PARANOID TIME.
Tracks: Not Advised.
■ 10″ . . . . SST 917
■ 7″ . . . . SST 002
■ CD Single . . . . .SST 002 CD
SST / May '93.

PROCESS OF WEEDING OUT.
Tracks: Process of weeding out.
■ LP . . . . SST 037
SST / Mar '86.
CD . . . . .SST 037 CD
SST / Sep '87 / Pinnacle.
■ 10″ . . . . SST 924
MC . . . . .SST 037 C
SST / May '93 / Pinnacle.

SIX PACK.
Tracks: Not Advised.
■ 10″ . . . . SST 920
■ 12″ . . . . .SST 00512
■ 7″ . . . . SST 005
■ CD Single . . . . .SST 005 CD
SST / May '93.

SLIP IT IN.
Tracks: Not Advised.
■ LP . . . . SST 029
SST / Sep '84.
CD . . . . .SST 029 CD
MC . . . . .SST 029 C
SST / May '93 / Pinnacle.

SLIP IT IN.
Tracks: Slip it in.
■ 12″ . . . . SST 12001
SST / Aug '84.

T.V. PARTY.
Tracks: T.V. party.
■ 7″ . . . . SST 012
SST / Feb '90.
■ 12″ . . . . .SST 01212
■ CD Single . . . . .SST 012 CD
SST / May '93.

WASTED..AGAIN.
Tracks: Wasted / T.V. party / Six pack / I don't care / I've had it / Jealous again / Slip it in / Annihilate this week / Loose nut / Gimmie gimmie / Louie Louie / Drinking and driving.
■ LP . . . . SST 166
SST / Jan '88.
CD. . . . . SST 166 CD
MC. . . . . SST 166 C
SST / May '93 / Pinnacle.

WHO'S GOT THE 10%.
Tracks: Not Advised.
CD. . . . . SST 060 CD
SST / Aug '87 / Pinnacle.
LP. . . . . SST 060
MC. . . . . SST 060 C
SST / May '93 / Pinnacle.

Black Hairy Tongue

BLACK HAIRY TONGUE SET.
Tracks: Not Advised.
■ 7" . . . . GB 01
Nuclear Blast / Oct '92.

Black Market Baby

BABY ON BOARD.
Tracks: Not Advised.
LP . . . . BC 1673
Bitzcore / '90 / Plastic Head.

BABY TAKES.
Tracks: Not Advised.
CD. BC 1663CD
■ LP . . . . BC 1663
Bitzcore / '88.

Black N' Blue

BLACK'N'BLUE.
Tracks: Strong will rock / School of hard knocks / Autoblast / Hold onto 18 / Wicked bitch / Action / Show me the night / One for the money / I'm the king / Chains around heaven.
■ LP . . . . GEF 26020
■ MC. 4026020
Geffen / Sep '84.

IN HEAT.
Tracks: Rock on / Sight for sore eyes / Heat it up burn it out / Suspicious / Snake / Live it up / Gimme your love / Get wise to the rise / Stranger / Great guns of fire.
■ LP . . . . K 9241801
■ MC. . . . . K 9241804
Geffen / Mar '88.

NASTY NASTY.
Tracks: Nasty nasty / I want it all / Does she or doesn't she / Kiss of death / 12 o'clock high / Do what you wanna do / I'll be there for you / Rules / Best of the West.
■ LP 9241111
■ MC. 9241114
Geffen / Oct '86.

Black Oak Arkansas

Southern rock/boogie outfit formed in 1965 by vocalist Jim 'Dandy' Mangrum, Pat Daugherty, Stanley Knight, Rickie Reynolds and Harvey Jett. Made a debut album for Stax, later reissued as *The Early Years*. Signed with Atlantic, built a reputation by non-stop touring. They had ten chart albums in the USA 1971-76 - *High On A Hog* and *Raunch And Roll* went gold. Paved the way for Lynyrd Skynyrd with their three-guitar lineup. Following many changes in personnel, Black Oak Arkansas split in 1980. Mangram has continued to tour/record as Jim Dandy.

10 YEAR OVERNIGHT SUCCESS.
Tracks: When the band was singin' 'shakin' all over' / Pretty, pretty / Can't blame it on me / Television indecision / Back it up / Bad boy's back in school / Love comes easy / You can't keep a good man down / Fireball.
■ LP . . . . MCF 2784
MCA / Feb '77.

BLACK ATTACK IS BACK (Black Oak Arkansas & Jim Dandy).
Tracks: Not Advised.
■ LP . . . . HMUSA 63
MC. . . . . HMAMC 63
Heavy Metal America / Apr '86 / FM Revolver / Sony.

EARLY TIMES.
Tracks: Someone something / When I'm gone / Let us pray / Sly fox / Mean woman / No one and the sun / Theatre / Collective thinking / Older than grandpa.
CD. . . . . CDSXE 067
Stax / Nov '92 / Pinnacle.

HOT & NASTY.
Tracks: Not Advised.
CD 812271146-2
WEA / Mar '93 / WEA.

RAUNCH & ROLL.
Tracks: Not Advised.
CD 8122713472
WEA / Jul '93 / WEA.

Black Riders

CHOSEN FEW.
Tracks: Not Advised.
■ LP . . . . GILP 555
G.I. / Mar '89.

Black Rose

BOYS WILL BE BOYS.
Tracks: Boys will be boys / Liar.
■ 7" . . . . BOL 9
Bullet / May '84.

BOYS WILL BE BOYS.
Tracks: Not Advised.
■ LP . . . . BULP 3
Bullet / Apr '84.

NO POINT RUNNING.
Tracks: No point running.
■ 7" . . . . TB 5
Teesbeat / Aug '82.

ROCK ME HARD.
Tracks: Rock me hard / Need a lot of lovin' / Nightmare / Breakaway.
■ 12". . . . . NEAT 48 12
Neat / Mar '85.

ROOM INSIDE.
Tracks: Not Advised.
CD. . . . . CONTECD 168
LP . . . . CONTE 168
Contempo / Oct '91 / Plastic Head.

WALK IT HOW YOU TALK IT.
Tracks: California USA / Ezly / Don't fall in love / Bright lights burnin' / Walk it how you talk it / Shout it out / I honestly love you / Part animal / Want you love.
■ LP . . . . NEAT 1034
Neat / Apr '87.
MC. . . . . NEATC 1034
Neat / May '87 / Grapevine Distribution.
VHS . . . . NEATVID 003V
Neat / '88 / Grapevine Distribution.

WE GONNA ROCK YOU (EP).
Tracks: We gonna rock you.
■ 12". . . . . BOLT 6
Bullet / Sep '83.

Black Sabbath

Since the classic line-up of Ozzy Osourne (vocals), Tony Iommi (guitar), Geezer Butler (bass) and Bill Ward (drums) entered the studio in April 1970 to record their eponymous debut album, Black Sabbath have overshadowed everyone else playing heavy metal. More than any other band, they can truly claim to have invented the genre. The first half-dozen studio albums they made with Ozzy remain the very best. Although the next two were less impressive, Sabbath had, as the title of his final outing with the band suggested, adopted a 'never say die' attitude that had seen them survive against all the odds. They overcame the loss of Ozzy (to a solo career) - and the wrath of the purist! - by replacing him with erstwhile Rainbow frontman Ronnie James Dio in 1979. Time has since turned the *Heaven And Hell* album into a classic and a masterpiece of reinvention. Subsequent singers and line-ups since 1983 have never matched their predecessors for creativity or commercial success but the Sabs have soldiered on to the point where they are nothing less than living legends today.

AM I GOING INSANE.
Tracks: Am I going insane / Hole in the sky.
■ 7" 6165 300
Nems / Feb '76.

BACKTRACKIN'.
Tracks: Paranoid / Iron man / Black Sabbath / Killing yourself to live / Snowblind / Sweet leaf / Into the void / Electric funeral / Sabbra cadabra / St. Vitus dance / Fairies wear boots / Superstarz / Children of the grave / Sabbath bloody Sabbath / Nib / Symptom of the universe / Planet caravan / War pigs / Rat salad / Am I going insane (radio) / Megalomania / Wizard / Cornucopia / Hole in the sky.
■ CD . . . . TRKCD 103
■ Double LP . . . . TRKLP 103
■ MC Set . . . . TRKMC 103
Backtrackin' / Jan '90.

BEST OF BLACK SABBATH.
Tracks: Not Advised.
■ LP . . . . STAR 301
Starcall (New Zealand) / Sep '88.

BLACK SABBATH.
Tracks: Black Sabbath / Wizard / Behind the walls of sleep / N.I.B. / Evil woman / Sleeping village / Warning.
■ LP .VO 6
Vertigo / Mar '70.
■ CD . . . . NELCD 6002
Nems / Dec '86.
■ LP . . . . NEL 6002
■ MC . . . . NELMC 6002
Nems / Dec '86.
CD. . . . . CLACD 196
MC. . . . . CLAMC 196
■ LP . . . . CLALP 196
Castle Classics / Oct '90.

BLACK SABBATH.
Tracks: Paranoid / Iron man / War pigs.
■ CD Single CD3-5
Special Edition / '88.

BLACK SABBATH 1970-1987.
Tracks: Not Advised.
■ LP 831 188-1
Vertigo / Dec '89.

BLACK SABBATH STORY, THE VOL. 1 (1970-1978).
Tracks: Not Advised.
■ VHS . . . . CMP 6070
Castle Music Pictures / '92.

BLACK SABBATH VOL 4.
Tracks: Wheels of confusion / Tomorrow's dream / Changes / FX / Supernaut / Snowblind / Cornucopia / Laguna sunrise / St. Vitus dance / Under the sun.
■ LP 6360 071
Vertigo / Sep '72.
■ LP . . . . NEL 6005
Nems / Nov '80.
■ CD . . . . NELCD 6005
■ MC . . . . NELMC 6005
Nems / '87.
CD. . . . . CLACD 199
MC. . . . . CLAMC 199
■ LP . . . . CLALP 199
Castle Classics / Oct '90.

BLACK SABBATH: INTERVIEW PICTURE DISC.
Tracks: Not Advised.
LP P.Disc . . . . BAK 2075
Baktabak / Nov '87 / Arabesque Ltd.

BLACKEST SABBATH.
Tracks: Black Sabbath / Paranoid / Iron man / Snowblind / Sabbath bloody Sabbath / Hole in the sky / Rock 'n' roll doctor / Never say die / Lady evil / Turn up the night / Sign of the southern cross / Heaven and hell (live) / Children of the sea / Digital bitch / Seventh star / Born to lose.
■ Double LP. 838 818 1
■ MC. 838 818 4
■ CD 838 818 2
Vertigo / Nov '89.

BORN AGAIN.
Tracks: Trashed / Stonehenge / Disturbing the priest / Park / Hot line / Zero the hero / Digital bitch / Born again / Keep it warm.
■ LP . . . . VERL 8
Vertigo / Sep '83.

COLLECTION: BLACK SABBATH.
Tracks: Paranoid / Behind the walls of sleep / Sleeping village / Warning / Warpigs / Hand of doom / Planet caravan / Electric funeral / Rat salad / Iron man / After forever / Supernaut / St. Vitus dance /

■ DELETED

Wheels of confusion / Snowblind / Killing yourself to
live / Sabbra cadabra / Writ.
■ **Double LP** . . . . CCSLP 109
■ **MC** .CCSMC 109
Castle Collector Series / Nov '85.
CD .CCSCD 109
Castle Collector Series / Jan '86 / BMG / Pinnacle /
Castle Communications.

CROSS PURPOSES.
Tracks: I witness / Cross of thorns / Psychophobia /
Virtual death / Immaculate deception / Dying for love
/ Back to Eden / Hand that rocks the cradle / Cardi-
nal sin / Evil eye.
CD . . . . EIRSCD 1067
LP . . . . EIRSLP 1067
MC . . . . EIRSC 1067
I.R.S. (Illegal) / Jan '94 / EMI.

CROSS PURPOSES LIVE (CD & Video Double Pack).
Tracks: Time machine / Children of the grave / I
witness / Mob rules (Video only) / Into the void /
Anno mundi (Video only) / Black sabbath / Neon
knights (Video only) / Psychophobia / Wizard / Cross
of thorns / Symptom of the universe / Headless cross
/ Paranoid / Iron man / Sabbath bloody sabbath.
VHS . . . . SAV 4913143
PMI / Jul '94 / Gold & Sons / TBD.

DEHUMANIZER.
Tracks: Computer god / After all / TV crimes / Letters
from Earth / Mastger of insanity / Time machine /
Sins of the father / Too late / I / Buried alive.
■ **LP** . . . . EIRSLP 1064
I.R.S. (Illegal) / Jun '92.
CD . . . . EIRSCD 1064
EMI / May '94 / EMI.
MC . . . . EIRSTC 1064
I.R.S. (Illegal) / May '94 / EMI.

DEVIL AND DAUGHTER.
Tracks: Devil and daughter.
■ **12"** . . . . .EIRST 115
■ **7"** . . . . EIRSB 115
■ **7"** . . . . EIRS 115
■ **7" P.Disc** . . . . .EIRSPD 115
I.R.S. (Illegal) / May '89.

DIE YOUNG.
Tracks: Die young / Heaven and hell (live).
■ **12"** . . . . .SAB 412
■ **7"** . . . . SAB 4
Vertigo / Dec '80.

ETERNAL IDOL, THE.
Tracks: Shining / Ancient warrior / Hard life to love /
Flory ride / Born to lose / Scarlet Pimpernel / Lost
forever / Eternal idol.
CD 832 708-2
■ **LP** . . . . VERH 51
■ **MC** . . . . .VERHC 51
Vertigo / Nov '87.

FEELS GOOD TO ME.
Tracks: Feels good to me / Paranoid / Heaven and
hell (Not on 7".).
■ **12"** . . . . .EIRST 148
■ **7"** . . . . EIRS 148
■ **CD Single** . . . . .EIRSCD 148
■ **MC Single** . . . . EIRSC 148
I.R.S. (Illegal) / Sep '90.

GREATEST HITS: BLACK SABBATH.
Tracks: Paranoid / Changes / Sabbath bloody Sab-
bath / Iron man / Black Sabbath / War pigs / Laguna
sunrise / Tomorrow's dream / Sweet leaf / N.I.B.
■ **LP** . . . . NEL 6009
Nems / Nov '80.
■ **CD** . . . . NELCD 6009
Nems / Nov '85.
■ **MC** . . . . NELMC 6009
Nems / Nov '85.
CD . . . . CLACD 200
MC . . . . CLAMC 200
■ **LP** . . . . CLALP 200
Castle Classics / Oct '90.
■ **CD** . . . . CTVCD 117
■ **MC** . . . . .CTVMC 117
Castle / Nov '93.

GUITAR THAT DRIVES BLACK SAB-BATH (Iommi, Tony).
Tracks: Not Advised.
VHS . . . . .CPMV 005
Cromwell Productions / Jun '92 / TBD.

HARD ROAD.
Tracks: Hard road / Symptom of the universe.
■ **7"** . . . . SAB 2
Vertigo / Oct '78.

HEADLESS CROSS.
Tracks: Headless cross (12" only) / Cloak and dagger / Headless cross (edit).
■ **12"** . . . . .EIRST 107
■ **12"** . . . . .EIRSPB 107
■ **7"** . . . . .EIRSCB 107
I.R.S. (Illegal) / Apr '89.

HEADLESS CROSS.
Tracks: Gates of hell / Headless cross / Devil and
daughter / When death calls / Kill in the spirit world /
Call of the wild / Black moon / Nightwing.
■ **LP** . . . . EIRSA 1002
■ **MC** . . . . EIRSAC 1002
I.R.S. (Illegal) / Apr '89.
CD . . . . EIRSACD 1002
I.R.S. (Illegal) / May '94 / EMI.

HEAVEN AND HELL.
Tracks: Neon knights / Children of the sea / Lady evil
/ Heaven and hell / Wishing well / Die young / Walk
away / Lonely is the world / Tomorrow's dream
■ **LP** 9102 752
Vertigo / Apr '80.
■ **LP** . . . . PRICE 10
■ **MC** . . . . .PRIMC 10
Vertigo / May '83.
■ **CD** 830 171-2
Vertigo / '87.
CD .550 0592
MC .550 0594
Spectrum (1) / Jun '93 / PolyGram.

INTERVIEW, THE.
Tracks: Not Advised.
CD P.Disc . . . . CBAK 4071
Baktabak / Feb '94 / Arabesque Ltd.

IRON MAN.
Tracks: Not Advised.
CD 550 7202
MC 550 7204
Spectrum (1) / Sep '94 / PolyGram.

LIVE AT LAST.
Tracks: Tomorrow's dreams / Sweet leaf / Killing
yourself to live / Cornucopia / War pigs / Laguna
sunrise / Paranoid / Wicked world.
■ **LP** . . . . NEL 001
MC . . . . NELMC 001
Nems / '87 / Pinnacle.
■ **CD** . . . . NELCD 6001
■ **LP** . . . . BS 001
■ **MC** . . . . .BSMC 001
Nems / Aug '89.
CD 832 704 4
■ **LP** 832 704 1
Vertigo / Jun '89.
CD . . . . CLACD 203
■ **LP** . . . . CLALP 203
■ **MC** . . . . CLAMC 203
Castle Classics / Oct '90.

LIVE EVIL.
Tracks: E 5 150 / Neon knights / N.I.B. / Children of
the sea / Voodoo / Black Sabbath / War pigs / Iron
man / Mob rules / Heaven and hell / Sign of southern
cross / Paranoid / Children of the grave / Fluff.
■ **Double LP** . . . . SAB 10
Vertigo / Mar '83.
■ **Double LP** . . . . PRID 11
■ **MC Set** . . . . PRIDC 11
Vertigo / Apr '86.

MASTER OF INSANITY.
Tracks: Master of insanity / Time machine / Neon
knights (live) (Not on Cdeirs 180) / T.V crimes (Only
on Cdeirs 180) / Die young (Only on Cdeirs 180) /
Children of the sea (live) (Only on Cdeirs 180).
■ **12" P.Disc.** . . . . 12 EIRSPD 180
■ **CD Single** . . . . .CDEIRS 180
MC Single . . . . .TCEIRS 180
I.R.S. (Illegal) / Oct '92 / EMI.

MASTER OF REALITY.
Tracks: Sweet leaf / After forever / Embryo / Chil-
dren of the grave / Lord of this world / Solitude / Into
the void / Orchid.
■ **LP** 6360 050
Vertigo / Jan '71.
■ **CD** . . . . NELCD 6004
■ **LP** . . . . NEL 6004
Nems / Nov '85.
■ **MC** . . . . NELMC 6004
Nems / Nov '85.
CD 832 707 4
■ **LP** 832 707 1
MC 832 707 2
Vertigo / Jun '89 / PolyGram.
CD . . . . CLACD 198
MC . . . . CLAMC 198
■ **LP** . . . . CLALP 198
Castle Classics / Oct '90.

MOB RULES.
Tracks: Turn up the night / Voodoo / Sign of the
Southern Cross / E 5150 / Mob rules / Country girl /
Slippin' away / Falling off the edge of the world /
Over and over.
■ **LP** 6302 119
Vertigo / Nov '81.
■ **LP** . . . . PRICE 77
■ **MC** . . . . .PRIMC 77
Vertigo / Jan '85.

MOB RULES.
Tracks: Mob rules / Die young.
■ **12"** . . . . .SAB 512
■ **7"** . . . . SAB 5
Vertigo / Nov '81.

NEON KNIGHTS.
Tracks: Neon knights.
■ **7"** . . . . SAB 3
Vertigo / Jul '80.

NEVER SAY DIE.
Tracks: Black Sabbath / Dirty women / Rock 'n' roll
doctor / Electric funeral / Children of the grave /
Paranoid / Snowblind / Never say die / Johnny Blade
/ Junior eyes / Hard road / Shockwaves / Air dance /
Over to you / Breakout / Swinging the chain.
■ **LP** 9102 750
Vertigo / Nov '76.
■ **LP** . . . . PRICE 9
■ **MC** . . . . .PRIMC 9
Vertigo / May '83.
CD 5501312
MC 5501314
Spectrum (1) / Oct '93 / PolyGram.

NEVER SAY DIE.
Tracks: Never say die / She's gone.
■ **7"** . . . . SAB 1
Vertigo / Jun '78.

NEVER SAY DIE.
Tracks: Not Advised.
■ **VHS** . . . . M 060 B
VCL / Sep '86.
■ **VHS** . . . . HEN 2020
Hendring Video / '88.

OZZY OSBOURNE YEARS.
Tracks: Black Sabbath / Wizard / Behind the wall of
sleep / N.I.B. / Evil woman / Sleeping woman /
Warning / War pigs / Paranoid / Planet Caravan /
Iron man / Hand of doom / Fairies wear boots /
Electric funeral / Sweet leaf / After forever / Embryo
/ Lord of the world / Solitude / Into this void / Wheels
of confusion / Tomorrow's dream / Changes / Super-
naut / Snowblind / Cornucopia / St. Vitus dance /
Under the sun / Sabbath bloody Sabbath / National
acrobat / Sabbra cadabra / Killing yourself to live /
Who are you / Looking for today / Spiral architect /
Hole in the sky / Symptom of the universe / Am I
going insane (radio) / Thrill of it all / Meglomania /
Writ.
CD Set . . . . ESBCD 142
■ **LP Set** . . . . ESBLP 142
Essential / Apr '91.

PARANOID.
Tracks: War pigs / Planet caravan / Iron man /
Electric funeral / Hand of doom / Rat salad / Fairies
wear boots / Wicked world / Paranoid.
■ **LP** 6360 011
Vertigo / Sep '70.
■ **CD** . . . . NELCD 6003
■ **MC** . . . . NELMC 6003
Nems / Jan '86.
■ **LP** . . . . NEL 6003
Nems / Jan '86.
CD 832 7014
■ **LP** 832 7011
MC 832 7012
Vertigo / Jun '89 / PolyGram.
CD . . . . CLACD 197
MC . . . . CLAMC 197
■ **LP** . . . . CLALP 197
Castle Classics / Oct '90.

PARANOID.
Tracks: Paranoid / Sabbath bloody Sabbath /
Snowblind.
■ **7"** 6059 010
Vertigo / Aug '70.
■ **7"** . . . . .NES 121
Nems / Aug '78.
■ **7"** . . . . .BSS 101
Nems / Sep '80.
■ **7" P.Disc** . . . . NEP 3
Nems / Sep '82.

PARANOID (EP).
Tracks: Paranoid / Iron man / Black Sabbath / War
pigs.

■ 12″. TOF 101
Archive 4 / Aug '86.

PARANOID (OLD GOLD).
Tracks: Paranoid / Electric funeral / Sabbath bloody sabbath.
7″. . . . . OG 9467
■ CD Single. . . . . OG 6129
Old Gold / Mar '89.

PRESENTATION BOX SET.
Tracks: Not Advised.
CD Set . . . . BSBCD 001
■ LP Set. . . . . BS 01BOX
Nems / '88.

SABBATH BLOODY SABBATH.
Tracks: Sabbath bloody sabbath / National acrobat / Fluff / Sabbra Cadabra / Killing yourself to live / Who are you / Looking for today / Spiral architect.
■ LP . . . . WWA 005
WWA / Dec '73.
■ CD . . . . NELCD 6017
■ LP . . . . NEL 6017
Nems / Nov '85.
■ MC. . . . . NELMC 6017
Nems / '87.
CD. 832 700 4
■ LP 832 700 1
MC. 832 700 2
Vertigo / Jun '89 / PolyGram.
CD. CLACD 201
MC. . . . . CLAMC 201
■ LP . . . . CLALP 201
Castle Classics / Oct '90.

SABBATH BLOODY SABBATH/ BLACK SABBATH.
Tracks: Sabbath bloody sabbath / National acrobat / Fluff / Sabbra Cadabra / Killing yourself to live / Who are you / Looking for today / Spiral architect / Black Sabbath / Wizard / Behind the walls of sleep / N.I.B. / Evil woman / Sleeping village / Warning.
■ Double LP. . . . . TFOLP 10
■ CD Set. . . . . TFOCD 10
■ MC. . . . . TFOMC 10
That's Original / Jun '88.

SABOTAGE.
Tracks: Hole in the sky / Don't start (too late) / Symptom of the universe / Megalomania / Thrill of it all / Superzar / Am I going insane / Writ.
■ LP 9119 001
Nems / Sep '75.
■ LP . . . . NEL 6018
Nems / Nov '85.
■ CD . . . . NELCD 6018
Nems / Jan '86.
■ MC. . . . . NELMC 6018
Nems / '87.
CD. 832 706 4
■ LP 832 706 1
MC. 832 706 2
Vertigo / Jun '89 / PolyGram.
CD. CLACD 202
MC. . . . . CLAMC 202
■ LP . . . . CLALP 202
Castle Classics / Oct '90.

SEVENTH STAR.
Tracks: In for the kill / No stranger to love / Turn to stone / Sphinx (The guardian) / Seventh star / Danger zone / Heart like a wheel / Angry heart / I memory..
CD. 826 704-2
■ LP . . . . VERH 29
■ MC. . . . . VERHC 29
Vertigo / Feb '86.

TECHNICAL ECSTASY.
Tracks: All moving parts / Backstreet kids / Dirty woman / Gypsy / It's alright / Rock 'n' roll doctor / She's gone / You won't change me.
■ LP . . . . PRICE 40
■ MC. . . . . PRIMC 40
Vertigo / Aug '83.
■ CD 838 224 2
Vertigo / Jun '89.

TURN UP THE NIGHT.
Tracks: Turn up the night / Lonely is the word.
■ 12″. . . . . SABP 6 12
■ 7″. . . . . SAB 6
■ 7″ P.Disc. . . . . SABP 6
Vertigo / Jan '82.

TV CRIMES.
Tracks: TV Crimes / Letters from the earth / Mob rules (live) (Only available on 12″PD.) / Heaven and hell (live) (Only available on CD Single.) / Paranoid (live) (Only available on CD Single (CDEIRSS 178)).
■ 12″ P.Disc. 12EIRSPD 178
■ 7″. . . . . EIRSP 178
■ CD Single. . . . . CDEIRS 178

■ CD Single. . . . . CDEIRSS 178
I.R.S. (Illegal) / Jun '92.

TYR.
Tracks: Not Advised.
■ LP . . . . EIRSA 1038
■ MC. . . . . EIRSAC 1038
I.R.S. (Illegal) / Aug '90.
CD . . . . EIRSCD 1038
I.R.S. (Illegal) / May '94 / EMI.

WE SOLD OUR SOUL FOR ROCK'N'ROLL.
Tracks: Black Sabbath / Wizard / Warning / Paranoid / Wicked world / Tomorrow's dream / Fairies wear boots / Changes / Sweat leaf / Children of the grave / Sabbath bloody sabbath / Am I going insane (radio) / Laguna sunrise / Snowblind.
■ Double LP. 6641 335
Nems / Feb '76.
■ Double LP. . . . . .NELD 101
Nems / Nov '80.
■ CD . . . . .RAWCD 017
■ Double LP. . . . . .RAWLP 017
■ MC. . . . . .RAWTC 017
Raw Power / Apr '86.
CD. . . . . CCSCD 249
■ Double LP. . . . . CCSLP 249
MC. . . . . .CCSMC 249
Castle Classics / Oct '90 / BMG / Castle Communications.

Black Sheep
BLACK SHEEP.
Tracks: Not Advised.
■ LP . . . . MACH 2
Razor / Jun '85.

Black Train Jack
NO REWARD.
Tracks: Not Advised.
CD . . . . CD RR 9070 2
LP . . . . RR LP 9070 1
Road Runner / Jun '93 / Pinnacle.

YOU'RE NOT ALONE.
Tracks: Not Advised.
CD . . . . RR 90172
LP . . . . RR 90171
Road Runner / Apr '94 / Pinnacle.

Blackeyed Susan
ELECTRIC RATTLEBONE.
Tracks: Electric rattlebone / Satisfaction / None of it matters / Sympathy / Ride with me / Old lady snow / Don't bring me down / Indica / She's so fine / How long / Best of friends / Holiday / Heart of the city.
■ LP 848 575-1
■ CD 848 575-2
■ MC. 848 575-4
Mercury / Jul '91.

Blackfoot
AFTER THE REIGN.
Tracks: Not Advised.
CD. . . . . CDVEST 15
Bulletproof / Jun '94 / Pinnacle.

DRY COUNTY.
Tracks: Dry county.
■ 7″. . . . . K 11686
Atco / Mar '82.

EVERY MAN SHOULD KNOW.
Tracks: Every man should know / Highway song.
■ 7″. . . . . K 11636
Atlantic / Jan '81.

GOOD MORNING.
Tracks: Good morning / Paying for it.
■ 7″. . . . . K 11673
Atco / Sep '81.

HIGHWAY SONG (Blackfoot live).
Tracks: Gimme, gimme, gimme / Every man should know / Good morning / Dry county / Rollin' and tumblin' / Road fever / Trouble in mind / Train train / Highway song / Howay the lads.
■ LP . . . . K 50910
Atco / Sep '82.

HIGHWAY SONG.
Tracks: Highway song / Rollin' and tumblin'.
■ 7″. . . . . K 11760
Atco / Aug '82.

MARAUDER.
Tracks: Good morning / Paying for it / Diary of a working man / Too hard to hand / Fly away / Dry county / Fire of the dragon / Rattlesnake rock 'n' roller / Searchin'.
■ MC. K4 50799
■ LP . . . . K 50799
Atco / Jul '81.

MEDICINE MAN.
Tracks: Doin' my job / Stealer / Sleazy world / Not gonna cry any more / Runnin', Runnin' / Chilled to d'bone / Guitar slingers song and dance.
CD . . . . .CDMFN 106
LP . . . . MFN 106
MC. . . . . .TMFN 106
Music For Nations / Oct '90 / Pinnacle.

MORNING DEW.
Tracks: Morning dew / Living in the city.
■ 12″. . . . . B 9690 T
■ 7″. . . . . .B 9690
Atlantic / Jun '85.

ON THE RUN.
Tracks: On the run / Street fighter / Train, train.
■ 7″. . . . . K 11601
Atco / Jul '83.

RICK MEDLOCKE AND BLACKFOOT (Medlocke, Rick & Blackfoot).
Tracks: Back on the streets / Staurday night / Closest thing to heaven / Silent type / Reckless boy / Private life / liar / Steady Rockin' / My wild romance / Rock 'n' roll tonight.
■ LP 781 743-1
■ MC. 781 743-4
Atlantic / Jun '87.

SEND ME AN ANGEL.
Tracks: Send me an angel / Drivin' fool / Wishing well.
■ 12″. . . . . B 9880 T
■ 7″. . . . . .B 9880
■ 7″ P.Disc . . . . B 9880 P
Atco / May '83.

SLIGO.
Tracks: Send me an angel / Crossfire / Heart's grown cold / We're goin' down / Teenage idol / Goin' in circles / Run for cover / White man's land / Sail away / Drivin' fool.
■ LP 790 081 0
■ LP . . . . .B 0080
Atco / Jul '83.

STRIKES.
Tracks: Road fever / I got a line on you / Left turn on a red light / Pay my dues / Baby blue / Wishing well / Run and hide / Train train / Highway song.
■ LP . . . . K 50603
Atlantic / Aug '79.
■ MC. K4 50603
WEA / Aug '79.

TEENAGE IDOL.
Tracks: Teenage idol / We're goin' down.
■ 12″. . . . . B 9845 T
■ 7″. . . . . .B 9845
Atco / Jul '83.

TOMCATTIN'.
Tracks: Warped / On the run / Dream on / Street fighter / Gimme gimme gimme / Every man should know / In the night / Reckless daughter / Spendin' cabbage / Fox chase.
■ LP . . . . K 50702
MC. K4 50702
Atco / Jul '80 / WEA.

TRAIN TRAIN.
Tracks: Train train / Baby blue.
■ 7″. . . . . .K 1147
Atlantic / Feb '80.

VERTICAL SMILES.
Tracks: Morning dew / Living in the limelight / Ride with you / Get it on / Young girl summer days / Legend never dies / Heartbeat and heels / In for the kill.
■ MC. 790 218-4
■ LP 790 218-1
Atco / Oct '84.

WHEN WILL I SEE YOU AGAIN.
Tracks: When will I see you again / Lay the real thing on me.
■ 7″. . . . . MCA 307
MCA / Jul '77.

■ DELETED

Blackhouse

5 MINUTES AFTER I DIE.
Tracks: Not Advised.
CD...........................BHCD 5
Nuclear Blast / Aug '93 / Plastic Head.

HOLY WAR.
Tracks: I make a choice / Fight / Whispers of love / Satan and his demons / Rhythmus II / Remember who / Took the fall / Power and wisdom / Repent / Holy war.
■ LP........................RRR 017
Ridgerunner (USA) / Feb '88.

HOPE LIKE A CANDLE.
Tracks: Not Advised.
CD............................ DV 12
Nuclear Blast / Aug '93 / Plastic Head.

PRO LIFE.
Tracks: Not Advised.
CD.......................... MHCD 006
Massacre / Nov '93 / Plastic Head.

WE WILL FIGHT BACK.
Tracks: Not Advised.
LP.........................081109
Parade Amourese / Sep '90.

Blackmore, Ritchie

Deep Purple guitarist who spent his early career playing with such rock luminaries as Screaming Lord Sutch, Joe Meek and Mike Dee. After leaving Deep Purple in 1975 dis-atisfied with their new 'funk' direction, Blackmore played with the U.S. band Elf, later recruiting the Elf singer Ronnie James Dio for the first line up of Rainbow. After a luke warm response to their debut album Blackmore initiated the first of numerous personnel changes, eventually replacing every other original member. Rainbow were finally laid to rest after a successful Deep Purple re-union in 1984 became more permanent.

MAN ON THE SILVER MOUNTAIN.
Tracks: Man on the silver mountain / Snake charmer.
■ 7".........................OYR 103
Oyster / Jan '75.

ROCK PROFILE VOL 1.
Tracks: Return of the outlaws / Texan spiritual / If you gotta take a baby / Big fat spider / Doo dah day / Thou shalt not steal / I'm not a bad guy / Ritchie Blackmore interview / Been invited to a party / Shake with me / Movin' in / Keep a knockin' / I shall be released / Playground / Wring that neck / Why didn't Rosemary / Living wreck / Guitar job / No, no, no / Highway star / A 200 / Gypsy / Hold on / Show me the way to go home.
CD.......................RPVSOPCD 143
■ Double LP............RPVSOPLP 143
MC..........................RPVSOPMC 143
Connoisseur Collection / Oct '89 / Pinnacle.

ROCK PROFILE VOL 2.
Tracks: Getaway / Little brown jug / Honey hush / Train kept a rollin' / Gemini suite: guitar movement / Bullfrog / Good golly Miss Molly / Great balls of fire / Hurry to the city / Still I'm sad / Man on the silver mountain / Lady of the lake / Sixteenth century greensleeves (live) / I call, no answer / Son of Alerik.
CD.......................RPVSOPCD 157
Double LP..............RPVSOPLP 157
Connoisseur Collection / Apr '91 / Pinnacle.

SESSION MAN.
Tracks: Not Advised.
CD.......................... RPM 120
RPM / Oct '93 / Pinnacle.

Blackthorne

AFTERLIFE.
Tracks: Cradle of the grave / Afterlife / We won't be forgotten / Breaking the chains / Over and over / Hard feelings / Baby you're the blood / Sex crime / Love from the ashes / All night long.
CD.......................CDMFN 148
LP.........................MFN 148
MC..........................TMFN 148
Music For Nations / May '93 / Pinnacle.

Blackwytch

OUT OF CONTROL.
Tracks: Not Advised.
■ LP......................METALP 111
Metal Masters / Apr '86.

Blade Runner

BACK STREET LADY.
Tracks: Not Advised.
■ LP......................... EBON 26
Ebony (Pinnacle) / Jan '85.

WARRIORS OF ROCK.
Tracks: Not Advised.
■ LP......................... EBON 35
Ebony (Pinnacle) / Mar '86.

Blasphemy

FALLEN ANGEL OF DOOM.
Tracks: Not Advised.
CD....................WRE 901CD
Wild Rags / Jan '91 / Plastic Head.
LP...................... WRE 901
Wild Rags / Jan '91 / Plastic Head.

Blind Fury

OUT OF REACH.
Tracks: Not Advised.
■ LP......................RR 9814
Road Runner / Jun '85.

Blind Guardian

BATTALIONS OF FEAR.
Tracks: Not Advised.
CD.........................859810
S.P.V. / Sep '89.

Blind Illusion

SANE ASYLUM, THE.
Tracks: Sane asylum / Vengeance is mine / Kamik-aze / Vicious vision / Bloodshower / Death noise / Smash the crystal / Metamorphosis of a monster.
■ LP.......................FLAG 18
Under One Flag / Mar '88.
CD....................CDFLAG 18
Under One Flag / Mar '88 / Pinnacle.

Blind Melon

L.A. quintet formed in 1991 and won Capitol deal within two months, probably unhin-dered by band's Guns N' Roses associa-tions; vocalist Shannon Hoon is Axl Rose's cousin, sang on Use Your Illusion and ap-peared in G N'R's Don't Cry video. 1993 debut album sold on back of successful third single No Rain.

BLIND MELON.
Tracks: Soak the sin / Tones of home / I wonder / Paper scratcher / Dear ol' dad / Change / No rain / Deserted / Sleepyhouse / Holy man / Seed to a tree / Drive / Time.
CD..........................CDEST 2188
LP..........................EST 2188
MC..........................TCEST 2188
Capitol / Mar '93 / EMI.

CHANGE.
Tracks: Change / Paper scratcher (Acoustic - live) (Features on 12" Picture Disc only.) / Time (Live) (Features on 12" Picture Disc & CDS only.) / No rain (Does not feature on 12" Picture Disc.).
12" P.Disc................12 CL 717
7".........................CL 717
CD Single..................CDCL 717
MC Single..................TCCL 717
EMI / Jun '94 / EMI.

NO RAIN.
Tracks: No rain / Soak the sin (12" only) / Paper scratcher (12" and CDS only) / Deserted (12" and CDS only) / I wonder (7" and MCS only).
■ 12"...................... 12 CLPD 699
■ 7"........................CLS 699
■ CD Single................CDCL 699
■ MC Single................TCCL 699
Chrysalis / Nov '93.

TONES OF HOME.
Tracks: Tones of home / No rain (live) / Drive (live) / Soak the sin.
■ 12".....................12CL 687
■ 12" P.Disc..............12CLPD 687
■ CD Single...............CDCL 687
EMI / Jun '93.

Blitzkrieg

BLITZKRIEG.
Tracks: Let's go / Life is just so-so / Mental case.
■ 7".......................LIG 504
Lightning / Jan '78.

BURIED ALIVE.
Tracks: Buried alive.
■ 7".......................NEAT 10
Neat / Oct '81.

CONCIOUS PRAYER.
Tracks: Concious prayer.
■ 7".......................SPH 3
Sexual Phonograph / Mar '83.

LEST WE FORGET.
Tracks: Lest we forget.
■ 7"...........................01 8
Nu Future / Jul '82.

READY FOR ACTION.
Tracks: Not Advised.
■ LP......................RR 9743
Road Runner / Nov '85.

TIME OF CHANGES, A.
Tracks: Ragnarok / Inferno / Blitzkreig / Pull the trigger / Armageddon / Hell to pay / Vikings / Time of changes / Saviour.
■ LP.....................NEAT 1023
Neat / '85.

Blood

FALSE GESTURES FOR A DEVIOUS PUBLIC.
Tracks: Done some brain cells last night / Degener-ate / Gestapo khazi / Well sick / Sewer brain / Sucker / Mesrine / Rule 43 / Joys of noise / Waste of flesh and bones / Throttle you blue.
■ LP.....................NOYZLP 1
Noise / Nov '83.

FULL TIME RESULT (Blood/Gonads).
Tracks: Stark raving normal / Meglomania / Such fun / Alconaut / Napalm job / Drunk addict / Coffin dodgers / Go mad with the gonads / I lost my love to a U.K. sub / Sandra Bigg really big / Got any Wrig-leys John / Punk rock will never die / Drinking song / Jobs not jails.
■ LP..................... LINK LP 024
Link / Feb '88.

IMPULSE TO DESTROY.
Tracks: Not Advised.
LP........................WRR 014
Wild Rags / '90 / Plastic Head.

MEGLOMANIA.
Tracks: Meglomania / Parasite in paradise / Calling the shots.
■ 7"........................01 122
No Future / Mar '83.

SICK KICKS FOR SHOCK ROCKERS.
Tracks: Not Advised.
■ LP...................... QUEST 3
Conquest / Jun '85.

STARK RAVING NORMAL.
Tracks: Stark raving normal / Mesrine.
■ 7".......................NOY 1
Noise / Oct '83.

Blood Feast

CHOPPING BLOCK BLUES.
Tracks: Not Advised.
CD....................FLAME 1016CD
LP..................... FLAME 1016
Flametrader / Nov '90 / Greyhound Records.

FACE FATE.
Tracks: Not Advised.
■ LP P.Disc............... NRPD 35
MC........................NRC 35
Mini LP.................. NRR 35
New Renaissance(USA) / Nov '87 / Pinnacle.

KILL FOR PLEASURE.
Tracks: Not Advised.
■ LP...................... NRR 16
MC........................NRC 16
New Renaissance(USA) / Nov '87 / Pinnacle.
CD.....................SHARK 013 CD
Shark / Apr '90 / Plastic Head.

Blood From The Soul

TO SPRITE THE GLAND THAT BREEDS.
Tracks: Painted life / Image and the helpless / On fear and prayer / Guinea pig / Nature's hole / Vascular / To spite / Suspension of my disbelief / Yet to be savoured / Blood from the soul.
CD . . . . MOSH 089CD
LP . . . . MOSH 089
MC . . . . MOSH 089MC
Earache / Oct '93 / Vital Distribution.

Bloodcum

HARDCORE DEMO SERIES, THE.
Tracks: Not Advised.
■ LP . . . . WRR 002
Wild Rags / Nov '88.

Bloodgood

ALL STAND TOGETHER.
Tracks: S.O.S. / All stand together / Escape from the fire / Say goodbye / Out of love / Kingdom come / Fear no evil / Help me / Rounded are the rocks / Lies in the dark / Streelight dance / I want to live in your heart.
CD . . . . CD 08793
MC . . . . C 08793
Broken / Jan '92 / Broken Records.

DETONATION.
Tracks: Not Advised.
■ CD . . . . CD 9019
■ LP . . . . RO 9019
■ MC . . . . CO 9019
Frontline (2) / Jul '88.

ROCK IN A HARD PLACE.
Tracks: Shakin' it / Presence / What have I done / Heaven on Earth / Do or die / She's gone / World / Seven.
■ CD . . . . CD 9036
■ LP . . . . RO 9036
■ MC . . . . CO 9036
Priority / Nov '88.

Bloodlust

GUILTY AS SIN.
Tracks: Not Advised.
■ LP . . . . RR 9744
Road Runner / Aug '86.

TERMINAL VELOCITY.
Tracks: Not Advised.
LP . . . . WRR 005
Wild Rags / Nov '88 / Plastic Head.

Bloodstar

ANYTIME ANYWHERE.
Tracks: Not Advised.
CD . . . . RR 90982
Road Runner / Feb '93 / Pinnacle.

Blue Blood

BIG NOISE, THE.
Tracks: Not Advised.
CD . . . . CDMFN 93
■ LP . . . . MFN 93
MC . . . . TMFN 93
Music For Nations / Oct '89 / Pinnacle.

BLUE BLOOD.
Tracks: Not Advised.
■ LP . . . . SNTF 615
Sonet / '87.

RUNNING BACK.
Tracks: Running back.
■ 12" 12KUT 133
■ 7" . . . . KUT 133
Music For Nations / Jun '89.

UNIVERSAL LANGUAGE.
Tracks: Not Advised.
CD . . . . MFNCD 112
LP . . . . MFN 112
MC . . . . MFNT 112
Music For Nations / Apr '91 / Pinnacle.

Blue Cheer

BLITZKRIEG OVER NUREMBERG.
Tracks: Babylon / Girl next door / Ride with me / Just a little bit / Summertime blues / Out of focus / Doctor please / Hunter.
CD . . . . CDTB 091

LP . . . . THBL 091
Thunderbolt / Sep '90 / TBD / Jazz Music.

HIGHLIGHTS AND LOWLIVES.
Tracks: Not Advised.
CD 23011421
LP 23010413
Nibelung / Nov '90.
CD . . . . CDTB 125
MC . . . . THBC 125
Thunderbolt / Jun '91 / TBD / Jazz Music.

Blue Murder

Shooting star trio masterminded by well-travelled guitarist John Sykes, originally featuring equally seasoned Carmine Appice on drums and former Firm bassist Tony Franklin; debut album (U.K. no. 45 in 1989) is worth tracking down by fans of Sykes' work with Whitesnake. Missing presumed deceased since 1989, band resurfaced in '93 with Nothing But Trouble.

BLUE MURDER.
Tracks: Riot / Valley of the kings / Blue murder / Billy / Black hearted woman / Sex child / Jelly roll / Out of love / Vtolemy.
■ CD 9242122
■ LP . . . . WX 245
■ MC . . . . WX 245C
Geffen / Apr '89.
CD . . . . GFLD 19225
MC . . . . GFLC 19225
Geffen / Aug '93 / BMG.

BLUE MURDER AT HOME.
Tracks: Settle down / Let's go / Not so sure anymore / Isabella / Start all over again / Straight to hell / Winter blues / Zabriskie Point / Ryu's song / Walk home my guitar.
■ LP . . . . EM 9604
Road Runner / Aug '87.

ENERGISE.
Tracks: Not Advised.
■ LP . . . . BM 002
Blue Murder / Mar '85.

NOTHING BUT TROUBLE.
Tracks: We all fall down / Itchycoo park / Cry for love / Runaway / Dance / I'm on fire / Save my love / Love child / Shouldn't have let you go / I need an angel / She knows.
CD . . . . GED 24419
MC . . . . GEC 24419
Geffen / Aug '93 / BMG.

TALK TALK TALK.
Tracks: Talk talk talk / Mr. Soul.
■ 7" 248845 7
WEA / Jun '86.

Blue Oyster Cult

American heavy metal band - Eric Bloom, Albert Bouchard, Joe Bouchard, Allen Lanier and Donald 'Buck Dharma' Roeser - formed in New York in 1970. Released debut eponymous LP in 1972, but it wasn't until the release of their third album, 1974's Secret Treaties, that they broke in the States. It was followed the next year by a live LP On Your Feet Or On Your Knees, which cemented their already strong live following and displayed their powerhouse concert appeal. Agents Of Fortune (1976) featured their classic (Don't Fear) The Reaper. From the late 1970's onwards, Blue Oyster Cult have continued to attract a large following among rock fans with their occult/biker image.

(DON'T FEAR) THE REAPER.
Tracks: (Don't fear) the reaper / R.U. ready 2 rock / I love the night.
■ 7" . . . . CBS 6333
CBS / May '78.
■ 7" . . . . A 4584
CBS / Jul '84.

(DON'T FEAR) THE REAPER (OLD GOLD).
Tracks: (Don't fear) the reaper / R U ready to rock.
7" . . . . OG 9398
Old Gold / Mar '90 / Pickwick.

AGENTS OF FORTUNE.
Tracks: This ain't the summer of love / True confessions / Don't fear the reaper / E.T.I. (Extra Terrestrial Intelegence) / Revenge of Vera Gemini / Sinful love / Tattoo vampire / Morning final / Tenderloin / Debbie Denise.

■ LP . . . . CBS 81385
CBS / Jul '76.
■ CD . . . . CD 32221
CBS / Jul '89.
■ LP . . . . CBS 32221
CBS / Jul '89.
CD 9827322
Pickwick/Sony Collector's Choice / Mar '94 / Pickwick / Pinnacle.

ASTRONOMY.
Tracks: Astronomy / Magna of illusion / (Don't fear) the reaper (Only on 12" & CD.) / Astronomy (wild mix) (Only on 12").
■ 12" 6529856
■ 7" 6529850
■ CD Single 6529852
CBS / Oct '88.
■ 12" 6529858
CBS / Jul '89.

BLUE OYSTER CULT.
Tracks: Transmission MC / I'm the lamb but I ain't no sheep / Then came the last days of May / Stairway to the stars / Before the kiss / Redcap / Screams / She's as beautiful as a foot / Cities on flame / Workshop of the telescopes / Redeemed.
■ LP . . . . CBS 32025
CBS / Mar '81.

BURNIN' FOR YOU.
Tracks: Burnin' for you / Heavy metal / Black and silver.
■ 12" . . . . A 13 1453
■ 7" . . . . A 1453
CBS / Aug '81.

CAREER OF EVIL.
Tracks: Cities on flame / Red and the black / Hot rails to hell / Dominance and submission / 7 screaming Diz-Busters / Me 262 / ETI (Extra Terrestrial Intellegence) / Beat 'em up / Black blade / Harvester of eyes / Flaming telepaths / Godzilla / (Don't fear) The reaper.
■ LP 4659291
MC 4659294
■ CD 4659292
CBS / Apr '90.

CLUB NINJA.
Tracks: White flags / Dancin' in the ruins / Rock not war / Perfect water / Spy in the house of the night / Beat 'em up / When the war comes / Shadow warrior / Madness to the method.
■ LP . . . . CBS 26775
■ MC 40 26775
CBS / Dec '85.
■ CD . . . . CD 26775
CBS / May '87.
CD 982841 2
Pickwick/Sony Collector's Choice / Mar '94 / Pickwick / Pinnacle.

CULT CLASSICS.
Tracks: Don't fear the reaper / E.T.I / M.E. 262 / This ain't the summer of love / Burning for you / O.D.D On life itself / Flaming telepaths / Godzilla / Astronomy / Cities on flame with rock 'n' roll / Harvester of eyes / Buck's boogie.
CD . . . . CDFRL 003
MC . . . . CFRL 003
Fragile / Apr '94 / Pinnacle.

CULTOSAURUS ERECTUS.
Tracks: Black blade / Monsters / Divine wind / Deadlines / Marshall plan / Hungry boys / Fallen angel / Lips in the hills / Unknown tongue.
■ LP . . . . CBS 86120
CBS / Jul '80.

DEADLINE.
Tracks: Deadline / Monsters.
■ 7" . . . . CBS 8986
CBS / Oct '80.

E.T.I.
Tracks: Dominance and submission / Cities on flame / Dr. Music / Red and the black / Joan Crawford / Burnin' for you / Roadhouse blues / Black blade / Hot rails to Hell / Godzilla / Veteran of the psychic wars / E.T.I. (Extra Terrestrial Intelligence) / Don't fear the Reaper.
■ Double LP. . . . . CBS 22203
CBS / May '82.

FALLEN ANGEL.
Tracks: Fallen angel / Lips in the hills.
■ 7" . . . . CBS 8790
CBS / Aug '80.

FIRE OF UNKNOWN ORIGIN.
Tracks: Fire of unknown origin / Burnin' for you / Veteran of the psychic wars / Sole survivor / Heavy

metal / Black and silver vengeance / After dark / Joan Crawford / Don't turn your back.
■ LP 85137
CBS / Jul '81.
CD . . . . CK 37389
CBS / '87 / Sony.

GOING THROUGH THE MOTIONS.
Tracks: Going through the motions / Searching for Celine.
■ 7" . . . . CBS 5889
CBS / Dec '77.

I LOVE THE NIGHT.
Tracks: I love the night / Nossertaur.
■ 7" . . . . CBS 6514
CBS / Aug '78.

IMAGINOS.
Tracks: I am the one you warned me of / Les invisibles / In the presence of another world / Del Rio's song / Siege and investiture of Baron von Frankenstein's castle / Astronomy / Magna of illusion / Blue Oyster Cult / Imaginos.
■ LP 4600361
MC 4600364
■ CD 4600362
CBS / Sep '88.
■ LP P.Disc 4600360
CBS / Mar '89.

LIVE 1976.
Tracks: Not Advised.
■ VHS . . . . CMP 6071
Castle Music Pictures / Oct '91.

LIVE: BLUE OYSTER CULT (1976).
Tracks: Not Advised.
CD . . . . CLACD 269
■ MC . . . . CLAMC 269
Castle / Oct '91.

MIRRORS.
Tracks: Dr. Music / Great sun jester / In thee / Mirrors / Moon crazy / Vigil / I am the storm / You're not the one / Lonely teardrops.
■ LP . . . . CBS 86087
CBS / Aug '79.

MIRRORS.
Tracks: Mirrors / Lonely teardrops.
■ 7" . . . . CBS 7783
CBS / Nov '79.

ON YOUR FEET OR ON YOUR KNEES.
Tracks: Subhuman / Harvester of eyes / Hot rails to hell / Red and the black / 7 screaming diz-busters / Buck's boogie / Then came the last days of May / Cities on flame / Me 262 / Before the kiss / I ain't got you / Born to be wild.
MC 4601134
■ LP 4601131
CBS / Sep '87.

REVOLUTION BY NIGHT.
Tracks: Take me away / Eyes on fire / Shooting shark / Veins / Shadow of California / Feel the thunder / Let go / Dragon lady / Light years of love.
■ LP . . . . CBS 25686
CBS / Nov '83.
CD . . . . CK 38947
Columbia (USA) / Dec '88 / Columbia (Imports).

SHOOTING SHARK.
Tracks: Shooting shark / Dragon lady.
■ 12" . . . . TA 4117
■ 7" . . . . A 4117
CBS / Jan '84.

SOME ENCHANTED EVENING.
Tracks: R U ready 2 rock / ETI (Extra Terrestrial Intellegence) / Astronomy / Kick out the jams / Godzilla / Don't fear the reaper / We gotta get out of this place.
■ MC .40 86074
■ LP . . . . CBS 86074
CBS / Sep '78.

SPECTRES.
Tracks: Godzilla / Golden age of leather / Death valley nights / Searchin' for Celine / Fire works / R.U. ready / Rock / Celestial the queen / Going through the motions / I love the night / Nosferatu.
■ LP . . . . CBS 86050
CBS / Jan '78.
■ LP . . . . CBS 32715
■ MC 40 32715
CBS / Feb '86.
CD . . . . .CDCBS 82371
CBS / Dec '88 / Sony.

TAKE ME AWAY.
Tracks: Take me away / Feel the thunder.
■ 12" . . . . TA 3937

■ 7" . . . . .A 3937
CBS / Dec '83.

WE'VE GOTTA GET OUT OF THIS PLACE.
Tracks: We've gotta get out of this place / Stairway to the stars.
■ 7" . . . . CBS 6909
CBS / Nov '78.

Bluuuurrgh

SUFFER WITHIN.
Tracks: Suffer within.
■ 7" . . . . KILL 001
Cannibalised Serial Killer / Jun '93.

Body Count

BODYCOUNT.
Tracks: Smoked pork / Body count's in the house / Now sports / Body count / Statistic / Bowels of the devil / Real problem / KKK Bitch / Note / Voodoo / Winner loses / There goes the neighborhood / Oprah / Evil dick / Body count athem / Momma's gotta die tonight / Ice T/Freedom of speech.
CD 9362451392
MC 9362451394
WEA / Mar '94 / WEA.

BORN DEAD.
Tracks: Not Advised.
CD . . . . RSYND 2
LP . . . . RSYN 2
MC . . . . RSYNC 2
Rhyme Syndicate / Sep '94 / EMI.

Bold

BOLD E.P.
Tracks: Not Advised.
■ 7" . . . . REVEL 011
■ CD Single . . . . REVEL 001CD
■ MC Single . . . . REVEL 011MC
Revelation / Apr '92.

SPEAK OUT.
Tracks: Talk is cheap / Nailed to the X / Now or never / Clear / Accept the blame / Change within / Search.
■ LP 8856182391
Revelation 9 (USA) / Sep '88.

Bolin, Tommy

GRIND.
Tracks: Grind / Homeward strut.
■ 7" . . . . K 10730
Atlantic / Mar '76.

PRIVATE EYES.
Tracks: Bustin' out of Rosey / Sweet burgundy / Post toastee / Shake the devil / Gypsy soul / Someday we'll bring our love home / Hello again / You told me that you loved me.
■ LP . . . . CBS 81612
CBS / Feb '77.
CD . . . . CCSCD 371
Castle / Aug '91 / BMG.
■ CD . . . . ESSCD 950
Essential / Aug '91.

TEASER.
Tracks: Grind / Homeward / Strut / Dreamer savannah woman / Teaser / People people / Marching powder / Wild dogs / Lotus.
CD .468016 2
MC .468016 4
Epic / May '94 / Sony.

ULTIMATE TOMMY BOLIN, THE.
Tracks: Sail on / See my people come together / Alexis / Spanish lover / Quadrant four / Time to move on / Nitroglycerin / Owed to 'G' / Wild dogs / People, people / Sweet burgundy / Brother brother / Cross the river / Showbizzy / Standing in the rain / Do it / Train / Golden rainbows / Gettin' tighter / You keep moving / Dreamer / Teaser / Shake the devil.
■ LP Set . . . . GHS 24248
Geffen / Dec '89.
■ LP Set 9242481
■ CD Set 9242482
■ MC Set 9242484
Geffen / Mar '90.

Bolt Thrower

4TH CRUSADE.
Tracks: Not Advised.
LP . . . . MOSH 070
MC. . . . . .MOSH 070MC
Earache / Oct '92 / Vital Distribution.

CD . . . . .MOSH 070CD
Earache / Sep '94 / Vital Distribution.

CENOTAPH.
Tracks: Cenotaph.
■ 12" . . . . MOSH 29 T
■ CD Single . . . . MOSH 29 CD
Earache / Jan '91.

IN BATTLE THERE IS NO LAW.
Tracks: Not Advised.
■ LP . . . . SOL 11
Vinyl Solution / Aug '88.
CD . . . . SOL 22 CD
Vinyl Solution / Feb '91 / RTM / Pinnacle.
■ MC . . . . SOL 11MC
Vinyl Solution / Oct '93.

PEEL SESSIONS: BOLT THROWER.
Tracks: Forgotten existence / Attack in the aftermath / Psychological warfare / In battle there is no law / Drowned in torment / Eternal war / Realm of chaos / Domination / Destructive infinity / Warmaster / After life / Lost souls domain / Forgotten existence.
CD . . . . SFRCD 116
LP . . . . SFRLP 116
Strange Fruit / Jun '91 / Pinnacle.

PEEL SESSIONS: BOLT THROWER.
Tracks: Not Advised.
■ 12" . . . . SFPS 056
Strange Fruit / Oct '88.

REALM OF CHAOS.
Tracks: Eternal war / Through the eye of terror / Dark millenium / All that remains / Lost souls domaine / Plague bearer / World eater / Drowned in torment / Realm of chaos.
■ LP . . . . MOSH 13
MC. . . . . .MOSH 13 MC
Earache / Oct '89 / Vital Distribution.
■ LP P.Disc . . . . MOSH 13 P
Earache / Jul '90.
CD . . . . MOSH 13 CD
Earache / Sep '94 / Vital Distribution.

SPEARHEAD.
Tracks: Spearhead (extended mix) / Crown of life / Dying creed / Lament.
■ 12" . . . . .MOSH 073T
■ CD Single . . . . MOSH 073 CD
Earache / Jan '93.

WAR MASTER.
Tracks: Not Advised.
LP . . . . MOSH 29
MC. . . . . MOSH 29MC
Earache / Sep '90 / Vital Distribution.
CD . . . . .MOSH 020CD
Earache / Sep '94 / Vital Distribution.

Bolton, Michael

Although now world famous for his bland pop soul ballads and the odd rock pose, Michael Bolton actually cut his teeth in a hard AOR mould releasing several well received albums including the album *Everybody's Crazy* which was given a KKKKK rating in the pages of Kerrang and heralded as an AOR classic, shame about that hair though.

(SITTIN' ON THE) DOCK OF THE BAY.
Tracks: (Sittin' on) the dock of the bay.
■ 12" 6513878
■ 7" 6513877
■ CD Single 6513872
CBS / Apr '88.

DRIFT AWAY.
Tracks: Drift away / White christmas (On CD singles only) / To love somebody (live version) (Only on 658865 2) / Back in my arms again (Only on 658865 5) / Fool's game (On 658865 5).
■ CD Single 658865 2
■ 7" 658865 5
■ CD Single 658865 5
■ MC Single 658865 4
Columbia / Dec '92.

EARLY YEARS, THE.
Tracks: Lost in the city / Everybody needs a reason / Your love / It's just a feelin' / Dream while you can / Take me as I am / These eyes / You mean more to me / If I had your love / Give me a reason / Tell me how you feel / Time is on my side.
CD . . . . ND 82157
RCA / Nov '90 / BMG.
CD . . . . ND 90593
RCA / Mar '92 / BMG.

EVERYBODY'S CRAZY.
Tracks: Everybody's crazy / Save our love / Can't turn it off / Call my name / Everytime / Desperate heart / Start breaking my heart / You don't want me bad enough / Don't tell me it's over.
CD. 4666622
MC. 4666624
Columbia / May '91 / Sony.

EVERYBODY'S CRAZY/MICHAEL BOLTON.
Tracks: Save our love / Everybody's crazy / Can't turn it off / Call my name / Everytime / Desperate heart / Start breaking my heart / You don't want me bad enough / Don't tell me it's over / Fool's game / She did the same thing / Hometown hero / Can't hold on, Let it go / Fighting for my life / Paradise / Back in my arms again / Carrie / I almost believed you.
CD Set 4683112
Columbia / Jul '92 / Sony.

GEORGIA ON MY MIND.
Tracks: Georgia on my mind / Take a look at my face / That's what love is all about (live) (Available on CD single format only.) / (Sittin' on) the dock of the bay (Available on CD single format only.)
■ 12". 6561968
■ 7". 6561967
■ CD Single. 6561962
■ MC Single. 6561964
CBS / Nov '90.

HOW AM I SUPPOSED TO LIVE WITH-OUT YOU.
Tracks: How am I supposed to live without you / Forever eyes (Not on CD single) / Soul provider (Not on Cassingle) / That's what love is all about (CD single only.) / Can't hold can't let go (CD single only.)
■ CD Single. 6553975
■ MC Single. 6553974
CBS / Feb '90.
■ 12". 6553976
■ 7". 6553977
CBS / Jan '90.

HOW CAN WE BE LOVERS.
Tracks: How can we be lovers / Hunger / Fools game / (Sittin' on) The dock of the bay (Live) / I almost believed you.
■ 12". 6559186
■ 7". 6559187
■ CD Single. 6559185
■ CD Single. 6559182
■ MC Single. 6559184
CBS / Apr '90.

HUNGER, THE.
Tracks: Hot love / Wait on love / (Sittin' on) the dock of the bay / Gina / That's what love is all about / Hunger / You're all I need / Take a look at my face / Walk away.
CD. . . . . CK 40473
Columbia (USA) / Oct '87 / Columbia (Imports).
■ LP. BFC 40473
Columbia (USA) / Sep '87.
CD. 4601632
■ LP. 4601631
MC. 4601634
CBS / Aug '90 / Sony.

LEAN ON ME.
Tracks: Lean on me / Time, love and tenderness (live) / To love somebody (live) (Available on CDS only) / How can we be lovers (live) (Available on CDS only).
■ 7". 660413 7
■ CD Single. 660413 2
■ CD Single. 660413 5
■ MC Single. 660413 4
Columbia / May '94.

LOVE IS A WONDERFUL THING.
Tracks: Love is a wonderful thing / Soul provider / Georgia on my mind (full length version) (Only on 12" and CD single) / When I'm back on my feet again (remix) (Only on 12" and CD single).
■ 12". 6567716
■ 7". 6567717
■ CD Single. 6567712
■ MC Single. 6567714
Columbia / Apr '91.

MICHAEL BOLTON.
Tracks: Fool's game / She did the same thing / Home town hero / Can't hold on, can't let go / Fighting for my life / Paradise / Back in my arms again / Carrie / I almost believed you.
■ LP. CBS 25342
CBS / Jul '83.
CD. 4667422
MC. 4667424
Columbia / Apr '92 / Sony.

MICHAEL BOLTON / EVERYBODY'S CRAZY / THE HUNGER.
Tracks: Not Advised.
CD Set 468327 2
Columbia / Jul '93 / Sony.

MISSING YOU NOW.
Tracks: Missing you now / It's only my heart / Love cuts deep (Only on CD single) / Walk away (Only on CD single).
■ 7". 6579917
■ MC Single. 6579914
■ CD Single. 6579912
Columbia / Apr '92.

ONE THING, THE.
Tracks: Said I loved you .. but I lied / I'm not made of steel / One thing / Soul of my soul / Completely / Lean on me / Ain't got nothing if you ain't got love / Time for letting go / Never get enough of your love / In the arms of love / Voice of my heart.
CD. 474355 2
LP. 474355 1
MC. 474355 4
MiniDisc. 474355 3
Columbia / Nov '93 / Sony.

REACH OUT I'LL BE THERE.
Tracks: Reach out I'll be there / New love / Forever isn't long enough (Available on CD single only.) / Stand up for love (Available on CD single only.)
■ 7". 658897 7
■ CD Single. 658897 2
■ MC Single. 658897 4
Columbia / Mar '93.

SAID I LOVED YOU..BUT I LIED.
Tracks: Said I loved you..but I lied / Soul provider / Time, love and tenderness (Available on CDS only.) / You send me (Available on CDS only).
■ 7". 659876 7
■ CD Single. 659876 2
■ MC Single. 659876 4
Columbia / Nov '93.

SOUL AND PASSION.
Tracks: Not Advised.
VHS .491222
Sony Music Video / Nov '92 / Sony.

SOUL OF MY SOUL.
Tracks: Soul of my soul / Voice of my heart / Soul of my soul (mix) (Available on CDS only) / Steel bars (live) (Available on CDS only).
■ 7". 660177 7
■ CD Single. 660177 5
■ CD Single. 660177 2
■ MC Single. 660177 4
Columbia / Feb '94.

SOUL PROVIDER.
Tracks: Soul provider / Georgia on my mind / It's only my heart / How am I supposed to live without you / How can we be lovers / You wouldn't know love / When I'm back on my feet again / From now on / Love cuts deep / Stand up for love.
CD. 4653432
MC. 4653434
■ LP. 4653431
CBS / Aug '89.
CD P.Disc. 4653439
CBS / Dec '90 / Sony.
MiniDisc. 465343-3
Columbia / Feb '93 / Sony.

SOUL PROVIDER.
Tracks: Soul provider (Only on 7" and CD single.) / Hunger / Soul provider (12" remix) (Only on 12" and CD single.) / Soul provider (7" edit) (Only on 12" single.) / (Sittin' on) the dock of the bay (Only on 12" and CD single.)
■ 7". 6549467
■ 12". 6549463
■ 12". 6549468
■ CD Single. 6549462
CBS / Jul '89.

SOUL PROVIDER.
Tracks: Not Advised.
VHS .498812
Sony Music Video / Mar '94 / Sony.

SOUL PROVIDER (SINGLE).
Tracks: Soul provider / Hunger / Soul provider (12" remix) (Available on 12" and CD single formats only.)
■ 12". 6558776
■ 7". 6558777
■ CD Single. 6558772
■ MC Single. 6558774
CBS / Sep '90.

SOUL PROVIDER - THE VIDEOS.
Tracks: Soul provider / How am I supposed to live without you / How can we be lovers / (Sittin' on) The dock of the bay / When I'm back on my feet again / That's what love is all about / Georgia on my mind.
VHS .490432
CMV Enterprises (Video) / Oct '90 / Sony.

STEEL BARS.
Tracks: Steel bars / How can we be lovers / Take a look at my face (CD single only.)
■ 7". 6577257
■ CD Single. 6577252
■ MC Single. 6577254
Columbia / Jan '92.

THAT'S WHAT LOVE IS ALL ABOUT.
Tracks: That's what love is all about / Take a look at my face / Fool's game (On 12" & CD single only) / Can't hold on, can't let go (On 12" & CD single only.)
■ 7". 6510590
CBS / '88.
■ 7". 6510597
CBS / Feb '88.
■ 12". 6510598
■ CD Single. 6510592
CBS / Jul '88.

TIME, LOVE AND TENDERNESS.
Tracks: Love is a wonderful thing / Time, love and tenderness / Missing you now / Forever isn't long enough / Now that I found you / When a man loves a woman / We're not makin' love anymore / New love / Save me / Steel bars.
CD. 4678122
■ LP. 4678121
MC. 4678124
Columbia / Apr '91 / Sony.
MiniDisc. 467012-3
Columbia / Feb '93 / Sony.

TIME, LOVE AND TENDERNESS.
Tracks: Time, love and tenderness / You wouldn't know love / Love is a wonderful thing (On 12" and CD single only) / (Sittin' on) The dock of the bay (On 12" and CD single only).
■ 12". 656989 6
■ 7". 656989 7
■ CD Single. 656989 2
Columbia / Jul '91.

TIMELESS (THE CLASSICS).
Tracks: Since I fell for you / To love somebody / Reach out I'll be there / You send me / Yesterday / Hold on / I'm coming / Bring it on home to me / Knock on wood / Drift away / White Christmas.
CD. 4723022
■ LP. 4723021
MC. 4723024
Columbia / Oct '92 / Sony.
MiniDisc. 472302-3
Columbia / Feb '93 / Sony.

TO LOVE SOMEBODY.
Tracks: To love somebody / When a man loves a woman (On 658455-5 only) / Georgia on my mind (On 658455-5 only) / (Sittin' on) the dock of the bay (On 658455-2/-5 only) / Now that I found you (Not on 658455-5 CDs).
■ 7". 658455-7
■ CD Single. 658455-2
■ CD Single. 6584555
■ MC Single. 658455-4
Columbia / Oct '92.

WHEN A MAN LOVES A WOMAN.
Tracks: When a man loves a woman / Save me / Love is a wonderful thing (Only on CD single).
■ 7". 6574887
■ CD Single. 6574885
■ MC Single. 6574884
Columbia / Oct '91.

WHEN I'M BACK ON MY FEET AGAIN.
Tracks: When I'm back on my feet again / Walk away / You're all that I need / I almost believed you / Home town.
■ 12". 6560776
■ 7". 6560777
■ CD Single. 6560772
■ CD Single. 6560775
■ MC Single. 6560774
CBS / Jul '90.

Bomb Disneyland

BOMB EVERYTHING.
Tracks: Faster bastard / World no.3 IOU / Wa'as sapennin / To the moon / Blood fuck / New one / Live in Grimsby / Hickory dickory death / Suicide 999 / Killer City / Fat pig / Bomb Disneyland / Prostitution / Woman / Blind faith.

                                         ■ DELETED

■ LP . . . . EFA 1711208
Sol 16 / May '89.

Bomb Everything

ALL POWERFUL FLUID, THE.
Tracks: Not Advised.
CD .CDDVN 10
LP . . . . DVN 10
MC .TDVN 10
Devotion / Jul '92 / Pinnacle.

FOUNTAINHEAD.
Tracks: Fountainhead.
■ 12" 12DVN 102
■ CD Single . . . . CDDVN 102
Devotion / Feb '92.

GUESS WHAT.
Tracks: Not Advised.
LP . . . . SOL 23
Vinyl Solution / Aug '90 / RTM / Pinnacle.

Bon Jovi

Formed in New Jersey by singer Jon Bon Jovi, band broke into mainstream with best-selling third album *Slippery When Wet*. The LP's trio of hits can take credit for new receptiveness of UK radio/TV to metal. Lengthy tour followed; pattern repeated after *New Jersey* in 1988. Bon Jovi and guitarist Richie Sambora took time off for solo projects; former's *Young Guns II* soundtrack produced his *Blaze Of Glory*. Regrouped in 1992 for *Keep The Faith*, whose chart-life maintained by yet more hits. Group's line-up remained unusually stable for first decade: Bon Jovi, Sambora, bassist Alec Jon Such, drummer Tico Torres and keyboardist David Bryan. In 1994, Such expressed desire to move on. Group's success unlikely to be affected.

7800 DEGREES FAHRENHEIT.
Tracks: In and out of love / Price of love / Only lonely / King of the mountain / Silent night / Tokyo road / Hardest part is the night / Always run to you / To the fire / Secret dreams.
■ LP . . . . .VERL 24
MC . . . . .VERLC 24
Vertigo / May '85 / PolyGram.
CD 824 509-2
Vertigo / Jan '90 / PolyGram.

ACCESS ALL AREAS (A Rock 'n' Roll Odyssey).
Tracks: Not Advised.
VHS . . . . CFM 2766
PMV / Dec '90 / PolyGram.

BAD MEDICINE.
Tracks: Bad medicine / 99 in the shade / Lay your hands on me (Only on 12" and CD single.).
■ CD Single . . . . JOVCD 3
■ 12" . . . . JOV 312
■ 12" . . . . JOVR 312
■ 7" . . . . JOV 3
■ 7" . . . . JOVS 3
Vertigo / Sep '88.

BAD MEDICINE (CD VIDEO).
Tracks: Bad medicine.
CD Video 080 566 2
Polygram Music Video / Sep '88 / PolyGram.

BED OF ROSES.
Tracks: Bed of roses.
■ 12" . . . . JOVXP 9
■ CD Single . . . . JOVCD 9
■ MC Single . . . . JOVMC 9
■ 7" . . . . JOV 9
Jambco / Jan '93.

BON JOVI.
Tracks: Runaway / She didn't know me / Shot through the heart / Love lies / Burning for love / Breakout / Come back / Get ready.
■ LP . . . . .VERL 14
MC . . . . .VERLC 14
Vertigo / Apr '84 / PolyGram.
CD 814 982-2
Vertigo / Jul '84 / PolyGram.

BON JOVI CD BOX SET.
Tracks: Not Advised.
■ CD Set. 838 605 2
Vertigo / Oct '89.

BON JOVI: INTERVIEW PICTURE DISC.
Tracks: Not Advised.
CD P.Disc. . . . . CBAK 4004
Baktabak / Apr '88 / Arabesque Ltd.

■ LP P.Disc . . . . BAK 2022
Baktabak / Apr '88.

BON JOVI: INTERVIEW PICTURE DISC COLLECTION.
Tracks: Not Advised.
7" Set . . . . BAKPAK 1007
Baktabak / Apr '88 / Arabesque Ltd.

BON JOVI: INTERVIEW PICTURE DISC, VOL 2.
Tracks: Not Advised.
LP P.Disc . . . . BAK 2106
Baktabak / Aug '88 / Arabesque Ltd.

BORN TO BE MY BABY.
Tracks: Born to be my baby / Love for sale / Wanted dead or alive (Only on 12" version.) / Runaway (Only on CD single.) / Livin' on a prayer (Only on CD single.) / Wanted dead or alive (live) (Only on JOVR 412 12" version.).
■ CD Single . . . . JOVCD 4
■ 12" . . . . JOV 412
■ 12" P.Disc. . . . . JOVR 412
■ 7" . . . . JOV 4
■ 7" . . . . JOVS 4
Vertigo / Nov '88.

BREAKOUT.
Tracks: In and out of love / Only lonely / Silent night / She don't know me / Hardest part of the night / Runaway.
■ VHS 041 386 2
Polygram Music Video / Jun '86.
VHS . . . . CFV 06112
Channel 5 / Oct '88 / Channel 5 Video / P.R.O. Video / Gold & Sons.

CHRIS TETLEY INTERVIEWS BON JOVI.
Tracks: Not Advised.
■ LP P.Disc . . . . CT 1001
Music & Media / Oct '87.

DEAD OR ALIVE (CD VIDEO).
Tracks: Not Advised.
CD Video 080 052 2
Polygram Music Video / Sep '89 / PolyGram.

DRY COUNTRY.
Tracks: Dry country / Stranger in this town (Live) (Not on JOVCD 13) / Blood money (Live) (On JOVBX 13 only) / It's only rock 'n' roll (Live) (On JOVCD 13 only.) / Waltzing Matilda (Live) (On JOVCD 13 only).
■ 7" . . . . JOV 13
■ CD Single . . . . JOVCD 13
■ CD Single . . . . JOVBX 13
■ MC Single . . . . JOVMC 13
Jambco / Mar '94.

HARDEST PART IS THE NIGHT.
Tracks: Hardest part is the night / Always run to you.
■ 12" . . . . .VERXR 22
■ 7" . . . . VER 22
■ 7" Set . . . . .VERDP 22
Vertigo / Aug '85.

I BELIEVE.
Tracks: I believe / Runaway (live) / Livin' on a prayer (live) (CDS only) / Wanted dead or alive (live) (CDS only).
■ 7" . . . . JOV 12
■ CD Single . . . . JOVCD 12
■ MC Single . . . . JOVMC 12
Jambco / Oct '93.

I'LL BE THERE FOR YOU.
Tracks: I'll be there for you / Homebound train / Wild in the streets (live) (Only on 12" single.) / Borderline (on CD single only.) / Edge of a broken heart (Available on CD only).
■ 7" . . . . JOVR 512
■ 12" . . . . JOV 512
■ 7" . . . . JOVPB 85
■ 7" . . . . JOVPB 5
■ 7" . . . . JOV 5
■ CD Single . . . . JOVCD 5
Vertigo / Apr '89.
■ MC Single . . . . JOVMC 5
Vertigo / Apr '89.

I'LL SLEEP WHEN I'M DEAD.
Tracks: I'll sleep when I'm dead.
■ 7" . . . . JOV 11
■ CD Single . . . . JOVCD 11
■ MC Single . . . . JOVMC 11
Jambco / Aug '93.

IN AND OUT OF LOVE.
Tracks: In and out of love / Roulette.
■ 12" . . . . .VERX 19
■ 7" . . . . VER 19
Vertigo / May '85.

IN THESE ARMS.
Tracks: In these arms.
■ MC Single . . . . JOVMC 10
■ CD Single . . . . .JOVCD 10
Jambco / May '93.

INTERVIEWS VOLUME 2, THE.
Tracks: Not Advised.
CD P.Disc. . . . . CBAK 4070
Baktabak / Feb '94 / Arabesque Ltd.

KEEP THE FAITH.
Tracks: Not Advised.
CD 5141972
MC 5141974
■ LP 5141971
Jambco / Nov '92.

KEEP THE FAITH.
Tracks: Keep the faith.
■ 7" . . . . JOV 8
■ CD Single . . . . JOVCD 8
■ MC Single . . . . JOVMC 8
Jambco / Oct '92.

KEEP THE FAITH.
Tracks: Not Advised.
VHS 865143
Polygram Music Video / Jul '93 / PolyGram.

LAY YOUR HANDS ON ME.
Tracks: Lay your hands on me / Bad medicine / Blood on blood / Born to be my baby (acoustic).
■ 10" . . . . JOV 612
■ 12" . . . . JOVS 661
■ 7" . . . . JOV 6
■ 7" . . . . JOVS 663
Vertigo / Aug '89.
■ CD Single . . . . JOVCD 6
Vertigo / Apr '89.
■ 10" . . . . JOVP 610
■ 12" . . . . JOVG 612
■ 7" . . . . JOVS 662
■ MC Single . . . . JOVMC 6
Vertigo / Aug '89.

LIVIN' ON A PRAYER.
Tracks: Livin' on a prayer / Wild in the streets / Edge of a broken heart / Livin' on a prayer(remix) (Extra track on 12"(VERXR 28) only).
■ 12" . . . . .VERXR 28
■ 12" . . . . .VERX 28
■ 7" . . . . VER 28
■ 7" . . . . .VERPA 28
■ 7" P.Disc . . . . .VERP 28
■ 7" Set . . . . .VERXG 28
Vertigo / Oct '86.

LIVIN' ON A PRAYER.
Tracks: Livin' on a prayer.
CD Video 080 042 2
Polygram Music Video / Oct '88 / PolyGram.

LIVING IN SIN.
Tracks: Living in sin / Love is war / Ride cowboy ride (12" & CD only.) / Stick to your guns (12" & CD only.).
■ 12" . . . . JOV 712
■ 7" . . . . JOV 7
■ CD Single . . . . JOVCD 7
■ MC Single . . . . JOVMC 7
Vertigo / Nov '89.
■ 12" . . . . JOVR 712
Vertigo / Nov '89.

NEVER SAY GOODBYE.
Tracks: Never say goodbye / Raise your hands.
■ 12" . . . . JOV 212
■ 7" . . . . JOV 2
■ MC Single . . . . JOVMC 2
Vertigo / Aug '87.

NEW JERSEY.
Tracks: Lay your hands on me / Bad medicine / Born to be my baby / Living in sin / Blood on blood / Stick to your guns / I'll be there for you / 99 in the shade / Love for sale / Wild is the wind / Ride cowboy ride.
CD 836 345-2
Vertigo / Nov '88 / PolyGram.
■ LP . . . . VERH 62
MC . . . . .VERHC 62
Vertigo / Sep '88 / PolyGram.
■ LP P.Disc. . . . . .VERHP 62
Vertigo / Jan '89.

NEW JERSEY.
Tracks: Not Advised.
VHS . . . . CFV 08892
Channel 5 / Nov '89 / Channel 5 Video / P.R.O. Video / Gold & Sons.

RUNAWAY.
Tracks: Runaway / Breakout.
■ 12" . . . . .VERX 14

■ 7″ . . . . VER 14
Vertigo / Oct '84.

SHE DON'T KNOW ME.
Tracks: She don't know me / Breakout.
■ 12″ . . . . .VERX 11
■ 7″ . . . . VER 11
Vertigo / May '84.

SLIPPERY WHEN WET.
Tracks: Let it rock / You give love a bad name / Livin' on a prayer / Social disease / Wanted dead or alive / Raise your hands / Without love / I'd die for you / Never say goodbye / Wild in the streets.
MC .VERHC 38
■ LP . . . . VERH 38
Vertigo / Sep '86.
■ LP P.Disc . . . . .VERHP 38
Vertigo / Aug '87.
CD 830 264-2
Vertigo / Sep '90 / PolyGram.

SLIPPERY WHEN WET.
Tracks: Not Advised.
VHS . . . . CFV 04002
Channel 5 / Jun '88 / Channel 5 Video / P.R.O. Video / Gold & Sons.
CD Video 080 296 1
Polygram Music Video / Oct '88 / PolyGram.
VHS . . . . LED 80092
4 Front / May '91 / PolyGram Video.

VERTIGO INTERVIEW.
Tracks: Not Advised.
■ 12″ P.Disc . . . . .WAXJOV 10
Vertigo / '88.

WANTED DEAD OR ALIVE.
Tracks: Wanted dead or alive / Shot through the heart / Social Disease (Extra track on 12″ version only.) / Silent night (Extra track in doublepack.) / Get ready (Extra track in doublepack.).
■ 7″ . . . . JOVS 1
Vertigo / Apr '87.
■ 12″ . . . . JOVR 112
■ 12″ . . . . JOV 112
■ 7″ . . . . JOV 1
■ CD Single . . . . JOVCD 1
■ 12″ . . . . JOVPB 112
Vertigo / Mar '87.

YOU GIVE LOVE A BAD NAME.
Tracks: You give love a bad name / Let it rock / Borderline.
■ 7″ P.Disc . . . . .VERP 26
■ 12″ . . . . .VERXR 26
■ 12″ .VERX 26
■ 7″ . . . . VER 26
Vertigo / Jul '86.

Bon Jovi, Jon

BLAZE OF GLORY.
Tracks: Blaze of glory / You really got me now / Blood money (12″ & CD single only).
■ 12″ . . . . JBJ 112
■ 7″ . . . . JBJ 1
■ CD Single . . . . .JBJCD 1
■ MC Single . . . . .JBJMC 1
Vertigo / Aug '90.

MIRACLE.
Tracks: Miracle / Bang a drum (Available on 7″ and cassette single.) / Dyin' ain't much of a livin' (Available on JBJ 212, JBJCD 2 and JBJP 212) / 8 minute interview with Jon Bon Jovi (Available on JBJ 212 only.)
■ 12″ . . . . JBJ 212
■ 12″ P.Disc . . . . JBJP 212
■ 7″ . . . . JBJ 2
■ CD Single . . . . .JBJCD 2
■ MC Single . . . . .JBJMC 2
Vertigo / Oct '90.

Bonesaw

ABANDONED.
Tracks: Not Advised.
CD . . . . LF 099CD
Lost & Found / Jun '94 / Plastic Head.

Bonfire

FIRE WORKS.
Tracks: Ready 4 reaction / Never mind / Sleeping all alone / Champion / Don't get me wrong / Sweet obsession / Rock me now / American nights / Fantasy / Give it a try / Cold days (Extra track on CD only.)
■ MC . . . . ZK 71518
■ LP . . . . ZL 71518
■ CD . . . . ZD 71518
Motown / Feb '88.

HARD ON ME.
Tracks: Hard on me / Freedom is my belief / You're back / Ready 4 reaction.
■ 12″ . . . . ZT 43194
■ 12″ . . . . ZT 43176
■ 7″ . . . . ZB 43081
■ 7″ . . . . ZB 43175
■ CD Single . . . . ZD 43194
RCA / Sep '89.

KNOCKOUT.
Tracks: Streets of freedom / Stroke / Dirty love / Rivers of glory / Home babe / Shake down / Hold you / Take my heart and run / All we got / Fight for love / Down and out.
CD . . . . PD 75093
■ LP . . . . PL 75093
■ MC . . . . PK 75093
RCA / Oct '91.

POINT BLANK.
Tracks: Bang down the door / Waste no time / Hard on me / Why is it never enough / Tony's roulette / Minestrone / You're back / Look of love / Price of loving you.
■ MC . . . . ZK 74249
■ CD . . . . ZD 74249
■ LP . . . . ZL 74249
RCA / Oct '89.

SWEET OBSESSION.
Tracks: Sweet obsession / Don't get me wrong / Angel in white.
■ 12″ . . . . ZT 41570 RB
■ 7″ . . . . ZB 41569 B
RCA / Jun '88.

WHO'S FOOLIN' WHO.
Tracks: Who's foolin' who / Who's foolin' who (version).
■ 12″ . . . . ZT 43506
■ 7″ . . . . ZB 43505
■ CD Single . . . . ZD 43506
Motown / Apr '90.

Bonham

DISREGARD OF TIME KEEPING, THE.
Tracks: Disregard of timekeeping / Wait for you / Bringing me down / Guilty / Holding on forever / Dreams / Don't wake away / Playing to win / Cross me and see / Just another day / Room for us all.
■ LP 465 693 1
MC 465 693 4
■ CD 465 693 2
WTG / Nov '89.

MADHATTER.
Tracks: Bing / Madhatter / Change of a season / So good / Six in Memphis / Storm / Ride on a dream / Hairy dog trumpet / Good with the bad / Waste no time / Los locos / Chimera.
■ LP 4694551
■ CD 4694552
■ MC 4694554
Sony Music / '92.

WAIT FOR YOU.
Tracks: Wait for you / Disregard of timekeeping / Cross me and see (Only on 12″.).
■ 12″ 6560246
■ 7″ 6560247
■ CD Single 6560242
■ EP 6560240
■ MC Single 6560244
Epic / May '90.

Bonnet, Graham

FORCEFIELD III (To Oz & Back) (Bonnet, Graham/Cozy Powell/Ray Fenwick/Jan Akkerman).
Tracks: Hit and run / Always / Stay away / Desire / Tokyo / Who'll be the next in line / Wings on my feet / Firepower / Hold on / Rendezvous.
CD . . . . PCOM 1100
■ LP . . . . PTLS 1100
MC . . . . PTLC 1100
President / Oct '89 / Grapevine Distribution / Target / Jazz Music / BMG.

GOODNIGHT AND GOOD MORNING.
Tracks: Goodnight and good morning / Wino song.
■ 7″ 2017110
Ring'O / Nov '77.

HERE COMES THE NIGHT.
Tracks: Not Advised.
CD . . . . PCOM 1114
LP . . . . PTLS 1114
MC . . . . PTLC 1114

President / Jul '91 / Grapevine Distribution / Target / Jazz Music / BMG.

IT'S ALL OVER NOW BABY BLUE.
Tracks: It's all over now baby blue / Heroes on my picture wall.
■ 7″ .2017 105
Ring'O / Jun '77.

LIAR.
Tracks: Liar / Bad days are gone.
■ 7″ . . . . VER 2
Vertigo / Jun '81.

LINE-UP.
Tracks: Night games / S.O.S / I'm a lover / Be my baby / That's the way that it is / Liar / Anthony boy / Dirty hand / Out on the water / Don't stand in the open / Set me free.
■ LP .6302 151
Mercury / Nov '81.

NIGHT GAMES.
Tracks: Night games / Out on the water.
■ 7″ . . . . VER 1
Vertigo / Mar '81.

THAT'S THE WAY THAT IT IS.
Tracks: That's the way that it is / Don't tell me to go.
■ 7″ . . . . VER 4
Vertigo / Oct '81.

WARM RIDE.
Tracks: Warm ride / 10/12 observation.
■ 7″ . . . . POSP 002
Ring'O / Mar '78.

Bored

JUNK.
Tracks: Burn / Clear my attic / Rain / Kick it in / Twisted / Descender / Drift away / She witch / Junk / Don't need you / Degenerate boy / 5.30 (think about you)
CD . . . . SUR 524CD
Survival (1) / Jun '93 / Vital Distribution.

MY PAL.
Tracks: My pal.
■ 7″ . . . . MR 70018
Munster Records / Apr '92.

Boston

Tom Scholz, technology graduate and Polaroid researcher, conceived Boston in 1975. Meticulously assembled demo won deal with Epic, who released *Boston* in 1976; album became biggest-selling debut in history and spawned worldwide hit *More Than A Feeling*. Contractual dispute followed less successful *Don't Look Back*, delaying release of *Third Stage* until 1986. A surprise hit on MCA, album included U.S. chart-topper *Amanda*. In intervening years, guitarist Barry Goudreau released solo album, while Scholz invented portable guitar amplifier, Rockman - first product of his Scholz Research & Development Inc. Recent album *Walk On* was eight years in making.

AMANDA.
Tracks: My destination / Amanda.
■ 12″ . . . . .MCAS 1901
■ 7″ . . . . .MCA 1091
MCA / Jan '87.

BOSTON.
Tracks: More than a feeling / Peace of mind / Foreplay (long time) / Rock 'n' roll band / Smokin' / Hitch a ride / Something about you / Let me take you home tonight.
■ LP . . . . EPC 32038
■ MC 40 32038
Epic / Mar '81.
■ MC 40 22155
CBS / Aug '83.
CD . . . . CD 81611
Epic / Mar '87 / Sony.
MiniDisc. 81611-3
Epic / Feb '93 / Sony.

CAN'TCHA SAY (YOU BELIEVE IN ME).
Tracks: Can'tcha say (you believe in me) / Still in love / Call the engines / Launch.
■ 12″ . . . . MCAT 1150
■ 7″ . . . . .MCA 1150
■ CD Single . . . . .DMCA 1150
MCA / May '87.

DON'T LOOK BACK.
Tracks: Journey / It's easy / Man I'll never be / Feeling satisfied / Part / Used to bad news / Don't be afraid.
■ LP . . . . EPC 86057
Epic / Jun '78.
■ LP . . . . EPC 32048
■ MC. 40 32048
Epic / Jun '81.
CD . . . . CD 86057
Epic / Mar '87 / Sony.
MiniDisc. MD 86057
Epic / Apr '93 / Sony.

DON'T LOOK BACK.
Tracks: Don't look back / Journey.
■ 7" . . . . EPC 6653
Epic / Oct '78.

FEELING SATISFIED.
Tracks: Feeling satisfied / Used to.
■ 7" . . . . EPC 7295
Epic / Apr '79.

FOR REAL.
Tracks: Not Advised.
CD . . . . MCD 10973
MC. . . . . MCC 10973
MCA / May '94 / BMG.

I NEED YOUR LOVE.
Tracks: I need your love.
■ CD Single . . . . MCSTD 1983
■ MC Single . . . . MCSC 1983
MCA / Jul '94.

LONG TIME.
Tracks: Long time / Let me take you home tonight.
■ 7" . . . . EPC 5043
Epic / Mar '77.

MAN I'LL NEVER BE.
Tracks: Man I'll never be / Don't be afraid.
■ 7" . . . . EPC 6837
Epic / Jan '79.

MORE THAN A FEELING.
Tracks: More than a feeling.
■ 7" . . . . EPC 4658
Epic / Jan '77.

MORE THAN A FEELING (OLD GOLD).
Tracks: More than a feeling / Don't look back.
■ 7" . . . . OG 9299
Old Gold / May '83.

PEACE OF MIND.
Tracks: Peace of mind / Foreplay.
■ 7" . . . . EPC 5288
Epic / Jun '77.

THIRD STAGE.
Tracks: Amanda / We're ready / Launch / Cool the engines / My destination / New world / To be a man / I think I like it / Can'tcha say / Still in love / Hollyann.
■ LP .MCG 6017
■ MC . . . . MCGC 6017
MCA / Oct '86.
■ CD . . . . DMCG 6017
MCA / Jan '87.
CD . . . . MCLD 19066
■ MC. MCLC 19066
MCA / Oct '92.

Boulevard

DO YOU WANNA DO THE DANCE.
Tracks: Do you wanna do the dance / Are angels flights of fancy.
■ 7" . . . . PB 5203
RCA / Jan '80.

DREAM ON.
Tracks: Dream on.
■ 12" . . . . MCAT 1308
■ 7" . . . . MCA 1308
■ CD Single . . . . DMCA 1308
MCA / Jan '89.

MAGIC MAN.
Tracks: Magic man / Magic men.
■ 7" . . . . CHOPD 5
Chopper / Jun '79.

NEVER GIVE UP.
Tracks: Never give up / When the lights go down.
■ 12". MCAT 1326

■ 7" . . . . .MCA 1326
MCA / May '89.

Boulton, Andy

AIN'T MISBEHAVIN' (Boulton, Andy & Tokyo Blade).
Tracks: Heartbreaker / Too much too soon / Watch your step / Movie star / Hot for love / Tokyo city / Love and hate / Don't walk away / Ain't misbehavin'.
■ LP 805336
Scratch (Germany) / Feb '88.

Bow Wow

YOU'RE MINE.
Tracks: You're mine / Don't cry baby.
■ 7" .HMINT 2
Heavy Metal / Nov '83.

Boyzz

TOO WILD TO TAME.
Tracks: Too wild to tame / Hoochie koochie / Wake it up, shake it up / Shady lady / Back to Kansas / Destined to die / Lean'n'mean / Dianne / Good life shuffle.
■ LP . . . . EPC 82995
Epic / Feb '79.

Brad

20TH CENTURY.
Tracks: 20th century / Screen / 20th Century (mixes) (On CD Single only).
■ CD Single 659248 2
■ 7" 659248 7
Epic / Jun '93.

SHAME.
Tracks: Buttercup / My fingers / Nadine / Screen / 20th Century / Raise love / Bad for the soul / Down / Rockstar / We.
CD 473596 2
LP 473596 1
MC 473596 4
Epic / May '93 / Sony.

Briar

CROWN OF THORNS.
Tracks: Not Advised.
■ LP . . . . UKPAL 002
UK / Dec '87.

EDGE OF A BROKEN HEART.
Tracks: Edge of a broken heart / Don't forget me when you're on your island / Boys are back in town (on 12" only).
■ 7" P.Disc . . . . .BRIAR P1
■ 7" P.Disc . . . . .BRIAR X1
PRT / Aug '87.
■ 12" . . . . .BRIAR T1
■ 7" P.Disc . . . . .BRIAR 1
PRT / Jul '87.

FRANKIE.
Tracks: Frankie.
■ 12" . . . . UKPT 003
■ 7" . . . . UKP 003
UK / Nov '87.

ONE MONKEY DON'T STOP NO SHOW.
Tracks: One monkey don't stop no show.
■ 12" . . . . AMY 456
■ 7" . . . . AM 456
A&M / Aug '88.

ONE MORE CHANCE.
Tracks: One more chance / Feelings.
■ 7" . . . . VHF 14
FM Records / Aug '85.

TOO YOUNG.
Tracks: Not Advised.
■ LP . . . . HMRLP 41
MC. . . . . HMRMC 41
Heavy Metal / Aug '85 / Sony / FM Revolver.

Bride

GOD GAVE ROCK & ROLL TO YOU.
Tracks: God gave rock & roll to you.
12" 12KUT 156
CD Single . . . . .CDKUT 156
Music For Nations / Jan '94 / Pinnacle.

SILENCE IS MADNESS.
Tracks: Not Advised.
CD . . . . .CMGCD 002

LP .CMGLP 002
Communique / Nov '90 / Plastic Head.

SNAKES IN THE PLAYGROUND.
Tracks: Not Advised.
CD .CDMFN 156
Music For Nations / Nov '93 / Pinnacle.

Brighton Rock

BRIGHTON ROCK.
Tracks: We came to rock / Game of love / Change of heart / Can't wait for the night / Assault attack / Jack is back / Save me / Nobody's hero / Barricade / Rock 'n' roll.
■ LP . . . . K 253 055 1
■ MC. . . . . K 253 055 4
Atlantic / Feb '87.

TAKE A DEEP BREATH.
Tracks: Can't stop the earth from shakin' / Outlaw / One more try / Rebels with a cause / Whose foolin' who / Unleash the rage / High and dry / Ride the rainbow / Power overload / Love slips away.
■ CD .255969 2
■ LP . . . . WX 272
■ MC. WX 272C
WEA / May '89.

British Lions

INTERNATIONAL HEROES.
Tracks: International heroes / Eat the rich.
■ 7" 6059201
Vertigo / Apr '78.

ONE MORE CHANCE.
Tracks: One more chance / Booster.
■ 7" 6059192
Vertigo / Feb '78.

TROUBLE WITH WOMEN.
Tracks: Trouble with woman / Any port in a storm / Lady don't fall backwards / High noon / Lay down your love / Waves of love / Electric chair / Won't you give him.
■ LP . . . . ARED 7
Cherry Red / '82.

Britny Fox

BITE DOWN HARD.
Tracks: Six guns loaded / Louder / Liar / Closer to your love / Over and out / Shot from my gun / Black and white / Look my way / Lonely too long / Midnight moses.
■ LP 7567917902
■ LP 7567917901
MC. 7567917904
East West / Nov '91 / WEA.

BOYS IN HEAT.
Tracks: In motion / Standing in the shadows / Hair of the dog / Livin' on a dream / She's so lonely / Dream on / Long way from home / Plenty of love / Stevie / Shine on / Angel in my heart / Left me / Stray / Long road.
CD. 4659542
■ LP 4659541
MC. 4659544
CBS / Dec '89 / Sony.

BRITNY FOX.
Tracks: Girlschool / Long way to love / Kick'n'fight / Save the weak / Fun in Texas / Rocky revolution / Don't hide / Gudbuy t'Jane / In America / Hold on.
CD. 4611112
■ LP 4611111
■ MC. 4611114
CBS / Sep '88.

GIRLSCHOOL.
Tracks: Girlschool / Kick and fight / Fun in Texas (Only on 12" version and CD single.).
■ 12". 6531446
■ 7" 6531447
■ CD Single 6531442
CBS / Oct '88.
■ 7" 6531440
CBS / Oct '88.

LONG WAY TO LOVE.
Tracks: Long way to love / Living on the edge / Long way to love (full length version) (12" only.) / Save the weak (12" only.).
■ 12". 6530186
■ 7" 6530187
■ 7" P.Disc 6530180
CBS / Oct '88.

STANDING IN THE SHADOWS.
Tracks: Standing in the shadows / Livin' on the edge / Girlschool (Not on 7") / Long way to love (Not on 7").
■ 12" 6554998
■ 7" 6554997
■ CD Single 6554992
CBS / Dec '89.

YEAR OF THE FOX.
Tracks: Not Advised.
VHS 490152
CMV Enterprises (Video) / Oct '89 / Sony.

Brock, Dave

AGENT OF CHAOS (Brock, Dave & The Agent Of Chaos).
Tracks: Not Advised.
CD . . . . SHARP 042CD
MC . . . . CSHARP 042
■ LP . . . . SHARP 042
Flicknife / Apr '88.

DAVE BROCK & THE AGENTS OF CHAOS (Brock, Dave & Agents Of Chaos).
Tracks: Not Advised.
■ LP . . . . SHARP 1842
Flicknife / Apr '89.

EARTHED TO THE GROUND.
Tracks: Earthed to the ground / Assassination / Green finned demon / Spirits / Sweet obsession / Oscillations / Machine dream / Now is the winter of our discontent / On the case.
■ LP . . . . SHARP 018
Flicknife / Apr '86.

SOCIAL ALLIANCE.
Tracks: Social alliance / Raping robots in the street.
■ 7" . . . . FLS 024
■ 7" P.Disc . . . . FLS 024P
Flicknife / Sep '83.

Broken Bones

BRAIN DEAD.
Tracks: Not Advised.
CD . . . . CDJUST 19
LP . . . . JUST 19
Rough Justice / Oct '92 / Pinnacle.

CRUCIFIX.
Tracks: Crucifix.
■ 7" . . . . FALL 025
Fall Out / '84.

DEATH IS IMMINENT.
Tracks: Not Advised.
CD . . . . .CLEO 93092
Jungle / Dec '93 / RTM / Pinnacle.

DECAPITATED.
Tracks: Not Advised.
■ LP . . . . FALL LP 043
■ LP P.Disc . . . . FALL LP 043P
Fall Out / Aug '87.

DECAPITATED.
Tracks: Decapitated.
■ 7" . . . . FALL 020
Scarlet / Jan '84.

DEM BONES.
Tracks: Not Advised.
■ LP . . . . FALL LP 028
■ LP P.Disc . . . . FALL LP 028P
Fall Out / Jul '84.
CD . . . . FALL CD 028
Fall Out / Dec '90 / RTM / Pinnacle.

F.O.A.D.
Tracks: FOAD / Kick down the doors / Teenage kamikaze / Programme control / SOTO / Missing link / Best of both worlds / Never say die / Decapitated (Part 1) / Problems / Secret agent / Liquidated brains / Gotta get out of here / I O U nothing / Seeing through my eyes / Anihilation No.3 / Decapitated (Part 2).
■ LP . . . . FALL LP 041
Fall Out / Feb '87.

F.O.A.D./BONECRUSHER.
Tracks: Not Advised.
CD . . . . FALLCD 041
Fall Out / May '93 / RTM / Pinnacle.

LIVE AT LEEDS.
Tracks: Fight the good fight / Who's to blame / Crucifix / Decapitated / City fodder / Big hard man /

Stand up / Problem / Wealth rules / Anihilation No.3 / Civil war / I.O.U.
VHS . . . . JE 129
Jettisoundz / Oct '84 / TBD / Visionary Communications.

LOSING CONTROL.
Tracks: Killing fields / Nowhere to run / Jump / Going down / Shutdown / Brain dead / Life's to fast / Bitching / Mercy / Maniac / Lesson.
■ LP . . . . HMRLP 133
■ CD . . . . HMRXD 133
■ MC . . . . HMRMC 133
Heavy Metal / Aug '89.
■ LP . . . . HMR LP 133
FM Records / Oct '92.

NEVER SAY DIE.
Tracks: Never say die.
■ 12" . . . . FALL 12039
Fall Out / Jul '86.

RELIGION IS RESPONSIBLE.
Tracks: Religion is responsible.
■ 12" 12HM 56
■ CD Single . . . . HEAVYXD 56
Heavy Metal / May '90.

SEEING THROUGH MY EYES.
Tracks: Seeing through my eyes.
■ 10" . . . . FALL 10034
■ 7" . . . . FALL 034
■ 7" P.Disc . . . . FALL 034P
Fall Out / Jan '85.

STITCHED UP.
Tracks: Not Advised.
CD . . . . CDJUST 18
LP . . . . JUST 18
MC . . . . TJUST 18
Music For Nations / Oct '91 / Pinnacle.

TRADER IN DEATH.
Tracks: Traders in death / Money, pleasure & pain / Whos care's about the cost / Stabbed in the back (still bleeding) / Booze for free / Crack attack / Trader in death / Blue lie blue life.
■ CD . . . . HMRCD 141
■ LP . . . . HMRLP 141
■ MC . . . . HMRMC 141
Heavy Metal / Mar '90.

TRADER IN DEATH.
Tracks: Trader in death.
■ 12" . . . . RFBSIN 4
RFB Recordings / Jun '87.

Broken Homes

SOMETHING'S GOTTA GIVE.
Tracks: Something's gotta give.
■ 12" . . . . MCAT 1450
■ 7" . . . . MCA 1450
MCA / Jan '91.

WING AND A PRAYER.
Tracks: Not Advised.
■ CD . . . . DMCG 6109
■ LP . . . . MCG 6109
■ MC . . . . MCGC 6109
MCA / Sep '90.

Bronz

SEND DOWN AN ANGEL.
Tracks: Send down an angel / Tiger / Stranded.
■ 12" . . . . BROX 183
■ 7" . . . . BRO 183
Bronze / Aug '84.

TAKEN BY STORM.
Tracks: Send down an angel / Heat of the night / Cold truth / Night runner / Taken by storm / Don't ever wanna lose ya / Sweet lady / Harder than diamond / Tiger / Loneliness is mine.
■ LP . . . . BRON 547
Bronze / Mar '84.

Bruce, Jack

Scottish born bassist, Jack Bruce played in Alexis Corner's Blues Incorporated, the Graham Bond Organisation, John Mayall's Bluesbreakers and Manfred Mann, befoe joining Eric Clapton and Ginger Baker in the legendary Cream. Bruce co-wrote their 1967 hit I Feel Free. Cream disbanded in 1969 and he joined short-lived supergroup Blind Faith. Later that year, recorded Songs For A Tailor LP. During the 1970's, he continued in the blues-rock vein, working with

Graham Bond, Chris Spedding, Dick Heckstall-Smith, John McLaughlin and Tony Williams. Recorded Harmony Row and Things We Like LPs. Also recorded with Robin Trower in B.L.T. in the early 1980's. In 1994, Jack Bruce joined Gary Moore and Ginger Baker to form BBM, releasing the hit album, Around The Next Dream.

AUTOMATIC.
Tracks: Make love (Part II) / Uptown breakdown / Travelling child / New World / E. Boogie / Green and blue / Swarm / Encore / Automatic pilot.
■ LP . . . . PTLS 1082
MC . . . . PTLC 1082
President / Jan '87 / Grapevine Distribution / Target / Jazz Music / BMG.

CITIES OF THE HEART.
Tracks: Can you follow / Running thro' our hands / Over the cliff / Statues / First time I met the blues / Smiles & grins / Bird alone / Neighbor, neighbor / Born under a bad sign / Ships in the night / Never tell your Mother she's out of tune / Theme from an imaginary western / Golden days / Life on earth / NSU / Sitting on top of the world / Politician / Spoonful / Sunshine of your love.
CD . . . . CMPCD 1004
MC . . . . .CMP 1004 CS
CMP / Feb '94 / Cadillac / New Note / Vital Distribution.
CD Set . . . . CMPCD 1005
CMP / Jul '94 / Cadillac / New Note / Vital Distribution.

COLLECTION: JACK BRUCE.
Tracks: Not Advised.
CD . . . . CCSCD 326
■ MC . . . . CCSMC 326
Castle Collector Series / Feb '92.

GREATEST HITS: JACK BRUCE.
Tracks: Not Advised.
■ Double LP 2658 137
MC Set 3524 218
Polydor / Nov '80 / PolyGram.

HOW'S TRICKS (Bruce, Jack Band).
Tracks: Not Advised.
■ LP .2394 180
RSO / Feb '77.

I FEEL FREE.
Tracks: I feel free / Make love.
■ 7" . . . . .VS 875
■ 12" . . . . VS 875-12
Virgin / Jun '86.

I'VE ALWAYS WANTED TO DO THIS.
Tracks: Hit and run / Running back / Facelift 318 / In this way / Mickey the fiddler / Dancing on air / Wind and the sea / Living without you / Out to lunch / Bird alone.
MC .40 84672
Epic / Dec '80 / Sony.
■ LP . . . . EPC 84672
Epic / Jan '81.

LIVE AT BOTTOM LINE (Bruce, Jack & friends).
Tracks: Not Advised.
CD . . . . TL 1324
Traditional Line / Nov '92 / Charly / A.D.A. Distribution / Koch International.

QUESTION OF TIME, A.
Tracks: Life on earth / Make love / No surrender / Flying / Hey now princess / Blues you can't lose / Obsession / Kwela / Let me be / Only playing games / Question of time.
■ LP 4656921
MC 4656924
Epic / Jan '90 / Sony.
CD 4656922
Epic / Jan '90 / Sony.

SONGS FOR A TAILOR.
Tracks: Never tell your mother / She's out of tune / Theme of an imaginary western / Tickets to water falls / Weird of Hermiston / Rope ladder to the moon / Ministry of bag / He the Richmond / Boston ball game, 1967 / To Isengard / Clearout.
■ LP 583-058
Polydor / Sep '69.
■ CD 835 242-2
Polydor / May '88.

TRUCE (Bruce, Jack & Robin Trower).
Tracks: Gonna shut you down / Gone too far / Thin ice / Last train to the stars / Take good care of yourself / Falling in love / Fat gut / Shadows touching / Little boy lost.
■ LP . . . . CHR 1352
■ MC . . . . ZCHR 1352

■ DELETED

Chrysalis / Jan '82.
CD S21 17609
One Way Records / May '94 / Topic Records / Direct Distribution.

WILLPOWER.
Tracks: Not Advised.
CD 837 806-2
■ LP 837 806-1
■ MC. 837 806-4
Polydor / May '89.

Brujeria

MATANDO GUEROS.
Tracks: Para de Venta / Leyes narcos / Sacrificio / Santa Lucia / Matando Gueros / Seis seis seis / Cruza la Frontera / Grenudos Locos / Chingo de Mecos / Narcos-Satanicos / Desperado / Culeros / Misas Negras (sacrificio III) / Chinga tu Madre / Verga del Brujo/Estan Chingados / Molestando Ninos Muertos / Machetazos (sacrificio II) / Castigo del Brujo / Christa de la Roca.
CD . . . . CD RR 9061 2
LP . . . . LP RR 9061 1
Road Runner / Jun '93 / Pinnacle.

Brutal Obscenity

DREAM OUT LOUD.
Tracks: Not Advised.
CD . . . . PROPH 3-2CD
LP . . . . PROPH 3-1
Prophecy (Semaphore) / Jul '90.

IT'S BECAUSE OF THE BIRDS AND THE FLOWERS.
Tracks: Death is a damn good solution / Straight and stoned / Mom or dad / 1,2,3 / God is just a fairy tale / No more feelings left / Overtaking / It's because of the birds and the flowers / Emotion suicide / It's cruel (part 2) / Useless immortality / Defensor minor / Hangover D.D.D.
CD . . . . CMFT 2CD
■ LP . . . . CMFT 2
CMFT / Jun '89.

SORRY BOYS AND GIRLS.
Tracks: Not Advised.
LP . . . . CCG 001
C.C.G. Underground / Jan '90 / Backs Distribution.

Brutal Truth

EXTREME CONDITIONS..
Tracks: Not Advised.
LP . . . . MOSH 069
MC. . . . . .MOSH 069MC
Earache / Sep '92 / Vital Distribution.
CD .MOSH 069CD
Earache / Sep '94 / Vital Distribution.

ILL NEGLECT.
Tracks: Ill neglect.
■ 7" . . . . 7 MOSH 080
Earache / Aug '92.

PERPETUAL CONVERSION.
Tracks: Perpetual conversion / Perpetual larceny / Walking corpse / Lord of this world / Bedsheet.
■ 12" . . . . .MOSH 084T
■ 7" . . . . 7 MOSH 084
■ CD Single . . . . MOSH 084 CD
Earache / Mar '93.

Brutality

SCREAMS OF ANGUISH.
Tracks: Not Advised.
CD .NB 075CD
LP . . . . NB 075
Nuclear Blast / Jul '93 / Plastic Head.

Budgie

Hard rock trio from Wales initially comprising Pete Boot, Tony Bourge and Burke Shelley, was formed in 1968. Released epoymous debut LP in 1971. Fourth album, In For The Kill (1974) was biggest seller reaching No. 29 on the UK album chart. 19/5's Bandolier was also an album chart hit. Night Flight in 1982, yielded a top 20 chart single with Keeping A Rendez-Vous. Budgie had many changes in personnel, nevertheless they continued to record and tour building a small but loyal following. The band finally disintegrated in 1983.

BANDOLIER.
Tracks: Not Advised.
■ LP .MCF 2723

MCA / Sep '75.
■ LP . . . . MCL 1795
MCA / Jul '84.
CD . . . . REP 4100-WZ
LP . . . . REP 2100
MC. REP 2100-TS
Repertoire (Germany) / Aug '91 / Pinnacle.

BEST OF BUDGIE.
Tracks: Breadfan / I ain't no mountain / I can't see my feelings / Baby please don't go / Zoom club / Breaking all the house rules / Parents / In for the kill / In the grip of a tyre-fitter's hand.
■ LP . . . . MCL 1637
■ MC. . . . . MCLC 1637
MCA / Feb '82.
■ CD . . . . DMCL 1637
MCA / Aug '89.
CD . . . . MCLD 19067
■ MC. . . . . MCLC 19067
MCA / Oct '92.

BORED WITH RUSSIA.
Tracks: Bored with Russia / Don't cry.
■ 7" .RCA 271
RCA / Sep '82.

BUDGIE.
Tracks: Not Advised.
CD . . . . REP 4012-WZ
LP . . . . REP 2012
MC. REP 2012-TS
Repertoire (Germany) / Aug '91 / Pinnacle.

CRIME AGAINST THE WORLD.
Tracks: Crime against the world / Hellbender.
■ 7" . . . . BUDGE 2
Active / Nov '80.

DELIVER US FROM EVIL.
Tracks: Bored with Russia / Don't cry / Truth drug / Young girl / Flowers in the attic / N.O.R.A.D.(domesday city) / Give me the truth / Alison / Finger on the button / Hold on to love.
■ LP . . . . RCALP 6054
■ MC. . . . . RCAK 6054
RCA / Oct '82.

I AIN'T NO MOUNTAIN.
Tracks: I ain't no mountain / Honey.
■ 7" . . . . MCA 175
MCA / Feb '75.

I TURNED TO STONE.
Tracks: I turned to stone.
■ 7" . . . . BUDGE 4
Active / Jul '81.

IN FOR THE KILL.
Tracks: Not Advised.
■ LP . . . . MCF 2546
MCA / Jun '74.
CD . . . . REP 4027-WZ
LP . . . . REP 2027
MC. REP 2027-TS
Repertoire (Germany) / Aug '91 / Pinnacle.

KEEPING A RENDEZVOUS.
Tracks: Keeping a rendezvous.
■ 7" . . . . BUDGE 3
Active / Oct '81.

NEVER TURN BACK.
Tracks: Breadfan / Baby please don't go / You're the biggest thing since powdered milk / You know I'll always love you / In the grip of a tyre-fitter's hand / Riding my nightmare / Parents / Apparatus / Superstar / Change your ways / Untitled lullaby.
■ LP . . . . MCL 1855
■ MC. . . . . MCLC 1855
MCA / Jun '87.

NEVER TURN YOUR BACK ON A FRIEND.
Tracks: Not Advised.
CD . . . . REP 4013-WZ
Repertoire (Germany) / Aug '91 / Pinnacle.

NIGHT FLIGHT.
Tracks: I turned to stone / Keeping a rendezvous / Reaper of glory / She used me up / Don't lay down and die / Apparatus / Superstar / Change your ways / Untitled lullaby.
■ LP . . . . RCALP 6003
■ MC. . . . . RCAK 6003
RCA / Oct '81.

POWER SUPPLY.
Tracks: Forearm smash / Hellbender / Heavy revolution / Gunslinger / Power supply / Secrets in my head / Time to remember / Crimes against the world.
■ LP . . . . ACTLP 1
Active / Nov '80.

■ LP . . . . RCALP 3046
■ MC. . . . . RCAK 3046
RCA / Sep '81.

SMILE BOY SMILE.
Tracks: Smile boy smile / All at sea.
■ 7" . . . . .AMS 7342
A&M / Mar '78.

SQUAWK.
Tracks: Whiskey river / Rocking man / Rolling home again / Make me happy / Hot as a docker's armpit / Drugstore woman / Bottled / Young is a world / Stranded.
■ LP . . . . MKPS 2023
MCA / Sep '72.
■ CD . . . . DMCL 1901
MCA / May '90.
CD . . . . REP 4026-WZ
LP . . . . REP 2026
MC. REP 2026-TS
Repertoire (Germany) / Aug '91 / Pinnacle.

WILD FIRE.
Tracks: Wild fire / High school girls / Panzer Division destroyed / Lies of Jim.
■ 7" . . . . BUDGE 1
Active / Jun '80.

Buffalo

BATTLE TORN HEROES.
Tracks: Battle torn heroes / Women of the night.
■ 7" . . . . HEAVY 3
Heavy Metal / Sep '81.

DEAD FOREVER.
Tracks: Not Advised.
CD . . . . REP 4141-WP
LP . . . . REP 2141
MC. REP 2141-SX
Repertoire (Germany) / Aug '91 / Pinnacle.

MEAN MACHINE.
Tracks: Mean machine / Rumour.
■ 7" . . . . .HEAVY 15
Heavy Metal / Nov '82.

Bulldozer

DAY OF WRATH.
Tracks: Not Advised.
■ LP .RR 9779
Road Runner / Jun '85.

FINAL SEPARATION, THE.
Tracks: Final separation / Ride hard,die fast / Cave / Sex symbol's bullshit / Don Andras / Never relax / Don't trust the saint / Death of the gods.
■ LP .RR 9711
Road Runner / Jul '86.

IX.
Tracks: Not Advised.
■ LP . . . . .SHARK 10
Shark / Apr '89.

Bullet LaVolta

DEAD WRONG.
Tracks: Not Advised.
■ LP . . . . FH 12012
Funhouse / Sep '89.
LP . . . . TAANG 22LP
Taang / Nov '92 / Plastic Head.

EVERY HUNGRY RABBIT.
Tracks: Every hungry rabbit.
■ 7" . . . . EFA 08125
Glitterhouse / Feb '91.

GIFT, THE.
Tracks: Not Advised.
■ LP . . . . .EM 9449 1
Emergo / '89.
CD . . . . .TAANG 29CD
Taang / Nov '92 / Plastic Head.

TAANG.
Tracks: Not Advised.
CD .T 029CD
Taang / Apr '89 / Plastic Head.

Bulletboys

BULLET BOYS.
Tracks: Hard as a rock / Smooth up in ya / Owed to Joe / Shoot the preacher down / For the love of money / Kissin' kitty / Hell on my heels / Crank me up / Badlands / F[8]X9.
CD 9257822
■ LP . . . . WX 213

■ DELETED

MC. .... **WX 213C**
WEA / Sep '88 / WEA.

FREAKSHOW.
Tracks: Hell yeah / Groove / Thrill that kills / Hang on
St. Christopher / Talk to your daughter / Freakshow /
Goodgirl / Do me raw / Ripping me / Say your
prayers / O me O my / Huge.
CD. 7599261682
■ LP 7599261681
MC. 7599261684
WEA / Apr '91 / WEA.

PIGS IN THE MUD.
Tracks: Not Advised.
VHS 7599382173
Warner Music Video / Oct '92 / WEA.

SMOOTH UP.
Tracks: Smooth up / Badlands.
■ 7" .... W 2876
WEA / Sep '89.

ZA-ZA.
Tracks: When pigs fly / Slow and easy / Rising / Sing
a song / Mine / 1-800-Goodbye / Show / For the
damned / Laughing with the dead / Fess / Crosstop.
CD. 9362450952
MC. 9362450954
Warner Bros. / Jun '93 / WEA.

Bullett

HANGED MAN.
Tracks: Hanged man / Contract man.
■ 7" 2058548
Polydor / Feb '75.

NO MERCY.
Tracks: Not Advised.
■ LP .... HMILP 15
Heavy Metal / Mar '84.

Burning Tree

BURNING TREE.
Tracks: Burning tree / Wigs, blues and high heeled
shoes / Fly on / Bakers song / Playing in the wind /
Masquerade / Crush / Last laugh / Mistreated lover /
Turtle.
MC. 4666334
■ CD 4666332
■ LP 4666331
Epic / Apr '90.

FLY ON.
Tracks: Fly on / Turtle (Available on 12" format only.)
/ Burning tree (live).
■ 12" 6563306
■ 7" 6563307
■ MC Single. 6563004
Epic / Oct '90.

Burtnick, Glenn

FOLLOW YOU.
Tracks: Follow you / Walls come down / Abalene (On
12" only).
■ 12" .... AMY 421
■ 7" .... AM 421
A&M / Dec '87.

HEARD IT ON THE RADIO.
Tracks: Heard it on the radio / Walls came down.
■ 12" .... AMY 437

HEROES AND ZEROS.
Tracks: Follow you / Spinning my wheel / Walls
came down / Stupid boys (suckers for love) / Love
goes on / Heard it on the radio / Abalene / Here
comes Sally / Scattered / Day your ship gets thru.
■ LP .... AMA 5166
■ MC. .... AMC 5166
A&M / Mar '88.

Burzum

HVIS LYSET TAR OSS.
Tracks: Not Advised.
CD. .... AMAZON 001
LP .... AMAZON 001LP
Misanthropy / Aug '94 / Plastic Head.

Bush, Stan

DIAL 818 888 8638.
Tracks: I got it bad for you / One kiss away / Total
surrender / Come to me / Hold you head up high /
Are you over me / Come on / In the name of love /
Hero of the heart / Take this heart / Take my love.
CD. .... CDVEST 7
Bulletproof / Mar '94 / Pinnacle.

**STAN BUSH AND BARRAGE (Bush, Stan
& Barrage).**
Tracks: Temptation / Primitive lover / Crank that
radio / Do you remember / Touch / Love don't lie /
Heart vs head / Gates of paradise / Take it like a
man / What is love.
■ LP .... INT 147318
Scotti Bros (USA) / Nov '87.
■ CD 832 787-2
■ LP 832 787-1
■ MC. 832 787-4
Polydor / Feb '88.

TOUCH, THE.
Tracks: Dare to be stupid / Touch.
■ 7" .... A 7318
Epic / Nov '86.

Butthole Surfers

BLIND EYE SEES ALL.
Tracks: Not Advised.
VHS .... TGV 1
Touch & Go / SRD.

BROWN REASONS TO LIVE.
Tracks: Not Advised.
LP .... VIRUS 32
Alternative Tentacles / Sep '93 / RTM / Pinnacle.

BUTTHOLE SURFERS.
Tracks: Not Advised.
■ LP .... VIRUS 32
Alternative Tentacles / Apr '84.

**CREAMED CORN FROM THE SOCKET
OF DAVIS EP.**
Tracks: Not Advised.
■ 12" .... PRAY 069
Fundamental / Oct '85.

HAIRWAY TO STEVEN.
Tracks: Not Advised.
CD. .... BFFP 29CD

■ LP .... BFFP 29
MC. .... BFFP 29C
Blast First / Feb '88 / RTM / Pinnacle.

HURDY GURDY MAN.
Tracks: Hurdy gurdy man / Barking dogs.
■ 7" .... RT 240
■ 12" .... RTT 240
■ CD Single .... RTT 240CD
Rough Trade / Sep '90.

INDEPENDENT WORM SALOON.
Tracks: Who was in my room last night / Wooden
song / Tongue / Chewin' George Lucas' chocolate /
Goofy's concern / Alcohol / Dog inside your body /
Strawberry / Some dispute over T-shirt sales / Danc-
ing fool / You don't know me / Annoying song / Dust
devil / Leave me alone / Edgar / Ballad of naked
men / Clean it up.
CD. .... CDEST 2192
■ LP .... EST 2192
■ MC. .... TCEST 2192
Capitol / Mar '93.

LIVE POP EP.
Tracks: Not Advised.
■ EP .... VIRUS 39
Alternative Tentacles / Jan '85.

LOCUST ABORTION TECHNICIAN.
Tracks: Sweat loaf / Graveyard (1) / Graveyard (2) /
Pittsburgh to Lebanon / Weber / Hay / Human can-
nonball / USSA / O-men / Kuntz / 22 going on 23.
CD. .... BFFP 15CD
■ LP .... BFFP 15
MC. .... BFFP 15C
Blast First / Jun '87 / RTM / Pinnacle.

PIOUHGD.
Tracks: Not Advised.
CD. .... R 20812602
LP .... R 20812601
MC. .... R 20812604
Hough Trade / Jun '91 / Pinnacle.

**PSYCHIC POWERLESS ANOTHER MANS
SAC.**
Tracks: Not Advised.
■ LP .... SAVE 005
Fundamental / Jul '85.
CD. .... SAVE 005CD
Fundamental / '88 / Plastic Head.

REMBRANDT PUSSYHORSE.
Tracks: Creep in the cellar / Sea ferring / American
woman / Waiting for Jimmy to kick / Strangersdie /
Perry / Whirling hall of knives / Mark says alright / In
the cellar.
■ LP .... RRELP 2
Red Rhino (Europe) / Apr '86.
CD. .... RRECD 2
Red Rhino (Europe) / May '88.

WIDOWERMAKER.
Tracks: Booze tobacco / Bong song / 1401 /
Helicopter.
■ 10" .... BFFP 41T
■ 12" .... BFFP 41
■ CD Single .... BFFP 41CD
Blast First / Jul '89.

C

C.I.A.

ATTITUDE.
Tracks: Not Advised.
CD .CDFLAG 68
LP . . . . .FLAG 68
Under One Flag / Jul '91 / Pinnacle.

IN THE RED.
Tracks: Extinction / In the red / N.A.S.A. / Flight 103 / Turn to stone / Natas / Buried alive / Mind over matter / Moby Dick (part 2) / Camantha.
CD . . . . CD FLAG 40
LP .FLAG 40
MC . . . . TFLAG 40
Music For Nations / May '90 / Pinnacle.

Cable Regime

ASSIMILATE AND DESTROY.
Tracks: Not Advised.
CD .PPP 110
PDCD / Sep '93 / SRD / Plastic Head.

KILL LIES ALL.
Tracks: Not Advised.
CD . . . . .STC 17CD
Sentrax Corporation / Aug '94 / Plastic Head.

LIFE IN THE HOUSE.
Tracks: Not Advised.
CD .PPP 108
PDCD / Sep '93 / SRD / Plastic Head.

LIFE IN THE HOUSE OF THE ENEMY.
Tracks: Not Advised.
CD . . . . CDPPP 108
Headdirt / Nov '92 / SRD.

Cacophony

GO OFF.
Tracks: X-ray eyes / Stranger / Black cat / Floating world / E.S.P. / Go off / Sword of the warrior / Images.
CD . . . . RR 94992
LP . . . . RR 94991
■ MC . . . . RR 94994
Road Runner / Feb '91.

SPEED METAL SYMPHONY.
Tracks: Not Advised.
CD . . . . RR 349577
■ LP . . . . RR 95771
■ MC . . . . RR 95774
Road Runner / Feb '91.

Cadaver

HALLUCINATING ANXIETY.
Tracks: Not Advised.
CD . . . . NECRO 4 CD
LP . . . . NECRO 4
MC . . . . .NECRO 4 MC
Necrosis / Dec '90 / Vital Distribution.

IN PAINS.
Tracks: Not Advised.
CD . . . . MOSH 071 CD
■ LP . . . . MOSH 071
■ MC . . . . MOSH 071 MC
Earache / Oct '92.

Cadaverous Condition

IN MELANCHOLY.
Tracks: Not Advised.
CD .LRC 008
Lethal / Feb '94 / Plastic Head.

Cancerous Growth

HMMLMMLUM.
Tracks: Something's here / One side / Cohata can you do / Diabolica fx / Youth of when / Prey for the weak / Black doomy theme / Satan's stupid / Von scenemaster.
LP . . . . NB 005
Nuclear Blast / Nov '88 / Plastic Head.

LATE FOR THE GRAVE.
Tracks: No chance / Stupid people / Decide / Be yourself / Something I don't need / Sick of it / Revolution / Keep my peace.
■ LP . . . . NB 004
Nuclear Blast / Nov '88.

Candlebox

CANDLEBOX.
Tracks: Don't you / Change / You / No sense / Far behind / Blossom / Arrow / Rain / Mothers dream / Cover me / He calls home.
CD 9362453132
MC 9362453134
Warner Bros. / Jul '93 / WEA.

FAR BEHIND.
Tracks: Far behind / You / Far behind (Live) (On CDs only.).
7" . . . . W 0258
CD Single . . . . .W 0258CD
MC Single . . . . .W 0258C
Warner Bros. / Aug '94 / WEA.

Candlemass

ANCIENT DREAMS.
Tracks: Not Advised.
■ LP . . . . ACTLP 7
Active / '88.
CD . . . . CDATV 7
Active / Feb '90 / Pinnacle.
CD . . . . ACTCD 7
Active / Jul '92 / Pinnacle.

AS IT IS, AS IT WAS (The Best Of Candlemass).
Tracks: Solitude / Bewitched / Dying illusion / Demon's gate / Mirror mirror (live) / Samarithan / Into the unfathomed tower / Bearer of pain / Where the runes still speak / At the gallows end / Mourner's lament / Tale of creation / Ebony throne / Under the oak / Well of souls (live) / Dark are the veils of death / Darkness in paradise / End of pain / Sorcerer's pleadge / Solitude '87 / Cyrstal ball '87 / Bullfest '93.
CD . . . . .CDMFN 166
Music For Nations / Oct '94 / Pinnacle.

CANDLEMASS LIVE IN STOCKHOLM 9TH JUNE 1990.
Tracks: Well of souls / Bewitched / Dark reflections / Demons gate / Through the infinitive halls of death / Mirror, mirror / Sorceror's pledge / Dark are the veils / Solitude / Under the oak / Bells of Acheron / Samaritan / Gallow's end.
CD . . . . .CDMFN 109
MC . . . . .TMFN 109
■ LP . . . . MFN 109
Music For Nations / Nov '90.

CHAPTER SIX.
Tracks: Not Advised.
CD . . . . .CDMFN 128
LP . . . . MFN 128
MC . . . . .TMFN 128
Music For Nations / May '92 / Pinnacle.

EPICUS DOOMICUS METALLICA.
Tracks: Not Advised.
CD . . . . .BDCD 013
Black Dragon / Jun '88.

NIGHTFALL.
Tracks: Not Advised.
■ CD . . . . .AXISCD 3
Active / Jun '88.
LP .ATV 3
Active / Jun '88 / Pinnacle.

SAMARITHAN.
Tracks: Samarithan / Solitude.
■ 12" 12AX 1
■ 7" 7AX 1
Axis / Mar '88.

TALES OF CREATION.
Tracks: Not Advised.
■ LP P.Disc . . . . MFN 95P
Music For Nations / Nov '89.
CD . . . . .MFNCD 95
■ LP . . . . MFN 95

MC . . . . MFNT 95
Music For Nations / Sep '89 / Pinnacle.

Cannibal Corpse

BLEEDING.
Tracks: Staring through the eyes of the dead / Fucked with a knife / Stripped, raped and strangled / Pulverized / Return to flesh / Pick-axe murders / She was asking for it / Bleeding / Force fed broken glass / An experiment in homicide.
CD . . . . .CDZORRO 67
LP . . . . ZORRO 67
MC . . . . .TZORRO 67
Metal Blade / Mar '94 / Pinnacle.

BUTCHERED AT BIRTH.
Tracks: Not Advised.
CD . . . . .CDZORRO 26
LP . . . . ZORRO 26
MC . . . . .TZORRO 26
Metal Blade / Aug '91 / Pinnacle.

EATEN BACK TO LIFE.
Tracks: Shredded humans / Put them to death / Scattered remains, splattered brains / Rotting head / Bloody chunks / Buried in the backyard / Edible autopsy / Mangled / Born in a casket / Undead will feast / Skull full of maggots.
CD . . . . .CDZORRO 12
LP . . . . ZORRO 12
MC . . . . .TZORRO 12
Metal Blade / Sep '90 / Pinnacle.

HAMMER SMASHED FACE.
Tracks: Hammer smashed face / Exorcist / Zero the hero / Meat hook sodomy / Shredded humans.
CD . . . . .CDMZORRO 57
LP . . . . MZORRO 57
Metal Blade / Apr '93 / Pinnacle.

TOMB OF THE MUTILATED.
Tracks: Not Advised.
CD . . . . .CDZORRO 49
LP . . . . ZORRO 49
MC . . . . .TZORRO 49
Zorro / Sep '92 / Pinnacle.

Captain Beyond

CAPTAIN BEYOND.
Tracks: Dancing madly backwards / Armworth / Myopic void / Mesmerization eclipse / Raging river of fear / Thousand days of yesterday / Frozen over / I can't feel nothin' / As the moon speaks / Astral Lady.
■ LP . . . . K 47503
Warner / Jul '72.

Carbonized

DISHARMONIZATION.
Tracks: Not Advised.
CD . . . . FDN 2006
Foundation 2000 / Sep '93 / Plastic Head.

NO CANNONIZATION.
Tracks: No cannonization.
■ 7" . . . . .THR 003
Thrash / Nov '92.

Carcass

Death metal band that has grown from a Napalm Death side-project (formed by Death guitarist Bill Steer in 1985) into a fully fledged, major-label force to be reckoned with. Early recordings with a nice line in tongue-in-cheek gore-ridden lyrics were issued via Earache whilst Steer continued to lead a double life by continuing with his original band - even touring with them to promote 1989's *Symphonies Of Sickness* on the now legendary Gods Of Grind Tour! Eventually he opted for Carcass full-time and brought the Liverpool based quartet to a new peak on the wonderfully tribal *Necrotism: Descanting The Insalubrious* and thence closer to the mainstream and a deal with Columbia Records almost unprecedented in death metal circles.

■ DELETED

HEARTWORK.
Tracks: Buried dreams / Carnal fudge / No love lost / Heartwork / Embodiment / This mortal coil / Albeit macht fleisch / Blind bleeding the blind / Doctrinal expletives / Death certificate.
LP . . . . MOSH 097
MC. .MOSH 097MC
Earache / Oct '93 / Vital Distribution.
CD . . . . .MOSH 097CD
Earache / Sep '94 / Vital Distribution.

HEARTWORK.
Tracks: Heartwork / This is your life / Rot 'n' roll.
12". . . . . .MOSH 108T
CD Single. . . . . .MOSH 108CD
Earache / Jan '94 / Vital Distribution.

NECROTICISM-DESCANTING THE INSALUBRIOUS.
Tracks: Inpropgation / Corporeal jigsore quandary / Symposium of sickness / Pedigree butchery / Incarnated solvent abuse / Carneous cacoffin / Lavaging expectorate of Lysergide composition / Forensic clinicism - The Sanguine article.
LP . . . . MOSH 042L
LP . . . . MOSH 042
MC. .MOSH 042MC
Earache / Oct '91 / Vital Distribution.
CD . . . . MOSH 042CD
Earache / Sep '94 / Vital Distribution.

PEEL SESSIONS: CARCASS.
Tracks: Not Advised.
■ 12" . . . . SFPS 073
Strange Fruit / '89.

REEK OF PUTRIFICATION.
Tracks: Genital grinder / Regurgitation of giblets / Pyosisisified / Carbonized eye-sockets / Frenzied detruncation / Vomited anal tract / Festerday / Fermenting innards / Excreted alive / Suppuration / Foeticide / Microwaved uterogestation / Splattered cavities / Psychopathologist / Burnt to a crisp / Pungent excruciation / Manifestation of verrucose urethra / Oxidised razor masticator / Malignant defecation.
■ LP . . . . MOSH 006
Earache / Jun '88.
MC. .MOSH 006MC
Earache / Jan '90 / Vital Distribution.
CD . . . . MOSH 006CD
Earache / Sep '94 / Vital Distribution.

SYMPHONIES OF SICKNESS.
Tracks: Not Advised.
■ LP . . . . MOSH 018
MC. .MOSH 018MC
Earache / Nov '89 / Vital Distribution.
■ LP P.Disc . . . . .MOSH 018P
Earache / Jul '90.
CD . . . . MOSH 018CD
Earache / Sep '94 / Vital Distribution.

TOOLS OF THE TRADE.
Tracks: Tools of the trade.
■ 12" . . . . MOSH 049T
CD Single. . . . . .MOSH 049CD
Earache / Mar '92 / Vital Distribution.

Carnivore

CARNIVORE.
Tracks: Predator / Male supremacy / Legion of doom / Thermonuclear warrior / Carnivore / Armageddon / God is dead / World wars III & IV.
■ LP . . . . RR 9754
Road Runner / Apr '86.
MC. . . . . .GWC 90534
New Renaissance(USA) / Apr '86 / Pinnacle.
CD . . . . RO 97542
Roadracer / Mar '90 / Pinnacle.

RETALIATION.
Tracks: Not Advised.
CD . . . . .RR 9597-2
■ LP . . . . RR 9597
Road Runner / Apr '89.

Cast Of Thousands

NOTHING IS FOREVER.
Tracks: Nothing is forever (7" mix) / New tomorrow.
■ 12" . . . . 12 FAA 108
Fun After All / Aug '87.

PASSION.
Tracks: This is love / Passion / September / Tear me down / Girl / Immaculate deception / Colour fields / This experience / Thin line / Nothing is forever.
CD . . . . CDAFTER 6
■ LP . . . . AFTER 6

MC. .TAFTER 6
Music For Nations / Jun '88 / Pinnacle.

SEPTEMBER.
Tracks: September.
■ 12". 12FAA 113
■ 7". . . . . .FAA 113
Fun After All / Oct '88.

Castle Blak

BABES IN TOYLAND.
Tracks: Not Advised.
■ LP . . . . HMUSA 60
Heavy Metal America / Jan '86.

Catalepsy

HOUSE OF DESPAIR.
Tracks: House of Despair.
■ CD Single . . . . .EL 108 CDS
Electrip / Sep '93.

Cathedral

ETHEREAL MIRROR, THE.
Tracks: Violet vortex / Ride / Enter the worms / Midnight mountain / Fountain of innocence / Grim luxuria / Jaded entity / Ashes you leave / Phantasmagoria / Imprisoned in flesh.
LP . . . . MOSH 077
MC. .MOSH 077MC
Earache / May '93 / Vital Distribution.
CD . . . . MOSH 077CD
Earache / Sep '94 / Vital Distribution.

FOREST OF EQUILIBRIUM.
Tracks: Not Advised.
LP . . . . MOSH 043
MC. .MOSH 043MC
Earache / Oct '91 / Vital Distribution.
CD . . . . MOSH 043CD
Earache / Sep '94 / Vital Distribution.

IN MEMORIUM EP.
Tracks: Mourning of a new day / All your sins / Ebony tears / March.
CD . . . . .RISE 008CD
LP . . . . RISE 008
Riseabove / Apr '94 / Vital Distribution.

SOUL SACRIFICE.
Tracks: Soul sacrifice.
■ 12" . . . . MOSH 040T
■ CD Single . . . . .MOSH 040CD
Earache / Mar '92.

STATIK MAJIK.
Tracks: Midnight mountain (Available on CDS only) / Hypnos 164 / Cosmic funeral / Voyage of the homeless sapien.
12". . . . . MOSH 106T
CD Single . . . . MOSH 106CD
Earache / Mar '94 / Vital Distribution.

Cats In Boots

KICKED AND KLAWED.
Tracks: Shotgun Sally / 9 lives (save me) / Her monkey / Whip it out / Long, long way from home / Coast to coast / Every sunrise / Evil angel / Bad boys are back / Judas kiss / Heaven on a heartbeat.
■ CD . . . . CDMTL 1049
■ LP . . . . MTL 1049
■ MC. . . . . .TCMTL 1049
EMI-Manhattan / Nov '89.

Celestial Season

FOREVER SCARLET.
Tracks: Not Advised.
CD . . . . .CDAR 015
Adipocre / Feb '94 / Plastic Head.

Celtic Frost

Rising from ashes of notorious Hellhammer, Celtic Frost are acknowledged as seminal death metal band; peaked with *Into The Pandemonium*. Released in 1987, album featured in Sounds' poll of decade's most important albums. Flirtation with glam-rock preceded return to earlier, avant-garde style. Drummer Reed St Mark also played with Mind Funk.

CELTIC FROST STORY, THE (Chris Tetley presents).
Tracks: Not Advised.
CD . . . . .ROHACD 1

■ LP P.Disc . . . . ROHALP 1
MC. . . . . .ROHAMC 1
EMI / Feb '90 / EMI.

COLD LAKE.
Tracks: Not Advised.
CD . . . . .NO 1253
LP . . . . NO 1251
MC. . . . . .NO 1252
Noise / Jul '92 / Pinnacle.

EMPEROR'S RETURN.
Tracks: Not Advised.
■ LP P.Disc . . . . .NUKPD 024
Noise / Sep '86.
CD . . . . .NCD 003
Noise / '88 / Pinnacle.
■ Mini LP . . . . .NUK 024
Noise / Oct '89.

I WON'T DANCE.
Tracks: I won't dance.
■ 12" . . . . .NOISE 094T
Noise / Feb '89.

INTO THE PANDEMONIUM.
Tracks: Mexican radio / Mesmerized / Inner sanctum / Sorrows of the moon / Babylon sell / Caress into oblivion / One in their pride / I won't dance / Rexirae (requiem) / Oriental masquerade.
CD . . . . .NO 067
LP . . . . NO 065
MC. . . . . .NO 066
Noise / Jul '92 / Pinnacle.

LIVE AT THE HAMMERSMITH ODEON.
Tracks: Not Advised.
VHS . . . . .NFV 101
Fotodisk Video / May '90.

MORBID TALES.
Tracks: Not Advised.
■ CD . . . . .CDNUK 001
Noise / Oct '89.
Mini LP . . . . NO 017
Noise / Jul '92 / Pinnacle.

MORBID TALES/EMPERORS RETURN.
Tracks: Not Advised.
CD . . . . .NCD 3
Noise / '88 / Pinnacle.

PARCHED WITH THIRST AM I, AND DYING (1984-1992).
Tracks: Idols of Chagrin / A.. descent to Babylon / Return to the Eve / Juices like wine / Inevitable factor / Heart beneath / Cherry orchards / Tristesses de la lune / Wings of solitude / Usurper / Journey into fear / Downtown Hanoi / Circle of the Tyrants / In the chapel, in the moonlight / I won't dance / Name of my bride / Mexican radio / Under Appolyon's sun.
CD NO191-2
LP NO191-1
MC. NO191-4
Noise / Mar '92 / Pinnacle.

TO MEGA THERION.
Tracks: Not Advised.
CD . . . . .NO 0313
LP . . . . NO 031
Noise / Jul '92 / Pinnacle.

VANITY/NEMESIS.
Tracks: Heart beneath / Wine in my hand (third from the sun) / Wings of solitude / Name of my bride / This island earth / Restless seas / Phallic tantrum / Kiss or a whisper / Vanity / Nemesis / Heroes (CD only.).
■ LP . . . . EMC 3576
■ MC. . . . . .TCEMC 3576
Noise (EMI) / Apr '90.
CD . . . . .NO 1992
Noise / Jul '92 / Pinnacle.

Cement

CEMENT.
Tracks: Living sound delay / Shout / I feel / Four / Prison love / Six / Blue / Too beat / Take it easy / Old days / Reputation shot / Chip away / KCMT.
CD 15715732
LP 15715731
World Service / Jun '93 / Vital Distribution.

MAN WITH THE ACTION HAIR, THE.
Tracks: Man with the action hair / Killing an angel / Pile driver / Crying / Dancing from the depths of the fire / Life on the sun / Sleep / Train / King Arthur / Hotel Aiablo / Bonnie Brae / Magic number / Power and the magic.
CD . . . . RTD 15717452
LP . . . . RTD 15717451
World Service / Aug '94 / Vital Distribution.

■ DELETED

Cemetary

EVIL SHADE OF GREY, AN.
Tracks: Dead red / Where the rivers of madness stream / Dark illusions / Evil shade of grey, An / Sidereal passing / Scars / Nightmare lake / Souldrain.
CD . . . . BMCD 020
LP . . . . .BMLP 020
MC. .BMCT 020
Black Mark / Jun '92 / Plastic Head.

GODLESS BEAUTY.
Tracks: Not Advised.
CD . . . . BMCD 33
MC. BMCT 33
Black Mark / Jul '93 / Plastic Head.

Cerebral Fix

BASTARDS.
Tracks: Not Advised.
LP . . . . RO 92861
■ CD . . . . RO 92862
■ MC. RO 92864
Roadracer / Nov '91.

DEATH EROTICA.
Tracks: Death erotica / World machine / Clarissa / Haunted eyes / Mind within mine / Splintered wings / Creator of outcasts / Angel's kiss / Still in mind / Raft of Medusa / Never again / Too drunk to funk / Burning / Livin' after midnight.
CD . . . . CDFLAG 75
LP . . . . .FLAG 75
MC. . . . . TFLAG 75
Under One Flag / Nov '92 / Pinnacle.

LIFE SUCKS AND THEN YOU DIE.
Tracks: Not Advised.
■ LP . . . . SOL 15
Vinyl Solution / Oct '88.

TOWER OF SPITE.
Tracks: Not Advised.
CD . . . . RO 93562
LP . . . . RO 93561
MC. RO 93564
Roadracer / Nov '90 / Pinnacle.

Cerebros Exprimidos

BONZOMANIA.
Tracks: Not Advised.
LP . . . . MR 016
Munster Records / Apr '92 / Plastic Head.

Cerebus

TOO LATE TO PRAY.
Tracks: Not Advised.
■ LP . . . . GWD 90542
MC. GWC 90542
New Renaissance(USA) / Nov '87 / Pinnacle.

Ceremonial Oath

BOOK OF TRUTH, THE.
Tracks: Prologue: sworn to avenge / Invocator / For I have sinned/The plague / Enthroned / Only evil prevails / Thunderworld / Lords of twilight / Ceremonial oath / Last name of God / Book of truth / Hellbound.
CD . . . . PRIM 003CD
LP . . . . PRIM 003
MC. PRIM 003MC
Modern Primitive / Jul '93 / Vital Distribution.

Chain Reaction

X RATED DREAM.
Tracks: Not Advised.
■ LP . . . . LAT 1135
Noir / Jul '82.

Chainsaw

HELL'S BURNIN' UP.
Tracks: Hell's burnin' up / Dungeon / Last fortress / Cut loose / Rage and revenge / Midnight hunter / Born to kill / He knows you are alone / Ageless force.
■ LP . . . . BONE 2
Bonebreaker (Germany) / Apr '86.

MASSACRE.
Tracks: Devil's daughter / Ballad of Mean Street / Rock 'n' roll gambler / Accident victim.
■ 12" . . . . THBE 1.006
Thunderbolt / Dec '84.

Chariot

ALL ALONE AGAIN.
Tracks: All alone again.
■ 12" . . . . SHADE 2
Shades / Mar '85.

BURNING AMBITION.
Tracks: Not Advised.
■ LP . . . . SHADE 4
Shades / Mar '86.

LIVE AT THE MARQUEE.
Tracks: Not Advised.
VHS . . . . .VID 01
Shades / '88 / Pinnacle.

WARRIOR, THE.
Tracks: Not Advised.
■ LP . . . . SHADES 1
Shades / Jul '85.
■ LP .SKULL 8392
Mausoleum / Jun '86.

Charon

CHARON.
Tracks: Not Advised.
■ LP . . . . HMILP 20
Heavy Metal / Sep '84.

Chastain

FOR THOSE WHO DARE.
Tracks: Mountain whispers / Please set us free / Night of anger / Light in the dark / Not much breathing / For those who dare / I am the rain / Barracuda / Secrets of the damned / Once before.
LP . . . . RR 93984
Road Runner / Aug '90 / Pinnacle.

MYSTERY OF ILLUSION.
Tracks: Black knight / Mystery of illusion / Endlessly / Fear on evil / We shall overcome / Winds of change / When the battle's over / I've seen tomorrow / Requiem / Night at the coods / March out.
■ LP .RR 9742
Road Runner / Oct '85.
CD . . . . RO 97422
Roadracer / Mar '90 / Pinnacle.

RULER OF THE WASTELAND.
Tracks: Not Advised.
■ LP .RR 9689
Road Runner / Oct '86.

VOICE OF THE CULT, THE.
Tracks: Voice of the cult / Live hard / Chains of love / Share yourself with me / Child of evermore / Soldiers of the flame / Evil for evil / Take me home / Fortune teller.
CD . . . . .RR 9548 2
■ LP .RR 9548 1
Road Runner / Jul '88.

WITHIN THE HEAT.
Tracks: Excursions into reality / Visionary / Nightmares / Zfunknc / In your face / Desert nights / It's still in your eyes / Pantheon.
CD . . . . .RR 9484 2
■ LP .RR 9484 1
■ MC. . . . . .RR 9484 4
Road Runner / Jan '89.

Chastain, David T.

7TH OF NEVER, THE.
Tracks: Not Advised.
■ LP . . . . BD 025
Black Dragon / Jul '87.

INSTRUMENTAL VARIATIONS.
Tracks: Not Advised.
CD . . . . .LD 872
■ LP . . . . .LA 872
Leviathan (USA) / Oct '87.

MOVEMENTS THROUGH TIME.
Tracks: Thunder and lightning / 827 / Fortunate and happenstance / Citizen of hell / Blitzkrieg / Oracle within / New York rush / We must carry on / Capricco / In E minor / No man's land / 7 Hills groove / Now or never / Trapped in the wind / Zoned in danger / Bargin.
CD . . . . KCLCD 1002
Killerwatt / Oct '93 / Kingdom Records.

NEXT PLANET PLEASE.
Tracks: Not Advised.
CD . . . . .CDVEST 9
Bulletproof / May '94 / Pinnacle.

WORLD GONE MAD.
Tracks: Not Advised.
■ LP . . . . BD 007
Black Dragon / Feb '86.

Cheap 'n' Nasty

BEAUTIFUL DISASTER.
Tracks: Not Advised.
CD . . . . WOLCD 1002
LP . . . . .WOL 1002
MC. WOLMC 1002
China / May '91 / Pinnacle.

BEAUTIFUL DISASTER.
Tracks: Beautiful disaster / Fantasy / Electric flag (Not available on 7" format only.).
■ 12" . . . . CHINX 34
■ 7" . . . . CHINA 34
■ CD Single . . . . CHICD 34
■ MC Single. . . . . CHICS 34
China / Feb '91.

MIND ACROSS THE OCEAN.
Tracks: Mind across the ocean.
■ 12" . . . . CHIXG 31
China / Dec '90.
■ 12" . . . . CHINX 31
■ 7" . . . . CHINA 31
■ CD Single . . . . CHICD 31
■ MC Single. . . . . CHICS 31
China / Nov '90.

Cheap Trick

Guitarist Rick Nielsen assembled Cheap Trick in 1973. Group spent early years establishing formidable live reputation; fittingly, breakthrough came with live *At Budokan* album and attendant hit *I want you to want me* in '79. Trick floundered in '80s before *The flame* topped U.S. singles chart in '88; group have since returned to mixed fortunes. Group are far more successful and influential in native U.S. than U.K.; blend of metal and Beatle-esque pop won fans in acts from Motley Crue to Nirvana.

AIN'T THAT A SHAME.
Tracks: Ain't that a shame / Elo kiddies.
■ 7" . . . . EPC 7839
Epic / Sep '79.

ALL SHOOK UP.
Tracks: Stop this game / Just got back / Baby loves to rock / Can't stop it but I'm gonna try / World's greatest lover / High priest of rhythmic noise / Love comes a-tumblin' down / I love you honey but I hate your friends / Go for the throat / Who'd king.
■ LP . . . . EPC 86124
Epic / Dec '80.
CD . . . . EK 36498
Pickwick/Sony Collector's Choice / Jun '88 / Pickwick / Pinnacle.

AT THE BUDOKAN.
Tracks: Hello there / Come on, come on / Lookout / Big eyes / Need your love / Ain't that a shame / I want you to want me / Surrender / Goodnight now / Clock strikes ten.
■ LP . . . . EPC 86083
Epic / Feb '79.
■ LP . . . . EPC 32595
MC. .40 32595
■ CD . . . . CD 86083
Epic / Feb '86.

BUSTED.
Tracks: Black 'n' blue / I can't understand it / Wherever would I be / If you need me / Can't stop fallin' into love / Busted / Walk away / You drive, I'll steer / When you need someone / Had to make you mine / Rock 'n' roll tonight.
■ CD 4668762
■ LP 4668761
■ MC. 4668764
Epic / Sep '90.

CALIFORNIA MAN.
Tracks: California man / Stiff competition.
■ 7" . . . . EPC 6427
Epic / Aug '78.

CAN'T STOP FALLIN' INTO LOVE.
Tracks: Can't stop fallin' into love / You drive, I'll steer / Flame.
■ MC Single. 6561484
■ 12" 6561486
■ 7" 6561487
■ CD Single 6561482
Epic / Aug '90.

CHEAP TRICK.
Tracks: Hot love / Speak now or forever hold your peace / He's a whore / Mandocello / Ballad of T.V. violence / Ello kiddies / Daddy should have stayed in High School / Taxman / Mr. Thief / Cry, cry / Oh Candy.
■ **LP** . . . . EPC 81917
Epic / Jun '80.
■ **LP** . . . . EPC 32070
MC. 40 32070
Epic / Nov '81 / Sony.
CD . . . . EK 34400
Pickwick/Sony Collector's Choice / Jun '88 / Pickwick / Pinnacle.

COLLECTION: CHEAP TRICK.
Tracks: Not Advised.
CD . . . . CCSCD 309
■ **MC.** . . . . .CCSMC 309
Castle / Oct '91.

DANCING THE NIGHT AWAY.
Tracks: Dancing the night away / I want you to want me / Surrender / Ain't that a shame.
■ **12"** . . . . TA 3743
Epic / Sep '83.

DOCTOR, THE.
Tracks: It's up to you / Rearview mirror romance / Doctor / Are you lonely tonight / Name of the game / Kiss me red / Good girls go to heaven (bad girls go everywhere) / Man-u-lip-u-lator / It's only love.
■ **LP** . . . . EPC 57087
MC. 40 57087
Epic / Nov '86 / Sony.
■ **CD** . . . . CD 57087
Epic / May '87.

DON'T BE CRUEL.
Tracks: Don't be cruel / I know what I want (live) / Ain't that a shame (12" and CD single only.) / California man (12" and CD single only.).
■ **CD Single** 6530053
CBS / '88.
■ **12"** 6528966
■ **7"** 6528967
Epic / Sep '88.
■ **7" P.Disc** 6528960
CBS / Sep '88.
■ **CD Single** 6528962
Epic / Sep '88.

DREAM POLICE.
Tracks: Dream police / Way of the world / House is rockin' / Gonna raise hell / I'll be with you tonight / Voices / Writing on the wall / I know what I want / Need your love.
■ **LP** . . . . EPC 83522
Epic / Oct '79.

EVERY TRICK IN THE BOOK.
Tracks: Can't stop falling in love / Wherever would I be / Never had a lot to lose / Ghost town / Don't be cruel / Flame / It's only love / Tonight it's you / I can't take it / If you want my love / She's tight / Surrender (live) / I want to want me (live) / Ain't that a shame (live) / Dream police / Way of the world / Voices.
■ **VHS** 490 492
CMV Enterprises (Video) / Sep '90.

FLAME, THE.
Tracks: Flame / Through the night / Flame (album version) (Track on 12" and CD single.) / I want you to want me (Track on 12" and CD single.) / If you want my love (Track on 12" and CD single.).
■ **7" P.Disc** 6514660
■ **12"** 6514666
■ **7"** 6514667
■ **CD Single** 6514662
Epic / May '88.

GREATEST HITS, THE.
Tracks: Magical mystery tour / Dream police / Don't be cruel / Tonight it's you / She's tight / I want you to want me (live) / If you want my love / Ain't that a shame (live) / Surrender / Flame / I can't take it / Can't stop fallin' into love / Voices.
CD 4690862
MC. 4690864
Epic / Apr '94 / Sony.

HEAVEN TONIGHT.
Tracks: Surrender / On top of the world / California man / High roller / Auf wiedersehen / Takin' me back / On the radio / Heaven tonight / Stiff competition / How are you / Oh Claire.
CD 982993 2
Pickwick/Sony Collector's Choice / Aug '93 / Pickwick / Pinnacle.

I WANT YOU TO WANT ME.
Tracks: I want you to want me / Oh boy.
■ **7"** . . . . EPC 5701
Epic / Oct '77.

I'LL BE WITH YOU TONIGHT.
Tracks: I'll be with you tonight / He's a whore / So good to see you.
■ **7"** . . . . EPC 8355
Epic / Apr '80.

IF YOU WANT MY LOVE.
Tracks: If you want my love / Four letter word.
■ **7"** . . . . EPCA 2406
Epic / Jul '82.

IN COLOR.
Tracks: Hello there / Big eyes / Drowned / I want you to want me / You're all talk / Oh Caroline / Clock strikes ten / Southern girls / Come on, come on / So good to see you.
MC. 40 82214
Epic / Nov '77.
CD . . . . EK 34844
Pickwick/Sony Collector's Choice / Jun '88 / Pickwick / Pinnacle.
CD 982933 2
MC. 982833 4
Pickwick / Nov '92 / Pickwick.

LAP OF LUXURY.
Tracks: Let go / No mercy / Flame / Space / Never had a lot to lose / Don't be cruel / Wrong side of love / All we need is a dream / Ghost town / All wound up.
CD 4607822
MC. 4607824
■ **LP** 4607821
Epic / May '88.
CD 982839 2
MC. 982839 4
Pickwick / Oct '92 / Pickwick.

LIVE AT THE BUDOKAN.
Tracks: Not Advised.
■ **CD** . . . . ESSCD 949
Castle / Jul '91.

NEXT POSITION PLEASE.
Tracks: I can't take it / Borderline / I don't love her anymore / Next position please / Younger girls / Dancing the night away / 3-D / You say jump / Y.O.Y.O.Y / Won't take no for an answer / Heaven's falling / Invaders of the heart.
■ **LP** . . . . EPC 25490
MC. 40 25490
Epic / Oct '83 / Sony.
CD . . . . EK 38794
Pickwick/Sony Collector's Choice / Jun '88 / Pickwick / Pinnacle.

ONE ON ONE.
Tracks: I want you / One on one / If you want my love / Oh la la la / Lookin' out for number one / She's tight / Time is runnin' / Saturday at midnight / Love's got a hold on me / I want to be a man / Four letter word.
■ **LP** . . . . EPC 85740
Epic / Jun '82.
■ **LP** . . . . EPC 32654
Epic / Aug '85.

SO GOOD TO SEE YOU.
Tracks: So good to see you / You're all talk.
■ **7"** . . . . EPC 6199
Epic / Mar '78.

STANDING ON THE EDGE.
Tracks: Little sister / Tonight it's you / She's got motion / Love comes / How about this / Standing on the edge / This time around / Rock all night / Cover girl / Wild wild women.
MC. 40 26374
■ **LP** . . . . EPC 26374
Epic / Nov '85.

STOP THIS GAME.
Tracks: Stop this game / Who'd be king.
■ **7"** . . . . EPC 9071
Epic / Oct '82.

SURRENDER.
Tracks: Surrender / Auf wiedersehen.
■ **7"** . . . . EPC 6394
Epic / May '78.

TONIGHT IT'S YOU.
Tracks: Tonight it's you / Wild wild women.
■ **12"** . . . . TX 6390
■ **7"** . . . . A 6390
Epic / Feb '86.

VOICES.
Tracks: Voices / Surrender.
■ **7"** . . . . EPC 7144
Epic / Nov '79.

WAY OF THE WORLD.
Tracks: Way of the world / Oh candy.
■ **7"** . . . . EPC 8114
Epic / Feb '80.

WORLD'S GREATEST LOVER.
Tracks: World's greatest lover / High priest of rhythmic noise.
■ **7"** . . . . EPC 9502
Epic / Feb '81.

Cheetah

MOMENT OF WEAKNESS.
Tracks: Moment of weakness / Kiss me Bwana.
■ **7"** . . . . GT 250
GTO / May '79.

PRESSURE DROP.
Tracks: Pressure drop / Don't stop making love.
■ **7"** . . . . SAFE 11
Safari / Nov '78.

SPEND THE NIGHT.
Tracks: Spend the night / I'm yours.
■ **7"** . . . . EPCA 1646
Epic / Jun '82.

Chemlab

BURN OUT AT THE HYDROGEN BAR.
Tracks: Codeine, glue & you / Suicide jag / Chemical halo / Neurozone / Elephant man / Rivethead / Derailer / Summer of hate.
CD . . . . .CDDVN 21
Devotion / Jun '93 / Pinnacle.

Chequered Past

CHEQUERED PAST.
Tracks: Not Advised.
■ **LP** . . . . HMUSA 53
MC. . . . . HMAMC 53
Heavy Metal America / Nov '85 / FM Revolver / Sony.

Cherry Bombz

COMING DOWN SLOW.
Tracks: Not Advised.
CD . . . . HD 021 CD
■ **LP** . . . . HD 021
MC. . . . . .HDT 021
High Dragon / Jun '87 / Pinnacle.

HOT GIRLS IN LOVE.
Tracks: Feeline feeling / Hot girls in love.
■ **12"** . . . . LIXT 3
■ **7"** . . . . LIX 3
Lick / Feb '86.

HOT GIRLS IN LOVE.
Tracks: Not Advised.
■ **VHS** . . . . HEN 2059
Hendring Video / Aug '87.

HOUSE OF ECSTASY.
Tracks: House of ecstasy / Declaration (On 7" only) / Countryfield inner city blues (On 12" only) / Running (back to your lover) (On 12" only).
■ **12"** . . . . LIXT 4
■ **7"** . . . . LIX 4
Lick / May '86.

Child, Desmond

DESMOND CHILD AND ROUGE (Child, Desmond & Rouge).
Tracks: Westside pow wow / Our love is insane / Lovin' your love / Fight / Main man / City in heat / Lazy love / Otti / Givin' in to my love.
■ **LP** . . . . EST 11908
Capitol / Apr '79.

DISCIPLINE.
Tracks: Price of lovin' you / Discipline / I don't want to be your friend / Love on a rooftop / Story of my life / According to the gospel of love / Do me right / Obsession / Gift of life / Ray of hope.
CD 7559610482
■ **LP** . . . . EKT 92
■ **MC.** . . . . .EKT 92C
Elektra / Aug '91.

GOODBYE BABY (Child, Desmond & Rouge).
Tracks: Goodbye baby / Imitation of love.
■ **7"** . . . . CL 16115
Capitol / Jan '80.

■ DELETED

OUR LOVE IS INSANE.
Tracks: Our love is insane / City in heat / Our love is insane (version).
■ 12" 12CL 16038
■ 7" . . . . CL 16038
Capitol / Apr '79.

RUNNERS IN THE NIGHT (Child, Desmond & Rouge).
Tracks: Truth comes out / My heart's on fire / Night was not / Goodbye baby / Runners in the night / Tumble in the night / Scared to live / Feeling like this / Imitation of love / Rosa.
■ LP .EST 11999
Capitol / Jan '80.

China

CHINA.
Tracks: Intro / Shout it out / Back to you / Fight is on / Wild jealousy / Rock city / Hot lovin' night / Living on the stage / I need your love / One shot to the heart / Staying alive.
■ CD 834 451-2
■ LP . . . . VERH 57
■ MC . . . . .VERHC 57
Vertigo / May '88.

SIGN IN THE SKY.
Tracks: Great wall / Dead lights / Animal victim / In the middle of the night / Won't give it up / Sign in the sky / Don't ever say goodbye / Broken dream / Second chance / Bitter cold / Take your time / Harder than hell / So long.
■ CD 847 247 2
■ LP 847 247 1
■ MC 847 247 4
Vertigo / Mar '90.

Christian Death

ALIVE.
Tracks: Not Advised.
CD . . . . FREUDCD 29
■ LP . . . . .FREUD 29
■ MC . . . . FREUDC 29
Jungle / Jul '89.

ANTHOLOGY OF BOOTLEGS.
Tracks: Not Advised.
CD . . . . .NOS 1006 CD
■ LP . . . . NOS 1006
Nostradamus / May '88.

ASHES.
Tracks: Not Advised.
■ LP . . . . NORMAL 15
Normal/Okra / May '88.
CD . . . . .NORMAL 15CD
Normal/Okra / May '94 / A.D.A. Distribution / Topic Records / Direct Distribution.

ATROCITIES.
Tracks: Not Advised.
■ LP . . . . NORMAL 18
Normal/Okra / May '88.
CD . . . . .NORMAL 18CD
Normal/Okra / May '94 / A.D.A. Distribution / Topic Records / Direct Distribution.

BELIEVERS OF THE UNPURE.
Tracks: Believers of the unpure.
■ 12" . . . . JUNG 24T
Jungle / Feb '86.

CATASTROPHE BALLET.
Tracks: Not Advised.
■ LP . . . . SD 5
Invitation Au Suicide / May '84.
CD . . . . CONTECD 105
■ LP . . . . CONTE 105
Contempo / Nov '87.

CHRISTIAN DEATH.
Tracks: Not Advised.
■ 7" Set . . . . NORMAL 48
Normal/Okra / Sep '87.

CHURCH OF NO RETURN.
Tracks: Church of no return.
■ 12" . . . . JUNG 40T
■ 7" . . . . JUNG 40
Jungle / May '88.

DEATHWISH.
Tracks: Not Advised.
■ LP . . . . SD 4
Invitation Au Suicide / Feb '84.
■ CD . . . . CONTECD 137
■ LP . . . . CONTAPE 137
Contempo / '90.
CD . . . . .NORMAL 84CD

Normal/Okra / May '94 / A.D.A. Distribution / Topic Records / Direct Distribution.

DOLL'S THEATRE.
Tracks: Not Advised.
CD . . . . CLEO 6208
L.A. / May '94 / Plastic Head.

DOLLS THEATRE.
Tracks: Not Advised.
CD . . . . .CLEO 62082
Cleopatra / Jun '94 / Plastic Head / Pinnacle.

HERETICS ALIVE.
Tracks: Prologue / Prelude / This is heresy / Wretched mankind / Sick of love / Nascent virion / Golden age / Erection / Chimere de si de-la / Four horsemen / Church of no return.
■ VHS . . . . JVD 6
Jungle Video Displays / Nov '90.

I HATE YOU.
Tracks: I hate you / We fall like love.
■ CD Single . . . . JUNG 055CD
Jungle / '88.

JESUS POINTS THE BONE.
Tracks: Not Advised.
CD . . . . FREUDCD 39
MC . . . . FREUDC 39
■ LP . . . . .FREUD 39
Jungle / Mar '92.

LIVE IN HOLLYWOOD.
Tracks: Not Advised.
LP . . . . CONTE 138
Contempo / Aug '93 / Plastic Head.

LOVE AND HATE.
Tracks: Not Advised.
CD Set . . . . FREUDBX 334
Jungle / Oct '92 / RTM / Pinnacle.

ONLY THEATRE OF PAIN.
Tracks: Cavity - First Communion / Figurative theatre / Burnt offerings / Mysterious Iniquitatis / Dream for mother / Deathwish / Romeo's distress / Dogs / Stairs - Uncertain journey / Spiritual cramp / Resurrection - Sixth Communion / Prayer / Desperate Hell / Cavity.
■ LP . . . . SD 1
Invitation Au Suicide / Feb '85.
CD . . . . .NORMAL 56CD
LP . . . . NORMAL 56
Normal/Okra / '90 / A.D.A. Distribution / Topic Records / Direct Distribution.
CD . . . . FCD 1007
CD . . . . 46032 L
LP . . . . 46031 L
MC . . . . 46034 L
Frontier / Aug '93 / Vital Distribution.

PART 1: ALL THE LOVE (All the Love, All the Hate).
Tracks: Not Advised.
CD . . . . FREUDCD 33
MC . . . . FREUDC 33
■ LP . . . . .FREUD 33
Jungle / Dec '89.

PART 2: ALL THE HATE (All the Love, All the Hate).
Tracks: Not Advised.
CD . . . . FREUDCD 34
■ LP . . . . .FREUD 34
MC . . . . FREUDC 34
Jungle / Dec '89 / RTM / Pinnacle.

PAST AND PRESENT.
Tracks: Not Advised.
CD .SHCD 163
Castle Showcase / Dec '87 / Arabesque Ltd.

PATH OF SORROW, THE.
Tracks: Not Advised.
CD . . . . .EFA 11906CD
LP . . . . EFA 11906
Appollyon / May '93 / SRD.
CD . . . . .CLEO 39932
Jungle / Mar '94 / RTM / Pinnacle.

RAGE OF ANGELS, THE.
Tracks: Not Advised.
CD . . . . .CLEO 81252
Cleopatra / May '94 / Plastic Head / Pinnacle.

SCRIPTURES.
Tracks: Not Advised.
■ LP . . . . .FREUD 18
■ CD . . . . FREUDCD 18
Normal/Okra / Dec '87.
CD . . . . NORMAL 65
Normal/Okra / May '94 / A.D.A. Distribution / Topic Records / Direct Distribution.

Normal/Okra / May '94 / A.D.A. Distribution / Topic Records / Direct Distribution.

SEX AND DRUGS AND JESUS CHRIST.
Tracks: Not Advised.
LP . . . . NORMAL 96
Normal/Okra / '90 / A.D.A. Distribution / Topic Records / Direct Distribution.

SEX, DRUGS AND JESUS CHRIST.
Tracks: Not Advised.
CD . . . . FREUDCD 25
MC . . . . FREUDC 25
■ LP . . . . .FREUD 25
Jungle / Nov '88.
LP P.Disc . . . . FREUDP 25
Jungle / Dec '90 / RTM / Pinnacle.

SEXY DEATH GOD.
Tracks: Not Advised.
CD . . . . CDVEST 26
Bulletproof / Aug '94 / Pinnacle.

SICK OF LOVE.
Tracks: Sick of love.
■ 12" . . . . JUNG 35T
■ 7" . . . . JUNG 35
Jungle / Sep '87.

TALES OF INNOCENCE.
Tracks: Not Advised.
CD . . . . CLEO 9109-2
Cleopatra / Dec '93 / Plastic Head / Pinnacle.

THEATRE OF PAIN.
Tracks: Not Advised.
■ LP . . . . FL 2
Future / Aug '83.

WHAT'S THE VERDICT.
Tracks: What's the verdict / This is not blasphemy.
■ 12" . . . . JUNG 45T
■ 7" . . . . JUNG 45
Jungle / Nov '88.

WIND KISSED PICTURES.
Tracks: Not Advised.
■ LP .SF 003
Supporti Fonograph (Italy) / Nov '87.
CD . . . . .NORMAL 76CD
Jungle / '88 / RTM / Pinnacle.

ZERO SEX.
Tracks: Zero sex.
■ 12" . . . . JUNG 050T
■ 7" . . . . JUNG 050
■ CD Single . . . . JUNG 050CD
Jungle / Jun '89.

Chrome Molly

ANGST.
Tracks: Thanx for the angst / Take me I'm yours / Don't let go / Come back / I want to find out / Take it or leave it / Living a lie / Cut loose / Too far gone / Set me free.
CD . . . . .DMIRF 1033
■ LP . . . . MIRF 1033
MC . . . . .MIRFC 1033
I.R.S. (Illegal) / Apr '88 / EMI.

I WANT TO FIND OUT.
Tracks: I want to find out.
■ 12" . . . . OHM 12 T
■ 7" . . . . OHM 12
Powerstation / Mar '86.

SHOOTING ME DOWN.
Tracks: Shooting me down.
■ 12" 12IRM 176
■ 7" . . . . IRM 176
I.R.S. (Illegal) / Nov '88.

SLAP HEAD.
Tracks: Out of our minds / Gimme that line again / Red hot red rock / Shotgun / Loosen up / Caught with the bottle again / Sitter the children / Assinine nation / Pray with me / Now / Little voodoo magic.
CD . . . . .CDMFN 98
LP . . . . MFN 98
MC . . . . TMFN 98
Music For Nations / May '90 / Pinnacle.

STICK IT OUT.
Tracks: C.M.A. / Breakdown / Something special / That's the way it is / Steel against the sky / Bob Geldof / Stand proud / Before you go / Look out for number one / Let go (Cassette only).
■ LP . . . . AMP 12
MC . . . . AMP 12C
Powerstation / May '87 / Powerstation Records.

TAKE IT OR LEAVE IT.
Tracks: Take it or leave it / Lonely / Don't let go.
■ 12" . . . . OHM 11 T
Powerstation / Aug '85.

TAKE ME I'M YOURS.
Tracks: Take me I'm yours / Don't fight dirty / Lose again (Available on 12" version only).
- 12" . . . . IRMT 152
- 7" . . . . IRM 152
- 7" P.Disc . . . . IRMP 152
I.R.S. (Illegal) / Apr '88.

THANX FOR THE ANGST.
Tracks: Thanx for the angst / Living a lie / One at a time (Extra track on 12".).
- 12" . . . . IRMT 158
- 7" . . . . IRM 158
I.R.S. (Illegal) / Mar '88.

WHEN THE LIGHTS.
Tracks: When the lights.
- 12" .BOLT 10
Bullet / May '84.

Chronical Diarrhoea

LAST JUDGEMENT.
Tracks: Not Advised.
- CD . . . . .NB 045CD
Nuclear Blast / Jul '91.

SALOMO SAYS.
Tracks: Not Advised.
- LP .NB 001R
Nuclear Blast / Oct '88.

Cinderella

After years of establishing themselves in and around their native Philadelphia, Cinderella were brought to a much wider audience after Jon Bon Jovi declared himself a fan. They signed with Vertigo and after supporting Bon Jovi and Dave Lee Roth their second album *Long Cold Winter* sold over a million copies. Unfortunately the follow up 'difficult third album' *Heartbreak Station* failed to repeat that success.

CINDERELLA: INTERVIEW PICTURE DISC.
Tracks: Not Advised.
LP P.Disc . . . . BAK 2084
Baktabak / Apr '88 / Arabesque Ltd.

DON'T KNOW WHAT YOU GOT (TIL IT'S GONE).
Tracks: Don't know what you got (till it's gone) / Fire and ice / Push, push (live) (Only on the Gatefold and CD versions) / Once around the ride (Only on gatefold sleeve.) / Long cold winter (On CD single only.)
- CD Single . . . . .VERCD 43
- 12" .VERX 43
- 7" .VERXG 43
- 7" . . . . VER 43
- 7" P.Disc . . . . .VERP 43
Vertigo / Feb '89.
- CD Video 0800982
Vertigo / Sep '89.

GYPSY ROAD.
Tracks: Gypsy road.
- 12" .VERX 40
- 12" . . . . .VERXG 40
- 7" . . . . VER 40
- CD Single . . . . .VERCD 40
Vertigo / Jul '88.

GYPSY ROAD (CD VIDEO).
Tracks: Gypsy road.
CD Video 080 402 2
Polygram Music Video / Oct '88 / PolyGram.

HEARTBREAK STATION.
Tracks: More things change / Love's got me doin' time / Shelter me / Heartbreak station / Sick for the cure / One for rock and roll / Dead man's road / Make your own way / Electric love / Love gone bad / Winds of change.
- LP 8480181
- CD 8480182
- MC 8480184
Vertigo / Nov '90.

HEARTBREAK STATION.
Tracks: Heartbreak station / Sick for the cure (Not on CD single.) / Falling apart at the seams (12" only.) / Move over (10" only.) / Gypsy road (CD single only.) / Shake me (CD single only.) / Somebody save me (CD single only.)
- 10" . . . . .VERSP 53
- 12" .VERX 53
- 7" . . . . VER 53
- CD Single . . . . .VERCD 53
Vertigo / Apr '91.

LONG COLD WINTER.
Tracks: Falling down / Gypsy road / Last mile / Long cold winter / If you don't like it / Coming home / Fire and ice / Take me back / Bad seamstress blues / Don't know what you got (til it's gone) / Second wind.
- CD 834 612-2
- LP . . . . VERH 59
- MC . . . . .VERHC 59
Vertigo / Jul '88 / PolyGram.

NIGHT SONGS.
Tracks: Night songs / Shake me / Nobody's fool / Nothin' for nothin' / Once around the ride / Hell on wheels / Somebody save me / In from the outside / Push push / Back home again.
- LP . . . . VERH 37
- MC . . . . .VERHC 37
Vertigo / Aug '86 / PolyGram.
- CD 830 076-2
Vertigo / Jan '87 / PolyGram.

NIGHT SONGS.
Tracks: Not Advised.
- VHS . . . . CFV 04192
Channel 5 / Nov '87 / Channel 5 Video / P.R.O. Video / Gold & Sons.

NOBODY'S FOOL.
Tracks: Nobody's fool / Shake me (live) / Galaxy blues.
- 12" .VERX 32
- 7" . . . . VER 32
Vertigo / May '87.

SAVE ME (CD VIDEO).
Tracks: Not Advised.
CD Video 080 020 2
Polygram Music Video / Sep '89 / PolyGram.

SHAKE ME.
Tracks: Shake me / Nightsongs / Hell on wheels.
- 12" .VERX 29
- 7" . . . . VER 29
Vertigo / Feb '87.

SHELTER ME.
Tracks: Shelter me / Love gone bad / Electric love (12" and CD single only.)
- 12" .VERX 51
- 7" . . . . VER 51
- CD Single . . . . .VERCD 51
- MC Single . . . . .VERMC 51
Vertigo / Nov '90.

TALES FROM GYPSY ROAD.
Tracks: Not Advised.
VHS . . . . CFM 02162
Polygram Music Video / '92 / PolyGram.

TALES FROM THE GYPSY ROAD.
Tracks: Not Advised.
VHS . . . . CFM 2162
Channel 5 / Nov '90 / Channel 5 Video / P.R.O. Video / Gold & Sons.

Circle Jerks

GROUP SEX.
Tracks: Not Advised.
LP . . . . WS 031
Weird Systems / Apr '88 / SRD.
CD . . . . WS 031 YZ
Weird Systems / Aug '88 / SRD.
CD . . . . 46002 L
LP . . . . 46001 L
MC . . . . 46004 L
Frontier / May '92 / Vital Distribution.

GROUP SEX/WILD IN THE STREET.
Tracks: Not Advised.
CD . . . . FCD 1002
Frontier / Aug '92 / Vital Distribution.

VI.
Tracks: Beat me senseless / Casulty vampire / Protection / American way / All wound up / Fortunate son / Patty's killing me / Tell me why / I'm alive / Status clinger / I don't / Living.
- LP . . . . RR 9584
Road Runner / Nov '87.
- CD . . . . RO 95842
Roadracer / Mar '90.

WILD IN THE STREETS.
Tracks: Not Advised.
- LP . . . . SFLP 8
Steppers / Jul '82.
LP 46171
MC 46174
Frontier / Jul '91 / Vital Distribution.

WONDERFUL.
Tracks: Not Advised.
- LP . . . . JUST 1
Rough Justice / Aug '89.

Circle Of Soul

HANDS OF FAITH.
Tracks: Not Advised.
CD . . . . HWDCD 11
LP . . . . HWDLP 11
MC . . . . HWDMC 11
Hollywood (2) / Oct '91 / Sony.

ONE MAN'S POISON.
Tracks: Not Advised.
CD . . . . IRS 975558
IRS (Holland) / Nov '93 / Pinnacle.

Circus Of Power

CIRCUS OF POWER.
Tracks: Call of the wild / Motor / Heart attack / in the wind / Machine / White trash mama / Needles / Crazy / Letters home / Backseat mama / Turn up the jams (Only on cassette and CD).
- CD . . . . PD 88464
- LP . . . . PL 88464
MC. . . . . PK 88464
RCA / Dec '88 / BMG.

MAGIC & MADNESS.
Tracks: Swamp devil / Evil woman / Heaven and hell / Circles / Poison girl / Shine / Dreams tonight / Mama Tequila / Black roses / Waitin' for the wizard / Outta my head / Slip away.
CD .472170 2
MC. 472170 4
Columbia / Jul '93 / Sony.

STILL ALIVE.
Tracks: Still alive and well / Motor (live) / Letters home (live) / White trash queen (live) / Heart attack (live) / Turn up the jams (live).
CD . . . . PD 90377
- LP . . . . PL 90377
- MC . . . . PK 90377
RCA / Jul '89.

VICES.
Tracks: Gates of love / Two river highway / Don't drag me down / Dr. Potion / Got hard / Junkie girl / Desire / Fire in the night / Vices / Last call Rosie / Los Angeles / Temptation / Simple man / Simple woman.
- LP . . . . PL 90461
- MC . . . . PK 90461
- CD . . . . PD 90461
RCA / Apr '90.

Cirith Ungol

KING OF THE DEAD.
Tracks: Not Advised.
- LP . . . . RR 9832
Road Runner / Aug '84.

ONE FOOT IN HELL.
Tracks: Not Advised.
- LP . . . . RR 9681
Metal Blade / Aug '86.

City Boy

5-7-0-5.
Tracks: 5-7-0-5 / Bad for business.
- 7" 6059 207
Vertigo / Jul '78.

5-7-0-5 (OLD GOLD).
Tracks: 5-7-0-5 / Run for home.
- 7" .OG 9899
Old Gold / '89.

BOOK EARLY.
Tracks: 5-7-0-5 / Summer in the school yard / Goodbye Laurelie / Raise your glass (to foolish me) / Cigarettes / What a night / Do what you do, do well / World loves a dancer / Beth / Moving in circles / Dangerous ground.
- LP .9102 028
Vertigo / '78.

CITY BOY.
Tracks: (Moonlight) shake my head and leave / Deadly delicious / Surgery hours (doctor doctor) / Sunset boulevard / Oddball dance / 5000 years / Don't know, can't tell / Hap-ki-do kid / Greatest story ever told / Haymaking time.
- LP .6360 126
Vertigo / '76.

■ DELETED

DAY THE EARTH CAUGHT FIRE.
Tracks: Day the earth caught fire / It's only the end of the world / Interrupted melody / Modern love affair / New York times / Up in the eighties / Machines / Ambition.
■ LP 9102036
Vertigo / Aug '79.

DAY THE EARTH CAUGHT FIRE, THE.
Tracks: Day the earth caught fire.
■ 7" 6059 238
Vertigo / Sep '79.

DINNER AT THE RITZ.
Tracks: Mommas boy / Walk on the water / Narcissus / Dinner at the Ritz / Goodbye blue Monday / Violin / State secrets - a thriller.
■ LP .6360 136
Vertigo / '76.

HAP KI DO KID.
Tracks: Hap-ki-do kid / Possessed.
■ 7" 6059 137
Vertigo / May '76.

HEADS ARE ROLLING.
Tracks: Mr. Shoes / Heads are rolling / Need a little loving / Change in the weather / Domino / Speechless / Bloody Sunday / Sound of the bell / You're leaving me / Heaven for the holidays / Life on the balcony.
■ LP .6359 024
Vertigo / Nov '80.

IN LOVE.
Tracks: In love.
■ 12" .CBD 001
City Boy / Feb '82.

LOVERS.
Tracks: Lovers / Exit the heavyweights.
■ 7" . . . . .CITY 1
Vertigo / Nov '81.

NEED A LITTLE LOVING.
Tracks: Need a little loving / Bloody Sunday.
■ 7" 6059363
Vertigo / Oct '80.

WHAT A NIGHT.
Tracks: What a night / Medicine.
■ 7" 6059 211
Vertigo / Oct '78.

YOUNG MEN GONE WEST.
Tracks: Dear Jean (I'm nervous) / Bordello night / Honeymooners / Young men gone West / I've been spun / One after tub / Runaround / Man who ate his car / Millionaire.
■ LP .6360 151
Vertigo / '77.

Civilised Society

SCRAP METAL.
Tracks: Not Advised.
■ LP . . . . ACHE 02
Manic Ears / Jan '87.

VIOLENCE SUCKS.
Tracks: Not Advised.
■ LP . . . . ACHE 07
Manic Ears / Aug '87.

YOU WERE WARNED.
Tracks: Not Advised.
CD . . . . ACHECD 021
LP . . . . ACHE 021
MC .ACHEMC 021
Manic Ears / Sep '90.

Clarke, Gilby

PAWNSHOP GUITARS.
Tracks: Not Advised.
CD .CDVUS 76
MC . . . . VUSMC 76
Virgin / Jul '94 / EMI.

Clawfinger

In the style of Rage Against The Machine, Clawfinger are one of a generation of new bands mixing rap and metal music with judicial use of samples and the f-word! Clawfinger are better than most, and stranger too because they come not from the states but from Stockholm. A quartet fronted by the lanky Zak Tell, they expand to a six-piece live and sound as heavy there

as they do on record. Clawfinger have already built a following across Europe and America won't be far behind.

DEAF, DUMB, BLIND.
Tracks: Nigger / Truth / Rosegrove / Don't get me wrong / I need you / Catch me / Warfair / Wonderful world / Sad to see your sorrow / I don't care.
CD .450993321-2
MC .450993321-4
East West / Aug '93 / WEA.

TRUTH, THE.
Tracks: Truth / Love / Get it (On CD single & 12" only) / Don't get me wrong.
■ 12" .YZ 786T
■ 7" . . . . .YZ 786
■ CD Single . . . . YZ 786CD
■ MC Single . . . . .YZ 786C
WEA / Oct '93.

WARFAIR.
Tracks: Warfair (Mixes) / Stars and stripes / Profit preacher (On CD1 only) / Truth (On CD2 only).
■ 7" . . . . .YZ 804
■ CD Single . . . . YZ 804CD1
■ CD Single . . . . YZ 804CD2
■ MC Single . . . . .YZ 804C
East West / Mar '94.

Clawhammer

PABLUM.
Tracks: Not Advised.
CD . . . . E 864252
LP . . . . E 86425
MC . . . . E 864254
Epitaph / Nov '92 / Plastic Head.

Cloven Hoof

CLOVEN HOOF.
Tracks: Nightstalker / March of the damned / Gates of Gehenna / Crack the whip / Laying down the law / Return of the passover.
■ LP . . . . NEAT 1013
MC . . . . NEATC 1013
Neat / '85 / Grapevine Distribution.

DOMINATOR.
Tracks: Rising up / Nova battlestar / Reach for the sky / Warrior of the wasteland / Invaders / Fugitive / Dominator / Road of eagles.
CD .HMRXD 113
FM Records / Aug '88 / FM Revolver / Sony.
■ LP . . . . HMRLP 113
■ MC . . . . HMRMC 113
Heavy Metal / Jul '88.

FIGHTING BACK.
Tracks: Not Advised.
■ LP . . . . CH 002
Receiver / Feb '87.

OPENING RITUAL.
Tracks: Opening ritual.
■ 7" . . . . TOA 1402
Cloven H' / Oct '82.

SULTAN'S RANSOM, A.
Tracks: Not Advised.
■ CD .HMRXD 129
■ LP .HMRLP 129
■ MC . . . . HMRMC 129
Heavy Metal / Aug '89.

SULTANS RANSOM, A.
Tracks: Astral rider / Forgotten heroes / D.V.R. / Jekyll and Hyde / 1001 Nights / Silver surfer / Notre dame / Mad, mad world / Highlander / Mistress of the forest.
■ LP . . . . HMR LP 129
FM Records / Oct '92.

Clutch

PASSIVE RESTRAINTS.
Tracks: Passive restraints / Impetus / High calibre consecrator.
■ 12" .MOSH 074T
■ CD Single . . . . .MOSH 074CD
Earache / Apr '93.

TRANS NATIONAL SPEEDWAY LEAGUE.
Tracks: Shogun named Marcus / El Jefe speaks / Binge and purge / 12 Ounce epilogue / Bacchanal / Milk of human kindness / Rats / Earthworm / Heirloom 13 / Walking in the great shining path of monster trucks / Effigy.
CD 7567922812
LP 7567922811
MC 7567922814
East West / Oct '93 / WEA.

Cochise

BEST OF COCHISE.
Tracks: Past loves / Trafalgar day / Moment and the end / Watch this space / China / That's why I sing the blues / Strange image / Down country girls / Home again / Another day / Love's made a fool of you / Cajun girl / Diamonds / Blind love / Thunder in the crib / Midnight moonshine.
CD .EDCD 254
Edsel / Sep '92 / Pinnacle.

Cockney Rejects

Punk/Oi! rabble-rousing East End band had minor hit single success and three Top 30 albums in 1979-1980. Biggest single was *Greatest Cockney Rip Off*, but best known was *War On The Terraces*. Evolved into a hard rock act with *Wild Ones* LP in 1982, which was produced by UFO's Pete Way.

BEST OF THE COCKNEY REJECTS, THE.
Tracks: Flares n slippers / Police car / I'm not a fool / East end / Bad man / Headbanger / Join the rejects / Where the hell is Babylon / War on the terraces / Oi oi oi / Hate of the city / Rocker / Greatest cockney rip off / We can do anything / Here we go again / Motorhead (Live) / Easy life (Live) / On the streets again / Power and the glory / Teenage fantasy.
CD .DOJOCD 82
Dojo / May '93 / Castle Communications / BMG.

EASY LIFE.
Tracks: Easy life / Motorhead / Hang 'em high.
■ 7" . . . . Z 20
Zonophone / Mar '81.

FLARES AND SLIPPERS.
Tracks: Flares and slippers.
■ 7" .SMALL 19
Small Wonder / Jan '79.

GREATEST COCKNEY RIP OFF.
Tracks: Greatest cockney rip off / Hate of the city.
■ 7" . . . . Z 2
Zonophone / May '80.

GREATEST HITS VOL. 3.
Tracks: Not Advised.
CD . . . . DOJOCD 168
Dojo / Nov '93 / Castle Communications / BMG.

GREATEST HITS VOL.1.
Tracks: I'm not a fool / Headbanger / Bad man / Fighting in the street / Shitter / Here they come again / Join the rejects / East End / New song / Police car / Someone like you / They're gonna put me away / Are you ready to ruck / Where the hell is Babylon / I'm forever blowing bubbles / West side boys.
CD . . . . DOJOCD 136
Dojo / Feb '94 / Castle Communications / BMG.

GREATEST HITS VOL.2.
Tracks: War on the terraces / In the underworld / Oi oi oi / Hate of the city / With the boys / Urban guerilla / Rocker / Greatest cockney rip off / Sitting in a cell / On the waterfront / We can do anything / It's alright / Subculture / Blockbuster / 15 Nights / We are the firm.
CD . . . . DOJOCD 138
Dojo / Feb '94 / Castle Communications / BMG.

GREATEST HITS VOLUME 3 (Live And Loud).
Tracks: Not Advised.

GREATEST HITS: COCKNEY REJECTS VOL 1.
Tracks: Rocker / Bad man / I'm not a fool / On the waterfront / On the run / Hate of the city / Easy life / War on the terraces / Fighting in the streets / Greatest cockney rip off / Join the Rejects / Police car / East end / Motorhead.
MC .TC ZONO 101
■ LP .ZONO 101
Zonophone / Apr '81.

GREATEST HITS: COCKNEY REJECTS VOL.2.
Tracks: War on the terraces / In the underworld / Oi oi oi / Hate of the city / With the boys / Urban guerilla / Rocker / Greatest cockney rip off / Sitting in a cell / On the waterfront / We can do anything / It's alright / Subculture / Blockbuster.
■ LP .ZONO 102
Zonophone / Oct '80.

I'M FOREVER BLOWING BUBBLES.
Tracks: I'm forever blowing bubbles / West side.
■ 7" . . . . .Z 4
Zonophone / May '80.

I'M NOT A FOOL.
Tracks: I'm not a fool.
■ 7" . . . . EMI 5008
EMI / Dec '79.

LETHAL.
Tracks: Not Advised.
CD . . . . NEATCD 1049
LP . . . . NEAT 1049
Neat / Aug '90 / Grapevine Distribution.

LIVE AND LOUD.
Tracks: Not Advised.
■ LP . . . . LINK LP 09
Link / Dec '87.

ON THE STREETS AGAIN.
Tracks: On the streets again / Lomdob.
■ 7" . . . . Z 21
Zonophone / May '81.

POWER AND THE GLORY.
Tracks: Power and the glory / Because I'm in love /
On the run / Lemon / Friends / Van Bollocks /
Teenage fantasy / It's over / On the streets again /
BYC / Greatest story ever told.
■ LP . . . . .ZONO 105
Regal Zonophone / Jul '81.
CD . . . . DOJOCD 174
Dojo / Nov '93 / Castle Communications / BMG.

TILL THE END OF THE DAY.
Tracks: Till the end of the day / Rock'n'roll dream.
■ 7" 7N 15981
Pye / Dec '65.
■ 7" . . . . .AKS 102
AKA / Nov '82.

UNHEARD REJECTS.
Tracks: Not Advised.
■ LP . . . . WOW LP 2
Wonderful World / Aug '85.

WE ARE THE FIRM.
Tracks: I'm forever blowing bubbles / War on the
terraces / On the water front / East end / Where the
hell is Babylon / Headbanger / Oi, oi, oi / Greatest
cockney rip off / Bad man / Power and the glory /
Join the Rejects / I'm not a fool / Police car /
Motorhead / We are the firm.
■ LP . . . . DOJOLP 32
Dojo / Aug '86.

WE ARE THE FIRM.
Tracks: We are the firm.
■ 7" . . . . Z 10
Zonophone / Oct '80.

WE CAN DO ANYTHING.
Tracks: We can do anything.
■ 7" . . . . .Z 6
Zonophone / Jul '80.

Coffin Break

CRAWL.
CD . . . . E 864132
LP . . . . E 864131
MC . . . . E 846314
Epitaph / Oct '91 / Plastic Head.

NO SLEEP TILL STARDUST MOTEL.
Tracks: Not Advised.
CD . . . . CZ 038
C/Z / Sep '94 / Vital Distribution / Plastic Head.

RUPTURE.
Tracks: Not Advised.
CD . . . . .TUPCD 20
LP . . . . .TUPLP 20
Tupelo / Jan '91 / Vital Distribution.

THIRTEEN.
Tracks: Not Advised.
CD . . . . E 864212
LP . . . . E 86421
Epitaph / Nov '92 / Plastic Head.

Cold Steel

BRACING THE FALL.
Tracks: Not Advised.
CD . . . . TURBO 008CD
Turbo Music / Nov '92 / Plastic Head.

DEAD BY DAWN.
Tracks: Not Advised.
LP . . . . CCG 004
C.C.G. Underground / Jan '90 / Backs Distribution.

FREAKBOY.
Tracks: Not Advised.
CD . . . . TURBO 005CD
LP . . . . TURBO 005LP
MC . . . . TURBO 005MC
Turbo Music / Nov '92 / Plastic Head.

Colour Trip

COLOURTRIP.
Tracks: Not Advised.
CD . . . . MASSCD 014
LP .MASS 014
Massacre / Feb '94 / Plastic Head.

Comecon

CONVERGING CONSPIRACIES.
Tracks: Not Advised.
CD . . . . CM 77075-2
MC . . . . CM 77057-4
Century Media / Jan '94 / Plastic Head.

Commander

HIGH 'N' MIGHTY.
Tracks: Not Advised.
■ LP . . . . IW 1028
Iron Works (USA) / Aug '88.

Company Of Wolves

COMPANY OF WOLVES.
Tracks: Call of the wild / Hangin' by a thread / Jilted /
Distance / Romance on the rocks / Can't leave ya,
can't leave ya / Hell's kitchen / St. James Infirmary /
My ship / I don't wanna be loved / Girl / Everybody's
baby.
■ CD 842 184 2
■ LP 842 184 1
■ MC 842 184 4
Phonogram / Feb '90.

Compulsion

BASKETCASE.
Tracks: Basketcase.
12" 95TP 12
CD Single 95TP7CD
One Little Indian / Jun '94 / Pinnacle.

CASSEROLE E.P.
Tracks: Not Advised.
■ 12" . . . . FLON 1202
Fabulon / Apr '93.

COMFORTER.
Tracks: Not Advised.
CD Set . . . . TPLP 59CDL
LP .TPLP 59
MC . . . . TPLP 59C
One Little Indian / Mar '94 / Pinnacle.

SAFETY.
Tracks: Not Advised.
CD . . . . TPLP 49MCD
MC . . . . TPLP 49MC
■ LP . . . . .TPLP 49M
One Little Indian / Oct '93.

Conception

LAST SUNSET.
Tracks: Prevision / Building a force / War of hate /
Bowed down with sorrow / Fairy's dance / Another
world / Elegy / Last sunset / Live to survive / Among
the Gods.
CD . . . . .N 0232-2
Noise / Jan '94 / Pinnacle.

PARALLEL MINDS.
Tracks: Not Advised.
CD . . . . .NO 2182
LP . . . . .NO 2181
Noise / Oct '93 / Pinnacle.

Concrete Sox

HERESY/CONCRETE SOX (see under
Heresy).

NO WORLD ORDER.
Tracks: Not Advised.
CD . . . . .LF 048
LP . . . . .LF 048 1
Lost & Found / Aug '93 / Plastic Head.

WHOOPS SORRY VICAR!.
Tracks: Prophecy / No trust no faith / Scientific
slaughter / Comparison / Rumour well out of hand /

Think now / False insight / Dream / Salt of the earth /
Facts / Moustache cacting / Like a maniac.
■ LP . . . . .ACHE 11
Manic Ears / Jan '88.

YOUR TURN NEXT.
Tracks: Not Advised.
■ LP . . . . GURT 10
Children Of The Revolution / Apr '86.

Condemned

HUMANOID.
Tracks: Not Advised.
LP . . . . NB 002
Nuclear Blast / Aug '92 / Plastic Head.

Coney Hatch

CONEY HATCH.
Tracks: Devil's deck / You ain't got me / Stand up /
No sleep tonight / Love poison / We've got the night /
Hey operator / I'll do the talking / Victim of rock /
Monkey bars.
■ LP . . . . MERS 15
MC . . . . MERSC 15
Mercury / Apr '83 / PolyGram.

CONEY HATCH: THE VIDEO SINGLE.
Tracks: Not Advised.
VHS 041 388 2
Polygram Music Video / Jun '86 / PolyGram.

FRICTION.
Tracks: This ain't love / She's gone / Wrong side of
town / Girls from last night's dream / Coming to get
you / Fantasy / He's a champion / State love /
Burning love.
■ LP . . . . .VERL 23
Vertigo / Apr '85.

HEY OPERATOR.
Tracks: Hey operator / Devils deck.
■ 12" . . . . .HATCH 12
■ 7" . . . . HATCH 1
Mercury / Mar '83.

OUTA HAND.
Tracks: Not Advised.
■ LP . . . . VERL 7
Vertigo / Aug '83.

THIS AIN'T LOVE.
Tracks: This ain't love / He's a champion.
■ 12" . . . . .VERX 18
■ 7" . . . . VER 18
Vertigo / Apr '85.

Confessor

CONDEMNED.
Tracks: Not Advised.
CD . . . . .MOSH 044CD
LP . . . . MOSH 44
■ MC . . . . MOSH 44MC
Earache / Oct '91.

CONDEMNED.
Tracks: Condemned.
■ 12" . . . . .MOSH 058T
Earache / Mar '92.

Confusion

HOPELESS.
Tracks: Hopeless.
■ 7" . . . . AMOK 005
Amok / Jun '93.

Connelly, Chris

COME DOWN HERE.
Tracks: Come down here.
■ 12" . . . . 12 DVN 108
CD . . . . .CDDVN 108
■ CD Single . . . . .CDVN 108
Music For Nations / Aug '92.

PHENOBARB BAM-BA-LAM.
Tracks: Not Advised.
CD . . . . .CDDVN 13
LP . . . . DVN 13
MC . . . . .TDVN 13
Music For Nations / Jul '92 / Pinnacle.

WHIPLASH BOYCHILD.
Tracks: Not Advised.
CD . . . . .CDDVN 14
LP . . . . DVN 14
MC . . . . .TDVN 14
Devotion / Oct '92 / Pinnacle.

Consolation

NEMBRIONIC HAMMERDEATH/CONSO-LATION SPLIT ALBUM (see under Nembrionic Hammerdeath).

Contagious

ANOTHER HUMAN INTEREST STORY.
Tracks: Not Advised.
■ CD................... RR 90872
Road Runner / Mar '93.

Contraband

ALL THE WAY FROM MEMPHIS.
Tracks: All the way from Memphis / All the way from
Memphis (balls to the wall version) / Loud guitars,
fast cars and wild wild livin'.
■ 12"..................... 12EMP 195
■ 7".................... EM 195
■ CD Single............... CDEM 195
■ MC Single.............. TCEM 195
Impact (EMI) / Jul '91.

CONTRABAND.
Tracks: All the way from Memphis / Kiss by kiss /
Intimate outrage / Bad for each other / Loud guitars,
fast cars & wild, wild livin' / Good rockin' tonight / If
this is love / Stand / Tonight you're mine / Hang onto
yourself.
■ CD................ CDEMC 3594
■ LP................ EMC 3594
■ MC................ TCEMC 3594
Impact (EMI) / Jun '91.

Controlled Bleeding

BODY SAMPLES.
Tracks: Not Advised.
CD................... EFA 5321 D
Dossier / Mar '93 / SRD.

CONTROLLED BLEEDING.
Tracks: Not Advised.
CD....................KK 025CD
K K / '89 / Plastic Head.
CD............... CLEO 1022CD
Cleopatra / Jan '94 / Plastic Head / Pinnacle.

CURD.
Tracks: Not Advised.
■ LP................... ST 7516
Dossier / Apr '87.
CD.................. EFA 7726 D
Dossier / Mar '93 / SRD.

FODDER SONG, THE.
Tracks: Fodder song.
■ 12".................. WAX 091
■ CD Single............ WAX 091CD
Wax Trax / Apr '90.

HEADCRACK.
Tracks: Not Advised.
■ LP.................... SR 12
Sterile / Jun '86.

LES NOUVELLES MISTIQUES DE CHAMBRE.
Tracks: Not Advised.
■ LP................. SUB 33015-20
Sub Rosa / '89.

MUSIC FOR GUILDED CHAMBERS.
Tracks: Not Advised.
LP....................SUB 33018-24
Sub Rosa / '90 / Vital Distribution / These Records.

MUSIC FROM THE SCOURGING GROUND.
Tracks: Not Advised.
■ LP................. SUB 33008-11
Sub Rosa / Dec '87.

MUSIC FROM THE VAULTS.
Tracks: Not Advised.
CD.................... DV 21
Dark Vinyl / Mar '94 / Plastic Head.

PENETRATION.
Tracks: Not Advised.
■ CD.................. TM 91652
Road Runner / Jun '92.

PETS FOR MEAT (Controlled Bleeding & Doc Wor Mirran).
Tracks: Not Advised.
CD................. EFA 12205-2
Crypt / Apr '94 / SRD.

SONGS FROM GRINDING WALL.
Tracks: Not Advised.
CD................... WAX 044 CD
Wax Trax / '89 / SRD.

SONGS FROM THE ASHES.
Tracks: Not Advised.
CD....................CLM 022CD
C'est La Morte / '89 / Rough Trade Inc.

SONGS FROM THE DRAIN.
Tracks: Not Advised.
■ LP................... ST 7550
Dossier / Nov '87.
CD.................. EFA 08547-2
Dossier / Jun '94 / SRD.

SONGS FROM THE GRINDING WALL.
Tracks: Songs from the grinding wall.
■ 12"...................WAXUK 044
Wax Trax / Mar '89.

TRUDGE.
Tracks: Not Advised.
CD................... WAX CD 090
LP................... WAX LP 090
Wax Trax / May '90 / SRD.

Convict

GO AHEAD..MAKE MY DAY.
Tracks: Not Advised.
■ LP.................... RR 9746
Road Runner / Sep '85.

Cooper, Alice

Self-proclaimed 'Worst band in LA' released three albums before UK/US success with *Killer* and *School's Out*. Latter's title track became Alice's anthem. Live and in studio, band mixed theatre and rock n' roll; a highly influential formula later adopted by Ozzy Osbourne and Kiss. Band split in 1974, lead singer (born Vincent Furnier) taking name for himself. Alice's solo career heralded by classic *Welcome To My Nightmare*. Alcoholism and declining sales made Cooper cult act until rejuvenation in mid-80s; two Top 10 albums and 1989 hit *Poison* are highlights of recent career. 1994 *Last Temptation*.. album harked back to Cooper concept albums of '70s.

ALICE COOPER LIVE 1968.
Tracks: Not Advised.
CD..................... EDCD 320
MC.....................CED 320
Edsel / Feb '92 / Pinnacle.

ALICE COOPER SHOW, THE.
Tracks: Under my wheels / Eighteen / Only women
bleed / Sick things / Is it my body / I never cry /
Billion dollar babies / Devil's food / Black widow /
You and me / I love the dead / Go to hell / Wish you
were here / School's out.
MC...................... K4 56439
■ LP.................... K 56439
WEA / Jan '78.

ALICE COOPER TRASHES THE WORLD.
Tracks: Trash / Billion dollars babies / I'm eighteen /
I'm your gun / Desperado / House of fire / No more
Mr. nice guy / This manics in love with you / Steven /
Welcome to my nightmare / Ballad of dwight fry /
Gutter Cats vs The Jets / Only woman blled / I love
the dead / Poison / Muscle of love / Spark in the dark
/ Bed of nails / School's out / Under my wheels /
Only my heart talkin'.
VHS......................490422
Sony Music Video / Mar '94 / Sony.

ALICE COOPER: INTERVIEW PICTURE DISC.
Tracks: Not Advised.
■ LP P.Disc............... CT 1015
Music & Media / Dec '87.
LP P.Disc................ BAK 2059
Baktabak / Sep '87 / Arabesque Ltd.

BEAST OF ALICE COOPER, THE.
Tracks: School's out / Under my wheels / Billion
dollar babies / Be my lover / Desperado / Is it my
body / Only women bleed / Elected / I'm eighteen /
Hello hooray / No more Mr. Nice Guy / Teenage
lament '74 / Muscle of love / Department of youth.
CD......................2417812
MC.................... WX 331C
■ LP.................... WX 331
WEA / Nov '89.

BED OF NAILS.
Tracks: Bed of nails / I'm your gun.
■ 12"....................ALICE Q3
■ 12"....................ALICE T3
■ 12" P.Disc...............ALICE P3
■ 7"....................ALICE G3
■ 7"....................ALICE R3
■ 7"..................... ALICE 3
■ 7" P.Disc..............ALICE B3
■ CD Single...............ALICE C3
■ MC Single.............ALICE M3
Epic / Sep '89.

BILLION DOLLAR BABIES.
Tracks: Hello hooray / Raped and freezin' / Elected /
Unfinished sweet / No more Mr. nice guy / Generation landslide / Sick things / Mary Ann / I love the
dead / Billion dollar babies.
■ LP.................... K 56013
WEA / '73.
CD................. 7599 27269-2
Warner Bros. / Jan '90 / WEA.

BOX SET.
Tracks: Not Advised.
■ VHS.................. HEN 2303
Hendring Video / Nov '90.

CONSTRICTOR.
Tracks: Not Advised.
■ CD................. DMCF 3341
■ LP................. MCF 3341
■ MC................ MCFC 3341
MCA / Oct '86.
■ MC................ MCLC 19068
MCA / Oct '92.
CD................. MCLD 19068
MCA / Jan '94 / BMG.

DA DA.
Tracks: Da da / Enough's enough / Former Lee
Warner / No man's land / Dyslexia / Scarlet and
Sheba / I love America / Fresh blood / Pass the gun
around.
■ LP.................. K 923969 1
WEA / Nov '83.

DEPARTMENT OF YOUTH.
Tracks: Department of youth / Cold ethyl.
■ 7"................... ANC 1012
Anchor (1) / Jan '75.

EASY ACTION.
Tracks: Not Advised.
CD Set.................. 773 391 2
Enigma (EMI) / Jul '90 / EMI.

ELECTED.
Tracks: Elected.
■ 7".................... K 16214
WEA / Oct '72.

FEED MY FRANKENSTEIN.
Tracks: Feed my frankenstein / Burning our bed /
Poison (Only available on 12"PD and CD Single.) /
Only my heart talkin' (Only available on 12"PD and
CD Single.).
■ 12" P.Disc............... 6580926
■ 7" P.Disc................ 6580927
■ CD Single................ 6580922
Epic / May '92.

FLUSH THE FASHION.
Tracks: Talk talk / We're all clones / Pain / Leather
boots / Aspirin damage / Nuclear infected / Grim
facts / Model citizen / Dance yourself to death /
Headlines.
■ LP.................... K 56805
■ MC................... K4 56805
WEA / '88.

FOR BRITAIN ONLY.
Tracks: For Britain only / Under my wheels.
■ 7".................... K 17940
■ 7" P.Disc.............. K 17940 P
WEA / May '82.

FREAK OUT SONG.
Tracks: Freak out song / Ain't that just like a woman /
Painting a picture / I've written home to mother /
Science fiction / Going to the river / A.C. Instrumental / Nobody likes me.
■ LP................... SHLP 115
MC.................... SHTC 115
Castle Showcase / Apr '86 / Arabesque Ltd.

FREEDOM.
Tracks: Freedom / Time to kill / School's out (live)
(Extra track on 12".).
■ 12"................. MCAX 1241
■ 12"................. MCAT 1241
■ 7"..................MCA 1241
MCA / Mar '88.

FROM THE INSIDE.
Tracks: From the inside / Wish I were born in Beverley Hills / Quiet room / Nurse Rozetta / Millie and Billie / Serious / How you gonna see me now / For Veronica's sake / Jack-knife Johnny / Inmates (we're all crazy).
■ **LP** . . . . K 56577
WEA / Dec '78.

GOES TO HELL.
Tracks: Go to hell / You gotta dance / I'm the coolest / Didn't we meet / I never cry / Give the kid a break / Guilty / Wake me gently / Wish you were here / I'm always chasing rainbows / Going home.
■ **LP** . . . . K 56171
WEA / Jun '76.

GREATEST HITS: ALICE COOPER.
Tracks: I'm eighteen / Is it my body / Desperado / Under my wheels / Be my lover / School's out / Hello hooray / Elected / No more Mr. nice guy / Billion dollar babies / Teenage lament '74 / Muscle of love.
■ **LP** . . . . K 56043
WEA / Aug '74.
■ **MC** K4 56043
WEA / Aug '74.
■ **CD** K2 56045
WEA / Jun '89.

HE'S BACK (THE MAN BEHIND THE MASK).
Tracks: Billion Dollar babies / He's back (the man behind the mask).
■ **12"** . . . . MCAT 1090
■ **7"** . . . . MCA 1090
MCA / Oct '86.

HELLO HURRAY.
Tracks: Hello hurray.
■ **7"** . . . . K 16248
WEA / Feb '73.

HEY STOOPID.
Tracks: Hey stoopid / Love's a loaded gun / Snakebite / Burning our bed / Dangerous tonight / Might as well be on Mars / Feed my Frankenstein / Hurricane years / Little by little / Die for you / Dirty dreams / Wind up toys.
CD 4684162
■ **LP** 4684161
■ **MC** 4684164
Epic / Jun '92.
MiniDisc 468416-3
Epic / Feb '93 / Sony.

HEY STOOPID.
Tracks: Hey stoopid / It rained all night (Only on 12" single) / Wind up toy.
■ **12"** 6569836
■ **12" P.Disc.** 6569838
■ **7"** 6569837
■ **CD Single** 6569839
Epic / Jun '91.

HOUSE OF FIRE.
Tracks: House of fire / This maniac's in love with you / Billion dollar babies (live) (on 12" and CD 5" only) / Under my wheels (live) (on 12" and CD 5" only) / Poison (Live).
■ **12"** . . . . ALICE T4
■ **7"** . . . . ALICE 4
■ **7"** . . . . ALICE Y4
■ **7"** . . . . ALICE R4
■ **7" P.Disc** . . . . ALICE P4
■ **CD Single** . . . . ALICE C4
■ **MC Single** . . . . ALICE M4
Epic / Nov '89.
■ **12"** . . . . ALICE S4
■ **7"** . . . . ALICE X4
■ **7"** . . . . ALICE L4
Epic / Nov '89.

HOW YOU GONNA SEE ME NOW.
Tracks: How you gonna see me now.
■ **7"** . . . . K 17270
WEA / Dec '78.

I AM THE FUTURE.
Tracks: I am the future / Zorro's ascent.
■ **7"** . . . . K 15004
WEA / Nov '82.

I LOVE AMERICA.
Tracks: I love America / Fresh blood / Pass the gun around.
■ **12"** . . . . ALICE 1T
WEA / Nov '83.

IT'S ME.
Tracks: It's me / Bad place alone / Poison (Live) (Does not feature on MCS.) / Sick things (Live) (Does not feature on MCS.).
12" P.Disc. 66056 3

CD Single 660563 2
Epic / Jul '94 / Sony.

KILLER.
Tracks: Under my wheels / Be my lover / Halo of flies / Desperado / You drive me nervous / Yeah, yeah, yeah / Dead babies / Killer.
■ **LP** . . . . K 56005
WEA.
CD .K 9272552
WEA / Sep '89 / WEA.

LACE AND WHISKEY.
Tracks: Damned if you do / My God / It's hot tonight / Lace and whiskey / Road rats / No more love at your convenience / Ubangi stomp / You and me / I never wrote those songs.
■ **LP** . . . . K 56365
WEA / May '77.

LADIES MAN.
Tracks: Freak out / Painting a picture / I've written home to mother / Science fiction / For Alice / Nobody likes me / Going to the river / Ain't that just like a woman.
■ **LP** . . . . .THBM 005
■ **MC** . . . . THBMC 005
Thunderbolt / Apr '87.
CD .CDTB 090
■ **MC** . . . . THBC 090
Thunderbolt / Feb '91.

LAST TEMPTATION, THE.
Tracks: Slideshow / Nothing's free / Lost in America / Bad place alone / You're my temptation / Stolen prayer / Unholy war / Lullaby / It's me / Cleansed by fire.
MiniDisc. 476594 8
Epic / Jul '94 / Sony.
CD 476594 2
LP 476594 1
LP 476594 0
MC 476594 4
Epic / Jun '94 / Sony.

LEGENDS IN MUSIC - ALICE COOPER.
Tracks: Not Advised.
CD . . . . LECD 085
Wisepack / Sep '94 / TBD / Conifer Records.

LIVE AT THE WHISKEY A GO GO, 1969.
Tracks: No longer umpire / Today Mueller / 10 minutes before the worm / Levity ball / Nobody likes me / B.B. on Mars / Sing low, sweet cheerio / Changing arranging.
CD . . . . NESTCD 903
LP . . . . NEST 903
Edsel / Mar '92 / Pinnacle.

LOST IN AMERICA.
Tracks: Lost in America / Hey stoopid (Live) / Billion dollar babies (Live) / No more Mr. Nice Guy (Live).
■ **12"** 660347 6
■ **CD Single** 660347 2
■ **MC Single** 660347 4
Epic / May '94.

LOVE AT YOUR CONVENIENCE.
Tracks: Love at your convenience / Hot tonight.
■ **7"** . . . . K 16935
WEA / Apr '77.

LOVE AT YOUR CONVENIENCE (RE-RELEASE).
Tracks: Love at your convenience / You and me.
■ **7"** . . . . K 17914
WEA / Feb '82.

LOVE IT TO DEATH.
Tracks: Caught in a dream / I'm eighteen / Long way to go / Black Juju / Is it my body / Hallowed be my name / Second coming / Ballad of Dwight Fry / Sun arise.
■ **LP** . . . . K 46177
WEA / Sep '72.
MC. K4 46177
WEA / Sep '87 / WEA.

LOVE'S A LOADED GUN.
Tracks: Love's a loaded gun / Fire / Eighteen (live) (Only on CD Single.).
■ **CD Single** 6574389
■ **MC Single** 6574644
■ **12" P.Disc.** 6574388
■ **7"** 6574387
Epic / Oct '91.

MUSCLE OF LOVE.
Tracks: Not Advised.
■ **LP** . . . . K 56018
WEA / Jan '74.

NIGHTMARE RETURNS, THE.
Tracks: Not Advised.
■ **VHS** . . . . HEN 2052
Hendring Video / '87.

NO MORE MR NICE GUY.
Tracks: No more Mr. nice guy.
■ **7"** . . . . K 16262
WEA / Apr '73.

POISON.
Tracks: Poison / Trash / Ballad of Dwight Fry (live) (Only on 12" (6550618) and CD single.) / I got a line on you (Only on CD single.) / Cold ethyl (live) (Only on 12" single (6550619)).
■ **12"** 6550619
■ **12"** 6550618
■ **7"** 6550617
■ **CD Single** 6550612
■ **CD Single** 6550652
Epic / Jul '89.

PRETTIES FOR YOU.
Tracks: Not Advised.
CD Set 773 362 2
Enigma (EMI) / Jul '90 / EMI.

PRIME CUTS.
Tracks: Not Advised.
VHS . . . . .CMP 6050
Castle Music Pictures / Jun '91 / BMG.

RAISE YOUR FIST AND YELL.
Tracks: Lock me up / Give the radio back / Freedom / Step on you / Not that kind of love / Prince of Darkness / Time to kill / Chop, chop, chop / Gail / Roses on white lace.
■ **LP P.Disc** . . . . MCFP 3392
■ **LP** . . . . MCF 3392
■ **MC** . . . . MCFC 3392
MCA / Oct '87.
■ **CD** . . . . DMCF 3392
MCA / Apr '88.
CD . . . . MCLD 19137
■ **MC** . . . . MCLC 19137
MCA / Nov '91.

ROCK LEGENDS VOL.2.
Tracks: Ain't that just like a woman / Painting a picture / An instrumental / I've written home to mother / Freak out song / Goin to the river / Nobody likes me / Science fiction.
CD . . . . SMS 054
Pickwick / Oct '92 / Pickwick.

SCHOOL'S OUT.
Tracks: Luney tune / Gutter cat vs the jets / Blue turk / My stars / Public animal no. 9 / Alma master / Grand finale / Schools out.
MC. K4 56007
WEA / Mar '85 / WEA.
■ **LP** . . . . K 56007
WEA / '88.
CD 9272602
WEA / Jun '89 / WEA.

SCHOOL'S OUT.
Tracks: School's out.
■ **7"** . . . . K 16188
WEA / Jul '72.
■ **7"** . . . . K 16287
WEA / Nov '76.

SCHOOL'S OUT (OLD GOLD).
Tracks: School's out / Elected.
■ **7"** .OG 9519
Old Gold / Sep '85.

SEVEN AND SEVEN IS (LIVE VERSION).
Tracks: Seven and seven is / Generation landslide.
■ **7"** . . . . K 17924
WEA / Mar '82.

SNAKES AND DEAD BABIES.
Tracks: Not Advised.
CD P.Disc. . . . . CBAK 4037
Baktabak / Apr '90 / Arabesque Ltd.

SPECIAL FORCES.
Tracks: Who do you think we are / Seven and seven is / Skeletons in the closet / You're no good / You want it, you got it / Vicious rumours / Prettiest cop on the block / Generation landslide '81 (Live) / You look good in rags / Don't talk old to me / Look at you over there, ripping the dust from my teddybear.
■ **LP** . . . . K 56927
WEA / Sep '81.
MC. K4 56927
WEA / Sep '81 / WEA.

TEENAGE FRANKENSTEIN.
Tracks: Teenage Frankenstein (live) / Schools out (live) / Only women bleed (This extra track on 12" only).

                                     ■ DELETED

■ 12″. . . . . MCAT 1113
■ 7″. . . . . .MCA 1113
MCA / Mar '87.

TEENAGE LAMENT '74.
Tracks: Teenage lament '74.
■ 7″ . . . . K 16345
WEA / Jan '74.

TORONTO ROCK 'N' ROLL REVIVAL.
Tracks: Not Advised.
■ LP . . . . PIXLP 3
Design / Jul '84.

TRASH.
Tracks: Poison / Spark in the dark / House of fire / Why trust you / Only my heart talkin' / Bed of nails / This maniac's in love with you / Trash / Hell is living without you / I'm your gun.
CD. 4651302
MC. 4651304
■ LP 4651301
Epic / Aug '89.

WE'RE ALL CLONES.
Tracks: We're all clones / Model citizens.
■ 7″ . . . . K 17598
WEA / May '80.

WELCOME TO MY NIGHTMARE.
Tracks: Not Advised.
■ VHS . . . . HEN 2072
Hendring Video / Mar '92.

YOU AND ME.
Tracks: You and me / My god.
■ 7″ . . . . K 16984
WEA / Jul '77.

ZIPPER CATCHES THE SKIN.
Tracks: Zorro's ascent / Make that money / I am the future / No baloney homosapiens / Adaptable (Anything for you) / I like girls / Remarkably insincere / Tag, you're it / I better be good / I'm alive (that was the day my dead pet return.
■ LP . . . . K 57021
WEA / '84.

Cop Shoot Cop

10 DOLLAR BILL.
Tracks: Not Advised.
■ 12″. . . . . ABB 053T
■ CD Single. . . . . ABBSCD 053
Big Cat / Jun '93.

ASK QUESTIONS LATER.
Tracks: Not Advised.
CD. . . . . ABBCD 045
LP . . . . .ABB 045
Big Cat / Apr '93 / Pinnacle.

CONSUMER REVOLT.
Tracks: Not Advised.
CD. . . . . ABB 033CD
LP . . . . .ABB 033
MC. . . . . ABB 033C
Big Cat / Apr '92 / Pinnacle.

RELEASE.
Tracks: Not Advised.
CD. . . . . ABB 69CD
LP . . . . ABB 69
Big Cat / Aug '94 / Pinnacle.

ROOM 429.
Tracks: Room 429.
■ 12″. . . . . ABB 054T
■ CD Single. . . . . ABBSCD 054
Big Cat / Dec '93.

SUCK CITY.
Tracks: Not Advised.
■ 12″. . . . . ABBO 39 T
CD. . . . . ABBSCDO 39
Big Cat / Sep '92 / Pinnacle.

WHITE NOISE.
Tracks: Not Advised.
CD. . . . . ABB 029CD
LP . . . . .ABB 029
MC. . . . . ABB 029C
Big Cat / Oct '91 / Pinnacle.

Coroner

Association with Celtic Frost (Coroner roadied for Frost and band's Tom G Warrior sang on early demos) won Coroner record deal in 1986. Band have since released five albums, of which 1993's *Grin* is the latest and 1989's *No More Color* the best. Lack of

international success attributed to infrequent touring.

GRIN.
Tracks: Dream path / Lethargic age / Internal conflicts / Cavaet (To the coming) / Serpent moves / Status: Still thinking / Theme for silence / Paralized, mesmerized / Grin (Nails hurt) / Host.
CD. . . . . .N 0210-2
LP . . . . .N 0210-1
MC. . . . . .N 0210-4
Noise / May '93 / Pinnacle.

MENTAL VORTEX.
Tracks: Not Advised.
CD. . . . . .NO 1772
LP . . . . .NO 1771
MC. . . . . .NO 1774
Noise / Aug '91 / Pinnacle.

NO MORE COLOUR.
Tracks: Not Advised.
■ CD . . . . .CDNUK 138
■ LP . . . . .NUK 138
■ MC. . . . . ZCNUK 138
Noise / Oct '89.

NO MORE COLOUR TOUR '90 (Live in East Berlin).
Tracks: Not Advised.
VHS . . . . .NFV 108
Fotodisk Video / Jun '90.

PUNISHMENT FOR DECADE.
Tracks: Not Advised.
■ CD . . . . .CDNUK 119
■ LP . . . . .NUK 119
■ MC. . . . . ZCNUK 119
Noise / Oct '89.

PURPLE HAZE.
Tracks: Purple haze.
■ 7″ 7HAZE 3
In Phaze / Oct '89.

R.I.P.
Tracks: Not Advised.
■ CD . . . . .CDNUK 075
■ LP . . . . .NUK 075
■ MC. . . . . ZCNUK 075
Noise / Oct '89.

Corpse Grinder

LEGEND OF CORPSE GRINDERS, THE.
Tracks: Not Advised.
■ LP . . . . .FC 004
Fan Club / May '84.

VALLEY OF FEAR.
Tracks: Not Advised.
■ LP . . . . ROSE 39
New Rose / Nov '84.

Corpus Rottus

RITUALS OF SILENCE.
Tracks: Not Advised.
LP . . . . DD 11711
With Your Teeth / Jan '94 / Plastic Head.

Corrosion Of Conformity

ANIMOSITY.
Tracks: Loss for words / Mad world / Consumed / Holier / Positive outlook / Prayer / Intervention / Kill death / Hungry child / Animosity.
■ LP . . . . RR 9764
Road Runner / Aug '85.
CD. . . . . .CDZORRO 44
Metal Blade / Apr '93 / Pinnacle.

BLIND.
Tracks: Not Advised.
CD. . . . . RO 92362
LP . . . . RO 92361
MC. . . . . RO 92364
Road Runner / Nov '91 / Pinnacle.

EYE FOR AN EYE.
Tracks: Tell me / Indifferent / Rabid dogs / Redneckkk / Minds are controlled / Broken will / L.S. / Co-exist / Dark thoughts / What / Positive outlook / College town / Eye for an eye / Poison planet / Negative outlook / No drunk / Not safe / Nothing's gonna change.
■ LP . . . . .TXLP 04
Toxic Shock.
■ CD . . . . CAROLCD 1356
■ LP . . . . CAROL 1356
■ MC. . . . . CAROLMC 1356
Product Inc. / Feb '90.

CD. . . . . INCDD 002/3
LP . . . . .INCLP 002
Product Inc. / Jun '94 / Vital Distribution.

EYE FOR AN EYE/SIX SONGS WITH MIKE SINGING.
Tracks: Tell me / Minds are controlled / Indifferent / Broken will / Rabid dogs / L.S. / Redneckkk / Coexist / Excluded / Dark thoughts / Poison planet / What / Negative outlook / Positive outlook / No drunk / College town / Not safe / Eye for an eye / Nothing's gonna change / Eye for an eye (2) / Center of the world / Citizen / Not for me / What (2) / Negative outlook (2).
CD. . . . . INCCD 002/3
Product Inc. / Jun '94 / Vital Distribution.

SIX SONGS WITH MIKE SINGING.
Tracks: Eye for an eye / Citizen / What / Center of the world / Not for me / Negative outlook.
■ LP . . . . CAROL 1365
■ MC. . . . . CAROLMC 1365
Product Inc. / Feb '90.
LP . . . . .INCLP 003
Product Inc. / Jun '94 / Vital Distribution.

TECHNOCRACY.
Tracks: Technocracy.
■ 12″. . . . . RR 125477
Metal Blade / May '87.

TECHNOCRACY.
Tracks: Technocracy / Hungry child / Happily ever after / Crawling / Ahh blugh / Intervention / Technocracy (2) / Crawling (2) / Happily ever after (2).
CD. . . . . .CDZORRO 53
Metal Blade / Apr '93 / Pinnacle.

VOTE WITH A BULLET.
Tracks: Vote with a bullet.
■ 12″. . . . . RR 23886
■ CD Single. . . . . RR 23883
Road Runner / Dec '92.

Count Raven

DESTRUCTION OF THE VOID.
Tracks: Until death do us part / Hippies triumph / Destruction of the void / Let the dead bury the dead / Northern lights / Leaving the warzone / Angel of death / Final journey / On ones hero / Europa.
CD. HELL019CD
Hellhound / Apr '94 / Plastic Head.

HIGH ON INFINITY.
Tracks: Jen / Children's holocaust / In honour / Madman from waco / Masters of all evil / Ode to Rebecca / High on infinity / An ordinary loser / Traitor / Dance / Coming / Lost world / Cosmos.
CD. . . . . HELL 026
Hellhound / Apr '94 / Plastic Head.

STORM WARNING.
Tracks: Intro: Count Raven / Inam naudemina / True revelation / In the name of rock 'n' roll / Sometimes a great nation / Within the garden of mirrors / Devastating age / How can it be / Social warfare.
■ LP . . . . ATV 16
Active / Dec '90.
CD. . . . . HELL 009CD
Hellhound / Apr '94 / Plastic Head.

Coverdale, David

Coverdale leapt from nowhere to stardom in 1973, when he replaced Ian Gillan as singer with Deep Purple. When they folded in 1976, Coverdale made two heroically unsuccessful solo albums before creating chartbusting Whitesnake. Contribution to *Days Of Thunder* soundtrack in 1990 hinted at solo career; however, Coverdale teamed up with Jimmy Page, then reconvened Whitesnake in '94.

BREAKDOWN.
Tracks: Breakdown / Only my soul.
■ 7″ . . . . .PUR 136
Purple / Feb '78.

HOLE IN THE SKY.
Tracks: Hole in the sky / Blindman.
■ 7″ . . . . .PUR 133
Purple / May '77.

LAST NOTE OF FREEDOM, THE.
Tracks: Last note of freedom / Car building / Gimme some lovin' (Available on all formats except 7″ single.) / Last note of freedom, The (LP version) (Available on CD single format only.).
■ 12″. 6562926
■ 7″ 6562920
■ 7″ 6562927

■ CD Single 6562922
■ MC Single 6562924
Epic / Sep '90.

NORTHWINDS.
Tracks: Keep on giving me love / Give me kindness /
Time and again / Queen of Hearts / Only my soul /
Say you love me / Breakdown / Northwinds.
■ LP . . . . TTS 3513
Purple / Feb '82.
■ LP . . . . FA 413 097 1
MC . . . . FA 413 097 4
Fame / Apr '84 / EMI.

WHITESNAKE.
Tracks: Lady / Blindman / Goldies place / Whites-
nake / Time on my side / Peace lovin' man / Sunny
days / Hole in the sky / Celebration.
■ LP . . . . TPS 3509
Purple / May '77.

WHITESNAKE/NORTHWINDS.
Tracks: Lady / Time on my side / Blindman / Goldies
place / Whitesnake / Peace lovin' man / Sunny days /
Hole in the sky / Celebration / Keep on giving me
love / Northwinds / Give me kindness / Time and
time again / Queen of hearts / Only my soul / Say
you love me / Breakdown.
CD . . . . VSOPCD 118
■ Double LP . . . . VSOPLP 118
MC . . . . VSOPMC 118
Connoisseur Collection / Nov '88 / Pinnacle.

Coverdale-Page

COVERDALE PAGE (Coverdale, David &
Jimmy Page).
Tracks: Shake my tree / Waiting on you / Take me for
a little while / Pride and joy / Over now / Feeling hot
/ Easy does it / Take a look at yourself / Don't leave
me this way / Absolution blues / Whisper a prayer
for the dying.
■ LP . . . . EMD 1041
EMI / Mar '93.
CD . . . . CDEMD 1041
MC . . . . TCEMD 1041
EMI / Jul '94 / EMI.

TAKE A LOOK AT YOURSELF.
Tracks: Take a look at yourself / Waiting on you /
Take a look at yourself (mixes) (Available on CDS
only).
■ 7" P.Disc . . . . EMPD 279
■ CD Single . . . . CDEM 279
■ MC Single . . . . TCEM 279
EMI / Aug '93.

TAKE ME FOR A LITTLE WHILE.
Tracks: Take me for a little while / Take me for a
little while (Mixes) / Shake my tree (The crunch mix)
(Features on 12" & CDS's only.) / Easy does it
(Features on 12" & MCS only.)
■ 12" 12EMPD 270
■ 12" . . . . CDEMS 270
■ CD Single . . . . CDEM 270
■ MC Single . . . . TCEM 270
EMI / Jun '93.

Craaft

CRAAFT.
Tracks: I wanna look in your eyes / Breakin' walls
ain't easy / Hold me / You're the best thing in my life
/ I guess you are the number one / Stranger / Don't
wanna wait no more / Now that you're gone / Wasted
years / Cool town lovers.
■ LP . . . . EPC 26880
Epic / Jul '86.
■ MC 40 26880
CBS / Jul '86.

I WANNA LOOK IN YOUR EYES.
Tracks: I wanna look in your eyes / I guess you are
the number one.
■ 7" . . . . A 6954
Epic / Jun '86.

SECOND HONEYMOON.
Tracks: Run away / Chance of your life / Gimme what
you got / Hey babe / Don't you know what love can
be / Right to your heart / Twisted up all inside / Jane
/ Running on love / Illusions / Are you ready to rock.
■ LP . . . . PL 71826
RCA / '88.
■ CD . . . . PD 71826
■ MC . . . . PK 71826
RCA / Jan '89.

Crackerbash

TIN TOY.
Tracks: Not Advised.
CD . . . . EFA 11397CD
Musical Tragedies / Aug '93 / SRD.

Cradle Of Filth

PRINCIPLE OF EVIL MADE FLESH.
Tracks: Not Advised.
CD . . . . NIHIL 1CD
LP . . . . NIHIL 1LP
Vinyl Solution / Mar '94 / RTM / Pinnacle.

Crash 'N' Burn

FEVER.
Tracks: Hot like fire / It takes two / Ride the rainbow /
So close to me / Dancing with the devil / Rio Corona
/ River of love / Wild cherry / Bump & grind / Fade
away / Singing the blues / Wheels of fire.
■ LP . . . . PL 74899
■ MC . . . . PK 74899
■ CD . . . . PD 74899
RCA / Sep '91.

HOT LIKE FIRE.
Tracks: Hot like fire.
■ CD Single . . . . PD 44278
■ 12" . . . . PT 44278
RCA / Aug '91.

Crawlpappy

DELUXE.
Tracks: Not Advised.
CD WB2-094CD
We Bite / Nov '92 / Plastic Head.

Cream

Much-imitated 'power trio' Cream formed in
1966; a successful union of drummer Ginger
Baker, bassist/vocalist Jack Bruce and guitarist Eric Clapton. Debut *Fresh Cream* set
pattern for future work: bluesy rock laced
with lengthy solos. 1967's *Disraeli Gears*
was huge success but, after two further
albums, internal friction prompted split in
November 1968. Singles *I Feel Free, Sunshine Of Your Love* and *White Room* - latter
two breaching U.S. Top Ten - became rock
standards. After split, only Clapton established career eclipsing that of Cream. Reformation of sorts occurred with creation of
BBM in 1994, Gary Moore assuming guitar
duties.

ALTERNATIVE ALBUM, THE.
Tracks: Not Advised.
CD . . . . ITM 960002
ITM Pacific / Oct '92 / Koch International / Complete
Record Co. Ltd.

ANYONE FOR TENNIS ("SAVAGE SE-
VEN" THEME).
Tracks: Anyone for tennis.
■ 7" 56 258
Polydor / Jun '68.

BADGE.
Tracks: Badge / Tales of brave Ulysses / White room
(Available on 12" only).
■ 7" 56 315
Polydor / Apr '69.
■ 12" . . . . RSOX 91
■ 7" . . . . RSO 91
Polydor / Jan '82.

BADGE.
Tracks: Badge.
■ 7" 2058 285
Polydor / Oct '72.

BEST OF CREAM.
Tracks: Not Advised.
■ LP 583 060
Polydor / Nov '69.
■ MC 3216 031
RSO / Nov '77.
■ LP . . . . ADAH 429
Arcade Music Gala / Apr '86.
MC 811 639-4
Polydor / Oct '90 / PolyGram.

CREAM.
Tracks: N.S.U. / Sleepy time time / Dreaming / Sweet
wine / Spoonful / Wrapping paper / Cat's squirrel /
Four until late / Coffee song / Rollin' and tumblin' /
I'm so glad / Toad.

■ LP 2384 067
Polydor / Jan '79.

CREAM 2.
Tracks: Not Advised.
■ MC 3228 005
RSO / Apr '78.

CREAM BOX SET.
Tracks: Not Advised.
■ LP Set 2658 142
Polydor / Oct '80.
CD Set . . . . CR 1
UFO / Oct '92 / Pinnacle.

CREAM FRESH CREAM.
Tracks: Not Advised.
VHS 879683
Polygram Music Video / Nov '93 / PolyGram.

CREAM: STRANGE BREW.
Tracks: Not Advised.
VHS 8536502573
Warner Music Video / Feb '92 / WEA.

DESERTED CITIES (THE CREAM
COLLECTION).
Tracks: Wrapping paper / Sitting on top of the world /
Passing on the time / NSU / Swlabr / Deserted cities
of the heart / Anyone for tennis / Born under a bad
sign / Dreaming / Take it back / Dance the night
away / Toad / Tales of brave Ulysses (Live) / I feel
free.
CD . . . . PWKS 4127P
MC . . . . PWKMC 4127P
Pickwick / Oct '92 / Pickwick.

DISRAELI GEARS.
Tracks: Strange brew / Sunshine of your love / World
of pain / Dance the night away / Blue condition /
Tales of brave Ulysses / We're going wrong / Out-
side woman blues / Take it back / Mother's lament.
CD 823 636-2
Polydor / PolyGram.
■ LP 594 003
Reaction / Nov '67.
■ LP 239 412 9
Polydor / Nov '77.
MC 823 636-4
Polydor / Nov '90 / PolyGram.

FAREWELL CONCERT.
Tracks: Not Advised.
VHS 041
Polygram Music Video / Oct '86 / PolyGram.
VHS . . . . CFV 01282
Channel 5 / Sep '87 / Channel 5 Video / P.R.O. Video
/ Gold & Sons.

FRESH CREAM.
Tracks: Not Advised.
CD 827 576-2
Polydor / PolyGram.
■ LP 593 001
Reaction / Dec '66.
■ LP 594 001
Reaction / Feb '69.
■ LP . . . . SPELP 42
Polydor / Sep '83.
MC 827 576-4
Polydor / Nov '90 / PolyGram.

GOODBYE CREAM.
Tracks: I'm so glad / Politician / Sitting on top of the
world / Badge / Doing that scrapyard thing / What a
bringdown.
■ LP 583 053
Polydor / Mar '69.
■ LP . . . . SPELP 75
■ MC . . . . SPEMC 75
RSO / Aug '84.
■ CD 823 660-2
Polydor / Jan '84.
MC 823 660-4
Polydor / Nov '90 / PolyGram.

GREATEST HITS: CREAM.
Tracks: Not Advised.
■ Double LP 2658 139
MC 3524 220
Polydor / Nov '80 / PolyGram.

HEAVY CREAM.
Tracks: Not Advised.
■ Double LP 2659 022
Polydor.
■ LP 2472 244
MC 3472 244
Karussell (Germany) / Mar '82.

I FEEL FREE.
Tracks: White room / I feel free / Badge / Anyone for
tennis / Spoonful / Wrapping paper / N.S.U. / Strange

brew / Sunshine of your love / I'm so glad / Politician / Take it back.
■ LP .2872 244
N/A / May '82.

I FEEL FREE.
Tracks: I feel free.
■ 7" 591 011
Reaction / Dec '66.
■ 7" . . . . POSP 812
Polydor / Jul '86.

I FEEL FREE (OLD GOLD).
Tracks: I feel free / Badge.
■ 7" .OG 9423
Old Gold / Jul '84.

LIVE 1968.
Tracks: Not Advised.
CD K880 803
Koine / Feb '89.

LIVE CREAM.
Tracks: N.S.U. / Sleepy time time / Lawdy mama / Sweet wine / Rollin' and tumblin'.
■ MC. . . . . SPEMC 93
RSO
■ LP . . . . SPELP 93
RSO / Mar '85.
■ MC. 827 577-4
Polydor / Nov '90.

LIVE VOL 1.
Tracks: Not Advised.
■ LP 2383 016
Polydor / Jul '70.
■ CD 827 577-2
Polydor / May '88.

LIVE VOL 2.
Tracks: Deserted cities of the heart / White room / Politician / Tales of brave Ulysses / Sunshine of your love / Steppin' out.
■ LP 2383 119
Polydor / Jun '72.
CD 823 661-2
Polydor / May '88 / PolyGram.

STORY OF CREAM VOL.1.
Tracks: Traintime / Toad / White room / Sitting on top of the world / Strange brew / Tales of brave Ulysses / Sunshine of your love / Take it back.
■ LP 2479 212
MC. 3215 038
Polydor / Oct '83 / PolyGram.

STORY OF CREAM VOL.2.
Tracks: I'm so glad / Politician / Spoonful / Born under a bad sign / Badge / Crossroads / N.S.U. / Passing the time / I feel free / Mothers Lament.
■ LP 2479 213
MC. 3215 039
Polydor / Oct '83 / PolyGram.

STRANGE BREW.
Tracks: Strange brew / Tales of brave Ulysses.
■ 7" 591 015
Reaction / Jun '67.

STRANGE BREW (OLD GOLD).
Tracks: Strange brew.
■ 7" .OG 9424
Old Gold / Jul '84.

STRANGE BREW - THE VERY BEST OF CREAM.
Tracks: Badge / Sunshine of your love / Crossroads / White room / Born under a bad sign / Swlabr / Strange brew / Anyone for tennis / I feel free / Tales of brave ulysses / Politician / Spoonful.
■ LP . . . . RSD 5021
MC. . . . . TRSD 5021
RSO / Feb '83 / PolyGram.

SUNSHINE OF YOUR LOVE.
Tracks: Sunshine of your love.
■ 7" 56 286
Polydor / Oct '68.

SUNSHINE OF YOUR LOVE (OLD GOLD).
Tracks: Sunshine of your love.
■ 7" .OG 9426
Old Gold / Jul '84.

VERY BEST OF CREAM, THE.
Tracks: White room / I feel free / Tales of brave Ulysses / I'm so glad / Toad / Sunshine of your love / Strange brew / NSU / Born under a bad sign / Badge / Crossroads.
■ LP 817 172-1
MC. 817 172-4
RSO / Jul '84 / PolyGram.
CD 811 639 2
RSO / May '90 / PolyGram.

WHEELS OF FIRE.
Tracks: White room / Sitting on top of the world / Passing the time / As you said / Pressed rat and warthog / Politician / Those were the days / Born under a bad sign / Deserted cities of the heart / Crossroads / Spoonful / Train time / Toad.
CD 825 414-2
Polydor / PolyGram.
■ LP 583 033
Polydor / Aug '68.
■ LP 2394 136
■ MC. 3216 036
Polydor / Nov '77.
CD 827 658-2
Polydor / Feb '89 / PolyGram.

WHEELS OF FIRE (In the studio - Live at the Fillmore).
Tracks: Not Advised.
■ Double LP. 583031 2
Polydor / Aug '68.
■ Double LP. 6PDLP 2
MC Set 3216 037
Polydor / Jan '84 / PolyGram.
CD Set 827 578 2
Polydor / '87 / PolyGram.
MC Set 827 578 4
Polydor / Nov '90 / PolyGram.

WHEELS OF FIRE (LIVE AT FILLMORE).
Tracks: Not Advised.
■ LP 2394 137
Polydor / Nov '77.

WHITE ROOM.
Tracks: White room.
■ 7" 56 300
Polydor / Jan '69.

WHITE ROOM (OLD GOLD).
Tracks: White room.
■ 7" .OG 9425
Old Gold / Jul '84.

WRAPPING PAPER.
Tracks: Wrapping paper.
■ 7" 591 007
Reaction / Oct '66.

Creaming Jesus

BARK.
Tracks: Bark.
■ 12" . . . . .JUNG 53T
Jungle / Jul '92.

DITCH DWELLER 5.
Tracks: Ditch dweller 5.
■ 12" . . . . JUNG 57 T
■ CD Single . . . . JUNG 57 CD
Jungle / Nov '91.

MUG.
Tracks: Mug.
■ 12" . . . . .JUNG 52T
Jungle / Nov '89.

NAILED UP FOR NOTHING.
Tracks: Nailed up for nothing.
■ 12" . . . . CREAM 1
Arkwright / Dec '90.

TOO FAT TO RUN, TO STUPID TO HIDE.
Tracks: Not Advised.
CD . . . . FREUDCD 36
LP . . . . .FREUD 36
Jungle / Dec '90 / RTM / Pinnacle.

Creation Of Death

PURIFY YOUR SOUL.
Tracks: Not Advised.
CD . . . . CDFLAG 62
LP . . . . .FLAG 62
Music For Nations / Sep '91 / Pinnacle.

Creek

CREEK.
Tracks: Love found me / Reach and touch / Arthur Whiteside / You don't owe me / Institute of rock 'n' roll / Six days to Sunday / Dialling numbers / Love will stay / Just another fool / Lead me down that road.
■ LP . . . . MFN 67
Music For Nations / Oct '86.

STORM THE GATE.
Tracks: Storm the gate / Foxy / I love / Passion / Fountain of youth / On my way / Rock me tonight / Girl is crying / Hanky panky / Climb / Bad light.
■ CD . . . . BEAVER 891CD

■ MC. . . . . BEAVER 891C
Beaver (Sweden) / Sep '89.
CD . . . . .CDMFN 102
LP . . . . MFN 102
Music For Nations / Jul '90 / Pinnacle.

Crematory

JUST DREAMING.
Tracks: Not Advised.
CD . . . . MASSCD 031
LP . . . . MASSLP 031
Massacre / Jun '94 / Plastic Head.

TRANSMIGRATION.
Tracks: Not Advised.
CD . . . . MASSCD 016
LP . . . . .MASS 016
Massacre / Nov '93 / Plastic Head.

Crimson Glory

Crimson Glory were formed in 1982 in Florida, musically compared with Queensryche and Iron Maiden, they were perhaps best known for the silver masks they wore. The debut album, Crimson Glory was a critical and commercial success and their masks became smaller the bigger they got. Ironically by the time of their third album Strange And Beautiful they dispensed with the masks all together and sank back into obscurity.

CRIMSON GLORY.
Tracks: Not Advised.
CD . . . . RR 349655
Road Runner / Dec '88 / Pinnacle.
■ LP . . . . .RR 9655
MC. . . . . RR 96554
Road Runner / Dec '88 / Pinnacle.

DREAM DANCER.
Tracks: Dream dancer.
■ 12" . . . . RR 24671
Road Runner / Apr '88.

LONELY.
Tracks: Lonely.
■ 12" . . . . RR 24481
■ 7" . . . . RR 54487
■ CD Single . . . . RR 24482
Road Runner / Apr '89.

STRANGE AND BEAUTIFUL.
Tracks: Not Advised.
■ LP . . . . RR 93011
■ MC. . . . . RR 93014
■ CD . . . . RR 93012
Road Runner / Aug '91.

TRANSCENDENCE.
Tracks: Not Advised.
CD . . . . .RR 9508 2
■ LP . . . . .RR 9508 1
MC. . . . . .RR 9508 4
Road Runner / Nov '88 / Pinnacle.

Crisis Party

RUDE AWAKENING.
Tracks: Not Advised.
■ LP . . . . EM 94421
Road Runner / Nov '89.

Cro-Mags

AGE OF QUARREL.
Tracks: Not Advised.
CD . . . . PCD 1218
Profile / May '87 / Vital Distribution.
MC. . . . . GWTC 9
■ LP . . . . .GWLP 9
GWR / May '87.
■ LP . . . . .RR 9613
Road Runner / Nov '87.

ALPHA OMEGA.
Tracks: Not Advised.
CD . . . . CM 9730CD
LP . . . . .CM 9730
MC. . . . . .CM 9730MC
Century Media / Jun '92 / Plastic Head.

BEST WISHES.
Tracks: Death camps / Only one / Crush the demoniac / Then & now / Days of confusion / Down but not out / Fugitive / Age of quarrel.
CD . . . . .FILCD 274
■ LP . . . . .FILER 274
■ MC. . . . . FILECT 274
Profile (USA) / Sep '89.

HARD TIMES IN AN AGE OF QUARREL.
Tracks: Not Advised.
CD . . . . CM 77072-2
Century Media / Jun '94 / Plastic Head.

NEAR DEATH EXPERIENCE.
Tracks: Not Advised.
CD . . . . CM 77050-2
LP . . . . CM 77050-1
MC . . . . CM 77050-4
Century Media / Sep '93 / Plastic Head.

Cronos

ROCK'N'ROLL DISEASE.
Tracks: Not Advised.
CD . . . . NEATCD 1051
Neat / Nov '93 / Grapevine Distribution.

Cross

COWBOYS AND INDIANS.
Tracks: Cowboys and indians / Love lies bleeding / Cowboys and indians (full length version) (12" only).
■ 12" . . . . VST 1007
■ MC Single . . . . VSTC 1007
■ 7" . . . . VS 1007
■ CD Single . . . . CDEP 10
Virgin / Sep '87.

HEAVEN FOR EVERYONE.
Tracks: Heaven for everyone / Love on a tightrope (like an animal) / Contact (Extra track on 12".).
■ 12" . . . . VST 1062
■ 7" . . . . VS 1062
Virgin / Mar '88.

MAD, BAD AND DANGEROUS TO KNOW.
Tracks: Top of the world ma / Liar / Closer to you / Breakdown / Penetration guru / Power to love / Sister blue / Foxy lady (Available on CD only) / Better things / Passion for trash / Old men (lay down) / Final destination.
CD . . . . CDPCS 7342
■ LP . . . . PCS 7342
■ MC . . . . TCPCS 7342
Parlophone / Mar '90.

MANIPULATOR.
Tracks: Manipulator / Stand up for love / Manipulator (extended version) (Available on 12" only).
■ 7" . . . . VS 1100
■ 12" . . . . VST 1100
Virgin / Jul '88.

POWER TO LOVE.
Tracks: Power to love / Passion for trash / Power to love (extended version) (Not available on 7").
■ CD Single . . . . CDR 6251
■ CD Single 147 497 2
■ 12" 12R 6251
■ 12" 147 497 6
■ 7" . . . . .R 6251
■ 7" 147 497 7
Parlophone / Apr '90.

SHOVE IT.
Tracks: Shove it / Heaven for everyone / Love on a tightrope (like an animal) / Cowboys and indians / Stand up for love / Love lies bleeding (she was a wicked, wily waitress) / Rough justice / 2nd shelf mix (CD only) / Contact.
■ LP . . . . V 2477
■ MC . . . . TCV 2477
Virgin / Nov '87.
CD . . . . CDV 2477
Virgin / '88 / EMI.
■ LP . . . . OVED 302
■ MC . . . . OVEDC 302
Virgin / Apr '90.

SHOVE IT.
Tracks: Shove it (Not on 12") / Rough justice (On all versions) / Shove it (extended mix) (Available on 12" and CD single only) / Shove it (metropolix) (12" only) / Cowboys and indians (Available on CD single only).
■ CD Single . . . . CDEP 20
Virgin / Apr '88.
■ 12" . . . . VST 1026
■ 7" . . . . VS 1026
Virgin / Jan '88.

Crowbar

CROWBAR.
Tracks: Not Advised.
CD . . . . IRSCD 981200
IRS (Holland) / Nov '93 / Pinnacle.

CROWBAR/LIVE + 1.
Tracks: High rate extinction / All I had (I gave) / Will that never dies / Fixation / No quarter / Self inflicted /

Negative pollution / Existance is punishment / Holding nothing / I have failed / Self inflicted (Live) / Fixation (Live) / I have failed (Live) / All I had (Live) / Numb sensitive (Live).
CD . . . . .CDVEST 5
Bulletproof / Apr '94 / Pinnacle.

OBEDIENCE THRU SUFFERING.
Tracks: Not Advised.
CD . . . . GCI 89802
Plastic Head / Jun '92 / Plastic Head.

Crowforce

CROWFORCE.
Tracks: Not Advised.
CD . . . . CDDVN 1
LP . . . . DVN 1
MC . . . . TDVN 1
N/A / Jul '92.

DON'T LOOK DOWN.
Tracks: Don't look down.
■ 12" 12DVN 101
■ CD Single . . . . CDDVN 101
Devotion / Nov '91.

Crown

ALL THAT ROCK AND ROLL.
Tracks: Harder way to live / Music is freedom / Love me my way / Magic time / Right thru / Feeling easy / Two sides of the life / All that rock 'n' roll music / I believe in tomorrow's love / Dance the night away.
■ LP . . . . THBL 019
Thunderbolt / Dec '84.

RED ZONE.
Tracks: Song for you / It's rock 'n' roll to me / Life in a minutes / You, oh you / Hollywood / Rising star / Lonely man / Ain't no coming back / Love is light in the night / Heaven or hell.
■ LP . . . . THBL 021
Thunderbolt / Apr '85.

Crown Of Thorns

DIAMOND JIM.
Tracks: Diamond Jim / World radio.
■ 7" . . . . IRS 109
I.R.S. (Illegal) / Aug '84.

KINGDOM COME.
Tracks: Kingdom come / Gone are the days.
■ 12" . . . . ILS 12035
I.R.S. (Illegal) / May '83.

PICTURES.
Tracks: Pictures / Treatment.
■ 12" . . . . PFPX 1029
■ 7" . . . . PFP 1029
I.R.S. (Illegal) / Nov '83.

Crucifixion

FOX.
Tracks: Fox / Death sentence.
■ 7" . . . . MIR 4
Miramar / Sep '80.

MOON RISING.
Tracks: Moon rising / Green eyes / Jailbait.
■ 7" .NEAT 37
Neat / Jan '84.

TAKE IT OR LEAVE IT.
Tracks: Take it or leave it / On the run.
■ 7" .NEAT 19
Neat / '88.

Cruella

VENGEANCE IS MINE.
Tracks: Not Advised.
CD . . . . US 13CD
■ LP . . . . US 013
U.S. Metal / Mar '89.

Crumbsuckers

BEAST ON MY BACK (B.O.M.B.).
Tracks: Breakout / Jimmie's dream / Charge / Initial shock / I am he / Connection / Rejuvenate / Remembering tomorrow / Beast on my back.
■ LP . . . . JUST 9
Music For Nations / Mar '88.

LIFE OF DREAMS.
Tracks: Not Advised.
■ LP . . . . JUST 4

Music For Nations / Jul '86.
CD . . . . .CDJUST 4
Music For Nations / Aug '91 / Pinnacle.

Cry Of Love

BAD THING.
Tracks: Bad thing / Gotta love me / I ain't superstitious (On CD single & 12" only).
■ 12" 660046 6
■ 7" .660046 7
■ CD Single 660046 2
Columbia / Jan '94.

PEACE PIPE.
Tracks: Peace pipe / Drive it home / Shade tree / Carnival (Available on 12 only) / Deathbed (Available on CDS only).
■ 12" 659746 6
■ CD Single 659746 2
Columbia / Sep '93.

Crybabys

CRYBABYS, THE.
Tracks: Not Advised.
CD . . . . .RRCD 142
■ LP .RRLP 142
MC .RRLC 142
Receiver / Apr '91 / Total / BMG / Grapevine Distribution.

Crypt Of Kereberos

WORLD OF MYTHS.
Tracks: Not Advised.
CD . . . . .CDAR 013
Adipocre / Feb '94 / Plastic Head.

Cryptic Slaughter

CONVICTED.
Tracks: Not Advised.
■ LP . . . . RR 9680
Metal Blade / Aug '86.

MONEY TALKS.
Tracks: Not Advised.
■ LP . . . . RR 9607
Metal Blade / Jun '87.

SPEAK YOUR PEACE.
Tracks: Born too soon / Insanity by the numbers / Deathstyles of the poor and lonely / Divided minds / Killing time / Still born, again / Co-exist / One thing or another / Speak your piece.
CD . . . . CDZORRO 6
LP . . . . ZORRO 6
Metal Blade / Jul '90 / Pinnacle.

STREAM OF CONSCIOUSNESS.
Tracks: Circus of fools / Aggravated / Last laugh / Overcome / Deteriorate / See through you / Just went back / Drift / Altered visions / One last thought / Whisker biscuit / Addicted.
CD .RR9 521 2
■ LP .RR9 521 1
Road Runner / Nov '88.

Cubanate

ANTIMATTER.
Tracks: Blackout / Bodyburn / Revolution time / Autonomy / Junky / Exert / Disorder / Sucker / Switch / Forceful / Bodyburn (remix) / Kill or cure.
CD . . . . DYCD 12
Dynamica / Sep '93 / Pinnacle.
CD DY1-2
M.A.B. / Jan '94 / Plastic Head.

BODY BURN.
Tracks: Body burn.
■ 12" . . . . DY 16
■ CD Single . . . . DY 13
Modern Music / Aug '93.

BODYBURN.
Tracks: Bodyburn.
CD Single . . . . MC 32-3
Machinery / Jan '94 / Plastic Head.

METAL.
Tracks: Metal.
12" . . . . DY 56
CD Single . . . . DY 53
Noise / Jun '94 / Pinnacle.

Cult

Initially punk/goth act, formed as Southern Death Cult in 1982 in Bradford by vocalist Ian Astbury. Evolved into Death Cult and after a handful of indie hits on Situation 2 became The Cult in 1984. Joined by ex-Theatre Of Hate guitarist, Billy Duffy, The Cult released *Dreamtime* on Beggar's Banquet. The Cult adopted a more rock orientated approach for the big selling *Love* LP in 1985. The album featured the now classic *She Sells Sanctuary* and *Rain*. Subsequent LP's; *Electric* (1987) and *Sonic Temple* (1989) were hugely derivative of Led Zeppelin et al but also very successful. 1991's *Ceremony* was a disappointing release in light of it's predecessors. New LP *The Cult* (1994) includes Cobain tribute *Sacred Life*.

BROTHERS GRIMM (Death Cult).
Tracks: Brothers Grimm / Christian / Ghost dance / House mine.
■ 12" . . . . SIT 23T
Situation 2 / Jul '83.

CEREMONY.
Tracks: Not Advised.
CD . . . . BEGA 122CD
■ LP . . . . BEGA 122
MC. . . . . BEGC 122
Beggars Banquet / Oct '91 / WEA / RTM / Pinnacle.

COMPLETE RECORDINGS (Death Cult).
Tracks: Gods zoo / Brothers grimm / Ghost dance / Horse nation / Christians / Gods zoo (these times).
CD . . . . SIT 2329CD
Situation 2 / '91 / RTM / Pinnacle.

CULT.
Tracks: Not Advised.
CD . . . . BBQCD 164
LP . . . . BBQLP 164
MC. . . . . BBQMC 164
Beggars Banquet / Sep '94 / WEA / RTM / Pinnacle.

CULT: INTERVIEW PICTURE DISC.
Tracks: Not Advised.
LP P.Disc . . . . BAK 2050
Baktabak / Jul '87 / Arabesque Ltd.

CULT: VIDEO SINGLE.
Tracks: Not Advised.
VHS . . . . VMS 001
One Plus One / '87.

DEATH CULT (Death Cult).
Tracks: Not Advised.
CD . . . . .SITU 2329 CD
Situation 2 / '89 / RTM / Pinnacle.

DREAMTIME.
Tracks: Horse nation / Butterflies / Flower in the desert / Bad medicine waltz / Spiritwalker / 83rd dream / Go West / Gimmick / Dreamtime / Rider in the snow.
■ LP P.Disc . . . . BEGA 57 P
■ CD . . . . BEGA 57 CD
■ LP . . . . BEGA 57
■ MC. . . . . BEGC 57
Beggars Banquet / Sep '84.
CD . . . . BBL 57 CD
■ LP . . . . BBL 57
MC. . . . . BBLC 57
Lowdown / Oct '88 / RTM / Pinnacle / WEA.

DREAMTIME AT THE LYCEUM.
Tracks: Not Advised.
VHS . . . . BB 001
Beggars Banquet / Sep '84 / WEA / RTM / Pinnacle.

EDIE (CIAO BABY).
Tracks: Medicine train (12" and CD only) / Love removal machine (live) (12" and CD only) / Revolution (live) (CD and cassette only.) / Edie (ciao baby) / Bleeding heart graffiti (Only on cassette single.) / Li'l devil (live) (Only on CD single picture disc.)
■ 12" . . . . BEG 230T
■ 7" . . . . .XEG 230G
■ 7" . . . . .BEG 230
■ CD Single . . . . BEG 230CP
■ CD Single . . . . BEG 230CD
■ MC Single . . . . BEG 230C
Beggars Banquet / Jun '89.

ELECTRIC.
Tracks: Wild flower / Peace dog / Li'l devil / Aphrodisiac jacket / Electric ocean / Bad fun / King country man / Born to be wild / Love removal machine / Outlaw / Memphis hip shake.
CD . . . . .BEGA 80CD
■ LP . . . . BEGA 80
MC. . . . . BEGC 80
Beggars Banquet / Jan '88 / WEA / RTM / Pinnacle.

ELECTRIC LOVE.
Tracks: She sells sanctuary / Rain / Revolution / Wild flower / Lil' devil / Love removal machine.
VHS . . . . BB 004
Beggars Banquet / Nov '87 / WEA / RTM / Pinnacle.

ELECTRIC MIXES.
Tracks: Not Advised.
CD . . . . BBP 3CD
Beggars Banquet / Nov '89 / WEA / RTM / Pinnacle.

FAT MAN (Southern Death Cult).
Tracks: Fat man / Moya.
■ 12" . . . . SIT 19T
■ 7" . . . . .SIT 19
Situation 2 / Dec '82.

FIRE WOMAN.
Tracks: Fire woman.
■ 12" . . . . BEG 228 T
■ 7" . . . . BEG 228
■ CD Single . . . . BEG 228 CD
Beggars Banquet / Mar '89.

GO WEST.
Tracks: Go West / Crazy spinning circles.
■ 12" . . . . BEG 115T
■ 7" . . . . .BEG 115
Beggars Banquet / Jul '84.

GOD'S ZOO (Death Cult).
Tracks: God's zoo.
■ 12" . . . . SIT 29T
■ 7" . . . . .SIT 29
Situation 2 / Nov '83.

GOING DOWN.
Tracks: Going down.
12" . . . . BBQ 40T
CD Single . . . . BBQ 40CD
Beggars Banquet / Aug '94 / WEA / RTM / Pinnacle.

HEART OF SOUL.
Tracks: Heart of soul.
■ 12" . . . . BEG 260T
■ 7" . . . . .BEG 260
■ CD Single . . . . BEG 260CD
■ MC Single . . . . BEG 260C
Beggars Banquet / Feb '92.

INTERVIEW DISC.
Tracks: Not Advised.
CD P.Disc. . . . . CBAK 4027
Baktabak / Sep '90 / Arabesque Ltd.

LIL' DEVIL.
Tracks: Li'l devil / Zap city / She sells sanctuary (live) (on 12" only) / Bone bag (live) (on 12" only) / Wild thing (On cassingle only.) / Louie Louie (On cassingle only.) / Phoenix (On cassingle only.)
■ 12" . . . . BEG 188T
■ 7" . . . . BEG 188
■ MC Single . . . . BEG 188C
■ CD Single . . . . BEG 188CD
Beggars Banquet / Apr '87.

LOVE.
Tracks: Nirvana / Big neon glitter / Love / Brother wolf, sister moon / Rain / Phoenix / Hollow man / Revolution / She sells sanctuary / Black angel.
CD . . . . BEGA 65 CD
■ LP . . . . BEGA 65
MC. . . . . BEGC 65
Beggars Banquet / Oct '85 / WEA / RTM / Pinnacle.

LOVE MIXES, THE.
Tracks: Not Advised.
CD . . . . BBP 2CD
Beggars Banquet / Nov '89 / WEA / RTM / Pinnacle.

LOVE REMOVAL MACHINE.
Tracks: Love removal machine.
■ 12" . . . . BEG 182T
■ 12" P.Disc. . . . . BEG 182TP
■ 7" . . . . .BEG 182
Beggars Banquet / Feb '87.
■ 7" Set . . . . BEG 182D
Beggars Banquet / Feb '87.

MANOR SESSIONS.
Tracks: Not Advised.
CD . . . . BBP 1CD
Beggars Banquet / Dec '88 / WEA / RTM / Pinnacle.

MUSIC AND MEDIA INTERVIEW PICTURE DISC.
Tracks: Not Advised.
■ LP P.Disc . . . . MM 1223
Music & Media / Feb '88.

PURE CULT.
Tracks: Not Advised.
CD . . . . BEGA 130CD
LP . . . . .BEGA 130

MC. . . . . .BEGC 130
Beggars Banquet / Jan '93 / WEA / RTM / Pinnacle.

PURE CULT (For Rockers, Ravers, Lovers and Sinners).
Tracks: She sells sanctuary / Rain / Revolution / Wild flower / Lil' devil / Love removal machine / Resurrection Joe / Heart of soul / Wild hearted son / Sweet soul sister / Edie (ciao baby) / Fire woman / She sells anctuary MCMXCIII.
VHS . . . . BB 015
Virgin Vision / Feb '93 / Gold & Sons / TBD.

RAIN.
Tracks: Rain / Little face.
■ 12" . . . . BEG 147 T
■ 7" . . . . .BEG 147
Beggars Banquet / Sep '85.

RESURRECTION JOE.
Tracks: Resurrection Joe.
■ 12" . . . . BEG 122 T
■ 7" . . . . .BEG 122
Beggars Banquet / Dec '84.

REVOLUTION.
Tracks: Revolution.
■ 12" . . . . BEG 152 T
■ 7" . . . . .BEG 152
■ 7" Set . . . . BEG 152 D
Beggars Banquet / Nov '85.

SHE SELLS SANCTUARY.
Tracks: She sells sanctuary.
■ 12" . . . . BEG 135 T
■ 7" . . . . .BEG 135
Beggars Banquet / May '85.

SHE SELLS SANCTUARY.
Tracks: She sells sanctuary / She sells sanctuary (mixes).
■ CD Single . . . . BEG 263CD1
■ CD Single . . . . BEG 263CD
Beggars Banquet / Jan '93.

SOLDIER BLUE.
Tracks: Soldier blue.
■ 12" . . . . BEG 205T
■ 7" . . . . .BEG 205
■ CD Single . . . . BEG 205CD
■ MC Single . . . . BEG 205C
Beggars Banquet / '87.

SONIC CEREMONY.
Tracks: Heart of soul / Wild hearted son / Sweet soul sister / Edie (Ciao baby) / Fire woman.
VHS . . . . BB 013
Beggars Banquet / Mar '92 / WEA / RTM / Pinnacle.

SONIC TEMPLE.
Tracks: Fire woman / Sun king / Sweet soul sister / Soul asylum / Soldier blue / Edie (ciao baby) / American horse / Automatic blues / Wake up time for freedom / New York City.
CD . . . . BEGA 98 CD
■ LP . . . . BEGA 98
MC. . . . . BEGC 98
Beggars Banquet / Mar '89 / WEA / RTM / Pinnacle.

SOUTHERN DEATH CULT (Southern Death Cult).
Tracks: All glory / Fat man / Today / False faces / Crypt / Crow / Faith / Vivisection / Apache / Moya.
■ LP . . . . BEGA 46
Beggars Banquet / Jun '83.
CD . . . . .BBL 46CD
■ LP . . . . BBL 46
MC. . . . . BBLC 46
Lowdown / Jul '88 / RTM / Pinnacle / WEA.

SPIRIT WALKER.
Tracks: Spirit walker.
■ 12" . . . . SIT 33T
■ 7" . . . . SIT 33
Situation 2 / Apr '84.

SUN KING.
Tracks: Sun king / Edie (ciao baby).
■ 12" . . . . BEG 235 T
■ 7" . . . . .BEG 235
■ CD Single . . . . BEG 235 CD
Beggars Banquet / Nov '89.

SWEET SOUL SISTER.
Tracks: Sweet soul sister / River / American horse (live) / Soul asylum (live).
■ 12" . . . . BEG 241TG
■ 12" . . . . BEG 241T
■ 12" P.Disc. . . . . BEG 241TP
■ 12" Remix. . . . . BEG 241TR
■ CD Single . . . . BEG 241CD
■ CD Single . . . . BEG 241CG
■ CD Single . . . . BEG 241CR

■ MC Single. . . . . .BEG 241MC
Beggars Banquet / Feb '90.

WILD HEARTED SON.
Tracks: Wild hearted son.
■ 7" . . . . .BEG 255
■ CD Single. . . . . BEG 255 CD
■ MC Single. . . . . BEG 255 C
Beggars Banquet / Sep '91.

WILDFLOWER, THE.
Tracks: Wildflower / Love trooper.
■ 12" . . . . .BEG 195T
■ 12" Remix. . . . . BEG 195TR
■ 7" . . . . .BEG 195
■ 7" P.Disc . . . . BEG 195P
■ MC Single. . . . . BEG 195C
■ 7" Set . . . . BEG 195D
■ CD Single. . . . . BEG 195CD
Beggars Banquet / Aug '87.

Cursed

RHAPSODY.
Tracks: Not Advised.
CD . . . . DW 20629CD
LP . . . . DW 20628
Deathwish / Jan '92 / Plastic Head.

Cutty Sark

DIE TONIGHT.
Tracks: Not Advised.
■ LP . . . . .SKULL 8339
MC. . . . . .TAPE 78339
Mausoleum / Jun '84 / Pinnacle.

HARD ROCK POWER.
Tracks: Hardrock power / Fire and ice / Dice / Attack.
■ 12" . . . . TEST 128330
Mausoleum / Jun '84.

HEROES.
Tracks: Not Advised.
■ LP . . . . .SKULL 8375
Mausoleum / Apr '85.

Cynic

FOCUS.
Tracks: Not Advised.
CD . . . . RR 91692
LP . . . . RR 91691
Road Runner / Sep '93 / Pinnacle.

Cyrka, Jan

BEYOND THE COMMON GROUND.
Tracks: Not Advised.
CD . . . . .CDGRUB 22
LP . . . . GRUB 22
MC. . . . . .TGRUB 22
Food For Thought / Mar '92 / Pinnacle.

SPIRIT.
Tracks: Not Advised.
CD . . . . .CDGRUB 29
MC. . . . . .TGRUB 29
■ LP . . . . GRUB 29
Food For Thought / Oct '93.

D

D.A.D.

DRAWS A CIRCLE.
Tracks: Not Advised.
- LP . . . . MRLP 3057
Megadisc / Sep '87.

NO FUEL LEFT FOR THE PILGRIMS.
Tracks: Sleeping my day away / Jhad / Point of view / Rim of hell / ZCMI / True believer / Girl nation / Lords of the atlas / Overmuch / Siamese twin / Wild talk / III will.
- CD 9259992
- LP . . . . WX 288
- MC . . . . WX 288C
WEA / Sep '89.

RISKIN' IT ALL.
Tracks: Bad craziness / D. Law / Day of the wrong moves / Rock 'n' rock radar / I won't cut my hair / Down that dusty 3rd world road / Makin' fun of money / Smart bot can't tell ya / Riskin' it all / Laugh 'n' a 1/2.
CD 7599267722
- LP 7599267721
MC 7599267724
WEA / Oct '91 / WEA.

SLEEPING MY DAY AWAY.
Tracks: Sleeping my day away / I will.
- 12" . . . . W 2775T
- 7" . . . . W 2775
- CD Single . . . . W 2775CD
- MC Single . . . . W 2775C
WEA / Sep '89.

D.A.M.

CAN YOU DIG IT.
Tracks: Can you dig it.
- 7" . . . . COX 001
Meantime / Dec '86.

HUMAN WRECKAGE.
Tracks: M.A.D / Death warmed up / Killing time / Left to rot / Prophets of doom / Terror squad / Total destruction / Infernal torment / Vendetta / Human wreckage / Aliens (CD only.) / F.O.D (CD only.).
- CD . . . . CDNUK 149
- LP . . . . NUK 149
- MC . . . . ZCNUK 149
Noise / Feb '90.

INSIDE OUT.
Tracks: Man of violence / House of cards / Appointment with fear / Winter's tears / Innocent one / My twisted mind / No escape / Beneath closed eyes / Thought for the day circles (Bonus track on CD only.).
- CD . . . . NO 1642
- LP . . . . NO 1641
- MC . . . . NO 1644
Noise / Apr '91.

KICKING ASS AT TJ'S.
Tracks: Army of fools / Christian fantasy land / Four more years / Shake your foundations / Kicking thought / Into the field / Madmen and the foul / Pressure point / Poster paint / Go with the brain / Blind ignorance / Attitude hits, An / Dream come true / Vicious circle / Cull / Et amour / Happy 1970.
- LP . . . . COX 013
Meantime / Apr '89.

WHERE HAVE ALL THE CHILDREN GONE.
Tracks: Ploppy's revenge / Deliverer / Into the field / Conversation / Cut the cord / Possession / Pressure point / Cull / Lust is greed / Office boys and cats / I think I should / Wall of fear.
- LP . . . . COX 002
Meantime / Mar '87.

D.I.

ANCIENT ARTIFACTS.
Tracks: Not Advised.
- LP 51006 1
Triple XXX (USA) / Aug '87.

HORSE BITES DOG CRIES.
Tracks: Not Advised.
- LP 51007 1
Triple XXX (USA) / Aug '87.

STATE OF SHOCK.
Tracks: Hated / Clownhouse / What is life / Run-around / Colors and blood / It's not right / Paranoid's demise / Dream / Better than expected / Martyr man / Lexicon devil.
CD . . . . CDVEST 14
Bulletproof / May '94 / Pinnacle.

TEAM GOON.
Tracks: Not Advised.
- LP XXX1002
Triple XXX (USA) / Aug '87.

TRAGEDY AGAIN.
Tracks: Tragedy again / Chiva / Nick the whip / Manhole / Sashu / Diablo I / Blue velvet / Backseat driver / Love to me is a sin / On our way / Diablo II.
CD . . . . EM 94262
- LP . . . . EM 94261
Road Runner / Dec '89.

WHAT GOOD IS GRIEF TO A GOD.
Tracks: Not Advised.
- LP . . . . .EM 9547 1
Emergo / '89.

D.O.A.

ASSASSINATION CLUB.
Tracks: Roger / Heaths lament / Africa / Enemy / War in the East / 13 / I'm right / You're wrong / Slum Lord / New wave sucks / Burn it down / War / D.O.A. / Rich bitch / Watcha gonna do / Our world / Liar for hire / Class war / America / General strike.
- VHS . . . . JE 122
Jettisoundz / '84.

BLOODIED BUT UNBOWED.
Tracks: Everything went black / Prisoner / Slumlord / Watcha gonna do / Two plus two / Smash the state.
- LP . . . . VIRUS 31
Alternative Tentacles / Feb '84.

BLOODY BUT UNBOWED/WAR ON 45.
Tracks: Not Advised.
CD . . . . LS 91852
LP . . . . LS 91851
Road Runner / Mar '92 / Pinnacle.

DAWNING OF A NEW ERROR.
Tracks: Not Advised.
CD . . . . VIRUS 106CD
Alternative Tentacles / Feb '92 / RTM / Pinnacle.

DISCO SUCKS.
Tracks: Disco sucks.
7" . . . . VIRUS 133
Alternative Tentacles / Jan '94 / RTM / Pinnacle.

DON'T TURN YOUR BACK (ON DESPERATE TIMES).
Tracks: Don't turn your back on desperate times.
- 12" . . . . VIRUS 42
Alternative Tentacles / Mar '85.

GREATEST SHITS.
Tracks: Not Advised.
CD . . . . QQP 019CD
LP . . . . QQP 019LP
QQP / Nov '92 / Plastic Head.

IT'S NOT UNUSUAL BUT IT'S UGLY.
Tracks: Not Advised.
CD . . . . VIRUS 120CD
Alternative Tentacles / Mar '93 / RTM / Pinnacle.

LOGGERHEADS.
Tracks: Not Advised.
CD . . . . VIRUS 130CD
LP . . . . VIRUS 130
Alternative Tentacles / Sep '93 / RTM / Pinnacle.

MURDER.
Tracks: Not Advised.
- CD . . . . LS 94132
- LP . . . . LS 94131
Road Runner / Mar '90.

ONLY THING GREEN.
Tracks: Only thing green.
- 7" . . . . VIRUS 131
Alternative Tentacles / Sep '93.

POSITIVELY D.O.A.
Tracks: Positively D.O.A.
- EP . . . . .VIRUS 7
Alternative Tentacles / Feb '82.

TALK - ACTION = 0.
Tracks: Not Advised.
CD . . . . LS 92512
LP . . . . LS 92511
Road Runner / Nov '91 / Pinnacle.

THIRTEEN FLAVOURS OF DOOM.
Tracks: Not Advised.
CD . . . . .VIKRUS 117
LP . . . . VIRUS 117
Alternative Tentacles / Oct '92 / RTM / Pinnacle.

WAR ON 45.
Tracks: Not Advised.
- LP . . . . VIRUS 24
Alternative Tentacles / May '84.

D.R.I.

22 SONGS.
Tracks: Not Advised.
- LP . . . . DRR 1983
Radical (USA) / Aug '87.

CROSSOVER.
Tracks: Not Advised.
- LP . . . . RR 9620
Road Runner / Jun '88.
CD . . . . RR 349620
MC . . . . RR 96204
Road Runner / Jun '88 / Pinnacle.

DEALING WITH IT.
Tracks: Snap / Marriage / Counter attack / Nursing home blues / Give my taxes back / Equal people / Bail out / Evil minds / I'd rather be sleeping / Yes ma'am / God is broke / I don't need society / Explorer / On my way home / Argument the war / Slit my wrist.
- LP . . . . .ARM 2
Armageddon / Sep '86.
- LP 720691
Death (USA) / Sep '87.
CD . . . . RR 98982
- LP . . . . RR 98981
Road Runner / Feb '89.

DEFINITION.
Tracks: Not Advised.
CD . . . . ROT 2093CD
LP . . . . ROT 2093LP
Rotten / Nov '92 / Plastic Head.

DIRTY ROTTEN LP.
Tracks: Not Advised.
- LP . . . . RR 95551
- CD . . . . RR 95552
Road Runner / May '88.

FOUR OF A KIND.
Tracks: All for nothing / Manifest destiny / Gone too long / Do the dream / Shut up / Modern world / Think for yourself / Slumlord / Dead in a ditch / Man unkind / guy / Man unkind.
CD . . . . RR 9538 2
- LP . . . . RR 9538 1
Road Runner / Aug '88.
CD . . . . .CDMZORRO 46
LP . . . . ZORRO 46
MC . . . . .TMZORRO 46
Metal Blade / Aug '92 / Pinnacle.

LIVE AT THE RITZ.
Tracks: Not Advised.
VHS . . . . RRV 9983
Road Runner / Jan '89 / Pinnacle.

THRASH ZONE.
Tracks: Not Advised.
- CD . . . . RO 94262
Road Runner / Oct '89.
LP . . . . RO 9429 1
Roadracer / Jan '90 / Pinnacle.

Damien Thorne

SIGN OF THE JACKAL, THE.
Tracks: Not Advised.
■ **LP** . . . . RR 9691
Road Runner / Aug '86.

Dammaj

MUTINY.
Tracks: Smuggler / Devils and angels / March of the gladiators / Without you / Mutiny / Leather master / Clashes of steel / To the bitter end.
■ **LP** . . . . RR 9636
Road Runner / Jan '87.

Damn Yankees

DAMN YANKEES.
Tracks: Coming of age / Bad reputation / Runaway / High enough / Damn yankees / Come again / Mysified / Rock city / Tell me how you want it / Piledriver.
■ **LP** 7599261591
■ **MC** 7599261594
WEA / Apr '90.
CD 7599261592
WEA / Mar '94 / WEA.

DON'T TREAD.
Tracks: Don't tread on me / Fifteen minutes of fame / Where you goin' now / Dirty dog / Mr. Please / Silence is broken / Firefly / Someone to believe / This side of hell / Double coyote / Uprising.
CD 9362450252
MC 9362450254
WEA / Aug '92 / WEA.

HIGH ENOUGH.
Tracks: High enough / Piledriver.
■ **MC Single** . . . . W 0006MC
■ **12"** . . . . W 0006T
■ **7"** . . . . W 0006
■ **CD Single** . . . . W 0006CD
WEA / Jan '91.

Damnation

HANGMAN.
Tracks: Hangman.
7" . . . . LF 090
Lost & Found / Jul '94 / Plastic Head.

Dan Band

LITTLE BLACK MAGIC.
Tracks: Can't resist it / Touch too much / Trying to get to you / Wild about you baby / Crossed / Driving too hard in the rain / China cup / Money / D'fer.
CD . . . . LLCD 134
■ **LP** . . . . LLP 134
MC . . . . LLK 134
Legacy / Jul '90 / Sony.

Dance Or Die

BEST OF DANCE OR DIE.
Tracks: Not Advised.
CD Single . . . . MA 49-3
Modern Music / Mar '94 / Plastic Head.

MOVE.
Tracks: Move.
■ **12"** . . . . MAD 12-5
Mad Cat / Jan '89.

PSYCHOBURBIA.
Tracks: Not Advised.
CD . . . . MA 232
Noise / Oct '92 / Pinnacle.

WILL OF THE WIND.
Tracks: Will of the wind.
■ **CD Single** . . . . MA 216
Noise / Dec '92.

Dandy, Jim

BLACK ATTACK IS BACK (see under Black Oak Arkansas).

READY AS HELL.
Tracks: Not Advised.
■ **LP** . . . . HMUSA 5
Heavy Metal America / Nov '84.
■ **LP P.Disc** . . . . HMPD 5
Heavy Metal / Aug '85.

READY AS HELL.
Tracks: Ready as hell / Black cat woman.
■ **7"** . . . . VHF 15
FM Records / Aug '85.

Danger

DANGER.
Tracks: Not Advised.
■ **LP** . . . . .SKULL 8305
Mausoleum / Oct '84.

Danger Danger

COMIN' HOME.
Tracks: Comin' home / Don't walk away / Crazy nites.
■ **CD Single** 6581332
Epic / Jun '92.

I STILL THINK ABOUT YOU.
Tracks: I still think about you / Rock America (Not on 7" single (1).) / Under the gun (Not on CD single or 7" single (1)) / Just what the Dr. ordered (Not on CD single or 7" single (2)) / Rock 'n' roll hoochie koo (live) (CD single only).
■ **12" P.Disc** 6578388
■ **7"** 6578387
■ **7"** 6578386
■ **CD P.Disc** 6578382
Epic / Mar '92.

MONKEY BUSINESS.
Tracks: Monkey business / Boys will be boys / Naughty naughty (Not on 7") / Bang bang (CD single only).
■ **12"** 6577516
■ **7"** 6577517
■ **CD Single** 6577512
Epic / Jan '92.

SCREW IT.
Tracks: Ginger snaps (intro) / Monkey business / Slipped her the big one / C'est loupe (prelude) / Beat the bullet / I still think about you / Get you s**t together / Crazy nites / Puppet show / Everybody wants some / Don't blame it on love / Comin' home / Horny S.O.B. / Find your way back home / Yeah, you want it / D.F.N.S.
■ **LP** 4686611
■ **MC** 4686614
■ **CD** 4686612
Epic / Feb '92.

Dangerous

DIAMONDS AND DOLLARS.
Tracks: Diamonds and dollars / Groupies lost her grip.
■ **7"** . . . . .MARQX 001
Marquee / Sep '90.

Dangerous Toys

DANGEROUS TOYS.
Tracks: Teas'n pleas'n / Scared / Bones in the gutter / Take me drunk / Feels like a hammer / Sport'n a woody / Queen of the Nile / Outlaw / Here comes trouble / Ten boots (stompin') / That dog.
CD 4654232
■ **LP** 4654231
MC 4654234
CBS / Dec '89 / Sony.

PISSED.
Tracks: Not Advised.
CD . . . . CDVEST 30
Bulletproof / Sep '94 / Pinnacle.

Danzig

Former leader of Misfits, Glenn Danzig has achieved greater notoriety than sales with his self-named band, formed 1988. Satanic image prompted MTV to ban *Mother* video and Danzig's mix of Sabbath-esque plod with Sinatra-esque singing has yet to infiltrate mainstream.

DANZIG.
Tracks: Twist of Cain / Not of this world / She rides / Soul on fire / Am I demon / Mother / Possession / End of time / Hunter / Evil thing.
■ **LP** 828 124-1
Mercury / Dec '88.
■ **LP** . . . . DEF 24208
American Recordings / Sep '88.
CD 838 487 2
■ **LP** 838 487 1

MC 838 487 4
Mercury / Dec '89 / PolyGram.

DANZIG.
Tracks: Not Advised.
VHS . . . . CFM 01922
Polygram Music Video / '92 / PolyGram.

DEMONSWEATLIVE.
Tracks: Not Advised.
CD 514 876-2
LP 514 876-1
MC 514 876-4
American Recordings / May '93 / PolyGram.

DIRTY BLACK SUMMER.
Tracks: Dirty black summer / When death had no name / Bodies.
■ **12"** . . . . DEFA 1712
■ **CD Single** . . . . .DEFCD 17
American Recordings / Jun '92.

HOW THE GODS KILL.
Tracks: Not Advised.
CD 512 270-2
LP 512 270-1
MC 512 270-4
American Recordings / Jun '92 / PolyGram.

LUCIFUGE.
Tracks: Long way back from hell / Killer wolf / I'm the one / Devil's plaything / Blood and tears / Pain in the world / Snakes of Christ / Tired of being alone / Her black wings / 777 / Girl.
CD 8463752
MC 8463754
■ **LP** 8463751
American Recordings / Jun '90.

MOTHER '94.
Tracks: Mother / Mother (Live) / When death had no name (On MOMDD/MOMX 1 only) / How the Gods kill (On MOMDD 1 only).
■ **12"** . . . . .MOMX 1
■ **7"** . . . . MOM 1
■ **CD Single** . . . . .MOMDD 1
■ **CD Single** . . . . .MOMCD 1
Phonogram / Apr '94.

Dare

ABANDON.
Tracks: Abandon / Last time / Precious (Only on 12" version.) / Love is the price (Only on 12" version.)
■ **CD Single** . . . . AMCD 470
■ **12"** . . . . AMY 470
■ **7"** . . . . AM 470
A&M / Sep '88.

ABANDON (REMIX).
Tracks: Abandon / Last time.
■ **12"** . . . . AMY 519
■ **12"** . . . . AMS 519
■ **7"** . . . . AM 519
■ **7" P.Disc** . . . . AMP 519
■ **CD Single** . . . . CDEE 519
A&M / Jul '89.

BLOOD FROM STONE.
Tracks: Not Advised.
■ **LP** 3953601
MC 3953604
■ **CD** 3953602
A&M / Aug '91.

HEARTBREAKER.
Tracks: Heartbreaker / King of spades / Runaway (live).
■ **12"** . . . . AMY 525
■ **7"** . . . . AM 525
■ **CD Single** . . . . CDEE 525
A&M / Sep '89.

NOTHING IS STRONGER THAN LOVE.
Tracks: Nothing is stronger than love / Valentino / If looks could kill (Only on CD single.).
■ **12"** . . . . AMY 493
■ **7"** . . . . AM 493
■ **CD Single** . . . . CDEE 493
A&M / Feb '89.

OUT OF THE SILENCE.
Tracks: Abandon / Into the fire / Nothing is stronger than love / Runaway / Under the sun / Raindance / King of spades / Heartbreaker / Return the heart / Don't let go.
MC . . . . AMC 5221
■ **LP** . . . . AMA 5221
■ **CD** . . . . CDA 5221
A&M / Oct '88.

RAINDANCE, THE.
Tracks: Raindance / Return the heart / No strings attached.

■ DELETED

```
■ 12"...................... AMY 483
■ 12"...................... AMP 483
■ 7"....................... AM 483
■ CD Single.............. CDEE 483
A&M / Apr '89.
```

REAL LOVE.
Tracks: Real love.
```
■ 12"...................... AMY 824
■ 12" P.Disc.............. AMP 824
■ 7"....................... AM 824
■ CD Single............. AMCD 824
A&M / Oct '91.
```

WE DON'T NEED A REASON.
Tracks: We don't need a reason.
```
■ 12"...................... AMY 775
■ 12" P.Disc.............. AMP 775
■ 7"....................... AM 775
■ CD Single............ AMCD 775
■ MC Single........... AMMC 775
A&M / Aug '91.
```

Dark Angel

DARKNESS DESCENDS.
Tracks: Darkness descends / Burning of Sodom / Hunger of the undead / Merciless death / Death is certain (life is not) / Black prophesies / Perish in flames.
```
■ LP..................... FLAG 6
Under One Flag / Nov '86.
CD.................... CDFLAG 6
Under One Flag / '89 / Pinnacle.
```

DECADE OF CHAOS - THE BEST OF DARK ANGEL.
Tracks: Not Advised.
```
CD................... CDFLAG 70
LP........................FLAG 70
MC...................... TFLAG 70
Under One Flag / Jul '92 / Pinnacle.
```

LEAVE SCARS.
Tracks: Not Advised.
```
■ LP......................FLAG 30
Under One Flag / Jan '89.
CD................... CDFLAG 30
■ MC................... TFLAG 30
Under One Flag / Jan '89.
```

LIVE SCARS.
Tracks: Not Advised.
```
CD................... CDFLAG 42
LP........................FLAG 42
MC..................... TFLAG 42
Under One Flag / Jul '89 / Pinnacle.
```

MERCILESS DEATH.
Tracks: Not Advised.
```
■ LP.................... MS 8602
Metalstorm / Jun '88.
```

TIME DOES NOT HEAL.
Tracks: Not Advised.
```
CD................... CDFLAG 54
Double LP ...............FLAG 54
MC Set................. TFLAG 54
Under One Flag / Feb '91 / Pinnacle.
```

WE HAVE ARRIVED.
Tracks: Not Advised.
```
■ LP.................... MS 8501
Metalstorm / Jan '88.
```

Dark Heart

SHADOWS OF THE NIGHT.
Tracks: Not Advised.
```
■ LP.................... RR 9849
Road Runner / Aug '84.
```

Dark Star

LADY OF MARS.
Tracks: Lady of Mars.
```
■ 7"......................AAA 105
Avatar / Aug '81.
```

ON TOUR.
Tracks: Not Advised.
```
■ LP................. AALP 5003
MC................. ZCAAA 5003
Avatar / Nov '81 / C.M. Distribution.
```

REAL TO REEL.
Tracks: Voice of America / Rock 'n' roll heroes / Only time will tell / Spy zone / Homicide on first and last / Stadium of tears / Sad day in London town / One way love / Going nowhere / Two songs don't make a right.
```
MC...................... WKFMMC 97
■ LP................... .WKFMLP 97
FM Records / Jul '87.
```

Dark Throne

BLAZE IN THE NORTHERN SKY.
Tracks: Blaze in the Northern sky.
```
■ 12".................... VILE 028
■ CD Single.......... VILE 028CD
Peaceville / Mar '92.
```

SOULSIDE JOURNEY.
Tracks: Not Advised.
```
CD.................... VILE 22CD
■ LP.................... VILE 22
Peaceville / Feb '91.
```

Dark Wizard

DEVIL'S VICTIM.
Tracks: Not Advised.
```
■ LP.................... FIST 8337
Mausoleum / Jun '84.
```

REIGN OF EVIL.
Tracks: Not Advised.
```
■ LP................... SKULL 8386
Mausoleum / Jul '85.
```

Darkness

BROKEN HARD.
Tracks: Not Advised.
```
CD..................... 15 389
MC...................... 79 389
Laserlight / Aug '91 / TBD / BMG / Target.
```

DARKNESS.
Tracks: Not Advised.
```
■ LP.....................805253
Scratch (Germany) / Jun '87.
```

DEFENDER OF JUSTICE.
Tracks: Not Advised.
```
■ LP.....................805855
Tales of Thrash / May '88.
```

Darkon

KILLED IN ACTION.
Tracks: Not Advised.
```
■ LP.................... WBLP 2
Wishbone/Earthshaker / Aug '84.
```

DC Lacroix

LIVING BY THE SECOND.
Tracks: Not Advised.
```
■ LP.....................721991
Metal Blade / Mar '88.
```

Dead Brain Cells

DBC.
Tracks: Deadlock / Monument / Lies / Power and corruption / Tempest / Public suicide / Negative reinforcement / Outburst / M.I.A. / Terrorist mind / Vice / Trauma X / Final act / Midnight special / Casey Jones / K.C. Moan / Take this hammer / Down by the riverside / Go down, old Hannah / Streamline train / Old Riley / Downbound train / Stack o lee blues / Mule skinner blues / Grey goose / Sporting life / House rent stomp / I can't sleep / This train / Midnight hour blues / Go down sunshine / Ella speed.
```
■ LP.....................JUST 10
Rough Justice / Jan '88.
```

DEAD BRAIN CELLS.
Tracks: Not Advised.
```
■ LP................ 88561-8161-1
Combat Core (USA) / Sep '87.
```

UNIVERSE.
Tracks: Not Advised.
```
CD.................... CDJUST 14
LP.......................JUST 14
Rough Justice / Jul '90 / Pinnacle.
```

Dead End

GHOST OF ROMANCE.
Tracks: Not Advised.
```
■ LP.....................722381
Metal Blade / Mar '88.
```

Dead On

ALL FOR YOU.
Tracks: Not Advised.
```
CD....................367 0005.3
LP.....................367 0005.0
Mausoleum / Oct '91 / Pinnacle.
```

DEAD ON.
Tracks: Salem girls / Beat a dead horse / Widower / Matador's nightmare / Full moon / Escape / Merry ship / Different breed / Dead on.
```
■ CD.................... K2 93249
■ LP.................... K1 93249
■ MC.................... K4 93249
SBK / Nov '90.
```

Deaf Dealer

KEEPER OF THE FLAMES.
Tracks: Not Advised.
```
■ LP.................... NEAT 1035
Neat / '88.
```

Death

FATE - THE BEST OF DEATH.
Tracks: Not Advised.
```
CD................... CDFLAG 71
LP........................FLAG 71
MC...................... TFLAG 71
Under One Flag / Jul '92 / Pinnacle.
```

HIGH COST OF LIVING, THE.
Tracks: High cost of living.
```
12".................... TROPE 010
Trope / Sep '94 / Vital Distribution.
```

HUMAN.
Tracks: Not Advised.
```
CD.................... RC 92382
LP.................... RC 92381
■ MC.................... RC 92384
Road Runner / Nov '91.
```

INDIVIDUAL THOUGHT PATTERNS.
Tracks: Overactive imagination / Jealousy / Trapped in a corner / Nothing is everything / Mentally blind / Individual thought patterns / Destiny / Out of touch / Philosopher / In human form.
```
CD................... RR 9079CD
LP......................RR 9079
MC.................... RR 9079 MC
Road Runner / Jun '93 / Pinnacle.
```

LEPROSY.
Tracks: Leprosy / Forgotten past / Pull the plug / Primitive ways / Born dead / Left to die / Open casket / Choke on it.
```
CD................... CDFLAG 24
■ LP......................FLAG 24
MC...................... TFLAG 24
Under One Flag / Oct '88 / Pinnacle.
■ LP P.Disc...............FLAG 24P
Under One Flag / May '89.
```

SCREAM BLOODY GORE.
Tracks: Infernal death / Zombie ritual / Denial of life / Sacrificial / Mutilation / Regurgitated guts / Baptized in blood / Torn to pieces / Evil dead / Scream bloody gore.
```
CD................... CDFLAG 12
■ LP......................FLAG 12
Under One Flag / Jun '87.
```

SPIRITUAL HEALING.
Tracks: Not Advised.
```
CD................... CDFLAG 38
MC...................... TFLAG 38
■ LP......................FLAG 38
Under One Flag / Jan '90.
```

Death Angel

ACT III.
Tracks: Not Advised.
■ LP 7599242801
■ CD 7599242802
■ MC 7599242804
Geffen / Apr '90.

FALL FROM GRACE.
Tracks: Not Advised.
LP . . . . RO 93331
MC . . . . RO 93334
■ CD . . . . RO 93332
Roadracer / Dec '90.

FROLIC THROUGH THE PARK.
Tracks: 3rd floor / Road mutants / Why you do this / Bored / Confused / Guilty of innocence / Open up / Shores of sin / Cold gin / Mind rape.
CD . . . . CDENV 502
■ LP . . . . ENVLP 502
■ MC . . . . TCENV 502
Enigma (EMI) / Aug '88.
CD 772549-2
Restless (1) / Jul '94 / Vital Distribution.

ULTRA-VIOLENCE.
Tracks: Thrashers / Evil priest / Voracious souls / Kill as one / Ultra violence / Mistress of pain / Final death / IPFS.
■ LP . . . . .FLAG 14
Under One Flag / May '87.
CD 772548-2
Restless (1) / Jul '94 / Vital Distribution.

Death In Action

TOXIC WASTE.
Tracks: Not Advised.
■ LP . . . . .WEBITE 032
We Bite / Jun '88.

Death Mask

SPLIT THE ATOM.
Tracks: Split the atom / I'm dangerous / Reign / Lust for fire / Tortured mind / Nightmare (a lesson for the innocent) / Hell rider / Walk alone / Death has no boundaries / Commando.
■ LP . . . . KILP 4004
Killerwatt / Oct '86.

Death SS

HEAVY DEMONS.
Tracks: Not Advised.
CD . . . . BABEDISCCD 002
LP . . . . BABEDISC 002
Plastic Head / Jul '92 / Plastic Head.

Deathcore

SPONTANEOUS.
Tracks: Not Advised.
CD 842976
LP 082976
Nuclear Blast / Sep '90 / Plastic Head.

SPONTANEOUS UNDERGROUND.
Tracks: Not Advised.
CD . . . . .NB 034CD
LP . . . . NB 034
Nuclear Blast / Oct '92 / Plastic Head.

Deathrow

DECEPTION IGNORED.
Tracks: Not Advised.
■ CD . . . . CDNUK 128
■ LP . . . . .NUK 128
■ MC . . . . ZCNUK 128
Noise / Oct '89.

RAGING STEEL.
Tracks: Not Advised.
■ LP . . . . .NUK 081
■ MC . . . . ZCNUK 081
Noise / Oct '89.

RIDERS OF DOOM.
Tracks: Not Advised.
■ LP . . . . .NUK 044
Noise / Oct '89.

Deathtrash

10,000 RPM GROOVE ORGY.
Tracks: Not Advised.
■ LP . . . . PIG 001
Metalworks / Nov '88.

Deathwish

AT THE EDGE OF DAMNATION.
Tracks: Not Advised.
■ LP . . . . .VOV 667
Metalworks / Sep '87.

DEMON PREACHER.
Tracks: Not Advised.
■ LP . . . . .RO 9478 1
Roadracer / '89.
CD . . . . GWMCD 33
GWR / Jun '90 / Pinnacle.
■ LP . . . . GWLP 33
MC . . . . GWTC 33
GWR / Jun '90 / Pinnacle.

TAILGATE.
Tracks: Tailgate.
■ 7" . . . . .LF 035
Plastic Head / Jun '92.

Decadence Within

SOULWOUND.
Tracks: Not Advised.
■ LP . . . . VILE 21
Peaceville / Dec '90.

THIS LUNACY.
Tracks: Not Advised.
■ LP . . . . VILE 010
Peaceville / Apr '89.

Deceased

LUCK OF THE CORPSE.
Tracks: Not Advised.
LP . . . . RR 001
MC . . . . RR 001MC
Nuclear Blast / Oct '92 / Plastic Head.

Decimator

CARNAGE CITY.
Tracks: Raider / Mutoids / F H Blood Island / C.C.S.M.P. / Devil's bridge / Rogue decimator / Dustbowl / Stealer of souls.
■ LP . . . . NEAT 1047
Neat / '89.

CARNAGE CITY STATE MOSH PATROL.
Tracks: Not Advised.
CD . . . . NEAT 1047D
Neat / '89 / Grapevine Distribution.

DIRTY, HOT & HUNGRY.
Tracks: Not Advised.
CD . . . . NEATCD 1052
MC . . . . NEATD 1052
Neat / Nov '92 / Grapevine Distribution.

Decollation

CURSED LANDS.
Tracks: Not Advised.
CD . . . . POSH 0004
Listenable / Oct '93 / Plastic Head.

Dedringer

DIRECT LINE.
Tracks: Not Advised.
■ LP . . . . DID 7
Dindisc / Feb '81.

DIRECT LINE.
Tracks: Direct line / She's not ready.
■ 7" . . . . .DIN 12
Dindisc / Jan '81.

HOT LADY.
Tracks: Hot lady / Hot licks / Rock 'n' roll.
■ 7" . . . . .NEAT 18
Neat / Nov '82.

MAXINE.
Tracks: Maxine / Innocent till proven guilty / Took a long time / We don't mind.
■ EP . . . . .DIN 11
Dindisc / Apr '81.

SECOND ARISING.
Tracks: Rock night / Going to the movies / Sold me lonely / I'm on the outside / Donna / Comin out fightin / Throw me the line / Never gonna lose it / Eagle never fails.
■ LP . . . . NEAT 1009
Neat / Jan '85.

Deep Purple

Formed in Germany by guitarist Ritchie Blackmore and keyboardist Jon Lord. 1968 U.S. hit *Hush* and first four albums gave little indication of hard rock style for which band became famous: exemplified by 1970's *Black Night* single and *In Rock* album. Critical change was addition of Ian Gillan on vocals; Blackmore, Lord, Gillan, drummer Ian Paice and bassist Roger Glover enjoyed massive success and formed best remembered line-up. Years of acrimonious reshuffles began with Gillan's departure in 1973, succeeded by future Whitesnake mainman David Coverdale. Band folded in '76 with only Lord and Paice remaining from original line-up. 1984 reformation yielded strong *Perfect Strangers* set, but hostility between Blackmore and Gillan ensured continuation of internal soap opera.

24 CARAT PURPLE.
Tracks: Woman from Tokyo / Fireball / Strange kind of woman / Never before / Black night / Speed king / Smoke on the water / Child in time.
■ LP . . . . TPSM 2002
Purple / May '75.
■ MC . . . . TC EXE 139
Purple / May '79.
■ LP . . . . FA 41 3133 1
■ LP . . . . FA 3132
MC . . . . FA 41 3132 4
Fame / Sep '85 / EMI.
CD . . . . CDFA 3132
Fame / Oct '87 / EMI.

ANTHOLOGY, THE (2).
Tracks: Hush / Mandrake root / Shield / Wring that neck / Bird has flown / Bloodsucker / Speed king / Black night / Child in time / Fireball / Strange kind of woman (live) / Highway star / Smoke on the water (live) / Pictures of home / Woman from Tokyo / Smooth dancer / Sail away / Lay down stay down / Burn (live) / Stormbringer / Hold on / Gypsy / Mistreated (live) / Gettin' tighter / Love child / You keep on moving / No one came.
CD Set . . . . CDEM 1374
■ LP Set . . . . EN 5013
■ MC Set . . . . TCEN 5013
EMI / Mar '91.

ANTHOLOGY: DEEP PURPLE.
Tracks: Hush / Emmaretta / Hallelujah / Shadows / Love help me / Wring that neck / Speed king / Black night / Grabsplatter / Child in time / Strange kind of woman / Freedom / Fireball / Highway star / Never before / When a blind man cries / Smoke on the water / Woman from Tokyo / Might just take your life / Coronarius redig / Soldier of fortune / You keep on moving.
■ Double LP . . . . .PUR 1
MC Set . . . . TCPUR 1
Harvest / Jun '85 / EMI.

BAD ATTITUDE.
Tracks: Bad attitude.
CD Video 080 088 2
Polygram Music Video / Oct '88 / PolyGram.

BATTLE RAGES ON, THE.
Tracks: Battle rages on / Lick it up / Anya / Talk about love / Time to kill / Ramshackle man / Twist in the tale / Nasty piece of work / Solitaire / One man's meat.
CD 74321 15420-2
MC 74321 15420-4
■ LP 74321 15420-1
RCA / Jul '93.

BEST OF DEEP PURPLE, THE.
Tracks: Speed king / Strange kind of woman / Black night / Fireball / Smoke on the water / Hush / Emmaretta / Woman from Tokyo / Demon's eye / Stormbringer.
■ CD . . . . TCD 2312
■ LP . . . . STAR 2312
■ MC . . . . STAC 2312
Telstar/Ronco / Nov '87.

BLACK NIGHT.
Tracks: Black night / Strange kind of woman.
■ 7" . . . . HAR 5178
Harvest / Mar '79.
■ 12" . . . . 12 HAR 5233
Harvest / Jun '85.

BOOK OF TALIESYN.
Tracks: Listen, learn, read on / Wring that neck / Kentucky woman / Exposition / We can work it out / Shield / Anthem / River deep, mountain high.
■ MC . . . . TCSHVL 751
■ LP . . . . SHVL 751
Harvest / Jun '69.

■ **CD** . . . . CDP 792 408 2
Harvest / Mar '89.

BURN.
Tracks: Burn / Might just take your life / Lay down,
stay down / Sail away / You fool no-one / What's
goin' on here / Mistreated / 'A' Zoo.
■ **MC.** . . . . .TCTPS 3505
EMI / Mar '74.
■ **LP** . . . . ATAK 11
MC. TCATAK 11
Purple / Mar '84 / EMI.
■ **LP** . . . . TPS 3505
EMI / Mar '84.
CD. . . . . CZ 203
Purple / Jul '89 / EMI.

BURN.
Tracks: Burn / Coronarias Redig / Mistreated.
■ **7"** . . . . .PUR 137
Purple / Sep '78.

BUTTERFLY BALL, THE/WIZARD'S CONVENTION (see under Glover, Roger).

CALIFORNIA JAM.
Tracks: Burn / Might just take your life / Mistreated /
Smoke on the water / You fool no one / Mule / Space
truckin'.
VHS . . . . BBCV 3000
BBC Video / Sep '84 / Sony / Gold & Sons / TBD.
■ **VHS** . . . . BBCV 4019
BBC Video / '88.
VHS . . . . CCV 1002
Connoisseur Collection / Sep '91 / Pinnacle.

CALL OF THE WILD.
Tracks: Call of the wild.
■ **12"** . . . . POSPX 843
■ **7" P.Disc** . . . . POSPP 843
■ **7"** . . . . POSP 843
Polydor / Feb '87.

COME TASTE THE BAND.
Tracks: Comin' home / Lady Luck / Gettin' tighter /
Dealer / I need love / Drifter / Love child / This time
around / Owed to 'G' / You keep on moving.
■ **LP** . . . . TPSA 7515
■ **MC** . . . . TC TPSA 7515
Purple / Nov '75.
CD. CZ 343
EMI / Jul '90 / EMI.

CONCERTO FOR GROUP AND ORCHESTRA.
Tracks: Not Advised.
■ **VHS** . . . . BBCV/B 3027
BBC Video / '88.
VHS . . . . CCV 1003
Connoisseur Collection / Apr '92 / Pinnacle.

CONCERTO FOR GROUP AND ORCHESTRA.
Tracks: Wring that neck / Child in time / Moderato -
allegro: First movement / Andante: Second move-
ment / Vivace - presto: Third movement.
■ **LP** . . . . SHVL 767
Harvest / Jan '70.
CD. CZ 342
EMI / Jul '90 / EMI.

DEEP PURPLE.
Tracks: Not Advised.
VHS . . . . VVCV 4019
Virgin Vision / '88 / Gold & Sons / TBD.

DEEP PURPLE IN CONCERT.
Tracks: Speed king / Wring that neck / Child in time /
Mandrake root / Highway star / Strange kind of
woman / Lazy / Never before / Space truckin' /
Lucille / Smoke on the water.
■ **MC** . . . . TCSHDW 412
■ **Double LP** . . . . .SHDW 412
Harvest / Dec '80.
CD Set . . . . .CDEM 1434
EMI / Feb '92 / EMI.

DEEP PURPLE IN ROCK.
Tracks: Speed king / Blood sucker / Child in time /
Flight of the rat / Into the fire / Living wreck / Hard
lovin' man.
■ **LP** . . . . SHVL 777
Harvest / Jun '70.
■ **LP** . . . . FA 3011
MC. TCFA 3011
Fame / May '82 / EMI.
■ **LP P.Disc** . . . . EJ 2603430
EMI / Jan '85.
■ **CD** . . . . CDFA 3011
Fame / Apr '88.

DEEP PURPLE: INTERVIEW PICTURE DISC.
Tracks: Not Advised.
LP P.Disc . . . . BAK 2039
Baktabak / Jun '87 / Arabesque Ltd.
CD P.Disc. . . . . CBAK 4054
Baktabak / Apr '92 / Arabesque Ltd.

DEEP PURPLE: VIDEO SINGLES.
Tracks: Not Advised.
VHS . . . . CFV 04182
Channel 5 / Nov '87 / Channel 5 Video / P.R.O. Video
/ Gold & Sons.
CD Video 080 390 9
Polygram Music Video / Oct '88 / PolyGram.

DEEPEST PURPLE.
Tracks: Black night / Speed king / Fireball / Strange
kind of woman / Child in time / Woman from Tokyo /
Highway star / Space truckin' / Burn / Demon's eye /
Stormbringer / Smoke on the water.
■ **LP** . . . . EMTV 25
■ **MC.** . . . . TC EMTV 25
EMI / Jul '80.
■ **CD** . . . . CDP 746 032 2
Harvest / Aug '84.
■ **LP** . . . . ATAK 138
MC. . . . . TCATAK 138
EMI / '89 / EMI.
CD. . . . . CDFA 3239
■ **LP** . . . . FA 3239
MC. . . . . TCFA 3239
Fame / Jul '90 / EMI.

DOING THEIR THING.
Tracks: Speed king / Wring that neck / Child in time /
Mandrake root.
■ **VHS** . . . . .CMP 3001
Castle Music Pictures / Oct '90.

FIREBALL.
Tracks: Fireball / No, no, no / Demon's eye / Mule /
Fools / No one came / Anyone's daughter.
■ **LP** . . . . SHVL 793
Harvest / Sep '71.
■ **LP** . . . . .FA 413093-1
Fame / Mar '84.
■ **LP P.Disc** . . . . EJ 2403440
EMI / Jan '85.
■ **LP** . . . . ATAK 105
MC. . . . . TCATAK 105
Harvest / Aug '87 / EMI.
■ **LP** . . . . EMS 1255
■ **MC** . . . . TCEMS 1255
Harvest / Oct '87.
CD. CZ 30
EMI / Jan '88 / EMI.

FIREBALL.
Tracks: Fireball / Anyone's daughter / Demon's eye.
■ **12"** . . . . 12 HAR 5235
Harvest / Jun '85.

GEMINI SUITE-LIVE.
Tracks: Guitar/Voice / Organ/Bass / Drums/Finale.
CD . . . . RPM 114
RPM / Jul '93 / Pinnacle.

HARD ROCK HEROES.
Tracks: Highway star / Hush / Stormbringer / Lady
double dealer / Strange kind of woman / Mandrake
root / Woman from Tokyo / Black night / Demons eye
/ Lay down, stay down / Hold on / Burn / Why didn't
Rosemary / Mistreated / Emeretta / Smoke on the
water / Help / Hey Joe / Speed king / Into the fire /
Child in time.
■ **MC** . . . . TCSHDW 412
■ **Double LP** . . . . .SHDW 412
Harvest / Dec '80.

HEAVY METAL PIONEERS.
Tracks: Not Advised.
VHS 8536502653
Warner Music Video / Oct '92 / WEA.

HOUSE OF BLUE LIGHT.
Tracks: Bad attitude / Unwritten law / Call of the wild
/ Mad dog / Black and white / Hard lovin' woman /
Spanish archer / Strange-ways / Mitzi dupree / Dead
or alive.
CD. 831 318-2
MC. . . . . .POLHC 32
■ **LP** . . . . POLH 32
Polydor / Jan '87.
■ **LP** 831 318-1
■ **MC.** 831 318-4
Polydor / Mar '91.

HUSH.
Tracks: Hush / Dead or alive / Bad attitude (12" and
CD single).
■ **12"** . . . . PZ 4
■ **7"** . . . . POC 4
■ **7"** . . . . PO 4
Polydor / May '88.

■ **CD Single** . . . . PZCD 4
Polydor / May '88.

KING OF DREAMS.
Tracks: King of dreams / Fire in the basement / King
of dreams (album version) (Available on 12" and CD
single.).
■ **12"** . . . . PT 49248
■ **7"** . . . . PB 49247
■ **CD Single** . . . . PD 49248
RCA / Sep '90.

KNEBWORTH LIVE 1985.
Tracks: Highway star / Nobody's home / Strange
kind of woman / Gypsy's kiss / Perfect strangers /
Lazy / Knocking at your backdoor / Space truckin' /
Difficult to cure / Speed king / Black night / Smoke on
the water.
CD. . . . . DPVSOPCD 163
LP . . . . .DPVSOPLP 163
MC. . . . . DPVSOPMC 163
Connoisseur Collection / Jun '91 / Pinnacle.

KNOCKING AT YOUR BACK DOOR.
Tracks: Not Advised.
CD. 511438-2
MC. 511438-4
Polydor / Mar '92 / PolyGram.

KNOCKING ON YOUR BACK DOOR.
Tracks: Knocking on your back door / Perfect
strangers.
■ **12"** . . . . POSPX 749
■ **7"** . . . . POSP 749
Polydor / Jun '85.

LIVE IN JAPAN.
Tracks: Highway star / Child in time / Mule (drum
solo) / Strange kind of woman / Lazy / Space trukin' /
Black night (encore) / Speed king (encore).
CD. . . . . CDEM 1510
EMI / Nov '93 / EMI.

LIVE IN LONDON: DEEP PURPLE.
Tracks: Burn / Might just take your life / Lay down,
stay down / Mistreated / Smoke on the water / You
fool no-one / Mule.
■ **MC** . . . . .TCSHSP 4124
■ **LP** . . . . SHSP 4124
Harvest / Aug '82.

LOVE CONQUERS ALL.
Tracks: Love conquers all / Truth hurts / Slow down
sister (Only on CD and 12" single).
■ **12"** . . . . PT 49212
■ **12" P.Disc.** . . . . PT 49224
■ **7"** . . . . PB 49225
■ **CD Single** . . . . PD 49226
■ **MC Single.** . . . . PK 49225
RCA / Feb '91.

MACHINE HEAD.
Tracks: Highway star / Maybe I'm a Leo / Pictures of
home / Never before / Smoke on the water / Lazy /
Space truckin'.
■ **LP** . . . . TPSA 7504
Purple / Apr '72.
■ **LP P.Disc** . . . . EJ 2603450
EMI / '85.
■ **LP** . . . . ATAK 39
■ **MC** . . . . TC-ATAK 39
Purple / '85.
■ **LP** . . . . .FA 3158
MC. . . . . TCFA 3158
Fame / Aug '86 / EMI.
■ **CD** . . . . CZ 83
EMI / Mar '87.
■ **CD** . . . . CDFA 3158
Fame / May '89.

MADE IN EUROPE (LIVE).
Tracks: Burn / Mistreated / Lady double dealer / You
fool no-one / Stormbringer.
■ **MC** . . . . .TCTPSA 7517
■ **LP** . . . . TPSA 7517
Purple / Nov '76.
CD . . . . CZ 344
EMI / Jul '90 / EMI.

MADE IN JAPAN.
Tracks: Highway star / Child in time / Smoke on the
water / Mule / Strange kind of woman / Lazy / Space
truckin'.
■ **Double LP.** . . . . TPSP 351
■ **MC Set** . . . . TC2 TPSP 351
Purple / Dec '72.
■ **CD** . . . . CDTPSP 351
Purple / Sep '88.
CD. . . . . CDFA 3268
MC. . . . . TCFA 3268
MFP / Oct '92 / EMI.

MALICE IN WONDERLAND (see under Paice, Ashton, Lord).

MARK 1 AND MARK 2.
Tracks: Hush / Mandrake root / Why didn't Rosemary / Hey Joe / Wring that neck / Emmaretta / Help / Chasing shadows / Black night / Speed king / Strange kind of woman / Into the fire / When a blind man cries / Smoke on the water / Woman from Tokyo / Highway star.

MARK 2 SINGLES.
Tracks: Black night / Smoke on the water / Child in time / Woman from Tokyo / Never before / When a blind man cries / Painted horse.
■ **LP** . . . . **TPS 3514**
Purple / Apr '79.

NEVER BEFORE.
Tracks: Never before.
■ **7"** . . . . **PUR 102**
Purple / Apr '72.

NEW LIVE AND RARE.
Tracks: Black night / Painted horse / When a blind man cries.
■ **EP** . . . . **PUR 135**
Purple / Oct '77.

NEW LIVE AND RARE - VOL.2.
Tracks: Not Advised.

NEW LIVE AND RARE - VOL.3.
Tracks: Smoke on the water / Bird has flown / Grabsplatter.
■ **EP** . . . . **SHEP 101**
Harvest / Oct '80.

NOBODY'S PERFECT.
Tracks: Highway star / Strange kind of woman / Perfect strangers / Hard lovin' woman / Bad attitude / Knocking on your back door / Child in time / Lazy / Black night / Woman from Tokyo / Smoke on the water / Space truckin'.
CD 835 897-2
■ **Double LP** . . . . **PODV 10**
■ **MC Set** . . . . **PODVC 10**
Polydor / Jun '88.
■ **LP** 835 897-1
■ **MC Set** 835 897-4
Polydor / Mar '91.

PERFECT STRANGERS.
Tracks: Knocking on your back door / Under the gun / Nobody's home / Mean streak / Perfect strangers / Gypsy's kiss / Wasted sunsets / Hungry daze / Not Responsible (Cassette only).
MC . . . . **POLHC 16**
■ **LP** . . . . **POLH 16**
Polydor / Nov '84.
■ **LP P.Disc** . . . . **POLHP 16**
Polydor / Jun '85.
CD 823 777-2
■ **LP** 823 777-1
MC 823 777-4
Polydor / Mar '91 / PolyGram.

PERFECT STRANGERS.
Tracks: Perfect strangers / Gypsy's kiss / Wasted sunsets (on 12" only) / Hungry daze (Available on 12" only).
■ **12"** . . . . **POSPX 719**
■ **7"** . . . . **POSP 719**
Polydor / Jan '85.

POWERHOUSE.
Tracks: Painted horse / Hush / Wring that neck / Child in time / Black night / Cry free.
■ **LP** . . . . **TPS 3510**
Purple / Jan '78.
■ **MC** . . . . **TCTPS 3510**
Purple / Jun '85.

PROGRESSION.
Tracks: Perfect strangers / Under the gun / Knocking at your back door / Gypsy's kiss / Not responsible / Black night (live) / Smoke on the water (live) / Hush / Bad attitude / Dead or alive / Hard lovin' woman / Call of the wild.
CD 550027-2
MC 550027-4
Spectrum (1) / May '93 / PolyGram.

SCANDANAVIAN NIGHTS.
Tracks: Wring that neck / Speed king / Into the fire / Paint it black / Mandrake root / Child in time / Black night.
CD Set . . . . **DPVSOPCD 125**
■ **Double LP** . . . . **DPVSOPLP 125**
MC Set . . . . **DPVSOPMC 125**
Connoisseur Collection / Oct '88 / Pinnacle.

SCANDANAVIAN NIGHTS (Live in Denmark, March 1972).
Tracks: Highway star / Strange kind of woman / Child in time / Mule / Lazy / Space Truckin' / Fireball / Lucille / Black night.

VHS . . . . **CCV 1000**
Connoisseur Collection / Jul '90 / Pinnacle.

SHADES OF DEEP PURPLE.
Tracks: And the address / Hush / One more rainy day / Prelude: happiness / I'm so glad / Mandrake root / Help / Love help me / Hey Joe.
■ **LP** . . . . **SHSM 2016**
Harvest / Mar '77.
■ **CD** . . . . **CZ 170**
Parlophone / Mar '89.

SINGLES - A'S & B'S.
Tracks: Hush / One more rainy day / Emmaretta / Wring that neck / Hallelujah / April, part 1 / Black night / Speed king / Strange kind of woman / I'm alone / Demon's eye / Fireball.
CD . . . . **CDFA 3212**
■ **LP** . . . . **FA 3212**
MC . . . . **TCFA 3212**
Fame / Nov '88 / EMI.

SINGLES A'S AND B'S.
Tracks: Hush / One more rainy day / Kentucky woman / Emmaretta / Bird has flown / Hallelujah / Speed king (Single version) / Black night / Strange kind of woman / I'm alone / Fireball / Demon's eye / Never before / When a blind man cries / Smoke on the water (US edit) / Black night (Live) / Might just take your life / Coronarias redig / You keep on moving / Love child.
CD . . . . **CDP 781 009 2**
■ **MC** . . . . **TCEMC 3658**
EMI / Jan '93.

SLAVES AND MASTERS.
Tracks: King of dreams / Cut runs deep / Fire in the basement / Truth hurts / Breakfast in bed / Love conquers all / Fortune teller / Too much is not enough / Wicked ways.
■ **CD** . . . . **PD 90535**
■ **LP** . . . . **PL 90535**
■ **MC** . . . . **PK 90535**
RCA / Oct '90.
DCC 07863524215
RCA / Jan '93 / BMG.
CD 7432118719-2
RCA / Apr '94 / BMG.

SMOKE ON THE WATER.
Tracks: Smoke on the water.
■ **7"** . . . .**PUR 132**
Purple / Mar '77.
■ **12"** **12HAR 5236**
Purple / Jun '85.

STORMBRINGER.
Tracks: Stormbringer / Love don't mean a thing / Holy man / Hold on / Lady double dealer / You can't do it right / High ball shooter / Gypsy / Soldier of fortune.
MC . . . . **TCATAK 70**
Purple / Jun '85 / EMI.
■ **MC** . . . .**TCTPS 3508**
EMI / Jun '85.
■ **LP** . . . . **ATAK 70**
Purple / Mar '86.
■ **LP** . . . . **TPS 3508**
EMI / Mar '86.
CD . . . . **CZ 142**
EMI / Oct '88 / EMI.

STRANGE KIND OF WOMAN.
Tracks: Strange kind of woman / I'm alone / Highway star.
■ **7"** . . . . **HAR 5033**
Harvest / Feb '71.
■ **12"** . . . . 12 HAR 5234
Harvest / Jun '85.

THIRD ALBUM.
Tracks: Chasing shadows / Blind / Lalena / Painter / Why didn't Rosemary / Bird has flown / April.
■ **MC** . . . . **TCSHVL 759**
■ **LP** . . . . **SHVL 759**
Harvest / Sep '69.
CD . . . . **CZ 172**
Harvest / Mar '89 / EMI.

WHO DO WE THINK WE ARE.
Tracks: Woman from Tokyo / Mary Long / Super trouper / Smooth dancer / Rat bat blue / Place in line / Our lady.
■ **LP** . . . . **ATAK 127**
■ **MC** . . . . **TCATAK 127**
EMI / Jan '73.
■ **MC** . . . . **TC TPSA 7508**
■ **LP** . . . . **TPSA 7508**
Purple / Jan '73.
CD . . . . **CZ 6**
EMI / Oct '87 / EMI.

Deep Throat

MOUTH ORGAN.
Tracks: Mouth organ.
12" . . . . **TRIP 9R**
Dodgey Beast / Mar '94 / RTM / Pinnacle.

VERSION 3.0.
Tracks: Not Advised.
CD . . . .**CDDVN 20**
LP . . . . **DVN 20**
Devotion / Jun '93 / Pinnacle.

Def Leppard

Formed in Sheffield in late '70s, Leppard found U.S. more receptive to blend of melody and metal. Astute management, heavy airplay and extensive touring formed background to 1983's nine-million selling *Pyromania*. Band shunned in U.K. until 1987's *Hysteria*, which sold 14 million worldwide; first two albums also million-sellers. Leppard are studio perfectionists: two versions of *Hysteria* - one produced by Jim Steinman - scrapped before final release. Other delays more tragic: drummer Rick Allen lost arm in 1984 car-crash and guitarist Steve Clark died in 1991. Band soldiered on; 1992's *Adrenalize* and 1993's *Retroactive* yielded further hits.

ACTION.
Tracks: Action / Miss you in heartbeat (demo) / She's too tough (demo) (CDS only) / Two steps behind (Joe's demo) (On 2nd CD single only) / Love bites (Live) (On 2nd CD only).
■ **7"** . . . . **LEP 13**
■ **CD Single** . . . .**LEPCX 13**
■ **CD Single** . . . .**LEPCD 13**
■ **MC Single** . . . .**LEPMC 13**
Bludgeon-Riffola / Jan '94.

ADRENALIZE.
Tracks: Let's get rocked / Heaven is / Make like a man / Tonight / White lightning / Stand up (kick love into motion) / Personal property / Have you ever / I wanna touch you / Tear it down.
CD 5109782
LP 5109781
MC 5109784
Bludgeon-Riffola / Mar '92 / PolyGram.

ANIMAL.
Tracks: Animal / Tear it down.
■ **7"** . . . . **LEP 1**
■ **12"** . . . . **LEPX 1**
Bludgeon-Riffola / Jul '87.

ANIMAL (CD VIDEO).
Tracks: Animal.
CD Video 080 626 2
Polygram Music Video / Sep '89 / PolyGram.

ARMAGEDDON IT.
Tracks: Armageddon it / Armageddon it (nuclear mix) (On 12"only) (*Track on 12" version.) / Ring of fire / Animal (Only on CD) / Pour some sugar on me.
■ **12"** . . . . **LEPXB 4**
■ **12"** . . . . **LEPX 4**
■ **7"** . . . . **LEP 4**
■ **CD Single** . . . . **LEPCD 4**
Bludgeon-Riffola / Mar '88.

BRINGING ON THE HEARTBREAK.
Tracks: Bringing on the heartbreak / You got me runnin'.
■ **12"** . . . . **LEPP 312**
■ **7"** . . . . **LEPP 3**
Vertigo / Jan '82.

CONVERSATIONALIZE.
Tracks: Not Advised.
CD P.Disc . . . . **CBAK 4029**
Baktabak / Feb '94 / Arabesque Ltd.

DEF LEPPARD CD BOX SET.
Tracks: Not Advised.
CD Set 838 606 2
Mercury / Oct '89 / PolyGram.

DEF LEPPARD: INTERVIEW PICTURE DISC (1).
Tracks: Not Advised.
■ **LP P.Disc** . . . . **CT 1011**
Music & Media / Dec '87.

DEF LEPPARD: INTERVIEW PICTURE DISC (2).
Tracks: Not Advised.
■ **12" P.Disc.** . . . .**LEPPARD 1**
Talkies / '87.

■ **DELETED**

DEF LEPPARD: INTERVIEW PICTURE DISC (3).
Tracks: Not Advised.
LP P.Disc . . . . BAK 2067
Baktabak / Nov '87 / Arabesque Ltd.

DEF LEPPARD: INTERVIEW PICTURE DISC (COLLECTION).
Tracks: Not Advised.
7" Set . . . . BAKPAK 1013
Baktabak / Dec '88 / Arabesque Ltd.

GETCHA ROCKS OFF.
Tracks: Getcha rocks off / Ride into the sun / Overture.
■ 7" 6059240
Vertigo / Aug '79.

HEAVEN IS.
Tracks: Heaven is.
■ 12" . . . . LEPX 9
■ 7" . . . . LEP 9
■ MC Single . . . . LEPMC 9
Bludgeon-Riffola / Jan '93.

HELLO AMERICA.
Tracks: Hello America / Good morning freedom.
■ 7" . . . . LEPP 1
Vertigo / Feb '80.

HIGH 'N' DRY.
Tracks: High 'n' dry (Saturday night) / You got me runnin' / Let it go / Another hit and run / Lady strange / On through the night / Mirror mirror (look into my eyes) / No, no, no / Bringin' on the heartbreak / Switch 625.
■ LP 6359 045
MC 7150 045
Vertigo / Sep '83 / PolyGram.
CD 818 836 2
■ LP 818 836 1
MC 818 836 4
Vertigo / Jan '89 / PolyGram.

HISTORIA.
Tracks: Hello America / Let it go / High 'n' dry / Bringin' on the heartbreak / Photograph / Rock of ages / Foolin' / Too late for love / Me and my wine / Women / Animal / Pour some sugar on me / Hysteria / Armageddon it (live) / Pour some sugar on me (live).
VHS 041 684 2
Polygram Music Video / Jun '88 / PolyGram.
CD Video 080 376 1
Polygram Music Video / Oct '88 / PolyGram.
VHS . . . . CFV 07892
Channel 5 / Sep '89 / Channel 5 Video / P.R.O. Video / Gold & Sons.

HYSTERIA.
Tracks: Women / Rocket / Animal / Love bites / Pour some sugar on me / Armageddon it / Gods of war / Don't shoot shot gun / Run riot / Hysteria / Excitable / Love and affection / I can't let you be a memory.
CD 830 675-2
■ LP . . . . HYSLP 1
MC . . . . HYSMC 1
Bludgeon-Riffola / '87 / PolyGram.
■ LP P.Disc . . . . HYSPD 1
Bludgeon-Riffola / Apr '88.

HYSTERIA.
Tracks: Hysteria / Ride into the sun / Love and affection (12"only).
■ 12" . . . . LEPX 3
■ 7" . . . . LEP 3
Bludgeon-Riffola / Nov '87.
■ CD Single . . . . LEPCD 3
Bludgeon-Riffola / Nov '8/.

IN THE ROUND - IN YOUR FACE (Live).
Tracks: Stagefright / Rock, rock (till you drop) / Women / Too late for love / Hysteria / Gods of war / Die hard the hunter / Bringin' on the heartbreak / Foolin' / Armageddon it / Animal / Pour some sugar on me / Rock of ages / Photograph.
CD Video 080 5981
Polygram Music Video / Nov '89 / PolyGram.
VHS . . . . CFV 08422
Channel 5 / Sep '89 / Channel 5 Video / P.R.O. Video / Gold & Sons.

LET IT GO.
Tracks: Let it go / Switch 625.
■ 7" . . . . LEPP 2
Vertigo / Aug '81.

LET'S GET ROCKED.
Tracks: Let's get rocked / Only after dark / Too late for love (live) (12" only) / Women (live) (CD single only).
■ 12" P.Disc . . . . DEFXP 7
■ 7" . . . . DEF 7

LOVE BITES.
Tracks: Love bites / Billy's got a gun (live).
■ 12" . . . . LEPXB 5
■ 7" . . . . LEPG 5
■ CD Single . . . . LEPCD 5
■ 12" . . . . LEPX 5
■ 7" . . . . LEP 5
Bludgeon-Riffola / Jul '88.

LOVE BITES (CD VIDEO).
Tracks: Love bites.
CD Video 080 458 2
Polygram Music Video / Oct '88 / PolyGram.

MAKE LOVE LIKE A MAN.
Tracks: Make love like a man / Miss you in a heartbeat / Action / Two steps behind (acoustic).
■ 12" P.Disc . . . . .LEPXP 7
CD P.Disc . . . . LEPCB 7
■ 7" . . . . LEP 7
■ MC Single . . . . LEPMC 7
Bludgeon-Riffola / Jun '92.

MUSIC AND MEDIA INTERVIEW PICTURE DISCS.
Tracks: Not Advised.
■ LP P.Disc . . . . DL 1021
Music & Media / Feb '88.

ON THROUGH THE NIGHT.
Tracks: Answer to the master / Hello America / It could be you / It don't matter / Overture / Rock brigade / Rocks off / Satellite / Sorrow is a woman / When the walls came tumblin down.
■ LP 9102 040
MC 7231 028
Vertigo / Mar '80 / PolyGram.
CD 8225 332
■ LP 8225 331
MC 8225 334
Vertigo / Jan '89 / PolyGram.

PHOTOGRAPH.
Tracks: Photograph / Bringing on the heartbreak.
■ 12" . . . . VERX 2
■ 7" . . . . VER 5
Vertigo / Jan '83.
■ 12" . . . . VERX 9
■ 7" . . . . VER 9
Vertigo / Feb '84.

POUR SOME SUGAR ON ME.
Tracks: Pour some sugar on me.
■ 7" . . . . LEP 2
Bludgeon-Riffola / Sep '87.

PYROMANIA.
Tracks: Rock rock ('til you drop) / Photograph / Stagefright / Too late for love / Die hard the hunter / Foolin' / Rock of ages / Comin' under fire / Action not words / Billy's got a gun.
■ LP . . . . VERS 2
MC . . . . VERSC 2
Vertigo / Mar '83 / PolyGram.
CD 810308-2
Vertigo / '88 / PolyGram.

RETRO ACTIVE.
Tracks: Not Advised.
CD 5183052
LP 5183051
MC 5183054
Bludgeon-Riffola / Oct '93 / PolyGram.
DCC 5183055
Phonogram / Jan '94 / PolyGram.

ROCK OF AGES.
Tracks: Rock of ages.
■ 7" . . . . VER 6
Vertigo / Aug '83.

ROCK OF AGES (CD VIDEO).
Tracks: Not Advised.
CD Video 080 034 2
Polygram Music Video / Sep '89 / PolyGram.

ROCKET.
Tracks: Rocket / Release me / Rocket (lunar mix) / Rock of ages (live).
■ CD Single . . . . LEPCD 6
■ 12" . . . . LEPX 6
■ 7" . . . . LEP 6
Bludgeon-Riffola / Jan '89.
■ 12" P.Disc . . . . .LEPXP 6
Bludgeon-Riffola / Jan '89.

ROCKET (CD VIDEO).
Tracks: Rocket.
CD Video 080 990 2
Polygram Music Video / Jan '89 / PolyGram.

CD Single
■ CD Single . . . . DEFCD 7
■ MC Single . . . . DEFMC 7
Bludgeon-Riffola / Mar '92.

TONIGHT.
Tracks: Tonight.
■ 7" . . . . LEP 10
■ CD Single . . . . .LEPCD 10
■ MC Single . . . . .LEPMC 10
Bludgeon-Riffola / May '93.

TOO LATE FOR LOVE.
Tracks: Too late for love / Foolin'.
■ 12" . . . . VERX 8
■ 7" . . . . VER 8
Vertigo / Dec '83.

TWO STEPS BEHIND.
Tracks: Two steps behind.
■ 7" . . . . LEP 12
■ CD Single . . . . LEPCD 12
■ MC Single . . . . .LEPMC 12
Bludgeon-Riffola / Sep '93.

WASTED.
Tracks: Wasted.
■ 7" 6059 204
Vertigo / Nov '79.

Defecation

PURITY DILUTION.
Tracks: Not Advised.
LP . . . . NB 018
Nuclear Blast / Sep '89 / Plastic Head.
CD . . . . .NB 018CD
Nuclear Blast / Nov '92 / Plastic Head.

Defiance

PRODUCT OF SOCIETY.
Tracks: Fault / Product of society / Lock jaw / Deadly intentions / Tribulation / Death machine / Forgotten / Insomnia / Aftermath / Hyperthermia.
CD . . . . RO 95042
■ LP . . . . RO 95041
Roadracer / Mar '89.

VOID, TERRA, FIRMA.
Tracks: Void terra firma / Questions / Slayground / Steamroller / Buried or burned / Deception of faith / Skitz - illusions / Killers / Checkmate / Last resort (welcome to poverty).
CD . . . . RO 93952
LP . . . . RO 93951
MC . . . . RO 93954
Roadracer / Apr '90 / Pinnacle.

Dehumanizers

END OF TIME.
Tracks: Not Advised.
■ LP . . . . NEGFX 006
Neg Effects / Jul '87.

Deicide

U.S. quartet, formed 1987, whose music is eclipsed by Black Metal posturing of leader Glen Banton. Self-proclaimed Satanist, Banton's environmentally-unfriendly treatment of wildlife prompted wrath of Animal Rights activists, maintaining tradition initiated by Alice Cooper and upheld by Ozzy Osbourne. 1993 album *Feasting the Beast* hinted at lack of enlightenment.

AMON : FEASTING THE BEAST.
Tracks: Lunatic of God's creation / Sacrificial suicide / Crucifixation / Carnage in the temple of the damned / Dead by dawn / Blasphererereion / Feasting the beast / Day of darkness / Oblivious to nothing.
CD . . . . RR 91112
MC . . . . RR 91114
Road Runner / Feb '93 / Pinnacle.

DEICIDE.
Tracks: Lunatic of God's creation / Oblivious to evil / Blasphererereion / Carnage in the temple of the damned / Day of darkness / Sacrificial suicide / Dead by dawn / Deicide / Mephistopheles / Crucifixion.
LP . . . . RO 93811
Roadracer / Sep '90 / Pinnacle.

LEGION.
Tracks: Not Advised.
CD . . . . RC 91922
MC . . . . RC 91924
■ LP . . . . RC 91921
Road Runner / Jun '92.

Del Lords

BASED ON A TRUE STORY.
Tracks: Crawl in bed / Judas kiss / Ashes to ashes / I'm gonna be around / Poem of the river / Cool and the crazy / Cheyenne / Lover's prayer / Whole lotta nothin' goin' on / River of justice.
CD . . . . CDENV 508
■ LP . . . . ENVLP 508
Enigma (EMI) / Sep '88.
MC. . . . . TCENV 508
Virgin / Sep '88 / EMI.

CHEYENNE.
Tracks: Cheyenne / River of justice / Hand to mouth (12" only).
■ 12" . . . . .ENVT 10
■ 7" . . . . ENV 10
Enigma (EMI) / Apr '89.

FRONTIER DAYS.
Tracks: How can a poor man stand such times and live / Get tough / Livin' on love / Double life / I play the drums / Burning in the flame of love / Pledge of love / Shame on you / Mercenary / Going home.
■ LP . . . . FIEND 53
Demon / Jul '85.

JOHNNY COMES MARCHING HOME.
Tracks: Heaven (Scott Kempner.) / love lies dying (Scott kempner) / Drug deal (Scott Kempner, Eric Ambel, Manny Caiate, Frank Funaro.) / Soldier's home (Scott Kempner) / St. Jake (Scott Kempner) / Dream come true (Scott Kempner) / True love (Scott Kempner) / Everlovin' (Scott Kempner) / Against my will (Scott Kempner) / No waitress no more (Scott Kempner).
MC. . . . . TCAML 3103
■ LP . . . . AML 3103
EMI-America / May '86.

JUDAS KISS.
Tracks: Judas kiss / Whole lotta nothin' goin' on.
■ 7" . . . . ENV 3
Enigma (EMI) / Oct '88.

LIVE: HOWLIN' AT THE HALLOWEEN MOON.
Tracks: True love / Jumpin' in the night / Wastin' time talkin' / Cool 'n the crazy / Judas kiss / I play the drums / Tallahassee lassie.
CD . . . . FIENDCD 162
Demon / Jan '90 / Pinnacle / A.D.A. Distribution.

POEM OF THE RIVER.
Tracks: Poem of the river / Get tough / Waitress (no more).
■ 12" . . . . .ENVT 14
■ 7" . . . . ENV 14
■ CD Single . . . . .ENVCD 14
Enigma (EMI) / Jun '89.

SOLDIER'S HOME.
Tracks: Soldier's home / No waitress no more.
■ 7" . . . . EA 215
EMI-America / May '86.

Deliverance

DEVIL'S MEAT.
Tracks: Not Advised.
■ LP . . . . .VOV 666
Metalworks / Apr '87.

EVIL FRIENDSHIP.
Tracks: Not Advised.
MC. . . . . .VOV 673C
■ LP . . . . .VOV 673
Metalworks / Jun '88.

FOOLISH HEARTS.
Tracks: Foolish hearts / Face the lady.
■ 7" . . . . EPC 8275
Epic / Mar '80.

LEAVING LA.
Tracks: Leaving LA / Face the lady.
■ 7" . . . . EPC 8904
Epic / Sep '80.

Demented Ted

PROMISE IMPURE.
Tracks: Existance lies beneath / Despair / Psychopathology / Incisions / Liquid remains / Geneticide / Between two eternities / Forgotten.
CD . . . . .CDVEST 2
Bulletproof / Mar '94 / Pinnacle.

Demolition Hammer

TIMEBOMB.
Tracks: Not Advised.
CD . . . . CM 77071-2
MC. . . . . CM 77071-4
Century Media / Aug '94 / Plastic Head.

TORTURED EXISTENCE.
Tracks: Not Advised.
CD 0897132
LP 0897131
MC. 0897134
Century Media / Sep '90 / Plastic Head.

Demon

NWOBHM pioneers, Demon - Chris Ellis, Dave Hill, Les Hunt, Mal Spooner and John Wright - were predictably into all things satanic. Debut album *Night Of The Demon* (1981), follow-up reached UK album chart, *The Unexpected Guest* (1982). Still recording/touring today and are particularly popular in Germany.

ANTHOLOGY - DEMON.
Tracks: Night of the demon - (Remix) / Into the nightmare / Father of time / Don't break the circle (Remix) / Spell / Sign of the madman / Plague / Nowhere to run (mix) / Blackheath (Alternative mix) / Touching the ice / From the outside / Hear of our time / Crossfire / Life on the wire / Breakout / Hollywood / England's glory.
MC. . . . . CLAYD 108
■ CD . . . . CLAYCD 108
Clay / Apr '93.

BLOW OUT.
Tracks: Not Advised.
CD . . . . SONICCD 11
Sonic (2) / May '92 / Total / BMG.
LP . . . . FT 30019LP
Flametrader / Nov '92 / Greyhound Records.

BREAKOUT.
Tracks: Not Advised.
■ LP . . . . CLAYLP 23
Clay / Jun '87.
■ CD . . . . CLAYCD 23
Clay / '88.
■ LP . . . . SONICLP 6
■ CD . . . . SONICCD 6
Sonic (2) / May '90.

BRITISH STANDARD APPROVED.
Tracks: Not Advised.
■ LP . . . . CLAYLP 15
Clay / Mar '85.
CD . . . . SONICCD 4
■ LP . . . . SONICLP 4
Sonic (2) / Sep '90.

HAVE WE BEEN HERE BEFORE?.
Tracks: Have we been here before / Victim of fortune.
■ 7" . . . . .CAR 249
Carrere / Jul '82.

HEART OF OUR TIME.
Tracks: Not Advised.
■ LP . . . . CLAYCLP 18
■ LP . . . . CLAYLP 18
Clay / Nov '85.
■ LP . . . . SONICLP 5
■ CD . . . . SONICCD 5
Sonic (2) / Sep '90.

HEART OF OUR TIME.
Tracks: Heart of our time.
■ 12" . . . . .PLATE 8
Clay / Nov '88.

HOLD ON TO THE DREAM.
Tracks: Not Advised.
■ CD . . . . SONICCD 10
■ LP . . . . SONICLP 10
Sonic (2) / Oct '91.

NIGHT OF THE DEMON.
Tracks: Full moon (Instrumental) / Night of the demon / Into the nightmare / Father of time / Decisions / Liar / Big love / Ride the wind / Fool to play the hard / One helluva night.
■ LP . . . . WEA 125
WEA / Aug '81.
■ LP . . . . CLAYLP 25
Clay / Apr '88.
■ CD . . . . SONICCD 1
■ LP . . . . SONICLP 1
Sonic (2) / Jun '90.

ONE HELLUVA NIGHT (Live in West Germany).
Tracks: Not Advised.
CD Set . . . . DEMONCD 1
■ Double LP. . . . . DEMONLP 1
Total Record Company / Aug '90.

ONE HELLUVA NIGHT.
Tracks: One helluva night.
■ 7" . . . . .CAR 226
Carrere / Mar '82.

PLAGUE, THE.
Tracks: Not Advised.
■ LP P.Disc . . . . CLAYLP 6P
■ LP . . . . CLAYLP 6
Clay / Jun '83.
■ CD . . . . CLAYCD 6
Clay / Aug '88.
■ CD . . . . SONICCD 3
■ LP . . . . SONICLP 3
Sonic (2) / Sep '89.

PLAGUE, THE.
Tracks: Plague / Only sane man.
■ 7" . . . . .CLAY 25
Clay / Aug '83.

RIDE THE WIND.
Tracks: Ride the wind / On the road.
■ 7" . . . . .CAR 185
Carrere / Jun '81.

TAKING THE WORLD BY STORM.
Tracks: Not Advised.
CD . . . . CLAYCD 27
■ LP . . . . CLAYLP 27
Clay / May '89.
■ MC . . . . SONICMC 8
■ LP . . . . SONICLP 8
■ CD . . . . SONICCD 8
Sonic (2) / May '89.

TONIGHT THE HERO IS BACK.
Tracks: Tonight the hero is back.
■ 7" Set . . . . .CLAY 48D
Clay / Apr '88.

UNEXPECTED GUEST, THE.
Tracks: Introduction / Observation, An / Don't break the circle / Spell / Total possession / Sign of a madman / Victim of fortune / Have we been here before / Strange institution / Grand illusion / Beyond the gates / Deliver us from evil.
■ LP . . . . .CAL 139
MC. . . . . CAC 139
Carrere / Jul '82 / WEA.
■ LP . . . . CLAYLP 22
Clay / Jan '87.
■ CD . . . . SONICCD 2
Sonic (2) / Sep '90.
■ LP . . . . SONICLP 2
Sonic (2) / Sep '90.

WONDERLAND.
Tracks: Wonderland.
■ 12" . . . . 12 CLAY 41
■ 7" . . . . .CLAY 41
Clay / Nov '84.

Depraved

COME ON DOWN.
Tracks: Not Advised.
■ LP . . . . GURT 6
Children Of The Revolution / Jan '86.

STUPIDITY MAKETH THE MAN.
Tracks: Not Advised.
■ LP . . . . GURT 14
Children Of The Revolution / Oct '86.

Des Barres, Michael

I'M ONLY HUMAN.
Tracks: Baited breath / I'm only human / Someone somewhere in the night / Nothing's too hard / Right or wrong / Dancin' on the brink of disaster / Boy meets car / Scandal papers / Five hour flight / Catch phrase / Bullfighter / I don't have a thing to wear / Outro.
■ LP 2394279
Dreamland / May '81.

I'M ONLY HUMAN.
Tracks: I'm only human / Catchphrase.
■ 7" . . . . DLSP 7
Dreamland / Jan '81.

■ DELETED

OBSESSION (Des Barres, Michael & Holly Knight).
Tracks: Obsession / Woman's weapon.
■ 12"...................... AMX 183
■ 7" .... AM 183
A&M / '84.

SOMEONE SOMEWHERE IN THE NIGHT.
Tracks: Someone somewhere in the night / Five hour flight.
■ 7" .... DLSP 9
Dreamland / Mar '81.

Descendents

ALL.
Tracks: Not Advised.
■ LP .... SST 112
MC........................ SST 112 C
SST / Jun '87 / Pinnacle.
CD................... SST 112 CD
SST / May '93 / Pinnacle.

BONUS FAT.
Tracks: Bonus fat.
■ LP .... SST 144
SST / Aug '87.
CD.................... SST 144 CD
MC..................... SST 144 C
SST / May '93 / Pinnacle.

ENJOY.
Tracks: Not Advised.
CD.................... SST 242 CD
LP .... SST 242
MC....................... SST 242 C
SST / Sep '90 / Pinnacle.

HALLRAKER.
Tracks: Not Advised.
■ LP .... SST 205
SST / Feb '89.
CD.................... SST 205 CD
MC..................... SST 205 C
SST / May '93 / Pinnacle.

I DON'T WANT TO GROW UP.
Tracks: Not Advised.
MC..................... SST 143 C
SST / Nov '87 / Pinnacle.
CD.................... SST 143 CD
SST / Feb '88 / Pinnacle.
LP .... SST 143
SST / May '93 / Pinnacle.

LIVEAGE.
Tracks: All / I'm not a loser / Silly girl / I wanna be a bear / Coolidge / Weinerschnitel / I don't want to grow up / Kids / Wendy / Get the time / Descendents / All-o-gistics / Myage / My dad sucks / Van / Surburban home / Hope / Clean sheets.
CD.................... SST 163 CD
■ LP .... SST 163
SST / Jan '88.
MC..................... SST 163 C
SST / May '93 / Pinnacle.

MILO GOES TO COLLEGE.
Tracks: Not Advised.
CD.................... SST 142 CD
LP .... SST 142
MC..................... SST 142 C
SST / May '93 / Pinnacle.

SOMERY.
Tracks: Not Advised.
CD.................... SST 259 CD
LP .... SST 259
MC..................... SST 259 C
SST / May '93 / Pinnacle.

TWO THINGS AT ONCE.
Tracks: Not Advised.
CD.................... SST 145 CD
MC..................... SST 145 C
SST / May '93 / Pinnacle.

Despair

DECAY OF HUMANITY.
Tracks: Decay of humanity / Delusion / Distant territory / Radiated / Cry for liberty / Victims of vanity / Silent screaming / Satanic verses.
CD..................... 8497122
LP 0897121
MC........................ 0897124
Century Media / Aug '90 / Plastic Head.

HISTORY OF HATE.
Tracks: Not Advised.
■ LP .... MB 1002
Metal Blast / Feb '89.

Destiny

ATOMIC WINTER.
Tracks: Not Advised.
CD..................... US 014 CD
■ LP .... US 014
U.S. Metal / Mar '89.

DESTINY.
Tracks: Destiny.
■ 12".................. 12 CUP 2
Cupido Disque / Apr '92.

DESTINY.
Tracks: Destiny.
■ 12"................. 12ELIC 11
Elicit / Jun '92.

MARATHON, THE.
Tracks: Marathon / Autumn gold.
■ 7" .... WML 1007
Windmill Music / Apr '84.

NOTHING LEFT TO FEAR.
Tracks: Not Advised.
CD...................... CDATV 18
LP .... ATV 18
Music For Nations / May '91 / Pinnacle.

Destruction

Formed in 1983, Germany's proficient and eclectic Destruction quickly built enviable international reputation. However, departure of bassist/frontman Schmier dealt band death blow; they split after 1991's *Cracked Brain*. Latter bears dubious distinction of being first thrash album recorded on 48-track tape.

CRACKED BRAIN.
Tracks: Not Advised.
■ CD .... CDNUK 136
■ LP .... NUK 136
■ MC.................... ZCNUK 136
Noise / Jun '90.

ETERNAL DEVASTATION.
Tracks: Not Advised.
■ LP .... SH 0046
Steamhammer (Germany) / Jul '86.

INFERNAL OVERKILL.
Tracks: Not Advised.
■ LP 081 086
Steamhammer (Germany) / Nov '85.

INFERNAL OVERKILL/SENTENCE OF DEATH.
Tracks: Not Advised.
CD...................... 857529
Steamhammer (Germany) / '89 / Pinnacle.

LIVE WITHOUT SENSE.
Tracks: Not Advised.
CD................... CDNUK 126
Noise / Feb '89 / Pinnacle.
■ LP 087578
Steamhammer (Germany) / Feb '89.
■ LP .... NUK 126
■ MC................... ZCNUK 126
Noise / Feb '89.

MAD BUTCHER.
Tracks: Not Advised.
Mini LP 601 897
Steamhammer (Germany) / Nov '87 / Pinnacle.

MAD BUTCHER/ETERNAL DEVASTATION.
Tracks: Not Advised.
CD...................... 851860
S.P.V. / '89.

SENTENCE OF DEATH.
Tracks: Not Advised.
Mini LP 601 838
Steamhammer (Germany) / Nov '87 / Pinnacle.

Destructor

BOMB HANOI, BOMB SAIGON, BOMB DISNEYLAND.
Tracks: Not Advised.
■ LP .... KILL 666
Carnage Benelux / Aug '84.

CRY HAVOC AND UNLEASH THE DOGS OF..
Tracks: Cry havoc and unleash the dogs of..
■ 12".................... CRI 12104
Criminal Damage / Aug '83.

FORCES OF LAW.
Tracks: Forces of law / Wild thing.
■ 12"..................... ILL 1912
■ 7"...................... ILL 19
Illuminated / Apr '83.

JAILBAIT.
Tracks: Jailbait.
■ 7"...................... ILL 14
Illuminated / Oct '82.

MEANINGLESS NAMES.
Tracks: Meaningless names / AK47 / Police state / Dachau / Death squad.
■ 7"..................... BOOK 2
Carnage / Jun '82.

RELIGION THERE IS NO RELIGION.
Tracks: Religion there is no religion / Soldier boy / Agent orange / Corpse gas.
■ EP .... KILL 2
Carnage / Jul '82.

Desultory

BITTERNESS.
Tracks: Not Advised.
CD.................... CDZORR 077
Metal Blade / Jun '94 / Pinnacle.

INTO ETERNITY.
Tracks: Not Advised.
■ CD .... CDZORRO 52
Metal Blade / Feb '93.

Detective

BAG BUSINESS.
Tracks: Hong Kong calls me / Rampage / As young as you feel / Green dream / Reagan is a moron / Green eyes / Reluctant hero / Can I please you / As young as you feel (slurry mix) / Red / End bag.
MC...................... PV 029
Peerless (USA) / Feb '87.

DETECTIVE.
Tracks: Recognition / Got enough love / Grim reaper / Nightingale / Detective man / Ain't none of your business / Deep down / Wild hot summer / One more heartache.
■ LP .... SSK 59405
Swansong / Jun '77.

IT TAKES ONE TO KNOW ONE.
Tracks: Help me up / Competition / Are you talkin' to me / Dynamite / Something beautiful / Warm love / Betcha won't dance / Fever / Tear jerker.
■ LP .... SSK 59406
Swansong / May '78.

Detente

RECOGNIZE NO AUTHORITY.
Tracks: Not Advised.
■ LP .... RR 9695
Road Runner / Aug '86.
CD...................... RO 96852
Roadracer / Mar '90 / Pinnacle.

Detest

DORVAL.
Tracks: Not Advised.
CD...................... NB 104
Nuclear Blast / Mar '94 / Plastic Head.

Dethrone

LET THE DAY BEGIN.
Tracks: Not Advised.
CD.................... CDFLAG 41
LP .... FLAG 41
Under One Flag / Sep '90 / Pinnacle.

Detritus

PERPETUAL DEFIANCE.
Tracks: Not Advised.
CD.................... CDFLAG 55
LP .... FLAG 55
MC..................... TFLAG 55
Under One Flag / May '91 / Pinnacle.

Devastation

DRAG YOU DOWN.
Tracks: Drag you down.
■ 7" . . . . REAL 8
Creative Reality / Nov '84.

SIGNS OF LIFE.
Tracks: Eye for an eye / Manic depressive / Retribution / Contaminated / Escape to violence / Desolation / Signs of life / Tomorrow we die / Fear of the unknown.
CD . . . . CDFLAG 44
LP . . . . .FLAG 44
MC . . . . TFLAG 44
Under One Flag / Jul '90 / Pinnacle.

VIOLENT TERMINATION.
Tracks: Not Advised.
■ LP . . . . ZR 0269
Zombo (USA) / Aug '87.

Deviated Instinct

GUTTERAL BREATH.
Tracks: Not Advised.
■ CD . . . . VILE 16 CD
■ LP . . . . VILE 16
■ MC . . . . VILE 16 MC
Peaceville / Feb '90.

NAILED.
Tracks: Not Advised.
Mini LP . . . . PRO 4
Prophecy / '90 / Plastic Head.

ROCK 'N' ROLL CONFORMITY.
Tracks: Pearls before swine / Laugh in your face / Conquest for eternity / House of cards / Putrid scum / Through the looking glass / Time and tide / When the chapter closes / Return of frost / Mechanical extinction / Rock 'n' roll conformity.
■ LP . . . . VILE 003
Peaceville / Apr '88.

Diamond

DIAMOND MISTRESS.
Tracks: Not Advised.
■ LP . . . . RR 9766
Road Runner / Aug '85.

Diamond Head

Diamond Head formed in 1977 and were leading lights of New wave of British Heavy Metal, scoring minor hits in 1982 with *In The Heat Of The Night* single and *Borrowed Time* album. 1983 follow-up, *Canterbury*, was ambitious but less successful; band splintered in 1985, launching variety of unsuccessful solo projects. Championed by Metallica, who covered Head's *Am I Evil?* and *Helpless*, band reformed for 1993 *Death And Progress* album, featuring members of Metallica, Black Sabbath and Megadeth.

AM I EVIL?.
Tracks: Am I evil / Heat of the night / Don't you ever leave me / Borrowed time / To Heaven from Hell / Dead reckoning / Lightning to the nations / Sucking my love.
■ LP . . . . .WKFMLP 92
■ MC . . . . WKFMMC 92
FM Records / May '87.
■ LP P.Disc . . . . WKFMPD 92
FM Records / May '88.
CD . . . . WKFMXD 92
FM Records / Sep '94 / FM Revolver / Sony.

BEHOLD THE BEGINNING.
Tracks: It's electric / Prince / Sweet & innocent / Sucking my love / Streets of gold / Play it loud / Shoot out the lights / Waited too long / Helpless.
■ LP . . . . METALP 110
Metal Masters / Apr '86.
CD . . . . .HMRXD 165
■ LP . . . . HMRLP 165
MC . . . . HMRMC 165
Heavy Metal / May '91 / Sony / FM Revolver.

BORROWED TIME.
Tracks: In the heat of the night / To Heaven from Hell / Call me / Lightning to the nations / Borrowed time / Don't you ever leave me / Am I evil.
■ LP . . . . DH 1001
MCA / Oct '82.
MC . . . . MCLC 1783
■ LP . . . . MCL 1783
MCA / Feb '84.

CALL ME.
Tracks: Call me / Trick or treat / Dead reckoning.
■ 12" . . . . .DHMT 101
■ 7" . . . . DHM 101
MCA / Nov '82.

CANTERBURY.
Tracks: Not Advised.
■ LP .DH 1002
MCA / Sep '83.

DEATH & PROGRESS.
Tracks: Not Advised.
CD . . . . ESSCD 192
MC . . . . ESSMC 192
■ LP . . . . ESSLP 192
Castle / Jun '93.

DIAMOND HEAD.
Tracks: Not Advised.
CD . . . . HMRXD 92
■ LP . . . . HMRLP 92
MC . . . . HMRMC 92
Heavy Metal / May '87 / Sony / FM Revolver.

DIAMOND HEAD - FRIDAY ROCK SHOW SESSIONS.
Tracks: Sweet and innocent / Lightning to the nations / Am I evil / In the heat of the night / Borrowed time / Don't you ever leave me / Sucking my love / Play it loud.
CD . . . . FRSCD 006
Raw Fruit / Mar '92 / Pinnacle.

DIAMOND HEAD - IN THE BEGINNING.
Tracks: Not Advised.
CD . . . . .WKFMCD 165
■ LP . . . . .WKFMLP 165
MC . . . . WKFMMC 165
FM Records / Feb '91 / FM Revolver / Sony.

DIAMOND LIGHTS.
Tracks: Diamond lights / We won't be back / I don't got / It's electric.
■ 12" . . . . DHM 005
Windsong / Sep '81.

IN THE HEAT OF THE NIGHT.
Tracks: In the heat of the night / Play it loud.
■ 12" . . . . .DHMT 102
■ 7" . . . . DHM 102
MCA / Sep '82.

MAKING MUSIC.
Tracks: Making music.
■ 7" . . . . DHM 103
MCA / Aug '83.

OUT OF PHAZE.
Tracks: Out of phaze / King maker.
■ 12" . . . . .DHMT 104
■ 7" . . . . DHM 104
MCA / Sep '83.

PLAY IT LOUD.
Tracks: Play it loud / Waited too long.
■ 7" . . . . DHM 004
Dhm / Mar '81.

SWEET AND INNOCENT.
Tracks: Not Advised.
CD . . . . METALMCD 122
Metal Masters / '88 / Pinnacle.

SWEET AND INNOCENT.
Tracks: Sweet and innocent / Streets of gold.
■ 7" . . . . SCREEN 1
Media / Aug '80.

Di'Anno, Paul

Di'Anno was the original Iron Maiden vocalist and stayed with them until 1981 when he 'quit' to concentrate on his own project. He formed Lonewolf, (later forced to change their name to Dianno) who had a much more American sound than the classic NWOBHM of Iron Maiden, but the band's only album *Dianno* was a critical and commercial failure and they split up. His next effort, Battlezone, after a promising start faded badly when their second album *Children Of Madness* was slated in the press.

CHILDREN OF MADNESS (Di'Anno, Paul Battlezone).
Tracks: Not Advised.
■ LP . . . . AMP 13
Powerstation / Jun '87.

FIGHTING BACK (Di'Anno, Paul Battlezone).
Tracks: Fighting back / Welcome to the battlezone / War child / In the darkness / Land God gave to Caine / Running blind / Too much to heart / Voice on the radio / Welfare warriors / Feel the rock.
■ LP . . . . RAWLP 020
MC . . . . RAWTC 020
Raw Power / Jul '86 / Pinnacle.

HEARTUSER.
Tracks: Heartuser / Tales of the unexpected / Antigue.
■ CD . . . . WKFMPD 1
■ LP . . . . WKFMLP 1
FM Records / Aug '84.

LIVE IN SOUTH AMERICA (Di'Anno, Paul Killers).
Tracks: Not Advised.
CD . . . . .SPVMAZE 084-46532
SPV / Jun '94 / Plastic Head.

SOUTH AMERICAN ASSAULT.
Tracks: Not Advised.
CD . . . . SPV 084-38952
SPV / Aug '94 / Plastic Head.

Dickinson, Bruce

Formerly singer with Samson, Bruce Dickinson achieved international fame with Iron Maiden. Tentative solo career - *Tattooed Millionaire* in 1990 - became permanent after Dickinson's strained split from Maiden in '93. CV also boasts two novels and several fencing trophies.

ALL THE YOUNG DUDES.
Tracks: All the young dudes / Darkness be my friend / Sin city (12" & CD single only).
■ CD Single . . . . .CDEM 142
■ 12" 12EMG 142
■ 7" . . . . EM 142
■ 7" P.Disc . . . . .EMPD 142
■ MC Single. . . . . .TCEM 142
EMI / Jun '90.

BALLS TO PICASSO.
Tracks: Cyclops / Hell no / Gods of war / 1000 Points of light / Laughing in the hiding bush / Change of heart / Shoot all the clowns / Fire / Sacred cowboy / Tears of the dragon.
CD . . . . CDEMDX 1057
LP . . . . EMD 1057
MC. . . . . TCEMD 1057
EMI / Jun '94 / EMI.

BORN IN '58.
Tracks: Born in '58 / Tattooed millionaire (live) / Son of a gun (live) (12" & CD single only).
■ 12" 12EM 185
■ 7" . . . . EM 185
■ CD Single . . . . .CDEM 185
■ MC Single . . . . .TCEM 185
EMI / Mar '91.

DIVE DIVE DIVE (World Tour 1990).
Tracks: Riding with the angels / Born in '58 / Lickin' the gun / Gypsy road / Dive dive dive / Ballad of Mutt / Zulu Lulu / Son of a gun / Hell on wheels / All the young dudes / Tattooed millionaire / No lies / Fog on the Tyne/Winds of change / Sin city / Black night / Bring your daughter..to the slaughter.
■ VHS . . . . MVN 9912713
PMI / Mar '91.

DIVE DIVE DIVE!.
Tracks: Riding with the angels / Sin city / Black night / Dive dive dive.
■ 12" 12EMP 151
■ 12" P.Disc. 12EMPD 151
■ 7" . . . . EM 151
■ CD Single . . . . .CDEM 151
■ MC Single . . . . .TCEM 151
EMI / Aug '90.

MUSIC AND MEDIA INTERVIEW PICTURE DISC.
Tracks: Not Advised.
■ LP P.Disc . . . . MM 1202
Music & Media / Feb '88.

TATTOOED MILLIONAIRE.
Tracks: Tattooed millionaire / Ballad of mutt / Winds of change (Not on 7" or cassingle.).
■ CD Single . . . . .CDEM 138
■ 12" 12EMP 138
■ 12" 12EM 138
■ 7" . . . . EM 138
■ 7" P.Disc . . . . .EMPD 138
■ MC Single. . . . . .TCEM 138
EMI / Apr '90.

■ DELETED

TATTOOED MILLIONAIRE.
Tracks: Son of a gun / Tattooed millionaire / Born in '58 / Hell on wheels / Gypsy road (Dive dive dive) / Dive dive dive / All the young dudes / Lickin' the gun / Zulu Lulu / No lies.

■ MC.	TCEMC 3574
■ LP	EMC 3574
■ CD	CDEMC 3574

EMI / May '90.

CD	CDEMS 1542

EMI / Jul '94 / EMI.

TEARS OF THE DRAGON.
Tracks: Tears of the dragon / Elvis has left the building (Features on EMPD 322.) / Fire child (Features on EM 322.) / Breeding house (Features on CDEMS 322.) / No way out..to be continued (Features on CDEMS 322.) / Winds of change (Features on CDEM 322.) / Spirit of joy (Features on CDEM 322.).

■ 7"	EMPD 322
■ 7"	EM 322
■ CD Single	CDEM 322
■ CD Single	CDEMS 322

EMI / May '94.

Dictators

1975 debut, *Dictators Go Girl Crazy*, flopped, but 1977's *Manifest Destiny*, yielded minor UK hit *Search And Destroy*. Subsequent albums returned Dictators to obscurity. Name-change to Manitoba's Wild Kingdom coincided with return of guitarist Ross the Boss (one-time Manowar member). Original Dictators periodically reform and plan new album at end of '94.

BLOOD BROTHERS.
Tracks: Faster and louder / Baby let's twist / No tomorrow / Minnesota strip / Stay with me / I stand tall / Borneo Jimmy / What it is / Slow death.

■ LP	K 53083

Asylum / Aug '78.

FU** 'EM IF THEY CAN'T TAKE A JOKE.
Tracks: Not Advised.

MC.	A 102

Reach Out International / '83 / Reach Out Int. Records / Windsong International Ltd.

MANIFEST DESTINY.
Tracks: Exposed / Heartaches / Sleepin' with the TV on / Disease / Hey boys / Steppin' out / Science gone too far / Young, fast scientific / Search and destroy.

■ LP	K 53061

Asylum.

SEARCH AND DESTROY.
Tracks: Search and destroy / Sleeping with the TV on.

■ 7"	K 13091

Asylum / Sep '77.

Die Cheerleader

60 HAYLOFT ACTION EP.
Tracks: Not Advised.

■ 12"	12 ABS 099
■ CD Single	ABSCD 099
■ 7"	ABS 099

Abstract / Jun '93.

DIE CHEERLEADER E.P.
Tracks: Not Advised.

■ 12"	12 ABS 097

Abstract / Nov '92.

FILTH BY ASSOCIATION.
Tracks: Not Advised.

CD	ABT 097CD
LP	ABT 097LP

Abstract Sounds Ltd. / Oct '93 / Pinnacle / Total / SRD.

SATURATION.
Tracks: Saturation.

■ 12"	12 ABS 098

Abstract Sounds Ltd. / Feb '93.

Die Kreuzen

CENTURY DAYS.
Tracks: Not Advised.

CD	TGLP 30CD
■ LP	TGLP 30

Touch & Go / Aug '88.

DIE KREUZEN.
Tracks: Not Advised.

■ LP	TGLP 4

Touch & Go / Oct '86.

GONE AWAY.
Tracks: Gone away.

■ 12"	TGEP 40

Touch & Go / Jul '89.

Die Krupps

1 (ONE).
Tracks: Not Advised.

CD	RTD 19512662
LP	RTD 19512661

Choice / Aug '92.

BOX, THE.
Tracks: Stahlwerksinfonie 1 / Stahlwerksinfonie 2 / Wahre arbeit - wahrer lohn / Stahlwerksinfonie (live) / Volle kraft voraus / Goldfinger / Fur einen augenbuck / Tod und teufel / Das ende der traume / Nieue helden / Wahre arbeit - wahrer lohn (2) / .. Denn du lebst nur einmal / Zwei herzen, ein rhythmus / Larm macht opaoo / Wahre arbeit - wahrer lohn (0) / True work - true pay / Risk / Rise and fall / Communication breakdown / Risky soul version / Gladiators / Your voice / Communication breakdown (don't speak mix) / This day is not the last / Risk (operatic intro) / Risk (metallic outro) / Machineries of joy / Machineries of joy (mix) / Machineries of joy (mix 2) / Join the rhythm of the machines.

CD Set	RTD 19515422

Our Choice / Sep '93 / Pinnacle.

CROSSFIRE.
Tracks: Crossfire.

12"	AXIST 008
CD Single	AXISCD 008

Equator / Jul '94 / Pinnacle.

FATHERLAND.
Tracks: Fatherland.

■ 12"	AXIST 002
■ CD Single	AXISCD 002

Equator / Oct '93.

FINAL OPTION.
Tracks: Not Advised.

CD	ATLASCD 004
LP	ATLASLP 004
MC.	ATLASMC 004

Equator / Oct '93 / Pinnacle.

FINAL REMIXES, THE.
Tracks: To the hilt / Paradise of sin / Language of reality / Fatherland / Worst case scenario / Shellshocked / Crossfire / Bloodsuckers / Iron man / Inside out / New temptation / Dawning of doom / Ministry of fear / Hi tech low life / Metal machine music / Rings of steel.

CD	ATLASCDD 006
LP Set	ATLASLPD 006

Equator / Sep '94 / Pinnacle.

GOLDFINGER.
Tracks: Goldfinger / Zuei herzen.

■ 12"	PST 03

Quiet / Jun '84.

MACHINERY OF JOY.
Tracks: Machinery of joy.

■ 12"	12MUTE 101
■ 7"	MUTE 101
■ CD Single	CDMUTE 101

Mute / May '89.

METALLE MASCHINEN MUSIK.
Tracks: Not Advised.

CD	KRUPPS 1CD
LP	KRUPPS 1

Grey Area / Aug '91 / RTM / Pinnacle.

TO THE HILT.
Tracks: To the hilt.

12"	AXIST 003
CD Single	AXISCD 003

Equator / Feb '94 / Pinnacle.

Diesel, Johnny

CRYIN' SHAME (Diesel, Johnny And The Injectors).
Tracks: Cryin' shame / Dry tears / Coming home (live) (Available on 12" only.) / Leave my girl alone (Available on 12" only.).

■ 12"	CHS 123466
■ 7"	CHS 3466

Chrysalis / Nov '89.

DON'T NEED LOVE (Diesel, Johnny And The Injectors).
Tracks: Don't need love.

■ 12"	CHS 123359
■ 7"	CHS 3359
■ CD Single	CHSCD 3359

Chrysalis / Apr '89.

■ 12" P.Disc.	CHSP 123359

Chrysalis / Jul '89.

JOHNNY DIESEL AND THE INJECTORS (Diesel, Johnny And The Injectors).
Tracks: Looking for love / Cry in shame / Comin' home / Dry tears / Get ya love / Parisienne hotel / Don't need love / Fire without a flame / Burn / Thang II.

■ CD	CCD 1672
■ LP	CHR 1672
■ MC.	ZCHR 1672

Chrysalis / Mar '89.

SOUL REVIVAL.
Tracks: Soul revival / Whose for better.

■ 12" P.Disc.	CHSP 123383

Chrysalis / Aug '89.

■ MC Single.	CHSMC 3383
■ 12"	CHS 123383
■ 7"	CHS 3383
■ CD Single	CHSCD 3383

Chrysalis / Jun '89.

Dio

Ronnie James Dio graduated from bar-band Elf, through Rainbow and Black Sabbath, to fronting own group. Well-received 1983 debut *Holy Diver* formed blue-print for series of albums, of which commercial highlight was *Sacred Heart*. Dio masterminded 'Hear n' Aid', metal's contribution to Live Aid charity, but own fortunes waned. He rejoined Sabbath in 1992, but has since revived solo project. Although unlikely to regain success, Dio can fairly claim to be one of metal's finest voices.

CHRIS TETLEY INTERVIEWS DIO.
Tracks: Not Advised.

■ LP P.Disc.	CT 1007

Music & Media / Oct '87.

DIAMONDS (The Best of Dio).
Tracks: Holy diver / Rainbow in the dark / Don't talk to strangers / We rock / Last in line / Evil eyes / Rock 'n' roll children / Sacred heart / Hungry for heaven / Hide in the rainbow / Dream evil / Wild one / Lock up the wolves.

CD	512206-2
■ LP	512206-1
■ MC.	512206-4

Vertigo / Jun '92.

DIO: INTERVIEW PICTURE DISC.
Tracks: Not Advised.

LP P.Disc.	BAK 2062

Baktabak / Sep '87 / Arabesque Ltd.

DREAM EVIL.
Tracks: Night people / Dream evil / Sunset superman / All the fools sailed away / Naked in the rain / Overlove / I could have been a dreamer / Faces in the window / When a woman cries.

CD	832 530-2
■ LP	VERH 46
MC.	VERHC 46

Vertigo / Aug '87 / PolyGram.

HEY ANGEL.
Tracks: Hey angel / Walk on water (Only on 7" single) / Rock'n'roll children (Only on 12" and CD single) / Mystery (Only on 12" and CD single) / Why are they watching me (Only on 12" singles).

■ 12"	DIO 912
■ 12" P.Disc.	DIOP 912
■ 7"	DIO 9
■ CD Single	DIOCD 9

Vertigo / Aug '90.

HOLY DIVER.
Tracks: Stand up and shout / Holy diver / Gypsy / Caught in the middle / Don't talk to strangers / Straight through the heart / Invisible / Rainbow in the dark / Shame on the night.

■ LP	VERS 5
MC.	VERSC 5

Vertigo / '83 / PolyGram.

CD	811 021-2
■ LP	PRICE 117
■ MC.	PRIMC 117

Vertigo / Mar '88.

HOLY DIVER.
Tracks: Holy diver / Evil eyes / Don't talk to strangers (Only on 12" single.).

■ 12"	DIO 112

Vertigo / Aug '83.

■ 7"	DIO 1

Vertigo / Aug '83.

■ DELETED

HUNGRY FOR HEAVEN.
Tracks: Hungry for heaven / Hide in the rainbow / Shine on the night (Extra track available on 12" version only.) / Egypt-the chains are on (Extra track available on 12" version only.).
■ 7" . . . . DIO 6
Vertigo / Nov '85.

HUNGRY FOR HEAVEN.
Tracks: Hungry for heaven.
■ 12" . . . . DIO 712
■ 12" P.Disc. . . . . DIOP 710
■ 7" . . . . DIO 7
■ 7" P.Disc. . . . . DIO P7
Vertigo / May '86.

I COULD HAVE BEEN A DREAMER.
Tracks: I could have been a dreamer / Night people / Sunset superman (Track on 12" version only.)
■ 12" . . . . DIO 812
■ 7" . . . . DIO 8
Vertigo / Jul '87.

INTERMISSION.
Tracks: King of rock 'n' roll / Rainbow in the dark / Sacred heart / Time to burn / Rock 'n' roll children / We rock.
■ Mini LP . . . . VERB 40
■ MC. .VERBC 40
Vertigo / Jun '86.

LAST IN LINE.
Tracks: We rock / Last in line / Breathless / I speed at night / One night in the city / Evil eyes / Mystery / Eat your heart out / Egypt-the chains are on.
■ LP . . . . .VERL 16
■ MC. . . . . .VERLC 16
Vertigo / '84.
■ CD 822 366-2
Vertigo / '86.

LIVE IN CONCERT: DIO.
Tracks: Not Advised.
VHS . . . . CFV 00142
Channel 5 / Apr '86 / Channel 5 Video / P.R.O. Video / Gold & Sons.

LOCK UP THE WOLVES.
Tracks: Wild one / Hey angel / Night music / Evil on Queen Street / Twisted / My eyes / Born on the sun / Between two hearts / Lock up the wolves / Walk on water / Why are they watching me.
■ LP 846 033 1
MC. 846 033 4
■ CD 846 033 2
Vertigo / May '90.

MYSTERY.
Tracks: Mystery.
■ 7" . . . . DIO 4
■ 7" P.Disc . . . . DIOP 4
Vertigo / '84.

RAINBOW IN THE DARK.
Tracks: Rainbow in the dark / Stand up and shout.
■ 7" . . . . DIO 2
Vertigo / '83.

ROCK 'N' ROLL CHILDREN.
Tracks: Rock 'n' roll children.
■ 12" . . . . DIO 512
■ 7" . . . . DIO 5
Vertigo / Aug '85.

SACRED HEART.
Tracks: Rock 'n' roll / Sacred heart / Another lie / Rock 'n' roll children / Hungry for heaven / Like the beat of a heart / Just another day / Fallen angels / Shoot shoot.
■ CD 834 848-2
■ LP . . . . VERH 30
■ MC. . . . . .VERHC 30
Vertigo / '85.

SPECIAL FROM THE SPECTRUM.
Tracks: Not Advised.
VHS 041 423 2
Polygram Music Video / Sep '86 / PolyGram.
VHS . . . . CFV 02232
Channel 5 / Sep '87 / Channel 5 Video / P.R.O. Video / Gold & Sons.

STRANGE HIGHWAYS.
Tracks: Not Advised.
CD. 518486-2
MC. 518486-4
■ LP 518486-1
Vertigo / Nov '93.

WE ROCK.
Tracks: We rock / Holy diver.
■ 12" . . . . DIO 312
■ 7" . . . . DIO 3
Vertigo / '84.

Dio, Ronnie James

Came to prominence with Elf and appeared on Roger Glover's *The Butterfly Ball* before continuing the Deep Purple connection by joining Ritchie Blackmore's Rainbow where he stayed for four albums, after a clash of personality with Blackmore he left to join the flagging Black Sabbath in 1979. Dio's songwriting and lyrical direction helped re-create Sabbath for the NWOBHM generation but after a strained world tour he stormed out. His next move was to create his own band, Dio, their epic supernatural songs were initially very popular but the formula was bringing little reward by the time of their final album *Lock Up The Wolves* .

CAROLINA COUNTRY BALL.
Tracks: Not Advised.
■ LP . . . . LONG 7
MC. . . . . LONGC 7
Safari / '84 / Pinnacle.

TRYING TO BURN THE SUN (see under Elf).

Dirty Looks

COOL FROM THE WIRE.
Tracks: Cool from the wire / It's not the way you rock / Can't take my eyes off you / Oh Ruby / Tokyo / Wastin' my time / Put a spell on you / No brains child / Get it right / It's a bitch / Get off.
■ CD . . . . K 781 836 2
■ LP . . . . K 781 836 1
■ MC. . . . . K 781 836 4
Atlantic / Apr '88.

DIRTY LOOKS.
Tracks: They got me covered / Love crimes / You can't love me / Lie to me / Take a life / Let go / 12 o'clock high / You're too old / Accept me / Disappearing / Drop that tan.
■ LP . . . . .SEEZ 22
■ MC. . . . . ZSEEZ 22
Stiff / Aug '80.

LET GO.
Tracks: Let go / Accept me.
■ 7" . . . . BUY 77
Stiff / May '80.

LIE TO ME.
Tracks: Lie to me / Rosario's ashes.
■ 7" . . . . BUY 66
Stiff / Mar '80.

TAILIN' YOU.
Tracks: Tailin' you / Automatic pilot.
■ 7" . . . . BUY 89
Stiff / Oct '80.

TURN IT UP.
Tracks: Daddy's gone / Living alone / Carrie / You've got it / Do we need it / Animal / Turn it up / Deceit / Hit list / Born again / Kiss of death / Time is up / It was.
■ LP . . . . .SEEZ 38
Stiff / Jun '81.

TURN OF THE SCREW.
Tracks: Turn of the screw (who's screwing you) / Nobody rides for free / C'mon Frenchie / Take what ya get / Hot flash jelly roll / Slammin' to the big beat.
■ CD 7819922
■ LP 7819921
■ MC. 7819924
WEA / Jul '89.

Dirty Tricks

HIT AND RUN.
Tracks: Hit and run / Get out on the street / Gambler / Road to Deriabay / I've had these dreams before / Walkin' tall / Last night of freedom / Lost in the past.
■ LP 2383 446
Polydor / Sep '77.

TOO MUCH WINE.
Tracks: Too much wine / Wait till Saturday.
■ 7" 2058 833
Polydor / Feb '77.

Dirty White Boy

BAD REPUTATION.
Tracks: Not Advised.
■ LP 841 959-1
■ MC. 841 959-4
■ CD 841 959-2
Polydor / Jun '90.

LAZY CRAZY.
Tracks: Lazy crazy.
■ 12" . . . . PZ 85
■ 7" . . . . PO 85
■ CD Single 877 397-2
Polydor / Jun '90.

LET'S SPEND MOMMA'S MONEY.
Tracks: Let's spend momma's money / Hard times.
■ MC Single . . . . POCS 96
■ 12" . . . . PZP 96
■ 12" . . . . PZ 96
■ 7" . . . . PO 96
■ CD Single . . . . PZCD 96
Polydor / Sep '90.

Disabuse

DISABUSE.
Tracks: Not Advised.
CD Single. . . . . DISC 3X
Mini LP . . . . DISC 3T
Discipline / Jun '94 / Plastic Head.

Discard

DEATH FROM ABOVE.
Tracks: Death from above.
■ 7" . . . . .JKR 001
Jesus Krust / Nov '92.

Discharge

Influential, uncompromising and under-rated punk band. Discharge out-lived most of their contemporaries and did not evolve into another punk turned metal act. They achieved considerable success in the Indie charts with their politico-punk well into the mid-1980's. Discharge recorded primarily for Stoke's Clay label. *Never Again* (1981), *Ignorance* (1985), were their biggest selling singles, and their 1982 LP *Hear Nothing, See Nothing, Say Nothing*, reached the top 40 album charts.

DECONTROL.
Tracks: Decontrol.
■ 7" . . . . CLAY 5
Clay / Jul '81.

DISCHARGE 1980-1986.
Tracks: Not Advised.
■ LP . . . . CLAYLP 24
Clay / Jul '87.

EXCREMENT OF WAR.
Tracks: Excrement of war.
■ 7" . . . . .FINNREC 006
Finn / Nov '92.

FIGHT BACK.
Tracks: Fight back.
■ 7" . . . . CLAY 3
Clay / Jul '81.

GRAVE NEW WORLD.
Tracks: Not Advised.
■ LP . . . . CLAYLP 19
Clay / Jul '86.

HEAR NOTHING, SEE NOTHING, SAY NOTHING.
Tracks: Hear nothing, see nothing, say nothing / Nightmare continues / Final bloodbath / Protest and survive / I won't subscribe / Drunk with power / Meanwhile / Hell on earth / Cries of help / Possibilities of lifes destruction / Q - and children? A - and children / Blood runs red / Free speech for the dumb / End.
■ CD . . . . CLAYCD 3
■ LP . . . . CLAYLP 3
Clay / Jan '90.

IGNORANCE.
Tracks: Ignorance / No compromise.
■ 12" . . . . 12 CLAY 43
■ 7" .CLAY 43
Clay / May '85.

LIVE AT CITY GARDEN.
Tracks: Warning / Nightmare continues / Never again / Blood runs red / Protest and survive / State violence/State control / More I see / Angel burning (encore) / Hear nothing, see nothing, say nothing / Where there is a will / Anger burning / Born to die in the gutter / In defence of our future / Price of silence / Decontrol / Blood runs red, The (encore).
■ CD . . . . CLAYCD 103
■ LP . . . . CLAY 103
Clay / Apr '93.

■ DELETED

MASSACRE DIVINE.
Tracks: City of fear / F.E.D. / Lost tribe rising / Challenge terror / White knuckle ride / New age / Terror police / Kiss tomorrow goodbye / Sexpolosion / Dying time / E 2.30 / F.E.D. (F2 mix).
MC. . . . . CLAYMC 110
Clay / Oct '91 / Plastic Head.
■ **CD** . . . . CLAYCD 110
■ **LP** . . . . CLAY 110
Clay / Apr '93.

MORE I SEE.
Tracks: More I see.
■ **12"** . . . . .12 CLAY 34
■ **7"** . . . . .CLAY 34
Clay / May '84.

NEVER AGAIN.
Tracks: Warning / Never again / Hear nothing, see nothing, say nothing / Nightmare continues / Where there is a will / Drunk with power / Final bloodbath / Anger burning / Two monstrous nuclear stockpiles / Price of silence / Protest and survive / Born to die in the gutter / Doomsday / More I see / State violence/ State control / In defence of our future / Decontrol.
■ **CD** .CLAYCD 12
■ **LP** . . . . CLAYLP 12
Clay / Apr '93.

NEVER AGAIN.
Tracks: Never again / Death dealers.
■ **7"** . . . . CLAY 6
Clay / Oct '81.

NIGHTMARE CONTINUES, THE.
Tracks: Never again / Hear nothing, see nothing, say nothing / Nightmare continues / Realities of war / State violence/State control / Hell on earth / Cries of help / Possibilities of lifes destruction / Final bloodbath / Protest and survive / Doomsday / Drunk with power / Why / Blood runs red / Two monstrous nuclear stockpiles / De-control.
MC. . . . . CLAYMC 107
■ **CD** .CLAYCD 107
■ **LP** . . . . CLAY 107
Clay / Apr '93.

PRICE OF SILENCE.
Tracks: Price of silence / Born to die in the gutter.
■ **7"** . . . . .CLAY 29
Clay / Mar '83.

PROTEST & SURVIVE.
Tracks: Never again / Hear nothing, See nothing, Say nothing / Nightmare continues / Realities of war / Ain't no feeble bastard / War's no fairytale / Anger burning / Hell on earth / Cries of help / Possibilities of lifes destruction / Visions of war / Stockpiles / More I see / Look at tomorrow / Society's victim / Protest and survive / Death dealers / Tomorrow belongs to us / Final bloodbath / Is this to be / Price of silence / Fight back / Doomsday / Why / Drunk with power / Religion instigates / Warning / Massacre of innocence / State violence / Decontrol.
■ **CD Set.** . . . . CLAYCD 113
Clay / Apr '93.

REALITIES OF WAR.
Tracks: Realities of war.
■ **7"** . . . . CLAY 1
Clay / Feb '87.

SEEING, FEELING, BLEEDING.
Tracks: Not Advised.
CD . . . . NB 085
LP . . . . .NBLP 085
MC. . . . . .NBMC 085
Nuclear Blast / Dec '93 / Plastic Head.

SHOOTIN' UP THE WORLD.
Tracks: Not Advised.
■ **CD** .CLAYCD 118
Clay / Oct '93.

STATE VIOLENCE.
Tracks: State violence / State control.
■ **7"** . . . . .CLAY 14
Clay / Oct '83.

WARNING - H.M.GOVERNMENT.
Tracks: Warning - H.M.Government.
■ **12"** . . . . .PLATE 5
Clay / Sep '83.

WHY.
Tracks: Vision of war / Look at tomorrow / Maimed and slaughtered / Ain't no feeble bastard / Massacre of innocents (air attack) / Doomsday / Does this system work / Why / Mania for conquest / Is this to be / State violence / State control.
LP . . . . PLATE 002
Clay / Apr '90 / Plastic Head.
CD . . . . .PLATE 002CD
Clay / Apr '93 / Plastic Head.

WHY?.
Tracks: Why.
■ **12"** . . . . .PLATE 2
■ **CD Single** . . . . .PLATECD 2
Clay / Jan '90.

Disembowelment
TRANSCENDENCE INTO THE PERIPHERAL.
Tracks: Not Advised.
CD . . . . NB 096-2
MC. . . . . NB 096-4
Nuclear Blast / Jan '94 / Plastic Head.

Disfear
BRUTAL SIGHT OF WAR, A.
Tracks: Not Advised.
CD . . . . LF 060CD
Lost & Found / Aug '93 / Plastic Head.

UNCURBED/SPLIT.
Tracks: Not Advised.
7" . . . . LF 065
Lost & Found / Feb '94 / Plastic Head.

Disgust
BRUTALITY OF WAR.
Tracks: Intro / Mother earth / Millions suffer and die / An horrific end / Thrown into oblivion / Civilisation decoys / Relentless slaughter / And still.. / Light of death / What kind of mind / You have no right / Sea of tears / Anguished cry / Heaps of flesh / Outro.
CD .MOSH 104CD
LP . . . . MOSH 104
■ **MC.** . . . . .MOSH 104MC
Earache / Nov '93.

Disharmonic Orchestra
EXPOSITIONSPROPHYLAXE.
Tracks: Not Advised.
CD 8429812
LP 0829811
Nuclear Blast / Dec '90 / Plastic Head.

PLEASURE DOME.
Tracks: Not Advised.
CD . . . . SPV 084-76772
SPV / Jun '94 / Plastic Head.

SPLIT LP (see under Pungent Stench).

Disincarnate
DREAMS OF THE CARRION KIND.
Tracks: Not Advised.
CD . . . . RR 91022
MC. . . . . RR 91024
■ **LP** . . . . RR 91021
Road Runner / Mar '93.

Dismember
INDECENT AND OBSCENE.
Tracks: Not Advised.
MC. . . . . NB 077
Nuclear Blast / Aug '93 / Plastic Head.
CD .NB 077CD
LP . . . . NB 007
Nuclear Blast / Jul '93 / Plastic Head.

PIECES.
Tracks: Not Advised.
CD .NB 060CD
Mini LP . . . . NB 060
Nuclear Blast / Apr '92 / Plastic Head.

SKIN HER ALIVE.
Tracks: Skin her alive.
■ **7" P.Disc** . . . . NB 047PDS
Nuclear Blast / Aug '92.

Disrupt
UNREST.
Tracks: Not Advised.
CD . . . . NB 109
Nuclear Blast / Jun '94 / Plastic Head.

Dissect
SWALLOW SWOUMING MASS.
Tracks: Not Advised.
CD . . . . .CYBERCD 5
Cyber / Sep '93 / Plastic Head.

Dixie Dregs
BEST OF DIXIE DREGS.
Tracks: Not Advised.
■ **LP** . . . . SLAM 2
Grand Slam (USA) / '89.

DREGS OF THE EARTH.
Tracks: Road expense / Pride o' the farm / Twiggs approved / Hereafter / Great spectacular / Broad Street strut / I'm freaking out / Old world.
■ **CD** 252207
Arista / Jun '88.

FREE FALL.
Tracks: Free fall / Holiday / Hand jig / Moe down / Refried funky chicken / Sleep / Cruise control / Cosmopolitan traveller / Big ditch / Wages of weirdness / Northern lights.
■ **LP** .2429 154
Capricorn / Oct '77.

NIGHT OF THE LIVING DREGS.
Tracks: Punk sandwhich / Country house shuffle / Riff raff / Long slow distance / Night of the living dregs / Bash / Leprechaun promenade / Patchwork.
■ **LP** .2429 181
Capricorn / Mar '79.

TAKE IT OFF THE TOP.
Tracks: Take it off the top / Little kids.
■ **7"** 2089061
Capricorn / Jul '78.

TAKE IT OFF THE TOP.
Tracks: Take it off the top / Belgian Tom's hat trick / Pickin' the blues.
■ **7"** .POSP 168
Polydor / Jan '82.

UNSUNG HEROES.
Tracks: Cruise control / Divided we stand / I'll just pick / Day 444 / Rock 'n' roll park / Attila the Hun / Kat food / Go for baroque.
■ **LP** . . . . AL 9548
Arista / Jul '81.

WHAT IF.
Tracks: Take it off the top / Odyssey / What if / Travel tunes / Ice cakes / Little kids / Gina Lola breakdown / Night meets light.
■ **LP** .2429 165
Capricorn / Aug '79.

D'Molls
D'MOLLS.
Tracks: Not Advised.
■ **LP** 781 791-1
Atlantic / Sep '88.

Dog Eat Dog
ALL BORO KINGS.
Tracks: Not Advised.
CD . . . . RR 90202
LP . . . . RR 90201
MC. . . . . RR 90204
Road Runner / Apr '94 / Pinnacle.

NO FRONTS.
Tracks: No fronts.
12" . . . . RR 23716
CD Single . . . . RR 23713
Road Runner / May '94 / Pinnacle.

WARRANT.
Tracks: Not Advised.
CD . . . . CD RR 9071 2
LP . . . . .RR LP 9071 1
Road Runner / Jun '93 / Pinnacle.

Dogs D'Amour
ALL OR NOTHING EP.
Tracks: Not Advised.
■ **MC Single** . . . . .WOKMC 2033
■ **12"** . . . . WOKT 2033
■ **CD Single** . . . . .WOKCDR 2033
■ **CD Single** . . . . WOKCD 2033
China / Jun '93.

BACK ON THE JUICE.
Tracks: Back on the juice / Victims of success (live) (Available on 12" format .) / Bullet proof poet (live) (Available on 12" format .) / Lie in this land (Available on CD single format.)
■ **12"** . . . . CHINX 30
■ **12" P.Disc.** . . . . CHIXP 30
■ **7"** . . . . CHINA 30
■ **CD Single** . . . . CHICD 30

■ MC Single. . . . . CHICS 30
China / Nov '90.

BOOTLEG ALBUM.
Tracks: Firework girl / Chains / Gold / Pourin' out my heart / Wait until I'm dead / How do you fall in love again / Kiss this joint / Heroine / Tales of destruction / Dynamite jet saloon / Swingin' the bottle.
■ LP . . . . WOL 7
China / Jul '88.

DOG'S HITS AND THE BOOTLEG ALBUM.
Tracks: Not Advised.
CD. . . . . WOLCD 1020
■ LP . . . . WOL 1020
■ MC. . . . . WOLMC 1020
China / Aug '91.

DOGS BOLLOX.
Tracks: Not Advised.
■ MC Set . . . . DOGSBOXMC
■ CD Set. . . . . DOGSBOXCD
China / Jun '93.

EMPTY WORLD.
Tracks: Empty world / Lady nicotine / Chiva / Heading for the target of insanity.
■ 12". . . . . CHIXB 27
■ 12". . . . . CHINX 27
■ 7". . . . . CHINA 27
■ CD Single . . . . CHICD 27
■ MC Single. . . . . CHICS 27
China / Aug '90.

ERROL FLYNN.
Tracks: Drunk like me / Hurricane / Errol Flynn / Princess valium / Trail of tears / Prettiest girl in the world / Goddess from the gutter / Satellite kid / Planetary pied piper / Dogs hair / Ballad of Jack / Girl behind the glass.
CD 8397002
■ LP 8397001
MC. 8397004
China / Sep '89 / Pinnacle.
CD . . . . WOLCD 1006
LP . . . . WOL 1006
■ MC. . . . . WOLMC 1006
China / Mar '91.

GRAVEYARD OF EMPTY BOTTLES, A.
Tracks: Not Advised.
MC. 8390744
Mini LP 8391741
China / Mar '89 / Pinnacle.
CD. . . . . WOLCD 1005
LP . . . . WOL 1005
■ MC. . . . . WOLMC 1005
China / Mar '91.

HOW COME IT NEVER RAINS.
Tracks: Baby glass (live) / Kirsten jet (live) (Extra track on 12" & CD single.) / How come it never rains (dynamite remix) (Extended version on CD single only) / How come it never rains.
■ CD Single . . . . CHICD 13
■ 12". . . . . CHINX 13
■ 12" P.Disc. . . . . CHIXP 13
■ 7". . . . . CHINA 13
■ 7". . . . . CHING 13
China / Jan '89.

I DON'T WANT YOU TO GO.
Tracks: I don't want you to go / Heroin / Ugly (Only on 12").
■ 12". . . . . CHINX 10
■ 7". . . . . CHINA 10
China / Sep '88.
■ 7". . . . . CHING 10
■ 12" P.Disc. . . . . CHIXP 10
China / Sep '88.

IN THE DYNAMITE JET SALOON.
Tracks: Debauchery / I don't want you to go / How come it never rains / Last bandit / Medicine man / Gonna get it right / Everything I want / Heartbreak / Billy two riders / Wait until I'm dead / Sometimes (Only available on CD.) / Kid from Kensington (Only available on CD.) / State I'm in (Only available on CD.)
CD. 837 368-2
MC. . . . . ZWOL 8
Polydor / Sep '88 / PolyGram.
■ LP . . . . WOL 8
China / Sep '88.
■ MC. . . . . WOLMC 1004
China / Jul '91.

KID FROM KENSINGTON, THE.
Tracks: Kid from Kensington / Everything I want / State I'm in (12" versions only.).
■ 12". . . . . CHINX 5
■ 7". . . . . CHINA 5
■ 7". . . . . CHING 5

■ 7" P.Disc . . . . CHIXP 5
China / May '88.

MORE UNCHARTERED HEIGHTS OF DISGRACE.
Tracks: Not Advised.
CD . . . . WOLCD 1032
■ LP . . . . WOL 1032
■ MC. . . . . WOLMC 1032
China / Apr '93.

PRETTY PRETTY ONCE.
Tracks: Pretty pretty once.
■ 7" . . . . WOKA 2038
■ CD Single . . . . WOKCD 2038
China / Aug '93.

SATELLITE KID.
Tracks: Satellite kid / She thinks too much of me / Drunk like me (12" only) / Things he'd do (12" only) / As I see the poppies (CD single only).
■ 12". . . . . CHINX 17
■ 7". . . . . CHINA 17
■ 7" P.Disc . . . . CHINP 17
■ CD Single . . . . CHICD 17
China / Jul '89.
■ 12" P.Disc. . . . . CHIXP 17
China / Jul '89.

STRAIGHT.
Tracks: Not Advised.
CD 8437962
LP 8437961
MC. 8437964
China / Sep '90 / Pinnacle.
CD . . . . WOLCD 1007
LP . . . . WOL 1007
■ MC. . . . . WOLMC 1007
China / Mar '91.

TRAIL OF TEARS.
Tracks: Trail of tears / Pourin' out my heart.
■ MC Single . . . . CHICS 20
■ 12". . . . . CHINX 20
■ 12" P.Disc. . . . . CHIXP 20
■ 7". . . . . CHINA 20
■ 7" P.Disc. . . . . CHINP 20
■ CD Single . . . . CHICD 20
China / Oct '89.

VICTIMS OF SUCCESS.
Tracks: Victims of success.
■ 12". . . . . CHINX 24
■ 7". . . . . CHINA 24
■ 7". . . . . CHINS 24
■ MC Single. . . . . CHICS 24
China / Jun '90.

Dokken

Formed by former Scorpions backing singer Don Dokken and signed by Elektra in 1982 after a well received debut album on Carrere in the U.S. Fairly middle of the road rock which sold well in the States where the final album *Beast from the East* went platinum. They split in 1988 after personality clashes between Dokken and guitarist George Lynch.

BACK FOR THE ATTACK.
Tracks: Kiss of death / Prisoner / Night by night / Standing in the shadows / Heaven sent / Mr. Scary / So many tears / Burning like a flame / Lost behind the wall / Stop fighting love / Cry of the gypsy / Sleepless nights / Dream warriors
■ CD 9607352
Elektra / Dec '87.
■ LP . . . . EKT 43
■ MC. . . . . EKT 43C
Elektra / Nov '87.

BACK IN THE STREETS.
Tracks: Not Advised.
CD. . . . . REP 4005-WG
LP . . . . REP 2005
MC. . . . . REP 2005-TO
Repertoire (Germany) / Aug '91 / Pinnacle.

BEAST FROM THE EAST.
Tracks: Unchain the night / Kiss of death / Tooth and nail / When Heaven comes down / Standing in the shadows (Not available on CD.) / Into the fire / Sleepless nights (Not available on CD.) / Mr. Scary / Dream warriors / Heaven sent / It's not love / Alone again / Just got lucky / Breaking the chains / In my dreams / Turn on the action (Not available on CD.) / Walk away.
MC. . . . . EKT 55 C
■ Double LP . . . . EKT 55
Elektra / Dec '88.

BREAKIN' THE CHAINS.
Tracks: Breakin' the chains / Seven thunders / I can see you / In the middle / We're illegal / Paris / Stick to your guns / Young girl / Felony / Nightrider.
■ LP . . . . CAL 136
Carrere / May '82.

BURNING LIKE A FLAME.
Tracks: Burning like a flame / Lost behind the wall.
■ 12". . . . . EKR 67T
■ 12" P.Disc. . . . . EKR 67TP
■ 7". . . . . EKR 67
Elektra / Feb '88.

IN MY DREAMS.
Tracks: In my dreams / Tell the living end / Alone again (12" only).
■ 7". . . . . EKR 37
■ 12". . . . . EKR 37 T
Elektra / Mar '86.

TOOTH AND NAIL.
Tracks: Without warning / Tooth and nail / Just got lucky / Heartless heart / Don't close your eyes / When Heaven comes down / Into the fire / Bullets to spare / Alone again / Turn on the action.
■ LP 9603761
Elektra / Oct '84.

UNDER LOCK AND KEY.
Tracks: Unchain the night / Hunter / In my dreams / Slippin' away / Lightning strikes again / It's not love / Jaded heart / Don't lie to me / Will the sun rise / Till the livin' end.
■ LP . . . . EKT 28
■ MC. . . . . EKT 28 C
Elektra / Mar '86.
CD. 9604582
Elektra / Mar '86 / WEA.

WE'RE ILLEGAL.
Tracks: We're illegal / Paris.
■ 7". . . . . CAR 229
Carrere / Apr '82.

Dokken, Don

Dokken got his first break when he was asked to provide vocals for The Scorpions album *Blackout* in 1982, with the spare studio time he was allowed to put together his own demo's which earnt him a deal with Carrere Records. The backing band he recruited included George Lynch (later of Lynch Mob) who, although a gifted guitarist, was to prove too much for Dokken and the band collapsed in 1988 after six volatile years. His solo albums have lacked the commercial impact of the band output.

UP FROM THE ASHES.
Tracks: Not Advised.
■ LP 7599243011
■ CD 7599243012
■ MC. 7599243014
Geffen / Sep '90.
■ CD . . . . GEFD 24301
■ MC. . . . . GEFC 24301
Geffen / Aug '91.

Dollface

METHEDRINE EP.
Tracks: Not Advised.
■ 7" . . . . KILL 706
■ CD Single . . . . KILLCD 006
Kill City / Aug '93.

ROCKSTARS.
Tracks: Rockstars.
12". . . . . KILL 1214
■ CD Single . . . . KILLCD 014
Trident / Jun '94 / Pinnacle.

Domain

CRACK IN THE WALL.
Tracks: Not Advised.
CD. . . . . FT 30016CD
LP . . . . FT 30015LP
Flametrader / Jan '92 / Greyhound Records.

OUR KINGDOM.
Tracks: Not Advised.
■ CD. 244722 2
WEA / '88.

Dominique, Lisa

Came to prominence as a pin-up in the British rock media as the singer in her brother Marino's band. Given a solo deal by Heavy Metal Records her debut album was ridiculed in the press and her pin-up appeal failed to translate to sales.

ALL FALL DOWN.
Tracks: All fall down / Time bomb / Dream maker.
- 12" . . . . .12 VHF 51
- 7" . . . . VHF 51
- CD Single . . . . .VHFXD 51
FM Records / Jan '90.

JEALOUS HEART.
Tracks: Jealous heart.
- 12" . . . . .12 VHF 47
FM Records / Apr '88.

LISA DOMINIQUE.
Tracks: Not Advised.
- LP . . . . ESSLP 148
- CD . . . . ESSCD 148
- MC . . . . ESSMC 148
Essential / Jul '91.

ROCK AND ROLL LADY.
Tracks: Rock 'n' roll lady / All fall down / Gamble / Somebody special / Holding on to your love / Time bomb / Jealous heart / Slow down / One foot back in your door / Trouble.
- CD . . . . .WKFMXD 117
- LP . . . . .WKFMLP 117
- MC . . . . .WKFMMC 117
FM Records / May '89.
- LP P.Disc . . . . .WKFMPD 117
FM Records / Feb '90.

Doom

DOOMED AGAIN.
Tracks: Not Advised.
LP . . . . DISCLP 5
Vinyl Japan / Sep '92 / Vital Distribution.

DOOMED FROM THE START.
Tracks: Not Advised.
LP . . . . DISC 5LP
Deathwish / Nov '92 / Plastic Head.

GREATEST INVENTION, THE.
Tracks: Not Advised.
CD . . . . DISCCD 10
LP . . . . DISCLP 10
Discipline / Aug '93 / Plastic Head.

PEEL SESSIONS: DOOM (29.5.79).
Tracks: Symptom of the universe / Multinationals / Expoitation / Circles / No religion / Relief / Sold out / War crimes / Means to an end / Dream to come true / Natural abuse / Days go by / Life lock / Bury the debt / Life in freedom / Money drug / Fear of the future.
CD . . . . SFPMCD 203
Mini LP . . . . SFPMA 203
Strange Fruit / '89 / Pinnacle.

TOTAL DOOM.
Tracks: Not Advised.
CD . . . . VILE 011CD
- LP . . . . VILE 011
Peaceville / Apr '89.

WAR CRIMES.
Tracks: Not Advised.
- LP . . . . VILE 4
Peaceville / Nov '89.

Doomstone

THOSE WHOM SATAN HATH.
Tracks: Not Advised.
CD. NOSF00ZCD
Nosferatu / Jun '94 / Plastic Head.

Doro

ANGELS NEVER DIE.
Tracks: Not Advised.
CD. 514 309-2
MC. 514 309-4
Vertigo / Mar '93 / PolyGram.

DORO.
Tracks: Unholy love / I had too much to dream last night / Rock on / Only you / I'll be holding on / Something wicked this way comes / Rare diamond / Broken / Alive / Mirage.
- CD 846 194 2
- LP 846 194 1
- MC 846 194 4
Vertigo / Jun '90.

FORCE MAJEURE (Doro & Warlock).
Tracks: White shade of pale / Mission of mercy / Beyond the trees / Hellraiser / Cry wolf / Bis aufs blut / Save my soul / Angels with dirty faces / Hard times / I am what I am / River of tears / Under the gun.
- LP 838 016 1
- CD 838 016 2
- MC 838 016 4
Vertigo / Mar '89.

RARE DIAMONDS (Doro & Warlock).
Tracks: Not Advised.
- LP 8483531
- CD 8483532
- MC 8483534
Mercury / Apr '91.

TRUE AT HEART.
Tracks: Not Advised.
DCC 510 102-5
Vertigo / Jan '93 / PolyGram.

Down By Law

BLUE.
Tracks: Not Advised.
CD. . . . . E 86419 2
LP . . . . E 86419 1
MC. . . . . E 86419 4
Epitaph / Nov '92 / Plastic Head.

DOWN BY LAW.
Tracks: Not Advised.
CD. . . . . E 86411 2
LP . . . . E 86411 1
MC. . . . . E 86411 4
Epitaph / Nov '92 / Plastic Head.

DOWN BY LAW/GIGANTOR (Down By Law/Gigantor).
Tracks: Not Advised.
CD . . . . LF 064CD
Lost & Found / Aug '93 / Plastic Head.

PUNKROCKACADEMYFIGHTSONG.
Tracks: Not Advised.
CD . . . . E 864312
LP . . . . E 864311
MC. . . . . E 864314
Epitaph / Jun '94 / Plastic Head.

Downset

ABOUT TA BLAST E.P.
Tracks: Not Advised.
7" .ABS 104
Abstract / May '94 / Pinnacle.

Dr. Know

WRECKAGE IN FLESH.
Tracks: War theatre / Mastermind / City wheels / Wreckage / Lake of fire.
- LP . . . . RR 94951
Road Runner / Dec '88.

Dr. Mastermind

DOCTOR MASTERMIND.
Tracks: Domination / Right way / Man of the year / We want the world / Control / Abuser / Black leather maniac / I don't wanna die.
CD . . . . RR 9605 2
- LP . . . . RR 9605
Road Runner / Dec '87.

Dragon

APRIL IN CUBA.
Tracks: April in Cuba / Mr. Thunder.
- 7" . . . . PRT 6699
PRT / Feb '79.

BODY AND THE BEAT.
Tracks: Rain / Promises (so far away) / Wilderworld / Cry / Cool down / Body and the beat / Witnessing / Magic / What am I gonna do / Fool.
MC. . . . . POLDC 5143
- LP . . . . POLD 5143

Polydor / Sep '84.
CD. 817 874-2
Polydor / '88 / PolyGram.

FALLEN ANGEL.
Tracks: Not Advised.
CD. . . . . CDFLAG 48
LP .FLAG 48
MC. . . . . .TFLAG 48
Music For Nations / Oct '90 / Pinnacle.

RAIN.
Tracks: Rain / Dreaded moroxy bird.
- 12" . . . . POSPX 672
- 7" . . . . POSP 672
Polydor / Mar '84.

SCREAM OF DEATH.
Tracks: Not Advised.
LP .FLAG 58
MC. . . . . .TFLAG 58
- CD . . . . CDFLAG 58
Music For Nations / Jun '91.

Dragster

AMBITIONS.
Tracks: Ambitions / Won't bring you back.
- 7" . . . . HEAVY 4
Heavy Metal / Feb '81.

I'M NOT AN AMERICAN.
Tracks: I'm not an American / Land of the giants.
- 7" . . . . .SNICK 2
Union City / Jul '87.

ROSEMARY.
Tracks: Rosemary.
- 12" . . . . SNICK 8T
Union City / Feb '88.
- 7" . . . . .SNICK 8
Union City / Jan '88.

WHERE IS THE HAMBURGER RELISH.
Tracks: Where is the hamburger relish / I wanna be an albino.
- 7" . . . . .SNICK 1
Union City / Nov '86.

Dread Zeppelin

5,000,000.
Tracks: Fab (part 1) / Stir it up / Do the claw / When the levee breaks / Misty mountain top / Train kept a rollin' / Nobody's fault (butt-mon) / Big ol' gold belt / Fab (part 2) / Stairway to heaven.
CD. . . . . EIRSACD 1057
- LP . . . . EIRSA 1057
MC. . . . . EIRSAC 1057
I.R.S. (Illegal) / May '91 / EMI.

HEARTBREAKER HOTEL.
Tracks: Heartbreaker hotel / Your time is gonna come.
- 12" . . . . EIRSTX 146
- 12" . . . . EIRST 146
- 7" . . . . EIRS 146
- CD Single . . . . .EIRSCD 146
I.R.S. (Illegal) / Aug '90.

STAIRWAY TO HEAVEN.
Tracks: Stairway to heaven / Jailhouse rock.
- 12" . . . . DREADT 2
- 12" P.Disc. . . . . .DREADPD 2
- 7" . . . . DREAD 2
- CD Single . . . . DREADCD 2
- MC Single. . . . . DREADC 2
I.R.S. (Illegal) / Apr '91.

UN-LED-ED.
Tracks: Black dog / Living loving maid / Bring it on home / Black mountain side / Heartbreaker (at the end of Lonely St) / Your time is gonna come / Whole lotta love / I can't suit you baby / Immigrant song / Moby Dick.
- LP . . . . EIRSA 1042
- MC . . . . EIRSAC 1042
- CD . . . . EIRSACD 1042
I.R.S. (Illegal) / Aug '90.

YOUR TIME IS GONNA COME.
Tracks: Your time is gonna come / All I want for Christmas is my two front teeth / Woodstock / Hey, hey, what can I do.
- 12" . . . . .DREADPB 1
- 12" Remix. . . . . DREADT 1
- 7" . . . . DREAD 1
- CD Single . . . . DREADCD 1
- MC Single. . . . . DREADC 1
I.R.S. (Illegal) / Nov '90.

Dream

DESIRES (AT HER CLOSEST).
Tracks: Desires (at her closest).
■ 12" 12REV 40
Black (1) / Dec '89.

DO THE TRIP.
Tracks: Do the trip / Wonderful world / Anything (12" only).
■ 7" . . . . REV 48
Revolver / Jul '88.
■ 12" .12 REV 48
Revolver / Jul '88.

DREAM, THE.
Tracks: Not Advised.
MC. . . . . REVMC 143
■ CD . . . . REVXD 143
■ LP . . . . REVLP 143
Black (1) / Apr '90.

Dream Theater

IMAGES IN WORDS.
Tracks: Not Advised.
VHS 853650537-3
Warner Music Video / Feb '94 / WEA.

LIVE.
Tracks: Metropolis / Fortune in lies / Bombay vindaloo / Surrounded / Another hand/The Killing Hand / Pull me under.
CD 756792286-2
MC. 756792286-4
Atlantic / Aug '93 / WEA.

WHEN DREAM AND DAY UNITE.
Tracks: Fortune in lies / Ytse Jake / Light / Status seeker / Killing hand.
■ CD . . . . DMCF 3445
■ LP . . . . MCF 3445
■ MC. MCFC 3445
MCA / Mar '89.

Driller Killer

BRUTALIZED.
Tracks: Not Advised.
CD . . . . DISTCD 8
Distortion / Jun '94 / Plastic Head.

Drive, She Said

DRIVE SHE SAID.
Tracks: If this is love / Don't you know / Love has no pride / Hold on / I close my eyes / Hard way home / But for you / Maybe it's love / If I told you / As she touches me.
CD .MFNCD 100
LP . . . . MFN 100
MC. .MFNC 100
Music For Nations / Apr '90 / Pinnacle.

DRIVIN' SHE SAID.
Tracks: Not Advised.
CD .CDMFN 118
LP . . . . MFN 118
MC. .TMFN 118
Music For Nations / Sep '91 / Pinnacle.

EXCELLERATOR.
Tracks: Not Advised.
CD .CDMFN 149
LP . . . . MFN 149
Under One Flag / Oct '93 / Pinnacle.

THINK OF LOVE.
Tracks: Think of love.
■ 12" 12KUT 139
■ 7" . . . . .KUT 139
Music For Nations / Sep '91.

Drivin' N' Cryin'

BUILD A FIRE.
Tracks: Build a fire / House for sale / Can't promise you the world / Saddle on the side of the ride.
■ 12" .12IS 531
■ 7" . . . . IS 531
■ 10" .10IS 531
■ CD Single . . . . CID 531
Island / May '92.

FLY ME COURAGEOUS.
Tracks: Not Advised.
CD . . . . CID 9991
LP . . . . .ILPS 9991
MC. . . . . .ICT 9991
Island (Germany) / May '92 / Pinnacle.

FLY ME COURAGEOUS.
Tracks: Fly me courageous / Toy never played with (demo) / Scarred but smarter (live) / With the people / Livin' by the book.
■ 12" .12IS 523
■ CD Single . . . . CID 523
■ MC Single. . . . . CIS 523
■ 7" . . . . IS 523
Island / Mar '92.

SMOKE.
Tracks: Not Advised.
CD . . . . CID 8008
MC. .ICT 8008
Island / Feb '93 / PolyGram.

Drop Acid

MAKING GOD SMILE.
Tracks: Not Advised.
CD . . . . LS 92502
LP . . . . LS 92501
Road Runner / Nov '91 / Pinnacle.

Drunken State

BAGS NOT CARRY THE COFFIN.
Tracks: Bags not carry the coffin.
■ 12" . . . . .DRUNK 101
Blast Furnace / Jan '89.

KILT BY DEATH.
Tracks: Not Advised.
MC. . . . . HMRMC 151
■ CD . . . . .HMRXD 151
■ LP . . . . .HMRLP 151
Heavy Metal / May '90.

Dumpy's Rusty Nuts

BOX HILL OR BUST.
Tracks: Box hill or bust / Got to be blues.
■ 7" . . . . CK 008
Cool King / Oct '82.

GET OUT ON THE ROAD.
Tracks: Not Advised.
■ LP . . . . METALP 118
Razor / Oct '87.

HOT LOVER.
Tracks: Not Advised.
■ LP . . . . GAS 4010
Gas / Sep '85.

JUST FOR KICKS.
Tracks: Just for kicks / Come ride with me.
■ 7" . . . . CK 006
Cool King / Aug '82.

RUN, RUN, RUN.
Tracks: Run, run, run / Rock city.
■ 7" . . . . DRN 21
A-Side / Jan '91.

SOMEWHERE IN ENGLAND.
Tracks: Not Advised.
■ LP . . . . LDLP 101
Landslide / Sep '84.
■ LP . . . . GAS 4013
Gas / Jan '86.

Dyoxen

FIRST AMONG EQUALS.
Tracks: Not Advised.
■ LP . . . . ATV 17
Active / Dec '90.
CD .CDATV 17
MC. .TATV 17
Active / Jul '92 / Pinnacle.

E

E.F. Band

DEEP CUT.
Tracks: Not Advised.
■ LP . . . . CULP 2
Bullet / Oct '83.

DEVIL'S EYE, THE.
Tracks: Devil's eye.
■ 7" . . . . RR 036
Red Ball / Oct '80.

LAST LAUGH IS ON YOU.
Tracks: Not Advised.
■ LP 6362 076
Mercury / Aug '81.

NIGHT ANGEL.
Tracks: Night angel.
■ 7" . . . . EF 1
E.F. Band / Apr '80.

SELF MADE SUICIDE.
Tracks: Self made suicide.
■ 7" . . . . RR 026
Red Ball / Feb '80.

Earth Christ

FIRESTORM.
Tracks: Not Advised.
CD . . . . VR 12-2
We Bite / Apr '94 / Plastic Head.

Earthshaker

BLONDIE GIRL.
Tracks: Blondie girl.
■ 12" . . . . 12 KUT 107
Music For Nations / Nov '83.

EARTH SHAKER.
Tracks: Not Advised.
■ LP . . . . MFN 13
Music For Nations / Nov '83.

FUGITIVE.
Tracks: Not Advised.
MC. . . . . TMFN 21
Music For Nations / Jan '85 / Pinnacle.

MIDNIGHT FLIGHT.
Tracks: Not Advised.
■ LP . . . . MFN 37
Music For Nations / Feb '86.

Easy Action

EASY ACTION.
Tracks: Rocket ride / Mental dance / End of the line / Don't cry don't crack / Another Saturday night / Round round round / We go rocking / Let's lose control / Rock things out / Number one / Rock on rockers.
■ LP 923973 1
Sire / Jun '85.

WE GO RACING.
Tracks: We go racing / Turn me on.
■ 12" . . . . W 9299T
■ 7" . . . . W 9299
Sire / Apr '84.

Edge Of Sanity

NOTHING BY DEATH REMAINS.
Tracks: Not Advised.
CD . . . . BMCD 10
LP . . . . BMLP 10
MC. . . . . BMCT 10
Black Mark / '92 / Plastic Head.

SPECTRAL SORROWS, THE.
Tracks: Not Advised.
CD . . . . BMCD 37
MC. . . . . BMCT 37
Black Mark / Nov '93 / Plastic Head.

UNORTHODOX.
Tracks: Unorthodox / Enigma / Incipience to the butchery / In the veins/Darker than black / Human

aberration (Cassette only) / Everlasting / After after-life / Beyond the unknown (CD only) / Nocturnal / Curfew for the damned / Cold sun / Day of maturity (CD only) / Requiscon by page / Dead but dreaming / When all is said.
CD. . . . . BMCD 018
LP . . . . .BMLP 018
MC. . . . . .BMCT 018
Black Mark / Jun '92 / Plastic Head.

UNTIL ETERNITY ENDS.
Tracks: Until eternity ends / Invisible Sun.
CD Single . . . . BMCD 58
Black Mark / Aug '94 / Plastic Head.

Electric Boys

ALL LIPS AND HIPS.
Tracks: All lips 'n' hips / Hallelujah / Funk-o-metal carpet ride.
■ 12" . . . . .VERX 48
■ 7" . . . . VER 48
■ CD Single . . . . .VERCD 48
Vertigo / Apr '90.
■ 12" P.Disc. . . . . .VERXP 48
Vertigo / Jul '90.

ELECTRIFIED.
Tracks: Electrified / Who are you / All lips 'n' hips (Not on 7") / Into the ditch (Not on 7").
■ 12" . . . . .VERX 50
■ 7" . . . . VER 50
■ CD Single . . . . .VERCD 50
Vertigo / Nov '90.

FREEWHEELIN'.
Tracks: Not Advised.
CD. 521722-2
MC. 521722-4
Polydor / Mar '94 / PolyGram.

FUNK O-METAL CARPET RIDE.
Tracks: Psychedelic eyes / All lips 'n' hips / Change / If I had a car / Captain of my soul / Rags to riches / Cheek to cheek / Electrified / Who are you / Into the woods.
■ LP 846 055 1
■ CD 846 055 2
■ MC. 846 055 4
Vertigo / May '90.

GROOVUS MAXIMUS.
Tracks: Not Advised.
■ LP 5122551
■ CD 5122552
■ MC. 5122554
Vertigo / Jun '92.

MARY IN THE MYSTERY WORLD.
Tracks: Mary in the mystery world / Why don't we do it in the road / Knee deep in you (Only available on 12", 12"PD and CD Single.) / All lips 'n' hips (Only available on 12" and CD Single.).
■ 12" . . . . .VERX 65
■ 12" P.Disc. . . . . .VERXP 65
■ 7" . . . . VER 65
■ CD Single . . . . .VERCD 65
Vertigo / May '92.

Electric Sun

EARTHQUAKE.
Tracks: Electric sun / Lilac / Burning wheels turning / Japanese dream / Sundown / Winter days / Still so many lives away / Earthquake.
■ LP 0060 196
Brain (Germany) / Dec '79.

FIRE WIND.
Tracks: Cast away your chains / Indian dawn / I'll be loving you always / Fire wind / Prelude in space minor / Just another rainbow / Children of the sea / Chaplin and I / Enola Gay / Tune of Japan / Attack / Lament.
■ LP 0060 378
Brain (Germany) / Mar '82.

Electro Hippies

ELECTRO HIPPIES LIVE.
Tracks: Not Advised.
■ LP . . . . VILE 013
Peaceville / Jun '89.

ONLY GOOD PUNK IS A DEAD ONE, THE.
Tracks: Faith / Acid rain / Run Ronald / Scum / B.P. / Unity / Terror eyes / So wicked / Profit / Freddy's revenge / Mistake / Things of beauty / Protest / Gas Joe Pearce / Lies / Tortured tears / D.I.Y. nor D.R.I / Suck / Deception.
■ LP . . . . VILE 002
Peaceville / Feb '88.
CD. . . . . VILE 002 CD
Peaceville / Feb '88 / Vital Distribution / Pinnacle.

PEEL SESSIONS: ELECTRO HIPPIES (12.7.87).
Tracks: Sheep / Starve the city (to feed the poorly) / Meltdown / Escape / Dead end / Thought / Chickens / Mother / Mega-Amageddon death.
■ 12" . . . . SFPS 042
Strange Fruit / Jul '87.

PLAY LOUD OR DIE.
Tracks: Acid rain / Wings of death / Theme toon / Reaper / Profit from death / Run Ronald / Terror eyes / Am I punk yet / Vivisection / Horns of Hades.
■ LP . . . . NECRO 1
Necrosis / Jun '89.

Electrocution

INSIDE THE UNREAL.
Tracks: Not Advised.
CD. . . . . BABECD 6
LP. . . . . .BABE 6
Rosemary's Baby (Metal) / Sep '93 / Plastic Head.

Elf

CAROLINA COUNTRY BALL (see under Dio, Ronnie James).

ELF.
Tracks: Not Advised.
■ LP . . . . CBS 26910
MC. 40 26910
CBS / Sep '86 / Sony.

ELF ALBUMS, THE.
Tracks: Carolina county ball / LA 59 / Ain't it all amusing / Happy / Annie New Orleans / Rocking chair rock'n'roll blues / Rainbow / Do the same thing / Blanche / Black swampy water / Prentice wood / When she smiles / Good time music / Liberty road / Shotgun boogie / Wonderworld / Streetwalker.
CD . . . . VSOPCD 167
Connoisseur Collection / Sep '91 / Pinnacle.

GARGANTUAN ELF ALBUM, THE.
Tracks: Not Advised.
CD . . . . .LONGCD 78
Safari / May '87 / Pinnacle.

TRYING TO BURN THE SUN (Elf & Ronnie James Dio).
Tracks: Not Advised.
■ LP . . . . LONG 8
MC. . . . . LONGC 8
Safari / Aug '84 / Pinnacle.

Elixir

ELIXIR.
Tracks: Not Advised.
■ LP . . . . GM 003
Goasco / Oct '88.

LETHAL POTION.
Tracks: Not Advised.
■ CD . . . . SONICCD 9
■ LP . . . . SONICLP 9
Sonic (2) / Apr '90.

■ DELETED

E 1

Eloy

CHRONICLES II.
Tracks: Not Advised.
CD EPV084-48192
A.C.I. / Jun '94 / Plastic Head.

CHRONICLES VOL.1.
Tracks: Not Advised.
CD SPV084-48182
SPV / Jul '94 / Plastic Head.

FOOLS.
Tracks: Fools / Heartbeat.
■ 7" . . . . HMINT 1
■ 7" P.Disc . . . . HMPD 1
Heavy Metal / Nov '83.

METROMANIA.
Tracks: Not Advised.
CD . . . . HMIXD 21
■ LP . . . . HMILP 21
MC . . . . HMIMC 21
Special . . . . HMIPD 21
Heavy Metal / Sep '84 / Sony / FM Revolver.

PERFORMANCE.
Tracks: In disguise / Shadow and light / Surrender / Heartbeat / Fools / Broken frame.
■ LP . . . . HMILP 12
■ LP P.Disc . . . . HMIPD 12
MC . . . . HMIMC 12
Heavy Metal / Apr '83 / Sony / FM Revolver.

PLANETS.
Tracks: Introduction / On the verge of darkening lights / Point of no return / Mysterious monolith / Queen of the night / At the gates of dawn / Sphinx / Carried by cosmic winds.
■ LP . . . . HMILP 1
■ LP P.Disc . . . . HMIPD 1
MC . . . . HMIMC 1
Heavy Metal / Jul '82 / Sony / FM Revolver.

RA.
Tracks: Not Advised
■ CD . . . . REVXD 120
■ LP . . . . REVLP 120
■ MC . . . . REVMC 120
Revolver / Aug '89.

TIME TO TURN.
Tracks: Through a sombre galaxy / Behind the walls of imagination / Illuminations / Time to turn / End of an odyssey / Flash / Say, is it really true.
■ LP . . . . HMILP 3
MC . . . . HMIMC 3
Heavy Metal / Jan '83 / Sony / FM Revolver.

Elvis Hitler

DISGRACELAND.
Tracks: Not Advised.
■ LP . . . . GWLP 37
GWR / Jan '89.

HELLBILLY.
Tracks: Not Advised.
CD . . . . LS 94362
Restless (USA) / Dec '89 / Vital Distribution.

Emerson, Lake & Palmer

Among rock's first 'supergroups', Keith Emerson (ex-Nice), Greg Lake (King Crimson) and Carl Palmer (Atomic Rooster) convened in 1970; pseudo-classical style delighted fans and appalled critics. Grandiose nature epitomised by live triple set *Welcome Back, My Friends, To The Show That Never Ends*. Return after three-year hiatus in 1977 proved music world had left ELP behind, despite hit *Fanfare For The Common Man*; band split at end of '78. Palmer and Lake enjoyed success with Asia in early '80s, while Emerson scored films. New ELP, with legendary Cozy Powell (ex-Whitesnake/Jeff Beck/Rainbow/etc) on drums, produced one forgotten album in '86; original trio reformed in 1992.

ALL I WANT IS YOU.
Tracks: All I want is you / Tiger in a spotlight.
■ 7" . . . . K 11225
Atlantic / '78.

ATLANTIC YEARS.
Tracks: Knife edge / Take a pebble / Lucky man / Tank / Tarkus / Excerpts from 'Pictures at an Exhibition' / Endless enigma / From the beginning / Karn evil 9 / First impression / Second impression / Third impression / Jerusalem / Still..you turn me on / Toccata / Fanfare for the common man / Pirates / I

believe in Father Christmas / Honky tonk train blues / Canario.
CD 7567824032
MC 7567824034
Atlantic / Aug '92 / WEA.

BEST OF EMERSON, LAKE AND PALMER, THE.
Tracks: Hoe down / Lucky man / Karn evil 9 / Trilogy / Fanfare for the common man / Still..you turn me on / Tiger in the spotlight / Jerusalem / Peter Gunn.
■ LP . . . . K 50757
MC K4 50757
Atlantic / '80 / WEA.
CD K2 50757
Manticore / '83 / WEA.

BRAIN SALAD SURGERY.
Tracks: Jerusalem / Toccata / Still..you turn me on / Benny the bouncer / Karn evil 9 / First impression (part 1) / First impression / Second impression / Third impression.
■ LP . . . . K 53501
■ MC K4 53501
Manticore / '73.
CD 781523 2
WEA / '89 / WEA.
CD 828468-2
Victory / Dec '93 / PolyGram.

E.L.P.
Tracks: Not Advised.
CD 781519 2
WEA / '89 / WEA.

EMERSON, LAKE & PALMER.
Tracks: Not Advised.
VHS 877783
Polygram Music Video / Nov '93 / PolyGram.

EMERSON, LAKE AND PALMER.
Tracks: Barbarian / Take a pebble / Knife edge / Three fates / Clotho / Lachesis / Auropos / Tank / Lucky man.
■ LP . . . . ILPS 9132
Island / Dec '70.
■ MC K4 43503
■ LP . . . . K 43503
Manticore / '74.
CD 191 20 2
Atlantic / '88 / WEA.
CD 828264-2
Victory / Dec '93 / PolyGram.

EMERSON, LAKE AND PALMER IN CONCERT.
Tracks: Introductory fanfare / Peter Gunn / Tiger in the spotlight / C'est la vie / Enemy god / Knife edge / Piano concerto no.1 / Pictures at an exhibition.
■ LP . . . . K 50652
■ MC K4 50652
Atlantic / Oct '79.

FANFARE FOR THE COMMON MAN.
Tracks: Fanfare for the common man / Brain salad surgery.
■ 7" . . . . K 10946
Atlantic / Jun '77.

IN THE HOT SEAT.
Tracks: Hand of truth / Daddy / One by one / Heart on ice / Thin line / Man in the long black coat / Change / Give me a reason to stay / Gone too soon / Street war / Pictures at an exhibition.
CD 828554-2
MC 828554-4
Victory / Aug '94 / PolyGram.

LIVE.
Tracks: Not Advised.
CD 8289332
MC 8283934
London / Jan '93 / PolyGram.

LIVE '77.
Tracks: Not Advised.
■ VHS . . . . HEN 2005
Hendring Video / '88.

LOVE BEACH.
Tracks: All I want is you / Love beach / Taste of my love / Gambler / For you / Canario / Memoirs of an officer and a gentleman / Prologue / Education of a gentleman / Love at first sight / Letters from the front / Honourable company.
■ LP . . . . K 50552
■ MC K4 50552
Atlantic / '78.
CD 828469-2
Victory / Dec '93 / PolyGram.

PETER GUNN.
Tracks: Peter Gunn / Knife edge.
■ 7" . . . . K 11416
Atlantic / Jan '80.

PICTURES AT AN EXHIBITION.
Tracks: Promenade / Gnome / Sage / Old castle / Blues variation / Hut of baba yaba / Curse of Baba Yaga / Great gate of Kiev / End, The - nutrocker.
■ LP . . . . HELP 1
Island / Dec '71.
■ LP . . . . K 33501
■ MC K4 33501
Manticore / '74.
■ CD 191 222
Cotillion / '88.
CD 781521 2
WEA / '89 / WEA.
CD 828466-2
Victory / Dec '93 / PolyGram.

PICTURES AT AN EXHIBITION.
Tracks: Not Advised.
VHS . . . . CFV 00502
Channel 5 / '88 / Channel 5 Video / P.R.O. Video / Gold & Sons.
■ VHS . . . . HEN 2254
Hendring Video / Aug '90.
■ VHS . . . . COL 1050
Castle Collector Series / Jun '92.

RETURN OF THE MANTICORE.
Tracks: Touch and go / Hang on to a dream / 21st Century schizoid man / Fire / Pictures at an exhibition / I believe in Father Christmas / Introductory Fanfare/Peter Gunn / Tiger in a spotlight / Toccata / Trilogy / Tank / Lucky man / Tarkus / From the beginning / Take a pebble / Knife edge / Paper blood / Hoedown / Rondo / Barbarian / Still .. you turn me on / Endless enigma / C'est la vie / Living sin / Karn evil 9 / Time and a place / Living sin / Karn evil 9 / Honky tonk train blues / Jerusalem / Fanfare for the common man / Black moon / Watching over you / Toccata con fuoco / For you / Prelude and fugue / Memoirs of an officer and a gentleman / Pirates / Affairs of the heart.
CD Set 828459-2
Victory / Dec '93 / PolyGram.

TARKUS.
Tracks: Tarkus / Eruption / Stones of years / Iconoclast / Mass / Manticore / Battlefield / Aquatarkus / Jeremy Bender / Bitches crystal / Only way / Infinite space (conclusion) / Time and a place / Are you ready Eddy.
■ LP . . . . ILPS 9155
Island / Jun '71.
■ MC K4 43504
■ LP . . . . K 43504
Manticore / '74.
CD . . . . K 7815202
WEA / Sep '89 / WEA.
CD 828465-2
Victory / Dec '93 / PolyGram.

TRILOGY.
Tracks: Endless enigma, The (part 1) / Fugue / Endless enigma, The (part 2) / From the beginning / Sheriff / Hoe down / Trilogy / Living sin / Aboddon's bolero.
■ LP . . . . ILPS 9186
Island / Jul '72.
■ MC K4 43505
■ LP . . . . K 43505
Manticore / '74.
CD . . . . K 7815222
Atlantic / '88 / WEA.

WELCOME BACK.
Tracks: Hoe down / Jerusalem / Toccata / Tarkus / Tarkus (conclusion) / Take a pebble / Piano improvisation / Jeremy Bender / Sheriff / Karn evil 9.
■ MC K4 63500
■ LP . . . . K 63500
Manticore / Aug '74.

WELCOME BACK MY FRIENDS TO THE SHOW THAT NEVER ENDS.
Tracks: Hoedown / Jerusalem / Toccata / Tarkus / Take a pebble / Piano improvisations / Jeremy Bender/The Sheriff / Karn evil 9.
CD 828474-2
Victory / Dec '93 / PolyGram.

WORKS LIVE.
Tracks: Introductory Fanfare / Peter Gunn / Tiger in a spotlight / C'est la vie / Watching over you / Maple leaf rag / Enemy God dances with the black spirits / Fanfare for the common man / Knife edge / Show me the way to go home / Abaddon's bolero / Pictures at an exhibition / Closer to believing / Piano concerto no. 1 / Tank.

CD 828477-2
Victory / Dec '93 / PolyGram.

WORKS VOL. 1.
Tracks: Piano concerto no. 1 / Lend your love to me
tonight / C'est la vie / Hallowed be thy name /
Nobody loves you like I do / Closer to believing /
Enemy God dances with the black spirits / L.A.
nights / New Orleans / Two part invention in D minor
/ Food for your soul / Tank / Fanfare for the common
man / Pirates.
CD 828470-2
Victory / Dec '93 / PolyGram.

WORKS VOL. 2.
Tracks: Tiger in the spotlight / When the apple blos-
soms bloom in the windmills of your mind / I'll be
your valentine / Bullfrogs / Brain salad surgery /
Barrelhouse shake down / Watching over you / So
far to fall / Maple leaf rag / I believe in Father
Christmas / Close but not touching.
■ LP . . . . K 50422
■ MC K4 50422
Atlantic / Dec '77.
■ CD 191 472
Atlantic / '88.
CD 781 538-2
Atlantic / Jun '89 / WEA.
CD .828473-2
Victory / Dec '93 / PolyGram.

WORKS: EMERSON, LAKE AND PALMER.
Tracks: Piano concerto no. 1 / Lend your love to me
tonight / C'est la vie / Hallowed be thy name /
Nobody loves you like I do / Closer to believing /
Enemy god / L.A. nights / New Orleans / Bach two
part invention in D minor / Food for your soul / Tank /
Fanfare for the common man / Pirates.
■ MC Set K4 80009
■ Double LP . . . . K 80009
Atlantic / Dec '74.
■ CD 700 02
Atlantic / '88.
CD 7814092
WEA / '89 / WEA.
CD 781 372-2
Atlantic / Jun '89 / WEA.

Emerson, Lake & Powell

EMERSON LAKE AND POWELL.
Tracks: Mars the bringer of war / Score / Learning to
fly / Miracle / Touch & go / Love blind / Step aside /
Lay down your guns.
■ CD 829 297-2
Polydor.
■ LP . . . . POLD 5191
■ MC . . . . POLDC 5191
Polydor / '86.

TOUCH AND GO.
Tracks: Touch & go / Learning to fly / Locomotion
(Extra track on 12" version only).
■ 12" . . . . POSPX 804
■ 7" . . . . POSP 804
Polydor / Jun '86.

English Dogs

BOW TO NONE.
Tracks: Not Advised.
CD . . . . IRC 023CD
LP . . . . .IRC 023LP
Impact / Aug '94 / Plastic Head.

FORWARD INTO BATTLE.
Tracks: Not Advised.
■ LP . . . . ASS 20
Rot / '85.

INVASION OF THE PORKY MEN.
Tracks: Not Advised.
■ LP . . . . CLAYLP 10
Clay / '84.

MAD PUNX AND ENGLISH DOGS.
Tracks: Mad punx and English dogs.
■ 12" . . . . .PLATE 6
Clay / '83.

METALMORPHOSIS.
Tracks: Nightmare of reality / Absolution / Let the
killing begin.
■ 12" . . . . 12 FLAG 101
Under One Flag / May '86.

TO THE END OF THE EARTH.
Tracks: To the end of the earth.
■ 7" . . . . ASS 17
Rot / '84.

WHERE LEGEND BEGAN.
Tracks: Not Advised.
■ LP . . . . FLAG 4
Under One Flag / Nov '86.

Enid

Cult band formed in mid-70s by ex-Barclay
James Harvest keyboardist Robert John
Godfrey. Nearly dragged down when record
label Pye collapsed, they won new following
as 1980s festival attraction. Loss of key personnel and record deals, coupled with disastrous attempts to break away from classi-
cal-esque sound, returned Enid to club status in '90s. Best work is 1984 reworking of
1976 debut, *In The Region Of The Summer
Stars*.

AERIE FAERIE NONSENSE.
Tracks: Prelude / Mayday galliard / Ondine / Childe
Roland / Fand: first movement / Fand: second
movement.
■ LP . . . . .ENID 6
Enid / '84.
■ LP . . . . EG 2603241
EMI / '84.
CD . . . . ENIDCD 6
Enid / '88 / Enid Records.
CD . . . . MNTLCD 6
Newt / May '94 / Plastic Head.

AT THE HAMMERSMITH.
Tracks: Not Advised.
CD . . . . .MNTLCD 10
Newt / May '94 / Plastic Head.

DAMBUSTERS MARCH.
Tracks: Dambusters march / Skye boat song.
■ 7" 7P 106
PRT / Jun '79.

ENID, THE.
Tracks: Fand / Raintown / Jessica / Then there were
none / Letter from America / Something wicked this
way comes / Encore.
VHS . . . . JE 133
Jettisoundz / May '89 / TBD / Visionary
Communications.

FAND SYMPHONIC TONE POEM.
Tracks: Not Advised.
■ LP . . . . .ENID 9
Enid / '85.

FINAL NOISE.
Tracks: Childe Roland / Hall of mirrors / Song for
Europe / Something wicked this way comes / Sheets
of blue / Chaldean crossing / La rage / Earth born /
Jerusalem.
CD . . . . ENID CD12
Wonderful Music Co. / Feb '90.
CD . . . . MNTLCD 3
Newt / May '94 / Plastic Head.

FOOL.
Tracks: Fool / Tico.
■ 7" 7P 187
PRT / Jul '80.

GOLDEN EARRINGS.
Tracks: Golden earrings / 665-The great bean.
■ 7" . . . . EMI 5109
EMI / Oct '80.

HEIGH HO.
Tracks: Heigh ho / Twinkle twinkle little star.
■ 7" . . . . BRO 134
Bronze / Oct '81.

IN THE REGION OF THE SUMMER STARS.
Tracks: Fool / Falling tower / Death, the reaper /
Lovers / Devil / Sun / Last judgement / In the region
of the Summer stars.
■ LP . . . . .ENID 7
Hyperion / '84.
■ LP . . . . EG 2603231
EMI / '84.
CD . . . . ENIDCD 7
Enid / '88 / Enid Records.
CD . . . . MNTLCD 7
Newt / May '94 / Plastic Head.

ITCHYCOO PARK.
Tracks: Itchycoo park.
■ 12" . . . . EDITL 3314
■ 7" . . . . EDIT 3314
Sedition / Sep '86.

JUBILEE (DAM BUSTERS MARCH).
Tracks: Jubilee (dam busters march) / Pomp and
circumstance (march no.1) / Omega.

■ 7" . . . . INT 534
EMI International / Jun '77.

LIVE AT HAMMERSMITH, VOL. 1.
Tracks: Not Advised.
■ LP . . . . .ENID 1
Enid / '84.

LIVE AT HAMMERSMITH, VOL. 2.
Tracks: Not Advised.
■ LP . . . . .ENID 2
Enid / '84.

LOVERS AND FOOLS.
Tracks: Fantasy on Scarborough fayre / Hall of mirrors / Sheets of blue / Lovers / Evensong / Bright
star / Flame of power / Fool / Falling tower / Something wicked this way comes / Summer / Flood / In
the region of the Summer stars.
■ Double LP . . . . DOJOLP 24
■ MC . . . . DOJOTC 24
Dojo / '87.

RHAPSODY IN ROCK.
Tracks: God save the Queen / Dies Irae / Song of
Fand / Punch and Judy man / Humoresque / Cortege
/ Wild things / Sanctus / Hall of mirrors / Dreamer.
■ Double LP . . . . .NSPD 18619
Pye / '80.

SALOME.
Tracks: O Salome / Streets of blue / Change / Jack /
Flames of power.
■ LP . . . . ENID 10
Enid / Mar '86.
CD . . . . MNTLCD 9
Newt / May '94 / Plastic Head.

SALOME.
Tracks: Salome.
■ 12" . . . . ENID 6999
■ 7" . . . . ENID 7999
■ CD Single . . . . ENID 2999
Wonderful Music Co. / Jun '90.

SEED AND THE SOWER, THE.
Tracks: Children crossing / Bar of shadow / La rage /
Longhome / Earth born.
CD . . . . ENIDCD 11
■ LP . . . . ENID 11
Enid / '88.
CD . . . . MNTLCD 2
Newt / Apr '94 / Plastic Head.

SIX PIECES.
Tracks: Sanctus / Once she was / Ring master /
Punch and Judy man / Hall of mirrors / Dreamer /
Joined by the heart (pt. 1) (CD only).
■ MC . . . . .ZCN 116
■ LP . . . . NH 116
Pye / '79.
■ LP . . . . .ENID 4
Hyperion / '84.
CD . . . . ENID CD4
Wonderful Music Co. / Feb '90.
CD . . . . MNTLCD 4
Newt / May '94 / Plastic Head.

SPELL, THE.
Tracks: Winter "The key" / Spring / Summer / Au-
tumn "Veni creator spiritus" (Come creative spritus)
/ Elephants never die / Sentimental side of Mrs
James (For the family and friends of Mark.) / Fand
(Live Hammersmith 1979). (CD only.).
■ LP . . . . .ENID 8
Hyperion / '84.
CD . . . . ENIDCD 8
Standz-Caroline / Jan '87 / Pinnacle.
CD . . . . ENID CD8
Wonderful Music Co. / Feb '90.

THEN THERE WERE NONE.
Tracks: Then there were / Letters from
America.
■ 7" . . . . .RAK 349
RAK / '83.
■ 12" 12EMI 5505
EMI / Nov '84.

TOUCH ME.
Tracks: Humoresque / Cortege / Elegy (touch me) /
Gallevant / Albion fair / Joined by the heart.
■ LP . . . . .NSPH 18593
Pye / '79.
■ MC . . . . ZCP 18593
PRT / '79.
■ LP . . . . .ENID 5
Enid / '84.
CD . . . . ENIDCD 5
Wonderful Music Co. / Feb '90.
CD . . . . MNTLCD 5
Newt / May '94 / Plastic Head.

■ DELETED

E 3

WHEN YOU WISH UPON A STAR.
Tracks: When you wish upon a star / Jessica.
■ 7" . . . . BRO 127
Bronze / Jul '81.

Enola Gay

PUTTING DENMARK.
Tracks: Putting Denmark.
■ 7" . . . . LF 029
Lost & Found / Apr '92.

Entombed

Issued cassette-only demos when called Nihilist as early as 1987, but didn't release any records until they changed their name to Entombed and secured a deal with the classic UK underground metal label Earache. Their debut, *Left Hand Path*, established them as Sweden's premier death metal outfit, who have gone from strength-to-strength (albeit with fluctuating five piece line-ups) ever since.

CLANDESTINE.
Tracks: Not Advised.
LP . . . . MOSH 037
MC . . . . MOSH 037MC
Earache / Oct '91 / Vital Distribution.
CD . . . . MOSH 037CD
Earache / Sep '94 / Vital Distribution.

HOLLOWMAN.
Tracks: Hollowman / Serpent speech / Wolverine blues / Bonehouse / Put off the scent / Hellraiser.
■ 12" . . . . MOSH 094T
■ CD Single . . . . MOSH 094CD
■ MC Single. . . . . MOSH 094MC
Earache / Apr '93.

LEFT HAND PATH.
Tracks: Left hand path / Drowned / Revel in flesh / When life has ceased / Supposed to rot / But life goes on / Bitter loss / Morbid devourment / Deceased / Truth beyond / Carnal leftovers.
LP . . . . MOSH 21
MC . . . . MOSH 21 MC
Earache / Jun '90 / Vital Distribution.
CD . . . . MOSH 21 CD
Earache / Sep '94 / Vital Distribution.

OUT OF HAND.
Tracks: Out of hand / God of thunder / Black breath.
12" . . . . MOSH 114T
7" 7MOSH 114
CD Single . . . . MOSH 114CD
Earache / Jul '94 / Vital Distribution.

STRANGER AEONS.
Tracks: Stranger aeons.
■ 12" . . . . MOSH 052T
■ CD Single . . . . MOSH 052CD
Earache / Jul '92.

WOLVERINE BLUES.
Tracks: Eyemaster / Rotten soil / Wolverine blues / Demon / Contempt / Full of hell / Blood song / Hollowman / Heavens die / Out of hand.
LP . . . . MOSH 082
MC . . . . .MOSH 082MC
Earache / Sep '93 / Vital Distribution.
CD . . . . MOSH 082CD
Earache / Sep '94 / Vital Distribution.

Enuff Z Nuff

Melodic rock quartet with an obvious Cheap Trick influence initially appeared in a blur of hideous flourescent outfits that have been toned down with the release of their second and third albums *Strength* and *Animals With Human Intelligence*. Both albums have sold well and received glowing critical reviews but recent upheavals in personnel may prove to be unsettling.

ANIMALS WITH HUMAN INTELLIGENCE.
Tracks: Superstitious / Black rain / Right by your side / Thes daze / Master of pain / Innocence / One step closer / Bring it on home / Takin' a ride / Love train / Maryanne lost her baby / Rock 'n' world.
CD 7822 18587-2
MC 7822 18587-4
Arista / Mar '93 / BMG.

ENUFF Z NUFF.
Tracks: New thing / Fly high Michelle / In the groove / For now / I could never be without you / She wants more / Hot little summer girl / Little indian angel / Kiss the clown / Finger on the trigger / Heaven or

hell / Missing you / Strength / In crowd / Hollywood ya / World is a gutter / Goodbye / Long way to go / Mother's eyes / Baby loves you.
CD K791 262 2
■ LP K791 262 1
MC K791 262 4
Atco / Aug '89 / WEA.

ENUFF Z NUFF.
Tracks: Not Advised.
VHS 8536501643
Warner Music Video / Oct '92 / WEA.

FLY HIGH MICHELLE.
Tracks: Fly high Michelle / Finger on the trigger / Hot little summer girl (Not on 7" single.).
■ 12" . . . . B 9135 T
■ 7" .B 9135
■ CD Single . . . . B 9135 CD
Atco / Jul '90.

NEW THING.
Tracks: New thing / Kiss the clown.
■ 12" . . . . B 8990T
■ 7" .B 8990
■ CD Single . . . . B 8990CD
East West / Apr '90.

RIGHT BY YOUR SIDE.
Tracks: Right by your side.
■ 12" 7432114592-1
■ 7" 7432114592-7
■ CD Single 7432114592-2
■ MC Single 7432114592-4
Arista / Apr '93.

STRENGTH.
Tracks: Goodbye / Long way to go / Mother's eyes / Baby loves you / Blue island / Way home, The/ Coming home / Something for free / Time to let you go.
CD 7567916382
■ LP 7567916381
MC 7567916384
Atco / Apr '91 / WEA.

Epidemic

DECAMERON.
Tracks: Not Advised.
CD . . . . .CDZORRO 50
MC . . . . TZORRO 50
Zorro / Sep '92 / Pinnacle.

EXIT PARADISE.
Tracks: Not Advised.
CD . . . . .CDZORRO 79
Metal Blade / Aug '94 / Pinnacle.

TRUTH OF WHAT WILL BE, THE.
Tracks: Not Advised.
CD . . . . CORE 4CD
LP . . . . CORE 4
Metalcore / Oct '90 / Pinnacle.

Erosion

EROSION III.
Tracks: Not Advised.
CD . . . . WB 095CD
We Bite / Nov '92 / Plastic Head.

Eulogy

ESSENCE.
Tracks: Not Advised.
CD . . . . SPV 077-140782
Nuclear Blast / Sep '94 / Plastic Head.

Europe

Swedish hard rock band formed in 1980, audibly influenced by Deep Purple. Self-titled LP went to No. 8 in Swedish charts in 1983. Following *Wings Of Tomorrow*, they were signed by CBS, and by end of 1984, were known outside Sweden, especially in Japan. International success came with release of *The Final Countdown* in May 1986. Title song topped charts in fourteen countries (including Britain) and made Top 10 in most others; making short-lived pin-up of singer Joey Tempest. Bar minor hit singles *Rock The Night* and *Superstitious*, subsequent releases have failed to consolidate position.

CARRIE.
Tracks: Carrie / Danger on the track (Only on 12" single.) / Love chaser.
■ 12" . . . . EURT 2

■ 7" . . . . EUR 2
Epic / Apr '87.

CARRIE (EP).
Tracks: Carrie / Love chaser / Open your heart / Dance the night away.
■ 12" . . . . EURD 2
Epic / Apr '87.

CHRIS TETLEY INTERVIEWS EUROPE.
Tracks: Not Advised.
■ LP P.Disc . . . . CT 1002
Music & Media / Oct '87.

EUROPE.
Tracks: In the future to come / Female / Seven doors hotel / King will return / Boyazant / Children of the time / Words of wisdom / Paradise beach / Memories.
■ LP . . . . .CHORD 008
Chord / Jan '87.
MC. . . . . CHORDTC 008
Chord / Jan '87 / EMI.

EUROPE 1982-1992.
Tracks: In the future to come / Seven doors hotel / Stormwind / Open your heart / Scream of anger / Dreamer / Final countdown / On broken wings / Rock the night / Carrie / Cherokee / Superstitious / Ready or not / Prisoners in paradise (Single edit) / I'll cry for you (Accoustic) / Sweet love child (Previously unreleased.) / Yesterday's news.
CD .473589 2
LP .473589 1
MC. 473589 4
Epic / Apr '93 / Sony.
MiniDisc. 473589 8
Epic / Aug '93 / Sony.

EUROPE: IN AMERICA.
Tracks: Final countdown / Seven doors hotel / Open your heart / Cherokee / Rock the night / Carrie.
VHS . . . . CFV 07682
Channel 5 / Aug '88 / Channel 5 Video / P.R.O. Video / Gold & Sons.
CD Video 080 370 1
Polygram Music Video / Oct '88 / PolyGram.

EUROPE: INTERVIEW PICTURE DISC.
Tracks: Not Advised.
LP P.Disc . . . . BAK 2041
Baktabak / May '87 / Arabesque Ltd.

FINAL COUNTDOWN (OLD GOLD).
Tracks: Final countdown / Carrie.
7" .OG 9946
Old Gold / Sep '90 / Pickwick.

FINAL COUNTDOWN WORLD TOUR, THE.
Tracks: Carrie / On the loose / Dreamer / Open your heart / Final countdown / Rock the night / Dance the night away / Broken wings / Cherokee.
■ VHS 490052
CMV Enterprises (Video) / Jun '89.

FINAL COUNTDOWN, THE.
Tracks: Love chaser / On the loose / Heart of stone / Time has come / Final countdown / Cherokee / Ninja / Danger on the track / Rock the night / Carrie.
■ LP . . . . EPC 26808
MC. 40 26808
Epic / Nov '86 / Sony.
CD . . . . CD 26808
Epic / Jan '87 / Sony.
CD 4663282
MC. 4663284
■ LP 4663281
Epic / Mar '90.
MiniDisc. 26808
Epic / Aug '93 / Sony.

FINAL COUNTDOWN, THE.
Tracks: Final countdown / On broken wings / Heart of stone (Only on 3"CD single.)
■ 12" . . . . TA 7127
■ 7" .A 7127
Epic / Oct '86.

HALFWAY TO HEAVEN.
Tracks: Half way to heaven / Yesterday's news / Final countdown (CD single only) / Open your heart (acoustic) (CD single only).
■ 12" 6578516
■ 7" 6578517
■ CD Single 6578512
■ MC Single 6578514
Columbia / Mar '92.

I'LL CRY FOR YOU.
Tracks: I'll cry for you / Seventh sign / Break free (Not on 7") / Prisoners in Paradise (CD single only.)
■ 12" 6576976
■ 7" 6576977

■ CD Single. 6576972
■ MC Single. 6576974
Epic / Jan '92.

LET THE GOOD TIMES ROCK.
Tracks: Let the good times rock / Never say die / Carrie (Only on CD single and 12".) / Seven doors hotel (Only on CD single and 12".).
■ 12". . . . . EURT 5
■ 7". . . . . EUR 5
■ CD Single. . . . . CDEUR 5
Epic / Mar '89.

OPEN YOUR HEART.
Tracks: Open your heart / Just the beginning / Rock the night (Only on 12" & CD single.) / Lyin' eyes (Only on 12" & CD single.).
■ 12". . . . . EUR T4
■ 7". . . . . EUR Q4
■ 7". . . . . EUR 4
■ CD Single. . . . . CDEUR 4
Epic / Oct '88.
■ 7". . . . . EUR B4
Epic / Oct '88.

OUT OF THIS WORLD.
Tracks: Superstitious / Let the good times rock / Open your heart / More than meets the eye / Coast to coast / Ready or not / Sign of the times / Just the beginning / Never say die / Lights and shadows / Tower's callin' / Tomorrow.
CD. 4624492
■ LP. 4624491
■ MC. 4624494
Epic / Sep '88.

OUT OF THIS WORLD/FINAL COUNT-DOWN/WINGS OF ..
Tracks: Not Advised.
■ CD Set. 4673932
Epic / Dec '90.

PRISONERS IN PARADISE.
Tracks: All or nothing / Halfway to Heaven / I'll cry for you / Little bit of lovin' / Talk to me / Seventh sign / Prisoners in paradise / Bad blood / Homeland / Got your mind in the gutter / 'Til my heart beats down your door / Girl from Lebanon.
CD. 4687552
MC. 4687554
■ LP. 4687551
Epic / Feb '92.
■ CD P.Disc. 4687559
Epic / Mar '92.
MiniDisc. 468755-3
Epic / Feb '93 / Sony.

ROCK THE NIGHT.
Tracks: Rock the night / Seven doors hotel / Storm wind (Only on EURQ 1 and 12" single.) / Wings of tomorrow (Only on EURQ 1 and 12" single.).
■ 12". . . . . EUR T1
■ 7". . . . . EUR Q1
■ 7". . . . . EUR 1
Epic / Feb '87.

ROCK THE NIGHT (OLD GOLD).
Tracks: Rock the night / Carrie.
12". . . . . OG 4228
Old Gold / Jun '92 / Pickwick.

SUPERSTITIOUS.
Tracks: Superstitious / Lights and shadows / Towers calling (Only on 12" and CD single.) / Final count-down (Only on 12" and CD single.).
■ 12". . . . . EUR T3
■ 7". . . . . EUR 3
■ 7". . . . . EUR C3
■ 7". . . . . EUR Q3
■ CD Single. . . . . CDEUR 3
Epic / Aug '88.

VIDEO EP: EUROPE.
Tracks: Final countdown / Rock the night / Carrie.
VHS. 5136 50
CBS-Fox / '87 / Sony / TBD.

WINGS OF TOMORROW.
Tracks: Stormwind / Scream of anger / Open your heart / Treated bad again / Aphasia / Wings of tomorrow / Wasted time / Lyin' eyes / Dreamer / Dance the night away.
■ LP. 4602131
■ MC. 4602134
Epic / Mar '88.
CD. 9826502
Pickwick/Sony Collector's Choice / Nov '91 / Pickwick / Pinnacle.

Every Mothers Nightmare

EVERY MOTHERS NIGHTMARE.
Tracks: Hard to hold / Bad on love / Love can make you blind / Dues to pay / Lord willin' / Ez come, ez go / Walls come down / Listen up / Long haired country boy / Nobody knows.
■ CD. 260921
■ LP. 210921
■ MC. 410921
Arista / Jul '90.

Eviction

WORLD IS HOURS AWAY, THE.
Tracks: Not Advised.
CD. CDZORRO 14
LP. . . . . ZORRO 14
Zorro / Nov '90 / Pinnacle.

Evil Dead

ANNIHILATION OF CIVILISATION.
Tracks: Not Advised.
CD. 847603
LP. 087602
Steamhammer (Germany) / '90 / Pinnacle.

RISE ABOVE.
Tracks: Not Advised.
CD. 557590
■ LP. 507577
Steamhammer (Germany) / '88 / Pinnacle.

Evil Mothers

CROSSDRESSER.
Tracks: Not Advised.
CD. . . . . CDDVN 26
Under One Flag / Dec '93 / Pinnacle.

PITCHFORKS & PERVERTS.
Tracks: Not Advised.
CD. . . . . CDDVN 30
Devotion / May '94 / Pinnacle.

Excalibur

BITTER END, THE.
Tracks: Not Advised.
■ LP. . . . . QUEST 5
Conquest / Sep '85.

CAROL-ANNE.
Tracks: Carol-Anne / Early in the morning / Sick & tired.
■ 12". . . . . 12 ATV 101
Active / Feb '90.

HOT FOR LOVE.
Tracks: Hot for love / Early in the morning / Come on and rock / Death's door.
■ 12". . . . . PLATE 9
Clay / Aug '88.

ONE STRANGE NIGHT.
Tracks: Una notte strana / Lights go down / round and 'round / Early in the morning / Running scared / Fight / Waiting / Frozen promises / Carole Ann / Death's door.
LP. . . . . ATV 10
Active / Mar '90 / Pinnacle.

Excessive Force

CONQUER YOUR HOUSE.
Tracks: Conquer your house.
■ 12". . . . . 12 DVN 107
■ CD Single. . . . . CDDVN 107
Music For Nations / Jul '92.

CONQUER YOUR WORLD.
Tracks: Not Advised.
CD. . . . . CDDVN 12
LP. . . . . DVN 12
MC. . . . . TDVN 12
Devotion / Jul '92 / Pinnacle.

Exciter

BETTER LIVE THAN DEAD.
Tracks: Stand up and fight / Heavy metal maniac / Victims of sacrifice / Under attack / Sudden impacts / Delivering to the master / I am the beast / Blackwitch / Long live the loud / Rising of the dead / Cry of the banshee / Pounding metal / Violence and force.
CD. . . . . CD BLEED 5
Bleeding Hearts / Mar '93 / Pinnacle.

FEEL THE KNIFE.
Tracks: Feel the knife / Violence and force.
■ 12". . . . . 12 KUT 113
Music For Nations / Jun '85.

HEAVY METAL MANIAC.
Tracks: Holocaust / Heavy metal maniac / Mistress of evil / Rising of the dead / Cry of the banshee / Stand up and fight / Iron dogs / Under attack / Blackwitch.
■ LP. . . . . RR 9710
Road Runner / Apr '86.
CD. . . . . RO 9710 2
Roadracer / Apr '89 / Pinnacle.

KILL AFTER KILL.
Tracks: Rain of terror / No life no future / Cold blooded murder / Smashin' 'em down / Shadow of the cross / Dog eat dog / Anger, hate and destruction / Second coming / Born to kill (live).
CD. . . . . N 0192-2
LP. . . . . N 0192-1
MC. . . . . N 0192-4
Noise / Apr '92 / Pinnacle.

LONG LIVE THE LOUD.
Tracks: Not Advised.
■ LP. . . . . MFN 47
Music For Nations / May '85.

OTT.
Tracks: Not Advised.
CD. 854603
■ LP. 084602
Maze / '89.

UNVEILING THE WICKED.
Tracks: Not Advised.
■ LP. . . . . MFN 61
MC. . . . . TMFN 61
Music For Nations / Aug '89 / Pinnacle.

VIOLENCE AND FORCE.
Tracks: Not Advised.
■ LP. . . . . MFN 17
Music For Nations / Feb '84.

Excrement Of War

CATHODE RAY COMA.
Tracks: Not Advised.
CD. . . . . FINNREC 07CD
Finn / Jun '94 / Plastic Head.

Excruciate

PASSAGE OF LIFE.
Tracks: Not Advised.
CD. . . . . THR 019
Thrash / Jul '93 / Plastic Head.

Executioner

BREAK THE SILENCE.
Tracks: Not Advised.
■ LP. . . . . NRR 24
New Renaissance(USA) / Aug '87.
MC. . . . . NRC 24
New Renaissance(USA) / Aug '87 / Pinnacle.

IN THE NAME OF METAL.
Tracks: Not Advised.
■ LP. GWD 90538
MC. . . . . GWC 90538
New Renaissance(USA) / Nov '87 / Pinnacle.

Exhorder

LAW, THE.
Tracks: Not Advised.
CD. . . . . RO 92342
Road Runner / Feb '93 / Pinnacle.

SLAUGHTER IN THE VATICAN.
Tracks: Not Advised.
CD. . . . . RO 9363 2
Road Runner / Feb '93 / Pinnacle.

Exodus

BONDED BY BLOOD.
Tracks: Bonded by blood / And then there were none / Metal command / No love / Strike of the beast / Exodus / Lesson in violence / Piranha / Deliver us to evil.
CD. . . . . CDMFN 44
■ LP. . . . . MFN 44
MC. . . . . TMFN 44
Music For Nations / Apr '85 / Pinnacle.

FABULOUS DISASTER.
Tracks: Not Advised.
CD . . . . CDMFN 90
■ LP P.Disc . . . . MFN 90P
MC . . . . TMFN 90
■ LP . . . . MFN 90
Music For Nations / Feb '89.

FORCE OF HABIT.
Tracks: Thorn in my side / Me, myself and I / Force of habit / Bitch / Fuel for the fire / One foot in the grave / Count your blessings / Climb beneath the fall / Architect of pain / When it rains it pours / Good day to die / Pump it up / Feeding time at the zoo.
■ LP . . . . EST 2179
■ MC . . . . TCEST 2179
■ CD . . . . CDEST 2179
Capitol / Sep '92.

GOOD FRIENDLY, VIOLENT FUN.
Tracks: Not Advised.
LP . . . . RO 92351
MC . . . . RO 92354
■ CD . . . . RO 92352
Road Runner / Nov '91.

IMPACT IS IMMINENT.
Tracks: Impact is imminent / A.W.O.L. / Lunatic parade / Within the walls of chaos / Objection overruled / Only death decides / Heads they win (tails you lose) / Changing of the guard / Thrash under pressure.
CD . . . . CDEST 2125
■ LP . . . . EST 2125
■ MC . . . . TCEST 2125
Capitol / Jun '90.

LESSONS IN VIOLENCE.
Tracks: Not Advised.
LP . . . . MFN 138M
MC . . . . TMFN 138M
Music For Nations / Jul '92 / Pinnacle.
CD . . . . CDMFN 138M
Music For Nations / Jul '92 / Pinnacle.

OBJECTION OVERRULED.
Tracks: Objection overruled / Changing of the guard / Free for all (Not on 7").
■ 12" 12CL 597
■ 12" P.Disc 12CLPD 597
■ 7" . . . . CL 597
Capitol / Nov '90.

PLEASURES OF THE FLESH.
Tracks: Deranged / Parasite / Faster than you'll ever live to be / 30 seconds / Chemi-kill / Till death do us part / Brain dead / Pleasures of the flesh / Seed of late / Choose your weapon.
■ LP . . . . MFN 77
MC . . . . TMFN 77
Music For Nations / Nov '87 / Pinnacle.
■ LP P.Disc . . . . MFN 77P
Music For Nations / Jan '88.
CD . . . . CDMFN 77
Music For Nations / Aug '89 / Pinnacle.

Exorcist

NIGHTMARE THEATRE.
Tracks: Not Advised.
■ LP . . . . RR 9700
Road Runner / Sep '86.

Exploited

Punk band - Gary, Big John, Dru Stix and Wattie - formed in 1980. Fronted by Wattie, the Exploited's music was anarchic, uncompromising and attracted a loyal army of unruly fans. The band had a few minor hit singles, including an infamous appearance on Top Of The Pops in October 1981, when they performed *Dead Cities*. Exploited LP's, *Punk's Not Dead* and *Troops Of Tomorrow* also reached the Top 20 during this period.

ARMY LIFE.
Tracks: Army life.
■ 7" . . . . EXP 1001
Exploited / Oct '80.
■ 7" . . . . SH 112
Secret / Apr '81.

ATTACK.
Tracks: Attack / Alternatives.
■ 7" . . . . .SHH 130
Secret / Jul '82.

COMPUTERS DON'T BLUNDER.
Tracks: Computers don't blunder / Addiction.
■ 7" . . . . .SHH 140
Secret / Oct '82.

DEAD CITIES.
Tracks: Dead cities / Punk's not dead / Army life / Barmy army.
■ 7" . . . . .SSH 120
Secret / Jul '82.
■ 12" . . . . TOF 107
Archive 4 / Aug '86.

DEATH BEFORE DISHONOUR.
Tracks: Not Advised.
■ LP . . . . JUST 6
Rough Justice / Aug '89.
CD . . . . .CDJUST 6
Rough Justice / Sep '90 / Pinnacle.

DOGS OF WAR.
Tracks: Dogs of war / Blown to bits.
■ 7" . . . . .SSH 110
Secret / Apr '81.

DON'T LET 'EM GRIND YOU DOWN (EP) (Exploited & Anti Pasti).
Tracks: Don't let 'em grind you down.
■ 7" . . . . EXP 1003
Superville / Oct '81.

EXPLOITED BARMY ARMY.
Tracks: Exploited barmy army.
■ 7" . . . . SH 113
Secret / Apr '81.

EXPLOITED ON STAGE.
Tracks: Not Advised.
■ LP . . . . .EXPLP 2001
Superville / Oct '81.

HORROR EPICS.
Tracks: Horror epics / Don't forget the chaos / Law and order / I hate you / No more idols / Maggie / Dangerous vision / Down below / Treat you like shit / Forty odd years ago / My life.
■ LP . . . . DOJOLP 37
Dojo / Aug '86.
■ MC . . . . DOJOTC 37
Dojo / '87.
CD . . . . DOJOCD 184
Dojo / Feb '94 / Castle Communications / BMG.

INNER CITY DECAY.
Tracks: Not Advised.
■ LP . . . . WAT 1
Snow / Mar '87.

JESUS IS DEAD.
Tracks: Drug squad man / Privacy invasion / Jesus is dead / Politician.
■ 12" . . . . 12 KORE 102
Rough Justice / Aug '86.

LET'S START A WAR (SAID MAGGIE ONE DAY).
Tracks: Let's start a war / Insanity / Safe below / Eyes of the vulture / Should we can't we / Rival leaders (re-mix) / God save the Queen / Kid ology / False hopes / Another day to go nowhere / Wankers.
■ LP . . . . PAX 18
Pax / Dec '83.
■ LP . . . . DOJOLP 10
■ MC . . . . DOJOTC 10
Dojo / '87.
CD . . . . DOJOCD 183
Dojo / Feb '94 / Castle Communications / BMG.

LET'S START A WAR/HORROR EPICS.
Tracks: Let's start a war (Said Maggie one day) / Insanity / Safe below / Eye's of the vulture / Should we, can't we / Rival leaders (Remix) / God saved the queen / Psycho / Kidology / False hope / Another day to go nowhere / Horror epics / Wankers / Don't forget the chaos / Law and order / I hate you / No more idols / Maggie / Dangerous vision / Down below / Treat you like shit / Forty odd years ago / My life.
CD . . . . LOMACD 3
Loma / Feb '94 / BMG.

LIVE AND LOUD.
Tracks: Law and order / Let's start a war / Horror epics / Cop cars / Blown to bits / Hitler's in the charts again / Belson was a gas / Alternative / I hate you / UK 82 / Rival leaders / Maggie / Troops of tomorrow / Sex and violence / Daily news / Crashed out / S.P.G. / Exploited barmy army / Dead cities / I believe in anarchy.
■ LP . . . . LINK LP 018
Link / Dec '87.
CD . . . . LINK CD 018
Street Link / Sep '93 / BMG.

LIVE AT THE PALM COVE.
Tracks: Barmy army / Army life / Cop cars / Alternative / Jimmy Boyle / Warhead / Dead cities / Belsen

was a gas / Computers don't blunder / Dogs of war / Blown to bits / Troops of tomorrow / I believe in anarchy / Punks not dead / Sex and violence.
■ VHS . . . . JE 107
Jettisoundz / '83.

LIVE AT THE WHITEHOUSE.
Tracks: Not Advised.
■ LP . . . . SDLP 2
Suck / Feb '86.

LIVE IN JAPAN.
Tracks: Not Advised.
■ VHS . . . . JE 237
Jettisoundz / Jan '93.

LIVE IN JAPAN.
Tracks: Let's start a war / Scaling the Derry Walls / Dogs of war / Massacre / UK 82 / About to die / Alternative / Rival leaders / Maggie / I still believe in anarchy / Death before dishonour / Dead cities / Troops of tomorrow / Army life / USA / Punk's not dead / Exploited barmy army / Sex and violence.
CD . . . . DOJOCD 109
Dojo / Feb '94 / Castle Communications / BMG.

LIVE ON STAGE 1981/LIVE AT THE WHITEHOUSE 1985.
Tracks: Cop cars / Crashed out / Dole Q / Dogs of war / Army life / Out of control / Ripper / Mod song / Exploited barmy army / Royalty / SPG / Sex and violence / Punk's not dead / I believe in anarchy / Let's start a war / Jimmy Boyle / Don't forget the chaos / God saved the Queen / Alternative / Horror epics / Wankers / Dead cities / Rival leaders / I hate you / Daily news.
CD . . . . LOMACD 2
Loma / Feb '94 / BMG.

LIVE ON THE APOCALYPSE NOW TOUR 1981.
Tracks: Not Advised.
■ LP . . . . APOCA 2
Chaos / Feb '87.

LIVE, LEWD LUST.
Tracks: Not Advised.
■ LP . . . . SLAM 7
Grand Slam (USA) / '89.

MASSACRE, THE.
Tracks: Not Advised.
CD . . . . .CDJUST 15
LP . . . . JUST 15
MC . . . . TJUST 15
Music For Nations / Sep '90 / Pinnacle.

ON STAGE.
Tracks: Cop cars / Crashed out / Dole Q / Dogs of war / Army life / Out of control / Ripper / Mod song / Exploited / Barmy army / Royalty / Sex and violence / Punks not dead / I believe in anarchy.
■ LP . . . . .DOJOLP 9
■ MC . . . . DOJOTC 9
Dojo / '87.
■ CD 10001 2
Continuum Records (USA) / Aug '92.

PUNK'S ALIVE.
Tracks: Punk's alive.
■ 12" . . . . EXPX 1
Skunx / Jul '88.

PUNK'S NOT DEAD.
Tracks: Punk's not dead / Mucky pup / Cop cars / Free flight / Army life / Blown to bits / Sex and violence / S.P.G. / Royalty / Dole Q / Exploited barmy army / Ripper / Out of control / Son of a copper / I believe in anarchy / Dogs of war / What you gonna do.
■ CD . . . . .STR CD 006
Street Link / Oct '92.
CD . . . . DOJOCD 106
Dojo / Mar '93 / Castle Communications / BMG.

PUNKS NOT DEAD.
Tracks: Punks not dead / Mucky pup / Cop cars / Free flight / Army life / Blown to bits / Sex and violence / SPG / Royalty / Dole Q / Exploited barmy army / Ripper / Out of control / Son of a copper / I believe in anarchy.
■ LP . . . . SEC 1
Secret / May '81.
■ MC . . . . TSEC 1
Secret / May '81.
■ LP . . . . RR 9995
Road Runner / '89.
■ LP . . . . LINK 065
Link / Mar '89.

■ DELETED

PUNKS NOT DEAD/TROOPS OF TOMORROW.
Tracks: Not Advised.
MC Set . . . . RR 49651
Road Runner / '89 / Pinnacle.

RIVAL LEADER.
Tracks: Rival leader.
■ 7" . . . . PAX 15
Pax / Oct '83.

SEXUAL FAVOURS.
Tracks: Sexual favours / War now / Let's start a war / Dogs of war / Jesus is dead / Alternative / Rival leaders / Drug squad man / Dead cities / Army life / Interview / Punks not dead.
■ VHS . . . . JE 163
Jettisoundz / '87.

SINGLES COLLECTION, THE.
Tracks: Army life / Fuck the mods / Crashed out / Exploited barmy army / I believe in anarchy / What you gonna do / Dogs of war / Blown to bits (Live) / Dead cities / Hitler's in the charts again / Class war / S.P.G. (Live) / Cop cars (Live) / Yop / Attack / Alternative / Troops of tomorrow / Computers don't blunder / Addiction / Rival leaders / Army style / Singalongabushell.
■ CD . . . . STR CD 018
Street Link / Oct '92.
CD . . . . DOJOCD 118
Dojo / Apr '93 / Castle Communications / BMG.

SINGLES, THE.
Tracks: Not Advised.
CD . . . . CLEO 5000CD
Cleopatra / Jan '94 / Plastic Head / Pinnacle.

TOTALLY EXPLOITED.
Tracks: Punk's not dead / Army life / F**k a mod / Barmy army / Dogs of war / Dead cities / Sex and violence / Yops / Daily news / Dole Q / Believe in anarchy / God save the queen / Psycho / Blown to bits / Insanity / SPG / Jimmy Boyle / U.S.A. / Attack / Rival leaders.
■ MC . . . . DOJOTC 1
Dojo / '86.
■ LP .DOJOLP 1
Dojo / Apr '86.
CD . . . . DOJOCD 1
Dojo / Jun '86 / Castle Communications / BMG.

TROOPS OF TOMORROW.
Tracks: Jimmy Boyle / Daily news / Disorder / Alternative / Rapist / Troops of tomorrow / UK 82 / Sid Vicious was innocent / War / They won't stop / So tragic / Germs / U.S.A.
■ MC . . . . .CQ 2
Major Richards / Jun '78.
■ LP . . . . SEC 8
Secret / Jun '82.
MC . . . . TSEC 8
Secret / '88.
■ LP . . . . RR 9981
Road Runner / '89.
■ LP . . . . LINK 066
Link / Mar '89.
LP . . . . SLAM 8
Grand Slam (USA) / Feb '90 / Pinnacle.
■ CD . . . . STR CD 007
Street Link / Oct '92.
CD . . . . DOJOCD 1
Dojo / Mar '93 / Castle Communications / BMG.

WAR NOW.
Tracks: War now.
■ 12" . . . . 12 KORE 103
Music For Nations / Apr '88.

Y.O.P.
Tracks: Y.O.P.
■ 12" . . . . SHH 136 12
Secret / Aug '82.

Export

EXPORT.
Tracks: Fast lane to your heart / Wheeler dealer / Too much in love with you / Lovin' you baby / You're my best friend / Someone, somewhere / Light in the dark / I'm sorry.
■ LP .VICE 1
His Master's Vice / '80.

JULIE BITCH.
Tracks: Julie Bitch / Nice to know you.
■ 7" . . . . K 11344
WEA / '79.

Extrema

TENSION AT THE SEAMS.
Tracks: Not Advised.
CD . . . . BABECD 5
LP . . . . BABE 5
Rosemary's Baby (Metal) / Sep '93 / Plastic Head.

Extreme
Although chiefly known for the hit ballad *More Than Words*, Extreme are actually a rock band trying hard to escape from that mold, which has sullied their reputation amongst hard rock fans. Formed in Boston, Massachusetts in 1985 by Nuno Bettencourt (an immensely gifted if occasionally temperamental guitarist) and drummer Paul Geary, they gained a solid reputation as a live act thanks to the athletic antics of singer Gary Cherone. Extreme broke world-wide with their second album *Pornograffiti* (featuring the aforementioned single) and despite losing their way a little with the follow-up, are looking for new drummer Mike Mangini to help the rebuilding process.

DECADENCE DANCE.
Tracks: Decadence dance.
■ 12" . . . . AMY 773
■ 7" . . . . AM 773
■ MC Single. . . . . AMMC 773
A&M / Sep '91.

EXTREME.
Tracks: Little girls / Wind me up / Kid ego / Watching waiting / Mutha (don't wanna go to school today) / Teachers pet / Big boys don't cry / Smoke signals / Flesh and blood / Rock a bye bye.
CD . . . . CDA 5238
■ LP . . . . AMA 5238
MC. . . . . AMC 5238
A&M / Mar '89 / PolyGram.

EXTREME II PORNOGRAFFITTI.
Tracks: Decadance dance / Li'l Jack horny / When I'm president / Get the funk out / More than words / Money (In God we trust) / It's a monster / Pornograffitti / When I first kissed you / Suzi (Wants her all day what) / He-man woman hater / Song for love / Whole hearted.
■ CD 3953132
■ MC. 3953134
A&M / Sep '90.
LP 3953131
A&M / Sep '90 / PolyGram.
DCC 395 313-5
A&M / Jan '93 / PolyGram.
CD . . . . CDMID 191
MC. . . . . CMID 191
A&M / May '94 / PolyGram.

HOLEHEARTED.
Tracks: Holehearted.
■ 12" . . . . AMY 839
■ CD Single . . . . AMCD 839
■ MC Single. . . . . AMMC 839
■ 7" . . . . AM 839
A&M / Nov '91.

III SIDES TO EVERY STORY.
Tracks: Not Advised.
CD 5400062
■ LP 5400061
MC. 5400064
A&M / Sep '92 / PolyGram.

MORE THAN WORDS.
Tracks: More than words.
■ 12" . . . . AMX 792
■ 7" . . . . AM 792
■ CD Single . . . . AMCD 792
■ MC Single. . . . . AMMC 792
A&M / Jul '91.

PHOTOGRAFFITI.
Tracks: Not Advised.
VHS 0898793
Polygram T.V. / Oct '91 / PolyGram.

SONG FOR LOVE.
Tracks: Song for love.
■ 12" . . . . AMY 698
■ 7" . . . . AM 698
■ CD Single . . . . AMCD 698
A&M / Apr '92.

TRAGIC COMIC.
Tracks: Tragic comic.
■ 12" . . . . AMY 156
■ MC Single. . . . . AMMC 156
■ 7" . . . . AM 156

■ CD Single. . . . . AMCD 156
■ CD Single . . . . .AMCDR 156
A&M / Jan '93.

Extreme Noise Terror

3 A.M. ETERNAL (Extreme Noise Terror & K.L.F.).
Tracks: 3 a.m. Eternal.
■ 7" . . . . ENT 1
Discipline / Nov '93.

FILTHKICK - IN IT FOR LIFE.
Tracks: Not Advised.
■ LP . . . . .SINK 1
Sink Below / Nov '89.

FROM ONE EXTREME TO ANOTHER.
Tracks: Deceived / False profit / Murder / We are the helpless / Use your mind / Take the strain / Bullshit propoganda / Conned thru life / Another nail in the coffin / Raping the earth / Show us you care.
■ VHS . . . . .JE 196
Jettisoundz / Sep '89.

HOLOCAUST IN YOUR HEAD.
Tracks: Statement / Take the strain / Show us you care / Use your mind / If your only in it for / Deceived / Conned thru life / Innocence to ignorance / Another nail in the coffin.
■ LP . . . . HURT 1
Hurt / Mar '89.

PEEL SESSIONS: EXTREME NOISE TERROR (10.11.87-16.2.90).
Tracks: False profit / Use your mind / Human error / Only in it for the music / Subliminal music / Punk, fact and fiction / Deceived / Another nail in the coffin / Carry on screaming / Conned thru life / Work for never / 3rd world genocide / I am a bloody fool / In it for life / Shock treatment.
CD . . . . SFPSCD 208
MC. . . . . SFPMC 208
Mini LP . . . . SFPMA 208
Strange Fruit / Aug '90 / Pinnacle.

PEEL SESSIONS: EXTREME NOISE TERROR.
Tracks: False profit / Another nail in the coffin / Use your mind / Carry on screaming / Human errors / Conned through life / Only in it for the music part 2.
■ 12" . . . . SFPS 048
Strange Fruit / Apr '88.

PRODUCT AND STRATEGY.
Tracks: Not Advised.
CD . . . . N 02012
Noise / Sep '92 / Pinnacle.

Exumer

POSSESSED BY FIRE.
Tracks: Not Advised.
■ LP 10005
Disaster (Germany) / Nov '87.

RISING FROM THE SEA.
Tracks: Not Advised.
■ LP 082566
Disaster (Germany) / Nov '87.

Eyehategod

TAKE AS NEEDED FOR PAIN.
Tracks: Not Advised.
CD . . . . .CM 77052-2
LP . . . . .CM 77052-4
Century Media / Sep '93 / Plastic Head.

Eyes

BLINK.
Tracks: 19th nervous breakdown / Immediate pleasure / I wanna be your man / When the night falls / Good day sunshine / Please don't cry / My degeneration / Man with money / You're too much / I'm rowed out.
■ LP . . . . .KIRI 028
Bam Caruso / Jun '84.

I LIKE IT.
Tracks: I like it / Once ain't enough.
■ 7" . . . . RAW 16
Raw / Mar '78.

SCENE BUT NOT HEARD.
Tracks: Not Advised.
■ LP . . . . MARI 038
Bam Caruso / Feb '87.

■ DELETED

EZO

EZO.
Tracks: House of 1,000 pleasures / Flashback heart attack / Mr. Midnight / Here it comes / I walk alone / Destroyer / Big changes / Kiss of fire / Desiree.
■ LP 9241431
■ MC 9241434
Geffen / Jun '87.

FIRE FIRE.

Tracks: Love junkie / Fire, fire / Burn down the night / Back to zero / She's ridin' the rhythm / Million miles away / Night crawler / Wild talk / Black moon / Cold blooded / Streetwalker.
■ CD . . . . K 9242302
■ LP . . . . K 9242301
■ MC . . . . K 9242304
Geffen / Jul '89.

Ezy Meat

ROCK YOUR BRAINS.
Tracks: Not Advised.
■ LP . . . . ES 0002
Electric Storm / Oct '88.

F

F.F.W.

KILLER (Freaky Fukin Weirdoz).
Tracks: Not Advised.
CD .EFA 15525CD
LP . . . . EFA 15525
Sub-up / Feb '92 / SRD.

WEIRDELIC.
Tracks: Not Advised.
CD .CDMFN 115
I P . . . . MFN 115
MC . . . . .TMFN 115
Music For Nations / May '91 / Pinnacle.

F.M.

Hardy U.K. band comprised of minor HM alumni. Solid touring resulted in five Top 75 singles between '87 and '90, with 1989 album *Tough It Out* reaching no. 34. Business hassles and well-established resistance of U.K. market to homegrown AOR prompted rethink in '92; band returned heavier but even less successful.

AMERICAN GIRLS.
Tracks: American girls / That girl / American girls (remix).
■ 12" 6500366
■ 7" 6500367
Portrait / Aug '86.

APHRODISIAC.
Tracks: Not Advised.
CD . . . . .CDMFN 141
LP . . . . MFN 141
MC . . . . .TMFN 141
Music For Nations / Oct '92 / Pinnacle.

BAD LUCK.
Tracks: Bad luck / This could be the last time / Hurt is where the heart is (Only on 12", CD and EP single.) / Bad luck (extended version) (Only on 12" and CD single.).
■ 12" 6550316
■ 7" 6550317
■ 7" P.Disc 6550319
■ CD Single 6550312
■ EP 6550310
■ MC Single 6550314
Epic / Jul '89.
■ 12" 6550318
Epic / Jul '89.

BLOOD & GASOLINE.
Tracks: Blood & Gasoline.
■ 12" . . . . 12 KUT 147
■ 7" .KUT 147
Music For Nations / Aug '92.

CITY OF FEAR.
Tracks: Krakow / Power / Truth of consequences / Lost and found / City of fear / Surface to air / Up to you / Silence / Riding the thunder / Nobody at all.
■ LP . . . . LOGO 1031
Logo / Sep '81.

EVERYTIME I THINK OF YOU.
Tracks: Everytime I think of you / Frozen heart (live) / Face to face (live) / Other side of midnight (live).
■ 10" . . . . .DINK QT2
■ 12" . . . . .DINK T2
■ 7" . . . . DINK 2
■ CD Single . . . . .DINK C2
■ CD Single . . . . .CDDINK 2
■ MC Single . . . . DINK M2
Epic / Feb '90.

FROZEN HEART.
Tracks: Frozen heart / Dangerous.
■ 12" . . . . TX 6613
■ 7" .A 6613
Portrait / Oct '85.

FROZEN HEART.
Tracks: Frozen heart / Love lasts forever / Other side of midnight (Only available on 12" version.) / Addicted to love (Only available on 7" Gatefold sleeve/ double pack.) / Hot legs (Only available on 7" Gatefold sleeve/double pack.).
■ 7" .DIDGE 1

■ 12" .DIDGE T1
Portrait / Feb '87.

HEARD IT THROUGH THE GRAPEVINE.
Tracks: Heard it through the grapevine.
■ 12" . . . . 12 KUT 142
■ 7" .KUT 142
■ CD Single . . . . .CDKUT 142
■ MC Single . . . . TKUT 142
Music For Nations / Nov '91.

INDISCREET.
Tracks: That girl / Other side of midnight / Love lies dying. / I belong to the night / American girls / Hot wired / Face to face / Frozen heart / Heart of the matter.
■ LP . . . . PRT 26827
■ MC .40 26827
Portrait / Sep '86.
■ CD . . . . CD 26827
Portrait / Sep '86 / Sony.
■ CD 4663392
■ LP 4663391
■ MC 4663394
Epic / Mar '90.
CD . . . . .BGOCD 184
Beat Goes On / Mar '93 / Pinnacle.

LET LOVE BE THE LEADER.
Tracks: Let love be the leader / Let love be the leader (live version) / I belong to the night (87 version).
■ 12" . . . . MERVB 1
■ 12" . . . . MERVT 1
■ 7" . . . . MERV 1
■ 7" P.Disc . . . . MERVP 1
Portrait / Jun '87.

LIVE ACOUSTICAL INTERCOURSE.
Tracks: Not Advised.
VHS . . . . VFN 12
Music For Nations / Feb '94 / Pinnacle.

LOVE WAS DYING.
Tracks: Love was dy.ng / Captured.
■ 12" . . . . TA 7233
■ 7" .A 7233
Portrait / Jun '86.

NO ELECTRICITY REQUIRED.
Tracks: Not Advised.
CD . . . . .CDMFN 155
Under One Flag / Oct '93 / Pinnacle.

ONLY THE STRONG (The Best Of FM 1984-1994).
Tracks: That girl / Other side of midnight / American girls / Face to face / Frozen heart / Tough it out / Don't stop / Bad luck / Burning my heart down / Let love be the leader / Heard it through the grapevine / Only the strong survive / Dangerous ground / Breathe fire / Blood & gasoline / All or nothing / Closer to heaven.
CD . . . . VSOPCD 203
Connoisseur Collection / Aug '94 / Pinnacle.

SOMEDAY (YOU'LL COME RUNNING).
Tracks: Someday (you'll come running) / Alibi / Obsession / Someday (you'll come running) (extended version) / Every time we touch.
■ EP . . . . .DINK B1
■ 12" . . . . .DINK T1
■ 7" . . . . DINK 1
■ 7" P.Disc . . . . .DINK P1
■ CD Single . . . . .DINK CD1
■ EP . . . . .DINK G1
■ MC Single . . . . DINK M1
Epic / Sep '89.

TAKIN' IT TO THE STREETS.
Tracks: Not Advised.
CD . . . . .CDMFN 119
LP . . . . MFN 119
MC . . . . .TMFN 119
Music For Nations / Oct '91 / Pinnacle.

THAT GIRL.
Tracks: That girl / American girls.
■ 7" .A 7005
Portrait / Mar '86.

TOUGH IT OUT.
Tracks: Tough it out / Bad luck / Everytime I think of you burning my .. / Obsession / Don't stop / Someday / Dream that died.
MC 4655894
■ LP 4655891
■ CD 4655892
Epic / Sep '89.

Failure

MAGNIFIED.
Tracks: Let it drip / Moth / Frogs / Bernie / Magnified / Wonderful life / Undone / Wet gravity / Empty friend / Small crimes.
CD .828487-2
MC .828487-4
Slash / Feb '94 / PolyGram.

Faith No More

Emerging from San Francisco in 1983, Faith No More can share credit with Red Hot Chili Peppers for now-ubiquitous metal/funk style. Independent, eponymous debut attracted attention of London records, who released *Introduce Yourself* in 1987. Album included early FNM anthem *We Care At Lot*. 1988 saw singer Chuck Mosely replaced by Mike Patton (ex-Mr Bungle; a group to which Patton has occasionally returned). FNM's *The Real Thing* was international smash, producing three hits and sell-out tour; pattern repeated on larger scale by 1992's *Angel Dust*. Departure of guitarist and band mascot 'Big Sick Ugly' Jim Martin demonstrated internal strife in wake of success.

ANGEL DUST.
Tracks: Not Advised.
CD 9293212
LP 9293211
MC 9293214
Slash / Jun '92 / PolyGram.
CD 828 401-2
MC 828 401-4
Slash / Jan '93 / PolyGram.

ANNE'S SONG.
Tracks: Anne's song / Anne's song (dance mix) / Greed.
■ 12" . . . . .LASHX 18
■ 7" . . . . .LASH 18
■ 7" P.Disc . . . . .LASHP 18
Slash / Apr '88.

EPIC.
Tracks: Epic / War pigs (live) / Surprise you're dead / Chinese arithmetic.
■ 12" . . . . .LASHX 21
■ 7" . . . . .LASH 21
■ 7" P.Disc . . . . .LASPD 21
■ CD Single . . . . .LASCD 21
Slash / Jan '90.

EPIC.
Tracks: Epic / Falling to pieces / Epic (live) (Not on picture disc.) / As the worm turns (12" & CD single only.).
■ 12" . . . . .LASHX 26
■ 12" P.Disc . . . . .LASPD 26
■ 7" . . . . .LASH 26
■ CD Single . . . . .LASCD 26
■ MC Single . . . . .LASCS 26
Slash / Aug '90.

EVERYTHING'S RUINED.
Tracks: Everything's ruined.
■ 12" . . . . .LASH 43
■ CD Single . . . . .LASHCD 43
■ MC Single . . . . .LASHC 43
Slash / Nov '92.

FALLING TO PIECES.
Tracks: Falling to pieces / We care a lot (live) / From out of nowhere (live) (Only on 12" and 7" (Gatefold).).
■ 12" . . . . .LASPX 25
■ 12" . . . . .LASHX 25
■ 7" . . . . .LASHP 25
■ 7" . . . . .LASHG 25
■ 7" . . . . .LASH 25

■ DELETED

F 1

■ MC Single. . . . . .LASCS 25
Slash / Jul '90.

FROM OUT OF NOWHERE.
Tracks: From out of nowhere.
■ 12" .LASHX 19
■ 7" . . . . .LASH 19
Slash / Oct '89.

FROM OUT OF NOWHERE (RE-RELEASE).
Tracks: From out of nowhere / Woodpecker from Mars (live) / Epic (live) (Only on 12", CD and LASHG 24 single.) / From out of nowhere (extended mix) / Real thing, The (live) (Only on 12" and CD single.).
■ 12" .LASHX 24
■ 12" P.Disc. . . . . .LASPX 24
■ 7" . . . . .LASH 24
■ 7" . . . . .LASHG 24
■ CD Single. . . . . .LASCD 24
■ MC Single. . . . . .LASCS 24
Slash / Apr '90.

I'M EASY/BE AGGRESSIVE.
Tracks: I'm easy / Be aggressive.
■ 7" . . . . .LASH 44
■ CD Single. . . . . .LACDP 44
■ MC Single. . . . . .LASCS 44
Slash / Jan '93.

INTERVIEW, THE.
Tracks: Not Advised.
MC. . . . . .MBAK 6020
Baktabak / Jun '91 / Arabesque Ltd.

INTRODUCE YOURSELF.
Tracks: Faster disco / Anne's song / Introduce yourself / Chinese arithmetic / Death march / We care a lot / R N' R / Crab song / Blood / Spirit.
■ LP . . . . .SLAP 21
MC. . . . . .SMAC 21
Slash / Apr '87 / PolyGram.
CD .828 051 2
London / Apr '87 / PolyGram.

LIVE AT THE BRIXTON ACADEMY.
Tracks: Epic / From out of nowhere / We care a lot / Falling to pieces / Real thing / Warriors / Zombie eaters / Edge of the world / Grade (Only on MC and CD.) / Cowboy song (Only on MC and CD.).
CD. 828 238 2
■ LP .828 238 1
MC. 828 238 4
Slash / Feb '91 / PolyGram.

MIDLIFE CRISIS.
Tracks: Midlife crisis.
■ 7" . . . . .LASH 37
■ CD Single. . . . . .LASCD 37
■ MC Single. . . . . .LASCS 37
Slash / Jun '92.

REAL THING, THE.
Tracks: From out of nowhere / Epic / Falling to pieces / Surprise, you're dead / Zombie eaters / Real thing / Underwater love / Morning after / Woodpecker from Mars / War pigs (Only on cassette and CD.) / Edge of the world (Only on cassette and CD.).
CD. 828 154 2
LP. .828 154 1
MC. 828 154 4
■ LP P.Disc. 828 217 1
Slash / Jun '89.

SMALL VICTORY, A.
Tracks: Small victory.
■ 12" .LASHX 39
■ 7" . . . . .LASH 39
■ CD Single. . . . . .LASHCD 39
■ MC Single. . . . . .LASCS 39
Slash / Aug '92.

VIDEO CROISSANT.
Tracks: Midlife crisis / Epic / Falling to pieces / Anne's song / We care a lot / Suprise you're dead / From out of nowhere / Small victory / Everything's ruined / Caffeine (Live).
VHS .085 552-3
Polygram Music Video / Jan '93 / PolyGram.

WE CARE A LOT.
Tracks: We care a lot / Jungle / Mark Bowen / Jim / Why do you bother / Greed / Pills for breakfast / As the worm turns / Arabian disco / New beginnings.
■ LP . . . . .MDR 1
Mordam / Feb '88.

WE CARE A LOT.
Tracks: Perfect day / Marguerite / We care a lot.
■ 12" .LASHX 17
■ 7" . . . . .LASH 17
Slash / Jan '88.

YOU FAT BASTARDS (Live at Brixton).
Tracks: From out of nowhere / Falling to pieces / Real thing / Underwater love / As the worm turns / Edge of the world / We care a lot / Epic / Woodpecker from Mars / Zombie eaters / War pigs.
VHS .0825343
London / Aug '90 / PolyGram.

Faithful Breath

GOLD 'N' GLORY.
Tracks: Not Advised.
■ LP . . . . .SKULL 8335
■ MC. . . . . .TAPE 78335
Mausoleum / '84.

Falcon, Billy

BLUE SMOKE.
Tracks: Blue smoke / Rocks in his head.
■ 7" .MCA 587
MCA / May '80.

FALCON AROUND.
Tracks: Not Advised.
■ LP . . . . .MCF 3065
MCA / Jun '80.

POWER WINDOWS.
Tracks: Power windows / Oh boy / Not funny anymore (Only on 12" and CD Single.).
■ 12" . . . . .MERX 355
■ 7" .MER 355
■ CD Single. . . . . .MERCD 355
Mercury / Jan '92.

PRETTY BLUE WORLD.
Tracks: Power windows / Heaven's highest hill / What she will / Pretty blue world / Die twice / Still got a prayer / Not funny anymore / My new girlfriend / This burning love / Gettin' married in the morning / Oh boy.
■ LP .8488001
■ CD .8488002
■ MC. 8488004
Jambco / Aug '91.

Fallen Angel

FALLEN ANGEL.
Tracks: Not Advised.
Mini LP . . . . .UN 12474
Plastic Head / Jul '92 / Plastic Head.

Fallout

ALTERED STATES.
Tracks: Altered states.
■ 12" .FF 1114
Fourth Floor (USA) / Jun '90.

BUTCHERY.
Tracks: Not Advised.
■ LP . . . . .FLP 2
I Records / Feb '84.

MORNING AFTER, THE.
Tracks: Morning after.
■ 12" .AZ 001
Azuli / Mar '90.

SALAMI TACTICS (EP).
Tracks: Salami tactics.
■ 7" F2
Mouth Too Small To Fight / Jan '83.

Faster Pussycat

DON'T CHANGE THAT SONG.
Tracks: Don't change that song / Cat house.
■ 12" .EKR 62T
■ 7" . . . . .EKR 62
Elektra / Sep '87.

FASTER PUSSYCAT.
Tracks: Don't change that song / Bathroom wall / No room for emotion / Cathouse / Babylon / Smash alley / Shooting you down / City has no heart / Ship rolls in / Bottle in front of me.
■ LP .9807301
MC. .9807304
Elektra / Jul '87 / WEA.

FASTER PUSSYCAT: INTERVIEW PICTURE DISC.
Tracks: Not Advised.
LP P.Disc . . . . .BAK 2127
Baktabak / '88 / Arabesque Ltd.

HOUSE OF PAIN.
Tracks: House of pain / Little dove (live).
■ 12" . . . . .EKR 112 T
■ 7" .EKR 112
Elektra / Jul '90.

POISON IVY.
Tracks: Poison ivy.
■ 12" . . . . .EKR 103 T
■ 7" .EKR 103
Elektra / Dec '89.

WAKE ME UP WHEN IT'S OVER.
Tracks: Where there's a whip there's a way / Crying shame / Little dove / House of pain / Pulling the weeds / Poison ivy / Gonna walk / Slip of the tongue / Tattoo / Ain't no way.
CD. . . . . .K 9608832
■ LP .EKT 64
■ MC. . . . . .EKT 64 C
Elektra / Sep '89.

WHIPPED.
Tracks: Nonstop to nowhere / Body thief / Jack the bastard / Big dictionary / Madam Ruby's love boutique / Only way out / Maid in wonderland / Friends / Cat bash / Loose booty / Mr. Lovedog / Out with a bang.
CD. 7559611242
■ LP .EKT 110
MC. . . . . .EKT 110C
Elektra / Aug '92 / WEA.

Fastway

Fastway were formed in 1982 by Motorhead guitarist 'Fast' Eddie Clarke and UFO bassist Pete Way - hence the name. Way sensibly jumped ship before band embarked on recording career; uncelebrated legacy of which is six, derivative albums - of these, only 1983 debut made even minor impression on U.K. chart.

ALL FIRED UP.
Tracks: All fired up / Misunderstood / Steal the show / Station / Non stop love / Hurtin' me / Tell me / Hung up on love / Stranger / Telephone / If you could see me.
■ LP .CBS 25958
CBS / Aug '84.

ALL FIRED UP.
Tracks: All fired up / Hurtin' me.
■ 12" .TA 4503
■ 7" . . . . .A 4503
CBS / Jun '84.

BAD BAD GIRLS.
Tracks: I've had enough (Only on CD.) / Bad bad girls / All shook up / Bod rock / Miles away / She won't rock (Only on CD.) / No repair / Death of me / Cut loose / Lucky to lose / Big beat no heart.
■ CD . . . . .LLCD 130
■ LP .LLP 130
■ MC. . . . . .LLK 130
Legacy / Mar '90.

BAD BAD GIRLS.
Tracks: Bad bad girls.
■ 7" .LGY 104
■ CD Single . . . . .LSYC 104
Legacy / May '90.

EASY LIVIN.
Tracks: Easy livin' / Say what you will / Far from home.
■ 12" . . . . .A 13 3196
■ 7" .A 3196
CBS / Mar '83.

FASTWAY.
Tracks: Easy livin' / Feel me touch me / All I need is your love / Another day / Heft / We become one / Give it all you got / Say what you will / You got me runnin' / Give it some action.
■ LP 25359
CBS / Apr '83.

FINE LINE, A.
Tracks: Fine line / Change of heart.
■ 7" . . . . .GWR 8
GWR / Feb '88.

I'VE HAD ENOUGH.
Tracks: I've had enough / All shook up.
■ 7" .LGY 105
Legacy / Aug '90.

ON TARGET.
Tracks: Not Advised.
CD. . . . . .GWCD 22
■ LP . . . . .GWLP 22

■ DELETED

■ MC. . . . . GWTC 22
GWR / Mar '88.
■ LP . . . . RR 9562 1
Road Runner / '89.

ON TARGET/BAD BAD GIRLS.
Tracks: Dead or alive / Change of heart / Fine line / Two hearts / You / Let him rock / She is in danger / Show some emotion / These dreams / Close your eyes / I've had enough / Bad bad girls / All shook up / Body rock / Miles away / She won't rock / No repair / Cut loose / Big beat no heart.
CD . . . . LOMCD 6
Loma / Feb '94 / BMG.

SAY WHAT YOU WILL - LIVE.
Tracks: Not Advised.
MC. . . . . RRMC 147
Receiver / Oct '91 / Total / BMG / Grapevine Distribution.
CD . . . . RRCD 147
LP . . . . RRLP 147
MC. RRLC 147
Receiver / Jul '93 / Total / BMG / Grapevine Distribution.

STRANGER, THE.
Tracks: Stranger / Hurtin' me.
■ 7" . . . . .A 4370
CBS / May '84.

WAITING FOR THE ROAR.
Tracks: Not Advised.
■ CD . . . . CD 26654
CBS / May '87.

WE BECOME ONE.
Tracks: We become one / Crazy dream.
■ 12" . . . . TA 3480
■ 7" . . . . .A 3480
CBS / Jun '83.

WORLD WAITS FOR YOU, THE.
Tracks: Waiting for the roar / Girl / Back door man / Doin' just fine / World waits for you / Kill me with your heart / Tired of your love / Change / Move over / Little by little / Rock on.
■ LP . . . . CBS 26654
MC. .40 26654
CBS / Feb '86 / Sony.

WORLD WAITS FOR YOU, THE.
Tracks: World waits for you.
■ 12" . . . . TA 6804
■ 7" . . . . .A 6804
CBS / Jan '86.

Fates Warning

AWAKEN THE GUARDIAN.
Tracks: Sorceress / Valley of the dolls / Fata Morgana / Guardian / Prelude to ruin / Giants love / Time long past / Exodus.
■ LP . . . . RR 9660
Road Runner / Jan '87.

INSIDE OUT.
Tracks: Not Advised.
CD . . . . MASSCD 037
LP . . . . MASSLP 037
MC. MASSMC 037
Massacre / Jun '94 / Plastic Head.

NIGHT ON BROCKEN.
Tracks: Not Advised.
■ LP . . . . RR 9823 1
Road Runner / '89.

NO EXIT.
Tracks: Not Advised.
CD . . . . .RR 9558 2
■ LP . . . . RR 95581
Road Runner / Apr '88.

NO EXIT/AWAKEN THE GUARDIAN.
Tracks: Not Advised.
CD . . . . .CDZORRO 39
Metal Blade / Jul '90 / Pinnacle.

PARALLELS.
Tracks: Not Advised.
CD .CDZORRO 31
LP . . . . ZORRO 31
MC. .TZORRO 31
Music For Nations / Nov '91 / Pinnacle.

PERFECT SYMMETRY.
Tracks: Not Advised.
CD . . . . .CDMZORRO 73
Metal Blade / May '94 / Pinnacle.

SPECTRE WITHIN, THE.
Tracks: Not Advised.
■ LP . . . . RR 9737
Road Runner / Nov '85.

SPECTRE WITHIN/NIGHTS ON BROCKEN.
Tracks: Not Advised.
CD . . . . .CDZORRO 38
Metal Blade / Jul '90 / Pinnacle.

Fear

LIVE FOR THE RECORD.
Tracks: Not Advised.
CD . . . . LS 92522
LP . . . . LS 92521
MC. LS 92524
Road Runner / Nov '91 / Pinnacle.

Fear Factory

FEAR IS THE MINDKILLER.
Tracks: Not Advised.
CD . . . . RR 90822
■ LP . . . . RR 90821
Road Runner / Apr '93.

SOUL OF A NEW MACHINE.
Tracks: Not Advised.
CD . . . . RR 91602
■ LP . . . . RR 91601
Road Runner / Sep '92.

Fear Of God

FEAR OF GOD.
Tracks: Fear of God.
■ 7" . . . . FAR OUT 10
Far Out / Jul '93.

TOXIC VOODOO.
Tracks: Not Advised.
CD . . . . .CDVEST 24
Bulletproof / Jul '94 / Pinnacle.

Femme Fatale

FALLING IN AND OUT OF LOVE.
Tracks: Falling in and out of love.
■ CD Single . . . . .DMCA 1309
■ 12" . . . . MCAT 1309
■ 7" . . . . .MCA 1309
MCA / Jan '89.

FEMME FATALE.
Tracks: Waiting for the big one / Falling in and out of love / Back in your arms again / Rebel / Fortune / If / Touch & go / Heat the fire / Cradle's rockin'.
■ CD . . . . DMCF 3433
■ LP . . . . MCF 3433
■ MC. . . . . MCFC 3433
MCA / Nov '88.

WAITING FOR THE BIG ONE.
Tracks: Waiting for the big one.
■ 12" . . . . MCATR 1286
■ 7" . . . . MCA 1286
MCA / Oct '88.

Fifth Angel

FIFTH ANGEL.
Tracks: Not Advised.
■ LP . . . . RR 96881
Road Runner / Jul '88.
CD . . . . RO 96882
Roadracer / Mar '90 / Pinnacle.

Fight

NAILED TO THE GUN.
Tracks: Nailed to the gun / Kill it / Nailed to the gun (mix) / Kill it (mix).
■ CD Single 659612 2
Epic / Oct '93.

WAR OF WORDS.
Tracks: Into the pit / Nailed to the gun / Life in black / Immortal sin / War of words / Laid to rest / For all eternity / Little crazy / Contortion / Kill it / Vicious / Reality, a new beginning.
CD .474547 2
LP .474547 0
MC. 474547 4
Epic / Sep '93 / Sony.

Films

BILL & TED'S BOGUS JOURNEY (Various Artists).
Tracks: Shout it out / Battle stations / God gave rock and roll to you II / Drinking again / Dream of a new day / Reaper / Perfect crime / Go to hell / Tommy the cat / Junior's gone wild / Showdown / Reaper rap.
CD 7567917252
■ LP 7567917251
MC. 7567917254
Interscope / Jan '92 / WEA.

BILL & TED'S EXCELLENT ADVENTURE (Film soundtrack) (Various Artists).
Tracks: Play with me / Boys and girls are doing it / Not so far away / Dancing with a gypsy / Father time / I can't breakaway / Dangerous / Walk away / In time / Two heads are better than one.
■ CD . . . . .CDA 391
■ LP . . . . AMA 391
■ MC. . . . . AMC 391
A&M / Apr '90.
■ CD 3939152
■ MC. 3939154
A&M / Feb '92.

BLAZE OF GLORY (Bon Jovi, Jon).
Tracks: Billy get your guns / Blaze of glory / Santa Fe / Never say die / Bang a drum / Guano City / Miracle / Blood money / Justice in the barrel / You really got me now / Dyin' ain't much of a livin'.
CD 846 473 2
MC. 846 473 4
■ LP 846 473 1
Vertigo / Aug '90.
DCC 846 473-5
Mercury / Jan '93 / PolyGram.

BUFFY THE VAMPIRE SLAYER (Various Artists).
Tracks: Keep it comin' (Dance til you can't dance no more) / Man smart, woman smarter / Silent city / We close our eyes / Little heaven / I ain't gonna eat out my heart anymore / Party with the animals / Zap city / I fought the law / Light comes out of black.
■ LP 472076-1
■ CD 472076-2
■ MC. 472076-4
Columbia / Oct '92.

CREEPERS (1985 film soundtrack) (Various Artists).
Tracks: Phenomena / Flash of the blade / Jennifer / Wind / Transmute / Sleepwalking / Jennifer's friend / Quick and the dead / Valley / Locomotive / Maggots.
■ LP . . . . HMILP 47
Heavy Metal / Feb '86.

CROW, THE (Original Soundtrack) (Various Artists).
Tracks: Not Advised.
CD .756782519-2
MC. 756782519-4
WEA / Mar '94 / WEA.

DAYS OF THUNDER (Film soundtrack) (Various Artists).
Tracks: Last moment of freedom / Deal for life / Break through the barrier / Hearts in trouble / Trail of broken hearts / Knockin' on Heaven's door / You gotta love someone / Show me heaven / Tinder box / Long live the night / Gimme some lovin'.
CD 4571592
MC. 4571594
■ LP 4571591
Epic / Aug '90.
CD P.Disc. 4571599
Epic / Dec '90 / Sony.

EAT THE RICH (1987 film soundtrack) (Various Artists).
Tracks: Eat the rich / Terrorists / Nosher in the bar / Arriba salsa / Dr. Rock / On the road / Car approach / Pistol in my pockets / Orgasmatron / Bess / End title.
■ LP . . . . MOMENT 108
■ MC. . . . . MOMENTC 108
■ CD . . . . MOMENTCD 108
Filmtrax / Nov '87.

HEAVY METAL (Film soundtrack) (Various Artists).
Tracks: Not Advised.
■ LP . . . . A 547
■ Double LP. . . . . EPC 88558
Epic / Nov '81.
■ MC. . . . . ZC 547
Asylum / Nov '81.

■ DELETED

HELLRAISER III (Various Artists).
Tracks: Not Advised.
```
CD. . . . . . . . . . . . . . . . . . . . . 8283602
LP . . . . . . . . . . . . . . . . . . . . . 8283601
MC. . . . . . . . . . . . . . . . . . . . . 8283604
```
London / Jan '93 / PolyGram.

HIGHLANDER II - THE QUICKENING (Film soundtrack) (Various Artists).
Tracks: Trust / One dream / Who's that man part 1 / Haunted / Here we go / As time goes by / It's a perfect, perfect world / Bird flight / Destroy shield / Sun shield/Dam escape.
```
CD. . . . . . . . . . . . . . . . . . . . . 9031736572
■ LP . . . . . . . . . . . . . . . . . . . . BWX 2
■ MC. . . . . . . . . . . . . . . . . . . . BWX 2C
```
Bronze / Apr '91.

JUDGEMENT NIGHT (Music From The Motion Picture) (Various Artists).
Tracks: I love you Mary Jane / Judgement night / Just another victim / Me, myself & my microphone / Disorder / Missing link / Fallin' / Freak momma / Another body murdered / Come and die / Real thing.
```
CD. . . . . . . . . . . . . . . . . . . . .474183-2
LP . . . . . . . . . . . . . . . . . . . . .474183-1
MC. . . . . . . . . . . . . . . . . . . . .474183-4
```
Epic / Oct '93 / Sony.

LAST ACTION HERO (Various Artists).
Tracks: Big gun / What the hell have I / Angry again / Real world / Two steps behind / Poison my eyes / Dream on / Little bitter - cock the hammer / Swim / Last action hero / Jack & the Ripper.
```
MiniDisc. . . . . . . . . . . . . . . . . . .473990-8
Columbia / Aug '93 / Sony.
CD. . . . . . . . . . . . . . . . . . . . .473990 2
LP . . . . . . . . . . . . . . . . . . . . .473990 1
MC. . . . . . . . . . . . . . . . . . . . .473990 4
```
Columbia / Jul '93 / Sony.

LESS THAN ZERO (Film Soundtrack) (Various Artists).
Tracks: Rockin' pneumonia and the boogie woogie flu / Life fades away / Rock and roll all nite / Going back to Cali / You and me (less than zero) / In a gadda-da-vida / Bring the noise / Are you my woman / She's lost you / How to love again / Hazy shade of winter.
```
■ LP . . . . . . . . . . . . . . . . . . . . 4604491
■ CD. . . . . . . . . . . . . . . . . . . . 4604492
■ MC. . . . . . . . . . . . . . . . . . . . 4604494
```
CBS / Nov '87.

LOST BOYS (Film soundtrack) (Various Artists).
Tracks: To the shock of Miss Louise / Good times / Lost in the shadows / Don't let the sun go down on me / Laying down the law / People are strange / Cry little sister / Power play / I still believe / Beauty has her way.
```
CD. . . . . . . . . . . . . . . . . . . . . 781 767-2
■ LP . . . . . . . . . . . . . . . . . . . . 781 767-1
MC. . . . . . . . . . . . . . . . . . . . . 781 767-4
```
Atlantic / Aug '87 / WEA.

MAGGOTS (Film Soundtrack) (Williams, Wendy O. & Plasmatics).
Tracks: Overture / Introduction (Spoken word) / You're a zombie / White's apartment / Four meal dinner (Spoken) / Day of the humans is gone / Central research laboratory / Valerie and Bruce on the phone / Destroyers / Bruce's bedroom / Brain dead / Propogators / White's bedroom fire escape / Finale.
```
■ LP . . . . . . . . . . . . . . . . . . . . GWLP 8
```
GWR / Mar '87.

REPO MAN (Film soundtrack) (Various Artists).
Tracks: Not Advised.
```
■ LP . . . . . . . . . . . . . . . . . . . . MCF 3223
■ MC. . . . . . . . . . . . . . . . . . . . MCFC 3223
```
MCA / Jun '84.

SINGLES (Various Artists).
Tracks: Would / Breath / Seasons / Dyslexic heart / Battle of Evermore / Cloe dancer/Crown of thorns / Birth ritual / State of love and trust / Overblown / Waiting for somebody / May this be love / Nearly lost you / Drown.
```
CD. . . . . . . . . . . . . . . . . . . . . 4714382
■ LP . . . . . . . . . . . . . . . . . . . . 4714381
MC. . . . . . . . . . . . . . . . . . . . . 4714384
```
Epic / Jul '92 / Sony.

SPEED (Various Artists).
Tracks: Speed / Million miles away / Soul deep / Let's go for a ride / Go outside and drive / Crash / Rescue me / Hard road / Cot / Cars ('93 sprint) / Like a motorway / Mr Speed.
```
CD. . . . . . . . . . . . . . . . . . . . . 7822 11018
```

```
MC. . . . . . . . . . . . . . . . . . . . .7822 110184
```
Arista / Aug '94 / BMG.

TRICK OR TREAT (Film Soundtrack) (Fastway).
Tracks: Trick or treat / After midnight / Don't stop the fight / Stand up / Tear down the wall / Get tough / Hold on to the nights / Heft / If you could see.
```
MC. . . . . . . . . . . . . . . . . . . . . 4504444
■ LP . . . . . . . . . . . . . . . . . . . . 4504441
CBS / Mar '87.
CD. . . . . . . . . . . . . . . . . . . . . 4504442
```
CBS / May '87 / Sony.

TRUE LIES (Various Artists).
Tracks: Sunshine of your love / Darkness Darkness / Alone in the dark / Entity / Sunshine of your love (remix) / Main title/Harry makes his entrance / Escape from the chateau / Harry's sweet home / Harry rides again / Spying on Helen / Juno's place / Caught in the act / Shadow lover / Island suite / Causeway/Helicopter rescue / Nuclear Kiss / Harry saves the day.
```
CD. . . . . . . . . . . . . . . . . . . . .476939-2
MC. . . . . . . . . . . . . . . . . . . . .476939-4
```
Columbia / Aug '94 / Sony.

WAYNE'S WORLD (Original Soundtrack) (Various Artists).
Tracks: Bohemian rhapsody / Hot & bothered / Rock candy / Dream weaver / Silkamikanico / Time machine / Wayne's world theme / Ballroom blitz / Foxy lady / Feed my Frankenstein / Why you wanna break my heart.
```
CD. . . . . . . . . . . . . . . . . . . . . 7599268052
MC. . . . . . . . . . . . . . . . . . . . . 7599268054
```
Reprise / May '92 / WEA.

WAYNE'S WORLD 2 (Original Soundtrack) (Various Artists).
Tracks: Dude (Looks like a lady) (live) / Shut up and dance / Louie Louie / Superstar / Frankenstein / Radar love / Spirit in the sky / Can't get enough / Out there / Idiot summer / Mary's house / Y.M.C.A.
```
CD. . . . . . . . . . . . . . . . . . . . .936245485-2
MC. . . . . . . . . . . . . . . . . . . . .936245485-4
```
WEA / Feb '94 / WEA.

Filthy Phil

CHRISTMAS CLASSICS (Filthy Phil & Fast Eddie).
Tracks: Not Advised.
```
■ LP . . . . . . . . . . . . . . . . . . . . RRLP 124
```
Receiver / Nov '89.

Fiona

BEYOND THE PALE.
Tracks: Tragedy / Hopelessly love you / Living in a boy's world / Thunder and lightning / Tender is the heart / Running out of night / In my blood / He's on my side / You better wait / Keeper of the flame.
```
■ LP . . . . . . . . . . . . . . . . . . . . 781 639-1
■ MC. . . . . . . . . . . . . . . . . . . . 781 639-4
```
Atlantic / May '86.

FIONA.
Tracks: Hang your heart on mine / Talk to me / You're no angel / Rescue you / James / Love makes you blind / Over now / Na na song.
```
■ MC. . . . . . . . . . . . . . . . . . . . 781 242-4
■ LP . . . . . . . . . . . . . . . . . . . . 781 242-1
```
Atlantic / Jun '85.

HEART LIKE A GUN.
Tracks: Not Advised.
```
■ CD. . . . . . . . . . . . . . . . . . . . K 781 903-2
■ LP . . . . . . . . . . . . . . . . . . . . K 781 903-1
■ MC. . . . . . . . . . . . . . . . . . . . K 781 903-4
```
Atlantic / Oct '88.

LIVING IN A BOYS WORLD.
Tracks: Keeper of the flame / Living in a boys world.
```
■ 7" . . . . . . . . . . . . . . . . . . . . A 9432
```
Atlantic / May '86.

SQUEEZE.
Tracks: Not Advised.
```
■ CD. . . . . . . . . . . . . . . . . . . . GEFD 24429
■ LP . . . . . . . . . . . . . . . . . . . . GEF 24429
■ MC. . . . . . . . . . . . . . . . . . . . GEFC 24429
```
Geffen / Mar '92.

TALK TO ME.
Tracks: June / Talk to me.
```
■ 7" . . . . . . . . . . . . . . . . . . . . A 9572
```
Atlantic / May '85.

Fire Merchants

IGNITION.
Tracks: Not Advised.
```
CD. . . . . . . . . . . . . . . . . . . . . MD 94352
■ LP . . . . . . . . . . . . . . . . . . . . MD 94351
```
Road Runner / Dec '89.

LANDLORDS OF ATLANTIS.
Tracks: Not Advised.
```
CD. . . . . . . . . . . . . . . . . . . . . EFA 13001-2
```
Ozone / May '94 / Grapevine Distribution / SRD.

Firehose

Formed from the ashes of pioneering American punk band The Minutemen after the tragic death of guitarist/singer D. Boon. George Hurley (drums) and Mike Watt (bass) were joined by Ed Crawford on guitar and vocals and released the fiery and inventive *Ragin' Full On* on cult label SST. Subsequent albums reproduced the spark of their debut until they were signed by major label Columbia. Sadly, the first fruits of the deal *Flyin' The Flannel* lacked much of the fire of their independent recordings, hopefully the follow up will be a return to form.

FROMOHIO.
Tracks: Not Advised.
```
CD. . . . . . . . . . . . . . . . . . . . .SST 235
■ LP . . . . . . . . . . . . . . . . . . . .SST 235
MC. . . . . . . . . . . . . . . . . . . . .SST 235 C
```
SST / Feb '89 / Pinnacle.

IF'N.
Tracks: Sometimes / Honey please / For the singer of REM / Anger.
```
■ LP . . . . . . . . . . . . . . . . . . . .SST 115
SST / Aug '88.
CD. . . . . . . . . . . . . . . . . . . . .SST 115 CD
MC. . . . . . . . . . . . . . . . . . . . .SST 115 C
```
SST / May '93 / Pinnacle.

MR MACHINERY OPERATOR.
Tracks: Formal introduction / Blaze / Herded into pools / Witness / Number seven / Powerful hankerin' / Rocket sled/Fuel tank / Quicksand / Disciples of the 3-way / More famous quotes / Sincerely / Hell-hole / 4.29.92 / Cliffs thrown down.
```
CD. . . . . . . . . . . . . . . . . . . . .472967 2
LP . . . . . . . . . . . . . . . . . . . . .472967 1
MC. . . . . . . . . . . . . . . . . . . . .472967 4
```
Columbia / Mar '93 / Sony.

RAGIN' FULL ON.
Tracks: Under the influence / Locked in / Brave captain / Under the influence of meat puppets / Chemical wire / Another theory shot to shit on your...
```
■ LP . . . . . . . . . . . . . . . . . . . .SST 079
SST / Jun '87.
CD. . . . . . . . . . . . . . . . . . . . .SST 079 CD
MC. . . . . . . . . . . . . . . . . . . . .SST 079 C
```
SST / May '93 / Pinnacle.

SOMETIMES.
Tracks: Rhymin' spielin' / She paints pictures / Sometimes.
```
■ 12". . . . . . . . . . . . . . . . . . . .SST 131
SST / Jun '88.
■ 10". . . . . . . . . . . . . . . . . . . .SST 919
■ CD Single. . . . . . . . . . . . . . . .SST 131 CD
```
SST / May '93.

Firehouse

DON'T TREAT ME BAD.
Tracks: Don't treat me bad / Overnight sensation / Lover's lane (Only available on 12"single & CD single).
```
■ 12". . . . . . . . . . . . . . . . . . . . 6567808
■ 7" . . . . . . . . . . . . . . . . . . . . 6567807
■ CD Single . . . . . . . . . . . . . . . 6567809
■ MC Single. . . . . . . . . . . . . . . 6567804
```
Epic / Jun '91.

FIREHOUSE.
Tracks: Rock on the radio / All she wrote / Shake and tumble / Don't treat me bad / Oughta be a law / Lover's lane / Home is where the heart is / Don't walk away / Seasons of change / Overnight sensation / Love of a lifetime / Helpless.
```
CD. . . . . . . . . . . . . . . . . . . . . 4674412
■ LP . . . . . . . . . . . . . . . . . . . . 4674411
■ MC. . . . . . . . . . . . . . . . . . . . 4674414
```
Epic / Jul '91.

FLYIN' THE FLANNEL.
Tracks: Down with the bass / Up Finnegan's ladder / Can't believe / Walking the cow / Flyin' the flannel / Epoxy for example / O'er the town of Pedro / Too

■ DELETED

long / First cuss / Anti-misogyny maneuver / Toolin'
song for Dave Alvin / Tien an man dream again /
Lost colors / Towin' the line / Losers, boozers and
heroes.

■ CD 4684222
■ LP 4684221
■ MC 4684224
Columbia / Oct '91.

HOLD YOUR FIRE.
Tracks: Reach for the sky / Rock you tonight / Sleeping with you / You're too bad / When I look into your
eyes / Get in touch / Hold your fire / Meaning of love
/ Talk of the town / Life in the real world / Mama
didn't raise no fool / Hold the dream.

CD 4692202
■ LP 4692201
■ MC 4692204
Sony Music / Jun '92.

WHEN I LOOK INTO YOUR EYES.
Tracks: When I look into your eyes.

■ 7" 650004 7
■ CD Single 658834 2
Epic / Dec '92.

Firm

Shortlived ('85-'87) collaboration between
Zeppelin guitarist Jimmy Page and Bad
Company/Free singer Paul Rodgers. Line-
up completed by drummer Chris Slade, now
with AC/DC, and future Blue Murder bassist
Tony Franklin. Sole tour - Page's first since
Zeppelin - attracted more attention than
group's two albums; eponymous debut
made no. 15 in U.K. but *Mean Business*
failed to crack Top 40. Page went on to
better things though not bigger things solo, while
Rodgers teamed with Who drummer Kenny
Jones in The Law.

ALL THE KINGS HORSES.
Tracks: All the kings horses / Fortune hunter.
■ 7" . . . . A 9458
Atlantic / Apr '86.

FIRM.
Tracks: Closer / Make or break / Someone to love /
Together / Radioactive / You've lost that lovin' feelin' /
Money can't buy satisfaction / Midnight moonlight /
Satisfaction guaranteed.

■ LP 781 239-1
■ MC 781 239-4
■ CD 781 239-2
Atlantic / Feb '85.

MEAN BUSINESS.
Tracks: Fortune hunter / Cadillac / All the kings
horses / Live in peace / Tear down the walls /
Dreaming / Free to live / Spirit of love.

■ LP . . . . WX 43
■ MC . . . . WX 43 C
■ CD 781 628-2
Atlantic / Apr '86.

RADIOACTIVE.
Tracks: Radioactive / Together / City sirens (on 12"
only) / Live in peace (on 12" only).

■ 12" . . . . A 9586T
■ 7" . . . . A 9586
Atlantic / Mar '85.

Fisc

HANDLE WITH CARE.
Tracks: Come run riot / Won't let go / Love fight /
Hold your head up / Let me leave / Live it up / Lover
under attack / Handle with care / Got to beat the
clock / Speed limit 55.

CD . . . . CDMFN 91
■ LP . . . . MFN 91
Music For Nations / Mar '89.

Fish

Former singer with Marillion, he left in 1989
quoting musical and personal differences.
He launched his solo career with the
warmly received *Vigil In The Wilderness Of
Mirrors* album, which, although stylistically
similar to Marillion failed to match their
sales level. The follow up *Internal Exile*
fared even worse and after one last attempt
he found himself without a label. He has
recently emerged unscathed with his own
label, Dick Bros. - a reference to his real
name, Derek Dick, and a new album *Suits*
which was released in May 1994.

BIG WEDGE.
Tracks: Big wedge / Jack & Jill / Faith healer (live)
(12" & CD single only.)

■ 12" 12EM 125
■ 12" P.Disc 12EMPD 125
■ 7" . . . . EMS 125
■ 7" . . . . EM 125
■ CD Single . . . . CDEM 125
■ MC Single . . . . TCEM 125
EMI / Jan '90.

FORTUNES OF WAR.
Tracks: Fortunes of war / Somebody special (Live)
(Features on CD 1 only.) / State of mind (Live)
(Features on CD 1 only.) / Lucky (Live) (Features on
CD 1 only.) / Warm wet circles (Live) (Features on
CD 2 only.) / Jumpsuit city (Live) (Features on CD 2
only.) / Company (Live) (Features on CD 2 only.) /
Kayleigh (Live) (Features on CD 3 only.) / Internal
exile (Live) (Features on CD 3 only.) / Just good
friends (Live) (Features on CD 3 only.) / Sugar mice
(Live) (Features on CD 4 only.) / Dear friend (Live)
(Features on CD 4 only.) / Lady let it lie (Live)
(Features on CD 4 only.).

CD Single . . . . DDICK 008CD2
CD Single . . . . DDICK 008CD4
CD Single . . . . DDICK 008CD1
CD Single . . . . DDICK 008CD3
Dick Bros. / Sep '94 / Vital Distribution.

GENTLEMAN'S EXCUSE ME, A.
Tracks: Gentleman's excuse me / Whiplash / Gentleman's excuse me, A (demo version) (12" & CD single
only.).

■ 12" 12EM 135
■ 12" P.Disc 12EMPD 135
■ 7" . . . . EM 135
■ 7" . . . . EMS 135
■ 7" P.Disc . . . . EMPD 135
■ CD Single . . . . CDEM 135
■ MC Single . . . . TCEM 135
EMI / Feb '90.

INTERNAL EXILE.
Tracks: Not Advised.

CD 5110492
■ LP 5110491
■ MC 5110494
Polydor / Nov '91.

INTERNAL EXILE.
Tracks: Internal exile / Carnival man.

■ 12" . . . . FISHS 1
■ 7" . . . . FISHY 1
■ CD Single . . . . FISCD 1
■ MC Single . . . . FISHC 1
Polydor / Sep '91.

LADY LET IT LIE.
Tracks: Lady let it lie / Out of my life / Black canal
(Not available on CDS 2) / Lady let it lie (live)
(Available on CDS 1 only) / Emperors song (live)
(Available on CDS 2 only) / Just good friends (Not
available on CDS 2).

12" . . . . DDICK 003PIC
CD Single . . . . DDICK 003CD2
CD Single . . . . DDICK 003CD1
MC Single . . . . DDICK 003CAS
Dick Bros. / Mar '94 / Vital Distribution.

SOMETHING IN THE AIR.
Tracks: Something in the air.

■ 12" . . . . FISHX 3
■ 7" P.Disc . . . . FISHP 3
■ CD Single . . . . FISHL 3
■ 7" . . . . FISHY 3
Polydor / Jun '92.

SONGS FROM THE MIRROR.
Tracks: Not Advised.

CD 5174992
LP 5174991
■ MC 5174994
Polydor / Jan '93.

STATE OF MIND.
Tracks: State of mind (edited version) (Not on CD
single.) / Voyeur, The (I like to watch) / State of mind
(Presidential mix) (Not on 7" or Cassingle.).

■ 12" 12EM 109
■ 12" P.Disc 12EMPD 109
■ 7" . . . . EM 109
■ CD Single . . . . CDEM 109
■ MC Single . . . . TCEM 109
EMI / Oct '89.

SUITS.
Tracks: 1470 / Lady let it lie / Emperor's song /
Fortunes of war / Somebody special / No dummy /
Pipeline / Jumpsuit city / Bandwagon / Raw meat.

CD . . . . DDICK 004CD
LP . . . . DDICK 004LP
LP P.Disc . . . . DDICK 004PIC
MC . . . . DDICK 004MC
Dick Bros. / May '94 / Vital Distribution.

SUSHI.
Tracks: Fearless / Big wedge / Boston tea party /
Credo / Family business / View from a hill / He
knows you know / She chameleon / Kayleigh / White
Russian / Company / Just good friends / Jeepster /
Hold your head up / Lucky / Internal exile / Cliche /
Last straw / Poets moon / 5 years.

CD Set . . . . DDICK 002CD
Dick Bros. / Mar '94 / Vital Distribution.

VIGIL IN THE WILDERNESS OF MIRRORS.
Tracks: Vigil / Big wedge / State of mind / Company /
Gentleman's excuse me / Voyeur, The (I like to
watch) (Not on album.) / Family business / View from
the hill / Cliche.

CD . . . . CDEMD 1015
■ LP . . . . EMD 1015
■ LP P.Disc . . . . EMDPD 1015
■ MC . . . . TCEMD 1015
EMI / Feb '90.

Fishbone

Funk-rock fusion outfit who lacked the depth
of material of many of their peers and have
failed to crossover in the way that Red Hot
Chili Peppers and Living Colour have. However their live shows were highly entertain-
ing and chaotic earning them rave reviews,
ultimately without the musical muscle to
back it up they have failed to capitalise on
their reputation.

EVERYDAY SUNSHINE.
Tracks: Everyday sunshine / Fight the youth / Freddie's dead (Only on CD single).

■ 6581936
■ 7" 6581937
■ CD Single 6581938
Columbia / Jul '92.

FISHBONE.
Tracks: Ugly / Another generation / Modern industry
/ Party at ground zero / V.T.T.O.T.F.D.G.F. / Lyin' ass
bitch.

■ LP . . . . CBS 20529
CBS / Sep '85.

FREDDIS'S DEAD.
Tracks: Freddie's dead / It's a wonderful life (gonna
have a good time) / Freddie's dead (Zeoniq mix) (CD
single & Picture Disc only.) / Freddie's dead (edit)
(CD single & Picture Disc only.) / I like to hide behind
my glasses (CD single single.).

■ 12" . . . . FSH T1
■ 12" P.Disc. . . . . FSH P1
■ 7" . . . . FSH 1
Epic / Sep '88.
■ CD Single . . . . CD FSH 1
Epic / Sep '88.

GIVE A MONKEY A BRAIN AND HE'LL SWEAR HE'S THE CENTRE..
Tracks: Swim / Servitide / Black flowers / Unyielding
conditioning / Properties of propaganda / Warmth of
your breath / Lemon meringue / They have all abandoned their hopes / End the reign / Drunk skitzo / No
fear / Nutt megalomaniac.

CD 473875 2
LP 473875 1
MC 473875 4
Sony Music / Jun '93 / Sony.
MiniDisc 473875 8
Columbia / May '94 / Sony.

MA AND PA.
Tracks: Ma and pa / Bonin in the boneyard / I like to
hide behind my glasses / In the name of swing (Only
on CD single.).

■ 7" P.Disc . . . . FSHP 2
■ CD Single . . . . CPFSH 2
■ 12" . . . . FSHT 2
■ 7" . . . . FSH 2
Epic / Mar '89.

PARTY AT GROUND ZERO.
Tracks: V.T.T.O.T.F.D.G.F. / Party at ground zero.
■ 12" . . . . TX 6544
■ 7" . . . . A 6544
CBS / Sep '85.

REALITY OF MY SURROUNDINGS, THE.
Tracks: Fight the youth / If I were a .I'd / So many
millions / Asswhippin' / Housework / Deathmarch /
Behaviour control technician / Pressure / Junkies
prayer / Prayer to the junkiemaker / Everyday sunshine / Naz-tee may'en / Babyhead / Those days are
gone / Sunless Saturday.

CD 4676152
■ LP 4676151
■ MC 4676154
Columbia / Jul '91.

REALITY OF MY SURROUNDINGS, THE.
Tracks: Not Advised.
VHS 490922
Sony Music Video / Nov '92 / Sony.

TRUTH AND SOUL.
Tracks: Freddie's dead / Ma and pa / Might long way / Pouring rain / Deep inside / Question of life / Bonin' in the boneyard / One day / Subliminal fascism / Slow bus movin' (Howard beach party) / Ghetto soundwave / Change.
CD 4611732
■ MC 4611734
■ LP 4611731
Epic / Oct '88.

Fist

BACK WITH A VENGEANCE.
Tracks: Feeling's right / Dog soldier / All I can do / Turn the hell on / Devil rise / S.S.Giro / Going wild tonight / Too hot / Lost and found.
■ LP . . . . NEAT 1003
Neat / '85.

COLLISION COURSE.
Tracks: Collision course / Law of the jungle.
■ 7" . . . . MCA 663
MCA / Jan '81.

FOREVER AMBER.
Tracks: Forever amber / Turn out the light.
■ 7" . . . . MCA 640
MCA / Aug '80.

NAME RANK AND SERIAL NUMBER.
Tracks: Name rank and serial number / You'll never get me up in one of those.
■ 7" . . . . .NEAT 04
Neat / Apr '80.
■ 7" . . . . MCA 615
MCA / Jul '80.

TURN THE HELL ON.
Tracks: Not Advised.
■ LP . . . . MAF 3082
MCA / Nov '80.

WANDERER.
Tracks: Wanderer / Too hot.
■ 7" . . . . .NEAT 21
Neat / Nov '82.

Fix

COLD DAYS.
Tracks: Not Advised.
LP . . . . .LF 015
Lost & Found / Apr '92 / Plastic Head.
CD . . . . .LF 078
Lost & Found / Mar '94 / Plastic Head.

LOST PLANES.
Tracks: Lost planes / I've been there before.
■ 7" . . . . CLUB 101
Polydor / Apr '81.

Flotsam & Jetsam

CUATRO.
Tracks: Natural enemies / Swatting at flies / Message / Cradle me now / Wading through the darkness / Double zero / Never to reveal / Forget about heaven / Secret sqaure / Hypodermic midnight snack / Are you willing / (Ain't nothing gonna) Save this world.
■ MC . . . . MCC 10678
■ CD . . . . MCD 10678
MCA / Feb '93.

DOOMSDAY FOR THE DECEIVER.
Tracks: Not Advised.
■ LP P.Disc 722081P
Metal Blade / Aug '87.
CD . . . . RR 349683
Road Runner / Jun '87 / Pinnacle.
MC. . . . . RR 96834
Road Runner / Oct '89 / Pinnacle.
■ LP . . . . RR 9683
Road Runner / Oct '89.
CD . . . . .ZORRO 36CD
LP . . . . ZORRO 36
MC. . . . . ZORRO 36T
Music For Nations / Sep '91 / Pinnacle.

FLOTZILLA.
Tracks: Flotzilla.
■ 12" . . . . RR 125471
Road Runner / Dec '87.

NO PLACE FOR DISGRACE.
Tracks: No place for disgrace / Dream of death / N.E.T. / Escape from within / Saturday night's alright for fighting / Hard on you / I live you die / Misguided fortune / T.A.A.B. / Jones.
■ LP . . . . RR 95491
MC. . . . . RR 95494
Road Runner / May '88 / Pinnacle.
CD . . . . RR 95492
Road Runner / Jan '94 / Pinnacle.

SATURDAY NIGHT'S ALRIGHT FOR FIGHTING.
Tracks: Saturday nights alright for fighting.
■ CD Single . . . . RR 24532
Road Runner / Dec '88.
■ 7" . . . . RR 24531
Road Runner / Dec '88.

WHEN THE STORM COMES.
Tracks: Master sleeps / Deviation / No more fun / 6, six, VI / E.M.T.E.K. / K.A.B. / Burned device / October thorns / Suffer the masses / Greed / Scars.
■ CD .DMCG 6084
■ LP .MCG 6084
■ MC .MCGC 6084
MCA / Apr '90.

Foghat

AKA ROCK & ROLL.
Tracks: Not Advised.
CD 812270890-2
WEA / Mar '93 / WEA.

BEST OF FOGHAT.
Tracks: Not Advised.
CD 8122700882
WEA / Jul '93 / WEA.

BEST OF FOGHAT - VOL.2, THE.
Tracks: Not Advised.
CD 8122705162
WEA / Jul '93 / WEA.

BEST OF FOGHAT VOL.2.
Tracks: Not Advised.
CD R2 705160
Rhino (USA) / Mar '92 / WEA.

BEST OF FOGHAT, THE.
Tracks: Not Advised.
■ LP .NEDLP 141
MC. . . . . .NEDMC 141
■ CD .NEXCD 141
Sequel / Sep '90.

ENERGIZED.
Tracks: Honey, hush / Step outside / Golden arrow / Home in my hand / Wild cherry / That'll be the day / Fly by night / Nothin' I won't do.
■ LP . . . . K 55500
Bearsville (USA).
CD 812270883-2
WEA / Mar '93 / WEA.

FOGHAT.
Tracks: I just want to make love to you / Trouble trouble / Leavin' again / Fools hall of fame / Sarah Lee / Highway (killing me) / Mabellene / Hole to hide in / Gotta get to know you.
■ LP . . . . K 45503
Bearsville (USA).
CD 812270887-2
WEA / Mar '93 / WEA.

FOGHAT (LIVE).
Tracks: Fool for the city / Home in my hand / I just want to make love to you / Road fever / Honey hush / Slow ride.
■ LP . . . . K 55518
Bearsville (USA) / '89.
■ LP . . . . NEXLP 112
■ CD . . . . NEXCD 112
■ MC .NEXMC 112
Sequel / Jun '90.
CD 812270884-2
WEA / Mar '93 / WEA.

FOGHAT 2.
Tracks: Ride ride ride / Feel so bad / Long way to go / It's too late / What a shame / Helping hand / Road fever / She's gone / Couldn't make her stay.
■ LP . . . . K 45514
Bearsville (USA).

FOOL FOR THE CITY.
Tracks: Fool for the city / My babe / Slow ride / Terraplane blues / Save your loving (for me) / Drive me home / Take it or leave it.
■ LP . . . . K 55507
Bearsville (USA).

CD 812270882-2
WEA / Mar '93 / WEA.

GIRLS TO CHAT AND BOYS TO BOUNCE.
Tracks: Second childhood / Wide boy / Love zone.
■ LP . . . . AALP 3578
MC. . . . . .BKR 3578
Bearsville (USA) / Jan '82.

I JUST WANNA MAKE LOVE TO YOU.
Tracks: I just wanna make love to you / Fool for the city.
■ 7" . . . . K 15227
Bearsville (USA) / Aug '78.

NIGHTSHIFT.
Tracks: Drivin' wheel / Don't run me down / Burning the midnight oil / Nightshift / Hot shot love / Take me to the river / I'll be standing by.
■ LP . . . . K 55511
Bearsville (USA).
CD 812270888-2
WEA / Mar '93 / WEA.

ROCK & ROLL OUTLAW.
Tracks: Not Advised.
CD 812270889-2
WEA / Mar '93 / WEA.

ROCK AND ROLL OUTLAWS.
Tracks: Eight days on the road / Hate to see you go / Dreamer / Trouble in my way / Rock and roll outlaws / Shirley Jean / Blue spruce woman / Chateau lafitte '59 boogie.
■ LP . . . . K 55502
Bearsville (USA).

STONE BLUE.
Tracks: Not Advised.
CD 812270881-2
WEA / Mar '93 / WEA.

THIRD TIME LUCKY.
Tracks: Third time lucky / Somebody's been sleeping in my bed.
■ 7" . . . . WIP 6582
Island / Mar '80.

TIGHT SHOES.
Tracks: Stranger in my hometown / Loose ends / Full time lover / Baby can I change your mind / Too late the hero / Dead end street / Be my woman / No hard feelings.
■ LP . . . . ILPS 9637
Island / Aug '80.

Forbidden

BEST OF (POINT OF NO RETURN), THE.
Tracks: Chalice of blood / Out of body (out of mind) / Feel no pain / Step by step / Off the edge / One foot in hell / Through the eyes of glass / Tossed away / March into fire / Victim of changes.
CD . . . . .CDMFLAG 73
LP . . . . .MFLAG 73
MC. . . . . .TMLAG 73
Under One Flag / Nov '92 / Pinnacle.

FORBIDDEN EVIL.
Tracks: Not Advised.
CD . . . . .CDFLAG 27
MC. . . . . .TFLAG 27
■ LP .FLAG 27
Under One Flag / Aug '89.

LIVE AT THE DYNAMO.
Tracks: Not Advised.
■ 12" .12FLAG 108
Music For Nations / Sep '89.

POINT OF NO RETURN - THE BEST OF FORBIDDEN.
Tracks: Not Advised.
CD . . . . .CDFLAG 73
LP . . . . .FLAG 73
MC. . . . . .TFLAG 73
Under One Flag / Jul '92 / Pinnacle.

TWISTED INTO FORM.
Tracks: Not Advised.
CD . . . . .CDFLAG 43
LP . . . . .FLAG 43
MC. . . . . .TFLAG 43
Under One Flag / Jul '89 / Pinnacle.

Ford, Lita

Came to prominence as the teenage guitar prodigy with all-girl band The Runaways, heading out on her own when the group fell apart. Her debut solo album *Out For Blood* was released in 1983 for Mercury, the same

label as The Runaways had used. After the poor showing of her second album she was dropped despite having completed a third, *The Bride Wore Black* , which was never released. Four years later she was on RCA and enjoying the biggest success of her career with the album *Lita* before finally hitting the Top 10 with *Close My Eyes Forever* a duet with Ozzy Osbourne.

BEST OF LITA FORD, THE.
Tracks: What do ya know about love / Kiss me deadly / Shot of poison / Hungry / Gotta let go / Larger than life / Only women bleed / Playin' with fire / Back to the cave / Lisa / Close my eyes forever.
CD	7863 66047-2
■ LP	7863 66047-1
MC.	7863 66047-4
RCA / Aug '92 / BMG.

CLOSE MY EYES FOREVER (Ford, Lita & Ozzy Osbourne).
Tracks: Close my eyes forever / Under the gun.
■ 12"	PA 49396
■ 12"	PT 49380
■ 7"	PB 49379
■ 12"	PT 49410
■ 7"	PB 49409
■ CD Single	PD 49409
RCA / May '89.

DANCIN ON THE EDGE.
Tracks: Not Advised.
■ LP	.VERL 13
MC.	.VERLC 13
Vertigo / May '84 / PolyGram.

DANGEROUS CURVES.
Tracks: Larger than life / What do ya know about love / Shot of poison / Bad love / Playin' with fire / Hellbound train / Black widow / Little too early / Holy man / Tambourine dream / Little black spider.
■ CD	PD 90592
■ LP	PL 90592
■ MC.	PK 90592
RCA / Jan '92.
CD 74321 16000-2	
RCA / Feb '94 / BMG.

GOTTA LET GO.
Tracks: Gotta let go.
■ 12"	.VERX 10
■ 7"	VER 10
Vertigo / Apr '84.

HUNGRY.
Tracks: Hungry.
■ 12"	PT 49262
■ 7"	PB 49265
■ CD Single	PD 49266
■ 12"	PT 49266
RCA / Jul '90.

INTERVIEW COMPACT DISC: LITA FORD.
Tracks: Not Advised.
CD P.Disc	CBAK 4020
Baktabak / Nov '89 / Arabesque Ltd.

KISS ME DEADLY.
Tracks: Kiss me deadly / Broken dreams / Kiss me deadly (inst) (12" only).
■ 12"	PT 49576
■ 7"	PB 49575
RCA / Apr '88.
■ 7" P.Disc	PA 49503
■ 7"	PB 49501
■ 7" P.Disc	PB 49575P
RCA / Apr '88.

LITA.
Tracks: Back to the cave / Can't catch me / Blueberry / Kiss me deadly / Falling in and out of love / Fatal passion / Under the gun / Broken dreams / Close my eyes forever.
■ CD	PD 86397
■ LP	PL 86397
■ MC.	PK 86397
RCA / Apr '88.
CD 74321 13887-2	
RCA / Feb '94 / BMG.

LITA FORD LIVE.
Tracks: Dancing on the edge / Broken dreams / Can't catch me / Hit and run / Fatal passion / Falling in and out of love / Kiss me deadly / Close my eyes forever / Back to the cave.
■ VHS 790 324	
BMG Video / Nov '89.

LITA FORD: INTERVIEW PICTURE DISC.
Tracks: Not Advised.
LP P.Disc	BAK 2133
Baktabak / Apr '89 / Arabesque Ltd.

MIDNIGHT SNACK, A.
Tracks: Hungry / Lita / Kiss me deadly.
VHS 790 457	
BMG Video / Oct '90 / BMG.

OUT FOR BLOOD (Ford, Lita Band).
Tracks: Out for blood / Stay with me baby / Just a feeling / Ready willing and able / Die for me only / Rock 'n' roll made what I am today / If you can't live with it / On the run / Any way that you want me / I can't stand it.
■ LP	MERL 26
■ MC.	MERLC 26
Mercury / Jul '83.

SHOT OF POISON.
Tracks: Shot of poison / Larger than life.
■ 7"	PB 49145
■ 12"	PT 49132
■ 12" P.Disc.	PT 49130
■ CD Single	PD 49146
RCA / Jan '92.

STILETTO.
Tracks: Your wake up call / Dedication / Lisa / Big gun / Bad boy / Cherry red / Hungry / Stiletto / Ripper / Only women bleed / Aces and high / Outro.
■ LP	PL 82090
■ CD	PD 82090
■ MC.	PK 82090
RCA / May '90.

Foreigner

Formed in 1976 by British musician Mick Jones and American singer Lou Gramm. 1977 debut *Foreigner* reached U.S. Top Five, staying on chart for months and spawning pair of Top 10 singles; formula repeated by 1978's *Double Vision*. Major UK success eluded band until 1981's *4* album and *Waiting For A Girl Like You* single. 1984's *Agent Provocateur* included transatlantic chart-topper *I Want To Know What Love Is* and was their first U.K. number one. Internal dissention prompted Gramm to go solo, then form Shadow King with Vivian Campbell (now with Def Leppard). New Foreigner personnel struggled on before Jones and Gramm reunited in 1992.

AGENT PROVOCATEUR.
Tracks: Tooth and nail / That was yesterday / I want to know what love is / Growing up the hard way / Reaction to action / Stranger in my own house / Love in vain / Down on love / Two different worlds / She's too tough.
CD	781 999-2
■ LP	781 999-1
MC.	781 999-4
Atlantic / Jan '85 / WEA.

BLUE MORNING BLUE DAY.
Tracks: Blue morning blue day / I have waited so long.
■ 7"	K 11236
Atlantic / Feb '79.

CLASSIC HITS LIVE.
Tracks: Double vision / Cold as ice / Damage is done / Women / Dirty white boy / Fool for you anyway / Head games / Feels like way / Waiting for a girl like you / Juke box hero / Urgent / Love maker / I want to know what love is / Feels like the first time.
CD	7567825252
MC.	7567825254
Atlantic / Dec '93 / WEA.

COLD AS ICE.
Tracks: Cold as ice / Reaction to action.
■ 7"	K 10986
Atlantic / Jul '78.
■ 12" Remix	A 9539T
■ 12" Remix	A 9539
Atlantic / Jun '85.

DON'T LET GO.
Tracks: Don't let go / Fool for you anyway.
■ 7"	K 11718
Atlantic / Mar '82.

DOUBLE VISION.
Tracks: Hot blooded / Blue morning, blue day / You're all I am / Back where you belong / Love has taken it's toll / Double vision / Tramontane / I have waited so long / Lonely children / Spellbinder.
CD	K250 476
■ LP	K 50476

■ MC.	K4 50476
Atlantic / Aug '78.

DOUBLE VISION.
Tracks: Double vision / Lonely children.
■ 7"	K 11199
WEA / '79.

FEELS LIKE THE FIRST TIME.
Tracks: Feels like the first time / Cold as ice / Long long way from home.
■ 7"	K 11086
Atlantic / May '78.

FEELS LIKE THE FIRST TIME.
Tracks: Feels like the first time / Woman oh woman.
■ 7"	K 10917
Atlantic / Apr '77.

FOREIGNER.
Tracks: Feels like the first time / Cold as ice / Starrider / Headknocker / Damage is done / Long long way from home / Woman oh woman / At war with the world / Fool for the anyway / I need you.
CD	250 356
■ LP	K 50356
■ MC.	K4 50356
Atlantic / Apr '77.

FOREIGNER 4.
Tracks: Night life / Juke box hero / Break it up / Waiting for a girl like you / Luanne / Urgent / I'm gonna win / Woman in black / Girl on the moon / Don't let go.
CD 250796	
Atlantic / '88 / WEA.

HEAD GAMES.
Tracks: Dirty white boy / Love on the telephone / Women I'll get even with you / Seventeen / Head games / Modern day / Blinded by science / Do what you like / Rev on the red line.
■ MC.	K4 50651
Atlantic / Nov '79.
■ LP	K 50561
WEA / Sep '79.
CD	250 651
Atlantic / Nov '85 / WEA.

HEAD GAMES.
Tracks: Head games / Do what you like.
■ 7"	K 11417
Atlantic / Mar '80.

HOT BLOODED.
Tracks: Hot blooded.
■ 7"	.K 1167
Atlantic / Oct '78.

I DON'T WANT TO LIVE WITHOUT YOU.
Tracks: I don't want to live without you / Face to face / Urgent (Track on CD single.).
■ 12"	A 9101 T
■ 7"	.A 9101
■ CD Single	A 9101 CD
Atlantic / May '88.

I WANT TO KNOW WHAT LOVE IS.
Tracks: I want to know what love is.
■ 12"	A 9596 T
■ 7"	.A 9596
Atco / Nov '84.

I'LL FIGHT FOR YOU.
Tracks: I'll fight for you / Moment of truth / Dirty white boy.
■ MC Single.	.A 7608MC
■ 12"	A 7608T
■ 7"	.A 7608
■ CD Single	A 7608CD
Atlantic / Sep '91.

I'LL GET EVEN WITH YOU.
Tracks: I'll get even with you / Blinded by science.
■ 7"	K 11602
Atlantic / Sep '80.

INSIDE INFORMATION.
Tracks: Heart turns to stone / Can't wait / Say you will / I don't want to live without you / Night to remember / Inside information / Beat of my heart / Face to face / Out of the blue / Counting every minute.
■ CD	781 808-2
Atlantic / Dec '87.
■ LP	WX 143
■ MC.	WX 143C
Atlantic / Nov '87.

JUKE BOX HERO.
Tracks: Jukebox hero / I'm gonna win.
■ 7"	K 11678
Atlantic / Oct '81.

RECORDS.
Tracks: Cold as ice / Double vision / Head games / Waiting for a girl like you / Feels like the first time / Urgent / Dirty white boy / Jukebox hero / Long long way from home / Hot blooded.
- ■ LP . . . . .A 0999
- MC . . . . .A 0999 4

Atlantic / Dec '82 / WEA.
- CD 780 999-2

Atlantic / '83 / WEA.

SAY YOU WILL.
Tracks: Say you will / Night to remember.
- ■ 12" . . . . A 9169 T
- ■ 7" . . . . .A 9269
- ■ CD Single . . . . A 9169 CD

Atlantic / Nov '87.

THAT WAS YESTERDAY.
Tracks: That was yesterday / Two different worlds.
- ■ 12" . . . . A 9571T
- ■ 7" . . . . .A 9571

Atlantic / Apr '85.

UNUSUAL HEAT.
Tracks: Only heaven knows / Lowdown and dirty / I'll fight for you / Moment of truth / Mountain of love / Ready for the rain / When the night comes down / Safe in my heart / No hiding place / Flesh wound / Unusual heat.
- MC . . . . WX 424C

East West / Dec '87 / WEA.
- CD 7567822992
- ■ LP . . . . WX 424

East West / Jun '91.

URGENT.
Tracks: Urgent / Girl on the moon.
- ■ 7" . . . . K 11665

Atlantic / Aug '81.
- ■ 7" . . . . K 11728

Atlantic / May '82.

VERY BEST OF FOREIGNER, THE.
Tracks: Not Advised.
- CD 7597805112
- ■ LP . . . . WX 469
- MC . . . . WX 469C

Atlantic / May '92 / WEA.

VERY BEST OF FOREIGNER..AND BEYOND.
Tracks: Soul doctor / Prisoner of love / With heaven on our side / Juke box hero / Hot blooded / Cold as ice / Head games / Waiting for a girl like you / Urgent / Double vision / I want to know what love is / Say you will / That was yesterday / I don't want to live without you / Rev on the red line / Dirty white boy / Feels like the first time.
- CD 7567899992
- MC 7567899994

Atlantic / Dec '92 / WEA.

WAITING FOR A GIRL LIKE YOU.
Tracks: Waiting for a girl like you / Feels like the first time / Cold as ice.
- ■ 7" . . . . K 11696

Atlantic / Dec '81.

WOMEN.
Tracks: Women / Modern day.
- ■ 7" . . . . K 11456

Atlantic / May '80.

Forgodsake

BLASTHEAD.
Tracks: Armchair enthusiast / Wake up now / If this it what it takes / Bad sex / Half past anything / Blasthead / Strange / Negative / In front of me / Crash / This one (Available on CD only.) / Not today (Available on CD only.) / Sky high (Available on CD only.) / Dumbtown (Available on CD only.).
- CD . . . . .CDBLEED 3
- LP . . . . BLEED 3

Bleeding Hearts / Apr '93 / Pinnacle.

Four Horsemen

NOBODY SAID IT WAS EASY.
Tracks: Nobody said it was easy / Homesick blues / Can't stop rockin' (Only on 12" and CD single).
- ■ 12" . . . . .DEFX 12
- ■ 7" . . . . .DEFA 12
- ■ 7" P.Disc . . . . .DEFP 12
- ■ CD Single . . . . .DEFCD 12

American Recordings / Sep '91.

NOBODY SAID IT WAS EASY.
Tracks: Nobody said it was easy / Rockin' is ma' business / Tired wings / Can't stop rockin' / Wanted man / Let it rock / Hot head / Moon shine / Home sick

blues / Seventy five again / Looking for trouble / I need a thrill/Somethin' good.
- CD 510047 2
- ■ LP 510047 1
- ■ MC 510047 4

American Recordings / Sep '91.

ROCKIN IS MA BUSINESS.
Tracks: Rockin is ma business / Moonshine / 75 again (Not on 7").
- ■ 12" P.Disc . . . . DEFAP 1512
- ■ 7" . . . . .DEFA 15
- ■ MC Single . . . . .DEFAC 15

American Recordings / Mar '92.

WELFARE BOOGIE.
Tracks: Welfare boogie / Shelley / High school rock'n'roller / Hard lovin' man.
- ■ 12" . . . . SICK 112
- ■ CD Single . . . . .SICCD 1

Phonogram / Jul '90.

Freak Of Nature

FREAK OF NATURE.
Tracks: Not Advised.
- CD . . . . .CDMFN 146
- LP . . . . MFN 146
- MC . . . . TMFN 146

Music For Nations / Mar '93 / Pinnacle.

GATHERING OF FREAKS.
Tracks: Not Advised.
- CD . . . . .CDMFN 169
- LP . . . . MFN 169
- MC . . . . TMFN 169

Music For Nations / Sep '94 / Pinnacle.

RESCUE ME.
Tracks: Rescue me / Turn the other way / What am I.
- ■ 12" 12KUT 153
- ■ CD Single . . . . CDKUT 153

Music For Nations / Jul '93.

Free

Formed in 1968, first success came in 1970: classic single *All Right Now* surged into Top Tens worldwide, while *Fire And Water* was big success on album charts. Success created problems within band, who split in early 1971. Failure of solo projects prompted swift reformation, although work was frequently disrupted by guitarist Paul Kossoff's drug problems (he died in 1976) and further friction. After classic *Heartbreaker* album and *Wishing Well* single, Free folded for good in June '73. Drummer Simon Kirke and singer Paul Rodgers promptly formed Bad Company. *All Right Now* lived on, returning to U.K. charts in 1973, '78, '82 and '91.

ALL RIGHT NOW.
Tracks: Wishing well / All right now / Little bit of love / Come together in the morning / Stealer / Sail on / Mr Big / My brother Jake the hunter / Be my friend / Travellin' in style / Fire and water / Travelling man / Don't say you love me.
- CD . . . . CIDTV 2
- ■ LP . . . . ILPTV 2
- MC . . . . ICTV 2

Island / Feb '91 / PolyGram.

ALL RIGHT NOW.
Tracks: All right now.
- ■ 7" . . . . WIP 6082

Island / Jun '70.

ALL RIGHT NOW (RE-RELEASE).
Tracks: All right now / I'm a mover / Get where I belong (Not available on 7" format.) / Get where I belong (version) (Not available on 7" format.).
- ■ 12" 12IS 486
- ■ 7" . . . . IS 486
- ■ CD Single . . . . CID 486
- ■ MC Single. . . . . CIS 486

Island / Jan '91.

BEST OF FREE.
Tracks: Mr. Big / Stealer / Ride on pony / My brother Jake / Be my friend / I'll be creepin' / Fire and water / Songs of yesterday / Love you so / All right now.
- VHS 0831683

Polygram Music Video / '92 / PolyGram.

COMPLETELY FREE.
Tracks: Not Advised.
- ■ LP . . . . ILPS 9719

Island / Oct '82.

FIRE & WATER/ HEARTBREAKER.
Tracks: Not Advised.
- CD 514 288-2
- CD Set . . . . ITSCD 3

Island / Nov '92 / PolyGram.

FIRE AND WATER.
Tracks: Oh I wept / Remember / Heavy load / Fire and water / Mr. Big / Dont say you love me / All right now.
- MC . . . . ICM 9120
- ■ CD . . . . CID 9120
- ■ LP . . . . .ILPM 9120

Island / Sep '86.
- MC 842 556 4

Island / '90 / PolyGram.
- CD . . . . .IMCD 80

Island / Apr '90 / PolyGram.
- LP . . . . ILPS 9120

Island / Jan '94 / PolyGram.

FREE.
Tracks: I'll be creepin' / Songs of yesterday / Lying in the sunshine / Trouble on double time / Mouthful of grass / Woman / Free me / Broad daylight / Mourning sad mourning.
- CD . . . . .IMCD 64

Island / '89 / PolyGram.

FREE.
Tracks: Stealer / My brother Jake / All right now / Mr. Big / Be my friend / Ride on pony / Songs of yesterday / I'll be creeping / Fire and water / Love you so.
- VHS . . . . IVA 020

Island Visual Arts / Oct '89 / PolyGram / TBD.

FREE (EP).
Tracks: All right now / My brother Jake / Wishing well.
- ■ EP . . . . IEP 6

Island / Feb '78.

FREE AT LAST.
Tracks: Catch a train / Soldier boy / Magic ship / Sail on / Travelling man / Little bit of love / Guardian of the Universe / Child / Goodbye.
- ■ LP . . . . .ILPS 9192

Island / Jun '72.
- ■ CD . . . . CID 9192

Island / Jun '88.
- CD . . . . .IMCD 82

Island / Feb '90 / PolyGram.

FREE LIVE.
Tracks: All right now / I'm a mover / Be my friend / Fire and water / Ride on pony / Mr. Big / Hunter / Get where I belong.
- ■ CD . . . . CID 9160
- ■ LP . . . . ILPS 9160

Island / Jun '88.
- CD . . . . .IMCD 73

Island / '89 / PolyGram.

FREE STORY, THE.
Tracks: Not Advised.
- ■ Double LP . . . . .ISLD 4

Island / Mar '74.
- ■ MC . . . . ZCID 104

Island / '75.

FREE STORY, THE (2).
Tracks: I'm a mover / I'll be creepin / Mourning sad morning / All right now / Heavy load / Fire and water / Be my friend / Stealer / Soon I will be gone / Mr. Big / Hunter / Get where I belong / Travelling man / Just for the box / Lady / My brother Jake / Little bit of love / Sail on / Come together in the morning.
- CD . . . . CID 9945
- ■ LP . . . . ILPS 9945
- MC . . . . ICT 9945

Island / Oct '89 / PolyGram.

FREE THE FREE.
Tracks: I'll be creepin / Songs of yesterday / Lying in the sunshine / Trouble on double time / Mouthful of grass / Woman / Free me / Broad daylight / Mourning sad morning.
- CD 842 782-2

Island / Sep '89 / PolyGram.

FREE'N'EASY.
Tracks: Hunter / Wishing well / Fire and water / Travellin' in style / Bodie / Walk in my shadow.
- ■ LP . . . . ILPS 9453

Island / Jan '77.

HEARTBREAKER.
Tracks: Wishing well / Come together in the morning / Travellin' in style / Heartbreaker / Muddy water / Common mortal man / Easy on my soul / Seven angels.
- ■ LP . . . . ILPS 9217
- ■ MC . . . . ICT 9217

■ DELETED

Island / Jan '78.
■ CD . . . . CID 9217
Island / Jun '88.
CD . . . . .IMCD 81
Island / Feb '90 / PolyGram.

HIGHWAY.
Tracks: Highway song / Stealer / On my way / Be my friend / Sunny day / Ride on pony / Love you so / Bodies / Soon I will be gone.
■ LP . . . . ILPS 9138
Island.
■ CD . . . . CID 9138
Island / Jun '88.
CD . . . . .IMCD 63
Island / '89 / PolyGram.

HUNTER, THE.
Tracks: Hunter / Worry.
■ 7" . . . . WIP 6351
Island / Oct '76.

I'LL BE CREEPIN'.
Tracks: I'll be creepin' / Songs of yesterday / Lying in the sunshine / Trouble on double time / Mouthful of grass / Woman / Free me / Broad daylight / Mourning sad morning.
■ LP . . . . ILPS 9104
Island.
■ CD . . . . CID 9104
Island / May '88.

LITTLE BIT OF LOVE.
Tracks: Little bit of love.
■ 7" . . . . WIP 6129
Island / May '72.

MOLTEN GOLD.
Tracks: I'm a mover / Hunter / Walk in my shadow / I'll be creepin' / Songs of yesterday / Woman / Broad daylight / Mouthful of grass / All right now / Oh I wept / Heavy load / Don't say you love me / Stealer / Highway song / Be my friend / Soon I will be gone / My brother Jake / Fire and water / Ride on pony / Mr big / Time away / Molten gold / Catch a train / Travelling man / Little bit of love / Sail on / Wishing well / Come together in the morning / Travellin' in style / Heartbreaker.
CD . . . . CRNCD 2
Island / May '94 / PolyGram.

MY BROTHER JAKE.
Tracks: My brother Jake.
■ 7" . . . . WIP 6100
Island / Aug '63.

MY BROTHER JAKE (REMIX).
Tracks: My brother Jake (remix) / Wishing well (remix) / Stealer, The (full) (Only on 12" and CD single) / Only my soul (Only on 12" and CD single).
■ 12" . . . . 12 IS 495
■ 7" . . . . IS 495
■ CD Single . . . . CID 495
■ MC Single . . . . CIS 495
Island / Apr '91.

TONS OF SOBS.
Tracks: Over the green hills (part 1) / Worry / Walk in my shadow / Wild Indian woman / Going down slow / I'm a mover / Hunter / Moonshine sweet tooth / Over the green hills (Part 2).
■ LP . . . . ILPS 9089
Island.
■ CD . . . . CID 9089
Island / Jun '88.
CD . . . . .IMCD 62
Island / '89 / PolyGram.

WISHING WELL.
Tracks: Wishing well / Woman.
■ 7" . . . . WIP 6146
Island / Jan '73.
■ 7" . . . . IS 221
■ 12" 12IS 221
Island / May '85.

Frehley's Comet

FREHLEY'S COMET.
Tracks: Rock soldiers / Breakout / Into the night / Something moved / We got your rock / Love me right / Calling to you / Dolls / Stranger in a strange land / Fractured too.
■ LP 781 749-1
■ MC 781 749-4
Atlantic / Jun '87.

INTO THE NIGHT.
Tracks: Into the night / Fracture too / Breakout.
■ 12" . . . . .A 9255 T
■ 7" . . . . .A 9255
WEA / Jun '87.

LIVE 4.
Tracks: Not Advised.
■ VHS . . . . HEN 2278
Hendring Video / Oct '90.

LIVE PLUS ONE.
Tracks: Rip it out / Breakout / Something / Something moved / Rocket ride / Words are not enough.
■ CD . . . . K 781 826 2
■ LP . . . . K 781 826 1
■ MC. K 781 826 4
Atlantic / '88.

SECOND SIGHTING.
Tracks: Insane / Time ain't runnin' out / Dancin' with danger / It's over now / Loser in a fight / Juvenile delinquent / Fallen angel / Separate / New kind of lover / Acorn is spinning.
■ CD 781 862-2
■ LP 781 862-1
■ MC. 781 862-4
Atlantic / Jun '88.

TROUBLE WALKING.
Tracks: Shot full of rock / Do ya / Five card stud / Hide your heart / Lost in limbo / Trouble walkin' / 2 young 2 die / Back to school / Remember me / Fractured III.
■ CD 782042 2
■ LP 782042 1
■ MC. .782042 4
WEA / Oct '89.

Friedman, Marty

DRAGON'S KISS.
Tracks: Not Advised.
CD . . . . .RR 9529 2
■ LP . . . . RR 9529 1
■ MC. . . . . RR 9529 4
Road Runner / '89.

SCENES.
Tracks: Tibet / Angel / Valley of enternity / Night / Realm of the senses / West / Trance / Triumph.
CD . . . . CDRR 9104 2
Road Runner / Nov '92 / Pinnacle.

Front 242

05:22:09:12 OFF.
Tracks: Animal - Cage / Animal - Gate / Animal - Guide / Modern angel / Junkdrome / Serial killers don't kill their girlfriend / Skin - Fur coat / GenEcide / Crushed / OffEND / Animal - Zoo / Serial killers don't kill their boyfriend / Happiness - More angels / Crushed - Obscene / Melt - Again / Speed angels.
CD . . . . RRE 022CD
LP . . . . RRE 022LP
MC. .RRE 022MC
Red Rhino Europe / Aug '93 / Vital Distribution.

06:21:03:11 UP EVIL.
Tracks: Crapage / Waste / Skin / Motion / Religion / Stratoscape / Hymn / Fuel / Melt / Flag / Mutilate / (S)crapage (Cd and MD only).
CD . . . . RRE 021CD
LP . . . . .RRE 021
MC. .RRE 021MC
MiniDisc. . . . . RRE 021MD
Red Rhino Europe / May '93 / Vital Distribution.

ANGELS VERSUS ANIMALS.
Tracks: Animal (radio) / Angel (wipe out) / Serial killers don't kill their dog either / Modern angel (mix) / Animal (extended) / Break me (female) / Der verfluchte engel / L'ange moderne / Born to breathe.
CD . . . . RRE 018CD
RRE / Nov '93 / Vital Distribution.

ANIMAL.
Tracks: Animal.
■ 12" . . . . RRE 018T
RRE / Nov '93.

BACK CATALOGUE (1981-1985).
Tracks: Not Advised.
■ CD .RRECD 004
Red Rhino (Europe) / Jan '87.
CD . . . . RRE 004CD
Red Rhino (Europe) / Jun '92.

ENDLESS RIDDANCE.
Tracks: Endless riddance.
■ 12" . . . . MK 003
Mask (Germany) / Nov '86.
■ CD Single . . . . MK 003CD
Red Rhino (Europe) / Aug '88.

FRONT BY FRONT.
Tracks: Until death us do part / Circling overland / In rhythms beliben / Felines / First in, first out / Blend the strengths / Headhunter V.30 / Work 01 / Terminal

state / Welcome to Paradise (June 1992 CD only) / Headhunter V1.0 (June 1992 CD only) / Never stop V1.0 (June 1992 CD only) / Work 242 N.Off is N.Off (June 1992 CD only) / Agony (until death) (June 1992 CD only) / Never stop V1.1 (June 1992 CD only) / Work 242.
■ LP . . . . RRELP 007
MC. RREMC 007
■ CD . . . . RRECD 007
Red Rhino (Europe) / Oct '88.
■ DAT . . . . RREDT 007
Red Rhino (Europe) / '89.
CD . . . . RRE 007CD
Red Rhino (Europe) / Jun '92.

GEOGRAPHY (1981-1983).
Tracks: Operating tracks / With your cries / Art and strategy / Geography II / U men / Dialogue / Least inkling / GVDT / Geography 1 / Black, white, blue / Kinetics / Kampferereit / Ethics (June 1992 CD release only) / Principles (June 1992 CD release only) / Body to body (June 1992 CD release only).
■ LP . . . . MK 001
Mask (Germany) / Nov '86.
■ CD . . . . CD MK 1
■ MC. . . . . MK 001MC
Mask (Germany) / '88.
■ CD . . . . MK 001CD
Mask (Germany) / Jun '92.

HEADHUNTER.
Tracks: Headhunter.
■ 12" . . . . RRET 6
Red Rhino / Oct '88.
■ 7" . . . . RRE 6
■ CD Single . . . . RRECD 6
Red Rhino (Europe) / Oct '88.

INTEGRATIOM EIGHT X TEN.
Tracks: Headhunter / Rhythm Of Time.
VHS . . . . .RRE 014
Red Rhino (Europe) / Nov '92.

INTEGRATION EIGHT X TEN.
Tracks: Take One - Live / Masterhit - Live / Tragedy for you / Quite Unusual / Funkahdafi - Live / Front By Front.
VHS . . . . .RRE 014
Red Rhino Europe / Nov '92 / Vital Distribution.

INTERCEPTION.
Tracks: Interception.
■ 7" . . . . .RRE 003
■ 12" . . . . RRET 003
Red Rhino (Europe) / Nov '86.
■ CD Single . . . . RRET 003CD
Red Rhino (Europe) / Aug '88.

LIVE TARGET.
Tracks: Rhythm of time / Soul manager / Don't crash / Im rhythmus bleiben / DSM 123 & Moldavia / No shuffle / Gripped by fear / Never stop / Headhunter / Tragedy for you / Welcome to paradise / Puncih your machine / Intro + Circling overland.
CD . . . . GUZZ 1888
Guzzi Records / Dec '92 / Vital Distribution.

MASTER HIT.
Tracks: Master hit / Master hit (version).
■ 12" . . . . RRET 009
Play It Again Sam / Jan '90.
■ CD Single . . . . RRECD 009
■ MC Single . . . . RREC 009
Red Rhino (Europe) / Jan '90.

MASTER HIT (REMIX).
Tracks: Master hit (remix).
■ 12" . . . . WAX 036
Wax Trax / Nov '87.

NEVER STOP.
Tracks: Never stop.
■ 7" . . . . RRE 8
■ CD Single . . . . RRECD 8
Red Rhino (Europe) / Apr '89.
■ 12" . . . . RRET 8
Red Rhino (Europe) / '89.

NO COMMENT (1984-1985).
Tracks: Commando mix / S. fr. nomenklatura pt 1/2 / Deceit / Lovely day / No shuffle / Special forces / See the future (live) (June 1992 CD release only) / In November (live) (June 1992 CD release only) / Special forces (demo) (June 1992 CD release only) / Body to body (June 1992 CD release only).
■ LP . . . . MK 002
Mask (Germany) / Jan '87.
MC. MK 002MC
■ CD . . . . CD MK 2
Mask (Germany) / '88.
CD . . . . MK 002CD
Mask (Germany) / Jun '92 / Vital Distribution.

NO SHUFFLE.
Tracks: No shuffle / Body to body.
■ 12" 12OPA 013
■ 7" . . . . OPA 13
Himalaya / Feb '86.

OFFICIAL VERSION (1985-1986).
Tracks: What you have is what you get / Re-run / Television station / Agressive due / Masterhit pt.1 / Slaughter / Quite unusual (June 1992 CD only) / Red team / Agressive angst / Masterhit pt.2 / Agresiva (June 1992 CD only) / Masterblaster (June 1992 CD only) / Hypnomix (June 1992 CD only).
■ CD . . . . RRECD 5
Red Rhino (Europe) / Jun '87.
■ LP . . . . RRELP 5
Red Rhino (Europe) / Jun '87.
■ MC . . . . RREMC 5
Red Rhino (Europe) / Mar '87.
CD . . . . RRE 005CD
Red Rhino (Europe) / Jun '92.

POLITICS OF PRESSURE.
Tracks: Politics of pressure.
■ 12" . . . . MK 004
Mask (Germany) / Nov '86.
■ CD Single . . . . MK 004CD
Mask (Germany) / Aug '88.

PRINCIPLES.
Tracks: Principles.
■ 7" . . . . ND 002
New Dance / May '82.

RELIGION.
Tracks: Religion / Crapage (Does not feature on 12" & CDS (RRE 016CD).).
■ 12" . . . . RRE 016T
■ 12" Remix . . . . RRE 016R
■ CD Single . . . . RRE 016CDR
■ CD Single . . . . RRE 016CD
Red Rhino Europe / Apr '93.
■ CD Single . . . . RRECDX 016
RRE / Nov '93.

TRAGEDY FOR YOU.
Tracks: Tragedy for you.
■ 12" . . . . RRET 010
■ CD Single . . . . RRECD 010
■ 7" . . . . RRE 010
Red Rhino (Europe) / Oct '90.

TWO IN ONE.
Tracks: Two in one.
■ 12" . . . . ND 009
242 / Feb '86.
■ CD Single . . . . ND 009CD
242 / Oct '88.

TYRANNY FOR YOU.
Tracks: Not Advised.
CD . . . . RRE CD 11
LP . . . . RRE LP 11
MC . . . . RRE MC 11
Red Rhino (Europe) / Dec '90.

U MEN.
Tracks: U men.
■ 7" . . . . ND 005
New Dance / May '82.

Frontline Assembly

BLADE, THE.
Tracks: Not Advised.
CD . . . . TM 91192
■ LP . . . . TM 91191
Road Runner / Sep '92.

CAUSTIC GRIP.
Tracks: Not Advised.
CD . . . . TMCD 50
LP . . . . TMLP 50
Third Mind / Sep '90 / Pinnacle.
CD . . . . TM 91162
Road Runner / Sep '92 / Pinnacle.

CONVERGENCE.
Tracks: On the cross / Collision and demonic / Right hand of heaven.
CD . . . . TMCD 002
Third Mind / Sep '88 / Pinnacle.
CD . . . . TM 91142
Road Runner / Sep '92 / Pinnacle.

CORROSION.
Tracks: Lurid sensation / Right hand of heaven / Concussion / On the cross / Conflict / Controversy / Dark dream / Wrack, The (part 2).
■ LP . . . . TMLP 21
Third Mind / Feb '88.

DIGITAL TENSION DEMENTIA.
Tracks: Digital tension dementia.
■ 12" . . . . TMS 11
■ CD Single . . . . TMSCD 11
Third Mind / Nov '88.

DISORDER.
Tracks: Not Advised.
■ LP . . . . TMLP 24
Third Mind / Jun '88.

FRONTLINE ASSEMBLY.
Tracks: Not Advised.
■ LP . . . . ST 7547
Dossier / Nov '87.

GASHED SENSES AND CROSSFIRE.
Tracks: No limit / Hypocrisy / Prayer / Big money / Sedation / Anti social / Shut down / Digital tension dimension / Fools game.
CD . . . . TMCD 031
■ LP . . . . TMLP 31
Third Mind / May '89.
CD . . . . TM 91152
Road Runner / Sep '92 / Pinnacle.

ICEOLATE.
Tracks: Iceolate / Mental distortion.
■ 12" . . . . TMS 052
■ CD Single . . . . TMSCD 052
Third Mind / Jul '90.

INITIAL COMMAND.
Tracks: Initial command.
CD . . . . KK 006CD
■ LP . . . . KK 001
K K / '88.

LIVE.
Tracks: Not Advised.
LP . . . . TMLP 047
Third Mind / '90 / Pinnacle.

NO LIMIT.
Tracks: No limit (damaged goods mix).
■ 12" . . . . TMS 043
■ CD Single . . . . TMSCD 043
Third Mind / '89.

PROVISION.
Tracks: Provision.
■ 12" . . . . TMS 57 T
■ 7" . . . . TMS 57
■ CD Single . . . . TMS 57 CD
Third Mind / Sep '90.

STATE OF MIND.
Tracks: Not Advised.
CD . . . . DCD 9005
Dossier / Aug '88 / SRD.

TACTICAL NEURAL IMPLANT.
Tracks: Not Advised.
CD . . . . TM 91882
■ LP . . . . TM 91881
Third Mind / Apr '92.

TOTAL TERROR VOL 1.
Tracks: Not Advised.
CD . . . . EFA 08451CD
Dossier / Nov '93 / SRD.

TOTAL TERROR VOL 2.
Tracks: Not Advised.
CD . . . . EFA 08452CD
Dossier / Nov '93 / SRD.

VIRUS.
Tracks: Virus / Virus (version).
■ 12" . . . . TMS 065
■ CD Single . . . . TMSCD 065
Third Mind / Jan '91.

Fudge Tunnel

COMPLICATED FUTILITY OF IGNOR-ANCE, THE.
Tracks: Random acts of cruelty / Joy of irony / Backed down / Cover up / Six eight / Long day / Excuse / Find your fortune / Suffering makes great stories / Circle of friends , circle of trends / Rudge with A G.
CD . . . . MOSH 119CD
LP . . . . MOSH 119
Earache / Sep '94 / Vital Distribution.

CREEP DIETS.
Tracks: Grey / Tipper Gore / Ten percent / Face down / Grit / Don't have time for you / Good kicking / Hot salad / Creep diets / Stuck / Always.
CD . . . . MOSH 064CD
LP . . . . MOSH 064

MC . . . . MOSH 064MC
Earache / Apr '93 / Vital Distribution.

HATE SONGS IN E.
Tracks: Not Advised.
CD . . . . MOSH 36CD
LP . . . . MOSH 36
MC . . . . MOSH 36MC
Earache / Jan '93 / Vital Distribution.

IN A WORD.
Tracks: Not Advised.
CD . . . . MOSH 099CD
LP . . . . MOSH 099LP
Earache / Aug '94 / Vital Distribution.

JOY OF IRONY, THE.
Tracks: Joy of irony / Rottweiler.
7" . . . . 7 MOSH 124
Earache / Sep '94 / Vital Distribution.

TEETH EP.
Tracks: Not Advised.
■ 12" . . . . MOSH 057T
■ CD Single . . . . MOSH 057CD
Earache / Mar '92.

Fugazi

FUGAZI.
Tracks: Not Advised.
LP . . . . DISCHORD 30
MC . . . . DISCHORD 30C
Dischord / Dec '88 / SRD.

IN ON THE KILLTAKER.
Tracks: Not Advised.
CD . . . . DIS 70D
LP . . . . DIS 70
MC . . . . DIS 70C
Dischord / Jun '93 / SRD.

MARGIN WALKER.
Tracks: Not Advised.
LP . . . . DISCHORD 35
Dischord / Jul '89 / SRD.
MC . . . . DISCHORD 35C
Dischord / Jul '89 / SRD.

REPEATER.
Tracks: Not Advised.
LP . . . . DISCHORD 44
Dischord / Mar '90 / SRD.

STEADY DIET OF NOTHING.
Tracks: Not Advised.
CD . . . . DISCHORD 60CD
LP . . . . DISCHORD 60
MC . . . . DISCHORD 60C
Dischord / Sep '91 / SRD.

THREE SONGS.
Tracks: Three songs.
■ 7" . . . . DISCHORD 43
Dischord / Feb '90.

Funhouse

BED OF NAILS.
Tracks: Bed of nails.
■ 7" . . . . FXS 007
Flux / May '84.

GENERATION GENERATOR.
Tracks: Not Advised.
■ CD . . . . HMAXD 160
■ LP . . . . HMUSA 160
■ MC . . . . HMAMC 160
Heavy Metal America / Oct '90.

OUT OF CONTROL.
Tracks: Out of control / This could be hell.
■ 7" . . . . ENY 222
Ensign / Mar '82.

Furlong, Michael

BREAKAWAY.
Tracks: Not Advised.
■ LP . . . . MFN 79
Music For Nations / Oct '87.

SAVIN' THE BEST FOR YOU.
Tracks: Savin' the best for you.
■ 12" . . . . 12 KUT 128
■ 7" . . . . KUT 128
Music For Nations / Aug '88.

USE IT OR LOSE IT.
Tracks: Careless / Use it or lose it / Head on rock 'n' roll / Back to the wall / On the firing line / Right-a-way / Don't start lovin' me / Two hearts / I've got news for you / Don't gimme the biz.
■ LP .780181 1
WEA / '85.

　　　　　　　　　　　　　　　　　　　　　　　　■ DELETED

G

G-Force

G-FORCE.
Tracks: You / White knuckles / Rockin' and rollin' / She's got you / I look at you / Because of your love / You kissed me sweetly / Hot gossip / Woman's in love / Dancin'.

CD	CLACD 212
■ LP	CLALP 212
■ MC	CLAMC 212

Castle Classics / Feb '91.

HOT GOSSIP.
Tracks: Hot gossip / Because of your love.

■ 7"	JET 183

Jet / Jun '80.

WHITE KNUCKLES.
Tracks: White knuckles / I look at you.

■ 7"	JET 7005

Jet / Nov '80.

YOU.
Tracks: You / Trust your livin'.

■ 7"	JET 194

Jet / Jul '80.

G.B.H.

UK punk group formed in 1980. Debut single, *Leather, Bristles, Studs And Acne*, was released in 1981 on Clay. In 1982 GBH made two brief appearances on the UK national charts: *No Survivors*, and *Give Me Fire*, both reached the top 75. Debut LP *City Baby Attacked By Rats*. Together with labelmates Discharge and Scotland's Exploited, GBH were at the forefront of 'grassroots' bands that kept punk alive when the media/public lost interest, although by the mid 1980's were more of a thrash metal act. Still touring and recording, but without the mohicans.

ATTACK AND REVENGE.
Tracks: Not Advised.

CD	RR 349678

Road Runner / '89 / Pinnacle.

BRIT BOYS ATTACKED BY BRATS.
Tracks: Not Advised.

■ VHS	JE 232

Jettisoundz / Apr '93.

CATCH 23.
Tracks: Catch 23 / Hell hole.

■ 7"	CLAY 22

Clay / Apr '83.

CHURCH OF THE TRULY WARPED.
Tracks: Pure greed / Not enough / Leather coffin / Candy man / Lords of discipline / Where the wild things are / Church of the truly warped / Back / I need energy / Evil Evar / All for the cause.

CD	CDJUST 21
LP	JUST 21
MC	TJUST 21

Rough Justice / Oct '92 / Pinnacle.

CITY BABIES REVENGE.
Tracks: Diplomatic immunity / Drugs party / In 526 / See the man run / Vietnamese blues / Womb with a view / Forbidden zone / Valley of death / City baby's revenge / Pins and needles / Christianised cannibals / Faster faster / High octane fuel / I feel alright / Skanga (Herby weed).

■ LP	CLAYCLP 8
■ LP	CLAYLP 8

Clay / Dec '83.

■ LP	RR 9877

Road Runner / '89.

■ CD	CLAYCD 8

Clay / May '90.

MC	CLAYMC 8

Clay / Apr '93 / Plastic Head.

CITY BABY ATTACKED BY RATS.
Tracks: Boston babies / Sick boy / Slit your own throat / Willie Whitelaw's willie / Big women / Heavy discipline / Bellend bop / Self destruct / No survivors / Passenger on the menu.

■ LP	RR 9949

Road Runner / '89.

MC	CLAYMC 4
■ CD	CLAYCD 4
■ LP	CLAYLP 4

Clay / May '90.

CITY BABY ATTACKED BY RATS/ LEATHER, BRISTLESS..
Tracks: Not Advised.

MC Set	RR 49643

Road Runner / '89 / Pinnacle.

CLAY YEARS 81-84, THE.
Tracks: Necrophilia / Generals / No survivors / Sick boy / Time bomb / I am the hunted / City baby attacked by rats / Give me fire / Catch 23 / Diplomatic immunity / Womb with a view / City baby's revenge / Christianised cannibals / Four men.

CD	CLAYCD 21
LP	CLAYLP 21
MC	CLAYMC 21

Clay / Apr '93 / Plastic Head.

DIPLOMATIC IMMUNITY.
Tracks: No survivors / Self destruct / Give me fire / Catch 23 / City baby attacked by rats / Time bomb / Maniac / I am the hunted / Sick boys / Boston babies / I feel alright / Slut / Diplomatic immunity / Pins & needles / Faster, faster / City baby's revenge / Necrophilia / Generals / Womb with a view / Christianised cannibals / Four men.

MC	CLAYMC 106
■ CD	CLAYCD 106
■ LP	CLAY 106

Clay / Apr '93.

DO WHAT YOU DO.
Tracks: Do what you do.

■ 12"	12 CLAY 36
■ 7"	CLAY 36

Clay / Aug '90.

DRIVEN TO DEATH.
Tracks: Not Advised.

MC	CLAYMC 105
■ CD	CLAYCD 105
■ LP	CLAY 105

Clay / Apr '93.

FRIDGE TOO FAR, A.
Tracks: Go home / Twenty floors below / Checking out / Needle inna haystack / See you bleed / Pass the axe / Crossfire / Captain Chaos / Fist of regret / Nocturnal journal.

CD	CDJUST 13
MC	TJUST 13

Rough Justice / Oct '89 / Pinnacle.

■ LP	JUST 13

Rough Justice / Oct '89.

FROM HERE TO REALITY.
Tracks: Not Advised.

CD	CDJUST 16
LP	JUST 16
MC	TJUST 16

Music For Nations / Oct '90 / Pinnacle.

GBH - THE CLAY RECORDINGS.
Tracks: Necrophilia / Generals / No survivors / Sick boy / Time bomb / City baby attacked by rats / Give me fire / Diplomatic immunity / City baby's revenge / Self destruct / Maniac / Boston babies / I feel alright / Slut / Faster faster / Race against time / Dead on arrival / Big women / Freak / Hell hole / Alcohol / Drugsparty in 526 / Vietnamese blues / Valley of death / Skanga (Herby weed) / War dogs / Gunned down / Heavy discipline / Do what you do / Children of dust.

■ CD Set	CLAYCD 112

Clay / Jul '93.

GIVE ME FIRE.
Tracks: Give me fire / Man-trap.

■ 7"	CLAY 16
■ 7" P.Disc	CLAY 16P

Clay / Nov '82.

KAWASALL LIVE.
Tracks: Not Advised.

■ VHS	JE 239

Visionary Communications / Oct '93.

LEATHER BRISTLES STUDS ACNE.
Tracks: Race against time / Knife edge / Lycanthropy / Necrophilia / Sick boy / State executioner / Dead on

arrival / Generals / Freak / War dogs / City baby attacked by rats / City baby's revenge.

MC	PLATEMC 3
■ CD	PLATECD 3
■ LP	PLATE 3

Clay / Apr '93.

LEATHER BRISTLES STUDS ACNE.
Tracks: Leather bristles, studs, acne.

■ 12"	UNKNOWN

Clay / Mar '84.

LEATHER, BRISTLES/NO SURVIVORS/ SICK BOYS.
Tracks: Race against time / Knife edge / Lycanthropy / Necrophilia / Sale executioner / Dead on arrival / Generals / No survivors / Self destruct / Big women / Sick boy / Slit your own throat / Am I dead yet freak.

■ LP	RR 9935

Road Runner / '89.

MC	CLAYMC 5
■ CD Set	CLAYCD 5

Clay / May '90.

■ LP	CLAYLP 5

Clay / Apr '93.

LIVE AT THE ACE BRIXTON.
Tracks: Maniac / Mantrap / Time bomb / Necrophilia / Hellhole / I am the hunted / Generals / Catch 23 / Give me fire / Slut / Dead on arrival / Knife edge / Freak of nature / City baby attacked by rats / Who wins / Boston baby / Big women / No survivors / Alcohol / Self destruct.

■ VHS	JE 103

Jettisoundz / '83.

LIVE IN JAPAN.
Tracks: Give me fire / New decade / Seed of madness / Checkin' out / Mass production / Just in time for the epilogue / C U Bleed / Drugs party in 526 / I / City baby's revenge / Race against time / Knife edge / Necrophilia / Moonshine / Freak.

CD	DOJOCD 112

Dojo / Feb '94 / Castle Communications / BMG.

MIDNIGHT MADNESS AND BEYOND.
Tracks: Not Advised.

MC	TJUST 2
■ LP	JUST 2

Rough Justice / Feb '86.

■ CD	CDJUST 2

Rough Justice / Aug '87 / Pinnacle.

NO NEED TO PANIC.
Tracks: Not Advised.

CD	CDJUST 7
■ LP	JUST 7

Rough Justice / '89.

NO SURVIVORS.
Tracks: Sick boy / Maniac / Time bomb / Necrophilia / I am the hunted / Generals / Catch 23 / Give me fire / City baby attacked by rats / No survivors / Alcohol / Bell end stop.

■ CD	CLAYCD 102
■ LP	CLAY 102

Clay / Apr '93.

NO SURVIVORS.
Tracks: No survivors / Self destruct / Big women.

■ 7"	CLAY 8

Clay / Jan '82.

OH NO IT'S GBH AGAIN.
Tracks: Oh no it's GBH again.

■ 12"	12 KORE 101

Rough Justice / Sep '86.

SICK BOY.
Tracks: Sick boy / Slit your own throat / Am I dead yet.

■ 7"	CLAY 11

Clay / Jun '82.

VIDEO TOO FAR, A (Live in Los Angeles).
Tracks: Not Advised.

VHS	VFN 1

Video For Nations / Aug '89 / Pinnacle.

WOT A BARGIN.
Tracks: Wot a bargin.
■ 12" . . . . 12 KORE 104
Music For Nations / Mar '88.

G.G.F.H.

ECLIPSE.
Tracks: Not Advised.
CD . . . . KTB 2CD
LP . . . . KTB 2
■ MC . . . . KTB 2MC
Dreamtime / Feb '91.

REALITY.
Tracks: Reality.
■ 12" .KTB 009
■ CD Single . . . . KTB 009CD
Dreamtime / Jul '92.

Gaines, Steve

ONE IN THE SUN.
Tracks: Give it to get it / It's alright / Black jack David / On the road / One in the sun / Talkin' about love / Nothin' is now / Take my time / Summertime's here.
■ CD . . . . WKFMXD 136
■ LP . . . . WKFMLP 136
■ MC . . . . WKFMMC 136
FM Records / Nov '89.

Galactic Cowboys

GALACTIC COWBOYS.
Tracks: I'm not amused / My school / Why can't you believe in me / Kaptain Krude / Someone for everyone / Sea of tranquility / Pump up the space suit / Ranch on Mars reprise / Speak to me.
■ CD . . . . DGCD 24324
■ LP . . . . DGC 24324
■ MC . . . . DGCC 24324
Geffen / Aug '91.
CD .GFLD 19202
■ MC . . . . GFLC 19202
Geffen / Jun '93.

SPACE IN YOUR FACE.
Tracks: Space in your face / You make me smile / I do what I do / Circles in the fields / If I were a killer / Blind / No problems / About Mrs Leslie / Where are you now / Ranch on Mars (Available on CD only) / Still life of peace (Available onm CD only).
CD . . . . GED 24524
MC . . . . GEC 24524
Geffen / Jun '93 / BMG.

Gamma

DIRTY CITY.
Tracks: Dirty city / Ready for action.
■ 7" . . . . K 12517
Elektra / Mar '81.

GAMMA 3.
Tracks: What's gone is gone / Right the first time / Moving violation / Mobile devotion / Stranger / Condition yellow / Modern girl / No way out / Third degree.
■ LP . . . . K 52355
Elektra / Apr '82.

GAMMA I.
Tracks: Thunder and lightning / I'm alive / Razor king / No tears / Solar heat / Ready for action / Wish I was / Fight to the finish.
■ LP . . . . K 53163
Asylum / Jul '80.

GAMMA II.
Tracks: Meanstreak / Four horsemen / Dirty city / Voyager / Something in the air / Cat on a leash / Skin and bone / Mayday.
■ LP . . . . K 52245
Elektra / Oct '80.
MC K4 52245
Elektra / Mar '81 / WEA.

RIGHT THE FIRST TIME.
Tracks: Right the first time / Condition yellow.
■ 7" . . . . K 12165
Elektra / Nov '82.

SOMETHING IN THE AIR.
Tracks: Something in the air / May day.
■ 7" . . . . K 12480
Elektra / Oct '80.

SPACE INVADERS.
Tracks: Space invaders / Innocent.
■ 7" . . . . MAG 158
Magnet / Nov '79.

THUNDER AND LIGHTNING.
Tracks: Thunder and lightning / Razor king.
■ 7" . . . . K 12459
Elektra / Jun '80.

Gamma Ray

FUTURE MADHOUSE.
Tracks: Not Advised.
CD . . . . .NO 2033
Noise / Jun '93 / Pinnacle.

HEADING FOR TOMORROW.
Tracks: Not Advised.
CD . . . . .N 0151-2
LP . . . . .N 0151-1
MC . . . . .N 0151-4
Noise / '91 / Pinnacle.

HEAVEN CAN WAIT.
Tracks: Heaven can wait (new version) / Sail on / Who do you think you are / Lonesome stranger / Mr. Outlaw.
■ CD . . . . CDNUK 1515
■ Mini LP . . . . NUK 1515
Noise / Sep '90.

INSANITY & GENIUS.
Tracks: Tribute to the past / No return / Last before the storm / Cave principle / Future madhouse / Gamma ray (edited version) / Insanity and genius / 18 Years / Your torn is over / Heal me / Brothers.
CD .N 0203-2
LP .N 0203-1
MC .N 0203-4
Noise / Jun '93 / Pinnacle.

LUST FOR LIVE.
Tracks: Tribute to the past / No return / Changes / Insanity & genius / Last before the storm / Heal me / Medley / Funny madhouse.
VHS . . . . NV 0030
Noise / Jan '94 / Pinnacle.

SIGN NO MORE.
Tracks: Not Advised.
CD . . . . .NO 1782
LP . . . . .NO 1781
MC . . . . .NO 1784
Noise / Oct '91 / Pinnacle.

Gang Green

ANOTHER WASTED NIGHT.
Tracks: Another wasted night / Skate to hell / Last chance / Alcohol / Have fun / 19th hole / Skate hate / Let's drink some beer / Protect and serve / Another bomb / Voices carry / Sold out Alabama.
■ LP .FH 12-002
Funhouse / Oct '87.
■ LP 086 401
Funhouse / May '89.
CD . . . . .FH 039
Funhouse / Jan '90.
CD . . . . TAANG 131CD
■ LP . . . . TAANG 131LP
Taang / Nov '92 / Plastic Head.

CAN'T LIVE WITHOUT IT.
Tracks: Let's drink some beer / Bartender / Lost chamber / We'll give it to you / We can do / Have fun / Last chance / Just one bullet / Born to rock / Rabies / Voices carry / Sold out / Bedroom of doom / Bomb / Alcohol.
LP . . . . RR 93801
MC . . . . RR 93804
Road Runner / Aug '90 / Pinnacle.

I81B4U.
Tracks: Not Advised.
■ LP . . . . RR 9500 1
■ MC . . . . RR 9500 4
■ CD . . . . RR 9500 2
Road Runner / Jan '89.

KING OF BANDS.
Tracks: Not Advised.
CD . . . . RR 92542
LP . . . . RR 92541
MC . . . . RR 92544
Road Runner / Nov '91 / Pinnacle.

LIVING LOVING MAID.
Tracks: Living loving maid.
■ 12" . . . . RR 24631
Road Runner / Jul '88.

OLDER .. BUDWEISER.
Tracks: Not Advised.
CD . . . . EM 94642
■ LP . . . . EM 94641
■ LP . . . . LM 9464 1

MC . . . . EM 94644
Emergo / Sep '89 / Pinnacle.

YOU GOT IT.
Tracks: Not Advised.
■ LP . . . . RR 9591
Road Runner / Nov '87.
CD . . . . RR 349591
MC . . . . RR 4951 1
Road Runner / '89 / Pinnacle.

Gargleblud

HOWLINYOWLINSCREAMINESS.
Tracks: Not Advised.
■ LP . . . . BLUD 001
Avalanche / Oct '90.

Gaye Bykers On Acid

ALL HUNG UP.
Tracks: All hung up / Afternoon tea with Dave Greenfield / All hung up (rough rider mix) (12" only) / All hung up (reprisal) (12" only).
■ 12" . . . . VST 1027
■ 7" . . . . VS 1027
Virgin / Nov '87.

CANCER PLANET MISSION.
Tracks: Not Advised.
LP . . . . .NBX 001
MC .NBX 001MC
Naked Brain / Mar '90.
CD . . . . NBXCD 001
Naked Brain / Mar '90.

DRILL YOUR OWN HOLE.
Tracks: Motorvate / Call me a liar / All hung up / Zen express / World war 7 blues / Git down / After blow there's suck / So far out / Drive in salvation / T.V.cabbage.
■ MC . . . . TCV 2478
■ LP .V 2478
Virgin / Nov '87.
■ CD . . . . CDV 2478
Virgin / Nov '87.

DRILL YOUR OWN HOLE.
Tracks: Not Advised.
VHS .VVD 266
Virgin Vision / Nov '87 / Gold & Sons / TBD.

EVERYTHING'S GROOVY.
Tracks: Everything's groovy.
■ 12" . . . . ITTI 040
■ 7" . . . . IT 040
In Tape / Nov '86.

GAYE BYKERS ON ACID.
Tracks: Not Advised.
CD .RRCD 160
LP .RRLP 160
Receiver / Jul '93 / Total / BMG / Grapevine Distribution.

GIT DOWN.
Tracks: Git down / Tolchocked by Kenny Pride / Go go in out, in out garotschka (On 12" only).
■ 12" . . . . VST 1008
■ 7" . . . . VS 1008
Virgin / Oct '87.

GROOVEDIVESOAPDISH.
Tracks: Not Advised.
■ LP .MLP 002
■ CD . . . . .DRYCD 002
■ MC . . . . .DRY 002
Bleed / Nov '89.

HOT THING.
Tracks: Hot thing / Rad dude / After blow there's suck (Available on 12" format only).
■ 10" . . . . VSA 1165
■ 12" . . . . VST 1165
■ 7" . . . . VS 1165
Virgin / Dec '88.

NIGHT TRACKS EP (3.5.87).
Tracks: Don't be human Eric - Let's be Frank / Ruby red lips / Get one up to get down / Space rape.
■ 12" . . . . SFNT 010
Night Tracks / Jan '89.

NOSEDIVE KARMA.
Tracks: Nosedive karma.
■ 12" . . . . ITTI 046
■ 7" . . . . IT 046
■ 10" . . . . IT 04610
In Tape / May '87.

■ DELETED

S.P.A.C.E.
Tracks: S.P.A.C.E.
■ 12" . . . . .NBT 121
Naked Brain / Sep '90.

STEWED TO THE GILLS.
Tracks: It is are you / Better off dead / M.A.D. / Hot thing / Testicle of God (and it was good) / III / Mass gyrate (Only on CD and cassette.) / Harmonious murder / Shoulders / Hair of dog / Sade dude / Teeth / Floydrix / Bedlam a go go (Only on CD and cassette.) / Fairway to heaven / It is are you (concept reprise).
■ CD . . . . CDV 2579
■ LP .V 2579
■ MC . . . . TCV 2579
Virgin / Feb '89.

Geddes Axe

ESCAPE FROM NEW YORK.
Tracks: Escape from New York.
■ 12" . . . . BOLT 4
Bullet / Jun '83.

RETURN OF THE GODS.
Tracks: Return of the gods.
■ 7" .ACS 1
ACS / May '81.

SHARPEN YOUR WITS.
Tracks: Sharpen your wits / Rock & roll is the way.
■ 7" .AXE 1
Steel City / Aug '82.

Geisha

PHANTASMAGORIA.
Tracks: You got what it takes / Shock rock school / Gangland sector 21 / Alive and scratching / Claws of sin / Underworld / S & M youth.
■ LP . . . . HMILP 88
Heavy Metal / Apr '87.

Generic

FOR A FREE AND LIBERATED SA.
Tracks: For a free and liberated SA.
■ 7" .FE 001
Flat Earth / Jul '86.

L.P. (Generic & Mortal Terror).
Tracks: Not Advised.
■ LP .COX 010
Meantime / '88.

SPARK INSIDE.
Tracks: Spark inside.
■ 7" . . . . TUNE 010
Loony Tunes / Feb '88.

Genitorturers

120 DAYS OF GENITORTURE.
Tracks: Not Advised.
CD . . . . CDFLAG 81
Under One Flag / Oct '93 / Pinnacle.

Genocide

BLACK SANCTUARY.
Tracks: Not Advised.
CD . . . . KCD 1004
■ LP . . . . KRK 1004
King Classic / Nov '89.

GENOCIDE.
Tracks: Genocide / Genocide (version).
■ EP .SAP 2
Safari / '80.

IMAGES OF DELUSION.
Tracks: Not Advised.
■ LP . . . . SAP 2 12
Safari / Nov '79.

SUBMIT TO GENOCIDE.
Tracks: Not Advised.
■ LP . . . . NRR 30
MC . . . . NRC 30
New Renaissance(USA) / Nov '87 / Pinnacle.

Geordie

British rock band consisted of Brian Gibson, Tom Hill, Brian Johnson and Vic Malcolm. Achieved four hit singles 1972/3 - *All Because Of You* was biggest seller - in a sub-Status-Quo vein. Subsequently faded into obscurity. In 1980, however, singer Brian Johnson leapt to sudden superstardom when he replaced late Bon Scott in AC/DC.

ALL BECAUSE OF YOU.
Tracks: All because of you.
■ 7" . . . . EMI 2008
EMI / Mar '73.

CAN YOU DO IT.
Tracks: Can you do it.
■ 7" . . . . EMI 2031
EMI / Jun '73.

DON'T BE FOOLED BY THE NAME.
Tracks: Not Advised.
CD . . . . .REP 4124-WZ
Repertoire (Germany) / Aug '91 / Pinnacle.

DON'T DO THAT.
Tracks: Don't do that / Keep on rocking.
■ 7" . . . . RZ 3067
Regal Zonophone / Dec '72.
■ 7" . . . . RBUS 58
Red Bus / Feb '81.

ELECTRIC LADY.
Tracks: Electric lady.
■ 7" . . . . EMI 2047
EMI / Aug '73.

GEORDIE FEATURING BRIAN JOHNSON (Geordie Featuring Brian Johnson).
Tracks: All because of you / Keep on rockin' / Natural born loser / Rocking with the boys / Going down / Black cat woman / Electric lady / Can you do it / Don't do that / Ain't it just like a woman / Hope you like it / Fire queen / Mercenary man / Treat her like a lady.
■ LP . . . . RBMP 5001
Red Bus / Jan '81.

GOT TO KNOW.
Tracks: Got to know / Ride on baby.
■ 7" . . . . EMI 2226
EMI / Feb '75.

HOPE YOU LIKE IT.
Tracks: Not Advised.
CD . . . . REP 4033-WZ
LP . . . . REP 2033
MC . . . . REP 2033-TS
Repertoire (Germany) / Aug '91 / Pinnacle.

NO SWEAT.
Tracks: No sweat / This time / Move away / Time to run / So you lose again / Rock & Roll / Oh no / Hungry / We make it rock.
■ LP . . . . NEAT 1008
Neat / May '85.

NUTBUSH CITY LIMITS.
Tracks: Nutbush City Limits / No sweat.
■ 7" . . . . AS 034
Armageddon / Apr '82.

George, Robin

In 1982 this British singer, guitarist and songwriter played with short-lived Byron Band, fronted by ex-Uriah Heep singer David Byron. Solo, George released singles *Go down fighting* (1983) and *Heartline* (1984). Latter reactivated in early 1985, becoming minor U.K./U.S. hit.

DANGEROUS MUSIC.
Tracks: Heartline / Spy / No news is good news / French kisses / Stolen from my heart / Shout / Showdown / Hitlist / Shoot on sight / Don't turn away.
■ LP . . . . .BRON 554
MC . . . . .BRONC 554
Bronze / Feb '85 / WEA.

DANGEROUS MUSIC.
Tracks: Not Advised.
VHS . . . . .VVD 100
Virgin Vision / Gold & Sons / TBD.

DON'T TURN AWAY.
Tracks: Don't turn away / Heartline.
■ 12" . . . . .BROX 195
■ 7" . . . . BRO 195
Bronze / Aug '85.

GO DOWN FIGHTING.
Tracks: Go down fighting / Daylite.
■ 7" . . . . .ROB 1
■ 7" P.Disc . . . . .ROBSD 1
Arista / Oct '83.

HEARTLINE.
Tracks: Heartline / Space kadett.
■ 12" . . . . .BROX 191

■ 7" . . . . BRO 191
Bronze / Mar '85.

SPY.
Tracks: Spy.
■ 12" . . . . .BROX 188
■ 7" . . . . BRO 188
Bronze / Jan '85.

Georgia Satellites

BATTLESHIP CHAINS.
Tracks: Battleship chains (kick and lick remix) / Hard luck boy.
■ 12" . . . . .EKR 58 T
■ 7" . . . . EKR 58
Elektra / Apr '87.

GEORGIA SATELLITES.
Tracks: Keep your hands to yourself / Railroad steel / Battleship chains / Red lights / Myth of love / I can't stand the pain / Golden lights / Over and over / Nights of mystery / Every picture tells a story.
■ CD 9604962
■ LP 9604961
■ MC 9604964
Elektra / Nov '86.
CD 7559 604962
MC 7559 604964
Pickwick / Jan '93 / Pickwick.

GEORGIA SATELLITES: INTERVIEW PICTURE DISC.
Tracks: Not Advised.
LP P.Disc . . . . BAK 2112
Baktabak / Jan '89 / Arabesque Ltd.

HIPPY HIPPY SHAKE.
Tracks: Hippy hippy shake / Hand to mouth / Powerful stuff (On 12" version only.).
■ 12" . . . . .EKR 86 T
■ 7" . . . . EKR 86
Elektra / Jan '89.

IN THE LAND OF SALVATION AND SIN.
Tracks: I dunno / Bottle o' tears / All over but the crying / Shake that thing / Six years gone / Games people play / Another choice / Bring down the hammer / Slaughter house / Stellazine blues / Sweet blue midnight / Days gone by / Crazy Dan takes five.
CD 9608872
■ LP . . . . EKT 62
■ MC . . . . .EKT 62C
Elektra / Oct '89.

KEEP THE FAITH.
Tracks: Not Advised.
■ LP . . . . SPRAY 301
Making Waves / Mar '85.
■ CD . . . . CDSPRAY 301
■ MC . . . . CSPRAY 301
Making Waves / Jul '87.

KEEP YOUR HANDS TO YOURSELF.
Tracks: Keep your hands to yourself / Can't stand the pain / Nights of mystery / I'm waiting for the man.
■ 12" . . . . .EKR 50 T
■ 7" . . . . EKR 50
Elektra / Aug '87.

LET IT ROCK (Best Of Georgia Satellites).
Tracks: Don't pass me by / Keep your hands to yourself / Battleship chains / Myth of love / Can't stand the pain / Nights of mystery / Let it rock (live) / Open all night / Sheila / Mon cheri / Down and down / Saddle up / Hippy hippy shake / I dunno / All over but the cryin' / Six years gone / Hard luck boy / Almost Saturday night/Rockin' all over the world / Dan takes five / Another chance.
CD 7559613362
MC 7559613364
WEA / Feb '93 / WEA.

ONE MORE CHANCE.
Tracks: One more chance / Open all night / Saddle up / That woman.
■ 12" . . . . .EKR 102T
■ 7" .EKR 102
Elektra / Oct '89.

OPEN ALL NIGHT.
Tracks: Open all night / Sheila / Whole lotta shakin' goin' on / Cool inside / Don't pass me by / Mon cheri / Down and down / Dunk 'n' dine / Baby so fine / Hand to mouth.
CD 9607932
■ LP . . . . EKT 47
■ MC . . . . .EKT 47C
Elektra / Jun '88.

SHEILA.
Tracks: Sheila / Hippy hippy shake / Battleship chains (live) (Only on 12".) / Railroad steel (live) (Only on 12".).
- 12" . . . . EKR 89 T
- 7" . . . . EKR 89
Elektra / May '89.

Giant

I'LL SEE YOU IN MY DREAMS.
Tracks: I'll see you in my dreams / Stranger to me / Hold back the night (Only on 12" & CD single).
- 12" . . . . AMY 564
- 7" . . . . AM 564
- CD Single . . . . AMCD 564
A&M / May '90.

I'M A BELIEVER.
Tracks: I'm a believer / No way out / The big pitch.
- 12" . . . . AMY 546
- 7" . . . . AM 546
- 7" . . . . AMS 546
- CD Single . . . . AMCD 546
A&M / Mar '90.

IT TAKES TWO.
Tracks: It takes two.
- 12" . . . . AMY 571
- 7" . . . . AM 571
- CD Single . . . . AMCD 571
A&M / Aug '90.

LAST OF THE RUNAWAYS.
Tracks: I'm a believer / Innocent days / I can't get close enough / I'll see you in my dreams / No way out / Shake me up / It takes two / Stranger to me / Hold back the night / Love welcome home / Big pitch.
- CD . . . . CDA 5272
- MC . . . . AMC 5272
- LP . . . . AMA 5272
A&M / Apr '90.

STAY.
Tracks: Stay / Get used to it / Time to burn (Only available on 12" and CD Single).
- 12" 6580986
- 7" 6580987
- CD Single 6580982
Epic / May '92.

TIME TO BURN.
Tracks: Thunder and lightning / Chained / Lay it on the line / Stay / Lost in paradise / Smoulder / Time to burn / I'll be there (when it's over) / Save me tonight / Where would I be without you / Now until forever / Get used to it.
- LP 4694571
- MC 4694572
- CD 4694572
Epic / May '92.

Gigantor

DOWN BY LAW/GIGANTOR (see under Down By Law).

MAGIC BOZO SPIN.
Tracks: Not Advised.
- CD . . . . LF 074CD
Lost & Found / May '94 / Plastic Head.

QUICKER THAN QUICK.
Tracks: Quicker than quick.
- 7" . . . . LF 036
Plastic Head / Jun '92.

Gillan

On leaving Deep Purple in 1973, released three jazzy albums as Ian Gillan Band. Personnel change yielded heavier *Mr Universe* album in 1979; now called Gillan, group enjoyed four years of success. Attempt to reform Purple collapsed; "I went out and joined Black Sabbath, I was so annoyed," said Gillan. Brief spell in Sabbath equally fraught; Purple reunion finally launched in 1984. Fired in 1989, Gillan released two small-selling solo albums, returning to Purple yet again in 1993.

ACCIDENTALLY ON PURPOSE (Gillan, Ian & Roger Glover).
Tracks: Clouds and rain / Evil eye / She took my breath away / Dislocated / Via Miami / I can't dance to that / Can't believe you wanna leave / Lonely Avenue / Telephone box / I thought no / Cayman Island (CD only) / Purple people eater (CD only) / Chet (CD only).
- CD . . . . CDV 2498
- LP . . . . V 2498
- MC . . . . TCV 2498
Virgin / Feb '88.

BEST OF GILLAN - TROUBLE, THE.
Tracks: Trouble / New Orleans / Fighting man / Living for the city / Helter skelter / Mr. Universe / Telephone box / Dislocated / Sleeping on the job / M.A.D. (Mutually Assured Destruction) / No laughing in heaven / Nightmare / Restless / Purple sky / Born to kill (live) / Smike on the water (live).
- CD . . . . CDVIP 108
- MC . . . . TCVIP 108
Virgin V.I.P. / Nov '93 / Pickwick / TBD.

CHILD IN TIME.
Tracks: Lay me down / You make me feel so good / Shame / My baby loves me / Down the road / Child in time / Let it slide.
- LP 2490 136
Polydor / Jul '76.
- CD . . . . CDVM 2606
Virgin / Apr '90 / EMI.

CLEAR AIR TURBULENCE.
Tracks: Clean air turbulence / Five moons / Money lender / Over the hill / Goodhand Liza / Angel Manchenio.
- LP . . . . VM 4
Virgin / Jul '82.
- LP . . . . OVED 76
Virgin / Aug '88.
- MC . . . . OVEDC 76
Virgin / Aug '88.
- CD . . . . CDVM 4
Virgin / Jan '90.

DISLOCATED (Gillan, Ian & Roger Glover).
Tracks: Dislocated / Chet / Purple people eater (12" only).
- 12" . . . . TENT 193
- 7" . . . . TEN 193
10 / Jul '87.

DOUBLE TROUBLE.
Tracks: I'll rip your spine out / Restless / Men of war / Sunbeam / Nightmare / Hadely bop bop / Life goes on / Born to kill / No laughing in Heaven / No easy way / Trouble / Mutually assured destruction / If you believe me / New Orleans.
- Double LP . . . . VGD 3506
Virgin / Oct '81.
- MC . . . . VGDC 3506
Virgin / Oct '81.
- CD . . . . CDVM 3506
Virgin / Nov '89 / EMI.

FUTURE SHOCK.
Tracks: Future shock / Night ride out of Phoenix / Ballad of the Lucitania Express / No laughing in Heaven / Sacre bleu / New Orleans / Bite the bullet / If I sing softly / Don't want the truth / For your dreams / One for the road (Only on CD.) / Bad news (Only on CD.) / Take a hold of yourself (Only on CD.) / M.A.D. (Only on CD.) / Maelstrom (Only on CD.) / Trouble (Only on CD.) / Your sisters on my list (Only on CD.) / Handles on her hips (Only on CD.) / Higher and higher (Only on CD.) / I might as well go home (mystic) (Only on CD.).
- LP . . . . VK 2196
- MC . . . . TCV 2196
Virgin / Apr '81.
- LP . . . . OVED 74
Virgin / Aug '88.
- MC . . . . OVEDC 74
Virgin / Aug '88.
- CD . . . . CDVM 2196
Virgin / '90 / EMI.

GLORY ROAD.
Tracks: Unchain your brain / Are you sure / Time and again / No easy way / Sleeping on the job / On the rocks / If you believe me / Running, white face, city boy / Nervous / Your mother was right (Only on CD.) / Red watch (Only on CD.) / Abbey of Thelema (Only on CD.) / Trying to get to you (Only on CD.) / Come tomorrow (Only on CD.) / Dragons tongue (Only on CD.) / Post-fade brain damage (Only on CD.).
- LP . . . . V 2171
Virgin / Aug '80.
- LP . . . . OVED 49
- MC . . . . OVEDC 49
Virgin / Mar '84.
- CD . . . . CDVM 2171
Virgin / Nov '89 / EMI.

JAPANESE ALBUM.
Tracks: Not Advised.
- CD . . . . RPM 113
RPM / Jul '93 / Pinnacle.

LIVE AT READING ROCK FESTIVAL 1980.
Tracks: Not Advised.
- CD . . . . FRSCD 002
- LP . . . . FRSLP 002
- MC . . . . FRSMC 002
Raw Fruit / Dec '90 / Pinnacle.

LIVE AT THE BUDOKAN.
Tracks: Clear air turbulence / My baby loves me / Scarabus / Money lender / Twin exhausted / Over the hill / Child in time / Smoke on the water / Mercury high / Woman from Tokyo.
- CD . . . . CDVM 3507
- Double LP . . . . VGD 3507
- MC Set . . . . VGDC 3507
Virgin / '87.

LIVING FOR THE CITY.
Tracks: Living for the city / Breaking chains.
- 7" . . . . VS 519
- 7" P.Disc . . . . VSY 519
Virgin / Aug '82.

LONG GONE.
Tracks: Long gone.
- 7" . . . . VS 537
Virgin / Oct '82.

MAGIC.
Tracks: What's the matter / Bluesy blue sea / Caught in a trap / Long gone / Driving me wild / Demon driver / Living a lie / You're so right / Living for the city / Demon driver (reprise) / Breaking chains (Only on CD.) / Fiji (Only on CD.) / Purple sky (Only on CD.) / South Africa (Only on CD.) / John (Only on CD.) / South Africa (12" extended version) (Only on CD.) / Helter skelter (Only on CD.) / Smokestack lightnin' (Only on CD.).
- LP . . . . V 2238
Virgin / Oct '82.
- LP . . . . OVED 75
Virgin / Aug '88.
- MC . . . . OVEDC 75
Virgin / Aug '88.
- CD . . . . CDVM 2238
Virgin / Nov '89 / EMI.

MR.UNIVERSE.
Tracks: Mr. Universe / Second sight / Secret of the dance / She tears me down / Roller / Vengeance / Puget sound / Dead of night / Message in a bottle / Fighting man / On the rocks (Only on CD.) / Bite the bullet (Only on CD.) / Mr. Universe (version) (Only on CD.) / Smoke on the water (Only on CD.) / Lucille (Only on CD.).
- LP . . . . ACRO 3
Acrobat / Oct '79.
- CD . . . . CDVM 2589
Virgin / Mar '83 / EMI.
- LP . . . . FA 3057
Fame / Mar '83.

MUTUALLY ASSURED DESTRUCTION.
Tracks: Mutually assured destruction / Maelstrom.
- 7" . . . . VS 403
Virgin / Feb '81.

NEW ORLEANS.
Tracks: New Orleans.
- 7" . . . . VS 406
Virgin / Mar '81.

NIGHTMARE.
Tracks: Nightmare.
- 7" . . . . VS 441
Virgin / Oct '81.

NO LAUGHING IN HEAVEN.
Tracks: No laughing in Heaven / Lucille / One for the road / Bad news.
- 7" . . . . VS 425
Virgin / Jun '81.

RESTLESS.
Tracks: Restless.
- 7" . . . . VS 465
Virgin / Jan '82.

SCARABUS.
Tracks: Scarabus / Twin exhausted / Poor boy hero / Mercury high / Pre-release / Slags to bitches / Apathy / Mad Elaine / Country lights / Fool's mate / My baby loves me (live).
- LP . . . . VM 3
Virgin / Jul '82.
- LP . . . . OVED 77
Virgin / Aug '88.
- MC . . . . OVEDC 77
Virgin / Aug '88 / EMI.
- CD . . . . CDVM 3
Virgin / Jan '90.

■ DELETED

SHE TOOK MY BREATH AWAY (Gillan, Ian & Roger Glover).
Tracks: She took my breath away / Cayman Island.
■ 12".....................VST 1041
■ 7".......................VS 1041
Virgin / Jan '88.

SLEEPIN' ON THE JOB.
Tracks: Sleepin' on the job / Higher and higher.
■ 7".......................VS 355
Virgin / Jun '80.

TROUBLE.
Tracks: Trouble.
■ 7".......................VS 377
Virgin / Oct '80.

TROUBLE - THE BEST OF GILLAN.
Tracks: Trouble / New Orleans / Fighting man / Living for the city / Helter skelter / Mr. Universe / Telephone box / Dislocated / Sleeping on the job / No laughing in heaven / Nightmare / Restless / Purple sky / Born to kill / Smoke on the water.
CD....................VVIPD 113
MC....................VVIPC 113
Virgin V.I.P. / May '91 / Pickwick / TBD.

VENGEANCE.
Tracks: Vengeance / Smoke on the water.
■ 7"...................BAT 12
Arista / May '81.

VERY BEST OF GILLAN.
Tracks: Sleeping on the job / Secret of the dance / Time and again / Vengeance / Roller / M.A.D. / Dead of night / Nightmare / Don't want the truth / If you believe me / Trouble / New Orleans / Living for the city / Restless / No laughing in heaven / Smoke on the water (live).
CD....................MCCD 032
MC....................MCTC 032
Music Club / Sep '91 / Gold & Sons / TBD / Video Collection / C.M. Distribution.

Gillan, Ian

CHERKAZOO & OTHER STORIES.
Tracks: Not Advised.
CD.......................RPM 104
RPM / Jul '93 / Pinnacle.

GARTH ROCKET & THE MOONSHINERS (see under Rocket, Garth).

GILLAN (Gillan, Ian Band).
Tracks: Not Advised.
■ LP....................STI 80000
Flyover / Feb '79.

GILLAN AT THE RAINBOW (Gillan).
Tracks: Not Advised.
VHS....................CFV 07022
Channel 5 / '88 / Channel 5 Video / P.R.O. Video / Gold & Sons.

IAN GILLAN - LIVE.
Tracks: Not Advised.
■ VHS...................CMP 6053
Castle Music Pictures / '92.

IAN GILLAN BAND (Gillan, Ian Band).
Tracks: Not Advised.
VHS....................SPC 07022
Spectrum (1) / Mar '90 / PolyGram.

LIVE AT THE RAINBOW (Gillan, Ian Band).
Tracks: Not Advised.
VHS....................SPC 00402
Spectrum (1) / Apr '90 / PolyGram.

LIVE AT THE RITZ '89 (see under Rockett, Garth).

LIVE AT THE RITZ '89 (see under Rockett, Garth).

MAD ELAINE (Gillan, Ian Band).
Tracks: Mad Elaine / Mercury high.
■ 7"...................WIP 6423
Island / Feb '78.

NAKED THUNDER.
Tracks: Gut reaction / No good luck / Sweet Lolita / Moonshine / Love gun / Talking to you / Nothing but the best / Nothing to lose / Long and lonely ride / No more can on the Brazos.
CD....................9031718990
■ LP....................9031718991
■ MC....................9031718994
East West / Jul '90.

NO GOOD LUCK.
Tracks: No good luck / Love gun / Rock 'n' roll girls.
■ 12"...................YZ 513T
■ 7"....................YZ 513
■ CD Single...............YZ 513CD
■ MC Single..............YZ 513C
East West / Aug '90.

SOLE AGENCY & REPRESENTATION (Gillan, Ian & The Javelins).
Tracks: Too much monkey business / It'll be me / You really got a hold on me / It's only make believe / Can I get a witness / Poison Ivy / Rave on / Blue Monday / You better move on / Somethin' else / Money / Love potion no.9 / Let's dance / Roll over Beethoven.
CD.......................RPM 132
RPM / Aug '94 / Pinnacle.

SOUTH AFRICA.
Tracks: South Africa / John / South Africa (extended version) (12" only).
■ 7"....................VS 1088
■ 12"...................VST 1088
Virgin / Jun '88.

TOOL BOX.
Tracks: Hang me out to dry / Toolbox / Dirty dog / Candy horizon / Don't hold me back / Pictures of hell / Dancing nylon shirt / Bed of nails / Gassed up / Everything I need / Dancing nylon shirt (part 2).
CD....................9031756412
■ LP....................9031756411
MC....................9031756414
East West / Oct '91 / WEA.

WHAT I DID ON MY VACATION.
Tracks: On the rocks / Scarabus / Puget sound / Mad Elaine (NOT on CD) / Time and again (NOT on CD) / Vengeance (NOT on CD) / No easy way / If I sing softly / I'll rip your spine out / New Orleans / Mutually assured destruction / Unchain your brain (NOT on CD) / You're so right / No laughing in Heaven (NOT on CD) / Long gone / If you believe me / Trouble / Bluesy blue sea.
■ MC Set................CDIXD 39
■ Double LP..............DIXD 39
■ CD...................DXDCD 39
10 / Jun '86.

Girl

NWOBHM act - Phil Collen, Dave Gaynor, Gerry Laffy, Simon Laffy and Philip Lewis - reached no. 33 with their debut album *Sheer Greed* (Jet). Following 1982's *Wasted Youth*, guitarist Phil Collen left to join Def Leppard. Girl disbanded shortly afterwards. Phil Lewis later joined L.A. Guns.

BLOOD, WOMEN, ROSES.
Tracks: Not Advised.
CD....................PRODCD 4
Product Inc. / May '87 / Vital Distribution.
■ LP....................33PROD 4
Product Inc. / May '87.

DO YOU LOVE ME?.
Tracks: Do you love me / Strawberries.
■ 7"...................JET 169
Jet / Jan '80.

HOLLYWOOD TEASE.
Tracks: Hollywood tease / You really got me / My number.
■ 7"...................JET 176
Jet / Apr '80.

LOVE IS A GAME.
Tracks: Love is a game / Little Miss Ann.
■ 10"...................JET 10191
■ 7"...................JET 191
Jet / Aug '80.

OLD DOGS.
Tracks: Old dogs / Passing clouds.
■ 7"...................JET 7019
Jet / Jan '82.

SHE NO RATTLE MY CAGE.
Tracks: She no rattle my cage.
■ 7"...................L 26500
K / Jan '88.

SHEER GREED.
Tracks: Hollywood tease / Things you say / Lovely Lorraine / Strawberries / Little Miss Ann / Doctor doctor / Do you love me / Take me dancing / What's up / Passing clouds / My number / Heartbreak America.
■ LP...................JETLP 224
MC....................JETCA 224
Jet / Jan '80 / Sony / Total / BMG.

WASTED YOUTH.
Tracks: Thru' the twilight / Old dogs / Ice in the blood / Wasted youth / Standard romance / Nice 'n' nasty / McKitty's back / 19 / Overnight angels / Sweet kids.
■ LP...................JETLP 238
Jet / Jan '82.

Girlschool

Female NWOBHM act - Denise Dufort, Kelly Johnson, Kim McAuliffe and Enid Williams - Girlschool were protegees of Motorhead. Formed in 1978, their debut single *Take It All Away* won them a support slot with Motorhead and a deal with Bronze Records. The *St. Valentine's Day Massacre* EP, which featured Motorhead and Girlschool duetting on a cover of Johnny Kid's classic *Please Don't Touch* was a top 5 hit. Williams left in 1982 after the big selling *Hit 'n' Run* LP. Girlschool moved to Polygram, ditched the denim and leather and had a hit with Gary Glitter in 1986.

1-2-3-4 ROCK AND ROLL.
Tracks: 1-2-3-4 rock and roll / Tush / Don't call it love / Emergency (Only on 12" single.).
■ 12"...................BROX 169
■ 7"....................BRO 169
Bronze / Aug '83.

20TH CENTURY BOY.
Tracks: 20th century boy / Breaking all the rules.
■ 12"...................BROX 171
■ 7"....................BRO 171
Bronze / Oct '83.

BEST OF GIRLSCHOOL, THE.
Tracks: Take it all away / It could be better / Emergency / Nothing to lose / Race with the devil / Demolition boys / C'mon let's go / Yeah right / Hit and run / Tonight (Live) / Kick it down / Please don't touch / Bomber / Wildlife / Don't call it love / Screaming blue murder / 1,2,3,4 Rock 'n' roll / Burning in the heat / 20th Century boy / Play dirty / I'm the leader of the gang / Play with fire / Fox on the run / Head over heels.
CD...................DOJOCD 103
Dojo / Feb '94 / Castle Communications / BMG.

BURNING IN THE HEAT.
Tracks: Burning in the heat / Surrender.
■ 12"...................BROX 176
■ 7"....................BRO 176
Bronze / Feb '84.

C'MON LET'S GO.
Tracks: C'mon let's go / Tonight / Demolition boys.
■ 7"...................BRO 126
Bronze / Jul '81.

CHEERS YOU LOT.
Tracks: C'mon let's go / Race with the devil / Wildlife / Screaming blue murder / Please don't touch / Breakout / Emergency / Yeah right / Bomber / Demolition boys / Take it from me / Tush.
■ LP...................METALPM 127
Razor / Sep '89.
CD....................METALMCD 127
Metal Masters / Jul '91 / Pinnacle.

COLLECTION: GIRLSCHOOL.
Tracks: 1-2-4 A rock & roll / Furniture fire / Take it all away / Kick it down / Midnight ride / Race with the devil / Play dirty / Yeah right / Emergency / Breakout (Knob in the media) / I'm your victim / Flesh and blood / Tush / Don't stop / Future flash / Rock me shock me / Screaming blue murder / Wild life / Bomber / Nothing to lose / Live with me / Like it like that / Tonight / Take it from me.
CD....................CCSCD 314
Castle / Dec '91 / BMG.

DEMOLITION.
Tracks: Demolition boys / Not for sale / Race with the devil / Take it all away / Nothing to lose / Breakdown / Midnight ride / Emergency / Baby doll / Deadline.
■ LP...................BRON 525
Bronze / Jul '80.

DEMOLITION/HIT AND RUN.
Tracks: Demolition boys / Not for sale / Race with the devil / Take it all away / Nothing to lose / Breakdown / Midnight ride / Emergency / Babydoll / Deadline / C'mon let's go / Hunter / (I'm your) Victim / Kick it down / Following the crowd / Tush / Hit and run / Watch your step / Back to start / Yeah right / Future flash.
CD....................LOMACD 1
Loma / Feb '94 / BMG.

EMERGENCY.
Tracks: Emergency / Furniture fire.
■ 7" . . . . BRO 89
Bronze / Feb '80.

FROM THE VAULTS.
Tracks: Nothing to lose / Furniture fire / Bomber / Demolition boys (Live) / 1234 Rock 'n' roll ("12" Extended version) / Tush (New version) / I'm the leader of the gang (I am) / Not for sale / Please dont' touch / Tonight / Don't stop / Don't call it love (New version) / Like it like that / Tonight (Live).
CD . . . . NEMCD 642
Sequel / Apr '94 / Castle Communications / BMG / Hot Shot.

GIRLSCHOOL.
Tracks: Not Advised.
CD . . . . .CMGCD 006
Communique / Nov '92 / Plastic Head.

HIT AND RUN.
Tracks: Hit and run / Tonight / Tush (12" only).
■ 12" . . . . .BROX 118
■ 7" . . . . .BRO 118
Bronze / Apr '81.

HIT AND RUN.
Tracks: Hit and run / C'mon let's go / Hunter / Victim / Kick it down / Following the crowd / Tush / Watch your step / Back to start / Yeah right / Future flash.
■ LP . . . . .BRON 534
Bronze / Apr '81.

I'M THE LEADER OF THE GANG (I AM)
(Girlschool & Gary Glitter).
Tracks: I'm the leader of the gang.
■ 12" . . . . .GWT 1
■ 7" . . . . .GWR 1
GWR / May '86.

NIGHTMARE AT MAPLE CROSS.
Tracks: Not Advised.
■ LP . . . . .GWLP 2
■ MC . . . . .GWTC 2
GWR / '86.

NIGHTMARE AT MAPLE CROSS/TAKE A BITE.
Tracks: All day all night / Play with fire / Danger sign / Never too late / Tiger feet / Back for more / Let's go crazy / You got me (Under your spell) / Let's break out / Turn it up / Action / Fox on the run / Girls on top / Tear it up / Love at first bite / Head over heels / Up all night / This time / Don't walk away / Too hot to handle.
CD . . . . LOMACD 8
Loma / Feb '94 / BMG.

NOTHING TO LOSE.
Tracks: Nothing to lose / Baby doll.
■ 7" . . . . .BRO 95
Bronze / May '80.

PLAY DIRTY.
Tracks: Going under / High and dry / Play dirty / 20th century boy / Breaking all the rules / Burning in the heat / Surrender / Rock me shock me / Running for cover / Breakout.
■ LP . . . . .BRON 548
Bronze / Nov '83.

PLAY DIRTY LIVE.
Tracks: Not Advised.
VHS 041 387 2
Polygram Music Video / Jun '86 / PolyGram.
VHS . . . . CFV 07442
Channel 5 / Jun '88 / Channel 5 Video / P.R.O. Video / Gold & Sons.

RACE WITH THE DEVIL.
Tracks: 1-2-3-4 rock and roll / Furniture fire / Take it all away / Kick it down / Midnight ride / Race with the devil / Play dirty / Yeah right / Emergency / Breakout (Knob in the media) / Flesh and blood / Tush / Don't stop / Future flash / Rock me shock me / Screaming blue murder / Wild life / Bomber / Nothing to lose / Live with me / Like it like that / Tonight / Take it from me.
■ LP . . . . .RAWLP 013
MC . . . . .RAWTC 013
Raw Power / Apr '86 / Pinnacle.

RACE WITH THE DEVIL.
Tracks: Race with the devil / Take it all away.
■ 7" . . . . .BRO 100
Bronze / Aug '80.

SCREAMING BLUE MURDER.
Tracks: Screaming blue murder / Live with me / Take it from me / Wildlife / Turns your head around / Don't call it love / Hell razor / When your blood runs cold you got me / Flesh and blood.

■ LP . . . . .BRON 541
■ MC . . . . .BRONC 541
Bronze / May '82.

SCREAMING BLUE MURDER/PLAY DIRTY.
Tracks: Scraming blue murder / Live with me / Take it from me / Wildlife / It turns your head around / Don't call it love / Hellrazor / When your blood runs cold / You got me / Flesh and blood / Going under / High 'n' dry / Play dirty / 20th Century boy / Breaking all the rules / Burning in the heat / Break out (Knob in the media) / Running for cover / Rock me shock me / Surrender.
CD . . . . LOMACD 4
Loma / Feb '94 / BMG.

St. VALENTINES DAY MASSACRE (see under Headgirl).

TAKE A BITE.
Tracks: Action / Girls on top / Fox on the run / Tear it up / Love at first bite / Up all night / Don't walk away / Head over heels / This time / Too hot too handle.
■ CD . . . . GWCD 21
■ LP . . . . GWLP 21
■ MC . . . . GWTC 21
GWR / Oct '88.
■ LP . . . . RR 9513 1
Road Runner / '89.

TAKE IT ALL AWAY.
Tracks: Take it all away.
■ 7" . . . . NIK 6
City / Sep '81.

WILDLIFE.
Tracks: Wildlife / Don't call it love / Don't stop.
■ EP . . . . BRO 144
Bronze / Apr '82.

YEAH RIGHT.
Tracks: Yeah right / Hunter.
■ 7" . . . . BRO 110
Bronze / Dec '80.

Giuffria

CALL TO THE HEART.
Tracks: Call to the heart / Out of the blue.
■ 12" . . . . .MCAT 935
■ 7" . . . . .MCA 935
■ 7" Set . . . . .MCAS 935
MCA / Mar '85.

GIUFFRIA.
Tracks: Do me right / Don't tear me down / Lonely in love / Turn me on / Awakening / Call to the heart / Dance / Trouble again / Line of fire / Out of the blue (too far gone).
■ LP . . . . .MCF 3244
■ MC . . . . .MCFC 3244
MCA / Feb '85.
■ LP . . . . .MCL 1844
■ MC . . . . .MCLC 1844
MCA / Mar '87.
■ CD . . . . DMCL 1844
MCA / Jun '89.

SILK AND STEEL.
Tracks: No escape / Love you forever / I must be dreaming / Girl / Change of heart / Radio / Heartache / Lethal lover / Tell it like it is / Dirty secrets.
■ LP . . . . IMCA 5742
■ MC . . . . IMCAC 5742
MCA / Aug '86.
■ CD . . . . MCAD 5742
MCA / '88.

Global Genocide Forget..

DISEASE (Global Genocide Forget Heaven).
Tracks: Room 213 (Frozen heart mix) / Hands / D.M.R.D. (Revenge mix) / Disease / Real (Nightmare mix) / Dark powers / Plasterchrist / Confession / Flesh.
CD . . . . KTB 007CD
LP . . . . .KTB 007
Dreamtime / Mar '93 / Vital Distribution.

Glover, Roger

ACCIDENTALLY ON PURPOSE (see under Gillan).

BUTTERFLY BALL, THE.
Tracks: Not Advised.
■ LP . . . . LONG 9
MC . . . . LONGC 9
Safari / Nov '84 / Pinnacle.

CD . . . . LICD 900013
Line / '89 / C.M. Distribution / Grapevine Distribution / A.D.A. Distribution / Conifer Records.

BUTTERFLY BALL, THE/WIZARD'S CONVENTION (1974 film musical) (Glover, Roger & Deep Purple).
Tracks: Dawn / Get ready / Saffron dormouse and Lizzy bee / Harlequin hare / Old blind mole / Magician moth / No solution / Behind the smile / Fly away / Aranea / Sitting in a dream / Waiting / Sir Maximus mouse / Dreams of Sir Bedivere / Together again / Watch out for the bat / Little chalk blue / Feast / Love is all / Homeward / Craig song / When the sun stops shining / Loose ends / Money to burn / Who's counting on me / Make it soon / Until tomorrow / Light of my life / She's a woman / Swanks and swells.
CD . . . . VSOPCD 139
■ Double LP . . . . VSOPLP 139
MC . . . . VSOPMC 139
Connoisseur Collection / Oct '89 / Pinnacle.

DISLOCATED (see under Gillan).

MASK & THE ELEMENTS.
Tracks: First a ring of clay / Next a ring of fire / Third rings watery flow / Fourth rings with the wind / Finale / Divided world / Getting stranger / Mask / Fake it / Dancin' again / (You're so) Remote / Hip level / Don't look down.
CD . . . . VSOPCD 183
MC . . . . VSOPMC 183
Connoisseur Collection / Apr '93 / Pinnacle.

MASK, THE.
Tracks: Divided word / Getting stranger / Mask / Fake it / Dancin' again / Remote / Hip level / Don't look down.
■ LP . . . . POLD 5139
Polydor / Jun '84.

MASK, THE.
Tracks: Mask / You're so remote.
■ 7" . . . . .POSP 678
Polydor / Jun '84.

SHE TOOK MY BREATH AWAY (see under Gillan).

God

BREACH BIRTH EP.
Tracks: Not Advised.
■ 12" . . . . SIT 65T
Situation 2 / Mar '90.

FOR LOVERS ONLY.
Tracks: For lovers only.
■ LP . . . . YEAHHUP 002
Shakin' Street / May '89.

GOD.
Tracks: Not Advised.
CD . . . . .PPP 106
PDCD / Jan '94 / SRD / Plastic Head.

GOD LIVE AT St. MARY'S CHURCH.
Tracks: Not Advised.
CD . . . . PPP 106CD
Pathological / Mar '92 / Cadillac.

POSSESSION.
Tracks: Pretty / F**ked / Return to hell / Soul fire / Hate meditation / Lord I'm on my way / Love / Black Jesus.
CD . . . . CDVE 910
■ MC . . . . TCVE 910
Venture / Mar '92.

SWEET LIFE.
Tracks: See smoke smell fire / Finger / Settling down / Lust / Wimps / Teste marce / Stomping ground / Sack B / So be it / Asset of punishment.
■ LP . . . . K 031/110
Konkurrel / May '88.

God Machine

DESERT SONG EP.
Tracks: Desert song / Prostitute / Commitment / Pictures of a bleeding boy.
■ 12" . . . . .FICSX 43
■ CD Single . . . . .FICCD 43
Fiction / May '92.

EGO.
Tracks: Ego / Temptation / Piano song.
■ 12" . . . . .FICSX 044
■ CD Single . . . . .FICCD 044
Fiction / Oct '92.

■ DELETED

HOME.
Tracks: Home.
■ **CD Single** . . . . **FICCD 47**
■ **12"** . . . . **FICSX 47**
Fiction / Jan '93.

ONE LAST LAUGH.
Tracks: Not Advised.
CD **523685-2**
MC **523685-4**
Polydor / Sep '94 / PolyGram.

PURITY EP.
Tracks: Not Advised.
■ **12"** . . . . **EVER 008 T**
Eve / Nov '91.

SCENES FROM A 2ND STOREY.
Tracks: Dream machine / She said / Blind man / I've seen the man / Desert song / Home / It's all over / Temptation / Out / Ego / Seven / Purity / Piano song.
CD **5171562**
MC **5171564**
■ **LP** **5171561**
Polydor / Jan '93.

Goddo

IF TOMORROW NEVER COMES.
Tracks: If tomorrow never comes / Feeling strange today.
■ **7"** . . . . **ATX 263**
Noir / Apr '82.

PRETTY BAD BOYS.
Tracks: Not Advised.
■ **LP** . . . . **LAT 1120**
MC . . . . **CAT 1120**
Noir / Jan '82 / Pinnacle / Jetstar.

Godflesh

COLD WORLD.
Tracks: Cold world.
■ **12"** . . . . **MOSH 056T**
■ **12"** . . . . **MOSH 056**
■ **CD Single** . . . . **MOSH 056CD**
Earache / Jul '92.

GODFLESH.
Tracks: Not Advised.
LP . . . . **FLESHLP 1**
Swordfish / Jan '92 / RTM / Pinnacle.
CD . . . . **MOSH 20 CD**
Earache / Feb '94 / Vital Distribution.

MERCILESS.
Tracks: Merciless / Blind / Unworthy / Flowers.
12" . . . . **MOSH 116T**
CD Single . . . . **MOSH 116CD**
Earache / Mar '94 / Vital Distribution.

PURE.
Tracks: Not Advised.
LP . . . . **MOSH 032**
MC . . . . **MOSH 032MC**
Earache / Sep '91 / Vital Distribution.
CD . . . . **MOSH 032CD**
Earache / Sep '94 / Vital Distribution.

SELFLESS.
Tracks: Xnoybis / Bigot / Black bored angel / Anything is mine / Empyreal / Crush my soul / Body dome light / Toll / Heartless / Mantra / Go spread your wings (On CD only.).
CD . . . . **MOSH 085CD**
LP . . . . **MOSH 085**
Earache / Sep '94 / Vital Distribution.

SLATE MAN.
Tracks: Slate man.
■ **12"** . . . . **MOSH 47T**
■ **CD Single** . . . . **MOSH 47CD**
Earache / Jan '93.

SLAVE STATE.
Tracks: Not Advised.
LP . . . . **MOSH 030**
MC . . . . **MOSH 030MC**
Earache / Jan '93 / Vital Distribution.

STREETCLEANER.
Tracks: Not Advised.
■ **LP** . . . . **MOSH 15**
MC . . . . **MOSH 15 MC**
Earache / Nov '89 / Vital Distribution.
CD . . . . **MOSH 15 CD**
Earache / Sep '94 / Vital Distribution.

TINY TEARS.
Tracks: Not Advised.
■ **LP** . . . . **TINY 1**
Swordfish / Jan '89.

TINY TEARS.
Tracks: Tiny tears.
■ **12"** **12FLESH 002**
Swordfish / Jan '89.

Godspeed

RIDET.
Tracks: Not Advised.
CD **756782573-2**
MC **756782573-4**
WEA / Mar '94 / WEA.

Godz

I'LL GET YOU ROCKIN'.
Tracks: Not Advised.
■ **LP** . . . . **HMUSA 48**
Heavy Metal America / Nov '85.

POWER ROCK FROM USA.
Tracks: go away / Baby, I love you / Guaranteed / Gotta keep a runnin' / Under the table / Cross country / Candy's going bad.
■ **LP** . . . . **XL 13051**
■ **MC** . . . . **XK 13051**
RCA / '83.

Gogmagog

I WILL BE THERE.
Tracks: I will be there.
■ **12"** . . . . **YUMT 109**
Food For Thought / Sep '85.

Golden Earring

Despite a mammoth career, international stardom has eluded Golden Earring apart from their huge selling *Radar Love* single in 1974. Often descibed as the Dutch equivilant of Status Quo - durable and hard working rockers - they remain big stars in their native country.

2ND LIVE.
Tracks: Not Advised.
■ **LP** **2625 042**
MC **3500 130**
Polydor (Import) / Sep '81 / Pinnacle / Silver Sounds (CD) / PolyGram.

BEST OF GOLDEN EARRING, THE.
Tracks: Not Advised.
CD . . . . **VSOPCD 171**
MC . . . . **VSOPMC 171**
Connoisseur Collection / Mar '92 / Pinnacle.

BLOODY BUCCANEERS.
Tracks: Making love to yourself / Temporary madness / When loves turns to pain / Joe / Planet blue / Going to the run / Bloody buccaneers / One shot / Away from paradise / In a bad moon / Pourin' my heart out again.
■ **CD** **4680932**
■ **LP** **4680931**
■ **MC** **4680934**
Columbia / '91.

BOMBAY.
Tracks: Bombay / Faded jeans.
■ **7"** **2121312**
Polydor / Feb '77.

CUT.
Tracks: Devil made me do it / Future / Baby dynamite / Last of the Mohicans / Lost and found / Twilight zone / Chargin' up my batteries / Secrets.
■ **LP** **6302 224**
MC **7144 224**
Philips / Apr '83 / PolyGram.

EIGHT MILES HIGH.
Tracks: Landing / Song of a devil's servant / One huge road / Everyday's torture / Eight miles high.
■ **CD** **825 371-2**
Polydor.

GOLDEN EARRING LIVE.
Tracks: Candy's going bad / She flies on strange wings / Mad love's comin' / Eight miles high / Vanilla queen / To the hilt / Fighting windmills / Con man / Radar love / Just like Vince Taylor.
■ **LP** **2625 034**
Polydor / Sep '77.
■ **LP** . . . . **SPELP 44**
Polydor / Oct '83.

GRAB IT FOR A SECOND.
Tracks: Movin' down life / Against the grain / Grab it for a second / Cell 29 / Roxanne / Leather / Temptin' / U-turn time.
■ **LP** **2310 639**
Polydor.

GREATEST HITS: GOLDEN EARING.
Tracks: Not Advised.
■ **Double LP** **2664 440**
MC **3578 487**
Polydor / Nov '80 / PolyGram.

GREATEST HITS: GOLDEN EARRING VOL.3.
Tracks: Radar love / She flies on strange wings / Instant poetry / Ce soir / Movin' down life / Bombay / Weekend love / Sleepwalking / Against the grain / I do rock 'n' roll / Long blond animal / No for an answer.
■ **LP** **2311 094**
MC **3100 609**
Polydor (Import) / Mar '84 / Pinnacle / Silver Sounds (CD) / PolyGram.

INSTANT POETRY.
Tracks: Instant poetry / From heaven to hell.
■ **7"** **2094-121**
Track / '74.

MOONTAN.
Tracks: Radar love / Candy's going bad / Vanilla queen / Big tree, blue sea / Are you receiving me.
■ **LP** **2406 112**
MC **3191 112**
Track / PolyGram.

N.E.W.S.
Tracks: Not Advised.
CD . . . . **CNR 100 014**
CNR (Holland) / '88 / EMI.

NAKED TRUTH, THE.
Tracks: Not Advised.
MiniDisc **472619-8**
Columbia / Apr '93 / Sony.

NORTH SOUTH EAST WEST.
Tracks: Not Advised.
■ **LP** . . . . **CAL 204**
MC . . . . **CAC 204**
Carrere / Apr '84 / WEA.

RADAR LOVE.
Tracks: Radar love / Just like Vince Taylor.
■ **7"** **2094 116**
Track / Dec '73.
■ **7"** **2121 335**
Polydor / Oct '77.

RADAR LOVE (OLD GOLD).
Tracks: Radar love / Twilight zone.
7" . . . . **OG 9582**
Old Gold / Mar '90 / Pickwick.

SLEEP WALKIN'.
Tracks: Sleep walkin' / Babylon.
■ **7"** **2001 626**
Polydor / Feb '76.

SWITCH.
Tracks: Plus minus absurdio / Love is a rodeo / Switch / Kill me / Tons of time / Daddy's gonna save my soul / Troubles and hassles / Lonesome DJ.
■ **LP** **2872 104**
MC **3472 104**
Karussell (Germany) / Aug '82.

TO THE HILT.
Tracks: Not Advised.
■ **LP** **248 033-1**
Polydor (Germany) / Oct '85.

TWILIGHT ZONE.
Tracks: Twilight zone / King Dark.
■ **12"** . . . . **MERX 122**
■ **7"** . . . . **MER 122**
Mercury / Oct '82.

VERY BEST OF VOL.1: GOLDEN EARRING.
Tracks: Not Advised.
■ **CD** **01290161**
Arcade / May '88.

VERY BEST OF VOL.2 : GOLDEN EARRING.
Tracks: Not Advised.
■ **CD** **01290261**
Arcade / May '88.

WHEN THE LADY SMILES.
Tracks: When the lady smiles / Orwell's year.
■ **12"** . . . . **CART 321**
■ **7"** . . . . **CAR 321**
Carrere / Apr '84.

Goldy, Craig

HIDDEN IN PLAIN SIGHT (Craig Goldy's Ritual).
Tracks: Not Advised.
CD . . . . CDMFN 125
LP . . . . MFN 125
MC . . . . TMFN 125
Music For Nations / Mar '92 / Pinnacle.

Golem

VISCERAL SCABS.
Tracks: Visceral scabs.
■ 7" . . . . KILL 002
Cannibalised Serial Killer / Jun '93.

Golgotha

SYMPHONY IN EXTREMIS.
Tracks: Not Advised.
CD . . . . CMGCD 009
Communique / Jul '93 / Plastic Head.

UNMAKER OF WORLDS.
Tracks: Not Advised.
CD . . . . CMGCD 003
LP . . . . CMGLP 003
Communique / Nov '90 / Plastic Head.

Goo Goo Dolls

HOLD ME UP.
Tracks: Not Advised.
LP . . . . AFTER 8
Fun After All / Dec '90 / Pinnacle.

JED.
Tracks: Out of sight / No way out / Down on the corner / Road to Salinas / Misfortune / Gimme shelter / Up yours / Sex maggot / Had enough / Em elbmuh / Artie / James Dean.
■ CD . . . . RO 9477 2
■ LP . . . . RO 94771
Roadracer / Apr '89.
CD . . . . CDZORRO 70
Metal Blade / Feb '94 / Pinnacle.

Goodwin, Myles

MYLES GOODWIN.
Tracks: Veil of tears / Do you know what I mean / Caviar / Sonya / Head on / Face the storm / Frank Sinatra can't sing / Giving it up (for your love) / Are you still loving me / Mama won't say (it's good).
■ CD . . . . K 781 821 2
■ LP . . . . K 781 821 1
■ MC . . . . K 781 821 4
Atlantic / Jun '88.

Gore

CRUEL PLACE, THE.
Tracks: Breeding / Cruel place / Garden of evil / Death has come.
CD . . . . MD 7905CD
■ LP . . . . MD 7905
Various / Apr '89.

LIFELONG DEADLINE.
Tracks: Not Advised.
CD MM1
Barooni / Mar '93 / SRD.

MEAN MAN'S DREAM.
Tracks: Not Advised.
■ LP . . . . CALCLP 029
Ediesta / Jul '87.

Goreaphobia

OMEN OF MASOCHISM.
Tracks: Omen of masochism.
■ 7" . . . . RR 015
Nuclear Blast / Sep '93.

Gorefest

EINDHOVEN INSANITY.
Tracks: Not Advised.
CD . . . . NB 091
LP . . . . NB 091 1
MC . . . . NB 091 4
Nuclear Blast / Aug '93 / Plastic Head.

ERASE.
Tracks: Not Advised.
CD . . . . NBCD 110
LP . . . . NB 110

MC . . . . NBMC 110
Nuclear Blast / Jul '94 / Plastic Head.

MINDLOSS.
Tracks: Not Advised.
CD . . . . FDN 8244CD
LP . . . . FDN 8244
Plastic Head / Jan '92 / Plastic Head.
CD . . . . NB 086
LP . . . . NB 086 1
MC . . . . NB 086 4
Nuclear Blast / Aug '93 / Plastic Head.

Gorguts

CONSIDERED DEAD.
Tracks: Not Advised.
■ LP . . . . RC 92731
■ MC . . . . RC 92734
Road Runner / Sep '91.
CD . . . . RC 92732
Road Runner / Jan '94 / Pinnacle.

EROSION OF SANITY.
Tracks: With the flesh he'll create / Condemned to obscurity / Erosion of sanity / Orphans of sickness / Hideous infirmity / Path beyond premonition / Odours of existence / Dormant misery.
CD . . . . RR 91142
Road Runner / Feb '93 / Pinnacle.

Gorky Park

GORKY PARK.
Tracks: Bang / Try to find me / Hit me with the news / Sometimes at night / Peace in our time / My genera- tion / Within your eyes / Child of the wind / Fortress / Danger.
■ CD 838 628 2
■ LP 838 628 1
■ MC 838 628 4
Vertigo / Oct '89.

Gothic Slam

JUST A FACE.
Tracks: Not Advised.
CD . . . . RO 94742
■ LP . . . . RO 94741
Roadracer / Dec '89.

KILLER INSTINCT.
Tracks: Not Advised.
■ LP . . . . RR 9554 1
Road Runner / '89.

Gramm, Lou

FOREIGNER IN A STRANGE LAND.
Tracks: Won't somebody take her home / Don't you know me, my friend / Better know your heart / I can't make it alone / How do you tell someone / Society's child / I wish today was yesterday / My baby / Headin' home / Watch you walk away.
CD . . . . CDTB 065
■ LP . . . . THBL 065
Thunderbolt / '88.

JUST BETWEEN YOU AND ME.
Tracks: Just between you and me / Day one / Mid- night blue.
■ 12" . . . . A 8755T
■ 7" . . . . A 8755
■ CD Single . . . . A 8755CD
Atlantic / Jan '90.

LONG HARD LOOK.
Tracks: I'll come running / Heart and soul / One dream / Warmest rising sun / Hangin' on my hip / Word gets around / I'll know when it's over / Light- nin' strikes again / Angel with a dirty face / Just between you and me / Broken dreams / True blue love / Tin soldier / Day one.
CD 7819152
■ LP . . . . WX 228
■ MC . . . . WX 228C
WEA / Jan '89.

MIDNIGHT BLUE.
Tracks: Midnight blue / Chain of love.
■ 12" . . . . A 9034 T
■ 7" . . . . A 9034
Atlantic / Mar '87.

READY OR NOT.
Tracks: Ready or not / Heartache / Midnight blue / Time / Not if I don't have you / She's got to know / Arrow thru your heart / Until I make you mine / Chain of love / Lover come back.
■ MC . . . . K 781 728 4
■ LP . . . . K 781 728 1

Atlantic / Feb '87.
■ CD 781 728-2
Atlantic / Feb '87.

TRY BLUE LOVE.
Tracks: Try blue love.
■ 7" . . . . A 7957
Atlantic / Aug '90.

Grand Funk Railroad

In early 70's, Grand Funk Railroad were rock's most critically reviled act. As hatred grew, so did audience - *Live Album* and *E Pluribus Funk* were particularly successful and they scored two U.S. chart-toppers with *The Locomotion* and *We're an American Band*. Group folded in '76, reforming briefly in 1981.

CAN YOU DO IT?.
Tracks: Can you do it / 1976.
■ 7" . . . . INT 523
EMI International / Aug '76.

CAPITOL   COLLECTORS   SERIES: GRAND FUNK RAILROAD.
Tracks: Time machine / Heartbreaker / Inside look- ing out / Closer to home/I'm your captain / Mean mistreater / Feeling alright / Gimme shelter / Foot- stompin' music / Rock 'n' roll soul / We're an Ameri- can band / Walk like a man (you can call me your man) / Loco-motion / Shinin' on / Some kind of wonderful / Bad time.
■ CD . . . . CZ 389
Capitol / Mar '91.

CAUGHT IN THE ACT.
Tracks: Introduction / Footstompin' music / Rock 'n' roll / Soul / Closer to home / Heartbreaker / Some kind of wonderful / Shinin' on the locomotion / Black licorice / Railroad / We're an American band / T.N.U.C / Inside looking out / Gimme shelter.
■ Double LP . . . . E STSP 15
Capitol / Nov '75.

COLLECTION: GRAND   FUNK RAILROAD.
Tracks: Not Advised.
CD . . . . CCSCD 332
■ MC . . . . CCSMC 332
Castle Collector Series / Apr '92.

GRAND FUNK LIVES.
Tracks: Good times / Queen bee / Testify / Can't be with you tonight / No reason why / We gotta get out of this place / Y.O.U. / Stuck in the middle / Greed of man / Wait for me.
■ LP . . . . K 99191
Full Moon (USA) / Feb '82.

GRAND FUNK RAILROAD (Capitol Col- lectors' Series).
Tracks: Not Advised.
■ CD . . . . CDP 7906082
Capitol / Mar '91.

INSIDE LOOKING OUT.
Tracks: Inside looking out.
■ 7" . . . . CL 15668
Capitol / Feb '71.

LIVE ALBUM: GRAND FUNK RAILROAD.
Tracks: Are you ready (Introduction) / Paranoid / In need / Heartbreaker / Inside looking out / Words of wisdom / Mean mistreater / Mark say's alright / T.N.U.C. / Into the sun.
■ Double LP . . . . ESTDW 1/2
Capitol / '71.

MARK, DON & MEL.
Tracks: Time machine / Into the sun / Heartbreaker / Feelin' alright / Inside looking out / Closer to home / Footstompin' music / Paranoid / Lonliness / Are you ready / Mean mistreater.
■ LP . . . . ESTSP 10
Capitol / Aug '72.

PHOENIX.
Tracks: Flight of the Phoenix / Trying to get away / Someone / She got to move me / Rain keeps fallin' / I just gotta know / So you won't have to die / Freedom is for children / Gotta find me a better day / Rock'n'- roll soul.
■ LP . . . . EAST 11099
Capitol / Feb '73.

WHAT'S FUNK.
Tracks: Rock and roll American style / Nowhere to run / Innocent / Still waitin' / Borderline / El Salvador / It's a man's world / I'm so true / Don't lie to me / Life in outer space.

■ DELETED

■ LP 923 750 1
Full Moon (USA) / '88.

Grave

AND HERE I DIE.
Tracks: Not Advised.
CD . . . . MC 770622
Century Media / Feb '94 / Plastic Head.

DEVOLUTION.
Tracks: Not Advised.
CD . . . . PRO 006CD
Prophet / Nov '92 / Pinnacle.

GRAVE/DEVOLUTION
(Grave/Devolution).
Tracks: Not Advised.
LP . . . . PRO 3
Prophecy / '90 / Plastic Head.

INTO THE GRAVE.
Tracks: Not Advised.
CD . . . . CM 9721CD
LP . . . . CM 9721
MC . . . . CM 9721MC
Century Media / '92 / Plastic Head.

SOULLESS.
Tracks: Not Advised.
CD . . . . CM 770702
LP . . . . CM 770701
MC . . . . CM 770704
Century Media / Jun '94 / Plastic Head.

Gravedigger

HEAVY METAL BREAKDOWN.
Tracks: Not Advised.
■ LP . . . . N 0007
Noise / Feb '89.

WAR GAMES.
Tracks: Not Advised.
■ LP . . . . N 0034
Noise / Feb '86.

WITCH HUNT.
Tracks: Not Advised.
CD . . . . NCD 002
■ LP . . . . N 0020
Noise / '88.

Graveyard Rodeo

ON THE VERGE.
Tracks: Not Advised.
CD . . . . CM 77069-2
MC . . . . CM 77069-4
Century Media / Aug '94 / Plastic Head.

Great Kat

BEETHOVEN ON SPEED.
Tracks: Beethoven on speed / Flight of the bumble-
bee / Funeral march / God / Sex and violins /
Gripping obsession / Worshipping bodies / Total
tyrant / Ultra-dead / Revenge of the mongrel / Kat
abuse / Made in Japan / Beethoven mosh (5th sym-
phony) / Paganini's 24th caprice / Guitar concerto in
blood minor / Bach to the future; for geniuses only.
CD . . . . RO 93732
MC . . . . RO 93734
■ LP . . . . RO 93731
Roadracer / Oct '90.

WORSHIP ME OR DIE.
Tracks: Not Advised.
■ LP . . . . RR 9589
Road Runner / Nov '87.
■ CD . . . . RO 95892
Roadracer / Mar '90.

Great White

BEST OF GREAT WHITE 1986 - 1992, THE.
Tracks: Step on you / All over now / Save your love /
House of broken love / Big goodbye / Rock me / Face
the day (blues mix) / Old rose motel / Once bitten
twice shy / Afterglow.
CD . . . . CDEST 2219
■ MC . . . . TCEST 2219
Capitol / Nov '93.

CALL IT ROCK 'N' ROLL.
Tracks: Call it rock 'n' roll / Hunter / Train to nowhere (Only on 12" and CD single).
■ 12" 12CL 625
■ 12" P.Disc. 12CLPD 625
■ 7" . . . . CL 625

■ CD Single. . . . . CDCL 625
■ MC Single. . . . . TCCL 625
Capitol / Aug '91.

CONGO SQUARE.
Tracks: Congo square (Not on 7" or cassingle.) /
South Bay cities / House of broken love (live) (Not on
7" or cassingle.) / Congo square (edit) (7" & cassingle only.).
■ 12" 12CLP 605
■ 12" P.Disc. 12CLPD 605
■ 7" . . . . CL 605
■ CD Single. . . . . CDCL 605
■ MC Single. . . . . TCCL 605
Capitol / Feb '91.

FACE THE DAY.
Tracks: Face the day.
■ 12" 12CL 424
■ 7" . . . . CL 424
Capitol / Jan '87.

GREAT WHITE.
Tracks: Out of the night / Stock it / Substitute / Bad
boys / On your knees / Streetkiller / No better than
hell / Hold on / Nightmares / Dead end.
MC . . . . TC AML240 087 4
■ LP . . . . AML 240 087 1
EMI-America / Mar '84.

HEART THE HUNTER.
Tracks: Heart the hunter / All over now / She shakes
me (12" & CD single only).
■ 12" 12CLP 555
■ 12" 12CL 555
■ 7" . . . . CL 555
■ 7" P.Disc . . . . CLPD 555
■ CD Single. . . . . CDCL 555
Capitol / Dec '89.

HOOKED.
Tracks: Call it rock 'n' roll / Original Queen of Sheba
/ Cold hearted lovin' / Can't shake it / Lovin' kind /
Heartbreaker / Congo square / South bay cities /
Desert moon / Afterglow.
MC . . . . TCEST 2138
■ CD . . . . CDEST 2138
■ LP . . . . EST 2138
Capitol / Feb '91.

HOUSE OF BROKEN LOVE.
Tracks: House of broken love / Red house (live) (Not
on 7".).
■ 12" 12CL 562
■ 7" . . . . CL 562
■ 7" P.Disc. . . . . CLPD 562
■ CD Single. . . . . CDCL 562
Capitol / Feb '90.

LIVE IN LONDON: GREAT WHITE.
Tracks: Move it / Heart the hunter / On your knees /
House of broken love / Face the day / All over now /
Once bitten twice shy.
CD . . . . TOCP 6147
Capitol / Aug '90 / EMI.

ONCE BITTEN.
Tracks: Lady red light / Gonna getcha / Rock me / All
over now / Fast road / What do you do (live) / Face
the day (US radio blues version) / Gimme some
lovin'.
MC . . . . TCEST 2039
■ LP . . . . EST 2039
Capitol / Nov '87.
CD . . . . CDEST 2039
Capitol / Apr '90 / EMI.
CD . . . . CDFA 3252
■ LP . . . . FA 3252
MC . . . . TCFA 3252
Fame / Oct '90 / EMI.

ONCE BITTEN, TWICE SHY.
Tracks: Once bitten twice shy / Wasted rock ranger /
Slow ride.
■ 12" 12CL 532
■ 12" P.Disc. 12CLPD 532
■ 12" P.Disc. 203 425 0
■ 7" . . . . CL 532
■ CD Single. . . . . CDCL 532
Capitol / Jul '89.

PSYCHO CITY.
Tracks: Psycho city / Step on you / Old Rose Motel /
Maybe someday / Big goodbye / Doctor me / I want
you / Never trust a pretty face / Love is a lie / Get on
home.
■ CD . . . . CDESTU 2182
■ LP . . . . ESTU 2182
■ MC . . . . TCESTU 2182
Capitol / Sep '92.

RECOVERY: LIVE.
Tracks: Immigrant song / Rock 'n' roll / Money (that's
what I want) / Red house / I don't need no doctor /

Shot in the dark / What do you do / Gonna getcha /
All over now.
■ LP . . . . EMS 1302
■ MC . . . . TCEMS 1302
Capitol / Jul '88.
■ CD . . . . CZ 127
Capitol / Jan '89.

ROCK ME.
Tracks: Rock me / Fast road / Immigrant song / Rock
'n' roll (This track is only on 12" format).
■ 12" 12CL 455
■ 7" . . . . CL 455
Capitol / Aug '87.

SAIL AWAY.
Tracks: Short overture / Mothers eyes / Cryin' /
Momma don't stop / Alone / All right / Sail away /
Gone with the wind / Livin' in the USA / If I ever saw
a good thing / Call it rock n' roll (Only on bonus live
CD.) / All over now (Only on bonus live CD.) / Love is
a lie (Only on bonus live CD.) / Old rose motel (Only
on bonus live CD.) / Babe (I'm gonna leave you)
(Only on bonus live CD.) / Rock me (Only on Live
bonus CD.) / Once bitten twice shy (Only on bonus
live CD.).
CD 72445 11080-2
MC 72445 11080-4
Zoo Entertainment / Aug '94 / BMG.

SUBSTITUTE.
Tracks: Substitute / No better than hell / Bad boys
(On 12" only).
■ 12" 12EA 167
■ 7" . . . . EA 167
EMI-America / '84.

TWICE SHY.
Tracks: Move it / Heart the hunter / Highway nights /
Angel song / Mista bone / Baby's on fire / House of
broken love / She only / Once bitten twice shy /
Wasted rock ranger.
■ LP . . . . ESTX 2096
■ MC . . . . TCESTX 2096
Capitol / Apr '89.
■ CD . . . . CDESTX 2096
■ LP . . . . EST 2096
■ MC . . . . TCEST 2096
Capitol / Apr '89.

TWICE SHY/LIVE AT THE MARQUEE
(Special Edition - Free Bootleg).
Tracks: Move it / Heart the hunter / Highway nights /
Angel song / Bitch / It's only rock 'n' roll / Women /
Mista bone / Baby's on fire / House of broken love /
She only / Once bitten twice shy / Wasted rock range
/ Shot in the dark / What do you do / Gonna getcha /
Money / All over now / Is anybody there / Face the
day / Rock me.
CD Set . . . . CDESTS 2096
■ Double LP. . . . . ESTS 2096
■ MC Set . . . . TCESTS 2096
Capitol / Dec '89.

Green Jelly

ANARCHY IN THE U.K.
Tracks: Anarchy in the u.k. / Green Jelly theme song
/ Three little pigs (mix) (On 12" & CD single only).
■ 7" 74321 15905-7
■ CD Single 74321 15905-2
■ MC Single. 74321 15905-4
■ 12". 74321 15905-1
Zoo Entertainment / Jul '93.

CEREAL KILLER.
Tracks: Obey the cowgod / Three little pigs / Ugly
truth / Cereal killer / Rock 'n' roll pumpkin / Anarchy
in the U.K. / Electric harley house (of love) / Trippin'
on XTC / Mis-adventures of Shit man / House me
teenage rave / Fight of the Skajaquada / Green Jelly
theme song.
CD 72445110382
LP 72445 110381
MC. 72445110384
Zoo Entertainment / Jun '93 / BMG.

CEREAL KILLER.
Tracks: Green Jelly theme song / Three little pigs /
Obey the cowgod / trippin' on xtc / Mis-adventures of
shit-man / Electric harley house (of love) / Fight of
the Skajaquada / House me teenage rave / Anarchy
in the U.K. / Rock 'n' roll pumpkin.
■ VHS 724451103638
BMG Video / Jun '93.

THREE LITTLE PIGS.
Tracks: Three little pigs.
■ 12". 7432115142-1
■ CD Single 7432115142-2

■ MC Single. 7432115142-4
■ 7″ 7432115142-7
RCA / May '93.

Green River

COME ON DOWN.
Tracks: Not Advised.
CD. . . . . HMS 031-2
Homestead / May '94 / SRD.

DRY AS A BONE.
Tracks: Unwind / This town / Baby takes / P.C.C. /
Ozzie.
CD. . . . . TUPCD 17
LP . . . . TUPLP 17
Tupelo / Jul '90 / Vital Distribution.

DRY AS A BONE/REHAB DOLL.
Tracks: Not Advised.
CD. . . . . SPCD 72
MC. . . . . SP 11A
Sub Pop / May '94 / RTM.

REHAB DOLL.
Tracks: Not Advised.
LP . . . . EFA 4465
LP . . . . .GR 0031
Glitterhouse / Feb '89 / SRD.

Grim Reaper

FEAR NO EVIL.
Tracks: Not Advised.
■ LP . . . . EBON 32
Ebony (Pinnacle) / Jun '85.

SEE YOU IN HELL.
Tracks: Not Advised.
■ LP . . . . EBON 16
Ebony (Pinnacle) / Nov '83.

Grin

AIN'T LOVE NICE.
Tracks: Ain't love nice.
■ 7″ . . . . EPC 1463
Epic / May '73.

Grin

PART OF ME.
Tracks: Part of me.
■ 7″ . . . . BEP 920709
Break Even Point / Jun '93.

Grinder

DAWN FOR LIVING.
Tracks: Not Advised.
CD. 853854
■ LP 083853
No Remorse / '88.

DEAD END.
Tracks: Agent orange / Blade is back / Just another
scar / Why / Dead end / Inside / Total control / Train
raid.
■ LP 083861
No Remorse / Jul '89.
CD. 853862
No Remorse / Jul '89.

NOTHING IS SACRED.
Tracks: Drifting for 99 seconds / Hymn for the iso-
lated / Spirit of violence / Nothing is sacred / None of
the brighter days / Superior being / Dear Mr. Sinister
/ Pavement tango / Nothing song / NME.
■ CD .NO 1652
■ LP .NO 1651
■ MC. . . . . .NO 1654
Noise / Apr '91.

SPIDERMAN.
Tracks: Spiderman / Furry dice / Other people.
■ 7″ . . . . EAR 2
Wax / Aug '79.

Gringos Locos

GRINGOS LOCOS.
Tracks: Higher than high / Sweet little sisters /
Jealousy / Mountain / I ain't braggin' / Mean rock 'n'
roller / Susie / Shout / Bad lucks lament / Tough kid /
Blues.
■ LP . . . . DIGLP 35
MC. . . . . .DIGMC 35
■ MC. 834 204 4
Dig It (Finland) / Apr '88.

Grip

AMERICAN DREAM.
Tracks: American dream.
■ 12″ . . . . ZT 43750
■ 7″ . . . . ZB 43749
■ 7″ P.Disc . . . . ZB 43751
■ CD Single . . . . ZD 43750
RCA / Jul '90.

BE YOURSELF.
Tracks: Crush on you / Two hearts / Rain comes
down / Baby blue / Ballad of Vera Daydream / Bet
your gonna lose her / She walks out / We don't want
it / Be yourself / Great balls of fire (live).
■ LP . . . . RAZ 29
Razor / Feb '88.
CD. . . . . RAZMCD 46
Razor / Jan '89 / Grapevine Distribution.

ENGLAND YOU'RE DEAD.
Tracks: England you're dead.
■ 12″ . . . . .RPG 001
Grip / Oct '87.

LOOK WHAT YOU'VE DONE.
Tracks: Look what you've done.
■ 12″ . . . . SUR 12 049
■ 7″ . . . . .SUR 049
Survival (1) / Oct '89.

TEENAGE BRIDE.
Tracks: Teenage bride / Silicon and wire / England
you're dead.
■ 12″ . . . . SUR 12048
■ 7″ . . . . .SUR 048
Survival (1) / Apr '89.

Grotus

LUDDITE.
Tracks: Luddite.
■ 12″ . . . . VIRUS 128
■ CD Single . . . . VIRUS 128CD
Alternative Tentacles / Aug '93.

OPIATE OF THE MASSES (Grotus & Transglobal Underground).
Tracks: Opiate of the masses.
12″. . . . . VIRUS 148
CD Single . . . . VIRUS 148CD
Alternative Tentacles / May '94 / RTM / Pinnacle.

SLOW MOTION APOCALYPSE.
Tracks: Not Advised.
CD. . . . . VIRUS 118CD
LP . . . . VIRUS 118
Alternative Tentacles / Mar '93 / RTM / Pinnacle.

Gruntruck

INSIDE YOURS.
Tracks: Not Advised.
CD. . . . . RO 92602
Road Runner / May '92 / Pinnacle.

PUSH.
Tracks: Tribe / Machine action / Racked / Crazy love
/ Above me / Push / Break / Slow scorch / Follow /
Body farm / Lose that way / Gotta believe.
CD. . . . . RR 91302
■ LP . . . . RR 91301
Road Runner / Oct '92.

GTR

GTR.
Tracks: When the heart rules the mind / Hunter /
Here I wait / Sketches in the sun / Jekyll and Hyde /
You can still get through / Reach out (never say no) /
Toe the line / Hackett to bits / Imagining.
■ LP 207716
■ CD .257716
■ MC. 407716
Arista / Jul '86.
■ CD .258980
■ LP .208980
■ MC. 408980
Arista / May '88.

WHEN THE HEART RULES THE MIND.
Tracks: When the heart rules the mind / Reach out
(never say no) / Sketches in the sun (Extra track on

12″ version only.) / Hackett to bits (Extra track on 12″
version only.).
■ 12″ . . . . .GTR 121
■ 7″ . . . . GTR 1
Arista / May '86.
■ 7″ P.Disc . . . . GTR SD 1
Arista / May '86.

Guardian

FIRST WATCH.
Tracks: I'll never leave you / Mystery man / Livin' for
the promise / Miracle / Saints battalion / Kingdom of
rock / Good life / One of a kind / World without love /
Rock in victory.
■ LP . . . . RR 94401
Road Runner / Sep '89.

Gun

RACE WITH THE DEVIL.
Tracks: Race with the devil.
■ 7″ . . . . CBS 3764
CBS / Nov '68.

RACE WITH THE DEVIL (OLD GOLD) (see under Ram Jam).

Gun

Formed in Glasgow, 1988, Gun scored three
U.K. hits from 1989 debut *Taking On The
World*. 1990 support slot with Rolling Stones
secured loyal European following, while
greatest success came with cover of Cameo's *Word Up* and parent album *Swagger*,
both of which made UK Top 10 in '94.

BETTER DAYS.
Tracks: Better days / When you love somebody /
Coming home (12″ & CD single only).
■ 12″ . . . . AMY 505
■ 7″ . . . . AM 505
■ CD Single . . . . CDEE 505
A&M / Jun '89.

DON'T SAY IT'S OVER.
Tracks: Don't say it's over / Steal your fire (580755-2/
7 only.) / Better days (Not on 580755-7) / Shame on
you (Not on 580755-7) / Money (Everybody loves her)
(On 580757-2 only.).
7″ 580754-7
CD Single. 580755-2
CD Single. 580757-2
A&M / Aug '94 / PolyGram.

GALLUS.
Tracks: Steal your fire / Money to burn / Long road /
Welcome to the real world / Higher ground / Bor-
rowed time / Freedom / Won't back down / Reach out
for love / Watching the world go by.
CD. 3953832
MC. 3953834
■ LP 3953831
A&M / Apr '92.

HIGHER GROUND.
Tracks: Higher ground.
■ 12″ . . . . AMY 869
■ 7″ . . . . AM 869
■ CD Single . . . . AMCD 869
A&M / Apr '91.

INSIDE OUT.
Tracks: Inside out / Back to where we started.
■ 12″ . . . . AMY 531
■ 7″ . . . . AMS 531
■ 7″ . . . . AM 531
■ 7″ P.Disc . . . . AMP 531
■ 7″ Set . . . . AMB 531
■ CD Single . . . . CDEE 531
A&M / Oct '89.

MONEY (EVERYBODY LOVES HER).
Tracks: Money (everybody loves her) / Prime time.
■ 12″ . . . . AMY 520
■ 12″ P.Disc. . . . . AMP 520
■ 7″ . . . . AM 520
■ CD Single . . . . CDEE 520
A&M / Sep '89.

SHAME ON YOU.
Tracks: Shame on you.
■ 12″ . . . . AMT 573
■ 12″ . . . . AMX 573
■ 12″ Remix. . . . . AMY 573
■ 7″ . . . . AM 573
■ CD Single . . . . AMCD 573
■ MC Single. . . . . AMMC 573
A&M / Jul '90.

PUNCHDRUNK.
Tracks: Not Advised.
■ CD .K 781 988 2
■ LP .K 781 988 1
■ MC. . . . . .K 781 988 4
Atlantic / Sep '89.

STEAL YOUR FIRE.
Tracks: Steal your fire / Don't blame me.
- 12" . . . . AMY 851
- 7" . . . . AM 851
- CD Single . . . . AMCD 851
- MC Single. . . . . AMMC 851
A&M / Feb '92.

SWAGGER.
Tracks: Stand in line / Find my way / Word up / Don't say it's over / Only one / Something worthwhile / Seems like I'm losing you / Crying over you / One reason / Vicious heart.
CD 540254-2
MC 540254-4
A&M / Jul '94 / PolyGram.

TAKING ON THE WORLD.
Tracks: Better days / Feeling within / Inside out / Money (Everybody loves her) / Taking on the world / Shame on you / Can't get any lower / Something to believe in / Girls in love / I will be waiting.
CD . . . . CDA 7007
- LP . . . . AMA 7007
MC. AMC 7007
A&M / Aug '90 / PolyGram.

TAKING ON THE WORLD.
Tracks: Taking on the world / Don't believe a word / Better days.
- 7" . . . . AMS 541
A&M / Feb '90.
- 12" . . . . AMY 541
- 7" . . . . AM 541
- CD Single . . . . CDEE 541
A&M / Jan '90.

TAKING ON THE WORLD.
Tracks: Better days / Money (Everybody loves her) / Inside out / Taking on the world / Shame on you.
VHS . . . . AMV 867
A&M Sound Pictures / Aug '90 / Gold & Sons / PolyGram Music Video / TBD.

WELCOME TO THE REAL WORLD.
Tracks: Welcome to the real world / Standing in your shadow / Steal your fire (12" only).
- 12" . . . . AMY 885
- 7" . . . . AM 885
A&M / Jun '92.

WORD UP.
Tracks: Word up (mixes) / Stay forever / Better days / Man I used to be (On 1st CD only) / Strange (On 1st CD only).
12" .580665-1
7" 580665-7
CD Single 580665-2
CD Single 580667-2
MC Single 580664-4
A&M / Jul '94 / PolyGram.

Gunjah

HEREDITY.
Tracks: Not Advised.
CD . . . . M 02082
LP . . . . N 02081
MC. N 02084
Modern / Feb '93 / Total / BMG.

WHOOZE IN DA HOUZE.
Tracks: Whooze in da houze.
CD Single . . . . NO 2413
Noise / Apr '94 / Pinnacle.

Guns N' Roses

Astute marketing of 'bad-boy' image snared front covers after first EP, *Live Like A Suicide*, but Guns N' Roses did not enjoy major success until year after release of *Appetite For Destruction* album. Single *Sweet Child O' Mine* topped US charts in 1988 and album followed. By December, the band had two albums in US Top Five - debut and *Lies* compilation - and joined Bon Jovi and Def Leppard as metal's biggest sellers. Volatile band relations delayed follow-up - double *Use Your Illusion* albums - until 1991. Two year tour ensued; notable events including departure of guitarist Izzy Stradlin and series of stadium dates with Metallica. Next release was 'covers' album *"The Spaghetti Incident"*; attendant controversy this time focussed on cover of Charles Manson song, *Look At Your Game, Girl*.

AIN'T IT FUN.
Tracks: Ain't it fun.
- CD Single . . . . GFSTD 62
- MC Single. . . . . GFSC 62
Geffen / Nov '93.

APPETITE FOR CONVERSATION (Interview Picture Disc).
Tracks: Not Advised.
LP . . . . BAK 6001
Baktabak / Mar '89 / Arabesque Ltd.
MC. . . . . MBAK 6001
Baktabak / Mar '89 / Arabesque Ltd.

APPETITE FOR DESTRUCTION.
Tracks: Welcome to the jungle / It's so easy / Nightrain / Out ta get me / Mr. Brownstone / Paradise city / My Michelle / Think about you / Sweet child o' mine / You're crazy / Anything goes / Rocket queen.
- LP . . . . WX 125
- MC. . . . . WX 125C
Geffen / Aug '87.
- CD 924148 2
Geffen / Dec '87.
CD. . . . . GEFD 24148
- LP . . . . GEF 24148
MC. . . . . .GEFC 24148
Geffen / Jan '91 / BMG.

CIVIL WAR E.P., THE.
Tracks: Not Advised.
- CD Single . . . . GFSTD 43
Geffen / May '93.

DON'T CRY.
Tracks: Don't cry.
- 12" . . . . GFST 9
- 7" . . . . GFS 9
- CD Single . . . . GFSTD 9
- MC Single . . . . GFSC 9
Geffen / Aug '91.

GARDEN OF EDEN.
Tracks: Not Advised.
- VHS . . . . GEFVS 40
Geffen / May '94.

GUNS 'N' ROSES.
Tracks: It's so easy (live) / Shadow of your love (live) / Move to the city (live) / Knockin' on heaven's door (live) / Whole lotta Rosie (live).

GUNS 'N' ROSES: INTERVIEW PICTURE DISC.
Tracks: Not Advised.
LP P.Disc. . . . . BAK 2079
Baktabak / Dec '87 / Arabesque Ltd.

GUNS 'N' ROSES: INTERVIEW PICTURE DISC.
Tracks: Not Advised.
- LP P.Disc. . . . . CT 1013
Music & Media / Dec '87.

GUNS N ROSES: INTERVIEW PICTURE DISC COLLECTION.
Tracks: Not Advised.
7" Set . . . . BAKPAK 1011
Baktabak / '88 / Arabesque Ltd.

INTERVIEW COMPACT DISC: GUNS 'N' ROSES.
Tracks: Not Advised.
CD P.Disc. . . . . CBAK 4015
Baktabak / Nov '89 / Arabesque Ltd.

IT'S SO EASY.
Tracks: It's so easy / Mr. Brownstone / Shadow of your love / Move to the city (live).
- 7" GEF22
Geffen / Jun '87.

KNOCKIN' ON HEAVEN'S DOOR.
Tracks: Knockin' on heaven's door.
- 12" . . . . GFST 21
- 7" . . . . GFS 21
- CD Single . . . . GFSTD 21
- MC Single. . . . . GFSC 21
Geffen / May '92.

LIES, THE SEX, THE VIOLENCE, THE SHOCKING TRUTH,.
Tracks: Reckless life / Patience / Nice boys / Used to love her / Move to the city / You're crazy / Mama kin / One in a million.
- CD 924198 2
- LP . . . . WX 218
- MC. . . . . WX 218C
Geffen / Dec '88.
CD. . . . . GEFD 24198
- LP . . . . GEF 24198
MC. . . . . .GEFC 24198
Geffen / Jan '91 / BMG.

LIVE AND LET DIE.
Tracks: Live and let die.
- 12" . . . . .GFST 17
- CD Single . . . . GFSTD 17
- 7" . . . . GFS 17
- MC Single. . . . . GFSC 17
Geffen / Dec '91.

MAKING OF ESTRANGED PART IV. OF THE TRILOGY.
Tracks: Estranged / Right next door to hell / Nightrain / Coma / Don't cry (Original lyrics) / November rain / Double talkin' jive.
VHS . . . . GEFV 39545
Geffen / Apr '94 / BMG.

MAKING VIDEOS PART 1.
Tracks: Don't cry (original lyrics) / Don't cry (alternate lyrics) / Shadow of your love / Heartbreak hotel / Don't cry (demo) / Rocket queen / Coma / You're crazy / 14 Years / Perfect crime.
VHS . . . . GEFV 39523
Geffen / Jun '93 / BMG.

MAKING VIDEOS PART 2.
Tracks: November rain (LP version) / Dead horse / You ain't the first / Estranged / Theme from "The Godfather" / So fine / Think about you / Locomotive.
VHS . . . . GEFV 39524
Geffen / Jun '93 / BMG.

NIGHT TRAIN.
Tracks: Night train / Reckless life.
- 12" . . . . .GEF 60T
- 7" . . . . GEF 60
- CD Single . . . . GEF 60CD
- MC Single . . . . GEF 60C
Geffen / Aug '89.

NOVEMBER RAIN.
Tracks: November rain / Sweet child o' mine / Patience (Only on 12" and CD Single).
- 12" . . . . .GFST 18
- 7" . . . . GFS 18
- CD Single . . . . GFSTD 18
- MC Single. . . . . GFSC 18
Geffen / Feb '92.

PARADISE CITY.
Tracks: Paradise city / Used to love her / Anything goes (Only on the 12" version.) / Sweet child o mine (Only on CD single.)
- 12" . . . . .GEF 50T
- 7" . . . . GEF 50
- CD Single . . . . GEF 50CD
Geffen / Mar '89.
- 7" . . . . GEF 50X
- 7" . . . . GEF 50P
- MC Single . . . . GEF 50C
Geffen / Mar '89.

PATIENCE.
Tracks: Patience / Rocket queen / Axl Rose Interview.
- 12" . . . . .GEF 56T
- 7" . . . . GEF 56
- CD Single . . . . GEF 56CD
- MC Single . . . . GEF 56C
Geffen / Jun '89.

SINCE I DON'T HAVE YOU.
Tracks: Since I don't have you.
- 7" . . . . GFS 70
- CD Single . . . . GFSTD 70
- CD Single . . . . GFSXD 70
- MC Single. . . . . GFSC 70
Geffen / May '94.

SPAGHETTI INCIDENT.
Tracks: Since I don't have you / New Rose / Down on the farm / Human being / Raw power / Ain't it fun / Buick Mackane / Hair of the dog / Attitude / Black leather / You can't put your arms around a memory / I don't care about you / What's your game.
CD. . . . . GED 24617
MC. . . . . GEC 24617
- LP . . . . GEF 24617
Geffen / Nov '93.

SWEET CHILD O' MINE.
Tracks: Sweet child o' mine / Out to get me / Rocket queen (Only on 12".).
- 12" . . . . .GEF 43T
- 7" . . . . GEF 43
Geffen / Aug '88.

SWEET CHILD O' MINE (RE-RELEASE).
Tracks: Sweet child o' mine / Out to get me / Move to the city (Only on CD single.) / It's so easy (Only on CD single.) / Whole lotta Rosie (Only on CD single.)
- 12" . . . . .GEF 55T
- 7" . . . . GEF 55
- 7" . . . . GEF 55X
Geffen / Nov '93.

■ CD Single. . . . . .GEF 55CD
Geffen / May '89.

TRUTH OR LIES THE INTERVIEW.
Tracks: Not Advised.
CD P.Disc. . . . . CBAK 4077
Baktabak / Feb '94 / Arabesque Ltd.

USE YOUR ILLUSION VOL.1.
Tracks: Not Advised.
CD. . . . . .GEFD 24415
■ LP . . . . GEF 24415
■ MC. . . . . .GEFC 24415
Geffen / Sep '91.

USE YOUR ILLUSION VOL.2.
Tracks: Not Advised.
CD. . . . . .GEFD 24420
■ LP . . . . GEF 24420
MC. . . . . .GEFC 24420
Geffen / Jul '91 / BMG.

USE YOUR ILLUSION WORLD TOUR - 1992 IN TOKYO, I.
Tracks: Nightrain / Mr. Brownstone / Live and let die / It's so easy / Bad obsession / Attitude / Pretty tied up / Welcome to the jungle / Don't cry / Double talkin' jive / Civil war / Wild horses / Patience / November rain.
VHS . . . . .GEFV 39521
Geffen / Dec '92 / BMG.
■ Laser Disc . . . . .GEI 39521
Geffen / Feb '93.

USE YOUR ILLUSION WORLD TOUR - 1992 IN TOKYO, II.
Tracks: You could be mine / Theme from "The Godfather" / Sweet child o' mine / So fine / Rocket queen / Move to the city / Knockin' on Heaven's door / Estranged / Paradise city.
VHS . . . . .GEFV 39522
Geffen / Dec '92 / BMG.
■ Laser Disc . . . . .GEI 39522
Geffen / Feb '93.

WELCOME TO THE JUNGLE.
Tracks: Welcome to the jungle / Whole lotta Rosie / It's so easy (12" only) / Knockin' on Heaven's door.
■ 7". . . . . GEF 30
■ 12". . . . . .GEF 30T
Geffen / Sep '87.

WELCOME TO THE JUNGLE (RE-RELEASE).
Tracks: Welcome to the jungle / Nightrain.
■ 12". . . . . .GEF 47T
■ 7". . . . . GEF 47
■ CD Single. . . . . .GEF 47CD
Geffen / Oct '88.

YESTERDAYS.
Tracks: Yesterdays / November rain.
■ 7" . . . . GFS 27
■ CD Single. . . . . .GFSTD 27
■ MC Single. . . . . GFSC 27
Geffen / Nov '92.

YOU COULD BE MINE.
Tracks: You could be mine.
■ 7" . . . . GFS 6

■ CD Single. . . . . GFSTD 6
■ MC Single. . . . . GFSC 6
Geffen / Jul '91.

Guns N' Wankers

HARDCORE.
Tracks: Nervous / Blows away / Blah blah blah / Surprise.
7" .DUMP 021
Rugger Bugger / Aug '94 / Vital Distribution.

METAL.
Tracks: 668 / Evergreen / Incoming.
7" .DUMP 022
Rugger Bugger / Aug '94 / Vital Distribution.

POP.
Tracks: Help / Skin deep / Raise your glass / Sunstroke.
7" .DUMP 020
Rugger Bugger / Aug '94 / Vital Distribution.

WANCHOR.
Tracks: Help / Skin deep / Raise your glass / Sunstroke / Nervous / Blows away / Blah blah blah / Suprise / 668 / Evergreen / Incoming.
CD . . . . SEEP 008
Rugger Bugger / Aug '94 / Vital Distribution.

Guttersnipes

ADDICTED TO LOVE.
Tracks: Addicted to love.
■ 7" . . . . GUTT 1
Razor / Jul '88.

POOR DRESS UP, THE.
Tracks: Funny old world / Forgotten men / Sale of the century / Addicted to love / On fire / Hate game / Time of our lives / Guns and rockets / Today / They're telling me.
LP . . . . RAZ 42
Razor / Feb '90 / Grapevine Distribution.

GWAR

AMERICA MUST BE DESTROYED.
Tracks: Not Advised.
CD . . . . CDZORRO 037
LP . . . . .ZORR 037
MC. . . . . TZORRO 037
Zorro / Mar '92 / Pinnacle.

HELL-O.
Tracks: Time for death / Americanized / Slutman city / War toy / Pure as the artic snow / Gwar theme / Ollie North / U ain't shit / Black and huge / A.E.I.O.U. / I'm in love with a dead dog / World o' filth / Captain crunch / Je m'appelle J. Cousteau / Bone meal / Techno's song / Rock 'n' roll party theme.
■ LP . . . . SHIMMY 010
MC. . . . . SHIMMY 010MC
Shimmy Disc / '89 / Vital Distribution.
CD. . . . . .CDZORRO 35
MC. . . . . TZORRO 35
Music For Nations / Sep '92 / Pinnacle.

MOVIE, THE.
Tracks: Not Advised.
VHS . . . . .LFV 117
Fotodisk Video / Aug '90.

PHALLUS IN WONDERLAND.
Tracks: Not Advised.
VHS . . . . VFN 5
Video For Nations / '92 / Pinnacle.

SCUMDOGS OF THE UNIVERSE.
Tracks: Not Advised.
■ CD . . . . .MASCD 001
■ LP . . . . MASLP 001
■ MC. . . . . MASMC 001
Mausoleum / May '90.

THIS TOILET EARTH.
Tracks: Not Advised.
CD. . . . . .CDZORRO 63
Metal Blade / Mar '94 / Pinnacle.

TOUR DE SCUM.
Tracks: Not Advised.
■ VHS . . . . VFN 9
Music For Nations / Aug '93.

Gypsy Kyss

WHEN PASSION MURDERED INNOCENCE.
Tracks: When passion murder innocence.
CD. 972210
■ LP 942210
FM Records / May '91.

Gypsy Queen

GYPSY QUEEN.
Tracks: Love is strange / I can't help it / Radio / Hey (are you ever satisfied) / Leave us alone / Don't rush me / Love is a shadow / I still care / Who are you / She wants to .. / Love is strange (remix) / Where does our love go.
CD. . . . . .LOPCD 500
■ LP . . . . LOPL 500
MC. . . . . .LOPC 500
Loop / Dec '87 / EMI.

SNARL 'N STRIPES EP.
Tracks: Radio (remix) / Doctor needs a doctor / War and peace / Where does our love go.
■ 12". . . . . 12 LOOP 100
■ EP . . . . .LOOP 100
Loop / Jan '88.

TAKE CARE OF YOURSELF.
Tracks: Take care of yourself.
■ 12". . . . . 12 LOOP 102
■ 7" . . . . .LOOP 102
Loop / Mar '89.

H

Hades

IF AT FIRST YOU DON'T SUCCEED.
Tracks: Not Advised.
CD . . . . RR 95332
■ LP . . . . RR 95331
Road Runner / Oct '88.

PITTER PATTER BISCUIT.
Tracks: Pitter patter biscuit.
■ 12" . . . . STORM 6
Vinyl Solution / Jun '90.

RESISTING SUCCESS.
Tracks: On to Iliad / Legal tender / Sweet revenge / Nightstalker / Resist success / Widows mite / Cross / Masque of the red death.
■ LP . . . . RR 9598
Road Runner / Aug '87.

Hagar, Sammy

Van Halen vocalist who rose to stardom with the revered Montrose - whose first album is regarded as one of the five best debut albums by Kerrang - before setting off on a solo career that was successful if not spectacular. After Dave Lee Roth's departure Hagar stepped in, at the personal invitation of Eddie Van Halen, to fill the vacant singers position. He has released one more solo album since joining Van Halen and while further solo ventures cannot be ruled out, Hagar seems to be devoting most of his energy to the band.

(SITTIN' ON THE) DOCK OF THE BAY.
Tracks: (Sittin' on) The dock of the bay / I've done everything for you.
■ 7" . . . . CL 16083
Capitol / '79.

BEST OF SAMMY HAGAR, THE.
Tracks: Not Advised.
■ CD . . . . K 9242552
■ LP . . . . WX 291
■ MC . . . . WX 291C
WEA / Aug '89.

BEST OF SAMMY HAGAR, THE.
Tracks: Red / (Sittin' on) The dock of the bay / I've done everything for you / Rock 'N' Roll weekend / Crusin' & boozin' / Turn up the music / Reckless / Trans am (highway wonderland) / Love or money / This planet's on fire / Plain Jane / Bad reputation / Bad motorscooter / You make me crazy.
CD C2 80262
Capitol / Apr '93 / EMI.

CENTRE HOLE.
Tracks: Red / Catch the wind / Cruisin' and boozin' / Free money / Rock 'n' roll weekend / Fillmore shuffle / Hungry / Pits / Love has found me / Little star/eclipse.
■ LP . . . . EST 11599
Capitol / May '80.

COLLECTION: SAMMY HAGAR.
Tracks: Not Advised.

DANGER ZONE.
Tracks: Love or money / 20th century man / Miles from boredom / Mommy says / In the night / Iceman / Bad reputation / Heartbeat / Run for your life / Danger zone.
■ LP . . . . EST 12069
Capitol / Jun '80.

GIVE TO LIVE.
Tracks: Give to live / When the hammer falls.
■ 12" . . . . GEF 23T
■ 7" . . . . GEF 23
Geffen / Aug '87.

HEARTBEAT.
Tracks: Heartbeat / Love or money.
■ 7" . . . . RED 1
Capitol / May '80.

HEAVY METAL.
Tracks: Heavy metal / Satisfied.
■ 12" . . . . EPCA 131600

I'VE DONE EVERYTHING FOR YOU.
Tracks: I've done everything for you / Red.
■ 7" . . . . EPCA 1600
Epic / Oct '81.

I'VE DONE EVERYTHING FOR YOU.
Tracks: I've done everything for you / Red.
■ 7" . . . . CL 16010
Capitol / Sep '78.
■ 7" 16120
Capitol / Feb '80.

LOOKING BACK.
Tracks: I'll fall in love again / There's only one way to rock / Heavy metal / Remember the heroes / Baby's on fire / Three lock box / Two sides of love / I can't drive 55 / I don't need love / Voa.
■ LP 9241271
■ MC 9241274
Geffen / Jan '87.

LOUD 'N' CLEAR.
Tracks: Not Advised.
CD . . . . .BGOCD 149
Beat Goes On / Aug '92 / Pinnacle.

LOUD AND CLEAR.
Tracks: Rock 'n' roll weekend / Make it last / Reckless / Turn up the music / I've done everything for you / Young girl blues / Bad motor scooter / Space station no. 5.
■ LP . . . . .EST 25330
Capitol / Mar '80.

MUSICAL CHAIRS.
Tracks: Turn up the music / It's gonna be alright kid / You make me crazy / Try / Don't stop me now / Straight from the hip kid / Hey boys / Someone out there / Crack in the world.
■ LP . . . . .GO 2021
Capitol Greenlight Series / Jul '81.
CD . . . . .BGOCD 201
Beat Goes On / May '94 / Pinnacle.

NINE ON A TEN SCALE.
Tracks: Keep on rockin' / Urban guerilla / Flamingos fly / China / Silver lights / All American / Confession (please come back) / Young girl blues / Rock 'n' roll Romeo.
■ LP . . . . .GO 2017
Capitol Greenlight Series / Jun '81.
■ LP . . . . FA 3068
MC . . . . TCFA 3068
Fame / May '83 / EMI.
CD . . . . .BGOCD 182
Beat Goes On / Apr '93 / Pinnacle.

PIECE OF MY HEART.
Tracks: Piece of my heart / Baby's on fire.
■ 7" . . . . GEFA 1884
Geffen / Jan '82.

PLAIN JANE.
Tracks: Plain Jane / Wounded in love.
■ 7" . . . . CL 16101
Capitol / Sep '79.

RED.
Tracks: Red / Catch the wind / Cruisin' and boozin' / Free money / Rock 'N' Roll weekend / Fillmore shuffle / Hungry / Pits / Love has found me / Little star/Eclipse.
CD . . . . .BGOCD 181
Beat Goes On / Apr '93 / Pinnacle.

RED ALERT, DIAL NINE.
Tracks: Red / Cruisin' and boozin' / Turn up the music / Reckless / This planet's on fire / Urban guerilla / Trans Am / Miles from boredom / 20th century man / Space station no.5 / I've done everything for you / Young girl blues.
■ LP . . . . .EST 26882
Capitol / Mar '82.

SAMMY HAGAR.
Tracks: Red / Catch the wind / Cruisin' and boozin' / Free money / Rock'n'roll weekend / Fillmore shuffle / Hungry / Pits / Love has found me / Little star / Eclipse.
■ LP . . . . .GO 2007
Capitol Greenlight Series / May '81.

SAMMY HAGAR.
Tracks: When the hammer falls / Hands and knees / Give to live / Boy's night out / Returning home / Standin' at the same old crossroads / Privacy / Back

into you / Eagle's fly / What the world needs now is love.
■ CD 9241442
■ LP . . . . WX 114
■ MC . . . . WX 114C
Geffen / Jul '87.

STANDING HAMPTON.
Tracks: There's only one way to rock / Baby's on fire / Can't get loose / I'll fall in love again / Heavy metal / Baby it's you / Surrender / Inside lookin' in / Sweet hitchhiker / Piece of my heart.
■ LP . . . . GEF 85456
Geffen / Feb '82.
■ LP 9020061
■ MC 9020064
Geffen / Sep '86.

STREET MACHINE.
Tracks: Never say die / This planet's on fire / Wounded in love / Falling in love / Growing pains / Child to man / Trans am (Highway wonderland) / Feels like love / Plain Jane.
■ LP . . . . .EST 11983
Capitol / Sep '79.
■ LP . . . . REV LP 72
Revolver / Jun '86.
CD . . . . .BGOCD 150
Beat Goes On / Oct '92 / Pinnacle.

THIS PLANET'S ON FIRE.
Tracks: This planet's on fire / Space station No. 5.
■ 7" 16114
Capitol / Dec '79.

THREE LOCK BOX.
Tracks: Three lock box / Remote love / Remember the heroes / Your love is driving me crazy / In the room / Rise of the animal / I wouldn't change a thing / Growing up / Never give up / I don't need love.
■ MC 4024254
Geffen / Dec '82.
■ LP 9020211
■ MC 9020214
Geffen / Sep '86.

THROUGH THE FIRE (Hagar, Schon, Aaronson, Shrieve).
Tracks: Top of the rock / Missing you / Animation / Valley of the kings / Giza / Whiter shade of pale / Hot and dirty / He will understand / My home town.
■ LP . . . . GEF 25893
Geffen / May '84.

TURN UP THE MUSIC.
Tracks: Turn up the music / Straight from the hip kid.
■ 7" . . . . CL 15983
Capitol / May '78.

TWO SIDES OF LOVE.
Tracks: Two sides of love / Burnin' down the city.
■ 7" . . . . .A 4696
Geffen / Aug '84.

UNBOXED.
Tracks: High hopes / Buying my way into heaven / I'll fall in love again / There's only one way to rock / Heavy metal / Eagles fly / Baby's on fire / Three lock box / Two sides of love / I can't drive / Give to live / I don't need love.
CD . . . . GED 24702
MC . . . . GEC 24702
Geffen / Mar '94 / BMG.

VOA.
Tracks: I can't drive 55 / Swept away / Rock is in my blood / Two sides of love / Dick in the dirt / Voa / Don't make me wait / Burnin' down the city.
■ LP 9240431
■ MC 9240434
Geffen / Sep '86.
■ CD 9240432
Geffen / '88.

WINNER TAKES IT ALL.
Tracks: Winner takes it all / Fight.
■ 7" 6504077
CBS / Apr '87.

YOU MAKE ME CRAZY.
Tracks: You make me crazy / Reckless.
■ 7" . . . . CL 15960
Capitol / Jan '78.

YOUR LOVE IS DRIVING ME MAD.
Tracks: Your love is driving me mad / I don't need love.
■ 7" . . . . GEFA 3043
Geffen / Jan '83.

Hallow's Eve

DEATH AND INSANITY.
Tracks: Not Advised.
■ LP . . . . RR 9676 1
Road Runner / '89.

MONUMENT.
Tracks: Not Advised.
■ LP . . . . RR 9583
Road Runner / Apr '88.

TALES OF TERROR.
Tracks: Not Advised.
■ LP . . . . RR 9772
Road Runner / Jun '85.
CD . . . . RO 97722
Roadracer / May '89 / Pinnacle.

Hamm, Stuart

KINGS OF SLEEP.
Tracks: Black ice / Surely the best / Call of the wild / Terminal beach / Count zero / I want to know / Prelude in C / Kings of sleep.
CD . . . . CDGRUB 13
LP . . . . GRUB 13
Food For Thought / Oct '89 / Pinnacle.

RADIO FREE ALBEMUTE.
Tracks: Not Advised.
CD . . . . CDGRUB 9
■ LP . . . . GRUB 9
MC . . . . TGRUB 9
Food For Thought / Oct '88 / Pinnacle.

Hammer

BLACK SHEEP.
Tracks: Jet stream / Heavy love / Black sheep / Light of dawn / Hey girl / Waiting no more / Between the sheets of music / Manic depression / Silent one.
■ LP . . . . K 53089
Asylum / '77.

CONTRACT WITH HELL.
Tracks: Not Advised.
■ LP . . . . EBON 29
Ebony (Pinnacle) / Apr '85.

TERROR.
Tracks: Not Advised.
CD . . . . SHARK 028
MC . . . . SHARKMC 028
Shark / Jul '92 / Plastic Head.

Hammerbox

HAMMERBOX.
Tracks: Not Advised.
CD . . . . CZ 029CD
■ LP . . . . CZ 029
Revolver / Oct '91.

Handsome Beasts

ALL RIOT NOW.
Tracks: All riot now / Mark of the beast.
■ 7" . . . . HEAVY 1
Heavy Metal / May '80.

BEAST WITHIN, THE.
Tracks: Mr. Mescalito / Hairy legs / Way I am / Chain gang / Beast within / Rough justice / Don't hold on / Sixth day / Let it go.
■ CD . . . . HMRXD 132
■ LP . . . . HMRLP 132
■ MC . . . . HMRMC 132
Heavy Metal / Feb '90.
■ LP . . . . HMR LP 132
FM Records / Oct '92.

BREAKER.
Tracks: Breaker / Crazy / One in a crowd.
■ EP . . . . HEAVY 2
Heavy Metal / Mar '81.

SWEETIES.
Tracks: Sweeties / You're on your own.
■ 7" . . . . HEAVY 11
Heavy Metal / Feb '82.

Hanoi Rocks

Hugely influential Scandanavian trash/glam metal outfit who split before achieving the massive fame predicted in the early 80's. Fronted by the impossibly beautiful Mike Monroe (who has since enjoyed limited solo success) and his chief songwriting partner Andy McCoy (guitar), Hanoi Rocks delivered full throttle rock 'n' roll like their lives depended on it. A live reputation second to few and series of patchy but cult classic independent releases on Lick led to a deal with Columbia. Sadly, however, after just one record for the label, drummer Razzle was killed in 1984 in a car driven by Motley Crue singer Vince Neil and the band splintered.

ALL THOSE WASTED YEARS.
Tracks: Not Advised.
MC Set . . . . LICKCAS 5/6
Lick / Mar '87 / Pinnacle.
■ Double LP . . . . LICKDLP 5/6
Lick / Mar '87.
CD Set . . . . LIC CD 5/6
Lick / Sep '91 / Pinnacle.

ALL THOSE WASTED YEARS.
Tracks: Pipeline / Oriental beat / Back to mystery city / Motorvatin' / Until I get you / Mental beat / Beer and a cigarette / Don't you ever leave me / Tragedy / Malibu beach / Taxi driver / I feel alright / Train kept a rollin' / Under my wheels / Blitzkrieg bop.
■ VHS . . . . HEN 2007
Hendring Video / '88.

BACK TO MYSTERY CITY.
Tracks: Strange boys play weird openings / Mental beat / Until I get you / Lick summer lover / Ice cream summer / Malibu beach nightmare / Tooting Bec wreck / Sailing down the years / Beating gets faster / Back to mystery city.
■ LP . . . . LICLP 1
MC . . . . LICK 1
Lick / Jun '83 / Pinnacle.
■ CD . . . . LIC CD 1
Lick / Sep '91.

BANGKOK SHOCKS SAIGON SHAKES.
Tracks: Not Advised.
■ LP . . . . LICLP 2
MC . . . . LICK 2
Lick / Aug '83 / Pinnacle.
CD . . . . LIC CD 2
Lick / Sep '91 / Pinnacle.

BEST OF HANOI ROCKS.
Tracks: Not Advised.
■ LP . . . . LICLP 8
MC . . . . LICK 8
Lick / Dec '85 / Pinnacle.
CD . . . . LIC CD 8
Lick / Nov '88 / Pinnacle.

DEAD BY CHRISTMAS.
Tracks: Oriental beat(live) / Back to Mystery city / Love's an injection / Lightning bar blues / Mental beat / Malibu beach / M.C. Baby / Village girl / 40 taxi driver / Tragedy / Visitor (live) / Ice cream summer / Whispers in the dark / Cheyenne / No law and order / Fallen star / Dead by Christmas / Lost in the city / Don't never leave me(live) / Under my wheels (live) / I feel alright (live).
■ LP . . . . RAWLP 016
MC . . . . RAWTC 016
Raw Power / Apr '86 / Pinnacle.

DON'T YOU EVER LEAVE ME.
Tracks: Don't you ever leave me / Shake / Magic carpet ride.
■ 12" . . . . TA 4685
■ 7" . . . . A 4685
CBS / Sep '85.

LEAN ON ME.
Tracks: Not Advised.
CD . . . . LICCD 11
MC . . . . LICK 11
Lick / Feb '93 / Pinnacle.

MALIBU BEACH.
Tracks: Malibu beach / Rebel on the run.
■ 7" . . . . LIX 1
Lick / May '83.
■ 12" . . . . LIXT 1
■ 7" P.Disc . . . . LIXPD 1
Lick / Oct '86.

MUSIC AND MEDIA INTERVIEW PICTURE DISCS.
Tracks: Not Advised.
■ LP P.Disc . . . . MM 1237
Music & Media / Feb '88.

NOTTINGHAM TAPES, THE (Live in Nottingham).
Tracks: Back to mystery city / Up around the bend / I can't get it / Motivatin' / Lightning bar blues / Boulevard of broken dreams / Don't you ever leave me / Tragedy / Malibu beach / Underwater world / Don't follow me / I feel alright / Taxi driver / Hey ho let's go.
VHS . . . . JE 169
Jettisoundz / '88 / TBD / Visionary Communications.

ORIENTAL BEAT.
Tracks: Not Advised.
MC . . . . LICK 3
Lick / Aug '83 / Pinnacle.
■ LP . . . . LICLP 3
Lick / Aug '83.
CD . . . . LIC CD 3
Lick / Sep '91 / Pinnacle.

ROCK 'N' ROLL DIVORCE.
Tracks: Not Advised.
■ LP . . . . BOOTLIC 7
Bootlick / Dec '86.

SELF DESTRUCTION BLUES.
Tracks: Not Advised.
MC . . . . LICK 4
Lick / Aug '83 / Pinnacle.
■ LP . . . . LICLP 4
Lick / Aug '83.
CD . . . . LICCD 4
Lick / Sep '91 / Pinnacle.

TRACKS FROM A BROKEN DREAM.
Tracks: Boulevard of broken dreams / Rebel on the run / Oil and gasoline / Shakes / Malibu calypso / Problem child / I can't get it / Do the duck / Two steps from the move / Magic carpet ride / I love you / Don't you ever leave me / Underwater world / Willing to cross the ocean / It's too late.
CD . . . . LICCD 10
LP . . . . LICLP 10
MC . . . . LICK 10
Lick / Oct '90 / Pinnacle.

TWO STEPS FROM THE MOVE.
Tracks: Up around the bend / High school / I can't get it / Underwater world / Don't you ever leave me / Million miles away / Boulevard of broken dreams / Boiler (Me boiler'n me) / Futurama / Cutting corners / Oriental beat / Back to Mystery City / Motorvatin' / Until Iget you / Mental beat / 11th Street kids / Tragedy / Malibu Beach / Taxi driver / Lost in the city / Under my wheels.
■ MC 40 26066
■ LP . . . . CBS 26066
CBS / Oct '84.
CD 4714172
MC 4714174
Columbia / Apr '92 / Sony.

UNDERWATER WORLD.
Tracks: Underwater world / Shakes / Magic carpet ride (on 12" only).
■ 12" . . . . TA 4732
■ 7" . . . . A 4732
CBS / Sep '84.

UNTIL I GET YOU.
Tracks: Until I get you / Tragedy / Oriental beat.
■ 12" . . . . LIXT 2
■ 7" . . . . LIX 2
Lick / Aug '83.

UP AROUND THE BEND.
Tracks: Up around the bend.
■ 12" . . . . TA 45 13
■ 7" . . . . A 4513
■ 7" Set . . . . DA 4513
CBS / Jun '84.

Hansen, Kai

HEADING FOR TOMORROW.
Tracks: Intro (welcome) / Space eater / Lust for life / Hold your ground / Heaven can wait / Money / Silence / Freetime / Heading for tomorrow / Look at yourself (CD only).
■ CD . . . . CDNUK 151
■ LP . . . . NUK 151
■ MC . . . . ZCNUK 151
Noise / Feb '90.

Hansen, Randy

RANDY HANSEN.
Tracks: Champagne and cocaine / Watch what you say / Time won't stop / I want to take you higher / Millionaire / Dancin' with me / Don't pretend.
■ LP . . . . EST 12119
Capitol / Jan '81.

■ DELETED

TRIBUTE TO JIMI HENDRIX.
Tracks: Not Advised.
■ CD 1890692
Trident / Nov '92 / Pinnacle.

Hard Corps

DIRTY.
Tracks: Dirty / Respirer.
■ 12" . . . . SUR 12 026
Survival (1) / Aug '84.

FLESH AND METAL.
Tracks: Not Advised.
■ CD . . . . CPRODCD 011
Concrete Productions / Sep '90.

JE SUIS PASSEE.
Tracks: Je suis passee.
■ 12" 12IMMAC 2
Immaculate / May '85.
■ 12" . . . . HARDX 1
■ 7" . . . . HARD 1
Polydor / May '85.
■ 7" . . . . IMMAC 2
Immaculate / May '85.

LUCKY CHARM.
Tracks: Lucky charm.
■ 12" . . . . .TYPE 3T
■ 7" . . . . TYPE 3
Transglobal / May '87.

TO BREATHE.
Tracks: To breathe / Metal and the flesh.
■ 12" . . . . HARDX 2
■ 7" . . . . HARD 2
Polydor / Oct '85.

Hard-Ons

DICKCHEESE.
Tracks: Made to love you / What am I supposed to do / Oozing for pleasure / Everytime I do a fart / Get away / Pretty face / There was a time / Mickey juice / Figaro / F**k society / Yuppies suck / Something about you / All washed up / Ache to touch you / Why don't you shut up / Nerds / Got a baby / Stairway to punchbowl.
■ LP . . . . SOL 10
Vinyl Solution / Apr '88.

HOT FOR YOUR LOVE BABY.
Tracks: All set to go / Love song for Cindy / Coffs harbour blues / School days / It's cold outside / Then I kissed her (Arabic version) / By my side / I'll come again / Fifteen / Keish's new song / From my window / Rock 'n' roll all nite.
■ LP . . . . SOL 8
Vinyl Solution / Feb '88.

LOVE IS A BATTLEFIELD.
Tracks: Love is a battlefield.
■ LP . . . . SOL 19
Vinyl Solution / Oct '89.

SMELL MY FINGER.
Tracks: Smell my finger.
■ 7" . . . . .DAMP 037
Waterfront / Sep '87.

TOO FAR GONE.
Tracks: Crazy crazy eyes / Notice me / If it makes you happy / Carphone / Test / I do I do I do / Lost / Blade / No one can stop you / Cat scan / If she only knew / It's up to me / Stressed out / Sleepy.
CD . . . . SUR 538CD
LP . . . . .SUR 538
Survival (1) / Sep '93 / Vital Distribution.

WHERE DID SHE COME FROM.
Tracks: Where did she come from.
■ 7" . . . . VS 27
Vinyl Solution / Jan '91.

YUMMY.
Tracks: Not Advised.
CD .SOL 26CD
LP . . . . SOL 26
MC . . . . SOL 26C
Vinyl Solution / Feb '91 / RTM / Pinnacle.

Hardline

HARDLINE.
Tracks: Not Advised.
■ LP . . . . .SKULL 8358
Mausoleum / Oct '84.

Harlequin

HARLEQUIN.
Tracks: Take this heart / Keep this fire alive / Don't waste my time / Memories / Can't turn it off / Calling / Trouble in paradise / Run for your life / Love in disguise.
■ LP . . . . EPC 26263
Epic / Jan '85.

ONE FALSE MOVE.
Tracks: Not Advised.
■ LP . . . . HMUSA 1
Heavy Metal America / Jun '84.

Harlow

HARLOW.
Tracks: Chain reaction / Don't say we're over / When you love someone / No escape / Pictures / Silence / Empty / Cry murder / Beyond control / Edge of love.
■ CD 7599258744
■ LP 7599258741
■ MC 7599258742
WEA / Jun '90.

Harter Attack

HUMAN HELL.
Tracks: Death bells of the apocalypse / Last temptation / Slaves of conformity / Message from God / Nuclear attack / Human hell / Culture decay / Thugs against drugs / Symbol of hate / Let the sleeping dogs die.
CD . . . . CORE 1CD
Metalcore / Jul '89 / Pinnacle.
■ LP . . . . CORE 1
Metalcore / Jul '89.

Harvey, Alex

Glasgow-born Harvey, was born in 1935 and once dubbed as Scotland's answer to Tommy Steele. Despite this, Harvey formed the R & B outfit, Alex Harvey Soul Band in 1958. Although building a big live following, the band split in 1966. In 1972 the Sensational Alex Harvey Band was formed - Zal Cleminson, Chris Glen, Hugh and Ted McKenna joining Harvey in a band that successfully fused vaudevillian theatrics with hybrid rock styles. The band became one of the top concert attractions of the mid-seventies. Inevitably they were bigger live than on record, although S.A.H.B. achieved Top 20 singles with 1975's live and irreverent recording of Tom Jones' *Delilah* and *The Boston Tea Party* (1976). S.A.H.B.'s Top 20 albums included *The Impossible Dream*, *Tomorrow Belongs To Me*, *Live*, *Penthouse Tapes* and *SAHB Stories*. Following Harvey's worsening back problem - injured during a live show - the band split in 1977. Tragically, Alex Harvey died of a heart attack in February 1981.

ALEX HARVEY.
Tracks: To make my life beautiful / Jesus man / Lucy / Hoodooin' of Miss Fanny de Berry / Ritual of Miss Fanny de Berry / So I'm down / Tulsa turnaround / Momma's waiting / Light of kindness / Delta dawn.
■ LP . . . . EST 789
Capitol / Feb '73.

ALEX HARVEY & HIS SOUL BAND (Harvey, Alex & His Soul Band).
Tracks: Framed / I ain't worrying baby / Backwater blues / Let the good times roll / Going home / I've got my mojo working / Teensville U.S.A. / New orleans / Bo Diddley is a gun slinger / When I grow to old to rock / Evil hearted man / I just wanna make love to you / Blind man / Reeling and rocking.
■ LP 831 887-1
MC 831 887-4
Polydor (Germany) / Oct '87 / PolyGram.

ALEX HARVEY BAND IN CONCERT (Harvey, Alex Band).
Tracks: Not Advised.
CD . . . . WINCCD 002
MC . . . . WINCMC 002
Windsong / Sep '91 / Pinnacle / A.D.A. Distribution.

ALL SENSATIONS (Harvey, Alex Sensational Band).
Tracks: Midnight moses / Action strasse / Delilah / St. Anthony / Sgt. Fury / Next / Give my compliments to the chef / Gang bang / Framed / Faith healer / Vambo marble eye / Anthem.
CD 512 201-2
■ MC 512 201-4
Vertigo / Jun '92.

AMOS MOSES (Harvey, Alex Sensational Band).
Tracks: Amos Moses.
■ 7" . . . . TOP 19
Mountain / Aug '76.

BBC LIVE IN CONCERT.
Tracks: Next / Faith healer / Give my compliments to the chef / Delilah / Boston tea party / Pick it up and kick it / Smouldering.
CD . . . . WHISCD 004
Windsong / Oct '94 / Pinnacle / A.D.A. Distribution.

BEST OF THE SENSATIONAL ALEX HARVEY BAND, THE (Harvey, Alex Sensational Band).
Tracks: Delilah / Faith healer / Framed / Sgt. Fury / Jungle rub out / Love story / School's out / Boston tea party / Gamblin' bar room blues / Next / Man in the jar / Snake bite / Give my compliments to the chef / Cheek to cheek.
■ LP . . . . NE 1368
MC . . . . CE 2368
K-Tel / Jul '87 / I & B Records / C.M. Distribution / Arabesque Ltd. / Mono Distributors (Jersey) Ltd. / Prism Leisure PLC / PolyGram / Ross Records / Prism Leisure PLC.
CD . . . . NCD 5139
K-Tel / Jun '87 / I & B Records / C.M. Distribution / Arabesque Ltd. / Mono Distributors (Jersey) Ltd. / Prism Leisure PLC / PolyGram / Ross Records / Prism Leisure PLC.

BEST OF THE SENSATIONAL ALEX HARVEY BAND, THE (Harvey, Alex Sensational Band).
Tracks: Delilah (live) / Cheek to cheek (live) / Jungle rubout / Man in the jar / Weights made of lead / Sgt. Fury / Boston tea party / Next / Gamblin' bar room blues / Tomorrow belongs to me (live) / Snake bite / School's out / Love story / Faith healer / Framed.
CD . . . . MCCD 001
MC . . . . .MCTC 001
Music Club / Feb '91 / Gold & Sons / TBD / Video Collection / C.M. Distribution.

BEST OF THE SENSATIONAL ALEX HARVEY BAND, THE (Harvey, Alex Sensational Band).
Tracks: Next / Framed / Faith healer / Tomahawk kid / Vambo / Man in the jar / Sgt. Fury / Tale of the giant stoneater / Action Strasse / Delilah / Weights made of lead / Boston tea party / Anthem / Runaway / Crazy horses / Big tree small axe / Mafia stole my guitar / Gang bang / Tomorrow belongs tome.
■ LP . . . . PL 70276
■ MC . . . . PK 70276
RCA / May '84.

BOSTON TEA PARTY, THE (Harvey, Alex Sensational Band).
Tracks: Boston tea party.
■ 7" . . . . TOP 12
Mountain / Jun '76.

CHEEK TO CHEEK (Harvey, Alex Sensational Band).
Tracks: Cheek to cheek / Jungle Jenny.
■ 7" 6059 173
Vertigo / Jun '77.

COLLECTION: ALEX HARVEY (Harvey, Alex Sensational Band).
Tracks: 25 dollars for a message / Tale of the giant stoneater / Action strasse / Gang bang / Next / Give my compliments to the chef / Framed / Tomorrow belongs to me / Dance to your daddy / Sgt. Fury / Sultan's choice / Delilah / Soul in chains / Faith healer / Boston tea party / Vambo / Dogs of war / There's no lights on the Christmas tree mother - they're bur / Giddy up a ding dong.
■ CD . . . . CCSCD 149
Castle Collector Series / '86.
■ Double LP . . . . CCSLP 149
■ MC . . . . CCSMC 149
Castle Collector Series / Sep '86.

COLLECTORS ITEMS (Harvey, Alex Sensational Band).
Tracks: Boston tea party / Action strasse / Give my compliments to the chef / Jungle Jenny / Vambo / Faith healer / Delilah / Sultan's choice / Dance to your daddy.
■ LP . . . . TOPS 129
Mountain / Oct '80.

DELILAH (Harvey, Alex Band).
Tracks: Delilah / Boston tea party / Faith healer.
■ 7" . . . . .HOT 2
Mountain / Jul '80.

DELILAH (Harvey, Alex Sensational Band).
Tracks: Delilah.
■ 7" . . . . ALEX 002
Vertigo / Jul '75.

DELILAH (Harvey, Alex Sensational Band).
Tracks: Not Advised.
CD 550 6632
MC 550 6634
Spectrum (1) / Aug '94 / PolyGram.

FOURPLAY (Harvey, Alex Band).
Tracks: Smouldering / Chase it into the night / Shake your way to heaven / Outer boogie / Big boy / Pick it up and kick it / Love you for a lifetime / Too much American pie.
■ LP . . . . TOPC 5006
Mountain / Feb '77.
■ LP . . . . SAH 113
Sahara / Nov '84.

FRAMED (Harvey, Alex Sensational Band).
Tracks: Not Advised.
CD . . . . SAMRCD 00119
Samurai / '86 / SRD.
■ LP . . . . SAH 119
MC . . . . SAH 119TC
Sahara / Jul '86.

GAMBLIN' BAR ROOM BLUES (Harvey, Alex Sensational Band).
Tracks: Gamblin' bar room blues.

IMPOSSIBLE DREAM, THE (Harvey, Alex Band).
Tracks: Not Advised.
■ LP 6360 112
Vertigo / Oct '74.
■ LP . . . . SAH 116
MC . . . . SAH 116TC
Sahara / May '86.

LEGEND (Harvey, Alex Sensational Band).
Tracks: Not Advised.
CD . . . . SAMRCD 00041
Samurai / '86 / SRD.

LEGEND, THE.
Tracks: Not Advised.
■ LP . . . . SAH 141
Sahara / Nov '85.

LIVE IN GLASGOW 1993 (Harvey, Alex Band).
Tracks: Faithhealer / St. Anthony / Framed / Gang bang / Amos moses / Boston tea party / Midnight moses / Vambo / Armed and ready / Delilah.
CD . . . . JIMBO 001
MC . . . . JIMMC 001
Grapevine / Apr '94 / A.D.A. Distribution / Grapevine Distribution.

LIVE: SENSATIONAL ALEX HARVEY BAND (Harvey, Alex Sensational Band).
Tracks: Compliments to the chef / Vambo / Delilah / Faith healer / Fanfare / Framed / Tomahawk kid.
CD . . . . SAHCD 00117
Samurai / '86 / SRD.
■ LP . . . . SAH 117
■ LP P.Disc . . . . SAH 117PD
MC . . . . SAH 117TC
Sahara / Apr '86.
MC . . . . TCFA 3161
Fame / Aug '86 / EMI.
■ LP . . . . FA 3161
Fame / Oct '86.

MAFIA STOLE MY GUITAR (Harvey, Alex New Band).
Tracks: Don's delight / Back in the depot / Wait for me Mama / Mafia stole my guitar / Shakin' all over / Whalers / Oh spartacus / Just a gigolo / I ain't got nobody.
■ LP . . . . PL 25257
RCA / Feb '80.
CD . . . . MAUCD 608
Demon / Sep '91 / Pinnacle / A.D.A. Distribution.

NEXT (Harvey, Alex Sensational Band).
Tracks: Swampsnake / Gang bang / Faith healer / Giddy up a ding dong / Next / Vambo marble eye / Last of the teenage idols.
■ LP 6360 103
Vertigo / Aug '75.
■ LP . . . . SAH 114
Sahara / Nov '84.
CD . . . . SAMRCD 00114
Samurai / '86 / SRD.

■ LP P.Disc . . . . SAH 114PD
Samurai / May '86.
MC . . . . TCFA 3169
■ LP . . . . FA 3169
Fame / Mar '87.

PENTHOUSE TAPES (Harvey, Alex Sensational Band).
Tracks: Not Advised.
■ LP 9102 007
Vertigo / Apr '76.
■ LP . . . . SAH 112
Sahara / Nov '84.
CD . . . . SAMRCD 00112
Samurai / '86 / SRD.

POET AND I.
Tracks: Poet and I.
■ 7" . . . . OHM 3
Powerstation / Nov '83.

PORTRAIT: SAHB (Harvey, Alex Sensational Band).
Tracks: Not Advised.
CD . . . . STFCD 1
■ LP . . . . STFL 1
MC . . . . STFC 1
Start / Sep '87 / TBD / Koch International.

ROCKDRILL (Harvey, Alex Band).
Tracks: Not Advised.
■ LP . . . . SAH 118
Sahara / Nov '84.

SAHB STORIES.
Tracks: Not Advised.
■ LP . . . . TOPS 112
Mountain / Jul '76.

SENSATIONAL (Harvey, Alex Band).
Tracks: Framed / Hammer song / Midnight Moses / Isobel Goudie / Buff's bar blues / I just want to make love to you / Hole in her stockings / There's no lights on the christmas tree mother / St Anthony.
■ LP 6360081
Vertigo / Jan '73.

SENSATIONAL ALEX HARVEY BAND (Harvey, Alex Band).
Tracks: Not Advised.
■ LP 6360 122
Vertigo / Sep '75.
■ LP . . . . SAH 115
Sahara / Nov '84.

SMALL AXE.
Tracks: Small axe / Whalers.
■ 7" . . . . PB 5252
RCA / May '80.

SOLDIER ON THE WALL, THE.
Tracks: Not Advised.
■ LP . . . . AMP 2
MC . . . . CAMP 2
Powerstation / Nov '83 / Powerstation Records.

SUNDAY SONG, THE.
Tracks: Sunday song / Horizons.
■ 7" . . . . F 12640
Decca / Jul '67.

TOMORROW BELONGS TO ME (Harvey, Alex Sensational Band).
Tracks: Not Advised.
■ LP 9102 003
Vertigo / May '75.
■ LP . . . . SAH 111
Sahara / Nov '84.
CD . . . . SAMRCD 00111
Samurai / '86 / SRD.

Hatrik

BEAST, THE.
Tracks: Not Advised.
■ LP . . . . RR 9761
Road Runner / Dec '85.

Haunted Garage

POSSESSION PARK.
Tracks: Not Advised.
CD . . . . CDZORRO 27
LP . . . . ZORRO 27
MC . . . . TZORRO 27
Metal Blade (USA) / Aug '91 / Pinnacle.

Havoc Mass

KILLING THE FUTURE.
Tracks: Not Advised.
CD . . . . MASSCD 019
Massacre / Dec '93 / Plastic Head.

Hawkwind

Since their inception in early 1969 Hawkwind have been a mainstay of the hippy-rock free festival circuit. They have made a bewildering number of albums with a vast array of personnel passing through. Perhaps the most famous ex-Hawklord is Lemmy who 'left' in 1975 and went on to fame and fortune with Motorhead. Hawkwind stubbornly carried on year in, year out and through constant touring have attracted a new generation of fans, with a certified classic in *Silver Machine* (originally a no. 3 in 1972) and vast back catalogue of chart albums, Hawkwind are without doubt the finest exponent of British psychedelic rock.

25 YEARS ON (Hawklords).
Tracks: PSI power / Free fall / Automotion / 25 years / Flying doctor / Only ones / Only the dead dreams of the cold war kid / Age of the micro man.
■ LP . . . . CD 4014
Charisma / Sep '76.
■ LP . . . . CHC 10
MC . . . . CHCMC 10
Charisma / Sep '83.
CD . . . . CDSCD 4014
Charisma / Apr '89 / EMI.

25 YEARS ON.
Tracks: 25 years on / Dead dream of the cold war kid.
■ 12" . . . . CB 33212
■ 7" . . . . CB 332
Charisma / May '79.

ACID DAZE.
Tracks: Not Advised.
CD Set . . . . RRCD 1X
■ LP Set . . . . RRBX 1
Receiver / May '90.

ACID DAZE VOLUME 1.
Tracks: Not Advised.
■ LP . . . . RRLP 125
Receiver / Apr '90.
CD . . . . RRCD 125
Receiver / Aug '93 / Total / BMG / Grapevine Distribution.

ACID DAZE VOLUME 2.
Tracks: Not Advised.
■ LP . . . . RRLP 126
Receiver / Apr '90.
CD . . . . RRCD 126
Receiver / Aug '93 / Total / BMG / Grapevine Distribution.

ACID DAZE VOLUME 3.
Tracks: Not Advised.
■ LP . . . . RRLP 127
Receiver / Apr '90.
CD . . . . RRCD 127
Receiver / Aug '93 / Total / BMG / Grapevine Distribution.

ANGELS OF DEATH.
Tracks: Angel voices / Nuclear drive / Rocky paths / Solitary mind games / Living on a knife edge / Fahrenheit 451 / Looking in the future / Choose your masks / Joker at the gate / Waiting for tomorrow / Last Messiah / Arrival in Utopia / Virgin of the world / Angels of death.
■ LP . . . . NL 71150
■ MC . . . . NK 71150
RCA / Jan '87.

ANGELS OF DEATH.
Tracks: Angels of death / Trans-dimensional man.
■ 7" . . . . RCA 137
RCA / Oct '81.

ANTHOLOGY - HAWKWIND.
Tracks: Not Advised.
CD Set . . . . ESBCD 168
Essential / Mar '92 / Total / BMG.

ANTHOLOGY-HAWKWIND VOL 1.
Tracks: Not Advised.
CD . . . . SAMRCD 00038
■ LP . . . . SAMR 038
■ LP P.Disc . . . . SAMR 038 PD
Samurai / Nov '86.

ANTHOLOGY-HAWKWIND VOL 2.
Tracks: Not Advised.
CD . . . . SAMRCD 00039
■ LP . . . . .SAMR 039
MC. TCSAMR 039
Samurai / Mar '86 / SRD.

ANTHOLOGY-HAWKWIND VOL 3.
Tracks: Not Advised.
MC. SAMR 040TC
Samurai / Jul '86 / SRD.

ASTOUNDING SOUNDS, AMAZING MUSIC.
Tracks: Reefer madness / Steppenwolf / City of Lagoons / Aubergine that ate Rangoon / Kerb crawler / Kadu flyer / Chronoglide skyway.
■ LP . . . . CDS 4004
Charisma / Sep '76.
■ LP . . . . CHC 14
■ MC. . . . . CHCMC 14
Charisma / '83.
CD . . . . CDSCD 4004
Charisma / May '89 / EMI.

BBC LIVE IN CONCERT.
Tracks: Not Advised.
■ CD . . . . WINCD 007
LP . . . . WINLP 007
MC. WINMC 007
Windsong / Nov '91 / Pinnacle / A.D.A. Distribution.

BEST OF HAWKWIND.
Tracks: Not Advised.
■ CD . . . . CDAR 1018
■ MC. ARLC 1018
Action Replay / May '90.

BEST OF HAWKWIND, THE.
Tracks: Not Advised.
MC. MATMC 293
Castle / Aug '94 / BMG.
CD . . . . MATCD 293
Castle / Mar '94 / BMG.

BEST OF: FRIENDS AND RELATIONS.
Tracks: Not Advised.
CD .SHARP 1724CD
Flicknife / Nov '88 / Pinnacle.

BRING ME THE HEAD OF YURI GAGARIN (Live at the Empire Pool - 1973).
Tracks: Ga-ga / Egg / Orgone accumulator / Wage war / Urban guerilla / Master of the universe / Welcome to the future / Sonic attack / Silver machine.
■ LP . . . . DM 002
Demi-Monde / '85.
CD . . . . CDCHARLY 40
Charly / Nov '86 / Charly.
CD .CDTB 101
Magnum / Dec '92 / TBD.

BRITISH TRIBAL MUSIC.
Tracks: Not Advised.
CD . . . . STFCD 2
■ LP . . . . STFL 2
MC. STFC 2
Start / Sep '87 / TBD / Koch International.

BUSINESS TRIP, THE.
Tracks: Altair / Quark strangeness & charm / LSD / Camera that could lie / Green finned demon / Do that / Day a wall came down / Berlin axis / Void of golden light / Right stuff / Wastelands / Dream goes on / Right to decide / Dream has ended / Future / Terra mystica (Features on DLP only).
CD . . . . EBSCD 111
CD . . . . EBSSCD 111
Double LP . . . . EBSLP 111
MC. EBSMC 111
Emergency Broadcast System / Sep '94 / Vital Distribution.

CALIFORNIA BRAINSTORM.
Tracks: Not Advised.
CD .ILCD 1014
Iloki / Aug '94 / Plastic Head.

CHOOSE YOUR MASQUES.
Tracks: Choose your masks / Dream worker / Arrival in Utopia / Utopia / Silver machine / Void city / Solitary mind games / Fahrenheit 451 / Scan / Waiting for tomorrow.
■ LP . . . . RCALP 6055
■ MC. . . . . RCAK 6055
RCA / '82.

CHRONICLE OF THE BLACK SWORD.
Tracks: Song of the swords / Shade gate / Sea king / Pulsing cavern / Elric the enchanter / Needle gun / Zarzinia / Demise / Sleep of a thousand tears / Chaos army / Horn of destiny.

CD . . . . SHARPD 033
■ LP . . . . SHARP 033
MC. SHARPC 033
Flicknife / Nov '85 / Pinnacle.
CD .DOJOCD 72
Dojo / Feb '94 / Castle Communications / BMG.

CHRONICLE OF THE BLACK SWORD.
Tracks: Not Advised.
■ VHS . . . . .JE 150
Jettisoundz / Aug '86.

CHURCH OF HAWKWIND.
Tracks: Angel voices / Nuclear drive / Star cannibal / Phenomeno of luminosity / Fall of Earth City / Church / Joker at the gate / Some people never die / Light specific data / Experiment with destiny / Last Messiah / Looking in the future.
■ LP . . . . RCALP 9004
RCA / '82.
CD .DOJOCD 86
Dojo / Jun '94 / Castle Communications / BMG.

COLLECTION: HAWKWIND (Parts 1 & 2).
Tracks: You shouldn't do that / We do it / Bring it on home / Silver machine / Born to go / Dealing with the devil / Urban guerilla / Masters of the universe / Who's gonna win the war / Hash cake '77 / Motorhead / Quark, strangeness and charm / Douglas in the jungle / Space is deep / Earth calling / Angels of death / Spirit of the age / Ghost dance.
■ Double LP . . . . CCSLP 148
■ MC. . . . . CCSMC 148
Castle Collector Series / Sep '86.
■ CD . . . . CCSCD 148
Castle Collector Series / Sep '86.

DECIDE YOUR FUTURE.
Tracks: Decide your future.
■ 12" 4 R2T
■ CD Single 4 R2CD
4 Real / Nov '93.

DOREMI FASOL LATIDO.
Tracks: Brainstorm / Space is deep / One change / Lord of the light / Down through the night / Time we left this world today / Watcher.
■ LP . . . . UAG 29364
■ MC. . . . . TCK 29364
United Artists / Dec '72.
■ LP . . . . ATAK 92
MC. TCATAK 92
Liberty / Jun '85 / EMI.

EARLY DAZE BEST OF.
Tracks: Hurry on sundown / Dreaming / Master of the universe / In the egg / Orgone accumulator / Sonic attack / Silver machine.
■ LP . . . . THBL 044
MC. THBC 044
Thunderbolt / Dec '87 / TBD / Jazz Music.
CD . . . . CDTB 044
Thunderbolt / Jun '88 / TBD / Jazz Music.

ELECTRIC TEPEE.
Tracks: Not Advised.
CD . . . . ESSCD 181
■ LP . . . . ESDLP 181
MC. ESDMC 181
Essential / May '92 / Total / BMG.

FRIENDS & RELATIONS.
Tracks: Who's gonna win the war / Golden void / Robot / Neesh / Good girl bad girl / Valium 10 / Human beings / Time centre.
■ LP .SHARP 01
Flicknife / Mar '82.

FRIENDS AND RELATIONS, VOL. 1.
Tracks: Not Advised.
LP . . . . SHARP 101
Flicknife / Oct '90 / Pinnacle.

FRIENDS AND RELATIONS, VOL. 2.
Tracks: Not Advised.
LP . . . . SHARP 107
Flicknife / Oct '90 / Pinnacle.

HALL OF THE MOUNTAIN GRILL.
Tracks: Psychedelic warlords (disappear in smoke) / Wind of change / D rider / Webb weaver / You'd better believe it / Hall of the mountain grill / Lost Johnny / Goat willow / Paradox.
■ LP . . . . UAG 29672
United Artists / Sep '74.
■ LP . . . . LBG 29672
■ MC. . . . . TC LBG 29672
Liberty / '85.
■ LP . . . . FA 3133
MC. FA 41 3133 4
MC. TCFA 3133
Fame / Sep '85 / EMI.
CD . . . . CDFA 3133
Fame / May '89 / EMI.

HAWKWIND.
Tracks: Hurry on sundown / Reason is / Be yourself / Paranoia part 1 / Paranoia part 2 / Seeing it as you really are / Mirror of illusion.
■ LP . . . . LBR 1012
Liberty / '80.
■ LP .SLS 1972 921
Sunset (Liberty) / Feb '84.
■ LP P.Disc . . . . .TCSLS 1972924
Sunset (Liberty) / Feb '84.
■ LP P.Disc . . . . SLSP 1972 921
Sunset (Liberty) / Feb '84.

HAWKWIND - CD BOX SET.
Tracks: Not Advised.
■ CD Set. . . . . .CLA BX 911
Castle Classics / Feb '92.

HAWKWIND - FRIDAY ROCK SHOW SESSIONS.
Tracks: Magnu/ Angels of death / Pulsing Cavern / Assault & battery / Needle gun / Master of the universe / Utopia / Dream worker / Assassins of Allah (Hassan I sahba) / Silver machine.
CD . . . . FRSCD 005
Raw Fruit / Mar '92 / Pinnacle.

HAWKWIND, FRIENDS & RELATIONS.
Tracks: Not Advised.
■ LP . . . . SHARP 024
Flicknife / Apr '85.

IN SEARCH OF SPACE.
Tracks: You shouldn't do that / You know you're only dreaming / Master of the universe / We took the wrong step years ago / Adjust me / Children of the sun.
■ LP . . . . UAS 29202
United Artists / Nov '71.
■ LP . . . . LBG 29202
Liberty / Mar '81.
■ LP . . . . ATAK 9
■ MC. . . . . TC-ATAK 9
Liberty / '85.
■ LP . . . . FA 3192
MC. TCFA 3192
Fame / Oct '87 / EMI.
CD . . . . CDFA 3192
Fame / May '89 / EMI.

IN THE BEGINNING.
Tracks: Master of the universe / Dreaming / Shouldn't do that / Hurry on sundown / Paranoia / See it as you really are / I do it / Came home.
■ LP . . . . DM 005
Demi-Monde / '85.
CD .CDTB 105
Thunderbolt / Jun '92 / TBD / Jazz Music.
CD . . . . CDCD 1131
Charly / Feb '94 / Charly.

INDEPENDENT DAYS - VOL.2.
Tracks: Not Advised.
■ LP . . . . SHARP 036
■ MC. . . . . SHARP 036C
Flicknife / Nov '86.

INDEPENDENTS DAY.
Tracks: Hurry on sundown / Motorway City / Motorhead / Over the top / Who's gonna win the war / Social alliance.
■ LP . . . . SHARP 019
Flicknife / '84.

IT'S THE BUSINESS OF THE FUTURE TO BE DANGEROUS.
Tracks: Not Advised.
CD . . . . ESSCD 196
MC. ESSMC 196
■ LP . . . . ESSLP 196
Essential / Oct '93.

LEVITATION.
Tracks: Levitation / Motorway city / Psychosis / World of tiers / Prelude / Who's gonna win the war / Space chase / Second of forever / Dust of time.
■ LP .BRON 530
Bronze / Nov '80.
CD . . . . CLACD 129
■ LP . . . . CLALP 129
Castle Classics / Jul '87.
■ MC. . . . . CLAMC 129
Castle Classics / Jul '87.

LEVITATION / LIVE '79.
Tracks: Levitation / Motorway city / Psychosis / World of tiers / Prelude / Who's gonna win the war / Space chase / Fifth second of forever / Dust of time / Shotdown in the night / Spirit of the age / Brainstorm

■ DELETED

H 5

/ Light house / Master of the universe / Silver machine (requiem).
■ **Double LP**. . . . . TFOLP 17
■ **CD Set**. . . . . TFOCD 17
■ **MC**. . . . . TFOMC 17
That's Original / '88.

LIVE (Hawklords).
Tracks: 25 Years / High rise / Death trap / Spirit of the age / Sonic attack / Over the top.
CD . . . . DOJOCD 71
Castle / Nov '92 / BMG.

LIVE '79.
Tracks: Not Advised.
CD. CLACD 243
Castle Classics / Jul '94 / BMG / Castle Communications.

LIVE 1979.
Tracks: Shot down in the night / Motorway city / Spirit of the age / Brainstorm / Lighthouse / Master of the universe / Silver machine.
■ **LP** . . . . BRON 527
Bronze / Aug '80.

LIVE 70/73.
Tracks: Sonic attack / Seven by seven / Wage war / Urban guerilla / Only dreaming / Hurry on a sundown / In the egg / Orgone accumulator (1972) / Welcome to the future / Masters of the universe.
■ **LP** . . . . DOJOLP 11
Dojo / Apr '86.
■ **CD** . . . . DOJOCD 11
Dojo / '87.

LIVE CHRONICLES.
Tracks: Not Advised.
■ **LP** . . . . GWSP 1
Legacy / Aug '89.

LIVE COLLECTION.
Tracks: Song of the sword / Dragons and fables / Narration / Sea king / Angels of death / Choose your masques / Flight sequence / Needle gun / Zarozinia / Lords of chaos / Dark Lords / Wizard of Pan Tang / Shade gate / Rocky paths / Pulsing cavern / Master of the universe / Dreaming city / Moonglum (Friend without a cause) / Elric the enchanter / Conjuration of magnu / Magnu dust of time / Horn of fate.
CD. . . . . CCSCD 321
■ **MC**. . . . . CCSMC 321
Castle / Apr '92.

LIVING LEGENDS.
Tracks: Not Advised.
■ **VHS** . . . . CMP 6005
Castle Music Pictures / Oct '90.

MASTERS OF THE UNIVERSE.
Tracks: Masters of the universe / Brainstorm / Sonic attack / Orgone accumulator / It's so easy / Lost Johnny.
■ **LP** . . . . FA 3008
■ **MC**. . . . . TCFA 3008
Fame / '82.
■ **LP** . . . . ATAK 103
■ **MC**. . . . . TCATAK 103
EMI / Aug '87.
CD. . . . . CDFA 3220
■ **LP** . . . . FA 3220
MC. TCFA 3220
Fame / May '89 / EMI.

MIGHTY HAWKWIND CLASSICS 1980-85.
Tracks: Hurry on sundown / Sweet mistress of pain / King of speed (live) / Motorhead / Valium ten / Night of the hawks / Green finned demon / Dream dancers / Dragons and fables / Over the top / Free fall / Death trap.
CD. CDMGRAM 86
Anagram / Apr '92 / Pinnacle.

MOTORHEAD.
Tracks: Motorhead / Valium ten.
■ **7"** . . . . FLS 205
Flicknife / Sep '81.
■ **12"** . . . . FLSEP 205
Flicknife / Sep '81.
■ **7"** . . . . FLS 034
Flicknife / Jul '86.

MOTORWAY CITY.
Tracks: Motorway city / Master of the universe.
■ **7"** . . . . FLS 025
Flicknife / '83.

NEEDLE GUN.
Tracks: Needle gun / Arioch.
■ **12"** . . . . FLST 032
■ **7"** . . . . FLS 032
Flicknife / '85.

NIGHT OF THE HAWK.
Tracks: Not Advised.
■ CD. POWCD 5502
Power House / May '89.
■ **LP** . . . . POW 5502
MC. POWC 5502
Power House / Jun '94 / Jetstar / Ichiban Records (UK) / Backs Distribution.

NIGHT OF THE HAWKS.
Tracks: Night of the hawks.
■ **7"** . . . . FLSEP 104
Flicknife / Feb '84.

NIGHT OF THE HAWKS.
Tracks: Ghost dance / Watching the grass grow / Dream worker / Ejection / Island / Uncle Sam's on Mars / Brainstorm / Sonic attack / PSI power / Silver machine.
■ **VHS** . . . . JE 123
Jettisoundz / Mar '93.

NIGHT OF THE HAWKS EP (Earth Ritual Preview).
Tracks: Night of the hawks / Green finned demon / Dream dancers / Dragons & fables.
■ **12"** . . . . FLEP 104
Flicknife / Jan '84.

NIGHTRIDING: HAWKWIND (Golden Decade Of Hawkwind).
Tracks: Not Advised.
■ **MC**. . . . . KNMC 10017
■ **CD** . . . . KNCD 10017
Nightriding / Jun '90.

OFFICIAL PICTURE LOGBOOK, THE.
Tracks: Not Advised.
■ **LP Set**. . . . . HWBOX 1
Flicknife / Oct '87.

OUT AND INTAKE.
Tracks: Turning point / Waiting for tomorrow / Cajun jinx / Solitary mind games / Starflight / Ejection / Assassins of Allah / Flight to Maputo / Confrontation / 5 to 4 / Ghost dance.
■ **LP** . . . . SHARP 040
■ **MC**. . . . . SHARP 040C
Flicknife / Apr '87.
CD. SHARP 040CD
Flicknife / Apr '87 / Pinnacle.

OVER THE TOP.
Tracks: Over the top / Free fall / Death trap.
■ **12"** . . . . FLEP 101
Flicknife / Nov '81.

P.S.I. POWER (Hawklords).
Tracks: P.S.I. Power / Age of the micro man.
■ **7"** . . . . CB 2323
Charisma / Oct '78.

PALACE SPRINGS.
Tracks: Not Advised.
CD. . . . . GWCD 104
LP. . . . . GWLP 104
MC. . . . . GWTC 104
GWR / May '91 / Pinnacle.

PXR5.
Tracks: Death trap / Jack of shadows / Uncle Sam's on Mars / Infinity / Life form / Robot / High rise / P.X.R.5.
■ **LP** . . . . CDS 4016
Charisma / Jun '79.
MC. CHCMC 25
Charisma / Mar '84.
■ **LP** . . . . CHC 25
CD. CDSCD 4016
Charisma / Apr '89 / EMI.

QUARK STRANGENESS AND CHARM.
Tracks: Spirit of the age / Damnation alley / Fable of a failed race / Quark, strangeness and charm / Hassan I sahba / Forge of vulcan / Days of the underground / Iron dream.
■ **LP** . . . . CDS 4008
Charisma / Jul '77.
■ **LP** . . . . CHC 50
■ **MC**. . . . . CHCMC 50
Charisma / Oct '86.
CD. CDSCD 4008
Charisma / Apr '89 / EMI.

QUARK STRANGENESS AND CHARM.
Tracks: Uncle Sam's on Mars (Red planet radio mix) / Quark strangeness and charm / Black sun / Uncle Sam's on Mars (Martian conquest mix).
12" . . . . EBT 110
CD Single . . . . EBCD 110
Emergency Broadcast System / Sep '94 / Vital Distribution.

QUARK STRANGENESS AND CHARM/PXR5.
Tracks: Spirit of the age / Damnation alley / Fable of a failed race / Quark, strangeness and charm / Hassan I sahba / Forge of Vulcan / Days of the underground / Iron dream / Death trap / Jack of shadows / Uncle Sam's on Mars / Infinity / Life form / Robot / High rise / P.X.R.5.
MC Set . . . . CASMC 110
Charisma / '88 / EMI.

REPEAT PERFORMANCE.
Tracks: Kerb crawler / Back on the streets / Spirit of the age / Quark, strangeness and charm / Steppenwolf / 25 years / PSI power / Only ones / High rise / Uncle Sam's on Mars.
■ **LP** . . . . BG 002
Charisma / Oct '80.

RIDICULE.
Tracks: Not Advised.
■ **LP** . . . . OBLP 1
Obsession / Nov '85.

ROADHAWKS.
Tracks: Hurry on Sundown / Paranoia / You shouldn't do that / Silver machine / Guerilla / Space is deep / Wind of change / Golden void.
■ **LP** . . . . UAK 29919
United Artists / Apr '76.
■ **LP** . . . . FA 413 096 1
MC. FA 413 096 4
Fame / Apr '84 / EMI.

SILVER MACHINE.
Tracks: Silver machine / Seven by seven.
■ **7"** . . . . RCA 276
■ **7" P.Disc** . . . . RCAP 276
RCA / Sep '82.
■ **12"** 12UP 35381
■ **7" P.Disc** . . . . UPP 35381
■ **7"** . . . . UP 35381
United Artists / Jan '83.
■ **12"** . . . . HW 12001
■ **7"** . . . . HW 7001
■ **7" P.Disc** . . . . HW 001
Samurai / May '86.

SILVER MACHINE (OLD GOLD).
Tracks: Silver machine / Urban guerilla.
7" . . . . OG 9981
Old Gold / '92 / Pickwick.

SOLSTICE AT STONEHENGE.
Tracks: Stonehenge decoded / Ghost dance / Watching the grass grow / Utopia / Sonic attack / Right stuff / Dawn / In the morning.
■ **VHS** . . . . JE 250
Visionary Communications / Oct '93.

SONIC ATTACK.
Tracks: Sonic attack / Rocky paths / Psychosonia / Virgin of the world / Angels of death / Living on a knife edge / Coded language / Disintegration / Streets of fear / Lost chances.
■ **MC**. . . . . RCAK 6004
■ **LP** . . . . RCALP 6004
RCA / Oct '81.

SPACE BANDITS.
Tracks: Not Advised.
CD. . . . . GWCD 103
■ **LP** . . . . GWLP 103
MC. . . . . GWTC 103
Legacy / Sep '90 / Sony.
CD. CLACD 282
Castle / Jul '92 / BMG.

SPACE RITUAL ALIVE.
Tracks: Not Advised.
■ **Double LP**. . . . . UAD 60037/8
United Artists / Jun '73.

SPACE RITUAL VOL.2.
Tracks: Space / Accumulator / Upside down sonic attack / Time we left / Ten seconds of forever / Brainstorm / Seven by seven / Master of the universe / Welcome to the future.
■ **LP** . . . . APK 8
MC. . . . . APKC 8
APK / Mar '85.
CD. . . . . CDTL 003
The CD Label / Apr '87 / Jazz Music / TBD.
CD. CDTB 099
Thunderbolt / Jan '91 / TBD / Jazz Music.

SPIRIT OF THE AGE.
Tracks: Master of the universe / Earth calling / Psychosis / Space chase / Angels of death / Motorway City / Born to go / Brainstorm (live) / Spirit of the age / Motorhead / Dealing with the devil / World of tiers / Fifth second of forever / Dust of time / Levitation / Silver machine (live).

■ DELETED

MC. . . . . ELITE 021 MC
Elite (Pickwick) / Oct '91 / Pickwick.
CD. . . . . .ELITE 021 CD
Elite (Pickwick) / Aug '93 / Pickwick.

SPIRIT OF THE AGE.
Tracks: Forge the Vulcan, The-introduction out-take /
Flying doctor / Steppenwolf / Hassan I sahba /
Twenty five years / Jack of shadows / PSI power /
Reefer madness / Fable of a failed race / High rise /
Quark, strangeness and charm / Back on the streets
/ Kerb crawler / Only the dead dreams of the cold
war kid / Spirit of the age.
CD. . . . . .COMCD 8
Virgin / '88 / EMI.

SPIRIT OF THE AGE (Solstice Remixes).
Tracks: Spirit of the age.
■ 12" . . . . 4 RIT
■ CD Single. . . . . 4 RID
■ MC Single. . . . . .4 RICS
Southern / Jun '93.

STASIS - THE UA YEARS 1971-1975.
Tracks: Urban guerilla / Psychedelic warlords (dis-
appear in smoke) / Brainbox pollution / Seven by
seven / Paradox / Silver machine / You'd better
believe it / Lord of light / Black corridor / Space is
deep / Earth calling (CD only) / Born to go (CD only.)
/ Down through the night (CD only.) / Awakening (CD
only.) / You shouldn't do that.
■ CD. . . . . CZ 297
■ LP. . . . . .NTS 300
■ MC. . . . . TCNTS 300
Note / Apr '90.
CD. . . . . CDFA 3267
■ MC. . . . . TCFA 3267
Fame / Apr '92.

TALES FROM THE ATOM HENGE.
Tracks: Hunky dory / Flying doctor / Steppenwolf /
Twenty five years / Hassan I sahba / Jack of shadows / PSI power / Reefer madness / Fable of a
failed race / Highrise / Quark, strangeness and
charm / Back on the streets / Dream of Isis / Kerb
crawler / Only the dreams of the cold war kid / Spirit
of the age.
CD. . . . . CDVM 9008
Charisma / Oct '92 / EMI.

TEXT OF THE FESTIVAL, THE.
Tracks: Master of the universe / Dreaming /
Shouldn't do that / Hurry on a sundown / Paranoia /
See it as you really are / I do it / Came home /
Sound..shouldn't / Improvise / Improvise..com-
promise / Reprise.
■ Double LP. . . . . JAMS 29
Illuminated / '83.
CD. . . . . CDTB 2068
■ Double LP. . . . . THBL 2068
Thunderbolt / Nov '88.

THIS IS HAWKWIND.. DO NOT PANIC.
Tracks: PSY power / Levitation / Circles / Space
chase / Death trap / Angel of death / Show down in
the night / Stonehenge decoded / Watching the grass
grow.
■ LP. . . . . SHARP 022
Flicknife / Nov '84.
■ MC. . . . . SHARP 022C
Flicknife / Oct '90.
CD. . . . . CDMGRAM 54
Anagram / Jun '92 / Pinnacle.

TRAVELLERS AID TRUST, THE.
Tracks: Not Advised.
CD. . . . . .SHARP 2045CD
■ Double LP. . . . . SHARP 2045
■ MC. . . . . CSHARP 2045
Flicknife / Dec '88.

UA YEARS, THE.
Tracks: Not Advised.
■ LP. . . . . LBG 5002
■ MC. . . . . TCLBG 5002
Liberty / '86.

URBAN GUERILLA.
Tracks: Urban guerilla.
■ 7" . . . . UP 35566
United Artists / Aug '73.

WARRIOR AT THE EDGE OF TIME.
Tracks: Assault and battery part 1 / Golden void part
II / Wizard blew his horn / Opa-loka / Demented man
/ Magnu / Standing at the edge / Spiral galaxy /
Warriors / Dying seas / Kings of speed / Motorhead.

WARRIOR BOXSET.
Tracks: Not Advised.
CD. . . . . .CYCL 015
Cyclops / Sep '94 / Pinnacle.

WARRIOR ON THE EDGE OF TIME.
Tracks: Assault & battery / Golden void / Wizard
blew his horn / Opa-loca / Demented king / Magno /
Standing at the edge / Spiral galaxy 28948 / Warriors
/ Dying seas / Kings of speed / Motorhead.
■ LP. . . . . UAG 29766
United Artists / Jun '85 / EMI.
MC. . . . . TCK 29766
CD. . . . . .DOJOCD 84
Dojo / Feb '94 / Castle Communications / BMG.

WHO'S GONNA WIN THE WAR (Hawklords).
Tracks: Who's gonna win the war / Time off.
■ 7" . . . . FLS 209
Flicknife / Jun '82

WHO'S GONNA WIN THE WAR.
Tracks: Who's gonna win the war / Nuclear toy.
■ 7" . . . . BRO 109
Bronze / Oct '82.

XENON CODEX, THE.
Tracks: War I survived / Wastelands of sleep / Neon
skyline / Lost chronicles / Tides / Heads / Mutation
zone / EMC / Sword of the East / Good evening.
■ CD. . . . . GWCD 26
■ LP. . . . . GWLP 26
■ MC. . . . . GWTC 26
GWR / May '88.
CD. . . . . .CLACD 281
Castle / Mar '93 / BMG.

YOUR LAST CHANCE.
Tracks: Your last chance.
■ 7" . . . . FLS 214
Flicknife / Jun '83.

ZAROZINIA.
Tracks: Zarozinia / Assault & battery / Sleep of a
thousand tears (This track on 12" version only.)
■ 12" . . . . FLST 033
■ 7" . . . . FLS 033
Flicknife / Mar '86.

ZONES.
Tracks: Zones / Dangerous vision / Running through
the back brain / Island / Motorway city / Utopia 84 /
Social alliance / Sonic attack / Dream worker /
Bainstorm.
MC. . . . . SHARP 014C
■ LP. . . . . SHARP 014
Flicknife / Oct '83.
CD. . . . . .CDMGRAM 57
Anagram / Jun '88 / Pinnacle.

ZONES/STONEHENGE.
Tracks: Not Advised.
CD. . . . . .SHARP 1422CD
Flicknife / Nov '88 / Pinnacle.

ZOO.
Tracks: Zoo / Hurry on sundown / Kings of speed /
Sweet mistress of Paris.
■ 12" . . . . FLEP 100
Flicknife / Dec '83.

Haywire

HAYWIRE'S THEME.
Tracks: Haywire's theme.
■ 12" . . . . PROCT 6
Rumour / Jul '92.

LET ME BE YOUR FANTASY.
Tracks: Let me be your fantasy.
■ 12" . . . . PROCT 3
Rumour / Nov '91.

PRIVATE SPELL.
Tracks: Not Advised.
CD. 846121
LP. 086121
We Bite / Jul '90 / Plastic Head.

Hazzard

HAZZARD.
Tracks: Not Advised.
■ LP. . . . . .SKULL 8371
MC. . . . . .TAPE 78371
Mausoleum / Apr '85 / Pinnacle.

Head Like A Hole

13.
Tracks: Not Advised.
CD. . . . . .NO 2162
Noise / Aug '94 / Pinnacle.

FISH ACROSS FACE.
Tracks: Fish across face / Air / Head of ignorance.
CD Single. . . . . .N 0216-3
Noise / Sep '94 / Pinnacle.

Headbutt

PISSING DOWN.
Tracks: Sandyard / Duffle bag / Through the slides /
Adding insult.. / Always scraping shit / Barbie skin.
CD. . . . . OINK 031 CD
LP. . . . . OINK 013
Pigboy / Jan '93 / Vital Distribution.

RANDY.
Tracks: Randy / Babysick / White cat / Flying saucers
are real.
■ 7" . . . . PIG 014
Pigboy / Sep '92.

SHOOTING PARTY.
Tracks: Shooting party.
7" 7DPROMS 20
Dirter Promotions / Jan '94 / Pinnacle.

Headgirl

St. VALENTINES DAY MASSACRE.
Tracks: Please don't touch / Emergency / Bomber.
■ EP . . . . BRO 116
Bronze / '81.

Headlock

IT FOUND ME.
Tracks: Not Advised.
CD . . . . CDVEST 31
Bulletproof / Sep '94 / Pinnacle.

Headmistress

BORN TO BE WILD.
Tracks: Born to be wild / Kids said rock.
■ 7" . . . . STYLE 222
Sunnyside / Sep '90.

Heads Up

DUKE.
Tracks: Not Advised.
CD . . . . EM 93192
LP . . . . EM 93191
MC . . . . EM 93194
Road Runner / Mar '91 / Pinnacle.

SOUL BROTHER CRISIS INTERVENTION.
Tracks: Not Advised.
CD. . . . . EM 73722
LP. . . . . EM 73721
MC. . . . . EM 73724
Emergo / Oct '90 / Pinnacle.
■ CD . . . . EM 93722
Road Runner / Feb '93.

UK DOMINATION TOUR 1991.
Tracks: Not Advised.
■ VHS . . . . AIM 003
Alternative Image / Mar '92.

Headswim

MOMENTS OF ONION E.P.
Tracks: Not Advised.
■ 12" . . . . 12 HEAD 2
■ CD Single. . . . . HEAD CD 2
Crush / Mar '94.

TENSE MOMENTS.
Tracks: Violent / My life (Is driving me crazy) / One
red eye / Chains and nails / Dead / Proud / Freedom
from faith / Inside of us.
10" 476990 0
MC Single 476990 2
Epic / Jun '94 / Sony.

TENSE NERVOUS HEAD.
Tracks: Violent / My life (is driving me crazy) / One
red eye / Chains and nails.
■ 12" . . . . 12 HEAD 001
■ CD Single . . . . HEADCD 001
Crush / Oct '93.

Hear'N'Aid

SESSIONS, THE.
Tracks: Not Advised.
VHS .VVC 168
Virgin Vision / Sep '86 / Gold & Sons / TBD.

STARS.
Tracks: Four and a half minute news / Stars.
■ 12" .HEAR 112
■ 7" . . . . HEAR 1
Vertigo / Apr '86.

Heart

Formed in Vancouver in 1974 by sisters Ann (vocals/guitar) and Nancy (guitar/vocals) Wilson, who then fronted a heavily Led Zeppelin-influenced, folk rock band. Initially they struggled to match their impressive live reputation with record sales, despite hits like *Crazy On You* (from *Dreamboat Annie*). A mid-80's liaison with Epic Records failed to elevate the band much further but something clicked in 1986 when they moved to Capitol, and launched themselves into a whole new dimension with an eponymous album, a new image and MTV friendly videos. 1987's *Bad Animals* took them a step further. These days, Heart (who have changed line-ups often but retain original guitarist Howard Leese) are cool enough to hang out with Alice In Chains and remain one of the classiest AOR metal acts around.

ALL I WANNA DO IS MAKE LOVE TO YOU.
Tracks: All I wanna do is make love to you (edit) / Call of the wild / Cruel tears (12" & CD single only).
■ 12" .12CL 569
■ 7" . . . . .CL 569
■ CD Single . . . . .CDCL 569
■ MC Single . . . . .TCCL 569
■ 12" P.Disc. 12CLPD 569
Capitol / Mar '90.

ALONE.
Tracks: Alone / Barracuda / Magic man.
■ MC Single . . . . .TCCL 448
■ 7" . . . . .CL 448
■ 12" .12CL 448
Capitol / May '87.

BAD ANIMALS.
Tracks: Who will you run to / Alone / There's the girl / I want you so bad / Wait for an answer / Bad animals / You ain't so tough / Strangers of the heart / Easy target / RSVP.
■ LP . . . . .EST 2032
■ LP . . . . .ESTU 2032
■ MC . . . . .TCESTU 2032
Capitol / May '87.
■ CD .CDFA 3266
■ MC .TCFA 3266
Fame / Apr '92.
DCC 7466765
Capitol / Jan '93 / EMI.
CD . . . . .CDEST 2032
MC . . . . .TCEST 2032
Capitol / Jul '94 / EMI.

BARRACUDA.
Tracks: Barracuda / Cry to me.
■ 7" . . . . .PRT 5402
Portrait / Sep '77.

BEBE LE STRANGE.
Tracks: Bebe le strange / Down on me / Silver wheels / Break / Rockin' heaven down / Even it up / Strange night / Raised on you / Pilot / Sweet darlin'.
■ LP .PRT 84135
Portrait / Apr '80.

BRIGADE.
Tracks: Wild child / All I wanna do is make love to you / Secret / Tall, dark handsome stranger / I didn't want to need you / Night / Fallen from grace / Under the sky / Cruel nights / Stranded / Call of the wild / I want your world to turn / I love you.
■ LP .ESTU 2121
Capitol / Apr '90.
CD .CDESTU 2121
MC .TCESTU 2121
Capitol / Feb '94 / EMI.

CRAZY ON YOU.
Tracks: Crazy on you / Soul of the sea.
■ 7" . . . . .ARIST 86
Arista / Feb '77.

DESIRE WALKS ON.
Tracks: Desire / Black on black II / Back to Avalon / Woman in me / Rage / In walks the night / My crazy

head / Ring them bells / Will you be there (in the morning) / Voodoo doll / Anything is possible / Avalon (reprise) / Desire walks on / La mujer que hay en mi / Te quedaras (en la manana).
CD .CDEST 2216
LP . . . . .EST 2216
MC .TCEST 2216
Capitol / Nov '93 / EMI.

DOG AND BUTTERFLY.
Tracks: Cook with fire / High time / Hijinx / Straight on / Dog and butterfly / Lighter touch / Nada one / Mistral wind.
■ LP .PRT 32803
■ MC .40 32803
Portrait / Aug '86.
CD 9826492
Pickwick/Sony Collector's Choice / Nov '91 / Pickwick / Pinnacle.

DREAMBOAT ANNIE.
Tracks: Magic man / Dreamboat Annie (fantasy child) / Crazy on you / Soul of the sea / Dreamboat Annie / White lightning and wine / Love me like music - I'll be your song / Sing child / How deep it goes / Dreamboat Annie (reprise).
■ LP .ARTY 139
■ MC . . . . .TCARTY 139
Arista / Oct '76.
■ CD . . . . .CDEST 2042
■ LP .EMS 1277
■ MC . . . . .TCEMS 1277
Capitol / Oct '87.

EVEN IT UP.
Tracks: Even it up / Pilot.
■ 7" . . . . .EPC 8270
Epic / Mar '80.

GREATEST HITS LIVE : HEART.
Tracks: Not Advised.
CD . . . . .EGK 36888
LP .PE 236888
MC . . . . .PE 36888
Epic / Dec '88 / Sony.

GREATEST HITS: HEART.
Tracks: Tell it like it is / Barracuda / Straight on / Dog and butterfly / Even it up / Bebe le strange / Sweet darlin / I'm down/Long tall Sally / Unchained melody / Rock and roll.
■ LP 4601741
CBS / '87.
CD 4601742
MC 4601744
CBS / Apr '94 / Sony.

HEART.
Tracks: If looks could kill / What about love / Never / These dreams / Wolf / All eyes / Nobody home / Nothin' at all / What he don't know / Shellshock.
■ LP . . . . .LOVE 1
■ MC .TCLOVE 1
Capitol / Oct '85.
CD .CDLOVE 1
Capitol / Feb '86 / EMI.

HEART BOX SET.
Tracks: Not Advised.
■ LP Set . . . . .HGIFT 1
■ MC Set . . . . .TCHGIFT 1
■ CD Set . . . . .CDHGIFT 1
Capitol / Oct '90.

HEART.
Tracks: Tell it like it is / Barracuda / Straight on / Dog and butterfly / Even it up / Bebe le strange / Sweet darlin' / I'm down/Long tall sally / Rock 'n' roll / Unchained melody.
■ LP .EPC 84829
Epic / '81.
■ LP 4601741
MC 4601744
Epic / '87 / Sony.

HEART: INTERVIEW PICTURE DISC.
Tracks: Not Advised.
LP P.Disc . . . . .BAK 2080
Baktabak / Dec '87 / Arabesque Ltd.

HEARTLESS.
Tracks: Heartless / Here song.
■ 7" . . . . .ARIST 140
Arista / Sep '77.

HOW CAN I REFUSE.
Tracks: How can I refuse / Barracuda / Little Queenie.
■ 12" . . . . .TA 3695
Epic / Sep '83.

I DIDN'T WANT TO NEED YOU.
Tracks: I didn't want to need you / Night / Will to love (12" & CD single only).

■ 12" 12CLP 580
■ 12" .12CL 580
■ 7" . . . . .CL 580
■ CD Single . . . . .CDCL 580
■ MC Single . . . . .TCCL 580
Capitol / Jun '90.

IF LOOKS COULD KILL.
Tracks: What about love / Never / These dreams / Nothin' at all / Alone / Who will you run to / There's the girl.
VHS . . . . .MVR 99 0075 3
PMI / Mar '88 / EMI / Gold & Sons / TBD.
CD Video 080 494 9
Polygram Music Video / Oct '88 / PolyGram.

INTERVIEW, THE.
Tracks: Not Advised.
CD P.Disc. . . . . .CBAK 4073
Baktabak / Feb '94 / Arabesque Ltd.

LITTLE QUEEN.
Tracks: Little queen / Treat me well / Say hello / Cry to me / Go on cry / Barracuda / Love alive / Sylvan song / Dream of the archer / Kick it out.
■ LP .PRT 82075
■ MC .40 82075
Portrait / Jun '86.
■ CD .CD 82075
Portrait / May '87.
CD 983278 2
Pickwick/Sony Collector's Choice / Mar '94 / Pickwick / Pinnacle.

MAGAZINE.
Tracks: Heartless / Just the wine / Without you / Magazine / Here song / Mother Earth blues / I've got the music in me / Devil delight.
■ CD . . . . .CDEST 2041
■ LP .EMS 1278
■ MC . . . . .TCEMS 1278
Capitol / Oct '87.

MAGAZINE.
Tracks: Magazine / Here song.
■ 7" . . . . .ARIST 206
Arista / Aug '78.

MAGIC MAN.
Tracks: Magic man / How deep it goes.
■ 7" . . . . .EPC 4708
Epic / Oct '76.

NEVER.
Tracks: Never (extended remix) / These dreams / Never (remix) / These dreams (7" version) / Heart of darkness (Available on CD single only) / If looks could kill.
■ 12" .12CL 482
■ 12" .12CLE 482
■ 7" . . . . .CLG 482
■ 7" . . . . .CL 482
■ 7" P.Disc . . . . .CLP 482
Capitol / Feb '88.
■ CD Single . . . . .CDCL 482
Capitol / Feb '88.

NOTHIN' AT ALL.
Tracks: Wolf / Nothin' at all.
■ 12" .12CL 406
■ 7" . . . . .CL 406
Capitol / May '86.

NOTHIN' AT ALL.
Tracks: Nothin' at all (remix) (7" & CD single only.) / Nothin' at all (ext. remix) (12" only.) / I've got the music in me / I want you so bad (ext. version) (12" only.) / I want you so bad (remix) (CD single only.)
■ 12" .12CL 507
■ 7" . . . . .CL 507
■ 12" P.Disc. 12CLP 507
■ CD Single . . . . .CDCL 507
Capitol / Oct '88.

PASSIONWORKS.
Tracks: How can I refuse / Blue guitar / Johnny moon / Sleep alone / Together now / Allies / Jealousy / Heavy heart / Love mistake / Language of love / Ambush.
■ LP .EPC 25491
Epic / Oct '83.

PRIVATE AUDITION.
Tracks: City's burning / Bright little girl / Perfect stranger / private audition / Angela / This man is mine / Situation / Hey darlin darlin / One word / Fast times / America.
■ LP .EPC 85792
Epic / Jun '82.
■ LP 4607021
■ MC .460702 4
Portrait / Feb '88.
CD 983429-2

Pickwick/Sony Collector's Choice / Apr '94 / Pickwick / Pinnacle.

ROCK THE HOUSE "LIVE".
Tracks: Wild child / Fallen from grace / Call of the wild / How can I refuse / Shell shock / Love alive / Under the sky / Night / Tall, dark handsome stranger / If looks could kill / Who will you run to / You're the voice / Way back machine / Barracuda.
- CD . . . . .CDESTU 2154
- ■ LP . . . . ESTU 2154
- ■ MC. . . . . .TCESTU 2154
Capitol / Aug '91.

SECRET.
Tracks: Secret / I love you / How can I refuse (live) (12" & CD single only).
- ■ 12". 12CL 603
- ■ 7" . . . . .CL 603
- ■ CD Single. . . . . .CDCL 603
- ■ MC Single. . . . . .TCCL 603
Capitol / Feb '91.

STRAIGHT ON.
Tracks: Straight on / Lighter touch.
- ■ 7" . . . . PRT 6704
PRT / Oct '78.

STRANDED.
Tracks: Stranded / Under the sky / I'll never stop loving you.
- ■ 12". 12CL 595
- ■ 12". 12CLG 595
- ■ 12" P.Disc 12CLPD 595
- ■ 7" . . . . .CL 595
- ■ CD Single. . . . . .CDCL 595
- ■ MC Single. . . . . .TCCL 595
Capitol / Sep '90.

TELL IT LIKE IT IS.
Tracks: Tell it like it is / Barracuda.
- ■ 7" . . . . EPC 9436
Epic / Jan '81.

THERE'S THE GIRL.
Tracks: There's the girl (12" remix) / Alone / Bad animals / There's the girl (7" remix).
- ■ 12". 12CL 473
- ■ 7" . . . . .CL 473
- ■ 7" P.Disc .CLP 473
- ■ CD Single. . . . . .CDCL 473
Capitol / Nov '87.
- ■ 12" P.Disc. 12CLP 473
- ■ MC Single. . . . . .TCCL 473
Capitol / Nov '87.

THESE DREAMS.
Tracks: These dreams / If looks could kill / Live (version) / Shellshock / What about love (Track on double pack only) / Heart of darkness (Track on double pack only) / There's the girl (rock-a-pella-version) / These dreams (remix) / These dreams (extended etched disc.) / These dreams (extended remix) (Track on special etched disc.) / These dreams (instrumental remix) (Track on special etched disc.) / Never (extended remix) (Track on special etched disc.).
- ■ 7" Set .CLD 394
- ■ 12". 12CL 394
- ■ 7" . . . . .CL 394
Capitol / Mar '86.
- ■ CD Single. . . . . .CDCL 477
Capitol / Mar '86.

THIS MAN IS MINE.
Tracks: This man is mine / America.
- ■ 7" . . . . EPCA 2436
Epic / Jun '82.

WHAT ABOUT LOVE?.
Tracks: What about love / Shellshock / Crazy on you (Only on CD single.) / Dreamboat Annie (Only on CD single.) / What about love (extended version) (Available on 12" only).
- ■ 7" . . . . .CL 361
Capitol / Jul '85.
- ■ 12". 12CLG 487
- ■ 12". 12CL 487
- ■ 7" . . . . .CL 487
- ■ 7" P.Disc .CLP 487
- ■ CD Single . . . . .CDCL 487
Capitol / May '88.

WHO WILL YOU RUN TO.
Tracks: Who will you run to / Nobody home / These dreams (Extra track on 12").
- ■ 12". 12CL 457
- ■ 7" . . . . .CL 457
- ■ 7" P.Disc .CLP 457
Capitol / Sep '87.

WILL YOU BE THERE (IN THE MORNING).
Tracks: Will you be there (in the morning).
- ■ 12". . . . . .CLPD 700
- ■ CD Single. . . . . .CDCL 700
- ■ CD Single. . . . . .CDCLS 700
- ■ MC Single. . . . . .TCCL 700
EMI / Dec '93.

WITH LOVE FROM..
Tracks: Not Advised.
- ■ CD Set. . . . . CDLOVE 2
- ■ LP Set. LOVE 2
- ■ MC Set . . . . TC LOVE 2
Capitol / Nov '88.

YOU'RE THE VOICE.
Tracks: You're the voice / Call of the wild / Barracuda.
- ■ 10". . . . . .10 CL 624
- ■ 7" . . . . .CLS 624
- ■ CD Single. . . . . .CDCL 624
- ■ MC Single. . . . . .TCCL 624
Capitol / Aug '91.

Heartland

CARRIE ANN.
Tracks: Carrie Ann.
- ■ 12". . . . . AMY 811
- ■ MC Single. . . . . AMMC 811
- ■ 7" . . . . AM 811
- ■ CD Single. . . . . AMCD 811
A&M / Aug '91.

FIGHT FIRE WITH FIRE.
Tracks: Fight fire with fire.
- ■ 10". . . . . AMX 761
- ■ 12". . . . . AMY 761
- ■ 7" . . . . AM 761
- ■ CD Single. . . . . AMCD 761
A&M / Jul '91.

HEARTLAND.
Tracks: Not Advised.
- ■ CD 3971212
- ■ LP 3971211
- ■ MC 3971214
A&M / Jan '91.

KICK, THE.
Tracks: Do you know the feeling / This can't be love / She's got it all / Heartland / Livin' it up / See you on the TV / Louise / On the beach / Don't fool around with love / Working in a parking lot.
CD. LICD 901202
Line / Jun '92 / C.M. Distribution / Grapevine Distribution / A.D.A. Distribution / Conifer Records.

Heathen

BREAKING THE SILENCE.
Tracks: Death by hanging / Goblins blade / Open the grave / Pray for death / Set me free / Breaking the silence / Worlds end / Save the skull.
- ■ LP . . . . MFN 75
Music For Nations / Aug '87.
- ■ CD . . . . CDMFN 75
Music For Nations / Aug '89 / Pinnacle.
MC. . . . . TMFN 75

VICTIMS OF DECEPTION.
Tracks: Not Advised.
- ■ CD . . . . RO 93312
Road Runner / Feb '93.

Heavy Load

METAL ANGELS IN LEATHER.
Tracks: Not Advised.
CD. 15 215
MC. 79 089
Laserlight / Aug '91 / TBD / BMG / Target.

Heavy Metal Kids

AIN'T NOTHING BUT A HOUSEPARTY.
Tracks: Ain't nothing but a house party.
- ■ 7" . . . . K 10671
Atlantic / Oct '75.

ANVIL CHORUS.
Tracks: Not Advised.
- ■ LP . . . . K 50143
Atlantic / '75.

CHELSEA KIDS.
Tracks: Overture / Chelsea kids / From heaven to hell and back again / Cry for me / She's no angel / Jackie the lad / Docking in / Squalliday inn / Delirious.

- ■ LP . . . . METALP 117
Razor / Aug '87.

CHELSEA KIDS.
Tracks: Chelsea kids / Jackie the lad.
- ■ 7" . . . . .RAK 258
RAK / Jun '77.

DELIRIOUS.
Tracks: Delirious / Chelsea kids.
- ■ 7" . . . . .RAK 262
RAK / Sep '77.

HEAVY METAL KIDS.
Tracks: Hangin' on / Ain't it hard / It's the same old song / Runaround eyes / Always plenty of women / Nature of my game / Kind of woman / Rock 'n' roll man / We gotta go.
- ■ LP . . . . K 50047
Atlantic / '74.

KITSCH.
Tracks: Not Advised.
- ■ LP . . . . .SRAK 523
RAK / '77.

Heavy Metal Outlaws

SEX FOR SEXISM'S SAKE.
Tracks: Not Advised.
- ■ CD .HMO SCD 1
Heavy Metal Outlaws / Oct '92.

SIXTIES MEANT NOTHING, THE.
Tracks: Can't stand the sixties / Yeah, yeah, yeah / Sixties meant nothing (Dead boring mix).
- ■ CD .HMO SCD 2
Heavy Metal Outlaws / Oct '92.

Heavy Pettin'

BIG BANG.
Tracks: Not Advised.
- ■ MC . . . . WKFMMC 130
- ■ CD . . . . WKFMXD 130
- ■ LP . . . . WKFMLP 130
FM Records / Nov '89.

IN AND OUT OF LOVE.
Tracks: In and out of love / Love on the run / Roll the dice.
- ■ 12". . . . . HEPX 1
- ■ 7" . . . . HEP 1
Polydor / Sep '83.

LETTIN' LOOSE.
Tracks: In and out of love / Broken heart / Love on the run / Love times love / Victims of the night / Rock me / Shout it out / Devil in her eyes / Hell is beautiful.
- ■ LP . . . . HEPLP 1
E.G. / '87.

LOVE TIMES LOVE.
Tracks: Love times love / Shout it out.
- ■ 7" P.Disc . . . . HEPP 3
- ■ 12". . . . . HEPX 3
- ■ 7" . . . . HEP 3
Polydor / Mar '84.

ROCK AIN'T DEAD.
Tracks: Rock ain't dead / Sole survivor / China boy / Lost in love / Northwinds / Angel / Heart attack / Dream time / Walkin' with the angels / Throw a party / Crazy (Extra track on CD only).
- ■ CD 825 897-2
Polydor / Jul '85.
- ■ LP . . . . HEPLP 4
Polydor / Jul '85.

ROCK ME.
Tracks: Rock me / Shadows of the night.
- ■ 12". . . . . HEPX 2
- ■ 7" . . . . HEP 2
Polydor / Nov '83.

ROLL THE DICE.
Tracks: Roll the dice (on 12" only) / Love x love.
- ■ 7" . . . . .NEAT 17
Neat / Aug '82.

ROMEO.
Tracks: Romeo / Don't call it love / City girl (Only on 12" single).
- ■ 12". . . . . POSPX 849
- ■ 7" . . . . POSP 849
Polydor / Apr '87.

SOLE SURVIVOR.
Tracks: Sole survivor / Crazy.
- ■ 12". . . . . HEPX 4
- ■ 7" . . . . HEP 4
Polydor / Jun '85.

Heir Apparent

GRACEFUL INHERITANCE.
Tracks: Not Advised.
■ LP . . . . BD 008
Black Dragon / Feb '86.

ONE SMALL VOICE.
Tracks: Not Advised.
CD. . . . . RO 94722
■ LP . . . . RO 94721
MC. . . . . RO 94724
Roadracer / Jul '89 / Pinnacle.

Helicon

HELICON.
Tracks: Not Advised.
CD . . . . N 0213-2
LP . . . . N 0213-1
Noise / Mar '93 / Pinnacle.

MELODIC METAL IS BACK.
Tracks: Not Advised.
CD MO2132
LP MO2131
Modern Music / Apr '93 / Plastic Head.

Helix

BACK FOR ANOTHER TASTE.
Tracks: Storm / That's life / Heavy metal cowboys / Back for another taste / Midnight express / Give it to you / Runing wild in the 21st century / Breakdown / Wild in the streets / Rockin' rollercoaster / Good to the last drop / Wheels of thunder.
■ CD . . . . GWCD 102
■ LP . . . . GWLP 102
■ MC. . . . . GWTC 102
GWR / Aug '90.
CD . . . . CLACD 346
Castle / May '94 / BMG.

GIMME GIMME GOOD LOVIN'.
Tracks: Gimme gimme good loving / When the hammer falls.
■ 7" . . . . CL 349
■ 7" P.Disc. . . . . CLP 349
Capitol / Jan '85.

HEAVY METAL LOVE.
Tracks: Heavy metal love / No rest for the wicked.
■ 12" 12CL 314
■ 7" . . . . CL 314
■ 7" P.Disc . . . . CLP 314
Capitol / Oct '83.

IT'S BUSINESS DOING PLEASURE.
Tracks: Not Advised.
CD . . . . CDIRS 986969
Intercord / Aug '93 / Pinnacle / C.M. Distribution.

LONG WAY TO HEAVEN.
Tracks: Kids are all shakin' / Deep cuts the knife / Ride the rocket / Long way to heaven / House on fire / Christine / Without you (Jasmine's song) / School of hard knocks / Don't touch the merchandise / Bangin' offa the bricks.
■ LP . . . . EJ 2403481
■ MC. . . . . EJ 2403484
Capitol / Sep '85.

NO REST FOR THE WICKED.
Tracks: Does a fool ever learn / Let's all do it tonight / Heavy metal love / Check out the love / No rest for the wicked / Don't get mad get even / Ain't no high like rock'n'roll / Dirty dog / Never want to lose you / White lace and black leather.
MC. . . . . TC EST 4001854
■ LP . . . . EST 4001851
Capitol / Aug '83.

ROCK YOU.
Tracks: Rock you / You keep me rockin'.
■ 7" . . . . CL 339
Capitol / Aug '84.

VIDEO EP: HELIX.
Tracks: Not Advised.
■ VHS . . . . MVS 99 0042 2
PMI / Jun '86.

WALKIN' THE RAZOR'S EDGE.
Tracks: Rock you / Young and wreckless / Animal house / Feel the fire / When the hammer falls / Gimme gimme good lovin' / My kind of rock / Anything you want / Six strings, nine lives / You keep me rockin'.
■ LP . . . . EJ 2401831
Capitol / Oct '84.

WHITE LACE AND BLACK LEATHER.
Tracks: Breaking loose / It's too late / Long-distance heartbreak / Time for a change / Hangman's tree / It's what I wanted / Mainline / Women, whisky and sin / Thoughts that bleed.
■ LP . . . . MOGO 4013
Logo / Jun '82.

WILD IN THE STREETS.
Tracks: Wild in the streets / Kiss it goodbye / Long way to heaven / Never gonna stop the rock / Dream on / What ya bringin' to the party / High voltage kicks / Give 'em hell / Shot full of love / Love hungry eyes / She's too tough.
■ LP . . . . EST 2046
■ MC. TC EST 2046
Capitol / Dec '87.

WILD IN THE STREETS.
Tracks: Wild in the streets.
■ 12" 12CL 468
Capitol / Oct '87.
■ 7" . . . . CL 468
Capitol / Oct '87.
■ 7" . . . . GWR 18
GWR / Oct '90.

Hell Bastards

HEADING FOR INTERNAL DARKNESS.
Tracks: We had evidence / Civilsed / Nazis killed / Death camp / Massacre / Heading for internal darkness / Pylons / Afrikkan beggar / Rise of crust.
■ LP . . . . COX 008
Meantime / May '88.

NATURAL ORDER.
Tracks: Not Advised.
CD . . . . MOSH 22 CD
LP . . . . MOSH 22
■ MC. MOSH 22 MC
Earache / Jun '90.

Hellanbach

ALL SYSTEMS GO.
Tracks: All systems go / Knocked out / Could have done better / Hot 'n' heavy express.
■ 12" . . . . NEAT 25 12
Neat / Mar '83.

BIG..H, THE.
Tracks: Beaten to the bone / Main man / Nobody's fool / Bandits run / S.P.G.C. / Saturday night / Panic state O.D. / Daddy dig those cats / When all is said and done / Urban paranoia.
■ LP . . . . NEAT 1019
Neat / '85.

NOW HEAR THIS.
Tracks: Dancin' / Times are getting harder / Look at me / All systems go / Maybe tomorrow / Motivated by desire / Taken by surprise / Let's get this show on the road / Kick it out / All the way / Everybody wants to be a cat.
■ LP . . . . NEAT 1006
Neat / '85.

Hellhammer

APOCALYPTIC RAIDS.
Tracks: Not Advised.
■ CD . . . . CDNUK 008
■ LP . . . . .NUK 008
Noise / Apr '90.

APOCALYPTIC RAIDS.
Tracks: Apocalyptic raids.
■ 12" . . . . N 008
■ CD Single . . . . N 008CD
Noise / '91.

Hellion

BLACK BOOK, THE.
Tracks: Not Advised.
CD . . . . .CDMFN 108
LP . . . . MFN 108
MC. . . . . TMFN 108
Music For Nations / Oct '90 / Pinnacle.

HELLION.
Tracks: Not Advised.
LP . . . . MFN 15
Music For Nations / Jan '84.

MINI-LP.
Tracks: Not Advised.
MC. . . . . NRC 28
Mini LP . . . . NRR 28
New Renaissance(USA) / Nov '87 / Pinnacle.

POSTCARDS FROM THE ASYLUM.
Tracks: Not Advised.
■ LP . . . . MFN 82
Music For Nations / Feb '88.

SCREAMS IN THE NIGHT.
Tracks: Screams in the night / Bad attitude / Better off dead / Upside down guitar solo / Hand / Explode / Easy action / Put the hammer down / Stick 'em / Children of the night / Tower of air.
■ LP . . . . MFN 73
Music For Nations / Mar '87.
■ CD . . . . CDMFN 73
Music For Nations / Aug '89.

Hellkrusher

BUILDINGS FOR THE RICH.
Tracks: Buildings for the rich / Third world exploitation / War, who needs it / Full of shit / Path to destruction / Chase is on / Sick / Conform / Dying for who / Smash the trash / Destined to die / System dictates / Threat of war / Burn a rock star / Who's system / War games / Clear the debt / Scared of change / Dead zone / Hellkrusher.
CD. . . . . CASE 004CD
LP . . . . .CASE 004
SMR / Feb '93 / Vital Distribution.

Hellmen

ELECTRIC CRAZY LAND.
Tracks: Not Advised.
LP . . . . MR 018
Munster Records / Apr '92 / Plastic Head.

Hellnation

COLLONIZED.
Tracks: Not Advised.
LP . . . . POLLUTE 09
Sound Pollution / Jul '93 / Plastic Head.

Helloween

Germany's answer to Iron Maiden, who made dizzy progression from speed metal origins in 1984. 1987's Keeper Of The Seven Keys Part One established reputation; after '88 Donington appearance, Keeper.. Part Two made no. 24 in U.K. Faintly ludicrous image ('Pumpkin Man' was Helloween version of Maiden's Eddie) took surreal turn with Pink Bubbles Go Ape album, which just missed UK Top 40. After one further effort, Helloween were dropped by EMI, lost half of personnel and returned to uncertain career with 1994's more straightforward Master Of The Rings.

BEST OF HELLOWEEN.
Tracks: Not Advised.
CD. . . . . .NO 1762
LP . . . . .NO 1761
MC. . . . . .NO 1764
Noise / Aug '91 / Pinnacle.

BEST, THE REST, THE RARE, THE (The Collection 1984-1988).
Tracks: Not Advised.
CD. . . . . N 01762
LP . . . . N 01761
MC. . . . . N 01764
Noise / Jan '92 / Pinnacle.

CHAMELEON.
Tracks: First time / When the sinner / I don't wanna cry no more / Crazy cat / Giants / Windmill / Revolution now/San Francisco (Be sure to wear some flowers in your hair) / In the night / Music / Step out of hell / I believe / Longing.
■ CD . . . . CDEMD 1045
■ LP Set . . . . EMD 1045
■ MC. . . . . TCEMD 1045
EMI / May '93.

DOCTOR STEIN.
Tracks: Dr. Stein / Savage / Livin' ain't no crime (Only on 3"CD single.) / Victim of fate (Only on 3"CD single.).
■ 12" P.Disc. . . . . .PHELLO 1
■ 12". 12HELLO 1
■ 7" 7HELLO 1
■ CD Single 3HELLO 1
Noise / Aug '88.

FUTURE WORLD.
Tracks: Future world.
■ 12". . . . . .NUK 083
Noise / Sep '87.

■ DELETED

■ 12" P.Disc. . . . . .NUKPD 083
Noise / Nov '89.

HELLOWEEN.
Tracks: Not Advised.
■ Mini LP . . . . .NUK 021
Noise / Oct '89.

I WANT OUT.
Tracks: I want out.
■ CD Single. 3HELLO 2
■ 12" 12HELLO 2
■ 7" . . . . 7 HELLO 2
■ 7" P.Disc . . . . .PHELLO 2
Noise / Oct '88.

JUDAS.
Tracks: Not Advised.
Mini LP 88561-8128-1
Combat Core (USA) / Sep '87.

JUDAS.
Tracks: Judas.
■ 12". . . . . .12 NUK 022
Noise / Sep '89.

KEEPER OF THE SEVEN KEYS.
Tracks: I'm alive / Future world / Halloween / Twilight of the gods.
■ LP . . . . .NUK 057
■ LP P.Disc . . . . .NUKPD 057
■ MC. . . . . .ZCNUK 057
Noise / Oct '89.

KEEPER OF THE SEVEN KEYS (PART 2).
Tracks: Eagle fly free / You always walk alone / March of time / Dr. Stein.
MC. . . . . .ZCNUK 117
■ CD . . . . .CDNUK 117
Noise / Nov '88.
■ LP . . . . .NUK 117
Noise / Sep '88.
■ LP P.Disc . . . . .NUKPD 117
Noise / Oct '89.

KEEPER OF THE SEVEN KEYS PARTS 1 & 2.
Tracks: Initiation / I'm alive / Little time / Twilight of the Gods / Tale that wasn't right / Future world / Halloween / Follow the sign / Invitation / Eagle fly free / You always walk alone / Rise and fall / Dr. Stein / We got the right / March of time / I want out / Keeper of the 7 keys / Save us / Don't run for cover / Livin' ain't no crime / Savage.
CD. . . . . .N 0240-2
Noise / Jan '94 / Pinnacle.

KIDS OF THE CENTURY.
Tracks: Kids of the century / Blue suede shoes / Exclusive Helloween interview (10" & 12" only.) / Shit and lobster (12" & CD single only.)
■ 12" 12EMS 178
■ 7" . . . . EM 178
■ CD Single . . . . .CDEM 178
■ MC Single . . . . .TCEM 178
■ 10" 10EMS 178
EMI / Feb '91.

LIVE IN THE UK.
Tracks: Little time / Dr. Stein / Future world / Rise and fall / We got the right / I want out / How many tears.
■ CD . . . . .CDEMC 3558
■ MC. . . . . .TCEMC 3558
■ LP . . . . .EMC 3558
Noise (EMI) / Apr '89.

MASTER OF THE RINGS.
Tracks: Not Advised.
CD. . . . . .RAWCD 101
LP . . . . .RAWLP 101
MC. . . . . .RAWMC 101
Raw Power / Aug '94 / Pinnacle.

MR. EGO.
Tracks: Mr. Ego.
CD Single. . . . . .RAWX 1001
Castle / Aug '94 / BMG.

PINK BUBBLES GO APE.
Tracks: Pink bubbles go ape / Kids of the century / Back on the streets / Number one / Heavy metal hamsters / Going home / Someone's crying / Mankind / I'm doin' fine - crazy man / Chance / Your turn.
■ LP . . . . .EMC 3588
■ CD . . . . .CDEMC 3588
■ MC. . . . . .TCEMC 3588
EMI / Mar '91.

WALLS OF JERICHO.
Tracks: Ride the sky / Metal invaders / Reptile / How many tears.
■ CD . . . . .CDNUK 088
■ LP . . . . .NUK 032

■ MC. . . . . .ZCNUK 032
Noise / Oct '89.

Hell's Belles

BARRICADES.
Tracks: Barricades.
■ 12". . . . . .RAWT 001
■ 7" . . . . .RAWS 001
Raw Power / Feb '86.

HELL'S BELLES.
Tracks: Looks like love / Overload / Desire me / Screaming for mercy / Hell's bells / Barricades / Strange love / Dirty girls / Storm break loose / Long legs.
■ LP . . . . .RAWLP 015
MC. . . . . .RAWTC 015
Raw Power / Apr '86 / Pinnacle.

Hellwitch

SYZYGIAL MISCREANCY.
Tracks: Not Advised.
LP . . . . WRE 902
Wild Rags / Dec '90 / Plastic Head.
CD. . . . . .WRE 902CD
Wild Rags / Jan '91 / Plastic Head.

TERRAASYMMETRY.
Tracks: Not Advised.
CD. . . . . .LMCD 1111
Lethal / Nov '93 / Plastic Head.

Helmet

New York alternative quartet who have grown heavier since 1990 debut Strap It On. Collaboration with House of Pain on Judgement Night soundtrack foreshadowed incorporation of hip-hop elements into Helmet sound on 1994's Betty.

BETTY.
Tracks: Not Advised.
CD. 654492404-2
MC. 654492404-4
Warner Bros. / Jun '94 / WEA.

BISCUITS FOR SMUT.
Tracks: Biscuits for smut / Milktoast / Flushings (On CDs only).
12". . . . . A 8291T
7" . . . . A 8291
CD Single. . . . . A 8291CD
East West / Jun '94 / WEA.

MEANTIME.
Tracks: In the meantime / Ironhead / Give it / Unsung / Turned out / He feels bad / Better / You borrowed / Fbla 11 / Role model.
CD. 7567921622
■ LP 7567921621
MC. 7567921624
Interscope / Jun '92 / WEA.

STRAP IT ON.
Tracks: Repitition / Rude / Bad mood / Sinatra / FBLA / Blacktop / Distracted / Make room / Murder.
CD. 756792235-2
MC. 756792235-4
Atlantic / Jul '93 / WEA.

UNSUNG.
Tracks: Better (Only on 12" and CDS format.) / FBLA (Live) (Only on 7" and MCS format.).
■ 12". . . . . .A 8484 T
■ 7" . . . . .A 8484
■ CD Single . . . . .A 8484 CD
■ MC Single . . . . .A 8484 C
WEA / Nov '92.

Helstar

BURNING STAR.
Tracks: Not Advised.
■ LP . . . . .MFN 20
Music For Nations / Apr '84.

DISTANT THUNDER, A.
Tracks: King is dead / Bitter end / Abandon ship / Tyrannicide / Scorcher / Genius of insanity / Whore of Babylon / Winds of love / He's a woman - she's a man.
CD. . . . . .RR 95242
■ LP . . . . .RR 95241
Road Runner / Aug '88.

NOSFERATU.
Tracks: Rhapsody in black / Baptized in blood / To sleep / Perchance to scream / Harker's tale (mass of

death) / Perseverance and desperation / Curse has passed away / Benediction / Harsh reality / Surling madness / Von am lebem destro sturm / Aleliaria and Everonn.
CD. . . . . .RO 94382
■ LP . . . . .RO 94381
Roadracer / Oct '89.

REMNANTS OF WAR.
Tracks: Not Advised.
■ LP . . . . .N 0043
Noise / Jul '86.

Hendrix, Jimi

Born in Seattle in 1942, Hendrix taught himself guitar. Playing in New York in 1966, he was discovered and brought to London by ex-Animal Chas Chandler. In first six months of 1967, Hendrix scored three UK Top 10 singles. U S success was signalled by appearance at 1967 Monterey Pop Festival, and reputation established as innovative musician and master showman. Albums Are You Experienced? (1967), Axis Bold As Love (1967) and Electric Ladyland (1968) were commercial and artistic triumphs. In September 1970, shortly after appearance at Isle of Wight Festival, Hendrix died in London. Voodoo Chile single was posthumous UK chart-topper. Subsequently, recordings were widely exploited, although more intelligently-compiled hits and rarities sets, and remastered studio albums, began to appear in 1990's.

10TH ANNIVERSARY BOX.
Tracks: Ain't no telling / All along the watchtower / And the gods made love / Angel / Are you experienced / Astroman / Beginnings / Belly button window / Bleeding heart / Blue suede shoes / Bold as love / Burning desire / Burning of the midnight lamp / Can you see me / Castles made of sand / Catastrophe / Changes / Come on / Coming down hard on me, baby / Crosstown traffic / Drifter's escape / Drifting / Drone blues / Easy blues / Exp / Ezy ryder / Fire / Freedom / Gypsy boy / Gypsy eyes / Have you ever been / Hear my train a comin' / Highway chile / House burning down / I don't live today / If six was nine / I'm your hoochie coochie man / In from the storm / Izabella / Jam 292 / Jimi / Jimmy jam / Johnny B. Goode / Little bears / Little Miss Lover / Little Miss Strange / Little wing / Long hot summer night / Love or confusion / Lover man / Machine gun / Manic depression / May this be love / Message of love / Midnight / Midnight lightning / Moon turn the tides / My friend / Night bird flying / Nine to the universe / 1983.. / Once I had a woman / One rainy wish / Peter Gunn / Power to love / Queen / Rainy day dream away / Red house / Remember / Sgt. Pepper's lonely hearts club band / Stars that play with laughing Sam's dice / Stepping stone / Still raining, still dreaming / Straight ahead / Tax free / 3rd stone from the sun / Trashman / Up from the skies / Voodoo chile / Wait until tomorrow / We gotta live together / Who knows / Young / You've got me floating / Foxy lady.
■ LP Set 2625 038
Polydor / Sep '80.

16 GREAT CLASSICS.
Tracks: Not Advised.
CD. 2615252
■ LP 2615251
MC. 2615254
Big Time / May '88.

20 GOLDEN PIECES: JIMI HENDRIX VOL 1.
Tracks: You got me running / Money / Let's go, let's go, let's go / You got what it takes / Sweet little angel / Walking the dog / There is something on your mind / Hard night / Hush now / Knock yourself out / Ballad of Jimi / No business / Gotta have a new dress / Don't accuse me / Flashing / Hang on, Sloopy / Twist and shout / Bo Diddley / Tutti frutti / Lucille.
■ LP . . . . .BDL 2010
MC. . . . . .BDC 2010
Bulldog Records / Jul '82.
Bulldog Records / '90 / President Records / Jazz Music / Wellard / TKO Records Ltd.

20 GOLDEN PIECES: JIMI HENDRIX: VOL 2.
Tracks: Good times / Voices / Suspicious / Whisper / Bessie Mae / Miracle worker / Feel that soul / Walking with Besse / Gotta find someone / Girl so fine / Soul food / Voices in the wind / Free spirit / Let me thrill your soul / Young generation / Get down / Funky / She's so fine / Let me go / Groove.
■ LP . . . . .BDL 2027
Bulldog Records / Nov '82.

ALL ALONG THE WATCHTOWER (Hendrix, Jimi Experience).
Tracks: All along the watchtower / Foxy lady / Purple haze / Manic depression.

■ 7" 604 025
Track / Oct '68.
■ 7" 2141 279
Polydor / Oct '80.
■ 12" . . . . POSPX 401
Polydor / Oct '80.

ALL ALONG THE WATCHTOWER (1990).
Tracks: All along the watchtower / Voodoo chile / Hey Joe / Crosstown traffic (12" only).

■ 12" . . . . PZ 100
■ 7" . . . . PO 100
■ CD Single . . . . PZCD 100
■ MC Single . . . . POCS 100
Polydor / Oct '90.

ALL ALONG THE WATCHTOWER (OLD GOLD) (Hendrix, Jimi Experience).
Tracks: All along the watchtower / Foxy lady.

■ 7" . . . . OG 9432
Old Gold / Jul '84.

ARE YOU EXPERIENCED?.
Tracks: Foxy lady / Manic depression / Red house / Can you see me / Love or confusion / I don't live today / May this be love / Fire / Third stone from the sun / Remember / Are you experienced / Purple haze / Hey Joe / Wind cries Mary.

■ LP 612 001
Track / May '67.
■ LP 613001
Polydor / Dec '81.
■ LP . . . . SPELP 97
MC . . . . SPEMC 97
Polydor / Sep '85 / PolyGram.
CD 825 416-2
Track / Sep '85 / PolyGram.
LP 847 234-1
■ CD 847 234-2
■ MC 847 234-4
Polydor / Jun '91.
CD 5210362
MC 5210364
Polydor / Oct '93 / PolyGram.

AT HIS BEST VOL. 4.
Tracks: Not Advised.

■ LP . . . . SM 3535
Joker (USA) / '88.

AT HIS BEST:VOL.1.
Tracks: She went to bed with my guitar / Free thunder / Cave man bells / Strokin' a lady on each hip / Baby chicken strut.

■ LP . . . . SM 3271
MC . . . . MC 3271
Joker (USA) / '87 / C.M. Distribution / Jazz Horizons / Jazz Music.

AT HIS BEST:VOL.2.
Tracks: Feels good / Fried cola / Monday morning blues / Jimi is tender too / Madagascar.

■ LP . . . . SM 3272
MC . . . . MC 3272
Joker (USA) / '87 / C.M. Distribution / Jazz Horizons / Jazz Music.

AT HIS BEST:VOL.3.
Tracks: Young Jim / Lift off / Down mean blues / Swift's wing / Spiked with heady dreams.

■ LP . . . . SM 3273
MC . . . . MC 3273
Joker (USA) / '87 / C.M. Distribution / Jazz Horizons / Jazz Music.

AT THE ATLANTA POP FESTIVAL.
Tracks: Purple haze / Red house / Fire / Foxy lady / Spanish castle magic / Voodoo chile / Stone free / Star spangled banner / Straight ahead / Hey Joe / All along the watchtower.

VHS 791279
BMG Video / Sep '92 / BMG.

AT THE ISLE OF WIGHT.
Tracks: Not Advised.

VHS 790 454
VHS . . . . 790 454 BX
BMG Video / Oct '90 / BMG.
Laser Disc 780 454
BMG Video / Aug '91 / BMG.

AT WOODSTOCK.
Tracks: Message to love / Izzabella / Red house / Jam back at the house / Voodoo chile / Star spangled banner / Purple haze / Woodstock improvisation / Villanova junction / Hear my train a comin'.
CD 74321 1102062
BMG Video / Nov '92 / BMG.

AT WOODSTOCK.
Tracks: Message to love / Fire / Izzabella / Redhouse / Jam back at the house / Voodoo chile / Star spangled banner / Purple haze / Woodstock improvisation / Villanova junction / Hear my train a comin'.
Laser Disc 74321110206
VHS 74321110203
BMG Video / Nov '92 / BMG.

AXIS BOLD AS LOVE.
Tracks: Experience / Up from the skies / Spanish castle magic / Wait until tomorrow / Ain't no telling / Little wing / If six was nine / You've got me floating / Castles made of sand / She's so fine / One rainy wish / Little Miss Lover / Bold as love.

■ LP 613-003
Track / Dec '67.
■ LP . . . . SPELP 3
MC . . . . SPEMC 3
Polydor / Aug '83 / PolyGram.
CD 813 572-2
Polydor / '87 / PolyGram.
LP 847 243-1
■ CD 847 243-2
■ MC 847 243-4
Polydor / Jun '91.

BAND OF GYPSIES.
Tracks: Who knows / Machine gun / Changes / Power to love / Message of love / We gotta live together / Hear my train / Foxy lady / Stop.

■ LP 2406-001
Track / Jul '70.
■ LP . . . . SPELP 16
■ MC . . . . SPEMC 16
Track / Aug '83.
CD 8219332
Track / May '88 / PolyGram.
CD 847 237-2
LP 847 237-1
■ MC 847 237-4
Polydor / Jun '91.

BAND OF GYPSIES (BOXED SET).
Tracks: Not Advised.

CD Set 839 875-2
Polydor / Dec '89 / PolyGram.

BEST OF AND THE REST OF, THE.
Tracks: Redhouse / Bleeding heart / Tomorrow never knows / Outside woman blues / Woke up this morning / Jam back at the house / Morrison's lament / Uranus rock / Sunshine of your love.

■ CD . . . . CDAR 1022
■ MC . . . . ARLC 1022
Action Replay / Mar '91.

BEST OF JIMI HENDRIX.
Tracks: Who knows / Machine gun / Hear my train a comin' / Foxy lady / Power to love / Message of love / Voodoo chile / Stone free / Ezy ryder.

■ CD . . . . CDP 746 485 2
EMI / May '87.

BURNING OF THE MIDNIGHT LAMP (Hendrix, Jimi Experience).
Tracks: Burning of the midnight lamp.

■ 7" 604 007
Track / Aug '67.

CONCERTS, THE.
Tracks: Fire / I don't live today / Red house / Stone free / Are you experienced / Little wing / Voodoo chile / Bleeding heart / Hey Joe / Wild thing / Hear my train a comin' / Foxy lady.

■ Double LP . . . . CBS 88592
CBS / Aug '82.
MC 40 22177
CBS / Sep '84 / Sony.
■ Double LP . . . . CBS 22177
CBS / Aug '88.
CD . . . . CCSCD 235
MC . . . . CCSMC 235
■ Double LP . . . . CCSLP 235
Castle Collector Series / Feb '90.

CORNERSTONES 1967-1970.
Tracks: Hey Joe / Purple haze / Wind cries Mary / Foxy lady / Crosstown traffic / All along the watchtower / Voodoo chile (slight return) / Have you ever been (to Electric Ladyland) / Star spangled banner (studio version) / Stepping stone / Room full of mirrors / Ezy ryder / Freedom / Drifting / In from the storm / Angel / Fire (Available on CD and cassette format only.) / Stone free (Available on CD and cassette format only.)

■ LP 847 231-1
Polydor / Oct '90.
CD 8472312
MC 8472314
Polydor / Jan '93 / PolyGram.

COSMIC TURNAROUND.
Tracks: No such animal (part 1) / Tomorrow / No such animal (part 2) / Come on baby / Down now / Louisville.

■ LP .AFELP 1002
MC . . . . ZCAFS 1002
Audio Fidelity(USA) / Feb '82 / Stage One Records.

CRASH LANDING.
Tracks: Message to love / Somewhere over the rainbow / Crash landing / Coming down hard on me baby / Peace in Mississippi / Power of soul / Stone free again / Captain Coconut.

■ LP 2310 398
Polydor / Aug '75.
■ LP . . . . SPELP 94
■ MC . . . . SPEMC 94
Polydor / Mar '83.
■ LP 847 263-1
■ CD 8472632
■ MC 8472634
Polydor / Jan '93.

CRASH LANDING/MIDNIGHT LIGHTNING.
Tracks: Message to love / Captain Coconut / Coming down hard on me, baby / Peace in Mississippi / Power of soul / Somewhere over the rainbow / Trashman / Midnight lightning / Machine gun / Gypsy boy / Blue suede shoes / Hear my train a comin' / Once I had a woman / Beginnings / Crash landing.

MC Set . . . . TWOMC 3
Polydor / Jun '83 / PolyGram.

CROSSTOWN CONVERSATION.
Tracks: Not Advised.

CD P.Disc . . . . CBAK 4082
Baktabak / Feb '94 / Arabesque Ltd.

CROSSTOWN TRAFFIC (Hendrix, Jimi Experience).
Tracks: Crosstown traffic.

■ 7" 604 029
Track / Apr '69.

CROSSTOWN TRAFFIC (RE-RELEASE).
Tracks: Crosstown traffic / Voodoo chile / All along the watchtower (Only on 12" single.) / Have you ever been (to electric ladyland) (Only on CD single.).

■ 12" . . . . PZ 71
■ 7" . . . . PO 71
■ CD Single . . . . PZCD 71
■ MC Single . . . . POCS 71
Polydor / Apr '90.

CRY OF LOVE.
Tracks: Freedom / Drifting / Easy rider / Night bird flying / My friend / Straight ahead / Astro man / Angel / In from the storm / Belly button window.

■ LP 2408101
Track / Apr '71.
■ LP 2302 023
MC 3194 025
Polydor / '74 / PolyGram.
■ LP . . . . SPELP 98
MC . . . . SPEMC 98
Polydor / Sep '85 / PolyGram.
CD 829 926-2
Polydor / Mar '89 / PolyGram.
CD 847 242-2
■ LP 847 242-1
MC 847 242-4
Polydor / Jun '91 / PolyGram.

ELECTRIC LADYLAND.
Tracks: And the gods made love / Electric ladyland / Voodoo Chile / Crosstown traffic / Still dreaming / House burning down / All along the watchtower / Long hot summer night / Little Miss Strange / Come on / Gipsy eyes / Burning of the midnight lamp / Rainy day / 1983 / Moon turn the tides / Gently, gently away.

■ Double LP 613-008/9
Track / Nov '68.
■ LP . . . . SPDLP 3
MC 350 011 2
Polydor / Jan '84 / PolyGram.
CD Set 823 359-2
Track / Nov '84 / PolyGram.
LP 847 233-1
■ CD 847 233-2
■ MC 847 233-4
Polydor / Jun '91.

ELECTRIC LADYLAND PART 1.
Tracks: Rainy day, dream away / 1983 / Moon, turn the tides.. / Gently, gently away / Still raining / Still

dreaming / House burning down / All along the watchtower / Voodoo chile (Slight return).
∎ LP 2310271
MC. .3100-197
Polydor / '74 / PolyGram.

ELECTRIC LADYLAND PART 2.
Tracks: And the Gods made love / Have you ever (been to electric ladyland) / Cross town traffic / Voodoo chile / Little Miss Strange / Long hot summer night / Come on (part 1) / Gipsy eyes / Burning of the midnight lamp.
∎ LP 2310 272
MC. 3100-198
Polydor / '74 / PolyGram.

ESSENTIAL JIMI HENDRIX, THE.
Tracks: Not Advised.
∎ Double LP. 261 203 4
∎ MC Set 350 012 2
Polydor / Jul '78.

ESSENTIAL VOL.2.
Tracks: Hey Joe / Fire / Foxy lady / Wind cries Mary / I don't live today / Crosstown traffic / Wild thing / Machine gun / Star spangled banner.
∎ LP .2311 014
Polydor / Feb '81.

EXPERIENCE.
Tracks: Suspicious / Room full of mirrors / Purple haze / Sunshine of your love / Fire / Bleeding heart / Smashing of amps / She's so fine / Wild thing.
MC. . . . . .MAMC 9201285
Masters (Holland) / Dec '88.

EXPERIENCE.
Tracks: Purple haze / Foxy lady / Voodoo chile / Wild thing / I don't live today / Up from the skies / Castles made of sand / Wait until tomorrow / Little Miss Lover / May this be love / Bold as love / If 6 was 9 / Folk blues acoustic.
VHS . . . . PVC 3015 M
Palace Video / Oct '87 / Palace Video.
VHS . . . . PVC 3015 X
Palace Video / Dec '91 / Palace Video.

EXPERIENCE.
Tracks: Not Advised.
Laser Disc 7432113701-6
BMG / Jan '94 / BMG.

EXPERIENCE (FILM) (1968 Film Soundtrack).
Tracks: Sunshine of your love / Room full of mirrors / Bleeding heart / Smashing of amps / Little ivy / Voodoo chile / Fire / Purple haze / Wild thing.
∎ LP . . . . NR 5057
Ember / Aug '71.
∎ LP . . . . BDL 4002
MC. BDC 4002
Bulldog Records / Jul '82 / President Records / Jazz Music / Wellard / TKO Records Ltd.
CD . . . . BDCD 40023
Bulldog Records / Nov '91 / President Records / Jazz Music / Wellard / TKO Records Ltd.

FIRE.
Tracks: Fire / Are you experienced.
∎ 12" . . . . A 132749
∎ 7" . . . . .A 2749
CBS / Sep '82.

FREE SPIRIT.
Tracks: Hey Leroy / Free spirit / House of the rising sun / Something you got / Let the God sing / She's a fox.
∎ LP . . . . PHX 1012
Phoenix (2) / Dec '81.

FREE SPIRIT (2).
Tracks: Good times / Voices / Suspicious / Whipper / Bessie Mae / Soul food / Voice in the wind / Free spirit.
∎ LP . . . . .THBM 006
Thunderbolt / Jun '87.
CD . . . . CDTB 094
Thunderbolt / Jan '91 / TBD / Jazz Music.

GANGSTER OF LOVE.
Tracks: Gangster of love / Let me go / Voice in the wind / Two + one goes / Good times / She's so fine / Soul food / Freedom and you / Win your love / Voices.
∎ LP . . . . TOP 124
MC. . . . . .KTOP 124
Topline / Jan '86 / Charly / Swift / Black Sun Records.

GET THAT FEELING (Hendrix, Jimi & Curtis Knight).
Tracks: Not Advised.
∎ LP . . . . HA 8349
London-American / May '68.

GOLD COLLECTION, THE.
Tracks: Not Advised.
CD D2CD03
MC. .D2MC03
Recording Arts / Dec '92 / TBD.

GRAFFITI COLLECTION.
Tracks: Not Advised.
CD . . . . GRCD 13
MC. GRMC 13
Graffiti Collection / Aug '90 / TBD.

GREATEST HITS: JIMI HENDRIX.
Tracks: Not Advised.
CD Set . . . . PULS 301
Pulsar / Mar '94 / BMG.

GYPSY EYES (Hendrix, Jimi Experience).
Tracks: Gypsy eyes / Remember.
∎ 7" 2094 010
Track / Oct '71.

HENDRIX 66.
Tracks: Not Advised.
∎ LP . . . . ENTF 1030
Enterprise / '75.

HENDRIX IN THE WEST.
Tracks: Johnny B. Goode / Lover man / Blue suede shoes / Voodoo chile / Queen / Sgt. Pepper's lonely hearts club band / Little wing / Red house.
∎ LP 230 201 8
Polydor / '74.
CD 831 312-2
Polydor / Apr '89 / PolyGram.

HEY JOE.
Tracks: Hey Joe / Purple haze / Wind cries Mary / Burning of the midnight lamp / Crosstown traffic / Foxy lady / Stone free / Voodoo chile / Gypsy eyes / Come on.
MC. .3186 025
Polydor (Import) / Oct '83 / Pinnacle / Silver Sounds (CD) / PolyGram.

HEY JOE (Hendrix, Jimi Experience).
Tracks: Hey Joe.
∎ 7" 56 139
Polydor / Jan '67.
∎ 7" 2608 001
Polydor/Dreyfus (USA) / Sep '80.

HEY JOE (OLD GOLD) (Hendrix, Jimi Experience).
Tracks: Hey Joe / Stone free.
∎ 7" . . . . .OG 9429
Old Gold / Jun '84.

IN THE BEGINNING.
Tracks: Stand by me / Bright lights, big city / Just a little bit / Satisfaction / Sugar pie honeybunch / You got what it takes / Day tripper / Land of a thousand dances / I'm a man / Hold on to what you've got / Twist and shout / Mr. Pitiful / What I'd say / Wooly bully / Walking the dog / Hang on, Sloopy.
∎ LP . . . . CBR 1031
MC. KCBR 1031
Premier (Sony) / '84 / Sony / Pinnacle.

INTERVIEW PICTURE DISC.
Tracks: Not Advised.
LP P.Disc . . . . VBAK 3008
Baktabak / Jun '91 / Arabesque Ltd.

INTERVIEWS.
Tracks: Not Advised.
CD 8122707712
WEA / Jul '93 / WEA.

INTROSPECTIVE: JIMI HENDRIX.
Tracks: Red house / Wake up this morning and find yourself dead / Interview part one / Bleeding heart / Interview part two.
CD .CINT 5006
LP . . . . LINT 5006
MC. MINT 5006
Baktabak / Apr '91 / Arabesque Ltd.

ISLE OF WIGHT/IN THE WEST.
Tracks: Not Advised.
∎ MC. 3577 377
Polydor / PolyGram.

JAM SESSION.
Tracks: Not Advised.
CD . . . . K 880 802
Koine / Feb '89.

JIMI HENDRIX.
Tracks: Voodoo chile (slight return) / Ezy ryder / Little wing / Love or confusion / House burning down / Johnny B. Goode / All along the watchtower / Little Miss Lover / Power to love / Drifters escape / Angel / Izabella.
∎ LP .2343 080
Polydor / Mar '75.

JIMI HENDRIX.
Tracks: Red house / Sweet thang / She's a fox / Free spirit / Good times / Go go shoes (part one) / House of the rising sun / Good feeling / Whoa eeh / Voice in the wind / Hot trigger / Girl so fine.
∎ VHS . . . . PEV 61267
Warner Home Video / Jun '86.
VHS . . . . PES 61267
Warner Home Video / Aug '94 / WEA / Hollywood Nites / Gold & Sons / TBD.

JIMI HENDRIX - BLUES.
Tracks: Hear my train a-comin' / Born under a bad sign / Red house / Catfish blues / Voodoo chile blues / Mannish boy / Once I had a woman / Bleeding heart / Jelly 292 / Electric Church Red house / Hear my train a-comin' (electric).
CD. 521037-2
MC. 521037-4
Polydor / Apr '94 / PolyGram.

JIMI HENDRIX - LIVE BOX.
Tracks: Not Advised.
CD Set 847 235-2
Polydor / Mar '91 / PolyGram.

JIMI HENDRIX ALBUM, THE.
Tracks: Coming down hard on me baby / Blue suede shoes / Jam 292 / Stars that play with laughing Sam's dice / Drifter's escape / Burning desire / I'm your hoochie coochie man / Have you ever been (to electric ladyland).
∎ LP . . . . CN 2067
∎ MC. CN4 2067
Contour / Nov '83.

JIMI HENDRIX AT THE MONTEREY POP FESTIVAL 1967.
Tracks: Not Advised.
CD . . . . ITM 960008
Koch / Sep '93 / Koch International.

JIMI HENDRIX AT WOODSTOCK.
Tracks: Not Advised.
CD .523384-2
MC. 523384-4
Polygram / Aug '94 / PolyGram.

JIMI HENDRIX BOX SET.
Tracks: Not Advised.
CD Set . . . . JH 1
UFO / Oct '92 / Pinnacle.

JIMI HENDRIX CONCERTS, THE.
Tracks: I don't live today / Stone free / Little wing / Bleeding heart / Wild thing / Red house / Are you experienced / Voodoo chile / Hey Joe / Hear my train a comin'.
CD .MEDIACD 1
∎ LP . . . . MEDIA 1
MC. . . . . .MEDIAC 1
Media Motion / Aug '89.

JIMI HENDRIX EXPERIENCE IN 1967 (Hendrix, Jimi Experience).
Tracks: Not Advised.
CD Set . . . . .JH 001
Revolver / Jul '92 / FM Revolver / Sony.

JIMI HENDRIX LIVE.
Tracks: Queen / Johnny B. Goode / All along the watchtower / Dolly dagger / Gloria / Wild thing / Little wing / Machine gun / Star spangled banner.

JIMI HENDRIX PLAYS BERKELEY.
Tracks: Johnny B. Goode / Hear my train a comin' / Star spangled banner / Purple haze / I don't live today / Hey baby (new rising sun) / Lover man / Machine gun / Voodoo chile.
VHS . . . . PVC 3008M
Palace Video / Jan '86 / Palace Video.
VHS 791.168
BMG Video / Oct '91 / BMG.

JIMI HENDRIX VOL 2.
Tracks: Freedom / Gypsy eyes / Remember / Castles made of sand / Stone free / Straight ahead / Red house / In from the storm / I don't live today /

Crosstown traffic / Are you experienced / Spanish castle magic / Long hot summer night / Bold as love.
■ LP 2343 086
Polydor / '76.

JIMI HENDRIX.
Tracks: Not Advised.
■ LP . . . . .COUNT 10
MC . . . . ZC CNT 10
Dakota (Countdown Series) / Oct '82.

JIMI HENDRIX: PROFILE.
Tracks: Not Advised.
■ LP 6.24782
MC CL4 24782
Teldec (1) / Dec '81 / Pinnacle / C.M. Distribution / Swift.

JIMI HENDRIX:VOL.1.
Tracks: Not Advised.
MC . . . . ZCGAS 703
Audio Fidelity(USA) / '84 / Stage One Records.

JIMI HENDRIX:VOL.2.
Tracks: Not Advised.
MC . . . . ZCGAS 704
Audio Fidelity(USA) / '84 / Stage One Records.

JIMI HENDRIX:VOL.3.
Tracks: Not Advised.
MC . . . . ZCGAS 732
Audio Fidelity(USA) / '88 / Stage One Records.

JIMI PLAYS MONTEREY.
Tracks: Killing floor / Foxy lady / Like a rolling stone / Rock me baby / Hey Joe / Can you see me / Wind cries Mary / Purple Haze / Wild thing.
CD 827 990-2
■ LP 827 990-1
MC 827 990-4
Polydor / Feb '86 / PolyGram.
CD 847 244-2
■ LP 847 244-1
MC 847 244-4
Polydor / Jun '91 / PolyGram.

JIMI PLAYS MONTEREY.
Tracks: Not Advised.
VHS . . . . VVD 198
Virgin Vision / Jun '86 / Gold & Sons / TBD.

JOHNNY B. GOODE.
Tracks: Not Advised.
VHS . . . . VVC 186
Virgin Vision / Gold & Sons / TBD.

JOHNNY B.GOODE.
Tracks: Voodoo Chile / Johnny B. Goode / All along the watchtower / Star spangled banner / Machine Gun.
■ LP . . . . FA 3160
■ MC . . . . TCFA 3160
Fame / Aug '86.

JOHNNY B.GOODE (Hendrix, Jimi Experience).
Tracks: Johnny B. Goode.
■ 7" 2001 277
Polydor / Feb '72.

KISS THE SKY.
Tracks: Are you experienced / I don't live today / Voodoo Chile / Stepping stone / Castles made of sand / Killing floor / Purple haze / Red house / Crowntown traffic / All along the watchtower.
MC 823 704-4
■ LP 823 704-1
■ CD 823 704-2
Polydor / Nov '84.
CD 847 261-2
■ LP 847 261-1
MC 847 261-4
Polydor / Jun '91 / PolyGram.

LAST EXPERIENCE CONCERT, THE (Hendrix, Jimi Experience).
Tracks: Not Advised.
CD . . . . ZET 517
Zeta / Jan '90.

LAST EXPERIENCE, THE.
Tracks: Not Advised.
CD . . . . CD 42
Bescol / '87 / C.M. Distribution.
MC . . . . MC 1627
Timeless Treasures / Sep '87 / TBD.

LEGEND, THE.
Tracks: Not Advised.
MC . . . . ADAHC 430
■ LP . . . . ADAH 430
Arcade Music Gala / Apr '86.

LEGENDARY JIMI HENDRIX, THE.
Tracks: Hey Joe / Stone free / Foxy lady / Red house / I don't live today / Wind cries Mary / Purple haze / All along the watchtower / Burning of the midnight lamp / Gypsy eyes / Little wing / Crosstown traffic / Voodoo chile / Straight ahead.

LIVE AND UNRELEASED - THE RADIO SHOW.
Tracks: Testify / Lawdy Miss Clawdy / I'm a man / Like a rolling stone / Red house / Hey Joe / Hoochie coochie man / Purple haze / Wind cries Mary / Foxy lady / Third stone from the wind / Wild thing / Look over yonder / Burning of the midnight lamp / Spanish castle magic / Driving south / Things that I used to do / All along the watchtower / Drifters escape / Cherokee mist / Voodoo chile (slight return) / 1983 / Merman I used to be / Voodoo chile / Come on (part 1) / Manic depression / Machine gun / Room full of mirrors / Angel / Rainy day shuffle / Valley of Neptune / Send my love to Linda / South Southern Delta / Dolly Dagger / Night bird flying.
■ CD Set . . . . HBCD 100
■ LP Set . . . . HBLP 100
■ MC Set . . . . HBMC 100
Castle Collector Series / Nov '89.

LIVE AT MONTEREY.
Tracks: Not Advised.
VHS 791192
BMG Video / Feb '94 / BMG.

LIVE AT THE ISLE OF WIGHT.
Tracks: Midnight lightning / Foxy lady / Lover man / Freedom / All along the watchtower / In from the storm / Intro god save the queen / Message to love / Voodoo Chile / Machine gun / Dolly dagger / Red house / New rising sun.
■ LP 2302 016
Polydor / Nov '71.
CD 831 313-2
■ LP . . . . SPELP 71
MC . . . . SPEMC 71
Polydor / Mar '89 / PolyGram.
■ LP 847 236-1
Polydor / Jun '91.
CD 8472362
MC 8472364
Polydor / Jan '93 / PolyGram.

LIVE AT WINTERLAND.
Tracks: Prologue / Fire / Manic depression / Sunshine of your love / Spanish castle magic / Red house / Killing floor / Tax free / Foxy lady / Hey Joe / Purple haze / Wild thing / Epilogue.
■ LP 833 004-1
MC 833 004-4
Polydor / Jul '87 / PolyGram.
CD 833 004-2
Polydor / Jul '87 / PolyGram.
CD 847 238-2
■ LP 847 238-1
MC 847 238-4
Polydor / Jun '91 / PolyGram.

LOOSE ENDS (Hendrix, Jimi Experience).
Tracks: Come down hard on me baby / Blue suede shoes / Jam 292 / Stars that play with laughing sams dice / Drifters escape / Burning desire / Born a hootchie kootchie man / Electric lady land.
CD 837 574-2
Polydor / Mar '89 / PolyGram.

MIDNIGHT LIGHTNING.
Tracks: Trashman / Hear my train a comin' / Blue suede shoes / Once I had a woman / Midnight lightning / Gypsy boy / Machine gun / Beginnings.
■ LP 2310 415
Polydor / Nov '75.
■ LP 825 166-1
MC 825 166-4
Polydor / Jun '89 / PolyGram.
CD 825 166-2
Polydor / Jun '89 / PolyGram.

MOODS.
Tracks: Mumblin' word / Miracle worker / From this day on / Human heart / Feel that soul / All alone / Get down / So-called friend / Girl so fine / Every little bit hurts / You say you love me.
■ LP . . . . PHX 1020
Phoenix (2) / Oct '82.

MORE EXPERIENCE (Hendrix, Jimi Experience).
Tracks: Little Ivy / Voodoo chile / Room full of mirrors / Fire / Purple haze / Wild thing / Bleeding heart.
■ LP . . . . BDL 4003

MC . . . . BDC 400
Bulldog Records / Jul '82 / President Records / Jazz Music / Wellard / TKO Records Ltd.

NIGHT LIFE.
Tracks: Good feeling / Hot trigger / Psycho / Come on baby (part 1) / Come on baby (part 2) / Night life / You got it / Woke up this morning / Lime line / Peoples people / Whoa eeh.
CD . . . . CDTB 07
LP . . . . THBL 07
Thunderbolt / Apr '90 / TBD / Jazz Music.

PEEL SESSIONS: JIMI HENDRIX EXPERIENCE (15.12.67).
Tracks: Radio 1 theme / Day tripper / Wait until tomorrow / Heary my train a comin' / Spanish castle magic.
■ 12" . . . . SFPS 06
■ CD Single . . . . SFPSCD 06
Strange Fruit / Dec '88.

PURPLE HAZE.
Tracks: Purple haze / 51st anniversary / All along the watchtower (Only on 12" and CD single) / Hey Joe (Only on CD single.)
■ 12" . . . . PZ 33
■ 7" . . . . PO 33
■ CD Single . . . . PZCD 33
Polydor / Jan '89.

PURPLE HAZE (Hendrix, Jimi Experience).
Tracks: Purple Haze.
■ 7" 604 001
Track / Mar '67.

PURPLE HAZE (OLD GOLD) (Hendrix, Jimi Experience).
Tracks: Purple haze / Wind cries Mary.
■ 7" . . . . OG 9430
Old Gold / Jul '84.

PURPLE HAZE IN WOODSTOCK.
Tracks: Not Advised.
CD . . . . ITM 960004
ITM Pacific / Feb '94 / Koch International / Complete Record Co. Ltd.

RADIO ONE SESSIONS.
Tracks: Stone free / Radio one theme / Day tripper / Killing floor / Love or confusion / Catfish blues / Drivin' South / Wait until tomorrow / Hear my train a comin' / Hound dog / Fire / Hoochie coochie man / Purple haze / Spanish castle magic / Hey Joe / Foxy lady / Burning of the midnight lamp.
CD . . . . CCSCD 212
MC . . . . CCSMC 212
■ Double LP . . . . CCSLP 212
Castle Collector Series / Feb '89.

RAINBOW BRIDGE (Film soundtrack).
Tracks: Dolly dagger / Earth blues / Pali gap / Room full of mirrors / Star spangled banner / Look over yonder / Hear my train a comin' / Hey baby (new rising sun).
■ CD . . . . K 233159
Reprise / Mar '87.

RAINBOW BRIDGE.
Tracks: Not Advised.
■ VHS . . . . HEN 2004
Hendring Video / Aug '88.

RARE HENDRIX.
Tracks: Good feeling / Voice in the wind / Go go shoes (part 1) / Good time / Bring my baby back / Suspicious / Hot trigger.
■ LP . . . . ENTF 3000
Enterprise / '76.

RE-EXPERIENCED.
Tracks: Hey Joe / Stone free / Wind cries Mary / Love or confusion / Red house / Third stone from the sun / Purple haze / Manic depression / If six was nine / Castles made of sand / All along the watchtower / Crosstown traffic / Voodoo chile / Electric ladyland / Rainy day dream away / 1983 / Moon, the tides / Angel / In from the storm / Stepping stone / Who knows / Little wing.

RECORDINGS FROM JIMI HENDRIX 1973 (Film soundtrack).
Tracks: Rock me baby / Wild thing / Machine gun / Interviews / Johnny B. Goode / Hey Joe / Purple haze / Like a rolling stone / Interviews II / Star spangled banner / Machine gun II / Hear my train a comin' / Interviews III / Red house / In the storm / Interviews IV.
■ LP . . . . K 64017
Reprise / '73.

REPLAY ON JIMI HENDRIX.
Tracks: Not Advised.
■ LP . . . . FEDB 5032
MC. . . . . CFEDB 5032
Sierra / May '86.

ROOTS OF HENDRIX.
Tracks: Wipe the sweat / Goodbye, Bessie Mae / Two in one goes / All I want / Under the table / Psycho.
■ LP . . . . PHX 1026
Phoenix (2) / Oct '82.

SESSIONS.
Tracks: Not Advised.
■ CD Set. 847 232-2
Polydor / Mar '91.

SINGLES ALBUM: JIMI HENDRIX.
Tracks: Hey Joe / Stone free / Purple haze / Wind cries Mary / 51st Anniversary / Highway chile / Burning of the midnight lamp / Stars that play with laughing Sam's dice / All along the watchtower / Long hot summer night / Crosstown traffic / Let me light your fire / Angel / Night bird flying / Gypsy eyes / Remember / Johnny B. Goode / Little wing / Foxy lady / Manic depression / 3rd stone from the sun / Gloria.
■ Double LP. . . . . PODV 6
MC Set . . . . PODVC 6
Polydor / Feb '83 / PolyGram.
CD Set 827 369-2
Polydor / Apr '86 / PolyGram.

SMASH HITS.
Tracks: Can you see me / 51st anniversary / Hey, Joe / Stone free / Purple haze / Fire / Wind cries Mary / Stars that play with laughing Sam's dice / Manic depression / Highway chile / Burning of the midnight lamp / Foxy lady.
■ LP 613-004
Track / Apr '68.
■ LP . . . . SPELP 15
MC. . . . . SPEMC 15
Track / Aug '83 / PolyGram.
CD 825 255-2
Polydor / Feb '85 / PolyGram.

STONE FREE.
Tracks: All along the watchtower / Angel / Are you experienced / Castles made of sand / Crosstown traffic / Drifter's escape / Ezy ryder / Johnny B. Goode / Little wing / Long hot summer night / Red house / Stone free.
■ LP 2343 114
Polydor / Aug '80.
■ LP . . . . SPELP 51
MC. . . . . SPEMC 51
Polydor / Nov '83 / PolyGram.

STRANGE THINGS.
Tracks: Fool for you baby / Oddball / Simon says / Come on baby (part 1) / Come on baby (part 2) / Blues blues / Lime line / Good feeling / Go go shoes (part one) / Bring my baby back / Psycho / Day tripper / Happy birthday / Don't accuse me / Welcome home / Hornets nest / Flashing / Strange things.
■ LP . . . . SHLP 101
MC. . . . . SHTC 101
Castle Showcase / Apr '86 / Arabesque Ltd.

SUPERSTAR (MUSIC FOR THE MILLIONS).
Tracks: Purple haze / Red house / Wind cries Mary / Let me light your fire / Freedom / Gypsy eyes / Voodoo chile / Angel / Who knows / Johnny B. Goode.
■ LP 823 434-1
MC. 823 434-4
Polydor (Holland) / Feb '85 / Pinnacle.

TOMORROW NEVER KNOWS.
Tracks: Red house / Wake up this morning and find yourself dead / Bleeding heart / Morrison's lament / Tomorrow never knows / Uranus rock / Outside woman blues / Sunshine of your love.
■ LP . . . . B 90166
MC. . . . . MB 90166
Happy Bird (Germany) / Jul '84.

TWO GREAT EXPERIENCES (Hendrix, Jimi & Lonnie Youngblood).
Tracks: Not Advised.
■ LP . . . . SM 3536
Joker (USA) / '88.

ULTIMATE EXPERIENCE, THE.
Tracks: All along the watchtower / Purple haze / Hey Joe / Wind cries Mary / Angel / Voodoo chile / Foxy lady / Burning of the midnight lamp / Highway chile / Crosstown traffic / Castles made of sand / Long hot summer night / Red house / Manic depression /

Gypsy eyes / Little wing / Fire / Wait until tomorrow / Star spangled banner / Wild thing.
CD 5172352
■ LP 5172351
MC. 5172354
Polydor / Oct '92 / PolyGram.
DCC 517 235-5
Polydor / Jan '93 / PolyGram.

VOICES IN THE WIND (Hendrix, Jimi & Tina Turner).
Tracks: Not Advised.
CD . . . . CDTBD 001
Thunderbolt / Jun '88 / TBD / Jazz Music.

VOODOO CHILE (Hendrix, Jimi Experience).
Tracks: Voodoo Chile.
■ 7" 2095 001
Track / Nov '70.
■ 12" . . . . POSPX 608
■ 7" . . . . POSP 608
Polydor / Sep '82.

VOODOO CHILE.
Tracks: Voodoo Chile / Power to love / Freedom / Spanish castle magic / Gypsy eyes / Love or confusion / 51st Anniversary / Little miss lover / I'm your hoochie coochie man / Izabella / House burning down / Bold as love.
■ LP 234 311 5
Polydor / Jul '82.
■ LP . . . . SPELP 52
MC. . . . . SPEMC 52
Polydor / Nov '83 / PolyGram.
■ LP . . . . MA 221285
MC. . . . . MAMC 9221285
Masters (Holland) / '88.

VOODOO CHILE (OLD GOLD).
Tracks: Voodoo Chile / Burning of the midnight lamp.
■ 7" . . . . OG 9431
Old Gold / Jul '84.

WAR HEROES.
Tracks: Bleeding heart / Highway chile / Tax free / Peter Gunn / Little bears / Catastrophe / Steeping stone / Midnight / Beginning / Izabella.
■ LP 2302 020
Polydor / Dec '72.
■ LP . . . . SPELP 4
■ MC . . . . SPEMC 4
Polydor / Aug '83.
CD 813 573-2
Polydor / Mar '89 / PolyGram.
■ LP 847 262-1
Polydor / Jun '91.
CD 847 262-2
Polydor / Jan '93 / PolyGram.
MC. 847 262-4
Polydor / Jun '93 / PolyGram.

WELL I STAND UP NEXT TO A MOUNTAIN.
Tracks: Not Advised.
LP P.Disc . . . . IFSIXWAS 9
Discussion / Dec '90.

WIND CRIES MARY, THE (Hendrix, Jimi Experience).
Tracks: Wind cries Mary.
■ 7" 604 004
Track / May '67.

WOKE UP THIS MORNING AND FOUND MYSELF DEAD.
Tracks: Red house / Wake up this morning and find yourself dead / Bleeding heart / Morrison's lament / Tomorrow never knows / Uranus rock / Outside woman blues / Sunshine of your love.
■ LP . . . . RL 015
Red Lightnin' / Sep '82.
CD . . . . RLCD 0068
Red Lightnin' / Nov '86 / A.D.A. Distribution / Swift / C.M. Distribution / Jazz Music / Cadillac / Arabesque Ltd. / Topic Records / Direct Distribution.
■ LP P.Disc . . . . RLP 0048
Red Lightnin' / Oct '88.
CD 26 20 332
MC. 26 20 334
Point (2) / '92 / Sound Solutions.
MC. . . . . SP 1038C
Stony Plain / Oct '93 / Projection / C.M. Distribution / Topic Records / Direct Distribution / A.D.A. Distribution.

13 ROCKING ANTHEMS.
Tracks: Everyday madness everyday / Ghettoised / Release / Consume / Face up to it / Unity - solidarity / Open up (D.Y.S.) / Break the connection / Network ends / Genocide / Into the grey / Street enters the house / Cornered rat.
LP . . . . FACE 007
In Your Face / Jan '90.

FACE UP TO IT.
Tracks: Consume / Face up to it / Too close to home / Flowers in concrete / Belief / Network of friends / When unity becomes solidarity / Acceptance / Cornered rat / Dedication from inspiration / Against the grain / Sick of the stupidity / Trapped in a scene / Believing a lie / Into the grey / Build up - knock down / Street enters the house / Make the connection.
■ LP . . . . FACE 1
In Your Face / Apr '88.
■ LP . . . . K 044 109
Konkurrel / May '88.

HERESY/CONCRETE SOX (Heresy & Concrete Sox).
Tracks: Not Advised.
■ LP . . . . MOSH 2
Earache / Mar '87.

VOICE YOUR OPINION.
Tracks: Not Advised.
CD . . . . LF 042CD
LP . . . . LF 042LP
Lost & Found / Nov '92 / Plastic Head.

WHO'S GENERATION.
Tracks: Who's generation.
■ EP . . . . FACE 4
In Your Face / Mar '89.

BREAKING POINT.
Tracks: Not Advised.
■ LP . . . . RR 95341
Road Runner / Aug '88.

BURNT AT THE STAKE.
Tracks: Water of vice / Keep on telling those lies / Fever of love / Watch me grow / Burnt at the stake.
■ 12" . . . . THBE 1.004
Thunderbolt / Apr '84.

TORTURE KNOWS NO BOUNDARY.
Tracks: Riding with the angels / Blood will tell / Portrait of faith / Whitechapel / Torture knows no boundary.
■ LP . . . . RR 9640
Road Runner / Feb '87.

BROTHERHOOD.
Tracks: Not Advised.
CD 367 0006.2
LP 367 0006.1
Mausoleum / Oct '91 / Pinnacle.

EVERYTIME.
Tracks: Everytime / Runaway.
■ 12" . . . . PZ 109
■ 7" . . . . PO 109
■ CD Single . . . . PZCD 109
■ MC Single. . . . . POCS 109
Polydor / Nov '90.

AWAKENING.
Tracks: Not Advised.
CD . . . . CDATV 19
LP . . . . ATV 19
Active / Aug '91 / Pinnacle.

EDGE OF ETERNITY.
Tracks: Not Advised.
CD . . . . CDATV 13
LP . . . . ATV 13
Music For Nations / May '90 / Pinnacle.

TRIBUTE TO INSANITY, A.
Tracks: Not Advised.
LP . . . . ACTLP 6
Active / Jul '89 / Pinnacle.

Hexx

QUEST FOR SANITY.
Tracks: Not Advised.
■ LP . . . . MFLAG 22
Under One Flag / Aug '89.
LP . . . . WRR 024
Wild Rags / '90 / Plastic Head.

WATERY GRAVES.
Tracks: Not Advised.
Mini LP . . . . WRR 025
Wild Rags / '90 / Plastic Head.

High Tide

DANCING IN MY MIND.
Tracks: Dancing in my mind / Electric blue.
■ 7" . . . . K 18930
WEA / Jan '82.

HIGH TIDE.
Tracks: Blankman cries again / Joke / Saneonymous.
■ LP . . . . PSYCHO 27
Psycho / May '84.

SEA SHANTIES.
Tracks: Futilists lament / Death warmed up / Pushed but not forgotten / Walking down their outlook / Missing out / Nowhere.
■ LP . . . . PSYCHO 26
Psycho / May '84.

SEA SHANTIES/HIGH TIDE.
Tracks: Futilist's lament / Death warmed up / Pushed, but not forgotten / Walking down their outlook / Missing out / Nowhere / Blankman cries again / Joke / Saneonymous.
CD . . . . CZ 530
EMI / Aug '94 / EMI.

Hinge

ACCIDENTAL MEETING OF MINDS.
Tracks: Pyramid club / Roar / Form / Rest / Quirky / Basilisk / Major 7th / Ransom / Rising man.
CD . . . . CDVEST 34
Bulletproof / Oct '94 / Pinnacle.

Hirax

HATE FEAR AND POWER.
Tracks: Not Advised.
■ LP . . . . R 9675
Road Runner / Oct '86.

Hittman

HITTMAN.
Tracks: Not Advised.
CD 857568
■ LP 087566
Steamhammer (Germany) / '88.

Hole

Talking to Courtney Love for the final time, her husband Kurt Cobain told her: "..no matter what happens, I want you to know that you made a really good record." Hole's *Live Through This* was indeed really good, Cobain's suicide giving it an unwelcome promotional boost. Previously, debut *Pretty on the Inside*, which shared release date with *Nevermind*, attracted widespread acclaim - prompting attempt by Madonna to sign band to her Maverick label (Hole instead joined Nirvana on Geffen). Second tragedy - death of bassist Kristen Pfaff - hit Hole in '94 but Love is true survivor likely to produce even better music in future.

BEAUTIFUL SON.
Tracks: Beautiful son.
■ 12" . . . . EFA 0491602
■ CD Single . . . . EFA 0491603
■ 7" . . . . .EFA 04914645
City Slang / Mar '93.

LIVE THROUGH THIS.
Tracks: Violet / Miss World / Plump / Asking for it / Jennifers body / Doll parts / Credit in the straight world / Softer, Softest / She walks on me / I think that I would die / Gutless / Rock star.
CD . . . . EFA 49352

LP . . . . EFA 49351
MC . . . . EFA 49354
■ LP . . . . EFA 40351
City Slang / Apr '94.

MS WORLD.
Tracks: Ms World / Rock star / Do it clean.
7" . . . . EFA 49367
CD Single . . . . EFA 49362
City Slang / Mar '94 / RTM / Pinnacle.

PRETTY ON THE INSIDE.
Tracks: Babydoll / Garbage man / Sassy / Good sister bad sister / Mrs. Jones / Berry / Loaded / Star belly / Pretty on the inside / Clouds / Teenage whore.
LP . . . . E 04071
MC . . . . E 04071C
City Slang / Oct '91 / RTM / Pinnacle.

TEENAGE WHORE.
Tracks: Teenage whore.
■ 7" . . . . EFA 407040
City Slang / Sep '91.

Hollywood Brats

GROWN UP WRONG.
Tracks: Not Advised.
CD . . . . LUSCD 6
LP . . . . LUSLP 6
Episode / Jul '90 / Grapevine Distribution.

HOLLYWOOD BRATS.
Tracks: Chez maximes / Another schoolday / Nightmare / Empty bottles / Courtesan / Then he kissed me / Tumble with me / Zurich 17 / Southern belles / Drowning sorrows / Sick on you.
■ LP . . . . ARED 6
Cherry Red / '82.
CD . . . . CDMRED 106
Cherry Red / Dec '93 / Pinnacle.

THEN HE KISSED ME.
Tracks: Then he kissed me / Sick on you.
■ 12" 12CHERRY 6
■ 7" . . . . CHERRY 6
Cherry Red / Apr '84.

Hollywood Rocks

ROCK ALBUM, A.
Tracks: Not Advised.
CD . . . . HWDCD 20
■ LP . . . . HWDLP 20
MC . . . . HWDMC 20
Hollywood (2) / Oct '91 / Sony.

Holocaust

COMING THROUGH.
Tracks: Coming through / Don't wanna be a loser / Good thing going.
■ 12" . . . . 12 PSP 4
Phoenix (Rock) / Apr '82.

HEAVY METAL MANIA.
Tracks: Heavy metal mania.
■ 12" . . . . 12 PSP 1
Phoenix (Rock) / Jul '80.

HOLOCAUST LIVE.
Tracks: Not Advised.
■ LP . . . . PSP LP 4
Phoenix (Rock) / May '83.

HYPNOSIS OF BIRDS.
Tracks: Hypnosis of birds / Tower / Book of seasons / Mercier and camier / Small hours / Into Lebanon / Summer tides / Mortal Mother / Cairnpapple hill / In the dark places of the earth / Caledonia.
CD . . . . TRMCD 010
Taurus Moon / Apr '93 / ACD Trading Ltd.

NO MAN'S LAND.
Tracks: Not Advised.
■ LP . . . . PSP LP 5
Phoenix (Rock) / Apr '84.

SOUND OF SOULS, THE.
Tracks: Not Advised.
■ CD . . . . .CROM 301CD
Chrome / '90.
LP . . . . CROM 301
Chrome / Jan '90.

Holosade

HELLHOUSE.
Tracks: Look into the mirror / Welcome to the hellhouse / Love it to death / Madame Guillotine / Psycho / Eternal life / Bittersweet / Nightmare reality.
■ LP . . . . AMP 016
Powerstation / Apr '88.

Holy Terror

MIND WARS.
Tracks: Not Advised.
CD . . . . .CDFLAG 25
■ LP . . . . .FLAG 25
MC . . . . .TFLAG 25
Under One Flag / Oct '88 / Pinnacle.

TERROR AND SUBMISSION.
Tracks: Black plague / Evil's rising / Blood of the saint / Mortal fear / Guardians of the Netherworld / Distant calling / Terror and submission / Tomorrow's end / Alpha omega.
■ LP . . . . .FLAG 10
Under One Flag / May '87.

Honeymoon Suite

BAD ATTITUDE.
Tracks: Bad attitude / Wounded.
■ 7" . . . . X 8772
WEA / Feb '86.

BIG PRIZE,THE.
Tracks: Bad attitude / Feel it again / Lost and found / What does it take (to win your love) / One by one / Wounded / Words in the wind / All along you knew / Once the feeling / Take my hand.
■ LP . . . . K 252824 1
■ MC . . . . K 252824 4
WEA / Mar '86.
■ CD . . . . K 925824 2
WEA / Jun '88.

FEEL IT AGAIN.
Tracks: Feel it again / One by one.
■ 12" . . . . U 8715 T
■ 7" . . . . U 8715
WEA / Mar '86.

NEW GIRL NOW.
Tracks: New girl in town / Wave babies.
■ 7" . . . . U 9486
WEA / Sep '85.

OTHER SIDE OF MIDNIGHT.
Tracks: Other side of midnight / Fast company / Feel it again (On 12" only.) / Stay in the light (On 12" only.).
■ 12" . . . . YZ 185 T
■ 7" . . . . .YZ 185
WEA / Jun '88.

RACING AFTER MIDNIGHT.
Tracks: Looking after no. 1 / Long way back / Cold look / Love fever / Other side midnight / Love changes everything / It's over now / Fast company / Tears on the page / Lethal weapon.
■ LP . . . . K 955445 1
■ MC . . . . K 955445 4
■ CD . . . . K 955445 2
WEA / Apr '88.
■ CD 255445 2
■ LP . . . . WX 196
■ MC . . . . WX 196C
WEA / Sep '88.

WAVE BABIES.
Tracks: It's your heart / Wave babies.
■ 7" . . . . U 9028
WEA / Jul '85.

Horse

HORSE.
Tracks: Not Advised.
■ LP . . . . WWDP 001
Diesel Power / Jul '89.

LIVE AT THE MARQUEE (Diesel Power).
Tracks: King Snake / She don't care / Little sunrise / Been a long time / Spirit / Into the fire / Thundering / Dealers wheels / Screwed, blued and tattooed / Babylon's burning.
■ VHS . . . . JE 207
Jettisoundz / Nov '90.

■ DELETED

House Of Lords

HOUSE OF LORDS, THE.
Tracks: Pleasure palace / Edge of your love / Love don't lie / Hearts of the world / Call my name / I wanna be loved / Looking for strange / Slip of the tongue / Under blue skies / Jealous heart.
- **LP** . . . . PL 88530
- **MC** . . . . PK 88530
- **CD** . . . . PD 88530
RCA / '88.

I WANNA BE LOVED.
Tracks: I wanna be loved / Call my name / Slip of the tongue (Only on 12" version.).
- **12"** . . . . PT 49486
- **7"** . . . . PB 49485
RCA / Mar '89.

SAHARA.
Tracks: Shoot / Chains of love / Can't find my way home / Heart on the line / Laydown staydown / Sahara / I ain't my love / Remember my name / American Babylon / Kiss of fire.
- **CD** . . . . PD 82170
- **LP** . . . . PL 82170
- **MC** . . . . PK 82170
RCA / Sep '90.

Housholder, Darren

DARREN HOUSEHOLDER.
Tracks: Cakewalk / Noodle surprise / Stand yer ground / Malt shop serenade / Dinner with Wolfgang / When the smoke clears / Pedal to the metal / Rubberneck / Deeper love / Johnny's bop / Misty / Detrick hates Jazz.
- **CD** . . . . RR 91212
Road Runner / Oct '92.

GENERATOR MAN.
Tracks: Not Advised.
CD . . . . RR 90232
Road Runner / Feb '94 / Pinnacle.

Howe, Greg

GREG HOWE.
Tracks: Not Advised.
CD . . . . RR 9531 2
- **LP** . . . . RR 9531 1
Road Runner / Aug '88.

Howe II

HIGH GEAR.
Tracks: High gear / Carry the touch / Strat o various / Disorderly conduct / Thinking of you / Standing on the line / Ferocious / Don't let the sloe gin (order the wine) / Party favours / Social fever.
- **LP** . . . . RR 94671
MC . . . . RR 94674
- **CD** . . . . RR 94672
Road Runner / Oct '89.

NOW HEAR THIS.
Tracks: Not Advised.
LP . . . . RR 92881
MC . . . . RR 92884
- **CD** . . . . RR 92882
Road Runner / Sep '91.

Hughes, Glenn

BLUES.
Tracks: Boy can sing the blues / I'm the man / Here comes the rebel / What can I do for ya / You don't have to save me anymore / So much love to give / Shake the ground / Hey buddy (you got me wrong) / Have you read the book / Life of misery / Can't take away my pride / Right to live.
CD . . . . RR 90882
MC . . . . RR 9088 4
Road Runner / Jan '93 / Pinnacle.

FROM NOW ON.
Tracks: Not Advised.
CD . . . . RR 90072
MC . . . . RR 90074
Road Runner / Feb '94 / Pinnacle.

I FOUND A WOMAN.
Tracks: I found a woman / L.A. cut off.
- **7"** . . . . SAFE 14
Safari / Nov '79.

PLAY ME OUT (CONNOISSEUR COLLECTION).
Tracks: I got it covered / Space high / It's about time / L.A. cut off / Well / Solution / Your love is like a fire / Destiny / I found a woman / Smile / There goes my

baby / Gypsy woman / Any day now / Glimmer Twins medley.
LP . . . . VSOPLP 153
- **CD** . . . . VSOPCD 153
- **MC** . . . . VSOPMC 153
Connoisseur Collection / Aug '90.

PLAY ME OUT (SAFARI).
Tracks: I got it covered / Space high / It's about time / L.A. cut off / Well / Soulution / Your love is like a fire / Destiny / I found a woman.
- **LP** . . . . LONG 2
Safari / Apr '78.
MC . . . . LONGC 2
Safari / Jul '88 / Pinnacle.

Hughes-Thrall

A short lived one-album liason between ex-Deep Purple and Trapeze man Glenn Hughes (bass/vocals) and Pat Thrall (guitar/vocals) who had just finished a stint in the Pat Travers Band (Drums were played by the much-travelled Frankie Banali, latterly of W.A.S.P.). A second album was rumoured to have been started but it's doubtful whether it could have topped the soaring vocals and crunching guitar of the first, a classic by any standards.

HUGHES AND THRALL.
Tracks: I got your number / Look in your eyes / Beg, borrow or steal / Where did the time go / Muscle and blood / Hold out your life / Who will you run to / Coast to coast / First step of love.
- **LP** . . . . EPC 25052
Epic / Jan '83.

Hunter, Ian

ALL AMERICAN ALIEN BOY.
Tracks: Not Advised.
- **LP** . . . . CBS 81310
CBS / May '79.

ALL OF THE GOOD ONES ARE TAKEN.
Tracks: All of the good ones are taken / Death'n'glory boys.
- **12"** . . . . TA 3541
- **7"** .A 3541
CBS / Jul '83.

ALL THE GOOD ONES ARE TAKEN.
Tracks: All the good ones are taken / Every step of the way / Fun / Speechless / Death 'n' glory boys / That girl is rock 'n' roll / Somethin's going on / Captain void 'n' video jets / Seeing double.
MC 40 25379
- **LP** . . . . CBS 25379
CBS / Aug '83.

AMERICAN MUSIC (Hunter-Ronson).
Tracks: American music / Tell it like it is / Sweet dreamer (Available on 12" format.).
- **12"** . . . . MERX 315
- **7"** . . . . MER 315
- **CD Single** . . . . MERCD 315
- **MC Single** . . . . MERMC 315
Mercury / Feb '90.

COLLECTION: IAN HUNTER.
Tracks: Not Advised.
CD . . . . CCSCD 290
- **MC** . . . . CCSMC 290
Castle Collector Series / Jul '91.

ENDLAND ROCKS.
Tracks: Endland rocks / Wild and free.
- **7"** . . . . CBS 5497
CBS / Jul '77.

IAN HUNTER.
Tracks: Once bitten, twice shy / Who do you love / Lounge lizard / Boy / 3,000 miles from here / Truth / Whole truth nuthin' but the truth / It aint' easy when you fall / Shades off / I get so excited.
- **LP** . . . . CBS 80710
CBS / Apr '75.
CD 477359-2
Columbia / Aug '94 / Sony.

JUSTICE OF THE PEACE.
Tracks: Justice of the peace / Little star.
- **7"** . . . . CBS 5229
CBS / May '77.

LISA LIKES ROCK 'N' ROLL.
Tracks: Lisa likes rock 'n' roll / Noises.
- **7"** . . . . CHS 2542
Chrysalis / Aug '81.

ONCE BITTEN, TWICE SHY.
Tracks: Once bitten twice shy.
- **7"** . . . . CBS 3194
CBS / May '75.

ROCKS.
Tracks: One bitten twice shy / Gun control / Central Park West / All the way from Memphis / I need your love / Noises / Just another night / Cleveland rocks / Irene Wilde / All the young dudes.
VHS . . . . CVHS 5033
Chrysalis Music Video / '89 / EMI.

SHIPS.
Tracks: Ships / Wild east.
- **7"** . . . . CHS 2346
Chrysalis / Aug '79.

SHORT BACK 'N' SIDES PLUS LONG ODDS & OUTTAKES.
Tracks: Central park 'n' west / Lisa likes rock 'n' roll / I need your love / Old records never die / Noises / Rain / Gun control / Theatre of the absurd / Leave me alone / Keep on burning / Detroit (Rough mix instrumental) / Na na na / I need your love (Rough mix) / Rain (Alternative mix) / I believe in you / Listen to the eight track / You stepped into my dreams / Venus in a bathtub / Theatre of the absurd (Wessex mix) / Detroit (Out take 5 - Vocal) / Na na na (Extended mix) / China (Ronson vocal) / Old records never die (Version 1).
CD Set . . . . CDCHR 6074
Chrysalis / May '94 / EMI.

SHORT BACK AND SIDES.
Tracks: Central Park N'West / Lisa likes rock 'n' roll / I need your love / Old records never die / Noises / Rain / Gun control / Theatre of the absurd / Leave me alone / Keep on burning.
- **LP** . . . . CHR 1326
Chrysalis / Aug '81.
MC . . . . ZCHR 1326
Chrysalis / '83 / EMI.

SOMETHIN'S GOIN' ON.
Tracks: Somethin's goin' on / All of the good ones are taken.
- **7"** .A 3855
CBS / Oct '83.

VERY BEST OF IAN HUNTER, THE.
Tracks: Not Advised.
CD 4675082
LP 4675081
MC 4675084
CBS (import) / Apr '91 / C.M. Distribution / Silva Screen.

WE GOTTA GET OUTTA HERE.
Tracks: We gotta get outta here / Once bitten twice shy / Bastard / Cleveland rocks / Sons and daughters / One of the boys.
- **7"** . . . . CHS 2434
Chrysalis / May '80.

WELCOME TO THE CLUB.
Tracks: F.B.I. / Once bitten twice shy / Angeline / Laugh at me / All the way from Memphis / I wish I was your mother / Irene Wilde / Just another night / Cleveland rocks / Standin' in my light / Bastard / Walkin' with a mountain / All the young dudes / Slaughter on Tenth Avenue / We gotta get out of here / Silver needles / Man 'o' war / Sons and daughters.
- **Double LP** . . . . CJT 6
Chrysalis / May '80.
MC . . . . ZCJT 6
Chrysalis / '83 / EMI.

WELCOME TO THE CLUB..
Tracks: F.B.I. / Once bitten twice shy / Angeline / Laugh at me / All the way from Memphis / I wish I was your mother / Irene Wilde / Just another night / Cleveland rocks / Standin' in my light / Bastard / Walking with a mountain/Rock 'n' roll Queen / All the young dudes / Slaughter on Tenth Avenue / One of the boys / Golden age of rock 'n' roll / When the daylight comes / Medley: Once bitten twice shy/ Bastard/Cleveland rocks / We gotta get out of here / Silver needles / Man o' war / Sons and daughters.
CD Set . . . . CDCHR 6075
Chrysalis / May '94 / EMI.

YOU'RE NEVER ALONE WITH A SCHIZOPHRENIC.
Tracks: Just another night / Wild east / Cleveland rocks / Ships / When the daylight comes / Life after death / Standin' in my light / Bastard / Outsider.
- **MC** . . . . ZCHR 1214
Chrysalis / '79.
- **LP** . . . . CHR 1214
Chrysalis / May '79.
CD CD25CR 03
Chrysalis / Mar '94 / EMI.

YUI ORTA (Hunter-Ronson).
Tracks: American music / Loner / Womens intuition / Cool / Big time / Livin' in a heart / Sons 'n' lovers / Beg a little love / Tell it like it is / Sweet dreamer.
■ CD 838 973 2
■ LP 838 973 1
■ MC 838 973 4
Mercury / Jan '90.

Hunters Club

BURNT ALIVE.
Tracks: Not Advised.
■ LP . . . . PIG 003
AVM / Sep '89.

GIMME YOUR SOUL.
Tracks: Gimme your soul.
■ 12" . . . . THC 12002
Trashcan / Sep '88.

TOO FAR GONE TO TURN AROUND.
Tracks: Play the game again / Lightning strikes / Sure feels good / Ain't seen nothing yet / Hit the street / Island of lies.
Mini LP . . . . THC LP 1
Trashcan / Mar '88.

YOU AIN'T SEEN NOTHING YET.
Tracks: You ain't seen nothin' yet / Trashcan.
■ 7" . . . . DTO 956
Trashcan / Apr '87.

Hurricane

AMERICA'S MOST HARDCORE (Hurricane & DFL).
Tracks: Hurra / Can we get along / Elbow room / Pizza man / America's most hardcore / U don't understand / Knucklehead nation / Think about the pit / Smoke bomb / My crazy life.
CD . . . . WIJ 034CD
LP . . . . WIJ 034V
MC . . . . WIJ 034C
Wiiija / Apr '94 / Vital Distribution.

I'M ON TO YOU.
Tracks: I'm on to you / Baby snakes / Girls are out tonight.
■ 12" . . . . ENV 7T
■ 7" . . . . ENV 7
Enigma (EMI) / Feb '89.

SLAVE TO THE THRILL.
Tracks: Reign of love / Next to you / Young man / Dance little sister / Don't wanna dream / Temptations / Ten thousand years / In the fire / Let it slide / Lock me up / Smiles like a child.
■ CD . . . . CDENV 1004
■ LP . . . . ENVLP 1004
■ MC . . . . TCENV 1004
Enigma (EMI) / Apr '90.

TAKE WHAT YOU WANT.
Tracks: Not Advised.
■ LP . . . . RR 9723
Road Runner / Jul '86.

Husker Du

Minneapolis trio who enjoyed massive critical acclaim during '80s, although only seventh album *Warehouse: Songs And Stories* made even minor impression on U.K. charts. Early punky style swiftly gave way to melodic and influential hardcore, but bitter internal relations caused band to split in '88. Legacy lives on in guitarist Bob Mould's Sugar.

CANDY APPLE GREY.
Tracks: Crystal / Don't know to know if you are lonely / I don't know for sure / Sorry somehow / Too far down / Hardly getting over it / Dead set on destruction / Eiffel Tower high / No promise have I made / All this I've done for you.
■ LP . . . . WX 40
MC . . . . WX 40 C
WEA / Apr '86 / WEA.
CD 7599253852
WEA / Nov '92 / WEA.

COULD YOU BE THE ONE.
Tracks: Could you be the one / Every time.
■ 12" . . . . W 8456T
■ 7" . . . . W 8456
WEA / Jan '87.

DON'T WANT TO KNOW IF YOUR LONELY.
Tracks: Don't want to know if your lonely / All work no play / Helter skelter (Live. Extra track available on 12" version only.).
■ 12" . . . . W 8746 T
■ 7" . . . . W 8746
WEA / Feb '86.

EIGHT MILES HIGH.
Tracks: Eight miles high / Masochism world.
■ 7" . . . . SST 025
SST / Apr '84.
■ CD Single . . . . SST 025 CD
SST / Dec '88.

EIGHT MILES HIGH / MAKES NO SENSE AT ALL.
Tracks: Not Advised.
■ 10" . . . . SST 915
SST / May '93.

EVERYTHING FALLS APART.
Tracks: Not Advised.
■ LP . . . . REFLEX D
Reflex / Jul '83.
CD 812271163-2
WEA / Mar '93 / WEA.

FLIP YOUR WIG.
Tracks: Not Advised.
■ LP . . . . SST 055
SST / Oct '85.
MC . . . . SST 055 C
SST / Oct '85 / Pinnacle.
CD . . . . SST 055 CD
SST / May '93 / Pinnacle.

ICE COLD ICE.
Tracks: Ice cold ice / Gotta lotta.
■ 12" . . . . W 8276T
■ 7" . . . . W 8276
WEA / Jun '87.

LAND SPEED RECORD.
Tracks: Not Advised.
CD . . . . SST 195 CD
■ LP . . . . SST 195
MC . . . . SST 195 C
SST / Nov '88 / Pinnacle.

LIVING END, THE.
Tracks: New day rising / Heaven hill / Standing in the rain / Back from somewhere / Ice cold ice / Everytime / Friend you're gonna fall / She floated away / From the gut / Target / It's not funny anymore / Hardly getting over it / Terms of psychic warfare / Powertime / Books about U.F.O's / Divide and conquer / Keep hangin' on / Celebrated Summer / Now that you know me / Ain't no water in the well / What's goin' on / Data control / In a free land / Sheena is a punk rocker.
CD 936245582-2
MC 936245582-4
Warner Bros. / May '94 / WEA.

MAKES NO SENSE.
Tracks: Not Advised.
■ VHS . . . . HEN 2029
Hendring Video / '88.

MAKES NO SENSE AT ALL.
Tracks: Makes no sense at all / Love is all around.
■ 7" . . . . SST 051
SST / Sep '85.
■ CD Single . . . . SST 051 CD
SST / Dec '88.

MAKES NO SENSE AT ALL / EIGHT MILES HIGH.
Tracks: Not Advised.
■ CD Single . . . . SST 270 CD
■ MC Single . . . . SST 270 C
SST / May '93.

METAL CIRCUS EP.
Tracks: Not Advised.
■ 12" . . . . SST 020
SST / Dec '83.
■ CD Single . . . . SST 020 CD
■ MC Single . . . . SST 020 C
SST / May '93.

NEW DAY RISING.
Tracks: Not Advised.
■ LP . . . . SST 031
SST / Feb '85.
CD . . . . SST 031 CD
MC . . . . SST 031 C
SST / May '93 / Pinnacle.

SORRY SOMEHOW.
Tracks: Sorry somehow / All this I've done for you / Flexible flyer (Extra track available on 12" version only.) / Celibated summer (Extra track available on 12" version only.).
■ 12" . . . . W 8612 T
■ 7" . . . . W 8612
■ 7" P.Disc . . . . W 8612 P
WEA / Sep '86.

WAREHOUSE SONGS AND STORIES.
Tracks: These important years / Charity, charity, prudence and hope / Standing in the rain / Back from somewhere / Ice cold ice / You're a soldier / Could you be the one / Too much spice / Friend, you've got to fall / She floated away / Bed of nails / Tell you why tomorrow / It's not peculiar / Actual condition / No reservations / Turn it around / She's a woman / Up in the air / You can live at home.
MC Set 925544 4
■ Double LP 925544 1
WEA / Jan '87.
CD 7599255442
WEA / Oct '92 / WEA.

ZEN ARCADE.
Tracks: Not Advised.
CD . . . . SST 027 CD
LP . . . . SST 027
MC . . . . SST 027 C
SST / May '93 / Pinnacle.

Hydra Vein

AFTER THE DREAM.
Tracks: Not Advised.
LP . . . . CMO 193
RKT / Jan '90.

RATHER DEATH THAN FALSE OF FAITH.
Tracks: Not Advised.
■ LP . . . . OTH 12
Metalother / Aug '88.
MC . . . . OTH 12C
Metalother / Aug '88 / Backs Distribution.

Hyperhead

METAPHASIA.
Tracks: Not Advised.
CD . . . . CDDVN 16
LP . . . . DVN 16
MC . . . . TDVN 16
Devotion / Dec '92 / Pinnacle.

TEENAGE MIND.
Tracks: Teenage Mind.
■ 12" . . . . 12 DVN 109
■ CD Single . . . . CDDVN 109
Music For Nations / Sep '92.

Hypocrisy

INFERIOR DEVOTIES.
Tracks: Not Advised.
CD . . . . .NB 098CD
Nuclear Blast / Mar '94 / Plastic Head.

OBSCULUM OBSCENUM.
Tracks: Not Advised.
CD . . . . NB 080
LP . . . . NB 080 1
MC . . . . NB 080 4
Nuclear Blast / Aug '93 / Plastic Head.

PENETRALIA.
Tracks: Not Advised.
CD . . . . .NB 067CD
LP . . . . .NB 067LP
MC . . . . NB 067MC
Nuclear Blast / Nov '92 / Plastic Head.

Hysteriah G.B.C.

SNAKEWORLD.
Tracks: Confess a lie / Land of democracy / Cafe of hope (slowly..) / Is the coffee ready yet / Snakes / How does it feel / Rope for rape.
■ CD . . . . HELLCD 011
■ LP . . . . HELLLP 011
Hellhound / Apr '92.

I Love You

I LOVE YOU.
Tracks: Not Advised.
■ CD . . . . .GEFD 24371
■ LP . . . . GEF 24371
■ MC. . . . . .GEFC 24371
Geffen / Apr '91.

LIVE.
Tracks: Not Advised.
CD. MD 2437-2
LP . . . . MD 2437-1
Medusa (USA) / Feb '90.

I Q Inc

SNAKES.
Tracks: Snakes.
■ 12". . . . . E 11543
■ CD Single . . . . E 11543 CD
Sub Pop / Mar '93.

Ice Age

LIFE'S A BITCH.
Tracks: Not Advised.
CD. HMIXD 154
■ LP . . . . HMILP 154
MC. . . . . HMIMC 154
FM Records / Aug '90 / FM Revolver / Sony.

Icon

RIGHT BETWEEN THE EYES.
Tracks: Right between the eyes / Two for the road / Take my breath away / Far cry / In your eyes / Forever young / Running under fire / Peace & love.
■ CD 782 010-2
■ LP . . . . K 820101
■ MC. . . . . K 820104
Atlantic / Sep '89.

SEX, LIES & SCANDAL.
Tracks: Sex, lies & scandal.
12" .12SUX 1
CD Single . . . . CDSUX 1
MC Single . . . . CASUX 1
Dodgey Beast / Aug '94 / RTM / Pinnacle.

SO SPECIAL.
Tracks: So special.
■ 12" . . . . RS 9113
Rham / Apr '91.

Iggy Pop

'Godfather Of Punk', Iggy Pop acheived notoriety as leader of seminal prototype punks, the Stooges. *The Stooges*, their 1969 debut LP for Elektra was produced by ex-Velvet John Cale is regarded as a classic. After a change of personnel, Iggy & The Stooges recorded *Raw Power* in 1973 which was produced by Iggy fan, David Bowie. In the mid 1970's, the band fell apart, blighted by Iggy Pop's drug habits. Further patronage from Bowie and interest from the burgeoning UK punk scene, re-kindled his career. *Lust For Life* and *The Idiot* were big selling LP's. Iggy Pop's erratic career has continued in between drug problems and acting, working at times with Bowie and ex-Pistol, Steve Jones. Although his studio work has veered towards fairly bland rock in recent years, as a live performer his awesome reputation is intact, and his influence on punk and beyond is undeniable.

AMERICAN CAESAR.
Tracks: Character / Wild America / Mixin' the colors / Jealousy / Hate / It's our love / Plastic and concrete / Fuckin' alone / Highway song / Beside you / Sickness / Boogie boy / Perforation problems / Social life / Louie Louie / Caesar / Girls of N.Y.
CD. .CDVUS 64
LP . . . . VUSLP 64
MC. VUSMC 64
Virgin America / Aug '93 / EMI.

BANG BANG.
Tracks: Bang bang / Sea of love.
■ 7" . . . . .ARIST 407
Arista / May '81.

BESIDE YOU.
Tracks: Beside you / Evil California (Features on 7" & MCS only.) / Home (Live) (Features on 7" and MCS only.) / Fuckin' alone (Features on MCS & 7" only.) / Les amanis (Features on CDS only.) / Louie Louie (Live) (Features on CDS only.) / Beside you (Acoustic version) (Features on CDS only.).
■ 10". . . . . VUSA 77
■ CD Single. . . . . .VUSCD 77
■ MC Single. . . . . VUSC 77
Virgin / May '94.

BLAH BLAH BLAH.
Tracks: Real wild child / Baby, it can't fall / Shades / Fire girl / Isolation / Cry for love / Blah, blah, blah / Hideaway / Winners and losers.
■ CD . . . . CDA 5145
A&M / Oct '86.
■ LP . . . . .AMA 5145
■ MC. . . . . .AMC 5145
A&M / Sep '86.
CD 395 145 2
A&M / '89 / PolyGram.
CD . . . . CDMID 159
MC. CMID 159
A&M / Oct '92 / PolyGram.

BRICK BY BRICK.
Tracks: Home / I won't crap out / Butt town / Moonlight lady / Neon forest / Pussy power / Brick by brick / Main Street eyes / Candy / Undefeated / Something wild / Starry night / My baby wants to rock and roll / Livin' on the edge of the night.
■ LP . . . . .VUSLP 19
■ MC. . . . . .VUSMC 19
Virgin America / Jul '90.
CD .CDVUS 19
MC. . . . . OVEDC 426
Virgin America / Apr '92 / EMI.

CANDY (Pop, Iggy & Kate Pierson).
Tracks: Candy / Pussy power / Undefeated (Only on 12" single.) / Butt town (Only on 12" single.) / My baby wants to rock'n'roll (Only on 10" single.).
■ 10". . . . . .TVUS 29
■ 12". . . . . .VUST 29
■ 7" . . . . VUS 29
■ MC Single. . . . . VUSC 29
■ CD Single . . . . .VUSCD 29
Virgin America / Sep '90.

CHINA GIRL.
Tracks: China girl / Baby.
■ 7" . . . . PB 9093
RCA / May '77.

CHOICE CUTS.
Tracks: Not Advised.
■ LP . . . . PL 84957
RCA (Germany) / Sep '84.

COLD METAL.
Tracks: Cold metal / Instinct / Tough baby (On 12" only).
■ 12". . . . . .AMY 452
■ 12" P.Disc. . . . . AMP 452
■ 7" . . . . AM 452
A&M / Aug '88.

COMPACT HITS: IGGY POP.
Tracks: Real wild child / Isolation / Cry for love / Shades.
■ CD Single . . . . AMCD 909
A&M / Apr '88.

CRY FOR LOVE.
Tracks: Cry for love / Winners and losers.
■ 12" . . . . AMY 358
■ 7" . . . . AM 358
A&M / Oct '86.

DEATH TRIP (Iggy & The Stooges).
Tracks: Not Advised.
■ LP P.Disc . . . . MIG 6P
Revenge (France) / Sep '88.

FIRE GIRL.
Tracks: Fire girl / Blah, blah, blah (live).
■ 12". . . . . AMY 392
■ 7" . . . . AM 392
A&M / Apr '87.

FIVE FOOT ONE.
Tracks: Five foot one / Pretty flamingo.
■ 7" P.Disc . . . . ARIPD 274
Arista / Jul '79.

FUN HOUSE (Iggy & The Stooges).
Tracks: Not Advised.
■ LP 4205579
Elektra / Mar '77.
CD 7559606692
WEA / Oct '93 / WEA.

GIMME DANGER (Iggy & The Stooges).
Tracks: Gimme danger.
■ 12". . . . . .CAX 3
Revenge (France) / May '88.

HIGH ON YOU.
Tracks: High on you / Squarehead.
■ 12". . . . . AMY 475
■ 7" . . . . AM 475
A&M / Dec '88.

HOME.
Tracks: Home / Lust for life.
■ 12". . . . . .VUST 22
■ 7" . . . . VUS 22
■ CD Single . . . . .VUSCD 22
■ MC Single. . . . . VUSC 22
Virgin America / Jun '90.

I GOT A RIGHT.
Tracks: I got a right / Sixteen.
■ 7" . . . . PB 9213
RCA / '79.

I GOT NOTHING (Iggy & The Stooges).
Tracks: I got nothing.
■ 12". 622336
■ CD Single. 622332
Skydog / Dec '90.

I'M BORED.
Tracks: I'm bored / African man.
■ 7" . . . . .ARIST 255
Arista / May '79.

I'M SICK OF YOU/KILL CITY.
Tracks: Kill city / Sell your love / Beyond the law / I got nothin' / Johanna / Night theme / Night theme (2) / Consolation prizes / No sense of crime / Lucky moments / Master charge / I'm sick of you / Tight pants / I got a right / Johanna (2) / Consolation prizes (2) / Scene of the crime / Gimme some skin / Jesus loves the stooges.
CD Set . . . . LICD 921175
Line / May '92 / C.M. Distribution / Grapevine Distribution / A.D.A. Distribution / Conifer Records.

IDIOT, THE.
Tracks: Sister midnight / Nightclubbing / Funtime / Baby / China girl / Dum dum boys / Tiny girls / Mass production.
■ LP . . . . PL 12275
■ MC. . . . . PK 12275
RCA / Apr '77.
CD . . . . CDOVD 277
MC. OVEDC 277
■ LP . . . . OVED 277
Virgin / Apr '90.

IGGY AND THE STOOGES (Iggy & The Stooges).
Tracks: Not Advised.
CD .890050
New Rose / May '94 / Pinnacle / Topic Records / Direct Distribution.

IGGY POP COMPACT COLLECTION.
Tracks: Not Advised.
CD TPAK21
Virgin / Jan '93 / EMI.

IGGY POP: INTERVIEW PICTURE DISC.
Tracks: Not Advised.
■ LP P.Disc . . . . BAK 2061
Baktabak / Sep '87.

INSTINCT.
Tracks: Cold metal / High on you / Strong girl / Tom Tom / Easy rider / Power and freedom / Lowdown / Instinct / Tuff baby / Squarehead.

CD	CDA 5198
■ LP	AMA 5198
■ MC	AMC 5198

A&M / Jun '88.

ISOLATION.
Tracks: Isolation / Shades (live) / Fire girl (remix) (on 12" only.).

■ 12"	AMY 397
■ 7"	AM 397

A&M / Jun '87.

KILL CITY.
Tracks: Kill city / I got nothing.

■ 7"	ADA 4

Radar / Mar '78.

KILL CITY (Pop, Iggy & James Williamson).
Tracks: Kill City / Sell your love / Beyond the law / I got nothing / Johanna / Night theme / Consolation prizes / No sense of crime / Lucky moments / Master charge.

■ LP	RAD 2

Radar.

CD	LICD 900131

Line / Oct '92 / C.M. Distribution / Grapevine Distribution / A.D.A. Distribution / Conifer Records.

KISS MY BLOOD.
Tracks: Not Advised.

VHS	VVD 882

Virgin Vision / Oct '91 / Gold & Sons / TBD.

LIVE AT THE WHISKEY A GO-GO (Stooges).
Tracks: Not Advised.

■ LP	MIG 7

Revenge (France) / Dec '88.

LIVE: CHANNEL BOSTON M.A. 1988.
Tracks: Not Advised.

CD	642005

New Rose / May '94 / Pinnacle / Topic Records / Direct Distribution.

LIVE: HIPPODROME, PARIS 1977.
Tracks: Not Advised.

CD	893334

New Rose / May '94 / Pinnacle / Topic Records / Direct Distribution.

LIVE: NEW YORK RITZ 1986.
Tracks: Not Advised.

CD	642044

New Rose / May '94 / Pinnacle / Topic Records / Direct Distribution.

LIVIN' ON THE EDGE OF THE NIGHT.
Tracks: Livin' on the edge of the night / Passenger / Nightclubbing (Only on 12" and CD singles) / China girl (Only on 12" and CD singles).

■ 12"	VUST 1228
■ CD Single	VUSCD 1228
■ MC Single	VSC 1228
■ 12"	VUSTG 18
■ 12" P.Disc.	VUSTE 18
■ 7"	VUS 18
■ MC Single	VUSC 18

Virgin America / Jan '90.

LUST FOR LIFE.
Tracks: Lust for life / Sixteen / Some wierd sin / Passenger / Tonight / Success / Turn blue / Neighbourhood threat / Fall in love with me.

■ LP	PL 12488

RCA / Oct '77.

■ LP	INTS 5114

RCA / Jan '82.

■ LP	NL 82488
■ MC	NK 82488

RCA / '84.

CD	CDOVD 278
■ LP	OVED 278
MC	OVEDC 278

Virgin / Apr '90 / EMI.

METALLIC KO (Iggy & The Stooges).
Tracks: Raw power / Head on the curb / Gimme danger / Search and destiny / Heavy liquid / I wanna be your dog / Recital / Open up and bleed / I got nothing / Rich bitch / Cock in my pocket / Louie Louie.

■ LP	IMP 1015

Skydog / '76.

CD	622322
■ LP	622321

Skydog / Apr '88.

MY GIRL HATES MY HEROIN (Stooges).
Tracks: Not Advised.

CD	890028

New Rose / Jun '94 / Pinnacle / Topic Records / Direct Distribution.

NEW VALUES.
Tracks: Tell me a stay / New values / Girls / I'm bored / Don't look down / Endless sea / Five foot one / How do you fix a broken heart / Angel / Curiosity / African man / Billy is a runaway.

■ LP	SPART 1092

Arista / May '79.

■ LP	1201144

Arista / Mar '87.

CD	260997
■ LP	210997
■ MC	410997

Arista / Nov '90.

NIGHT OF DESTRUCTION (Stooges).
Tracks: Not Advised.

CD	642100

New Rose / Jun '94 / Pinnacle / Topic Records / Direct Distribution.

NO FUN (Featuring Iggy Pop) (Stooges).
Tracks: 1969 / Real cool time / No fun / Dirt / Down on the street / Loose / T.V. eye / I wanna be your dog / I feel alright.

■ LP	K 52234

Elektra / Aug '80.

OPEN UP AND BLEED (Iggy & The Stooges).
Tracks: Not Advised.

CD	HTM 16

Revenge (France) / May '88 / Pinnacle.

PARTY.
Tracks: Pleasure / Rock and roll party / Eggs on plate / Sincerity / Houston is hot tonight / Pumpin' for Jill / Happy man / Bang bang / Sea of love / Time won't let me.

■ LP	SPART 1158

Arista / Jun '81.

■ LP	203806
■ MC	403806

Arista / Jan '87.

CD	253 806

RCA / Sep '89 / BMG.

PASSENGER, THE.
Tracks: Passenger / Nightclubbing.

■ 7"	GOLD 549

RCA Golden Grooves / May '82.

POP SONGS.
Tracks: Loco mosquito / Bang bang / Pumpin' for Jill / Tell me a story / Take care of me / Mr. Dynamite / I'm bored / Sea of love / Play it safe / Endless sea / Pleasure / Five foot one / Houston is hot tonight / Dog food.

CD	262178
■ MC	412178

Arista / Jan '92.

RAW POWER (Pop, Iggy & The Stooges).
Tracks: Search and destroy / Gimme danger / Your pretty face is going to hell / Penetration / Raw power / I need somebody / Shake appeal / Death trip.

■ LP	CBS 31464

Embassy / Jun '77.

■ LP	CBS 32083

CBS / Dec '81.

■ LP	ESSLP 005
■ MC	ESSMC 005
■ CD	ESSCD 005

Essential / May '89.

CD	476610 2
MC	476610 4

Columbia / Apr '94 / Sony.

RAW STOOGES VOL.1 (Iggy & The Stooges).
Tracks: Not Advised.

■ LP	190069

Electric (Germany) / Dec '88.

RAW STOOGES VOL.2 (Iggy & The Stooges).
Tracks: Not Advised.

■ LP	190070

Electric (Germany) / Dec '88.

REAL WILD CHILD.
Tracks: Little Miss Emperor / Real wild child.

■ 12"	AMY 368
■ 7"	AM 368

A&M / Nov '86.

RUBBER LEGS (Iggy & The Stooges).
Tracks: Not Advised.

■ LP	FC 037

Fan Club / Dec '87.

■ CD	FC 037CD

Fan Club / Oct '88.

CD	422351

New Rose / May '94 / Pinnacle / Topic Records / Direct Distribution.

RUN LIKE A VILLAIN.
Tracks: Run like a villain / Platonic.

■ 7"	CHFLY 2634

Animal / '82.

SHADES.
Tracks: Baby it can't fall / Cry for love (12" only).

■ 12"	AMY 374
■ 7"	AM 374

A&M / Feb '87.

SHE CREATURES OF HOLLYWOOD HILLS (Iggy & The Stooges).
Tracks: She creatures of Hollywood Hills.

■ 12"	CAX 4

Revenge (France) / Dec '88.

SOLDIER.
Tracks: Loco mosquito / Ambition / Take care of me / Get up and get out / Play it safe / I'm a conservative / Dog food / I need more / Knocking 'em down (in the city) / Mr. Dynamite / I snub you.

■ LP	SPART 1117

Arista / Feb '80.

CD	251160
■ LP	210160
■ MC	410160

Arista / Apr '91.

STOOGES, THE (Iggy & The Stooges).
Tracks: Not Advised.

■ LP	K 42032

Elektra / Mar '77.

CD	7559606672

WEA / Oct '93 / WEA.

STOOGES, THE (Stooges).
Tracks: What you gonna do (live cut '68) (Previously unreleased.) / Gimme danger (live 73) / Ron Asheton interview.

■ 12"	CAXBOX 1

Revenge (France) / Dec '88.

SUCCESS.
Tracks: Success / Passenger.

■ 7"	PB 9160

RCA / '79.

SUCK ON THIS.
Tracks: Not Advised.

CD	642 050
■ MC	644 050

Trident / May '93.

TAKE CARE OF ME.
Tracks: Take care of me / Locomosquito.

■ 7"	ARIST 327

Arista / Feb '80.

TILL THE END OF THE NIGHT (Stooges).
Tracks: Not Advised.

CD	642042

New Rose / Jun '94 / Pinnacle / Topic Records / Direct Distribution.

TV EYE (1977 LIVE).
Tracks: TV eye / Funtime / Sixteen / I got a right / Lust for life / Dirt / Nightclubbing / I wanna be your dog.

■ MC	PK 12796

RCA / '79.

■ LP	PL 12796

RCA / Apr '83.

CD	CDOVD 448

Virgin / Jun '94 / EMI.

ZOMBIE BIRDHOUSE.
Tracks: Run like a villain / Villagers / Angry hills / Life of work / Ballad of Cookie McBride / Ordinary bummer / Eat or be eaten / Bulldozer / Platonic / Horse song / Watching the news / Street crazies.

■ MC	ZCHR 1399
■ LP	CHR 1399

Animal / Sep '82.

■ DELETED

Ignite

SCARRED FOR LIFE.
Tracks: Not Advised.
CD . . . . LF 104CD
Lost & Found / Aug '94 / Plastic Head.

Ignorance

CONFIDENT RAT, THE.
Tracks: Not Advised.
CD .CDZORRO 17
LP . . . . ZORRO 17
MC . . . . .TZORRO 17
Metal Blade / Feb '91 / Pinnacle.

POSITIVELY SHOCKING.
Tracks: Not Advised.
CD .CDZORRO 48
LP . . . . ZORRO 48
MC . . . . .TZORRO 48
Zorro / Sep '92 / Pinnacle.

Illdisposed

FOUR DEPRESSIVE SEASONS.
Tracks: Not Advised.
CD . . . . NB 103
Nuclear Blast / Apr '94 / Plastic Head.

RETURN FROM TOMORROW.
Tracks: Not Advised.
CD . . . . NB 116
Nuclear Blast / Aug '94 / Plastic Head.

Immolation

DAWN OF POSSESSION.
Tracks: Not Advised.
■ MC . . . . RC 93104
■ LP . . . . RC 93101
RC Records / Aug '91.
CD . . . . RC 93102
RC Records / Jan '94 / Pinnacle.

Immortal

PURE HOLOCAUST.
Tracks: Not Advised.
CD . . . . OPCD 19
Osmose / Dec '93 / Plastic Head.

Impaled Nazarene

UGRA KARMA.
Tracks: Not Advised.
CD .OPCD 018
LP . . . . .OPLP 018
Osmose / Apr '94 / Plastic Head.

Impaler

CARNAL DEITY.
Tracks: Not Advised.
CD . . . . DEAF 007CD
LP . . . . DEAF 007
Deaf / Apr '92 / Vital Distribution.

Impellitteri

STAND IN LINE.
Tracks: Stand in line / Since you've been gone / Secret love / Somewhere over the rainbow / Tonight I'll fry / White and perfect / Goodnight and goodnight / Playing with fire / Leviathan.
CD . . . . CDMFN 87
MC . . . . TMFN 87
Music For Nations / Aug '88 / Pinnacle.
■ LP . . . . MFN 87
Music For Nations / Aug '88.

Impetigo

HORROR OF THE ZOMBIES.
Tracks: Not Advised.
CD . . . . WRR 035
Wild Rags / Aug '93 / Plastic Head.

ULTIMO MONDO CANNIBALE.
Tracks: Not Advised.
LP . . . . WRE 904
Wild Rags / Dec '90 / Plastic Head.
CD .WRE 904CD
Wild Rags / Jan '92 / Plastic Head.

Impulse Manslaughter

HE WHO LAUGHS LAST LAUGHS ALONE.
Tracks: Not Advised.
LP . . . . NB 011
Nuclear Blast / Oct '88 / Plastic Head.
LP . . . . NB 003
Nuclear Blast / Feb '89 / Plastic Head.

LOGICAL END.
Tracks: Not Advised.
CD .NB 013CD
LP . . . . NB 013
Nuclear Blast / Jun '89 / Plastic Head.

Inbred

KISSIN' COUSINS.
Tracks: Not Advised.
■ LP . . . . K 001/118
Konkurrel / Oct '88.

Incubus

BEYOND THE UNKNOWN.
Tracks: Not Advised.
CD .NB 039CD
LP . . . . NB 039
Nuclear Blast / Jan '91 / Plastic Head.

SERPENT TEMPTATION.
Tracks: Not Advised.
■ LP .VOV 674
Metalworks / May '89.

TO THE DEVIL A DAUGHTER.
Tracks: Not Advised.
■ LP . . . . GRC 2165
Guardian / Aug '84.

Indestroy

INDESTROY.
Tracks: Not Advised.
■ LP . . . . NRR 10
MC . . . . NRC 10
New Renaissance(USA) / Nov '87 / Pinnacle.

Infectious Grooves

GROOVE FAMILY CYCO.
Tracks: Violent & funky / Boom boom boom / Frustrated again / Rules go out the window / Groove family cyco / Die like a pig / Do what I tell ya / Cousin Randy / Why / Made it.
CD 475929 2
LP 475929 1
MC 475929 4
Epic / May '94 / Sony.

PLAGUE THAT MAKES YOUR BOOTY MOVE, THE (It's The Infectious Grooves).
Tracks: Punk it up / Therapy / I look funny / Stop funk'n with my head / I'm gonna be my King / Closed session / Infectious grooves / Infectious blues / Monster skank / Back to the people / Turn your head / You lie..and yo breath stank / Do the sinister / Mandatory love song / Infecto groovalistic / Thanx but no thanx.
CD 4687292
■ LP 4687291
■ MC 4687294
Epic / Sep '91.

SARSIPPIUS ARK.
Tracks: Intro / Turtle wax (Funkaholics anonymous) / No cover/ 2 drink minimum / Immigrant song / Caca De Kick / Don't stop spread the jam / Three headed mind pollution / Slo-Motion slam / Legend in his own mind (Ladies love 'sip) / Infectious grooves / These freaks are here to party / Man behind the man / Fame / Savor da flavor / No Budget/ Dust off the 8-Track / Infectious grooves (2) / You pick me up (Just throw me down)"Therapy" / Do the sinister / Big big butt, by infectiphibian / Spreck.
CD 473591 2
LP 473591 1
MC 473591 4
Epic / Mar '93 / Sony.

Infernal Majesty

NONE SHALL DEFY.
Tracks: Not Advised.
■ LP .RR 9609
MC . . . . .RR 49609
Road Runner / '89 / Pinnacle.

Inferno

INFERNO/EXECUTE (Inferno/Execute).
Tracks: Not Advised.
■ LP 0012-06
Pusmort / Dec '86.

Inhuman Conditions

DESERVE NO RESPECT.
Tracks: Not Advised.
LP 082931
Nuclear Blast / Dec '90 / Plastic Head.

SUPPORT.
Tracks: Support.
■ 7" . . . . AMOK 004
Amok / Jun '93.

Intense Degree

PEEL SESSIONS:INTENSE DEGREE (28.2.88).
Tracks: Hangin' on / Vagrants / Skate-bored / All the guys / Day dreams / Take no chances / Future shock / Politician / Allegiance / Bursting.
■ 12" . . . . SFPS 053
Strange Fruit / Aug '88.

WAR IN MY HEAD.
Tracks: Not Advised.
■ LP .MOSH 9
Earache / Feb '89.

Internal Void

STANDING ON THE SUN.
Tracks: Not Advised.
CD .HELL018CD
Hellhound / Nov '92 / Plastic Head.

Intrinsic

INTRINSIC.
Tracks: Not Advised.
■ LP 8856182431
No Wimp (USA) / Aug '88.

Intruder

HIGHER FORM OF KILLING, A.
Tracks: Time of trouble / Martyr / Genetic genocide / Second chance / (I'm not your) stepping stone / Killing winds / Sentence is death / Agents of the dark (MIB) / Antipathy.
■ LP . . . . RO 94521
Roadracer / Oct '89.

INTRUDER.
Tracks: Not Advised.
■ LP P.Disc . . . . IW 1024
Iron Works (USA) / Oct '87.

LIVE TO DIE.
Tracks: Not Advised.
■ LP . . . . IW 1023
Iron Works (USA) / Jan '88.

PSYCHO SAVANT.
Tracks: Not Advised.
CD .CDZORRO 25
LP . . . . ZORRO 25
MC . . . . .TZORRO 25
Metal Blade / Jul '91 / Pinnacle.

Invocator

EXCURSION DEMISE.
Tracks: Not Advised.
CD 8410582
LP 0810581
Black Mark / Jan '92 / Plastic Head.

WEAVE THE APOCALYPSE.
Tracks: Not Advised.
CD . . . . BMCD 34
MC . . . . BMCT 34
Black Mark / Jul '93 / Plastic Head.

Iron Angels

HELLISH CROSSFIRE.
Tracks: Not Advised.
■ LP 081 853
Steamhammer (Germany) / Jan '86.

WINGS OF WAR.
Tracks: Not Advised.
■ LP . . . . SH 0047
Steamhammer (Germany) / Jul '86.

Iron Brew

IRON BREW.
Tracks: Not Advised.
■ CD . . . . .LLMCD 132
■ LP . . . . .LLM 132
Legacy / Apr '90.

Iron Butterfly

Regarded as American challengers to Led Zeppelin and Cream's rock supremacy, Butterfly were successful but short-lived. 1968 debut, *Heavy*, appeared in U.S. charts for 50 consecutive weeks, although band are best remembered for next album; multi-million selling *In-A-Gadda-Da-Vida*; title track of which was minor hit and later co-vered by Slayer. Butterfly disbanded in 1971, reformed to scant acclaim in '74 and split again in '75. Reunion loomed in '90s.

HEAVY.
Tracks: Not Advised.
CD .REP 4128-WZ
Repertoire (Germany) / Aug '91 / Pinnacle.

IN-A-GADDA-DA-VIDA.
Tracks: Most anything you want / My mirage / Termination / Are you happy / In a gadda-da-vida / Flowers and beads.
■ LP . . . . K 40022
Atlantic / '74.
■ CD . . . . K 240022
WEA / Jul '87.

LIGHT & HEAVY.
Tracks: Not Advised.
CD 812271166-2
WEA / Mar '93 / WEA.

TWO ORIGINALS OF IRON BUTTERFLY (Ball and Metamorphosis).
Tracks: In the time of our lives / Soul experience / Lonely boy / Real fright / In the crowds / It must be love / Her favourite style / Filled with fear / Belda bear / Free flight / New day / Shady lady / Best years of our lives / Slower than guns / Stone believer / Soldier in out town / Easy rider (let the wind pay the way) / Butterfly bleu.
■ LP . . . . K 80003
Atlantic.

Iron Fist

MOTORSEXLE MANIA.
Tracks: Not Advised.
CD . . . . FDN 2009-2
Foundation 2000 / Jul '94 / Plastic Head.

Iron Horse

EVERYTHING IS GREY.
Tracks: Not Advised.
■ LP . . . . K 50730
Scotti Bros (USA) / Nov '80.

IRON HORSE.
Tracks: One and only / Sweet Lui-Louise / Jump back in the light / You gotta let go / Tumbleweed / State line blues / Watch me fly / Old fashioned / She's got it / There ain't no cure.
■ LP . . . . K 50598
Scotti Bros (USA) / '77.

ONE AND ONLY.
Tracks: One and only / She's got it.
■ 7" . . . . K 11319
WEA / '79.

SWEET LUI-LOUISE.
Tracks: Sweet Lui-Louise / Watch me fly.
■ 7" . . . . K 11271
Scotti Bros (USA) / Apr '79.

WHAT'S YOUR HURRY DARLIN'.
Tracks: What's your hurry darlin' / Try a little harder.
■ 7" . . . . K 11497
Scotti Bros (USA) / Nov '80.

Iron Maiden

Figureheads of New Wave of British Heavy Metal in 1979, Iron Maiden swiftly became UK's biggest hard rock act since Led Zeppelin. Shifting line-up in early years culminated in departure of singer Paul Di'anno

after first two albums, although replacement Bruce Dickinson (ex-Samson) led band to mammoth success. Maiden enjoy consistent - and, in the metal field, unprecedented - success in UK charts; 1982 album *Number Of The Beast* and 1991 single *Bring Your Daughter To The Slaughter* both entered at number one. Huge international concert draw, band have twice headlined UK's 'Monsters of Rock' festival. Further line-up changes in '90s included departure of Dickinson, although principal songwriter Steve Harris remains. Now fronted by Blaze Bayley, ex-Wolfsbane, Maiden can rely on loyal support from large audience.

2 MINUTES TO MIDNIGHT.
Tracks: 2 minutes to midnight / Rainbow's gold.
■ 12" .12EMI 5489
■ 7" . . . . EMI 5489
EMI / Aug '84.

ACES HIGH.
Tracks: Aces high / King of twilight / Number of the beast.
■ 7" . . . . EMI 5502
■ 12" P.Disc. 12EMIP 5502
■ 12" 12EMI 5502
EMI / Oct '84.

BE QUICK OR BE DEAD.
Tracks: Be quick or be dead / Nodding donkey blues / Space station No. 5 (Not on 7").
■ 12" 12EMG 229
■ 12" P.Disc. 12EMPD 229
■ 7" . . . . EM 229
■ CD Single . . . . .CDEM 229
EMI / Apr '92.

BEHIND THE IRON CURTAIN VIDEO EP.
Tracks: Aces high / Hallowed be thy name / 2 minutes to midnight / Run to the hills.
■ VHS . . . . MVR 99 0039 2
PMI / Jun '86.
■ VHS . . . . MVA 012
PMI / Jun '90.
VHS .MC 2060
Music Club Video / Mar '91 / Video Collection / Gold & Sons / TBD.

BRING YOUR DAUGHTER..TO THE SLAUGHTER.
Tracks: Bring your daughter..to the slaughter / I'm a mover / Communication breakdown (Not on 7" pic. disc, etched disc or cassingle.).
■ 12" 12EMP 171
■ 12" P.Disc. 12EMPD 171
■ 7" P.Disc . . . . .EMPD 171
■ CD Single . . . . .CDEM 171
■ MC Single . . . . .TCEM 171
■ 7" . . . . EMS 171
EMI / Dec '90.

CAN I PLAY WITH MADNESS.
Tracks: Can I play with madness / Black Bart blues / Massacre (Only on 12" and CD.).
■ 12" .12EM 49
■ 7" . . . . EMS 49
■ 7" . . . . EM 49
■ 7" P.Disc . . . . EMP 49
■ CD Single . . . . CDEM 49
EMI / Mar '88.

CAN I PLAY WITH MADNESS/THE EVIL THAT MEN DO.
Tracks: Can I play with madness / Black Bart blues / Massacre / Evil that men do / Prowler '88 / Charlotte the harlot '88 / Listen with Nicko part IX.
■ CD Single . . . . .CDIRN 9
■ 12" . . . . IRN 9
EMI / Mar '90.

CLAIRVOYANT, THE.
Tracks: Clairvoyant / Prisoner, The (live) / Heaven can wait (live) (Not on 7".).
■ 12" .12EM 79
■ 12" .12EMG 79
■ 7" P.Disc . . . . EMP 79
■ CD Single . . . . CDEM 79
■ 7" . . . . EM 79
■ 7" . . . . EMS 79
EMI / Nov '88.

CLAIRVOYANT/INFINITE DREAMS.
Tracks: Clairvoyant, The (live) / Prisoner, The (live) / Heaven can wait (live) / Infinite dreams (live) / Killers (live) / Still life (live) / Listen with Nicko part X.
■ CD Single . . . . .CDIRN 10

■ 12" .IRN 10
EMI / Mar '90.

DONINGTON LIVE 1992.
Tracks: Be quick or be dead / Number of the beast / Wrathchild / From here to eternity / Can I play with madness / Wasting love / Tailgunner / Evil that men do / Afraid to shoot strangers / Fear of the dark / Bring your daughter..to the slaughter / Clairvoyant / Heaven can wait / Run to the hills / 2 minutes to midnight / Iron Maiden / Hallowed be thy name / Trooper / Sanctuary / Running free.
VHS . . . . MVN 4911563
PMI / Nov '93 / EMI / Gold & Sons / TBD.

EVIL THAT MEN DO, THE.
Tracks: Evil that men do / Prowler '88 / Charlotte the harlot '88.
■ 12" .12EMS 64
■ 7" . . . . EM 64
■ 7" . . . . EMG 64
■ 7" P.Disc . . . . EMP 64
■ CD Single . . . . CDEM 64
■ 12" .12EM 64
EMI / Aug '88.

FEAR OF THE DARK.
Tracks: Be quick or be dead / From here to eternity / Afraid to shoot strangers / Fear is the key / Childhood's end / Wasting love / Fugitive / Chains of misery / Apparition / Judas be my guide / Weekend warrior / Fear of the dark.
■ CD . . . . CDP 799 161 2
■ LP . . . . .EMD 1032
EMI / May '92.
CD. . . . . .CDEMD 1032
MC. . . . . TCEMD 1032
EMI / Jul '94 / EMI.

FEAR OF THE DARK (LIVE).
Tracks: Fear of the dark (Live) / Hooks in you (Live) / Tailgunner (Live) / Bring your daughter..to the slaughter (Live).
■ 7" . . . . EMP 263
■ 7" P.Disc . . . . .EMPD 263
■ CD Single . . . . .CDEMS 263
EMI / Mar '93.

FIRST TEN YEARS, THE (THE VIDEOS).
Tracks: Women in uniform / Wrathchild / Run to the hills / Number of the beast / Flight of Icarus / Prowler / 2 minutes to midnight / Aces high / Running free with madness / Evil that men do / Clairvoyant / Infinite dreams (live) / Holy smoke.
VHS . . . . MVN 991 246 3
PMI / Oct '90 / EMI / Gold & Sons / TBD.

FLIGHT OF ICARUS.
Tracks: Flight of Icarus / I've got the fire.
■ 7" . . . . EMI 5378
EMI / May '82.

FLIGHT OF ICARUS/THE TROOPER.
Tracks: Flight of Icarus / I've got the fire / Trooper / Cross-eyed Mary / Listen with Nicko part V.
■ CD Single . . . . .CDIRN 5
■ 12" . . . . IRN 5
EMI / Mar '90.

FROM HERE TO ETERNITY.
Tracks: From here to eternity / Roll over Vic Vella (Not on 7" picture disc.) / Public enema number one (Only on CD single) / No prayer for the dying (Only on CD single) / I can't see my feeling (Only on 7" picture disc.).
■ 12" 12EMP 240
■ 7" . . . . EMS 240
■ 7" P.Disc . . . . .EMPD 240
■ CD Single . . . . .CDEM 240
EMI / Jun '92.

FROM HERE TO ETERNITY.
Tracks: Woman in uniform / Wrathchild / Run to the hills / Number of the beast / Flight of Icarus / Prowler / Two minutes to midnight / Aces high / Running free / Wasted years / Stanger in a strange land / Can I play with madness.
VCD . . . . PMCD 4912842
PMI / Jul '94 / EMI / Gold & Sons / TBD.

HALLOWED BE THY NAME.
Tracks: Hallowed be thy name.
■ 12" 12EMPD 288
■ 7" . . . . EMP 288
■ CD Single . . . . .CDEM 288
EMI / Nov '93.

HOLY SMOKE.
Tracks: Holy smoke / All in your mind / Kill me ce soir (Not on 7" or cassingle.).
■ 12" 12EMP 153
■ 12" P.Disc. 12EMPD 153
■ 7" . . . . EM 153
■ CD Single . . . . .CDEM 153

■ MC Single. . . . . .TCEM 153
EMI / Sep '90.

INFINITE DREAMS.
Tracks: Infinite dreams (live) / Killers (live) / Still life (live) (12", Special & CD single only.).
■ 12". 12EMPX 117
■ 12". 12EM 117
■ 7". EMS 117
■ 7". EM 117
■ 7" P.Disc . . . . .EMPD 117
■ CD Single . . . . .CDEM 117
■ MC Single. . . . . .TCEM 117
EMI / Nov '89.

IRON MAIDEN.
Tracks: Prowler / Remember tomorrow / Running free / Phantom of the opera / Transylvania / Strange world / Charlotte the harlot / Iron Maiden.
■ LP . . . . EMC 3330
EMI / Apr '80.
■ LP . . . . FA 3121
■ MC. . . . . FA 41 3121 4
Fame / May '85.
■ CD . . . . CDFA 3121
Fame / Oct '87.
CD . . . . CDEMS 1538
EMI / Jul '94 / EMI.

IRON MAIDEN (Monsters of rock special).
Tracks: Not Advised.
VHS . . . . MHV 4910213
PMI / Aug '92 / EMI / Gold & Sons / TBD.

IRON MAIDEN EP.
Tracks: Running free / Remember tomorrow / Killers / Innocent exile.
■ 12". 12EMI 5219
EMI / Aug '81.

IRON MAIDEN: INTERVIEW PICTURE DISC.
Tracks: Not Advised.
LP P.Disc . . . . BAK 2037
Baktabak / May '87 / Arabesque Ltd.

KILLERS.
Tracks: Ides of March / Wrathchild / Murders in the Rue Morgue / Another life / Genghis Khan / Innocent exile / Killers / Prodigal son / Purgatory / Drifter.
■ LP . . . . EMC 3357
EMI / Feb '81.
■ LP . . . . FA 3122
MC. TCFA 3122
Fame / May '85 / EMI.
■ CD . . . . CDFA 3122
Fame / Oct '87.
CD . . . . CDEMS 1536
EMI / Jul '94 / EMI.

LIVE AFTER DEATH (World Slavery Tour).
Tracks: Aces high / Two minutes to midnight / Trooper / Revelations / Flight of Icarus / Rime of the ancient mariner / Powerslave / Number of the beast / Hallowed be thy name / Iron Maiden / Run to the hills / Running free / Wrathchild / Twenty two Acacia Avenue / Children of the damned / Die with your boots on / Phantom of the opera.
■ Double LP. . . . . RIP 1
■ Double LP. . . . . ATAK 99
■ MC Set . . . . TCATAK 99
■ MC Set . . . . TC RIP 1
EMI / Oct '85.
■ CD . . . . CZ 123
EMI / Jan '86.
CD . . . . CZ 250
■ Double LP. . . . . ATAK 141
■ MC Set . . . . TCATAK 141
EMI / '89.
■ CD . . . . CDFA 3248
■ Double LP. . . . . FAD 3248
■ MC Set . . . . TCFAD 3248
Fame / Jun '91.
CD . . . . CDEMS 1535
MC. TCEMS 1535
EMI / Jul '94 / EMI.

LIVE AFTER DEATH.
Tracks: Aces high / Two minutes to midnight / Trooper / Revelations / Flight of Icarus / Rime of the ancient mariner / Powerslave / Number of the beast / Hallowed be thy name / Iron Maiden / Run to the hills / Running free / Sanctuary.
VHS . . . . MVP 99 1094 2
■ VHS . . . . MVN 99 1094 2
PMI / Jun '86.
■ CD Video 080 508 1
Polygram Music Video / '88.

VHS .MC 2139
Video Collection / Sep '94 / Gold & Sons / Video Collection / TBD.

LIVE AT DONINGTON 1992.
Tracks: Be quick or be dead / Number of the beast / Wrathchild / From here to eternity / Can I play with madness / Wasting love / Tailgunner / Evil that men do / Afraid to shoot strangers / Fear of the dark / Bring your daughter to the slaughter / Clairvoyant / Heaven can wait / Run to the hills / 2 minutes to midnight / Iron Maiden / Hallowed be thy name / Trooper / Sanctuary / Running free.
■ CD . . . . CDDON 1
■ LP .DON 1
■ MC. . . . . TCDON 1
EMI / Nov '93.

LIVE AT THE RAINBOW.
Tracks: Wrathchild / Killers / Remember tomorrow / Transylvania / Phantom of the opera / Iron Maiden.
■ VHS . . . . MVR 99 1022 2
■ VHS . . . . MVR 99 0018 2
PMI / Oct '84.

MAIDEN ENGLAND.
Tracks: Moonchild / Evil that men do / Prisoner / Still life / Die with your boots on / Infinite dreams / Killers / Can I play with madness / Heaven can wait / Wasted years / Clairvoyant / Seventh son of a seventh son / Number of the beast / Hallowed be thy name / Iron Maiden.
■ VHS . . . . MVP 99 1195 3
PMI / Nov '89.
■ VHS . . . . MVN 99 1195 3
PMI / Jun '90.

MAIDEN ENGLAND (CD & Video Double Pack).
Tracks: Moonchild / Evil That Men Do / Prisoner / Still Life / Die With Your Boots On / Infinite Dreams / Killers / Can I Play With Madness (Video only) / Heaven Can Wait / Wasted Years / Clairvoyant / Seventh Son Of A Seventh Son / Number Of The Beast / Hallowed Be Thy Name (Video only) / Iron Maiden.
VHS . . . . SAV 4913103
PMI / Jul '94 / EMI / Gold & Sons / TBD.

MAIDEN JAPAN.
Tracks: Maiden Japan / Running free / Remember tomorrow / Killers / Innocent exile.
■ 12". . . . . EMI 125219
■ 7". . . . . EMI 5219
EMI / Sep '81.

NO PRAYER FOR THE DYING.
Tracks: Tailgunner / Holy smoke / No prayer for the dying / Public enema number one / Fates warning / Assassin / Run silent run deep / Hooks in you / Bring your daughter..to the slaughter / Mother Russia.
CD. . . . . CDEMD 1017
MC. . . . . TCEMD 1017
■ LP . . . . EMD 1017
EMI / Oct '90.
■ LP P.Disc . . . . EMDPD 1017
EMI / Oct '90.
CD . . . . CDEMS 1541
EMI / Jul '94 / EMI.

NUMBER OF THE BEAST.
Tracks: Invaders / Children of the damned / Prisoner / 22, Acacia Avenue / Number of the beast / Run to the hills / Gangland / Hallowed be thy name.
■ MC. . . . . TCEMC 3400
EMI / '82.
■ LP . . . . EMC 3400
EMI / Mar '82.
■ LP . . . . FA 3178
■ MC. . . . . TCFA 3178
Fame / May '87.
■ CD . . . . CDFA 3178
Fame / Apr '88.
CD . . . . CDEMS 1533
MC. . . . . TCEMS 1533
EMI / Jul '94 / EMI.

NUMBER OF THE BEAST.
Tracks: Number of the beast / Remember tomorrow.
■ 7". . . . . EMI 5287
EMI / May '82.

PIECE OF MIND.
Tracks: Where eagles dare, Theme from / Revelations / Flight of Icarus / Die with your boots on / Trooper / Still life / Quest for fire / Sun and steel / To tame a land.

■ LP . . . . ATAK 97
■ MC. . . . . TCEMA 800
■ LP . . . . EMA 800
EMI / May '83.
■ CD . . . . CZ 82
EMI / Dec '86.
CD . . . . CZ 248
■ LP . . . . ATAK 139
MC. . . . . TCATAK 139
EMI / '89 / EMI.
■ LP . . . . FA 3245
■ CD . . . . CDFA 3245
■ MC. . . . . TCFA 3245
Fame / Jun '91.
CD . . . . CDEMS 1540
MC. . . . . TCEMS 1540
EMI / Jul '94 / EMI.

PLAYING WITH MADNESS.
Tracks: Not Advised.
CD P.Disc . . . . CBAK 4035
Baktabak / Jan '92 / Arabesque Ltd.

POWERSLAVE.
Tracks: Aces high / 2 Minutes to midnight / Losfer words (big 'Orra) / Flash of the blade / Duellists / Black in the village / Powerslave / Rime of the ancient mariner.
■ LP P.Disc . . . . POWERP 1
■ LP . . . . POWER 1
■ MC. . . . . TC POWER 1
EMI / Sep '84.
■ CD . . . . CZ 81
EMI / Sep '84.
CD . . . . CZ 249
■ LP . . . . ATAK 140
MC. . . . . TCATAK 140
EMI / '89 / EMI.
■ LP . . . . FA 3244
■ CD . . . . CDFA 3244
■ MC. . . . . TCFA 3244
Fame / Jun '91.
CD . . . . CDEMS 1539
MC. . . . . TCEMS 1539
EMI / Jul '94 / EMI.

PURGATORY.
Tracks: Purgatory / Genghis Khan.
■ 7". . . . . EMI 5184
EMI / Jun '81.

PURGATORY/MAIDEN JAPAN.
Tracks: Purgatory / Genghis Khan / Running free / Remember tomorrow / Killers / Innocent exile / Listen with Nicko Part III.
■ CD Single. . . . . .CDIRN 3
■ 12". IRN 3
EMI / Feb '90.

RAISING HELL.
Tracks: Be quick or be dead / Trooper / Evil that men do / Clairvoyant / Hallowed be thy name / Wrathchild / From here to eternity / Fear of the dark / Transylvania / Number of the beast / Bring your daughter to the slaughter / Two minutes to midnight / Afraid to shoot strangers / Heaven can wait / Sanctuary / Run to the hills / Iron Maiden.
VHS . . . . MVN 4912643
PMI / May '94 / EMI / Gold & Sons / TBD.

REAL DEAD ONE, A.
Tracks: Number of the beast / Trooper / Prowler / Transylvania / Remember tomorrow / Where eagles dare / Sanctuary / Running free / 2 minutes to midnight / Iron maiden / Hallowed be thy name.
CD. . . . . CDEMD 1048
LP . . . . EMD 1048
MC. . . . . TCEMD 1048
EMI / Oct '93 / EMI.

REAL LIVE ONE, A.
Tracks: Be quick or be dead / From here to eternity / Can I play with madness / Wasting love / Tailgunner / Evil that men do / Afraid to shoot strangers / Bring your daughter..to the slaughter / Heaven can wait / Clairvoyant / Fear of the dark.
CD. . . . . CDEMD 1042
LP . . . . EMD 1042
MC. . . . . TCEMD 1042
EMI / Mar '93 / EMI.

RUN TO THE HILLS.
Tracks: Run to the hills / Total eclipse.
■ 7" P.Disc . . . . EMIP 5263
■ 7". . . . . EMI 5263
EMI / Jan '82.

RUN TO THE HILLS (LIVE).
Tracks: Run to the hills (live) / Phantom of the opera.
■ 7". . . . . EMI 5542
■ 12" P.Disc. 12EMIP 5542
■ 12". 12EMI 5542
EMI / Dec '85.

RUN TO THE HILLS/THE NUMBER OF THE BEAST.
Tracks: Run to the hills / Total eclipse / Number of the beast / Remember tomorrow (live) / Listen with Nicko Part IV.
- 12" . . . . IRN 4
- CD Single . . . . .CDIRN 4
EMI / Mar '90.

RUNNING FREE.
Tracks: Running free / Burning ambition.
- 7" . . . . EMI 5032
EMI / Feb '80.

RUNNING FREE (LIVE).
Tracks: Running free (live) / Sanctuary.
- 12" 12EMI 5532
- 7" . . . . EMI 5532
EMI / Sep '85.

RUNNING FREE/RUN TO THE HILLS.
Tracks: Running free / Sanctuary / Murders in the Rue Morgue / Run to the hills / Phantom of the opera / Losfer words (big 'orra) / Listen with Nicko (part VII).
CD . . . . .CDIRN 7
- 12" . . . . IRN 7
EMI / Mar '90.

RUNNING FREE/SANCTUARY.
Tracks: Running free / Burning ambition / Sanctuary / Drifter / I've got the fire / Listen with Nicko Part I.
- 12" . . . . IRN 1
- CD Single . . . . .CDIRN 1
EMI / Feb '90.

SANCTUARY.
Tracks: Sanctuary / Drifter.
- 7" . . . . EMI 5065
EMI / Jun '80.

SEVENTH SON OF A SEVENTH SON.
Tracks: Moonchild / Infinite dreams / Can I play with madness / Evil that men do / Seventh son of a seventh son / Prophecy / Clairvoyant / Only the good die young.
- CD . . . . CDEMD 1006
- LP . . . . EMD 1006
- MC. . . . . TCEMD 1006
EMI / Apr '88.
- LP P.Disc . . . . EMDP 1006
EMI / Apr '88.
- LP . . . . .ATAK 143
MC. TCATAK 143
EMI / '89 / EMI.
- LP . . . . FA 3247
- MC. TCFA 3247
Fame / Jun '91.
- CD . . . . CZ 252
EMI / Jun '91.
CD . . . . CDEMS 1534
MC. TCEMS 1534
EMI / Jul '94 / EMI.

SOMEWHERE IN TIME.
Tracks: Caught somewhere in time / Wasted years / Sea of madness / Heaven can wait / Loneliness of

---

the long distance runner / Stranger in a strange land / Deja-vu / Alexander the great.
- LP . . . . ZONE 1
- MC . . . . TC ZONE 1
EMI / Jul '86.
- CD . . . . CZ 120
- LP . . . . EMC 3512
- MC. . . . . TCEMC 3512
EMI / Sep '86.
CD. . . . . CZ 251
- LP . . . . ATAK 142
MC. TCATAK 142
EMI / '89 / EMI.
CD . . . . CDFA 3246
- LP . . . . FA 3246
- MC. TCFA 3246
Fame / Jun '91.
CD . . . . CDEMS 1537
MC. TCEMS 1537
EMI / Jul '94 / EMI.

STRANGER IN A STRANGE LAND.
Tracks: Stranger in a strange land / That girl / Juanita.
- 7" . . . . EMI 5589
- 12" P.Disc 12EMIP 5589
EMI / Nov '86.

TROOPER, THE.
Tracks: Trooper / Cross-eyed Mary.
- 7" . . . . EMI 5397
- 7" P.Disc . . . . EMIP 5397
EMI / Jun '83.

TWELVE WASTED YEARS.
Tracks: Stranger in a strange land / Charlotte the harlot / Drifter / Prowler / Phantom of the opera / Running free / Women in uniform / She's a roller / Murders in the Rue Morgue / Number of the beast / Total eclipse / Iron Maiden / Sanctuary / Prisoner / Caught somewhere in time / Run to the hills / 22 Acacia Avenue / Wasted years / Trooper.
VHS . . . . MVN 99 1152 2
PMI / Nov '87 / EMI / Gold & Sons / TBD.

TWILIGHT ZONE.
Tracks: Twilight zone / Wrathchild.
- 12" 12EMI 5145
- 7" . . . . EMI 5145
EMI / Mar '81.

TWO MINUTES TO MIDNIGHT/ACES HIGH.
Tracks: Two minutes to midnight / Rainbow's gold / Mission from 'Arry / Aces high / King of twilight / Number of the beast (live) / Listen with Nicko part VI.
- 12" . . . . IRN 6
- CD . . . . .CDIRN 6
EMI / Mar '90.

VIDEO PIECES (Video EP).
Tracks: Run to the hills / Number of the beast / Flight of Icarus / Trooper.
- VHS . . . . MVS 99 0002 2
PMI / Jul '83.

WASTED YEARS.
Tracks: Wasted years / Reach out / Sheriff of Huddersfield (Extra track available on 12" version only.).
- 7" P.Disc . . . . EMIP 5583
- 7" . . . . EMI 5583
- 12" 12EMI 5583
EMI / Aug '86.

WASTED YEARS/STRANGER IN A STRANGE LAND.
Tracks: Wasted years / Reach out / Sheriff of Huddersfield / Stranger in a strange land / That girl / Juanita / Listen with Nicko (part VIII).
- CD Single . . . . .CDIRN 8
- 12" . . . . IRN 8
EMI / Mar '90.

WOMEN IN UNIFORM.
Tracks: Women in uniform / Invasion / Phantom of the opera (Only on 12" single.).
- 12" 12EMI 5105
- 7" . . . . EMI 5105
EMI / Oct '80.

WOMEN IN UNIFORM/TWILIGHT ZONE.
Tracks: Women in uniform / Invasion / Phantom of the opera / Twilight zone / Wrathchild / Listen with Nicko Part II.
- CD Single . . . . .CDIRN 2
- 12" . . . . IRN 2
EMI / Feb '90.

Iron Man

BLACK NIGHT.
Tracks: Not Advised.
CD. . . . . HELL 022
Hellhound / Jul '93 / Plastic Head.

Isengard

VINTERSKUGGE.
Tracks: Vinterskugge / Gjennom skoggen til blaafjellene ut i vannets dyp hvor morke / Dommedagssalme / In the halls and chambers of stardust the crystallic heavens / Fanden lokker til stupet (nytrad) / Naglfar / Thy gruesome death / Death cult / Rise from below / Dark lord of Gorgoroth / Trollwandering (ojtro) / Fog / Storm of evil / Bergtrollets gravferd / Our Lord will come.
CD . . . . DEAF 016CD
Deaf / Mar '94 / Vital Distribution.

It's Alive

MATAPOLIS.
Tracks: It's alive.
- 12" . . . . 12 ATV 103
- 7" . . . . ATV 103
- CD Single . . . . CDSTV 103
Active / Dec '92.

J

Jackyl

JACKYL.
Tracks: I stand alone / Dirty little mind / Down on me / When will it rain / Redneck punk / Lumberjack / Reach for me / Back off brother / Brain drain / Just like a devil / She loves my cock.
CD . . . . GED 24489
MC . . . . GEC 24489
■ LP . . . . GEF 24489
Geffen / Nov '92.

PUSH COME TO SHOVE.
Tracks: Push come to shove.
■ 12" . . . . GFSTP 76
■ CD Single . . . . GFSTD 76
Geffen / Jul '94.

PUSH COMES TO SHOVE.
Tracks: Not Advised.
CD . . . . GED 24710
MC . . . . GEC 24710
Geffen / Aug '94 / BMG.

Jacob's Mouse

DOT (EP), THE.
Tracks: Sign / Enterprise / Hey dip sugar / Ho-hum / Microflesh.
12" . . . . LIVES 001
Liverish / Oct '94 / SRD.

FANDANGO WIDEWHEELS.
Tracks: Fandango widewheels / B12 marmite / 3 pound apathy / Keen apple.
7" . . . . WIJ 032V
CD Single . . . . WIJ 032CD
Wiiija / Mar '94 / Vital Distribution.

GOOD.
Tracks: Good / Dusty / Lip and cheek.
■ 7" . . . . WIJ 026V
■ CD Single . . . . WIJ 026CD
Wiiija / Oct '93.

GROUP OF SEVEN.
Tracks: Group of 7 / Palace / Sag bag.
■ 7" . . . . WIJ 027V
■ CD Single . . . . WIJ 027CD
Wiiija / Nov '93.

I'M SCARED.
Tracks: Kettle / Deep cavass lake / This room / Zig zag / Solo / Coalmine dog / Thin sound / Ash tray / Body shop / Box hole / Colum.
CD . . . . WIJ 021CD
LP . . . . WIJ 021V
Wiiija / Apr '93 / Vital Distribution.
MC. 31058-4
Wiiija / Jan '94 / Vital Distribution.

NO FISH SHOP PARKING.
Tracks: Tumbleswan / Twist / She is dead / Place to go / Carfish / Caphony / Justice / Vase.
CD . . . . BLIT 001CD
LP . . . . BLIT 001
Blithering Idiot / Oct '94 / SRD.

TON UP EP.
Tracks: Not Advised.
■ 12" . . . . WIJ 015V
■ CD Single . . . . WIJ 015CD
Wiiija / Aug '92.

WRYLY SMILERS.
Tracks: Good / Dusty / Group of seven / Palace / Sag bag / Fandango widewheels / B12 Marmites / 3 Pound apathy / Keen apple / Lip & cheek.
CD . . . . JCOB 001CD
LP . . . . JCOB 001V
Wiiija / Oct '94 / Vital Distribution.

Jade

IF YOU'RE MAN ENOUGH.
Tracks: Not Advised.
■ LP . . . . RR 9755
Road Runner / Nov '85.

Jaded Angel

CRAZY WORLD.
Tracks: Crazy world / Red light killer / Smokin' in the boys room.
■ MC Single. . . . . JADE 001
Jaded Angel / Jun '90.

ROCK ON.
Tracks: Rock on / Under fire.
■ MC Single. . . . . JADE 002
Jaded Angel / Mar '90.

Jag Panzer

AMPLE DESTRUCTION.
Tracks: Licensed to kill / Warfare / Symphony of terror / Harder than steel / Generally hostile / Watching / Reign of tyrants / Cardiac arrest / Crucifix.
■ LP . . . . IW 1001
Iron Works (USA) / Jul '85.
CD . . . . PRD 70062
Barricade / Dec '90 / Pinnacle.

JEFFEREY.
Tracks: Jefferey.
CD Single . . . . SPV 050-62303CDS
Rising Sun / Aug '94 / Plastic Head.

Jagged Edge

FUEL FOR YOUR SOUL.
Tracks: Liar / You don't love me / Smooth operator / Fuel for your soul / Loving you too long / Money talking / Out in the gold / Hell ain't a long way / Sweet Lorraine / Law of the land / Burning up / All through the night.
CD 847 108-2
■ LP 847 108-1
■ LP 847 201-1
■ MC. 847 108-4
Polydor / Sep '90.

HELL AIN'T A LONG WAY.
Tracks: Hell ain't a long way.
■ 12" . . . . PZ 132
■ 7" . . . . PO 132
■ CD Single . . . . PZCD 132
■ MC Single . . . . POCS 132
Polydor / Mar '91.

OUT IN THE COLD.
Tracks: Out in the cold.
■ 12" . . . . PZ 105
■ 7" . . . . PO 105
■ 7" P.Disc . . . . POP 105
■ CD Single . . . . PZCD 105
■ MC Single . . . . POCS 105
Polydor / Oct '90.

TROUBLE.
Tracks: Trouble / You don't love me / Wolf / Rosie Rosie / Crash and burn / Good golly Miss Molly.
MC. 841 983-4
■ Mini LP 841 983-1
■ CD 841 983-2
Polydor / Feb '90.

YOU DON'T LOVE ME.
Tracks: You don't love me.
■ 12" . . . . PZ 97
■ 12" P.Disc . . . . PZP 97
■ 7" . . . . PO 97
■ CD Single . . . . PZCDG 97
■ MC Single . . . . POCS 97
Polydor / Sep '90.

Jaguar

AXE CRAZY.
Tracks: Axe crazy / War machine.
■ 7" . . . . NEAT 16
Neat / Aug '82.

BACK STREET WOMAN.
Tracks: Backstreet woman / Chasing the dragon.
■ 7" . . . . HEAVY 10
Heavy Metal / Nov '81.

POWER GAMES.
Tracks: Dutch connection / Out of luck / Fox / Master game / No lies / Run for your life / Prisoner / Ain't no fantasy / Raw deal / Cold heart.
■ LP . . . . NEAT 1007
Neat / Jan '85.

THIS TIME.
Tracks: Not Advised.
■ LP . . . . RR 9851
Road Runner / Jul '84.

Jane's Addiction

The brainchild of singer Perry Farrell, who combined performance art, androgyny and rock in a truly unique band. His band's eponymous debut was intriguing, not least for its Doors-like approach, but it was the second album, *Nothing's Shocking*, which lit the blue touch paper; belying its title and warping the parameters of what metal could sound like. Controversy followed the band everywhere and stories of drugs and terminal illness seemed to be actively courted by Farrell at the time of the release of their final album *Ritual De Lo Habitual* in 1990. They split up in 1991 by design rather than accident and Farrell went on to launch the groundbreaking touring festival, Lollapalooza, and to front Porno For Pyros. Guitarist David Navarro, once tipped to replace Izzy Stradlin in Guns N' Roses, eventually joined The Red Hot Chili Peppers.

BEEN CAUGHT STEALING.
Tracks: Been caught stealing / Had a dad.
■ 12" . . . . W 0011T
■ CD Single . . . . W 0011CD
■ 12" . . . . W 0011TB
■ 7" . . . . W 0011
■ MC Single . . . . W 0011C
WEA / Mar '91.

CLASSIC GIRL.
Tracks: Classic girl.
■ 12" . . . . W 0031T
■ MC Single . . . . W 0031C
■ 7" . . . . W 0031
■ CD Single . . . . W 0031CD
WEA / Jun '91.

GIFT, THE.
Tracks: Not Advised.
VHS 7599381853
WEA / Jul '93 / WEA.

JANE'S ADDICTION.
Tracks: Trip away / Rock 'n' roll / I would for you / Jane says / Pigs in zen / My time / Whores / Sympathy / Chip away / 1%.
■ LP XXX1004
Triple XXX (USA) / Aug '87.
■ LP 510041
Triple XXX (USA) / Dec '88.
CD 7599265992
Triple XXX (USA) / Apr '91 / Pinnacle.
■ LP 7599265991
MC. 7599265994
WEA / May '91 / WEA.

NOTHING'S SHOCKING.
Tracks: Up the beach / Had a dad / Standing in the shower / Jane Says / Thank you boys / Mountain song / Summertime rolls / Ted, just admit it.
■ LP 925727 1
■ MC. 925727 4
WEA / Sep '88.
CD K925727-2
LP . . . . WX 216
MC. . . . . WX 216C
WEA / Mar '94 / WEA.

RITUAL DE LO HABITUAL.
Tracks: Stop / No one's leaving / Ain't no right / Obvious / Been caught stealing / Three days / Then she did / Of course / Classic girl.
CD 7599259932
■ LP . . . . WX 306
MC. . . . . WX 306 C
WEA / Sep '90 / WEA.

SHOCKING EP : MOUNTAIN SONG.
Tracks: Mountain song / Jane says / Had a dad (live).
■ 12" . . . . . W 7520 T
WEA / May '89.

THREE DAYS (PART 1).
Tracks: Three days (part 1).
■ 12" . . . . . W 9584 T
■ 7" . . . . . W 9584
■ CD Single . . . . . W 9584 CD
■ MC Single . . . . . W 9584 C
WEA / Aug '90.

Jawbox

FOR YOUR OWN SPECIAL SWEETHEART.
Tracks: Not Advised.
CD . . . . . EFA 49322
LP . . . . . EFA 49321
City Slang / Mar '94 / RTM / Pinnacle.

GRIPPE.
Tracks: Not Advised.
CD . . . . . DIS 52CD
LP . . . . . DIS 52V
MC . . . . . DIS 52C
Dischord / May '94 / SRD.

JACKPOT PILS.
Tracks: Jackpot pils.
■ 7" . . . . . DIS 77V
Dischord / Feb '93.

NOVELTY.
Tracks: Not Advised.
CD . . . . . DIS 69CD
LP . . . . . DIS 69V
MC . . . . . DIS 69C
Dischord / May '94 / SRD.

Jawbreaker

24 HOUR REVENGE THERAPY.
Tracks: Boat dreams from the hill / Indictment / Boxcar / Outpatient / Ashtray monument / Condition Oakland / Ache / Do you still hate me / West bay invitational / Jinx removing / In saddling around.
CD . . . . . TUP 049-2
LP . . . . . TUP 049-1
MC . . . . . TUP 049-4
Tupelo / Feb '94 / Vital Distribution.

BIVOUAC.
Tracks: Not Advised.
CD . . . . . TUP 382
LP . . . . . TUP 381
MC . . . . . TUP 384
Tupelo / Nov '92 / Vital Distribution.

CHESTERFIELD KINGS.
Tracks: Not Advised.
Mini LP . . . . . TUPLP 0351
Tupelo / May '92 / Vital Distribution.

Jellyfish

San Francisco pop rockers with neat line in '70s revivalism. Four UK chart singles and no. 21 placing for second album *Spilt Milk* (1993) demonstrated small but enthusiastic market for ELO pastiches performed by renegades from the Kiss Army.

BABY'S COMING BACK.
Tracks: Baby's coming back / All I want is everything (live).
■ 12" . . . . . CUST 2
■ MC Single . . . . . CUSC 2
■ 7" . . . . . CUSS 2
■ CD Single . . . . . CUSCD 2
Charisma / Apr '91.

BELLYBUTTON.
Tracks: Man I used to be / That is why / King is half undressed / I wanna stay home / She still loves him / All I want is everything / Now she knows she's wrong / Bed spring kiss / Baby coming back / Calling Sarah.
■ LP . . . . . CUSLP 3
MC . . . . . CUSMC 3
■ CD . . . . . CDCUS 3
Charisma / May '91.
CD . . . . . CDCUX 3
Charisma / Feb '92 / EMI.

GHOST AT NUMBER ONE, THE.
Tracks: Ghost at number one.
■ 7" CUSS10
■ CD Single CUSDG10
■ MC Single CUSC10
Charisma / Jan '93.

I WANNA STAY HOME.
Tracks: I wanna stay home.
■ 12" . . . . . CUSA 4
■ 7" . . . . . CUSS 4
■ MC Single . . . . . CUSC 4
Charisma / Nov '91.

KING IS HALF UNDRESSED, THE.
Tracks: King is half undressed / Calling Sarah.
■ CD Single . . . . . CUSX 1
■ 12" . . . . . CUST 1
■ 7" . . . . . CUSS 1
■ MC Single . . . . . CUSC 1
■ CD Single . . . . . CUSCD 1
Charisma / Jan '91.

NEW MISTAKE.
Tracks: New mistake / He's my best friend (Not available on CDS 1) / All is forgiven (Available on CD 2 only) / Russian hill (Available on CD 2 only) / Sebrina, paste and plato (Available on CD 1 only) / Man I used to be (Available on CD 1 only) / Bed-spring kiss (Available on CD 1 only).
■ 7" . . . . . CUSS 11
■ CD Single . . . . . CUSCD 11
■ CD Single . . . . . CUSDG 11
■ MC Single . . . . . CUSC 11
Charisma / Jul '93.

SCARY-GO-ROUND.
Tracks: Scary-go-round.
■ 12" . . . . . CUST 3
■ MC Single . . . . . CUSC 3
■ 7" . . . . . CUSS 3
Charisma / Aug '91.

SPILT MILK.
Tracks: Joining a fan club / Sebrina, Paste & Plato / New mistake / Glutton of sympathy / Ghost at number one / Bye, bye, bye / All is forgiven / Russian hill / He's my best friend / Too much, too little, too late / Brighter day.
CD . . . . . CDCUS 20
LP . . . . . CUSLP 20
MC . . . . . CUSMC 20
Charisma / May '93 / EMI.

Jesus Lizard

Alternative outfit best-known for patronage of Nirvana, with whom they shared double A-sided single in 1992. Band have been around since 1989, although commercial success has been hindered by cacophonous material and appalling name.

CHROME.
Tracks: Chrome.
■ 7" . . . . . TGLP 53
Touch & Go / Feb '90.

FLY ON THE WALL.
Tracks: Fly on the wall.
7" . . . . . TG 128
CD Single . . . . . TG 128CD
Touch & Go / Jan '94 / SRD.

GOAT.
Tracks: Not Advised.
CD . . . . . TG 68CD
LP . . . . . TGLP 68
MC . . . . . TG 68C
Touch & Go / Feb '91 / SRD.

HEAD.
Tracks: Not Advised.
LP . . . . . TGLP 54
Touch & Go / Jun '90 / SRD.
CD . . . . . TGCD 54
Touch & Go / Jul '93 / SRD.

LIAR.
Tracks: Not Advised.
CD . . . . . TGLP 100CD
LP . . . . . TGLP 100
MC . . . . . TGLP 100C
Touch & Go / Oct '92 / SRD.

PURE.
Tracks: Not Advised.
LP . . . . . TG 30
Touch & Go / Jul '93 / SRD.

Jet Red

JET RED.
Tracks: Not Advised.
CD . . . . . CDMFN 94
■ LP . . . . . MFN 94
Music For Nations / Aug '89.

Jethro Tull

Classic rock band who command fanatical following, not least among members of Anthrax and Iron Maiden; latter covered band's *Cross Eyed Mary* and emulated Tull-style wholesale on *Seventh Son of a Seventh Son* album. With over 20 chart albums to their credit - of which 1971's *Aqualung* is most-renowned - Tull can afford to ignore critical jibes and wrath that descended on them when they beat Metallica to Best Hard Rock Act title in 1989 Grammy ceremony.

20 YEARS OF JETHRO TULL.
Tracks: Stormy Monday blues / Love story / New day yesterday / Summerday sands / Coronach / March the mad scientist / Pibroch (pee break) / Black satin (instrumental) / Lick your fingers clean / Overhand / Crossword / Saturation / Jack-a-Lynn / Motoreyes / Part of the machine / Mayhem / Maybe / Kelpie / Under wraps 2 / Wond'ring aloud / Dun ringill / Life's a long song / Nursie grace / Witch's promise / Teacher / Living in the past / Aqualung / Locomotive breath.
CD . . . . . CCD 1655
■ LP . . . . . CJT 7
■ MC . . . . . ZCJT 7
Chrysalis / '91.

20TH ANNIVERSAY (BOX SET).
Tracks: Song for Jeffrey / Love story / Fat man / Bouree / Stormy Monday blues / New day yesterday / Cold wind to Valhalla / Minstrel in the gallery / Velvet green / Grace / Clasp / Pibroch (pee-break/ black satin dancer) / Fallen on hard times / Jack frost and the hooded crow / I'm your gun / Down at the end of your road / Coronach / Summerday sands / Too many too / March the mad scientist / Pan dance / Strip cartoon / King Henry's madrigal / Sitch in time / 17 / One for John Gee / Aeroplane / Sunshine day / Lick your fingers clean / Chateau D'Isaster / Saturation / Jack-a-lynn / Motoreyes / Blues (instrumetal) (untitled) / Rhythm in gold / Part of the machine / Mayhem / Maybe / Overhang / Kelpie / Living in these hard times / Under wraps 2 / Only solitaire / Cheap day return / Wond'ring aloud / Dun ringill / Salamander / Moths / Nursie / Life's a long song / One white duck / Nothing at all / Songs from the wood / Living in the past / Teacher / Aqualung / Locomotive breath / Witch's promise / Bungle in the jungle / Farm on the freeway / Thick as a brick / Sweet dream.
■ CD Set . . . . . TBOXCD 1
Chrysalis / Aug '88.
■ Double LP . . . . . TBOX 1
■ MC Set . . . . . ZTBOX 1
Chrysalis / '91.

25 YEARS OF JETHRO TULL.
Tracks: Teacher / Witch's promise / Story of the hare who losts his spectacles / Aqualung / Kissing Willie / Rocks on the road / Living in the past / Nothing is easy / Minstrel in the gallery / Thick as a brick / Songs from the wood / Too old to rock 'n' roll: Too young to die / My God / New day yesterday.
VHS . . . . . MVP 4911263
PMI / Jun '94 / EMI / Gold & Sons / TBD.

25TH ANNIVERSARY BOX SET.
Tracks: My Sunday feeling (mix) / Song for Jeffrey remix / Living in the past remix / Teacher remix / Sweet dreams (mix) / Cross-eyed Mary remix / Witch's promise, The remix / Life is a long song remix / Bungle in the jungle remix / Minstrel in the gallery (mix) / Cold wind to Valhalla remix / Too old to rock 'n' roll remix / Too young to die remix / Songs from the wood remix / Heavy horses remix / Black Sunday remix / Broadsword remix / Nothing is easy / My God / With you there to help me / Song for Jeffrey / To cry you a song / Sossity, you're a woman / Reasons for waiting / We used to know / Guitar solo / For a thousand mothers / So much trouble / My Sunday feeling / Someday the sun won't shine for you / Living in the past / Bouree / With you there to help me (2) / Thick as a brick / Cheerio / New day yesterday / Protect and survive / Jack-a-Lynn / Whistler / My God (2) / Aqualung / To be sad is a mad way to be (Live) / Back to the family (Live) / Passion play extract (Live) / Wind-up/Locomotive breath/Land of Hope and Glory/Wind-up / Seal driver (Live) / Nobody's car (Live) / Pussy-Willow (Live) / Budapest (Live) / Nothing is easy (Live) / Kissing Willie (Live) / Still loving you tonight (Live) / Beggar's farm' Passion Jig (Live) / Song for Jeffrey (Live) / Living in the past (Live).
CD . . . . . CDCHR 6004
Chrysalis / Apr '93 / EMI.

A.
Tracks: Crossfire / Flyingdale flyer / Working John, working Joe / Black Sunday / Protect and survive / Batteries not included / Uniform / 4 WD (low ratio) / Pine martin's jig / And further on / Bod.

J 2
■ DELETED

■ LP . . . . CHR 1301
■ LP . . . . CDL 1301
■ MC. . . . . ZCHR 1301
Chrysalis / Sep '80.
CD. . . . . CCD 1301
Chrysalis / Jan '89 / EMI.

ANOTHER CHRISTMAS SONG.
Tracks: Another Christmas song / Solstice bells / Jack Frost (Available on 12" format).
■ 12". . . . . CHS 123405
■ 7" . . . . CHS 3405
■ CD Single. . . . . TULLCD 5
Chrysalis / Nov '89.

AQUALUNG.
Tracks: Aqualung / Cross-eyed Mary / Cheap day return / Mother goose / Wond'ring aloud / Up to me / My God / Hymn 43 / Slipstream / Locomotive / Breath / Wind up.
■ LP . . . . ILPS 9145
Island / Apr '71.
■ LP . . . . CHR 1044
■ MC. . . . . ZCHR 1044
Chrysalis / '74.
CD. . . . . CCD 1044
Chrysalis / Jan '91 / EMI.
MiniDisc. 321044-3
Chrysalis / Feb '93 / EMI.
DCC 3210445
Chrysalis / Jan '93 / EMI.
CD. CD25CR 08
Chrysalis / Mar '94 / EMI.

BENEFIT.
Tracks: With you there to help me / Nothing to say / Alive and well and living in / Son for Michael Collins / Jeffrey and me / To cry you a song / Time for everything / Inside / Play in time / Sossity / You're a woman.
■ LP . . . . ILPS 9123
Island / May '70.
■ LP . . . . CHR 1043
MC. . . . . ZCHR 1043
Chrysalis / Jan '74 / EMI.
CD. . . . . CPCD 1043
Chrysalis / Jun '87 / EMI.

BEST OF THE ANNIVERSARY COLLECTION, THE.
Tracks: Song of Jeffrey / Beggars farm / Christmas song / New day yesterday / Bouree / Nothing is easy / Living in the past / To cry you a song / Teacher / Sweet dream / Cross-eyed Mary / Mother goose / Aqualung / Locomotive breath / Life is a long song / Thick as a brick (Extract) / Passion play / Skating away on the thin ice of the new day / Bungle in the jungle / Minstrel in the gallery / Too old to rock and roll / Too young to die / Songs from the wood / Jack in the green / Whistler / Heavy horses / Dun ringill / Flyingdale flyer / Jack-a-Lynn / Pussy willow / Broadsword / Under wraps 11 / Steel monkey / Farm on the freeway / Jump start / Kissing Willie / This is not love.
CD. . . . . CDCHR 6001
MC. . . . . TCCHR 6001
Chrysalis / May '93 / EMI.

BROADSWORD.
Tracks: Broadsword / Fallen on hard times.
■ 7" . . . . CHS 2619
■ 7" P.Disc . . . . CHSP 2619
Chrysalis / May '82.

BROADSWORD AND THE BEAST, THE.
Tracks: Beastie / Clasp / Fallen on hard times / Flying colours / Slow marching / Broadsword / Pussy willow / Watching me watching you / Seal driver / Cheerio.
CD. . . . . CCD 1380
■ LP . . . . CDL 1380
MC. . . . . ZCDL 1380
Chrysalis / Apr '82 / EMI.

CATFISH RISING.
Tracks: This is not love / Occasional demons / Rocks on the road / Thinking round corners / Still loving you tonight / Doctor to my disease / Like a tall thin girl / Sparrow on the schoolyard wall / Roll yer own / Gold-tipped boots, black jacket and tie.
CD. . . . . CCD 1886
■ LP . . . . CHR 1886
MC. . . . . ZCHR 1886
Chrysalis / Sep '91 / EMI.

CORONACH.
Tracks: Coronach / Jack Frost.
■ 7" . . . . TULL 2
■ MC Single. . . . . ZTULL 2
Chrysalis / Jun '86.

CREST OF A KNAVE.
Tracks: Steel monkey / Farm on the freeway / Jump start / Said she was a dancer / Budapest / Mountain men / Raising steam / Waking edge (Extra on cassette and CD) / Dogs in the midwinter (Extra on cassette and CD).
CD. . . . . CCD 1590
■ LP . . . . CDL 1590
MC. . . . . ZCDL 1590
Chrysalis / Sep '87 / EMI.

HEAVY HORSES.
Tracks: And the mouse police never sleeps / Acres wild / No lullaby / Moths / Journey man / Rover / One brown mouse / Heavy horses / Weathercock.
MC. . . . . ZCHR 1175
■ LP . . . . CHR 1175
Chrysalis / Apr '78.
CD. . . . . CCD 1175
Chrysalis / '86 / EMI.

LAP OF LUXURY.
Tracks: Lap of luxury / Astronomy / Automotive engineering (on 12" only) / Tundra (on 12" only).
■ 12". . . . . TULLX 1
■ EP. . . . . TULL 1
Chrysalis / Sep '84.

LIFE IS A LONG SONG.
Tracks: Life is a long song / Up the pool.
■ 7" . . . . WIP 6106
Island / Sep '71.

LITTLE LIGHT MUSIC, A.
Tracks: Some day the sun won't shine for you / Living in the past / Life is a long song / Under wraps / Rocks on the road / Nursie / Too old to rock 'n' roll, too young to die / One white duck / New day yesterday / John Barleycorn / Look into the sun / Christmas song / From a dead beat to an old greaser / Bouree / Pussy willow.
CD. . . . . CCD 1954
■ Double LP. CHR19543219541
MC. . . . . ZCHR 1954
Chrysalis / Sep '92 / EMI.

LIVE - BURSTING OUT.
Tracks: No lullaby / Sweet dream / Skating away on the thin ice of the new day / Jack in the green / One brown mouse / New day yesterday / Flute solo improvisation / God rest ye merry gentlemen / Bouree / Thick as a brick / Hunting girl / Too old to rock 'n' roll, too young to die / Conundrum / Minstrel in the gallery / One-eyed Mary / Quatrain / Aqualung / Locomotive breath / Dambusters march.
■ Double LP. . . . . CJT 4
■ MC Set . . . . ZCJT 4
Chrysalis / Jan '78.

LIVE AT HAMMERSMITH 1984.
Tracks: Not Advised.
CD. . . . . FRSCD 004
MC. . . . . FRSMC 004
■ LP . . . . FRSLP 004
Raw Fruit / Dec '90.

LIVING IN THE PAST.
Tracks: Witches promise / Song for Jeffrey / Love story / Christmas song / Living in the past / Driving song / Bouree / Sweet dreams / Singing all day / Witches' promise / Inside / Just trying to be / By kind permission of you / Dharma for one / Wondering again / Locomotive breath / Life is a long song / Up the 'Pool / Dr. Bogenbroom / For later / Nursie.
■ Double LP. . . . . CJT 1
■ MC Set . . . . ZCJT 1
Chrysalis / Jan '74.
■ CD. . . . . CCD 1035
Chrysalis / Oct '87.
CD. . . . . CCD 1575
MC. . . . . ZCJTD 1
Chrysalis / Feb '94 / EMI.

LIVING IN THE PAST.
Tracks: Living in the past / Hard liner (Features on 7" only.) / Living in the (Slightly more recent past) (Live) (Features on CDSS 3970 only.) / Silver river turning (Features on CDSS 3970 only.) / Rosa on the factory floor (Features on CDSS 3970 only.) / I don't want to be me (Features on CDSs 3970 only) / Living in the past (mixes) (Features on 12" only.) / Truck stop runner (Features on CDCHS 3970 only.) / Man of principle (Features on CDCHS 3970 only.).
■ 12". 12CHS 3970
■ 7" . . . . CHS 3970
■ CD Single. . . . . CDCHSS 3970
■ CD Single. . . . . CDCHS 3970
Chrysalis / May '93.

LIVING IN THE PAST (OLD GOLD).
Tracks: Living in the past.
■ 7" . . . . OG 9673
Old Gold / Aug '87.

LIVING IN THE PAST (ORIGINAL).
Tracks: Living in the past.
■ 7" . . . . WIP 6056
Island / May '69.
■ 7" . . . . CHS 2081
Chrysalis / May '69.

LOVE STORY.
Tracks: Love story.
■ 7" . . . . WIP 6048
Island / Jan '69.

M.U. BEST OF.
Tracks: Teacher / Aqualung / Thick as a brick / Bungle in the jungle / Locomotive breath / Fat man / Living in the past / Passion play / Skating away on the thin ice of the new day / Rainbow blues / Nothing is easy.
■ LP . . . . CHR 1078
MC. . . . . ZCHR 1078
Chrysalis / '85 / EMI.
CD. . . . . ACCD 1078
Chrysalis / Dec '85 / EMI.
DCC 3210785
Chrysalis / Jan '93 / EMI.

MINSTREL IN THE GALLERY.
Tracks: Minstrel in the gallery / Cold wind to Valhalla / Black satin dancer / Requiem / One white duck / O 10 equals nothing at all / Baker St. muse / Including pig me and the whore / Nice little tune / Crash barrier waltzer / Mother England reverie / Grace.
■ LP . . . . CHR 1082
MC. . . . . ZCHR 1082
Chrysalis / Sep '75 / EMI.
CD. . . . . CCD 1082
Chrysalis / '86 / EMI.

MU/REPEAT.
Tracks: Not Advised.
MC Set . . . . ZCDP 105
Chrysalis / Dec '82 / EMI.

NIGHT CAP - THE UNRELEASED MASTERS 1972-1991.
Tracks: First post / Animelee / Tiger toon / Look at the animals / Law of the bungle / Law of the bungle (part II) / Left right / Solitaire / Critique oblique / Post last / Scenario / Audition / No rehearsal / Paradise steakhouse / Sealion II / Piece of cake / Quartet / Silver river turning / Crew nights / Curse / Rosa on the factory floor / Small cigar / Man of principle / Commons brawl / No step / Drive on the young side of life / I don't want to be me / Broadford bazaar / Lights out / Truck stop runner / Hard liner.
CD Set . . . . CDCHR 6057
Chrysalis / Nov '93 / EMI.

ORIGINAL MASTERS.
Tracks: Living in the past / Aqualung / Too old to rock 'n' roll too young to die / Locomotive breath / Skating away on the thin ice of the new day / Bungle in the jungle / Sweet dreams / Songs from the wood / Witches promise / Thick as a brick / Minstrel in the gallery / Life is a long song.
■ LP . . . . JTTV 1
MC. . . . . ZJTTV 1
Chrysalis / Nov '85 / EMI.
CD. . . . . CCD 1515
Chrysalis / Apr '86 / EMI.

PASSION PLAY, A.
Tracks: Not Advised.
■ LP . . . . CHR 1040
MC. . . . . ZCHR 1040
Chrysalis / Jan '73 / EMI.
CD. . . . . CCD 1040
Chrysalis / Jan '89 / EMI.

REPEAT, VOL.II.
Tracks: Minstrel in the gallery / Cross eyed Mary / New day yesterday / Bouree / Thick as a brick / War child / Passion play / To cry you a song / Too old to rock 'n' roll, too young to die / Glory row.
■ LP . . . . CHR 1135
Chrysalis / Oct '77.
■ MC. . . . . ZCHR 1135
Chrysalis / '83.
CD. . . . . CCD 1135
Chrysalis / Apr '86 / EMI.

RING OUT SOLSTICE BELLS (EP).
Tracks: Ring out solstice bells / March the mad scientist / Christmas song / Pan dance.
■ EP . . . . CXP 2
Chrysalis / Dec '76.

ROCK ISLAND.
Tracks: Kissing Willie / Rattlesnake trail / Ears of tin / Undressed to kill / Rock Island / Heavy water / Another Christmas song / Whaler's dues / Big riff and Mando / Strange avenues.
CD. . . . . CCD 1708
■ LP . . . . CHR 1708
MC. . . . . ZCHR 1708
Chrysalis / Aug '89 / EMI.

ROCKS ON THE ROAD.
Tracks: Rocks on the road.
■ 12".............................TULLX 7
■ CD Single....................TULLCD 7
■ MC Single...................TULLMC 7
Chrysalis / Mar '92.

SAID SHE WAS A DANCER.
Tracks: Said she was a dancer / Dogs in the midwinter / Down at the end of your road (Extra track on CD only) / Too many too (Extra track on CD only).
■ 12".............................TULLX 4
■ 7"...............................TULL 4
■ CD Single....................TULLCD 4
Chrysalis / Dec '87.

SLIPSTREAM.
Tracks: Black Sunday / Dun ringill / Flyingdale flyer / Songs from the wood / Heavy horses / Sweet dream / Too old to rock 'n' roll, too young to die / Skating away / Aqualung / Locomotive breath.
VHS................................CVHS 5018
Chrysalis Music Video / Jan '84 / EMI.

SONGS FROM THE WOOD.
Tracks: Songs from the wood / Jack in the green / Cup of wonder / Hunting girl / Ring out- Solstice bells / Velvet green / Whistler / Pibroch (cap in hand) / Fire at midnight.
MC.................................ZCHR 1132
■ LP................................CHR 1132
Chrysalis / Feb '77.
CD.................................ACCD 1132
Chrysalis / '86 / EMI.

STAND UP.
Tracks: New day yesterday / Jeffrey goes to Leicester Square / Bouree / Back to the family / Look into the sun / Nothing is easy / Fat man / We used to know / Reasons for waiting / For a thousand mothers.
■ LP................................CHR 1042
■ MC...............................ZCHR 1042
Chrysalis / '69.
■ LP................................ILPS 9103
Island / Aug '69.
■ LP.............................FA 41 30861
MC............................TCFA 41 30864
Fame / Nov '83 / EMI.
CD.................................ACCD 1042
Chrysalis / '86 / EMI.
CD.................................CCD 1042
Chrysalis / Jan '89 / EMI.

STEEL MONKEY.
Tracks: Steel monkey / At the end of the road / Too many too (Extra track on 12") / I'm your gun (extra track on 12".).
■ 12"...........................CHS 123172
■ 7"..............................CHS 3172
■ 7"...............................TULL 3
■ 12".............................TULLX 3
Chrysalis / Oct '87.

STORM WATCH.
Tracks: North Sea oil / Orion / Home / Dark ages / Warm sporran / Something's on the move / Old ghosts / Dunringill / Flying Dutchman / Elegy.
■ LP................................CDL 1238
MC.................................ZCDL 1238
Chrysalis / Sep '79 / EMI.
CD.................................CCD 1238
Chrysalis / Jan '89 / EMI.

SWEET DREAM.
Tracks: Sweet dream.
■ 7"..............................WIP 6070
Island / Nov '69.

THICK AS A BRICK.
Tracks: Not Advised.
■ LP................................CHR 1003
■ MC...............................ZCHR 1003
Chrysalis / Jan '74.
CD.................................ACCD 1003
Chrysalis / '86 / EMI.
CD.................................UDCD 510
Mobile Fidelity Sound Lab(USA) / Apr '89.

THIS IS NOT LOVE.
Tracks: This is not love / Night in the wilderness / Jump start.
■ 7"...............................TULL 6
■ CD Single....................TULLCD 6
■ 12".............................TULLX 6
■ MC Single..................TULLXMC 6
Chrysalis / Aug '91.

THIS IS THE FIRST 20 YEARS.
Tracks: Not Advised.
VHS.................................VVD 398
Virgin Vision / '88 / Gold & Sons / TBD.

THIS WAS.
Tracks: My Sunday feeling / Someday the sun won't shine / For you / Beggar's farm / Move on alone / Serenaded a cuckoo / Dharma for one / It's breaking me / Cat's squirrel / Song for Jeffrey / Round.
■ LP................................ILPS 9085
Island / Nov '68.
■ LP................................CHR 1041
MC.................................ZCHR 1041
Chrysalis / Jan '74 / EMI.
CD.................................CCD 1041
Chrysalis / '86 / EMI.

TOO OLD TO ROCK AND ROLL.
Tracks: Quizz kid / Crazed institution / Salamander / Taxi grab / From a dead beat to an old greaser / Bad eyed and loveless / Big dipper / Too old to rock 'n' roll; too young to die / Pied piper / Chequered flag (dead of alive).
MC.................................ZCHR 1111
Chrysalis / Apr '76 / EMI.
■ LP................................CHR 1111
Chrysalis / May '76.
CD.................................CCD 1111
Chrysalis / '86 / EMI.

TOO OLD TO ROCK'N'ROLL, TOO YOUNG TO DIE.
Tracks: Too old to rock 'n' roll, too young to die / Rainbow blues.
■ 7"..............................CHS 2086
Chrysalis / '83.

UNDER WRAPS.
Tracks: Lap of luxury / Under wraps (part 1) / European legacy / Later the same evening / Saboteur / Radio free Moscow / Nobody's car / Heat / Under wraps (part 2) / Paparazzi / Apologee.
CD.................................CCD 1461
■ LP................................CDL 1461
MC.................................ZCDL 1461
Chrysalis / Sep '84 / EMI.

WAR CHILD.
Tracks: War child / Queen and country / Ladies / Back door angels / Sea lion / Skating away on the thin ice of the new day / Bungle in the jungle / Only solitaire / Third hoorah / Two fingers.
■ LP................................CHR 1067
MC.................................ZCHR 1067
Chrysalis / Sep '74 / EMI.

WHISTLER.
Tracks: Whistler / Strip cartoon.
■ 7"..............................CHS 2135
Chrysalis / Feb '77.

WITCHES PROMISE.
Tracks: Witches promise / Teacher.
■ 7"..............................WIP 6077
Island / Jan '70.

WORKING JOHN WORKING JOE.
Tracks: Working John working Joe.
■ 7"..............................CHS 2468
Chrysalis / Oct '80.

Jett, Joan

After split of Runaways (featuring metal queen Lita Ford) guitarist Joan Jett formed the Blackhearts in 1980. 1982 cover of Arrow's I Love Rock 'N' Roll topped U.S. chart for seven weeks, reaching no. 4 in U.K. Subsequent career was briefly rejuvenated by inclusion of hit in 1994's Wayne's World 2.

ALBUM (Jett, Joan & The Blackhearts).
Tracks: Fake friends / Handy man / Everyday people / Hundred feet away / Secret love / French song / Tossin' and turnin' / Why can't we be happy / I love playin' with fire / Coney Island whitefish / Had enough.
■ LP................................EPC 25414
MC..................................40 25414
Epic / Sep '83 / Sony.

BAD REPUTATION.
Tracks: Not Advised.
MC..................................40 25045
■ LP................................EPC 25045
Epic / Oct '82.

CRIMSON AND CLOVER (Jett, Joan & The Blackhearts).
Tracks: Crimson and clover / Oh woe is me.
■ 7"..............................EPCA 2485
Epic / Jul '82.

DIRTY DEEDS DONE CHEAP.
Tracks: Dirty deeds done cheap.
■ 12" P.Disc..................CHSP 123518

■ 7"..............................CHS 3518
■ 12"...........................CHS 123518
■ CD Single.................CHSCD 3518
■ MC Single................CHSMC 3518
Chrysalis / Mar '90.

DIRTY DEEDS DONE CHEAP.
Tracks: Not Advised.
■ MC.............................K 450323
East West / Nov '76.
CD................................K 250323
East West / Aug '87 / WEA.

DO YA WANNA TOUCH ME (Jett, Joan & The Blackhearts).
Tracks: Do ya wanna touch me / Jezebel.
■ 7"..............................EPCA 2674
Epic / Sep '82.

EVERYDAY PEOPLE (Jett, Joan & The Blackhearts).
Tracks: Everyday people / Why can't we be happy.
■ 7"................................A 3790
Epic / Sep '83.

FAKE FRIENDS (Jett, Joan & The Blackhearts).
Tracks: Fake friends / Coney Island whitefish.
■ 12"...............................TA 3615
■ 7"................................A 3615
Epic / Aug '83.

GLORIOUS RESULTS OF A MISPENT YOUTH (Jett, Joan & The Blackhearts).
Tracks: Cherry bomb / Someday / I love you love me love / Frustrated / hold me / Long time / Talking about my baby / Love like mine / I need someone / New Orleans / Push and stomp / I got no answers.
■ LP................................EPC 25993
Epic / Jan '85.

GOOD MUSIC.
Tracks: Good music.
■ 12"...........................POSPX 877
■ 7"..............................POSP 877
Polydor / Aug '87.

GOOD MUSIC (Jett, Joan & The Blackhearts).
Tracks: Not Advised.
■ CD.............................833 078-2
■ LP.............................833 078-1
■ MC.............................833 078-4
Polydor / Sep '87.

HIT LIST, THE.
Tracks: Dirty deeds done dirt cheap / Love hurts / Pretty vacant / Up from the skies / Time has come today / Celluoid heroes / Love me two times / Have you ever seen the rain / Tush / Roadrunner USA.
■ CD.............................CCD 1773
■ LP..............................CHR 1773
■ MC............................ZCHR 1773
Chrysalis / Mar '90.

I HATE MYSELF FOR LOVING YOU (Jett, Joan & The Blackhearts).
Tracks: I hate myself for loving you / Love is pain (live) / I can't control myself (12" and CD single only.) / I hate myself for loving you (live) (Only on CD single.).
■ CD Single...................887 644 2
■ 12"............................LONX 195
■ 7"..............................LONP 195
■ 7"...............................LON 195
■ CD Single.................LONCD 195
London / Aug '88.

I LOVE PLAYING WITH FIRE (Jett, Joan & The Runaways).
Tracks: Saturday night special / Eight days a week / Mama weer all crazee now / I'm a million / Right now / Take over / My buddy and me / Lost little girls / Black leather / Blackmail / Don't abuse me / I love playin' with fire.
■ LP..............................LAKER 1
Cherry Red / Apr '82.

I LOVE ROCK 'N' ROLL (Jett, Joan & The Blackhearts).
Tracks: I love rock 'n' roll / I'm gonna run away / Love is pain / Nag / Crimson and clover / Victim of circumstance / Bits and pieces / Be straight / You're too possessive / Oh woe is me.
■ LP..............................EPC 85686
MC..................................40 85686
Epic / Apr '82 / Sony.
■ LP P.Disc.................EPC 11-85686
Epic / Aug '82.

I LOVE ROCK 'N' ROLL (Jett, Joan & The Blackhearts).
Tracks: I love rock 'n' roll / Love is pain.
- 7" . . . . EPCA 2087
Epic / Jul '82.

I LOVE ROCK 'N' ROLL (Jett, Joan & The Blackhearts).
Tracks: I love rock 'n' roll.
- 7" . . . . W 0232
- CD Single. . . . . .W 0232CD
- MC Single. . . . . .W 0232C
Reprise / Feb '94.

I LOVE YOU LOVE ME LOVED (Jett, Joan & The Blackhearts).
Tracks: I love you love me loved / Long time.
- 12" . . . . TA 4851
- 7" . . . . A 4851
Epic / Oct '84.

I NEED SOMEONE (Jett, Joan & The Blackhearts).
Tracks: I need someone / Talkin' bout my baby / French song.
- 12" . . . . TA 4392
- 7" . . . . A 4391
Epic / Apr '85.

JEZEBEL.
Tracks: Jezebel / Bad reputation.
- 7" . . . . ARO 242
Ariola / Sep '80.

LOVE HURTS.
Tracks: Love hurts / Up from the skies / Tush (Not on 7" single).
- 12" . . . . CHS 123546
- 7" . . . . CHS 3546
- CD Single. . . . . CHSCD 3546
- MC Single. . . . . CHSMC 3546
Chrysalis / Jun '90.

MAKE BELIEVE.
Tracks: Make believe / Call me lightning.
- 7" . . . . ARO 227
Ariola / May '80.

NOTORIOUS (Jett, Joan & The Blackhearts).
Tracks: Backlash / Ashes in the wind / Only good thing (you ever said was goodbye) / Lie to me / Don't surrender / Goodbye / Machismo / Treadin' water / I want you / Wait for me.
- CD 9070802
- MC. 9070804
Silenz / Jun '92 / BMG.

UP YOUR ALLEY (Jett, Joan & The Blackhearts).
Tracks: I hate myself for loving you / Ridin' with James Dean / Little liar / Tulane / I wanna be your dog / I still dream about you / You want in I want out / Just like in the movies / Desire / Back it up / Play that song again.
- CD 837 158-2
- MC. . . . . LONC 67
- LP . . . . LONLP 67
London / Jul '88.

YOU DON'T KNOW WHAT YOU'VE GOT.
Tracks: You don't know what you've got / I'm gonna run away.
- 7" . . . . EPCA 2880
Epic / Oct '82.

YOU DON'T KNOW WHAT YOU'VE GOT.
Tracks: You don't know what you've got / Don't abuse me.
- 7" . . . . ARO 235
Ariola / Jun '80.

Jezebelle

BAD ATTITUDE.
Tracks: Ain't no lady / Leave me alone / Travel on gypsy / Other side / Scandal / No mercy / Satisfaction garanteed / Boulevard / Bum.
- CD . . . . .HMRXD 148
- LP . . . . .HMRLP 148
- MC. . . . . .HMRMC 148
Heavy Metal / May '90 / Sony / FM Revolver.

Jingo De Lunch

AXE TO GRIND.
Tracks: Different world / Steamed / Flapjax / Axe to grind / Did you ever / Kick and run / Tender prey / Seen and done / Chill out / Jinxed / Trouble / Shot down.
- CD 856 803

- LP 086802
Hellhound / Apr '89.

PERPETUUM MOBILE.
Tracks: Lies / Utopia / Peace of mind / Jingo / Illusions / Perpetuum mobile / Fate / Scratchings / Scarecrow / What you see / Thirteen.
- LP . . . . WEBITE 27
We Bite / May '88.

Johansen, David

BUSTER POINDEXTER (Poindexter, Buster).
Tracks: Smack dab in the middle / Bad boy / Hot hot hot / Are you lonely for me baby / Screwy music / Good morning judge / Oh me oh my (I'm a fool for you baby) / Whadaya want / House of the rising sun / Cannibal / Heart of gold.
- CD . . . . PD 86633
- LP . . . . PL 86633
- MC. . . . . PK 86633
RCA / Jul '88.

FUNKY BUT CHIC.
Tracks: Funky but chic / Let go song.
- 7" . . . . SKY 6663
Blue Sky / Jun '78.

HEAR THE NEWS.
Tracks: Hear the news / King of Babylon.
- 12" . . . . .TEN 46 12
- 7" . . . . TEN 46
10 / Mar '85.

HERE COMES THE NIGHT.
Tracks: She loves strangers / Bohemian love pad / You fool you / My obsession / Marquesa De Sade / Here comes the night / Havin' so much fun / Rollin' job / Heart of gold.
- LP . . . . SKY 84504
Blue Sky / Sep '81.

HOT HOT HOT (Poindexter, Buster).
Tracks: Hot hot hot / Cannibal.
- 12" . . . . PT 49582
- 7" . . . . PB 49581
RCA / Jun '88.

IN STYLE.
Tracks: Melody / She / Big city / She knew she was falling in love / Swaheto woman / Justine / In style / You touched me too / Wreckless crazy / Flamingo road.
- LP . . . . SKY 83175
Blue Sky / Nov '79.

SWAHETO WOMAN.
Tracks: Swaheto woman / She knew she was falling in love.
- 7" . . . . SKY 8125
Blue Sky / Mar '80.

SWEET REVENGE.
Tracks: Not Advised.
- LP . . . . DIX 8
10 / '85.

Johnny Crash

NEIGHBOURHOOD THREAT.
Tracks: Hey kid / No bones about it / All the way in love / Thrill of the kill / Axe to the wax / Sink or swim / Crack of dawn / Freedom road / Halfway to heaven / Trigger happy / Baby's like a piano.
- MC. 4662244
- CD 4662242
- LP 4662241
Epic / Apr '90.

Jones, Steve

FIRE AND GASOLINE.
Tracks: Not Advised.
- CD . . . . .DMCG 6067
- LP . . . . .MCG 6067
- MC. . . . . .MCGC 6067
MCA / Oct '89.

FREEDOM FIGHTER.
Tracks: Freedom fighter.
- 12" . . . . MCAT 1371
- 7" . . . . MCA 1371
- CD Single. . . . . DMCAT 1371
MCA / Oct '89.

I NEED YOU.
Tracks: I need you.
- 7" . . . . PFD 001
P Flight / Dec '84.

MERCY.
Tracks: Give it up / That's enough / Raining in my heart / With or without you / Pleasure and pain / Pretty baby / Drugs suck / Through the night / Love letters / Mercy.
- LP . . . . MCF 3384
- MC. . . . . MCFC 3384
MCA / Apr '87.
- CD . . . . DMCF 3384
MCA / Jun '87.

MERCY.
Tracks: Mercy.
- 12" . . . . IRMT 1184
- 7" . . . . IRM 1184
I.R.S. (Illegal) / Aug '87.

Jordan, Sass

Blistering Canadian singer who avoided 'big in Canada' trap by moving to L.A. after 1989 debut *Tell Somebody* and teaming with former George Clinton/Rod Stewart guitarist Stevie Salas. Latter put own; acclaimed band Colorcode on ice to add extra raunch to Jordan's 1994 *Rats* album.

HIGH ROAD EASY.
Tracks: High road easy / Rescue me / Big blue plantation / Funk 49 (Live).
- CD Single. . . . . .CDEM 335
EMI / Jul '94 / EMI.

RACINE.
Tracks: Make you a believer / If you're gonna love me / You don't have to remind me / Who do you think you are / Windin' me up / I want to believe / Goin' back again / Do what you want / Cry baby / Where there's a will / Time flies.
- CD . . . . CDP 7450082
EMI / Aug '94 / EMI.

RATS.
Tracks: Damaged / Slave / Pissin' down / High road easy / Sun's gonna rise / Head / Ugly / I'm not / Honey / Wish / Breakin' / Give.
- CD . . . . CDEMC 3675
- MC. . . . . TCEMC 3675
EMI / Apr '94 / EMI.

TELL SOMEBODY.
Tracks: Not Advised.
- CD . . . . .REV XD 193
- MC. . . . . REV MC 193
FM Records / Nov '92 / FM Revolver / Sony.

Joshua

INTENSE DEFENCE.
Tracks: Reach up / I've been waiting / Only yesterday / Crying out for love / Living on the edge / Tearing at my heart / Remembering you / Look to the sky / Don't you know / Stand alone.
- CD . . . . PD 71905
- LP . . . . PL 71905
- MC. . . . . PK 71905
RCA / Mar '89.

SURRENDER.
Tracks: Surrender love / Heart full of soul / Your love is gone / Hold on / Back to the rock / Rockin' the world / Stay alive / Loveshock / Reprise.
- CD . . . . .WKFMXD 64
- LP . . . . .WKFMLP 64
- MC. . . . . .WKFMMC 64
FM Records / Mar '86.

Journey

Formed in San Francisco in 1973, Journey took five years and six line-ups to make it big. Driving force was guitarist Neil Schon, ex-Santana. Breakthrough came with 1978's *Infinity* - first Journey LP to feature frontman Steve Perry. *Escape*, released 1981, reached No.1 in U.S., was still listed on chart at close of '82, and yielded trio of Top 10 singles; band never won U.K. success. 1984 saw release of *Street Talk* by Perry and *Through The Fire* by HSAS (Schon with Sammy Hagar, Kenny Aaronson and Michael Schrieve). Journey regrouped for *Raised On Radio* in 1986, then split; reunion was mooted in 1994, but without Perry, who released second solo album in 1994.

AFTER THE FALL.
Tracks: After the fall / Rubicon / Anyway you want it / Don't stop believin.
- 12" . . . . TA 3692
- 7" .A 3692
CBS / Sep '83.

ANYWAY YOU WANT IT.
Tracks: Anyway you want it / Do you recall.
■ 12″ 128558
■ 7″ . . . . CBS 8558
CBS / May '80.

BE GOOD TO YOURSELF.
Tracks: Be good to yourself / Only the young / Anyway you want it* / Stone in love (Only on 12″ single.) / Separate ways / After the fall (Only in Double Pack.) / Rubicon (Only on double pack.).
■ 12″ . . . . TA 7095
■ 7″ . . . . .A 7095
■ 7″ P.Disc . . . . DA 7095
CBS / Apr '86.

CAPTURED.
Tracks: Majestic / Where were you / Just the same way / Line of fire / Lights / Stay awhile / Too late / Dixie highway / Feeling that way / Anytime / Do you recall / Walks like a lady / La do da / Lovin' touchin' squeezin' / Squeezin' / Wheel in the sky / Anyway you want it / Party's over.
■ Double LP . . . . CBS 88525
CBS / '81.
■ Double LP 4511321
CBS / Sep '87.
■ MC 4511324
CBS / Sep '87 Sony.
■ CD . . . . CD 88525
CBS / Sep '87 Sony.
■ CD 4511322
CBS / Jun '89.

DEPARTURE.
Tracks: Anyway you want it / Walks like a lady / Someday soon / People and places / Pecious time / Where were you / I'm cryin' / Line of fire / Departure / Good morning girl / Stay a while / Home made love.
■ LP . . . . CBS 84101
CBS / Jul '80.
■ CD . . . . CD 84101
■ LP . . . . CBS 32714
■ MC .40 32714
CBS / Feb '86.

DON'T STOP BELIEVIN'.
Tracks: Don't stop believin' / Open arms / Who's crying now / Lovin', touchin', squeezin'.
■ 7″ . . . . .A 1728
CBS / Feb '82.
■ 12″ . . . . A 12 1728
■ MC Single . . . . A 40 2908
CBS / Feb '82.

ESCAPE.
Tracks: Don't stop believin' / Stone in love / Who's crying now / Keep on running / Still they ride / Escape / Lay it down / Dead or alive / Mother, Father / Open arms.
■ LP . . . . CBS 85138
CBS / Mar '82.
CD . . . . CD 85138
CBS / May '87 Sony.
■ LP .460185 1
■ MC .460185 4
Epic / Feb '88.
CD 4602852
CBS / Apr '89 Sony.

EVOLUTION.
Tracks: Too late / Lovin' touchin' squeezin' / City of the angels / When you're alone it ain't easy / Sweet and simple / Lovin' you is easy / Just the same way / Do you recall / Daydream / Lady Luck / Majestic.
■ LP . . . . CBS 83566
CBS / Apr '79.
■ LP . . . . CBS 32342
■ MC .40 32342
CBS / Jul '83.
■ CD . . . . CD 83566
CBS / Mar '87.
CD 9827372
Pickwick/Sony Collector's Choice / Mar '94 / Pickwick / Pinnacle.

FAITHFULLY.
Tracks: Faithfully / Edge of the blade.
■ 7″ . . . . .A 3358
CBS / Apr '83.

FRONTIERS.
Tracks: Separate ways / Send her my love / Chain reaction / After the fall / Faithfully / Edge of the blade / Troubled child / Back talk / Frontier / Rubicon.
MC 40 25261
■ LP . . . . CBS 25261
CBS / Feb '83.
CD . . . . .CD CBS 252 61
CBS / '88 / Sony.

FRONTIERS AND BEYOND.
Tracks: Not Advised.
VHS . . . . CFV 08032
Channel 5 / Mar '89 / Channel 5 Video / P.R.O. Video / Gold & Sons.

FRONTIERS/ ESCAPE.
Tracks: Not Advised.
■ Double LP . . . . .CBS J 241
CBS / Aug '87.

GIRL CAN'T HELP IT.
Tracks: Girl can't help it / It could have been.
■ 7″ 6501167
CBS / Nov '86.

GREATEST HITS: JOURNEY.
Tracks: Only the young / Don't stop believin' / Wheel in the sky / Faithfully / I'll be alright without you / Anyway you want it / (Ask) the lonely / Who's crying now / Separate ways / Lights / Lovin' touchin' squeezin' / Open arms / Girl can't help it / Send her my love / Be good to yourself.
CD 4631492
MC 4631494
■ LP 4631491
CBS / Dec '88.
MiniDisc. 463149-3
Columbia / Apr '93 / Sony.

IN THE BEGINNING.
Tracks: Journey of a lifetime / Topaz / Kohoutek / On a Saturday night / It's all too much / In my lonely feeling / Conversations / Mystery mountain / Spaceman / People / Anyway / You're on your own / Look into the future / Nickel and dime / I'm gonna leave you.
■ Double LP . . . . CBS 22073
CBS / Oct '80.

INFINITY.
Tracks: Lights / Feeling that way / Anytime / La do da / Patiently / Wheel in the sky / Somethin' to hide / Winds of March / Can do / Open the door.
■ CD . . . . CD 82244
CBS / '88.

JOURNEY.
Tracks: Of a lifetime / In the morning day / Kohoutek / To play some music / Topaz / In my lonely feeling/conversations.
■ LP . . . . CBS 80724
CBS / '75.
CD 983313 2
Pickwick/Sony Collector's Choice / Oct '93 / Pickwick / Pinnacle.

JOURNEY - CASSETTE EP.
Tracks: Don't stop believin' / Who's crying now / Open arms / Lovin', touchin', squeezin'.
■ MC 40 2908
CBS / Dec '82.

LIGHTS.
Tracks: Lights / Open the door.
■ 7″ . . . . CBS 6392
CBS / Jun '78.

LOOK INTO THE FUTURE.
Tracks: On a Saturday nite / It's all too much / Anyway / She makes me (feel alright) / You're on your own / Look into the future / Midnight dreamer / I'm gonna leave you.
■ LP . . . . CBS 69203
CBS / '76.
■ LP . . . . CBS 32102
CBS / May '82.

NEXT.
Tracks: Spaceman / People / I would find you / Here we are / Hustler / Next / Nickel and dime / Karma.
■ LP . . . . CBS 81554
CBS / '77.

ONLY THE YOUNG.
Tracks: Only the young / I'll fall in love again.
■ 7″ . . . . .A 6058
Geffen / Mar '85.

PARTY'S OVER.
Tracks: Party's over / Wheel in the sky.
■ 7″ . . . . CBS 9578
CBS / Mar '81.

RAISED ON RADIO.
Tracks: Girl can't help it / Positive touch / Suzanne / Be good to yourself / Once you love somebody / Happy to give / Raised on radio / I'll be alright without you / It could have been you / Eyes of a woman / Why can't this night go on forever.
■ LP . . . . CBS 26902
CBS / May '86.
■ CD . . . . CD 26902
CBS / May '86.
CD 4679922
■ MC 4679924
Columbia / Apr '91.

SEPARATE WAYS.
Tracks: Separate ways / Frontiers.
■ 12″ . . . . A 13 3077
■ 7″ .A 3077
CBS / Feb '83.

STONE IN LOVE.
Tracks: Stone in love / Only solutions.
■ 7″ . . . . .A 2890
CBS / Oct '82.

SUZANNE.
Tracks: Suzanne / Ask the lonely (on 12″ only.) / Raised on radio (on 12″ only).
■ 7″ . . . . CBS 7265
■ 12″ . . . . TA 7265
CBS / Jul '86.

TIME.
Tracks: Of a lifetime / Kohoutek / I'm gonna leave you / Cookie Duster & Nickel & Dime / For you / Velvet curtains/ Anytime / Anytime / Patiently / Good times / Majestic / Too late / Sweet and simple / Just the same way / Little girl / Anyway you want it / Someday soon / Good morning girl / Where you were / Line of fire / Homemade love / Natural thing / Lights / Stay awhile / Walks like a lady / Lovin', Touchin', Squeezin' / Dixie highway / Wheel in the sky / Party's over (Hopelessly in love) / Don't stop believin' / Stone in love / Keep on running / Who's crying now / Still they ride / Open arms / Mother, Father / La raza del sol / Only solutions / Liberty / Separate ways (Worlds apart) / Send her my love / Faithfully / After the fall / All that really matters / Eyes of a woman / Why can't this night go on forever / Once you love somebody / Happy to give / Be good to yourself / Only the young / Ask the lonely / With a tear / Into your arms / Girl can't help it / I'll be alright without you.
CD Set 472810 2
MC Set 472810 4
Columbia / Jan '93 / Sony.

WHEEL IN THE SKY.
Tracks: Wheel in the sky / Can do.
■ 7″ . . . . CBS 6238
CBS / Apr '78.

WHO'S CRYING NOW.
Tracks: Who's crying now / Don't stop believing.
■ 7″ . . . . .A 2725
CBS / Sep '82.

WHO'S CRYING NOW.
Tracks: Who's crying now / Open arms / Suzanne / Don't stop believin'.
■ 7″ . . . . .A 1467
CBS / Aug '81.
■ 12″ 6545416
■ 7″ 6545417
■ CD Single 6545412
CBS / Jan '89.

Judas Priest

Formed in 1972 in metal hotbed of Birmingham, Priest released first album *Rocka Rolla* in 1974, made U.K. chart debut with *Sin After Sin* (1977) and were among few HM groups to sustain success during punk era. In 1979, single *Take On The World* and live album *Unleashed In The East* both reached U.K. Top 20. Follow-up *British Steel* reached Top Five and spawned three Top 30 singles, including classic *Living After Midnight*. Although 1980 was peak chart year in Britain, Priest continued as major U.S. attraction. In late '80s, band were accused of placing subliminal messages in songs, allegedly prompting two fans in Reno to shoot one another (band won resultant court case). Early '90s saw Halford form new band, Fight, and guest with Black Sabbath, but Priest could return.

6 TRACK HITS.
Tracks: Sinner / Exciter / Hell bent for leather / Ripper / Hot rockin' / Green manalishi.
■ EP 7SR 5018

■ DELETED

MC. 7SC 5018
Scoop 33 / Sep '83.

BEFORE THE DOWN.
Tracks: Before the down / Rock forever.
■ 7" . . . . CBS 6794
CBS / Oct '78.

BEST OF JUDAS PRIEST.
Tracks: Dying to meet you / Never satisfied / Rocka
rolla / Diamonds and rust / Victim of changes / Island
of domination / Ripper / Deceiver.
■ LP . . . . GULP 1026
Gull / Feb '78.
■ MC. . . . . ZCGUL 1026
Gull / Feb '78.
CD . . . . GUCD 1026
Gull / May '87 / Pinnacle.

BETTER BY YOU, BETTER THAN ME.
Tracks: Better by you, better than me / Invader.
■ 7" . . . . CBS 6077
CBS / Feb '78.

BREAKING THE LAW.
Tracks: Breaking the law / Metal gods / Living after
midnight / Take on the world (Available on cassingle
only.) / United (Available on cassingle only.)
■ 7" . . . . CBS 8644
CBS / Jun '80.
■ MC Single. . . . . A 40 3067
CBS / Feb '83.

BRITISH STEEL.
Tracks: Rapid fire / Metal gods / Breaking the law /
Grinder / United / You don't have to be old to be wise
/ Living after midnight / Race / Steeler.
■ LP . . . . CBS 84160
CBS / Apr '80.
■ CD . . . . CD 84160
■ LP . . . . CBS 32412
■ MC 40 32412
CBS / Jan '84.
CD 9827252
Pickwick/Sony Collector's Choice / Mar '94 / Pick-
wick / Pinnacle.

BRITISH STEEL/SCREAMING FOR VEN-GEANCE/STAINED GLASS.
Tracks: Breaking the law / Rapid fire / Metal gods /
Grinder / United / Living after midnight / You don't
have to be old to be wise / Rage / Steeler / Helion /
Electric eye / Riding on the wind / Bloodstone /
(Take these) Chains / Pain and pleasure / Screaming
for vengeance / You've got another thing comin' /
Fever / Devil's child / Exciter / White heat, red hot /
Better by you, better than me / Stained glass /
Invader / Saints in hell / Savage / Beyond the realms
of death / Hero's end.
CD Set 468328 2
Columbia / Feb '93 / Sony.

CHAINS.
Tracks: Chains / Judas Priest audio file.
■ 7" . . . . .A 2822
CBS / Oct '82.

COLLECTION: JUDAS PRIEST.
Tracks: One for the road / Rock a rolla / Winter /
Deep freeze / Winter retreat / Cheater / Never satis-
fied / Run of the mill / Dying to meet you / Victim of
changes / Ripper / Dream deceiver / Prelude /
Tyrant / Genocide / Epitaph / Island of domination.
CD . . . . CCSCD 213
■ Double LP. . . . . CCSLP 213
■ MC. . . . . CCSMC 213
Castle Collector Series / Apr '89.

DEFENDERS OF THE FAITH.
Tracks: Freewheel burning / Jawbreaker / Rock hard
ride free / Sentinel / Love bites / Eat me alive / Some
heads are gonna roll / Night comes down / Heavy
duty / Defenders of the faith.
■ LP . . . . CBS 25713
CBS / Jan '84.
■ CD . . . . CD 25713
CBS / Jul '84.

DIAMONDS AND RUST.
Tracks: Diamonds and rust / Dissident aggressor.
■ 7" . . . . CBS 5222
CBS / May '77.

EVENING STAR.
Tracks: Evening star / Beyond the realms.
■ 7" . . . . CBS 7312
CBS / May '79.

EVENING STAR.
Tracks: Evening star / Starbreaker.
■ 7" . . . . CBS 6719
CBS / Sep '78.

FREEWHEEL BURNING.
Tracks: Freewheel burning / Breakin' the law.
■ 12" . . . . TA 5054
■ 7" . . . . A 4054
CBS / Jan '84.

HERO HERO.
Tracks: Not Advised.
CD . . . . LICD 900414
Line / Nov '87 / C.M. Distribution / Grapevine Distri-
bution / A.D.A. Distribution / Conifer Records.
■ Double LP. . . . . GUD 2005/6
MC Set . . . . ZCGUD 2005/6
Gull / '88 / Pinnacle.

HOT ROCKIN'.
Tracks: Hot rockin' / Trouble shooter / Breakin' the
law.
■ 12" . . . . A 13 1153
■ 7" . . . . .A 1153
CBS / Apr '81.
■ 7" . . . . CBS 9520
CBS / Apr '81.

JOHNNY B. GOODE.
Tracks: Rock you all around the world / Turbo lover
(Available on 12" only) / Johnny B. Goode.
■ 12" . . . . A 9114 T
■ 7" . . . . A 9114
Atlantic / May '88.

JUDAS PRIEST.
Tracks: Not Advised.
■ LP . . . . PGLP 1026
Shanghai / Aug '86.

JUDAS PRIEST LIVE.
Tracks: Riding the wind / Heading out to the highway
/ Hellion/Electric eye / Metal gods / Bloodstone /
Breaking the law / Sinner / Desert plains / Ripper /
Diamonds and rust / Devil's child / Screaming for
vengeance / You've got another thing coming / Vic-
tim of changes / Living after midnight / Green mana-
lishi / Hell bent for leather.
VHS . . . . VVD 233
Virgin Vision / '87 / Gold & Sons / TBD.
VHS 498202
CMV Enterprises (Video) / Jun '89 / Sony.

JUDAS PRIEST: INTERVIEW PICTURE DISC.
Tracks: Not Advised.
LP P.Disc . . . . BAK 2054
Baktabak / Jul '87 / Arabesque Ltd.

KILLING MACHINE.
Tracks: Not Advised.
■ LP . . . . CBS 83135
CBS / Nov '78.
■ LP . . . . CBS 32218
CBS / Oct '82.

LIVING AFTER MIDNIGHT.
Tracks: Living after midnight / Delivering the goods.
■ 7" . . . . CBS 8379
CBS / Mar '80.

LIVING AFTER MIDNIGHT (OLD GOLD).
Tracks: Living after midnight / Breaking the law.
■ 7" . . . . OG 9864
Old Gold / Feb '89.

LOCKED IN.
Tracks: Locked in / Reckless.
■ 12" . . . . TA 7144
■ 7" . . . . QTA 7144
CBS / May '86.

METAL WORKS '73 - '93.
Tracks: Hellion / Electric eye / Victim of changes /
Painkiller / Eat me alive / Devil's child / Dissident
aggressor / Delivering the goods / Exciter / Breaking
the law / Hell bent for leather / Blood red skies /
Metal gods / Before the dawn / Turbo lover / Ram it
down / Metal meltdown / Screaming for vengeance /
You've got another thing comin' / Beyond the realms
of death / Solar angels / Bloodstone / Desert plains /
Wild nights, Hot & Crazy Days / Heading out to the
highway / Living after midnight / Touch of Evil / Rage
/ Night comes down / Sinner / Freewheel burning /
Night crawler.
CD Set 473050 2
LP Set 473050 1
MC Set 473050 4
Columbia / Apr '93 / Sony.

NIGHT CRAWLER.
Tracks: Night crawler (Edit) / Living after midnight
(Live) / Ripper (On CDs only.) / Breaking the law
(Live) (On CDs only.) / I'm a rocker (On CDs only.)
■ 7" 659097 7
■ CD Single. 659097 2
Columbia / Apr '93.

PAINKILLER.
Tracks: Painkiller / Hell patrol / All guns blazing /
Leather rebel / Metal meltdown / Night crawler /
Between the hammer and the anvil / Touch of evil /
Battle hymn / One shot at glory.
CD 4672902
■ LP 4672901
■ MC. 4672904
CBS / Sep '90.

PAINKILLER.
Tracks: Painkiller / United / Better by you, better
than me.
■ 12" 6562736
■ 7" 6562737
■ CD Single. 6562732
■ MC Single. 6562734
CBS / Sep '90.

PAINKILLER.
Tracks: Painkiller / Locked in / Love bites / Hot
rockin' / You've got another thing comin' / Breaking
the law / Living after midnight / Freewheel burning /
Touch of evil.
VHS 499042
Sony Music Video / '91 / Sony.

POINT OF ENTRY.
Tracks: Heading out to the highway / Don't go / Hot
rockin' / Turning circles / Desert plains / Solar
angels / You say yes / All the way / Troubleshooter /
On the run.
MC. 40 84833
CBS / Feb '81 / Sony.
■ LP . . . . CBS 84834
CBS / Mar '81.

PRIEST..LIVE.
Tracks: Out in the cold / Heading out to the highway /
Metal gods / Breaking the law / Love bites / Some
heads are gonna roll / Sentinel / Private property /
Rock you all around the world / Electric eye / Turbo
lover / Freewheel burning / Parental guidance /
Living after midnight / You've got another thing
comin.
CD 4506392
CBS / Jul '87 / Sony.
■ LP 4506391
■ MC. 4506394
CBS / Jun '87.

RAM IT DOWN.
Tracks: Ram it down / Heavy metal / Love zone /
Come and get it / Hard as iron / Blood red skies / I'm
a rocker / Johnny B. Goode / Love you to death /
Monsters of rock.
■ LP 4611081
■ CD 4611082
■ MC. 4611084
CBS / May '88.

RIPPER.
Tracks: Ripper / Never satisfied / Victim of changes.
■ 12" . . . . GULS 7112
Gull / Aug '80.

ROCKA ROLLA.
Tracks: One for the road / Rocka rolla / Winter /
Deep freeze / Winter retreat / Cheater / Never satis-
fied / Run of the mill / Dying to meet you / Caviar and
meths.
■ LP . . . . GULP 1005
Gull / Sep '77.
■ LP . . . . FA 41 3137 1
■ MC. . . . . FA 41 3137 4
Fame / Nov '85 / EMI.
CD . . . . LICD 900101
Line / Nov '87 / C.M. Distribution / Grapevine Distri-
bution / A.D.A. Distribution / Conifer Records.

SAD WINGS OF DESTINY.
Tracks: Victim of changes / Ripper / Dreamer de-
ceiver / Deceiver / Prelude / Tyrant / Genocide /
Epitaph / Island of domination.
■ LP . . . . GULP 1015
Gull / Sep '77.
CD . . . . LICD 900112
Line / Nov '87 / C.M. Distribution / Grapevine Distri-
bution / A.D.A. Distribution / Conifer Records.

SCREAMING FOR VENGEANCE.
Tracks: Hellion / Electric eye / Riding on the wind /
Bloodstone / Pain and pleasure / (Take these) chains
/ Screaming for vengeance / You've got another
thing comin' / Fever / Devil's child.
■ LP . . . . CBS 85941

CBS / Jul '82.
■ **LP** .... CBS 32712
■ **MC** .... .40 32712
CBS / Feb '86.

SIN AFTER SIN.
Tracks: Sinner / Diamonds and rust / Starbreaker / Last rose of summer / Let us prey / Call for the priest / Raw deal / Here come the tears / Dissident aggressor.
■ **LP** .... CBS 82008
CBS / May '77.
■ **LP** .... CBS 32005
CBS / Mar '81.
CD .... .983286 2
Pickwick/Sony Collector's Choice / Nov '93 / Pickwick / Pinnacle.

SOME HEADS ARE GONNA ROLL.
Tracks: Some heads are gonna roll / Green Manalishi.
■ **12"** .... TA 4298
■ **7"** .... .A 4289
CBS / Mar '84.

STAINED CLASS.
Tracks: Exciter / White heat / Red hot / Better by you, better than me / Stained glass / Invader / Saints in hell / Savage / Beyond the realms of death / Hero's end.
■ **LP** .... CBS 82430
CBS / Feb '78.
■ **LP** .... CBS 32075
CBS / Nov '81.
CD .... CD 32075
■ **MC** .... .40 32075
Columbia / Apr '91.
MiniDisc. 82430-3
Columbia / Feb '93 / Sony.

TAKE ON THE WORLD.
Tracks: Take on the world / Star breaker.
■ **7"** .... CBS 6915
CBS / Jan '79.

TOUCH OF EVIL.
Tracks: Touch of evil / Between the hammer and the anvil / You've got another thing comin' (Only on 12" and CD single.).
■ **12"** 6565896
■ **7"** 6565897
■ **7" P.Disc** 6565890
■ **CD Single** 6565892
■ **MC Single.** 6565894
Columbia / Mar '91.

TURBO.
Tracks: Turbo lover / Locked in / Private property / Parental guidance / Rock you all around the world / Out in the cold / Wild nights, hot and crazy days / Hot for love / Reckless.
CD .... CD 26641
CBS / '86 / Sony.
■ **LP** .... CBS 26641
■ **MC** .... .40 26641
CBS / Apr '86.
■ **CD** 4633652
■ **LP** 4633651
■ **MC** 4633654
CBS / Feb '89.

TURBO LOVER.
Tracks: Turbo lover / Hot for love.
■ **7"** .... .A 7048
CBS / Apr '86.

TYRANT.
Tracks: Tyrant / Rocka rolla / Genocide.
■ **12"** .... GULS 7612
Gull / Jun '83.

UNITED.
Tracks: United / Grinder.
■ **7"** .... CBS 8897
CBS / Jul '80.

UNLEASHED IN THE EAST.
Tracks: Exciter / Running wild / Sinner / Ripper / Green manalishi / Diamonds and rust / Victim of changes / Genocide / Tyrant.
■ **LP** .... CBS 83852
CBS / Oct '79.
■ **CD** .... CD 83852
CBS / '88.
CD 4686042
MC. 4686044
Columbia / Apr '94 / Sony.

YOU'VE GOT ANOTHER THING COMIN'.
Tracks: You've got another thing comin' / Exciter.
■ **7"** .... .A 2611
■ **7" P.Disc** .... .112611
CBS / Aug '82.

Juggernaut

BLACK PAGODA.
Tracks: Shedding / Bitter / Decide / Difference / Green lightening / I.O. / Reality easel / Whisper / Make it so hard / Machine / Cry me a river / Master of pricks / Searchin' for a better high.

CD .... .N 0215-2
Noise / Sep '94 / Pinnacle.

TROUBLE WITHIN.
Tracks: Not Advised.
■ **LP** .... RR 9590
Road Runner / Sep '87.

Junior Manson Slags

HUMAN SKIN SUIT.
Tracks: Human skin suit.
■ **12"** .... .VERT 4T
Blipvert / Oct '89.

PLASTIC SMILE (EP).
Tracks: Not Advised.
■ **12"** .... VERT 001T
Blipvert / Dec '88.

SILVER TRAIN.
Tracks: Silver train.
■ **12"** .... .VERT 002 T
Blipvert / Jun '89.

Junk Monkeys

BLISS.
Tracks: Not Advised.
CD. .... .CDZORRO 51
Metal Blade / Aug '92 / Pinnacle.

Junkyard

JUNKYARD.
Tracks: Blooze / Shot in the dark / Life sentence / Can't hold back / Hands off / Simple man / Hollywood / Long way home / Texas.
CD. 924 227 2
■ **LP** .... WX 266
MC. .... WX 266C
Elektra / Apr '89 / WEA.
■ **CD** .... .GEFD 24227
■ **MC** .... .GEFC 24227
Geffen / Aug '91.

SIXES, SEVENS AND NINES.
Tracks: Not Advised.
■ **CD** .... .GEFD 24372
■ **LP** .... GEF 24372
■ **MC** .... .GEFC 24372
MCA / May '91.

K

K.M.F.D.M.

DON'T BLOW YOUR TOP.
Tracks: Don't blow your top / No meat no man / Oh look / What a race / King Kong / No news.
■ LP . . . . SAW 006
Skysaw / Nov '88.

DON'T BLOW YOUR TOP.
Tracks: Don't blow your top.
■ 12" . . . . SKY 8
Skysaw / '88

GODLIKE.
Tracks: Godlike.
■ 12" . . . . WAX 132
■ CD Single . . . . WAX 132 CD
Wax Trax / Jul '90.

MONEY.
Tracks: Money / Bargeld.
■ 12" . . . . TRAN 05T
■ CD Single . . . . TRAN 05CD
Transglobal / Apr '92.

MONEY (REMIX).
Tracks: Money (remix).
■ 12" . . . . TRAN 07T
■ 7" 7TRAN 07
■ CD Single . . . . TRAN 07CD
Outer Rhythm (R & S) / Apr '92.

NAIVE.
Tracks: Not Advised.
CD . . . . WAXCD 148
LP . . . . WAXLP 148
Wax Trax / Sep '90 / SRD.

NAIVE (REMIX) (K.M.F.D.M. & Thrill Kill Kult).
Tracks: Naive (remix) / Days of swine and roses (remix).
■ 12" . . . . WAX 160
■ CD Single . . . . WAX 160CD
Wax Trax / Oct '90.

VIRUS.
Tracks: Virus.
■ 12" . . . . SBR 034T
Strike Back / Nov '89.

WHAT DO YOU KNOW DEUTSCHLAND.
Tracks: Not Advised.
CD . . . . CDSAW 004
■ LP . . . . SAW 004
Skysaw / Feb '88.

WORLD VAIOE.
Tracks: Not Advised.
CD . . . . SBR 032 CD
■ LP . . . . SBR 032
Strike Back / May '89.

Kansas

Formed in 1972, Kansas cracked U.S. charts with '77's Leftoverture, boosted by hit Carry On Wayward Son; no. 51 placing for latter constitutes band's entire U.K. chart success. Next album Point Of No Return was another U.S. Top Ten album and yielded million-selling Dust In The Wind. Band remain intermittently active.

ALL I WANTED.
Tracks: All I wanted / We're not alone anymore.
■ 12" . . . . MCAS 1116
■ 7" . . . . MCA 1116
MCA / Jan '87.

AUDIO VISIONS.
Tracks: Relentless / Anything for you / Hold on / Loner / Curtain of iron / Got to rock on / Don't open your eyes / No one together / No room for a stranger / Back door.
■ LP . . . . KIR 84500
Kirshner (USA) / Nov '80.

BEST OF KANSAS.
Tracks: Carry on wayward son / Point of no return / Fight fire / No one together / Play the game tonight / Wall.
■ LP . . . . EPC 26065

■ MC. 40 26065
Epic / Sep '84.
■ CD . . . . CD 26065
CBS / Nov '85.
■ CD 4610362
Epic / Aug '90.

CARRY ON WAYWARD SON.
Tracks: Carry on wayward son / Questions of my childhood.
■ 7" . . . . EPC 4932
Epic / May '77

DRASTIC MEASURES.
Tracks: Fight fire with fire / Everybody's my friend / Mainstream / Andi / Going through the motions / Get rich / Don't take your love away / End of the age / Incident on a bridge.
■ LP . . . . EPC 25561
Epic / Sep '83.
MC. 40 25561
Epic / Jul '87 / Sony.

DUST IN THE WIND.
Tracks: Dust in the wind / Paradox.
■ 7" . . . . KIR 6205
Kirshner (USA) / Mar '78.

FIGHT FIRE WITH FIRE.
Tracks: Fight fire with fire / Carry on wayward son / Dust in the wind.
■ 12" . . . . TA 3696
Epic / Sep '83.

IN THE SPIRIT OF THINGS.
Tracks: Ghosts / One big sky / Inside of me / One man, one heart / House on fire / Once in a lifetime / Stand beside me / I counted on love / Preacher / Rainmaker / T.O. Witcher / Bells of Saint James.
■ LP . . . . MCA 6254
MCA / '88.

KANSAS.
Tracks: Can I tell you / Bringing it back / Lonely wind / Belexes / Journey from Mariabronn / Pilgrimage / Apercu / Death of Mother Nature suite.
■ LP . . . . EPC 80174
Epic / '74.
CD 9827332
Pickwick/Sony Collector's Choice / Apr '92 / Pickwick / Pinnacle.

KANSAS BOXED SET, THE.
Tracks: Can I tell you / Death of mother nature suite / Journey from Maria Bronn / Song for America / Devil game / Incomudro-hymm to the atman / Child of innocence / Icarus / Borne on wings of steel / Mysteries and mayhem / Pinnacle / Carry on wayward son / Wall / What's on my mind / Opus insert / Magnum opus / Father Padilla meets the perfect gnat / Howling at the moon / Industry on parade / Release the beavers / Gnat attack / Point of no return / Portrait (He Knew) / Dust in the wind / Closet chronicles / People of the south wind / On the other side / Glimpse of home / Relentless / Loner / Hold on / Wheels.
CD Set . . . . CD 47364
Legacy / Jul '94 / Sony.

LEFT OVERTURE.
Tracks: Not Advised.
CD. 982837 2
MC. 982841 4
MC. 982837 4
Pickwick / Nov '92 / Pickwick.

LEFTOVERTURE.
Tracks: Carry on wayward son / Wall / What's on my mind / Miracles out of nowhere / Opus insert / Questions of my childhood / Cheyenne anthem / Magnum opus / Father Padilla meets the perfect gnat / Howling at the moon / Man overboard / Industry on parade / Release the beavers / Great attack.
■ LP . . . . EPC 81728
Epic / '76.

MASQUE.
Tracks: It takes a woman's love (to make a man) / Two cents worth / Icarus - born on the wings of steel / All the world / Child of innocence / It's you / Mysteries and mayhem / Pinnacle.
■ LP . . . . PZ 33806
Kirshner (USA) / '75.

MONOLITH.
Tracks: On the other side / People of the south wind / Angels have fallen / How my soul cries out for you / Glimpse of home / Away from you / Stay out of trouble / Reason to be.
■ LP . . . . KIR 83644
Kirshner (USA) / '79.

PLAY THE GAME TONIGHT.
Tracks: Play the game tonight / Play on.
■ 7" . . . . KIR 2409
Kirshner (USA) / Jul '82.

POINT OF NO RETURN.
Tracks: Point of no return / Closet chronicles.
■ 7" . . . . KIR 5820
Kirshner (USA) / Mar '78.

POINT OF NO RETURN, THE.
Tracks: Point of know return / Paradox / Spider / Portrait (he knew) / Closet chronicles / Lightning's hand / Dust in the wind / Sparks of the tempest / Nobody's home / Hopelessly human.
■ CD . . . . CD 32361
CBS / Jul '89.

POWER.
Tracks: Silhouettes in disguise / Power / All I wanted / Secret service / We're not alone anymore / Musicatto / Taking in the view / Three pretenders / Tomb 19 / Can't cry anymore.
■ LP . . . . MCG 6021
■ MC. . . . . MCGC 6021
MCA / Dec '86.

SONG FOR AMERICA.
Tracks: Down the road / Song for America / Lamplight symphony / Lonely street / Devil game / Incomudro - hymn to the Atman.
■ LP . . . . EPC 80740
Epic / '75.

TWO FOR THE SHOW.
Tracks: Song for America / Point of no return / Paradox / Dust in the wind / Icarus / Borne on wings of steel / Portrait / Carry on wayward son / Journey from Mariabronn.
■ LP . . . . KIR 88228
Kirshner (USA) / Feb '79.

VINYL CONFESSIONS.
Tracks: Play the game tonight / Right away / Fair exchange / Chaining shadows / Diamonds and pearls / Face it / Windows / Borderline / Play on / Crossfire.
■ LP . . . . KIR 85714
Kirshner (USA) / Aug '82.

Kataklysm

MYSTICAL GATE OF REINCARNATION.
Tracks: Not Advised.
CD . . . . NB 093-2
MC. . . . . NB 093-4
Nuclear Blast / Feb '94 / Plastic Head.

Keel

BECAUSE THE NIGHT.
Tracks: Because the night.
■ 12" . . . . KEELX 1
■ 7" . . . . KEEL 1
Vertigo / Mar '86.

FINAL FRONTIER.
Tracks: Final frontier / Rock and roll animal / Because the night / Here today and gone tomorrow / Arm and a leg / Raised on rock / Just another girl / Tears of fire / Nightfall / No pain no gain.
■ CD 826 815-2
■ LP . . . . VERH 33
■ MC. . . . . VERHC 33
Vertigo / Apr '86.

KEEL.
Tracks: United nations / Somebody's waiting / Cherry Lane / Calm before the storm / King of the rock / It's a jungle out there / I said the wrong thing to the right girl / Don't say you love me / If love is a crime (I wanna be convicted) / 4th of July.
■ LP . . . . MCF 3393
■ MC. . . . . MCFC 3393

■ CD . . . . DMCF 3393
MCA / Jul '87.

LAY DOWN THE LAW.
Tracks: Not Advised.
■ LP . . . . SH 1014
Shrapnel (USA) / Aug '87.

RIGHT TO ROCK, THE.
Tracks: Right to rock / Back to the city / Let's spend the night together / Easier said than done / So many girls, so little time / Electric love / Speed demon / Get down / You're the victim (I'm the crime).
■ LP . . . . VERL 26
■ MC . . . . VERLC 26
Vertigo / Apr '85.

Kerbdog

DRY RISER.
Tracks: Dry riser / Xenophobia / Self inflicted (On 12"/CDs) / Same with the hammer (On 7" only).
■ 12" . . . . VERCX 83
■ 7" . . . . VER 83
■ CD Single . . . . VERCD 83
Vertigo / Jan '94.

DUMMY CRUSHER.
Tracks: Dummy crusher / Kennedy (On 1st CD only) / Debaser (On 1st CD only) / Mr. Clean (On 12" only) / Don't stand in line (On 12" only) / Too much too young (On 7" only) / Mildred Pierce (On 2nd CD only) / This is not a love song (On 2nd CD only).
12" . . . . VERX 86
7" . . . . VER 86
CD Single . . . . VERCD 86
CD Single . . . . VERDD 86
Vertigo / Jul '94 / PolyGram.

TOTALLY SWITCHED.
Tracks: End of green / Dry riser / Dead anyway / Cleaver / Earthworks / Dummy crusher / Inseminator / Clock / Schism / Scram.
CD .518866-2
LP 518 866-1
MC .518866-4
Vertigo / Apr '94 / PolyGram.

Kidd Glove

GOOD CLEAN FUN.
Tracks: Good clean fun / Street angel.
■ 7" . . . . TMG 1337
Morocco (USA) / Mar '84.

KIDD GLOVE.
Tracks: Good clean fun / Killer instinct / Street angel / Spirit of the night / Fade to black / Hellzarockin' / Somewhere in a song / Secrets / Susie wants to be a star.
■ LP . . . . ZL 72149
MC . . . . ZK 72149
Morocco (USA) / Apr '84 / BMG.

Kik Tracee

NO RULES.
Tracks: Don't need rules / Mrs. Robinson / You're so strange / Trash city / Hard time / Big western sky / Generation express / Soul shaker / Tangerine man / Lost / Velvet crush / Rattlesnake eyes (Strawberry jam) / Romeo blues (CD only.) / Fade Dunaway.
■ LP . . . . PL 82189
■ CD . . . . PD 82189
■ MC . . . . PK 82189
RCA / Jun '91.

Killdozer

FOR LADIES ONLY.
Tracks: Not Advised.
LP . . . . TGLP 39
Touch & Go / Oct '90 / SRD.

INTELLECTUALS ARE THE SHOESHINE BOYS OF THE ..
Tracks: Not Advised.
LP . . . . TGLP 47
Touch & Go / Jan '90 / SRD.

LITTLE BABY BUNTIN'.
Tracks: Not Advised.
■ LP . . . . TGLP 26
Touch & Go / Mar '88.

LITTLE BABY BUNTIN' LIVE.
Tracks: Cinnamon girl / I am I said / King of sex / Hamburger martyr / La grange / Hottentot / One for the people / Cranberries / Sonnet / Sweet home Alabama / Fifty seven / Going to the beach.
VHS . . . . JE 193

Jettisoundz / Jan '90 / TBD / Visionary Communications.

SNAKEBOY.
Tracks: Not Advised.
■ LP . . . . TGLP 6
Touch & Go / Aug '88.

TWELVE POINT BUCK.
Tracks: Not Advised.
■ LP .TGLP 48
Touch & Go / Nov '89.

Killer

FATAL ATTRACTION.
Tracks: Not Advised.
CD .367 0001.2
LP .367 0001.1
Mausoleum / Oct '91 / Pinnacle.

MURDER ONE.
Tracks: Impaler / Beast arises / Children of the revolution / S & M / Takin' no prisoners / Marshall Lokjaw / Protector / Dream keeper / Awakening / Remember tomorrow.
CD . . . . PD 90643
MC . . . . PK 90643
■ LP . . . . PL 90643
RCA / May '92.

READY FOR HELL.
Tracks: Not Advised.
■ LP . . . . .SKULL 8301
MC . . . . TAPE 78301
Mausoleum / May '84 / Pinnacle.

ROCKIN' MOOD.
Tracks: Rockin' mood / Killers boogie.
■ 7" . . . . RH 100
Red Hot / '79.

SHOCK WAVES.
Tracks: Not Advised.
■ LP . . . . .SKULL 8320
Mausoleum / Apr '84.
MC . . . . TAPE 78320
Mausoleum / Apr '84 / Pinnacle.

WALL OF SOUND.
Tracks: Not Advised.
■ LP . . . . .SKULL 8302
MC . . . . TAPE 78302
Mausoleum / May '84 / Pinnacle.

YOUNG BLOOD.
Tracks: Not Advised.
■ LP .941310
Powerstation / Jul '86.

Killer Dwarfs

BIG DEAL.
Tracks: Tell me please / We stand alone / Startin' to shine / Breakaway / Union of pride / Lifetime / Power / I'm alive / Burn it down / Desperados.
■ LP 4608121
■ MC 4608124
CBS / Jun '88.

DIRTY WEAPONS.
Tracks: Dirty weapons / Nothin' gets nothin' / All that we dream / Doesn't matter / Last laugh / Comin' through / One way out / Appeal / Not foolin' / Want it bad.
CD .4659082
■ LP 4659081
MC 4659084
Epic / Apr '90 / Sony.

KILLER DWARFS.
Tracks: Not Advised.
■ LP . . . . LAT 1178
Noir / Nov '83.
■ LP . . . . GWLP 35
GWR / Aug '89.

Killing Joke

Fronted by singer/keyboard player Jaz Coleman, this British rock band was formed in 1979. In late 1980, group's cult following pushed eponymous debut album to no. 39 in U.K. Band chalked up seven minor U.K. hits, finally cracking Top 20 with 1985's *Love Like Blood*. Hiatus in '90s - during which bassist Youth became star producer - was ended by '94's *Pandemonium*. In the meantime, Joke were credited among influences on acts like Nirvana and Pearl Jam.

(LET'S ALL GO TO THE) FIRE DANCES.
Tracks: (Let's all go to the) fire dances / Dominator.
■ 12" . . . . EGOX 11
■ 7" . . . . EGO 11
E.G. / Jun '83.

ADORATION.
Tracks: Adorations / Exile / Ecstasy (On 12" Double Pack version only.).
■ 7" . . . . EGO 27
E.G. / Aug '86.

AMERICA.
Tracks: America / America (extended mix) (CD & 12" only) / Jihad / Change (CD only).
■ 7" . . . . EGO 40
■ 12" . . . . EGOX 40
E.G. / Apr '88.
■ CD Single . . . . EGOCD 40
E.G. / Aug '88.

BIRDS OF A FEATHER.
Tracks: Birds of a feather.
■ 12" . . . . EGOX 10
■ 7" . . . . EGO 10
E.G. / Oct '82.

BRIGHTER THAN A 1000 SUNS.
Tracks: Adorations / Sanity / Chessboards / Twilight of the moral / Love of the masses / Southern sky / Winter gardens / Rubicon / Goodbye to the village (CD & cassette only) / Victory (CD & cassette only) / Exile.
CD . . . . EGCD 66
■ LP . . . . EGLP 66
■ MC . . . . EGMC 66
E.G. / Nov '86.

CHANGE.
Tracks: Change.
■ 12" . . . . VST 1432
■ CD Single . . . . VSCDT 1432
■ CD Single . . . . VSCDX 1432
■ MC Single . . . . VSC 1432
Virgin / Sep '92.

CHOP CHOP.
Tracks: Chop chop / Good samaritan.
■ 7" .EGO 7
E.G. / Jun '82.

COURTAULD TALKS, THE.
Tracks: Not Advised.
LP Set . . . . INV 004
Invisible / Aug '94 / Plastic Head.

EIGHTIES.
Tracks: Eighties.
■ 12" . . . . EGOX 16
■ 7" . . . . EGO 16
E.G. / Mar '84.

EMPIRE SONG.
Tracks: Empire song / Brilliant.
■ 7" .EGO 4
E.G. / Mar '82.

EXORCISM.
Tracks: Exorcism.
10" .BFLT 11
CD Single . . . . BFLD 11
Big Life / Mar '94 / Pinnacle.

EXTREMITIES, DIRT AND VARIOUS RE-PRESSED EMOTIONS.
Tracks: Money is not our God / Age of greed / Beautiful dead / Extremities / Intravenous / Inside the termite mound / Solitude / North of the border / Slipstream / Kaliyuga / Struggle.
CD . . . . AGR 0544
LP . . . . AGR 0541
MC . . . . AGR 0542
Noise / Nov '90 / Pinnacle.

FIRE DANCES.
Tracks: Gathering / Fun and games / Rejuvenation / Frenzy / Harlequin / Feast of blaze / Song and dance / Dominator / Let's all go (to the fire dances) / Lust almighty.
■ LP . . . . EGMD 60
■ MC . . . . EGMDC 60
E.G. / Jul '83.
CD . . . . EGCD 60
E.G. / '87 / EMI.
■ LP . . . . EGLP 60
■ MC . . . . EGMC 60
E.G. / Jan '87.

■ DELETED

FOLLOW THE LEADERS.
Tracks: Follow the leader / Tension.
- ■ 10"..........................EGMDX 101
- ■ 7"...........................EGMDS 101

E.G. / May '81.

HA - KILLING JOKE LIVE.
Tracks: Psyche / Sun goes down / Pandys are coming / Take take take / Unspeakable / Wardance.
- ■ MC...........................EGMDC 4
- ■ Mini LP......................EGMDT 4

Malicious Damage / Nov '82.
- ■ LP............................EGMLP 3
- ■ MC...........................EGMMC 3

E.G. / '84.

KILLING JOKE.
Tracks: Requiem / War Dance / Tomorrow's World / Bloodsport / Wait / Complications / S.O. 36 / Primitive.
- ■ LP............................EGMD 545
- ■ MC...........................EGMDC 545

E.G. / Oct '80.
- CD.............................EGCD 57

E.G. / '87 / EMI.
- ■ LP............................EGLP 57
- ■ MC...........................EGMC 57

E.G. / Jan '87.

KINGS AND QUEENS.
Tracks: Kings and queens / Madding crowd.
- ■ 12"..........................EGOX 21
- ■ 7"...........................EGO 21

E.G. / Mar '85.

LAUGH I NEARLY BOUGHT ONE!.
Tracks: Turn to red / Pssyche / Requiem / Wardance / Follow the leaders / Unspeakable / Butcher / Exit / Hum / Empire song / Chop-chop / Sun goes down / Eighties / Darkness before dawn / Love like blood / Wintergardens / Age of greed.
- CD.............................CDV 2693
- ■ MC...........................TCV 2693

E.G. / Oct '92.

LOVE LIKE BLOOD, A.
Tracks: Love like blood / Blue feather.
- ■ 12" Remix....................EGOY 20
- ■ 12"..........................EGOX 20
- ■ 7"...........................EGO 20

E.G. / Jan '85.

ME OR YOU?.
Tracks: Me or you / Wilful days.
- ■ 12"..........................EGOX 14
- ■ 7"...........................EGO 14
- ■ 7" Set.......................EGOD 14

E.G. / Oct '83.

MONEY IS NOT OUR GOD.
Tracks: Money is not our God.
- ■ 12"..........................AG 054-6
- ■ CD Single....................AG 054-3

Noise / Dec '90.

MY LOVE OF THIS LAND.
Tracks: My love of this land (On all versions) / Darkness before dawn (On all versions) / Follow the leader (dub) (Not on 7") / Psyche (live) (On 12" only) / Sun goes down (On 10" only).
- ■ 7"...........................EGO 43
- ■ 10"..........................EGOT 43
- ■ 12"..........................EGOX 43

E.G. / Jul '88.

NERVOUS SYSTEM.
Tracks: Almost red / Nervous system / Are you recieving / Turn to red.
- ■ 12"..........................12WIP 6550

Island / Jan '80.

NEW DAY, A.
Tracks: New day / Dance day.
- ■ 12"..........................EGOX 17
- ■ 7"...........................EGO 17

E.G. / Jul '84.

NIGHT TIME.
Tracks: Night time / Darkness before dawn / Love like blood / Kings and Queens / Tabazan / Multitudes / Europe / Eighties.
- CD.............................EGCD 61
- MC.............................EGMC 61
- ■ LP............................EGLP 61

E.G. / Jan '87.

OUTSIDE THE GATE.
Tracks: America / My love of this land / Stay one jump ahead / Unto the ends of the earth / Calling / Obsession / Tiahuanaco / Outside the gate / America (extended mix) (CD only) / Stay one jump ahead (extended mix) (Only on CD).
- CD.............................EGCD 73
- ■ MC...........................EGMC 73

- ■ LP............................EGLP 73

E.G. / May '88.

PANDEMONIUM.
Tracks: Pandemonium / Exorcism / Millennium / Communion / Black moon / Labyrinth / Jana / Whiteout / Pleasures of the flesh / Mathematics of chaos.
- CD.............................BFLCD 09
- LP Set.........................BFLLP 9
- MC.............................BFLMC 09

Big Life / Jul '94 / Pinnacle.

PANDEMONIUM.
Tracks: Pandemonium.
- 12"............................BFLT 17
- MC Single.....................BFTC 17

Big Life / Jul '94 / Pinnacle.

PANDEMONIUM PART 1.
Tracks: Pandemonium part 1.
- CD Single.....................BFLDA 17

Big Life / Jul '94 / Pinnacle.

PANDEMONIUM PART 2.
Tracks: Pandemonium part 2.
- ■ CD Single....................BFLDB 17

Big Life / Jul '94.

PSYCHE.
Tracks: Psyche / War dance.
- ■ 7"...........................MD 540

Malicious Damage / Mar '80.

REVELATIONS.
Tracks: Hum / Empire Song / We have joy / Chop chop / Pandys are coming / Chapter 2 / Have a Nice Day / Land of Milk and Honey / Good Samaritan / Dregs.
- ■ LP............................EGMD 3
- ■ MC...........................EGMDC 3

Malicious Damage / Apr '82.
- ■ LP............................EGLP 59
- ■ CD...........................EGCD 59
- ■ MC...........................EGMC 59

E.G. / Jan '87.

SANITY.
Tracks: Sanity / Goodbye to the village.
- ■ 12"..........................EGOX 30
- ■ 7"...........................EGO 30

E.G. / Oct '86.

WHAT'S THIS FOR.
Tracks: Fall of because / Tension / Unspeakable / Butcher / Who told you how / Follow the leader / Madness / Exit.
- ■ LP............................EGMD 550
- ■ MC...........................EGMDC 550

E.G. / Jun '81.
- CD.............................EGCD 58

E.G. / '87 / EMI.
- ■ MC...........................EGMC 58
- ■ LP............................EGLP 58

E.G. / Jan '87.

Kilzer, John

BUSMAN'S HOLIDAY.
Tracks: Not Advised.
- ■ CD...........................GEFD 24322
- ■ LP............................GEF 24322
- ■ MC...........................GEFC 24322

Geffen / Jul '91.

MEMORY IN THE MAKING.
Tracks: Green, yellow and red / Heart and soul / Red blue jeans / Memory in the making / Pick me up / Give me a highway / Loaded dice / Dream queen / If sidewalks talked / When fools say love / Dirty dishes / I love you.
- ■ CD...........................9241902
- ■ LP............................WX 170
- ■ MC...........................WX 170C

Geffen / Apr '88.

Kinetic Dissent

I WILL FIGHT NO MORE FOREVER.
Tracks: Not Advised.
- CD.............................RO 93272
- LP.............................RO 93271
- MC.............................RO 93274

Roadracer / Jul '91 / Pinnacle.

King Axe

ROCK THE WORLD.
Tracks: Rock the world / Chain / Red line / Devachan / Warrior / We still remember / Great escape / Medusa / Dark crusade / Magic man.
- ■ LP............................RR 9611

Road Runner / Jun '87.

King Crimson

Archetypal art-rockers who occasionally dabbled in hard rock; notably on best-known track *21st Century Schizoid Man*. Have split and reformed twice with modest success. Band leader Robert Fripp has been involved with variety of projects, including Peter Gabriel's early solo career; other Crimson luminaries include Yes drummer Bill Bruford, Bowie/Zappa guitarist Adrian Belew and ELP bassist Greg Lake.

BEAT.
Tracks: Neal and Jack and Me / Heartbeat / Sartori in Tangier / Waiting man / Neurotica / Two Hands / Howler / Requiem.
- CD.............................EGCD 51
- ■ MC...........................EGMC 51
- ■ LP............................EGLP 51

E.G. / Jan '87.

COMPACT COLLECTION.
Tracks: Not Advised.
- CD.............................TPAK 28

Virgin / Nov '93 / EMI.

COMPACT KING CRIMSON, THE.
Tracks: Discipline / Thel hun ginjeet / Matte Kudasai / Three of a perfect pair / Frame by frame / Sleepless / Heartbeat / Elephant talk / 21st century schizoid man / I talk to the wind / Epitaph / March for no reason (part of Epitaph) / Tomorrow and tomorrow (part of Epitaph) / Red (LP & cassette only) / Cat food (LP & cassette only) / Court of the crimson king / Return of the fire witch / Dance of the puppets.
- CD.............................EGCD 68
- ■ Double LP....................EGLP 68
- ■ MC Set.......................EGMC 68

E.G. / Jan '86.

CONCISE KING CRIMSON, THE.
Tracks: 21st Century schizoid man / Epitaph / In the court of the Crimson King (abridged) / Cat food / Ladies in the road / Starless (abridged) / Red / Fallen angel / Elephant talk / Frame by frame / Matte kudesai / Heartbeat / Three of a perfect pair / Sleepless.
- CD.............................CDV 2721
- MC.............................TCV 2721

Virgin / Oct '93 / EMI.

DISCIPLINE.
Tracks: Elephant talk / Frame by frame / Matte Kudasai / Indiscipline / Thel hun ginjeet / Sheltering sky / Discipline.
- ■ MC...........................EGMC 49

E.G. / Jan '87.
- CD.............................EGCD 49
- ■ LP............................EGLP 49

E.G. / Jun '88.

EARTHBOUND.
Tracks: 21st century / Schizoid man / Peoria / Sailors tale / Earthbound / Groon.
- ■ LP............................2343 092

Polydor / Oct '77.

GREAT DECEIVER, THE.
Tracks: Not Advised.
- CD.............................KCDIS 1

Virgin / Nov '92 / EMI.

HEARTBEAT.
Tracks: Heartbeat.
- ■ 7"...........................EGO 6

E.G. / Jun '82.

IN THE COURT OF THE CRIMSON KING.
Tracks: 21st century schizoid man / I talk to the wind / Epitaph / Tomorrow and tomorrow (part of Epitaph) / Moonchild / Illusion (Part of Moonchild.) / Court of the Crimson King / Return Of The fire witch / Dance of the puppets / March for no reason (part of Epitaph) / Dream, The (part of Moonchild).
- ■ LP............................ILPS 9111

Island / Nov '69.
- ■ CD...........................800 030-2

Polydor / May '83.
- CD.............................EGCD 1
- MC.............................EGMC 1
- ■ LP............................EGLP 1

E.G. / Jan '87.

IN THE WAKE OF POSEIDON.
Tracks: Peace a beginning / Pictures of a city / Cadence and cascade / In the wake of Poseidon / Peace-A theme / Cat food / Devil's triangle / Merday Morn (part 1 of the Devil's Triangle) / Hand of Sceiron (Part 2 of the Devil's Triangle) / Garden of worm (part 3 of the Devil's triangle) / Peace-an End.
- ■ LP............................ILPS 9127

Island / May '70.

■ DELETED

MC. . . . . .EGMC 2
■ CD . . . . .EGCD 2
■ LP . . . . .EGLP 2
E.G. / Jan '87.

ISLANDS.
Tracks: Formentera lady / Sailor's tale / Letter /
Ladies of the road / Prelude: song of the gulls /
Islands.
■ LP . . . . ILPS 9175
Island / Jan '72.
■ LP 2302 060
■ MC. 3100 360
Polydor / Apr '77.
■ MC. . . . . .EGMC 5
■ CD . . . . .EGCD 5
■ LP . . . . .EGLP 5
E.G. / Jan '87.

KING CRIMSON BOX SET (Court of the Crimson King / Larks Tongues in Aspic).
Tracks: Not Advised.
CD Set . . . . .EGBC 6
MC Set . . . . .EGBM 6
E.G. / Nov '89 / EMI.

LARK'S TONGUES IN ASPIC, A.
Tracks: Lark's tongues in aspic, (part 1) / Book of
Saturday / Exiles / Easy Money / Talking drum /
Lark's tongues in aspic, (part 2).
■ LP . . . . ILPS 9230
Island / Apr '73.
MC. . . . . .EGMC 7
■ CD . . . . .EGCD 7
■ LP . . . . .EGLP 7
E.G. / Jan '87.

LIZARD.
Tracks: Cirkus / Indoor games / Happy family / Lady
of the dancing water / Lizard / Prince Rupert awakes
(part 1 of Lizard) / Bolero (The peacocks tale) /
Battle of glass tears / Dawn song (part a of battle of
glass tears) / Last skirmish (part b of Battle of Glass
Tears) / Prince Rupert's lament (Part C of Battle of
Glass Tears) / Big top.
■ LP . . . . ILPS 9141
Island / Jan '71.
■ LP . . . . .EGLP 4
■ MC. . . . . .EGMC 4
E.G. / Jan '87.
CD. . . . . .EGCD 4
E.G. / '88 / EMI.

MATTE KUDASAI.
Tracks: Matte Kudasai / Elephant talk.
■ 7" . . . . .EGO 2
E.G. / Dec '81.

RED.
Tracks: Red / Fallen angel / One more red nightmare
/ Providence / Starless.
■ LP . . . . ILPS 9308
Island / Oct '74.
■ LP 2302 066
■ MC. 3100 366
Polydor / Apr '77.
CD. . . . . .EGCD 15
■ LP . . . . .EGLP 15
■ MC. . . . . .EGMC 15
E.G. / Jan '87.

SLEEPLESS.
Tracks: Sleepless / Nuages.
■ 12" . . . . .EGOX 15
■ 7" . . . . .EGO 15
E.G. / Mar '84.

STARLESS AND BIBLE BLACK.
Tracks: Great deceiver / Lament / We'll let you know
/ Night watch / Trio / Mincer / Starless and bible
black / Fracture.
■ LP . . . . ILPS 9275
Island / Apr '74.
■ LP 2302 065
■ MC. 3100 365
Polydor / Mar '77.
CD. . . . . .EGCD 12
E.G. / '87 / EMI.
■ LP . . . . .EGLP 12
■ MC. . . . . .EGMC 12
E.G. / Jan '87.

THREE OF A PERFECT PAIR.
Tracks: Model man / Sleepless / Man with an open
heart / Nuages (that which passes, passes like
clouds) / Dig me / No warning / Lark's tongues in
aspic, (part 3) (In digital stereo) / Three of a perfect
pair / Industry.
■ CD 817 882-2
E.G. / Feb '84.
CD. . . . . .EGCD 55
■ MC. . . . . .EGMC 55
■ LP . . . . .EGLP 55
E.G. / Jan '87.

USA.
Tracks: Lark's tongues in aspic, (part 2) / Lament /
Exiles / Asbury Park (Sandy) / Easy money / 21st
century / Schizoid man.
■ LP 2302 067
Polydor / Dec '79.
■ LP . . . . .EGLP 18
E.G. / '82.

YOUNG PERSON'S GUIDE TO KING CRIMSON.
Tracks: Epitaph / Cadence and cascade / Ladies of
the road / I talk to the wind / Red / Starless / Night
watch / Book of Saturday / Peace - a theme / Cat
food / Groon / Coda from lark's tongue in aspic part
2 / Moonchild / Dream / Illusion / Trio / Court of the
Crimson King / Return of the fire witch / Dance of the
puppets.
■ Double LP 2612 035
■ MC. 3500 123
Polydor / Mar '77.
■ LP . . . . .EGLP 22
E.G. / '80.
CD. . . . . .EGCD 22
E.G. / '86 / EMI.

King Diamond

ABIGAIL.
Tracks: Not Advised.
CD. . . . . RR 349622
■ LP P.Disc. . . . . RR 69622
■ LP . . . . RR 9622
■ MC. . . . . RR 49622
Road Runner / Jun '87.

CONSPIRACY.
Tracks: At the graves / Lies / Wedding dream /
Something weird / Let it be done / Sleepless nights /
Visit from the dead / Amon belongs to them / Victi-
mized / Cremation.
CD. . . . . RR 9461-2
■ LP . . . . RR 9461-1
MC. . . . . RR 9461-4
Road Runner / Aug '89 / Pinnacle.
■ LP P.Disc. . . . . RR 9461 6
Road Runner / Sep '89.

DARK SIDES, THE.
Tracks: Halloween / Tem / No presents for Christmas
/ Shrine / Lake / Phone call.
CD. . . . . RR 24552
■ LP . . . . RR 24551
Road Runner / Oct '88.

EYE, THE.
Tracks: Not Advised.
CD. . . . . RR 93462
LP . . . . RR 93461
MC. . . . . RR 93464
Road Runner / Nov '90 / Pinnacle.

FAMILY GHOST.
Tracks: Family ghost.
■ 12" . . . . RR 125476
Road Runner / '89.

FATAL PORTRAIT.
Tracks: Not Advised.
■ LP . . . . RR 9721
Road Runner / Feb '86.
MC. . . . . RR 97214
Road Runner / Feb '86 / Pinnacle.
CD. . . . . RR 349721
Road Runner / '87 / Pinnacle.

IN CONCERT 1987.
Tracks: Not Advised.
CD. 92872
LP 92871
MC. 92874
Road Runner / Dec '91 / Pinnacle.

LIVE IN EUROPE '87.
Tracks: Not Advised.
CD. . . . . RR 9287 2
Road Runner / Feb '93 / Pinnacle.

NO PRESENTS FOR CHRISTMAS.
Tracks: No presents for Christmas.
■ 12" . . . . RR 125485
Road Runner / Jul '87.

THEM.
Tracks: Not Advised.
CD. . . . . RR 95502
■ LP . . . . RR 95501
MC. . . . . RR 95504
Road Runner / Jul '88 / Pinnacle.

King Kobra

HOME STREET HOME.
Tracks: Home street home / Iron eagle (never say
die).
■ 12" . . . . .12 VHF 35
FM Records / Jan '87.

IRON EAGLE.
Tracks: Iron eagle (never say die) / This raging fire.
■ 7" . . . . .CL 397
Capitol / May '86.

KING KOBRA III.
Tracks: Not Advised.
■ LP . . . . MFN 86
■ MC. . . . . TMFN 86
Music For Nations / Aug '89.
CD. . . . . CDMFN 86
Music For Nations / Aug '89 / Pinnacle.

THRILL OF A LIFETIME.
Tracks: Second time around / Dream on / Feel the
heat / Thrill of a lifetime / Only the strong survive /
Iron eagle (never say die) / Home street home /
Overnight sensation / Raise your hands to rock /
Party animals.
■ LP . . . . .WKFMLP 83
MC. . . . . .WKFMMC 83
FM Records / Mar '87 / FM Revolver / Sony.

Kingdom Come

BAD IMAGE.
Tracks: Passion departed / You're the one / Fake
believer / Friends / Mad queen / Pardon the differ-
ence (but I like it) / Little wild thing / Can't resist /
Talked too much / Glove of stone / Outsider.
CD. 450993148-2
LP 450993148-1
MC. 450993148-4
WEA / Feb '94 / WEA.

CROWN OF THORNS.
Tracks: Crown of thorns / Gone are the days.
■ 7" . . . . ILS 0035
I.R.S. (Illegal) / Feb '83.

DO YOU LIKE IT.
Tracks: Do you like it.
■ 12" . . . . .KCX 3
■ 12" . . . . .KCCV 3
■ 12" P.Disc . . . . KCPDX 3
■ 7" . . . . .KCS 3
■ CD Single . . . . KCCDS 3
Polydor / Apr '89.

GET IT ON.
Tracks: Get it on / 17 / Loving you (Track on 12" and
CD single.).
■ 12" . . . . .KCX 1
■ 12" P.Disc. . . . . .KCXP 1
■ 7" . . . . .KCS 1
■ CD Single . . . . .KCCD 1
Polydor / Mar '88.

GET IT ON (CD VIDEO).
Tracks: Get it on.
CD Video 080 312 2
Polygram Music Video / Oct '88 / PolyGram.

HANDS OF TIME.
Tracks: Not Advised.
■ LP 849 329-1
MC. 849 329-4
■ CD 849 329-2
Polydor / Jun '91.

IN YOUR FACE.
Tracks: Do you like it / Wind / Highway 6 / Just like a
wild rose / Mean dirty Joe / Who do you love / Gotta
go (can't wage a war) / Faith hope and love / In your
face / Moonlight sonata / Waiting on you / Perfect 'O'
/ Overrated / Stargazer.
■ LP 839 192-1
■ MC. 839 192-4
■ CD 839 192-2
Polydor / May '89.

KINGDOM COME.
Tracks: Living out of touch / Pushin' hard / What love
can be / 17 / Shuffle / Get it on / Now 'forever after' /
Hideaway / Loving you / Shout it out.
■ LP . . . . .KCLP 1
■ MC. . . . . .KCMC 1
■ CD 835 368-2
Polydor / Mar '88.

KINGDOM COME: INTERVIEW PICTURE DISC.
Tracks: Not Advised.
LP P.Disc . . . . .BAK 2149
Baktabak / Oct '89 / Arabesque Ltd.

OVERRATED.
Tracks: Overrated.
- 12".................................KCX 4
- 7".................................KCCV 4
- CD Single......................KCCDS 4
- 10".............................KCCVX 4
- 7".................................KCS 4

Polydor / Sep '89.

WHAT LOVE CAN BE.
Tracks: What love can be.
- CD Single.......................KCCD2
- 12".................................KCX 2
- 12".................................KCXG2
- 7".................................KCS 2
- 7".................................KCSC 2

Polydor / Jul '88.

KingOfTheHill

I DO U.
Tracks: I do U (CHR mix) (Not on 12") / Something
'bout you / I do U (single version) (12" & CD single
only) / Take it or leave it (Kingadahill) (12" & CD
single only).
- 12"..............................12KOTH 1
- 7"................................KOTHS 1
- 7"................................KOTH 1
- CD Single....................CDKOTH 1

SBK / Jun '91.

IF I SAY.
Tracks: If I say / Purple haze / I do u (Only on CD
Single.).
- 12".............................12KOTHP 2
- 7"...............................KOTHS 2
- CD Single...................CDKOTH 2

EMI / Oct '91.

KING OF THE HILL.
Tracks: Party in my pocket / Freak show / I do u / If I
say / Roses / Take it or leave it (Kingadahill) /
Something 'bout you / Place in my heart / Big groove
/ Electric riot.
- LP................................SBKLP 15
- MC................................SBKTC 15
- CD................................SBKCD 15

SBK / Aug '91.

Kings Of Sun

BLACK LEATHER.
Tracks: Black leather / Bad love.
- 12"................................PT 49536
- 7"................................PB 49535

RCA / Sep '88.

FULL FRONTAL ATTACK.
Tracks: Crazy / Lock me up / Drop the gun / There is
danger / Hooked on it / Vampire / Rescue me / Full
frontal attack / Howling wind / I get lonely / Haunt
you baby / Overdrive.
- CD................................PD 90470
- LP................................PL 90470
- MC...............................PK 90470

RCA / Sep '90.

KINGS OF THE SUN.
Tracks: Serpentine / Get on up / Black leather /
Tomboy / Hot to trott / Vicious delicious / Jealous /
Bottom of my heart / Cry 4 love / Medicine man / Bad
love / Wildcat (CD only).
- MC...............................PK 86826
- LP................................PL 86826

RCA / Nov '88.
- CD................................PD 86826

RCA / Nov '88.

Kings X

CHRONICLES.
Tracks: Not Advised.
- VHS..........................8536501943

Warner Music Video / Oct '92 / WEA.

DOGMAN.
Tracks: Dogman / Shoes / Pretend / Flies and blue
skies / Black the sky / Fool you / Don't care /
Sunshine rain / Complain / Human behaviour / Ci-
garettes / Go to hell / Pillow / Manic depression.
- CD.............................756782558-2
- LP.............................756782558-1
- MC............................756782558-0

WEA / Jan '94 / WEA.

FAITH, HOPE, LOVE.
Tracks: We are finding who we are / It's love / I'll
never get tired of you / Fine art of friendship / Mr.
Wilson / Moanjam / Six broken soldiers / I can't help
it / Talk to you / Everywhere I go / We were born to
be in love / Faith, hope, love / Legal kill.
- CD.............................7567821452

- LP.................................7567821451
- MC................................7567821454

Megaforce / Oct '90 / Pinnacle.

GRETCHEN GOES TO NEBRASKA.
Tracks: Out of the silent planet / Over my head /
Summerland / Everybody knows a little bit of some-
thing / Difference, The (in the garden of St. Anne's-
On-The-Hill) / I'll never be the same / Mission / Fall
on me / Pleiades / Don't believe it (it's easier said
than done) / Send a message / Burning down.
- CD.................................781 997-2
- LP....................................WX 279
- MC.................................WX 279C

Atlantic / Jun '89.

IT'S LOVE.
Tracks: It's love / You were born to be love / Six
broken soldiers (Not available on 7" format.).
- 7"....................................A 7791
- MC Single.........................A 7791C
- 12"..................................A 7791T
- CD Single.........................A 7791CD

Megaforce / Jan '91.

KINGS X.
Tracks: World around me / Prisoner / Big picture /
Lost in Germany / Chariot song / Ooh song / Junior's
gone wild / Now just for the dead / What I know about
love / Black flag / Dream in my life / Silent wind.
- LP.............................7567805061
- MC............................7567805064

Atlantic / Mar '92 / WEA.
- CD.............................7567805062

Atlantic / Mar '94 / WEA.

OUT OF THE SILENT PLANET.
Tracks: In the new age / Goldilox / Power of love /
Wonder / Sometimes / King / What is this / Far, far,
away / Shot of love / Visions.
- CD..............................K 781825-2
- LP...............................K 781825-1
- MC.............................K 781825-4

Megaforce / Mar '88.

OVER MY HEAD.
Tracks: Over my head / King / Shot of love / I'll never
be the same.
- 12"..................................A 8982T
- 7"...................................A 8982
- MC Single.........................A 8982C

Atlantic / Mar '90.

Kiss

Among the best-selling and most influential
of metal bands, Kiss were formed in 1972,
although breakthrough came only with 1975
Alive! album. Reputation was enhanced by
refusal to be photographed without elabor-
ate make-up and costumes. Emphasis on
image and merchandising obscured series
of high-quality albums, of which 1975's Destroyer is best-regarded. Declining fortunes
led to removal of make-up in 1983. Highlights of subsequent career include hit singles Crazy, Crazy Nights and God Gave
Rock And Roll To You. 1994 tribute album
Kiss My Ass featured diverse cast, including Garth Brooks, Anthrax, Stevie Wonder
and Dinosaur Jr.

2000 MAN.
Tracks: 2000 man / I was made for loving you / Sure
know something.
- EP.................................NB 1001

Casablanca / Feb '80.

ACE FREHLEY SOLO ALBUM (see under
Frehley, Ace).

ALIVE.
Tracks: Deuce / Strutter / Got to choose / Hotter than
hell / Firehouse / Nothin' to lose / C'mon and love
me / Parasite / She / Watchin' you / 100,000 years /
Black diamond / Rock bottom / Cold gin / Rock and
roll all nite / Let me go rock 'n' roll.
- Double LP....................CALD 5004

Casablanca / Dec '77.
- Double LP........................6640026

Casablanca / Apr '82.
- Double LP..........................PRID 3
- MC Set...........................PRIDC 3

Casablanca / Sep '84.
- CD.................................822 780-2

Casablanca / Apr '87.

ALIVE VOL 3.
Tracks: Creatures of the night / Deuce / I just wanna
/ Unholy / Heaven's on fire / Watchin' you / Domino /

I was made for lovin' you / I still love you / Rock 'n
roll all night / Lick it up / Forever / Take it off / I love
it loud / Detroit rock city / God gave rock 'n' roll to
you / Star spangled banner.
- CD.................................514 827-2
- MC................................514 827-4

Vertigo / May '93 / PolyGram.

ANIMALIZE.
Tracks: I have had enough (Into the fire) / Heaven's on
fire / Burn bitch burn / Get all you can take / Lonely
is the hunter / Under the gun / Thrills of the night /
While the city sleeps / Murder in high heels.
- CD.................................822 495-2

Vertigo / Nov '84 / PolyGram.
- LP....................................VERL 18
- MC.................................VERLC 18

Vertigo / Sep '84 / PolyGram.

ANIMALIZE (Live Un-Censored).
Tracks: Not Advised.
- VHS................................EV 5606

Embassy Home Video / Jan '86 / Sony.
- VHS..............................CFV 06322

Channel 5 / Apr '87 / Channel 5 Video / P.R.O. Video
/ Gold & Sons.

ASYLUM.
Tracks: King of the mountain / Any way you slice it /
Who wants to be lonely / Trial by fire / I'm alive /
Love's a deadly weapon / Tears are falling / Secretly
cruel / Radar for love / Uh all night.
- CD.................................826 099-2
- LP...................................VERH 32
- MC.................................VERHC 32

Vertigo / Sep '85 / PolyGram.

BEST OF SOLO ALBUMS.
Tracks: Not Advised.
- MC................................7144060

Casablanca / Nov '87.

CRAZY CRAZY NIGHTS.
Tracks: Not Advised.
- LP...................................VERH 49
- MC.................................VERHC 49

Vertigo / Oct '87 / PolyGram.
- CD.................................832 626-2

Vertigo / Feb '91 / PolyGram.

CRAZY CRAZY NIGHTS.
Tracks: Crazy crazy nights / No, no, no / Lick it up
(Only on 12" single.) / Uh all night (Only on 12"
single.).
- 12"..................................KISS 712
- 12" P.Disc.....................KISSP 712
- 7"....................................KISS 7
- 7" P.Disc.......................KISSP 7

Vertigo / Sep '87.

CRAZY CRAZY NIGHTS.
Tracks: Not Advised.
- VHS..............................CFV 07782

Channel 5 / Aug '88 / Channel 5 Video / P.R.O. Video
/ Gold & Sons.
- CD Video.......................080 232 2

Polygram Music Video / Oct '88 / PolyGram.

CREATURES OF THE NIGHT.
Tracks: Creatures of the night / Saint and sinner /
Keep me comin' / Rock and roll hell / Danger / I love
it loud / I still love you / Killer / War machine.
- LP....................................CANL 4

Casablanca / Jun '82.
- CD.................................8241542

Casablanca / Aug '88.

CREATURES OF THE NIGHT.
Tracks: Creatures of the night / Rock 'n' roll all nite.
- 12"..................................KISS 412
- 7"....................................KISS 4

Casablanca / Apr '83.

DESTROYER.
Tracks: Detroit rock city / King of the night time
world / God of thunder / Great expectations / Flaming youth / Sweet pain / Shout it out loud / Beth / Do
you love me.
- LP...............................CBSP 4008

Casablanca / May '76.
- LP....................................6399064

Casablanca / Apr '82.
- LP....................................PRICE 41
- MC.................................PRIMC 41

Casablanca / Oct '83.
- CD.................................824 149-2

Casablanca / Apr '87.

DOUBLE PLATINUM.
Tracks: Strutter 78 / Do you love me / Hard woman /
Calling Dr. Love / Let me go Rock 'n' Roll / Love gun
/ God of thunder / Firehouse / Hotter than hell / I
want you / Deuce / 100,000 Years / Detroit rock city /

■ DELETED   K 5

She / Rock and Roll all nite / Beth / Making love /
C'mon and love me / Cold gin / Black diamond.
■ **LP** 6641907
Casablanca / '78.
CD 824 499 2
■ **LP** . . . . .PRID 8
■ **MC** . . . . .PRIDC 8
Casablanca / Mar '85.
CD 824 155-2
Casablanca / Apr '87.

DRESSED TO KILL.
Tracks: Room service / Two timer / Ladies in waiting
/ Get away / Rock bottom / C'mon and love me /
Anything for my baby / She / Love her all I can / Rock
and roll all nite / Detroit rock city / King of the night
time world / God of thunder / Great expectations /
Flaming youth / Sweet pain / Shout it out loud / Beth
/ Do you love me.
■ **LP** 6399 059
MC 7199 059
Casablanca / Feb '82.
CD 8241482
Casablanca / Aug '88.

DYNASTY.
Tracks: I was made for lovin' you / 2,000 man / Sure
know something / Dirty livin' / Charisma / Magic
touch / Hard times / X-ray eyes / Save your love /
Dynasty.
■ **LP** . . . . CALH 2051
Casablanca / Jul '79.
■ **LP** 9128024
Casablanca / Apr '82.
MC . . . . PRIMC 42
■ **LP** . . . . PRICE 42
Casablanca / Oct '83.
CD 8127702
Casablanca / Aug '88.

ELDER, THE.
Tracks: Oath / Fanfare / Just a boy / Dark light / Only
you / Under the rose / World without heroes / Mr.
Blackwell / Escape from the island / Odyssey / I.
■ **LP** 6302 163
MC 7144 163
Casablanca / Nov '81.
■ **CD** 825 153-2
Casablanca / Jun '89.

EXPOSED.
Tracks: Not Advised.
VHS 041 489 2
Polygram Music Video / Oct '87 / PolyGram.
CD Video 080 100 1
Polygram Music Video / Oct '88 / PolyGram.
VHS . . . . CFV 08072
Polygram Music Video / Sep '89 / PolyGram.
VHS 0835443
4 Front / '91 / PolyGram Video.

FIFTEEN YEARS ON THE INTERVIEW.
Tracks: Not Advised.
CD P.Disc . . . . CBAK 4002
Baktabak / Apr '88 / Arabesque Ltd.

FOREVER (REMIX).
Tracks: Forever (remix) / Street giveth and the street
taketh away / All American men (12" only) / Shandi
(12" only) / Oath (12" only) / Creatures of the night /
Lick it up / Heaven's on fire (CD only) / Deuce
(original demo version) (12" Gatefold only) / Strutter
(original demo version) (12" Gatefold only).
■ **12"** . . . . KISSX 11
■ **7"** . . . . KISS 11
■ **CD Single** . . . . KISCD 11
■ **12"** . . . . KISXG 11
■ **7" P.Disc** . . . . KISSP 11
Vertigo / Mar '90.

FRAMED (Interview Picture Disc).
Tracks: Not Advised.
LP . . . . BAK 6005
MC . . . . MBAK 6005
Baktabak / Jun '90 / Arabesque Ltd.

GENE SIMMONS SOLO ALBUM (see under Simmons, Gene (1)).

GOD GAVE ROCK 'N' ROLL TO YOU II.
Tracks: God gave rock 'n' roll to you II / Junior's
gone wild / Shout it out (Only on 12PD & CD single.).
■ **12" P.Disc** . . . . 88696 TP
■ **7"** 88696
■ **CD Single** . . . . 88696 CD
■ **MC Single** . . . . 88696 C
East West / Dec '91.

HEAVEN'S ON FIRE.
Tracks: Heaven's on fire / Lonely is the hunter.
■ **12"** . . . . .VERX 12
■ **7"** . . . . VER 12
Vertigo / Sep '84.

HIDE YOUR HEART.
Tracks: Hide your heart.
■ **10"** . . . . KISP 1010
■ **12"** . . . . KISSX 10
■ **7"** . . . . KISR 10
■ **7"** . . . . KISS 10
■ **CD Single** . . . . KISCD 10
■ **MC Single** . . . . KISMC 10
Vertigo / Oct '89.

HOT IN THE SHADE.
Tracks: Rise to it / Betrayed / Hide your heart /
Prisoners of love / Read my body / Love's a slap in
the face / Forever / Silver spoon / Cadillac dreams /
King of hearts / St. Giveth St. Taketh Away / You love
me to hate you / Somewhere between heaven and
hell / Little Caesar / Boomerang.
■ **CD** 8389132
■ **LP** 8389131
■ **MC** 8389134
Fontana / Oct '89.

HOTTER THAN HELL.
Tracks: Get to choose / Parasite / Goin' blind / Hotter
than hell / Let me go rock 'n' roll / All the way /
Watchin' you / Mainline / Comin' home /
Strangeways.
■ **LP** 6399 058
MC 7199 058
Casablanca / Feb '82.
CD 8241472
Casablanca / Aug '88.

I WAS MADE FOR LOVING YOU.
Tracks: I was made for lovin' you / Hard times.
■ **7"** . . . . .CAN 152
Casablanca / Jun '79.

I WAS MADE FOR LOVING YOU (IMPORT).
Tracks: I was made for loving you / Hard times.
■ **12"** 6000562
Casablanca / Sep '88.

KILLER.
Tracks: Killer / Love it loud / I was made for lovin'
you.
■ **7"** . . . . KISS 312
Casablanca / Dec '82.

KILLERS.
Tracks: I'm a legend tonight / Down on your knees /
Could gin / Love gin / Shout it out loud / Sure know
something / Nowhere to run / Partners in crime /
Detroit rock city / God of thunder / I was made for
loving you / Rock and roll all nite.
■ **LP** . . . . CANL 1
Casablanca / Jun '82.

KISS.
Tracks: Strutter / Nothin' to lose / Firehouse / Cold
gin / Let me know / Kissin' time / Deuce / Kiss love
theme / 100,000 years / Black diamond.
■ **LP** . . . . PRICE 68
■ **MC** . . . . PRIMC 68
Casablanca / Jul '84.
■ **CD** 8241462
Casablanca / Aug '88.

KISS ALIVE, 2.
Tracks: Detroit rock city / King of the night time
world / Ladies room / Making love / Love gun /
Calling Dr. Love / Christine sixteen / Shock me /
Hard luck woman / Tomorrow and tonight / I stole
your love / Beth / God of thunder / I want you / Shout
it out loud / All American men / Rockin' in the USA /
Larger than life / Rocket ride / Anyway you want it.
■ **LP** . . . . .CBSP 401
Casablanca / Jun '76.
■ **Double LP** 6685 043
MC 7599 512
Casablanca / Feb '82.
CD 822 781-2
Casablanca / May '89.

KISS: INTERVIEW PIC DISC COLLECTION.
Tracks: House arrest / Jack's back.
7" Set . . . . BAKPAK 1002
Baktabak / Oct '87 / Arabesque Ltd.

KISS: INTERVIEW PICTURE DISC.
Tracks: Not Advised.
■ **LP P.Disc** . . . . CT 1012
Music & Media / Dec '87.
LP P.Disc . . . . BAK 2026
Baktabak / Jun '87 / Arabesque Ltd.

LICK IT UP.
Tracks: Not Advised.
CD 814 297 2
Vertigo / '83 / PolyGram.
■ **LP** . . . . VERL 9

■ **MC** . . . . VERLC 9
Vertigo / Oct '83.

LICK IT UP.
Tracks: Lick it up / Not for the innocent.
■ **12"** .KISS 005 12
■ **7"** . . . . KISS 005
Casablanca / Oct '83.

LICK IT UP (CD VIDEO).
Tracks: Not Advised.
CD Video 080 044 2
Polygram Music Video / Sep '89 / PolyGram.

LOVE GUN.
Tracks: I stole your love / Christine sixteen / Got love
for sale / Shock me / Tomorrow and tonight / Love
gun / Hooligan / Almost human / Plaster caster /
Then she kissed me.
■ **LP** 6399063
Casablanca / Apr '82.
■ **LP** . . . . PRICE 69
■ **MC** . . . . PRIMC 69
Casablanca / Jul '84.
CD 8241512
Casablanca / Aug '88.

MUSIC AND MEDIA INTERVIEW PIC-TURE DISC.
Tracks: Not Advised.
■ **LP P.Disc** . . . . KISS 1001
■ **LP P.Disc** . . . . MM 1205
Music & Media / Feb '88.

NOTHIN' TO LOSE.
Tracks: Nothin' to lose.
■ **7"** . . . . .CBX 503
Casablanca / Jan '75.

PAUL STANLEY SOLO ALBUM (see under Stanley, Paul).

PHANTOM OF THE PARK, THE.
Tracks: Not Advised.
■ **VHS** . . . . .IVSV 1051
IVS (video) / Apr '87.
■ **VHS** . . . . HEN 2063
Hendring Video / Dec '87.

REASON TO LIVE.
Tracks: Reason to live / Thief in the night / Who
wants to be lonely (Only on 12" and CD single.) /
Thrills in the night / Tears are falling (Only on CD
single.) / Crazy crazy nights (Only on CD single.).
■ **MC Single** . . . . .KISS MC8
Vertigo / Dec '87.
■ **12"** . . . . KISS 812
■ **7"** . . . . .KISS 8
■ **CD Single** . . . . KISCD 8
Vertigo / Nov '87.
■ **7" P.Disc** . . . . KISSP 8
Vertigo / '88.

REVENGE.
Tracks: Unholy / Take it off / Tough love / Spit / God
gave rock 'n' roll to you II / Domino / Heart of chrome
/ Thou shall not / Every time I look at you / Paralyzed
/ I just wanna / Carr jam 1981.
■ **LP** 8480371
■ **CD** 8480372
■ **MC** 8480374
Mercury / Apr '92.
DCC 848 037-5
Mercury / Jan '93 / PolyGram.

ROCK AND ROLL ALL NITE.
Tracks: Rock and roll all nite / Anything for my baby.
■ **7"** . . . . .CBX 510
Casablanca / Jun '75.

ROCK AND ROLL OVER.
Tracks: I want you / Take me / Calling Dr. Love /
Ladies room / Baby driver / Love 'em and leave 'em
/ Mr. Speed / See you in your dreams / Hard luck
woman / Making love.
■ **LP** 6399 060
MC 7199 060
Casablanca / Feb '82.
CD 8241502
Casablanca / Aug '88.

ROCKET RIDE.
Tracks: Rocket ride / Detroit rock city / Love gun.
■ **7"** . . . . .CAN 117
Casablanca / Feb '78.

SMASHES, TRASHES AND HITS.
Tracks: Let's put the 'x' in sex / Crazy crazy nights /
(You make me) rock hard / Love gun / Detroit rock
city / I love it loud / Deuce / Lick it up / Heaven's on
fire / Strutter / Beth (Lead vocals: Eric Carr.) / Tears
are falling / I was made for lovin' you / Rock and roll
all nite / Shout it out loud.
CD 836 427-2

■ **DELETED**

■ LP 836 427-1
■ MC. 836 427-4
Vertigo / Nov '88.

TALK TO ME.
Tracks: Talk to me / She's so European.
■ 7" . . . . MER 19
Mercury / Jun '80.

TEARS ARE FALLING.
Tracks: Tears are falling / Heaven's on fire.
■ 12" . . . . KISS 612
■ 7" . . . . KISS 6
Vertigo / Oct '85.

TEARS ARE FALLING (CD VIDEO).
Tracks: Not Advised.
CD Video 080 058 2
Polygram Music Video / Sep '89 / PolyGram.

TURN ON THE NIGHT.
Tracks: Turn on the night / Hell or high water / King of the mountain (Only on 12") / Any way you slice it (Only on 12") / Crazy crazy nights / Reason to live.
■ 12" . . . . KISS 912
■ 7" . . . . KISS 9
■ 7" P.Disc . . . . KISSP 9
■ CD Single . . . . KISCD 9
Vertigo / Aug '88.

UNHOLY.
Tracks: Unholy / God gave rock 'n' roll to you II (Only available on 7" MC and CD Single.) / Partners in crime (Only available on 7" MC and CD Single.) / Deuce (Only available on 12" and CD Single.) / Strutter (Only available on 12" and CD Single.).
■ 12" . . . . KISS 1212
■ CD Single . . . . KISCD 12
■ 7" . . . . KISS 12
■ MC Single . . . . KISMC 12
Mercury / Apr '92.

UNMASKED.
Tracks: Is that you / Shandy / What makes the world go round / Talk to me / Naked city / Torpedo / Tomorrow / Two sides of the coin / She's no European / Easy as it seems / Tears are falling.
CD 800 041-2
Casablanca / May '83.
■ LP 6302032
Casablanca / Nov '87.

WHAT MAKES THE WORLD GO ROUND.
Tracks: What makes the world go round / Naked city.
■ 7" . . . . KISS 1
Mercury / Sep '80.

WORLD WITHOUT HEROES, A.
Tracks: World without heroes / Mr. Blackwell.
■ 7" . . . . KISS 2
Casablanca / Feb '82.

Kiss Of The Gypsy

TAKE THIS OLD HEART.
Tracks: Take this old heart / Straight talk / Tough enough (Only on 12" and CD single) / Easy does it (Only on 12" single) / Infatuation (Only on CD single).
■ 12" . . . . A 7474 T
■ 7" . . . . A 7474
■ CD Single . . . . A 74 74 CD
■ MC Single . . . . A 7474 C
Atlantic / May '92.

WHATEVER IT TAKES.
Tracks: Whatever it takes.
■ 10" . . . . A 5994 TE
■ CD Single . . . . A 5994 CD
Atlantic / Sep '91.

Kix

BLOW MY FUSE.
Tracks: Blow my fuse / Boomerang / Dirty boys / Cold blood / Get it while it's hot / She dropped me the bomb / Piece of pie.
■ LP . . . . K 781 877 1
■ CD . . . . K 781 877 2
■ MC. K 781 877 4
Atlantic / Sep '88.

COOL KIDS.
Tracks: Cool kids / Mighty mouth.
■ 7" . . . . A 9810
Atlantic / Jun '83.

DON'T CLOSE YOUR EYES.
Tracks: Don't close your eyes / Get it while it's hot / She dropped me the bomb (Available on 12" format only.).
■ 12" . . . . A 7889T
■ 7" . . . . A 7889
Atlantic / Jan '90.

FEAR OF FLYING.
Tracks: Fear of flying / Werewolf talking.
■ 7" . . . . CR 205
Creole / Aug '80.

HOT WIRE.
Tracks: Hot wire / Girl money / Luv-a-holic / Tear down the walls / Bump the la la / Rock & roll overdose / Cold chills / Same Jane / Pants on fire (liar, liar) / Hee bee jee bee crush.
CD 7567917142
■ LP 7567917141
MC. 7567917144
East West / Jul '91 / WEA.

MIDNITE DYNAMITE.
Tracks: Midnite dynamite / Red hot / Bang bang / Layin' rubber / Walking away / Scarlet fever / Cry baby / Cold shower / Lies like a rug / Sex.
■ LP 781 267-1
Atlantic / Oct '85.

Konkhra

SEXUAL AFFECTIVE DISORDER.
Tracks: Not Advised.
CD . . . . NB 105CD
LP . . . . NB 105
Nuclear Blast / Mar '94 / Plastic Head.

STRANDED.
Tracks: Not Advised.
CD . . . . CD 7913002
Progress Red / Jun '93 / Plastic Head.

Kooga

DON'T BREAK MY HEART.
Tracks: Don't break my heart / Lay down your love.
■ 7" . . . . KO 1
Beserkley / Mar '88.

Kossoff, Paul

BACK STREET CRAWLER.
Tracks: I'm ready / Time away / Molton gold / Back-street crawler / Tuesday morning.
■ MC. ICM 9264
■ LP . . . . ILPM 9264
Island / Apr '87.
CD . . . . IMCD 84
Island / Feb '90 / PolyGram.

BLUE SOUL.
Tracks: Over the green hills (Part 1) / Worry / Moonshine / Trouble on double time / Crossroads / Oh I wept / We got time / Oh how we danced / Stealer / Hold on / Catch a train / Come together in the morning / Molten gold / I know why the sun don't shine / Tricky Dicky rides again / I'm ready / Blue soul.
■ LP . . . . PKSP 100
Island / Apr '86.
MC. . . . . PKC 100
Island / Oct '86 / PolyGram.
CD . . . . IMCD 144
Island / Jul '92 / PolyGram.

CROYDON - JUNE 15TH 1975.
Tracks: Not Advised.
■ Double LP . . . . SDLP 1002
Street Tunes / Sep '83.

HUNTER, THE.
Tracks: Not Advised.
■ LP . . . . STLP 001
Street Tunes / Aug '83.

KOSS.
Tracks: Worm / Song of yesterday / Mr. Big / Time away / Hole in the head / You and me / You've taken hold of me / Molten gold / Side kick to the stars / Never take me alive / Band plays on / It's a long way down to the top / Train song / Hunter / We won / Bird dog blues.
■ Double LP . . . . SDLP 1001
Street Tunes / Aug '83.
■ MC. CLAMC 127
■ LP . . . . CLALP 127
Castle Classics / '87.
■ CD . . . . CLACD 127
Castle Classics / Jul '87.

KOSSOFF, KIRKE, TETSU, RABBIT (Kossoff/Kirke/Tetsu/Rabbit).
Tracks: Bluegrass / Sammy's alright / Anna / Just for the box / Hold on / Fool's life / Yellow house / Dying fire / I'm on the run / Colours.
■ LP . . . . ILPS 9188
Island / '72.
CD . . . . IMCD 139

■ MC. ICM 9188
Island / Aug '91 / PolyGram.

LEAVES IN THE WIND.
Tracks: Not Advised.
■ LP . . . . STLP 002
Street Tunes / Aug '83.

MR BIG.
Tracks: Not Advised.
MC. . . . . STC 0012
Street Tunes / Nov '83 / Pinnacle.

Kotzen, Richie

ELECTRIC JOY.
Tracks: Not Advised.
CD . . . . RR 9290 2
LP . . . . RR 9290 1
■ MC. RR 9290 4
Road Runner / Sep '91.

FEVER DREAM.
Tracks: Not Advised.
CD . . . . RR 93672
LP . . . . RR 93671
■ MC. RR 93674
Road Runner / Sep '90.

RICHIE KOTZEN.
Tracks: Squeeze play / Strut it / Unsafe at any speed / Rat trap / Cryptic script / Plaid plesiosaur / Spider legs / Jocose Jenny / Noblesse oblige.
■ LP . . . . RR 9468 1
MC. . . . . RR 94684
■ CD . . . . RR 9468 2
Road Runner / Jul '89.

Kreator

Kreator smashed out of Essen in 1985 with *Endless Pain*, spearheading avalanche of German thrash metal. After series of well-received albums, of which best is *Pleasure To Kill*, 1992's *Renewal* album widened style to encompass industrial influence. Mainman Mille Petrozza also threatened thrash version of Pink Floyd's *The Wall*.

AFTER THE ATTACK.
Tracks: Not Advised.
■ LP P.Disc . . . . N 0072
Noise / May '87.

BEHIND THE MIRROR.
Tracks: Behind the mirror / Gangland.
■ 12" . . . . NOISE 084T
Noise / Oct '87.

COMA OF SOULS.
Tracks: Not Advised.
■ CD . . . . CDNUK 158
■ MC. ZCNUK 158
Noise / Nov '90.
■ LP . . . . NUK 158
Noise / Oct '90.

ENDLESS PAIN.
Tracks: Endless pain / Total death / Storm of the beast / Son of evil / Flag of hate / Cry war / Bonebreaker / Living in fear / Dying victims.
■ CD . . . . CDNUK 025
■ LP . . . . NUK 025
Noise / Oct '89.

EXTREME AGGRESSION.
Tracks: Extreme aggression / No reason to exist / Love us or hate us / Stream of consciousness / Some pain will last / Betrayer / Don't trust / Bringer of torture / Fatal energy.
■ CD . . . . CDNUK 129
■ LP . . . . NUK 129
■ MC. ZCNUK 129
Noise / Feb '89.
■ LP P.Disc . . . . NUKPD 145
Noise / Nov '89.

EXTREME AGGRESSION TOUR 89/90.
Tracks: Not Advised.
VHS . . . . NFV 107
Fotodisk Video / May '90.

FLAG OF HATE.
Tracks: Not Advised.
■ 12" 12NUK 047
■ 12" P.Disc. . . . . NUKPD 084
Noise / Oct '89.

OUT OF THE DARK.
Tracks: Not Advised.
CD . . . . N 02002
Noise / Sep '92 / Pinnacle.

OUT OF THE DARK, INTO THE LIGHT.
Tracks: Not Advised.
■ Mini LP . . . . .NUK 118
Noise / Aug '88.

PLEASURE TO KILL.
Tracks: Not Advised.
■ LP . . . . .N 0037
Noise / Apr '86.
■ CD .CDNUK 037
■ LP . . . . .NUK 037
Noise / Oct '89.

RENEWAL.
Tracks: Not Advised.
CD . . . . .NO 1932
LP . . . . .NO 1931
MC . . . . .NO 1934
Noise / Oct '92 / Pinnacle.

TERRIBLE CERTAINTY.
Tracks: Blind faith / Storming with menace / Terrible certainty / As the world burns / Toxic trace / No escape / One of us / Behind to mirror.
■ CD .CDNUK 086
Noise / Nov '89.
■ LP . . . . .NUK 086
■ MC .ZCNUK 086
Noise / Oct '89.

Krokus

Krokus were briefly musical ambassadors for Switzerland, a nation unremarked for rock success stories. Formed in 1978, by 1981 their UK following was sufficent to place second album *Hardware* at no. 44. Band split in 1990 after minor U.S. success, personnel upheavals and series of derivative albums.

ALIVE AND SCREAMIN'.
Tracks: Long stick goes boom / Eat the rich / Screaming in the night / Hot shot city / Midnite maniac / Bedside radio / Lay me down / Stayed awake all night / Headhunter.
■ LP 208025
■ MC 408025
■ CD 258025
Arista / Feb '87.

AMERICAN WOMAN.
Tracks: American woman / Long stick goes boom.
■ 7" .ARIST 468
Arista / '82.

BAD BOYS RAG DOLLS.
Tracks: Bad boys rag dolls / Save me.
■ 7" .ARIST 451
Arista / '82.

BALLROOM BLITZ.
Tracks: Ballroom blitz / Ready to rock.
■ 12" . . . . .ARIST 12579
■ 7" .ARIST 579
Arista / Nov '84.

BLITZ, THE.
Tracks: Midnite maniac / Out of control / Boxes nite out / Our love / Out to lunch / Ballroom blitz / Rock the nations / Hot stuff / Ready to rock.
■ LP 206494
■ MC 406494
Arista / Aug '84.
CD 610198
Arista / '88 / BMG.

CHANGE OF ADDRESS.
Tracks: Now / Hot shot city / School's out / Let this love begin / Burning up the night / Say goodbye / World on fire / Hard luck hero / Long way from home.
■ MC 407.647
■ LP 607.647
Ariola / Jun '86.

HARDWARE.
Tracks: Celebration / Easy rocker / Smelly nelly / Mr. 69 / She's got everything / Burning bones / Rock city / Winning man / Mad racket.
■ LP .ARL 5064
■ MC . . . . .ZCART 5064
Arista / Feb '81.

HEADHUNTER.
Tracks: Headhunter / Eat the rich / Screaming in the night / Ready to burn / Night wolf / Stayed awake all night / Stand and be counted / White din / Russian Winter.
■ LP 205255
■ MC 405255
Arista / Apr '83.
■ CD 255255
Arista / Apr '88.
■ LP 209080
Arista / May '88.
■ MC 409080
Arista / Apr '88.

HEART ATTACK.
Tracks: Everybody rocks / Wild love / Let it go / Winning man / Axx attack / Rock 'n' roll / Flyin' high / Shoot down the night / Bad bad girl / Speed up.
■ LP . . . . .IMCA 42087
■ MC . . . . .UNCAC 42087
■ CD . . . . .MCAD 42087
MCA / Mar '88.

HEATSTROKES.
Tracks: Heatstrokes / Shy kid.
■ 7" . . . . .ARO 233
Ariola / Jun '80.

INDUSTRIAL STRENGTH (EP).
Tracks: Bedside radio / Easy rocker / Celebration / Bye bye baby.
■ 7" . . . . .ARO 258
Ariola / May '81.

METAL RENDEZVOUS.
Tracks: Heatstrokes / Bedside radio / Come on / Streamer / Shy kid / Tokyo nights / Lady double dealer / Fire / No way / Backseat rock 'n' roll.
■ LP .ARL 5056
■ MC . . . . .ZCARL 5056
Ariola / Sep '82.
■ CD 259048
Arista / Jun '88.

ONE VICE AT A TIME.
Tracks: Long stick goes boom / Bad boys / Rag dolls / Playing the outlaw / To the top / Down the drain / American woman / I'm on the run / Save me / Rock 'n' roll.
■ LP . . . . .SPART 1189
■ MC . . . . .TCART 1189
Arista / Feb '82.

ROCK CITY.
Tracks: Rock city / Mr. 69 / Mad racket.
■ 7" . . . . .ARO 254
Ariola / Feb '81.

TOKYO NIGHT.
Tracks: Tokyo night / Bedside radio / Shy kid.
■ 12" . . . . .AROD 241
■ 7" . . . . .ARO 241
Ariola / Sep '80.

Kruiz

KRUIZ.
Tracks: Knight on the road / Brave new world / Heaviest in town / Avenger / In flames / Dream 5000 years long / Iron rock / Possessed.
■ CD . . . . K 243869-2
■ LP . . . . K 243869-1
■ MC . . . . K 243869-4
WEA / Dec '88.

Kublai Khan

ANNIHILATION.
Tracks: Death breath / Mongrel horde / Down to the inferno / Liars dice / Passing away / Clash of the swords / Battle hymn of the Republic / Kublaikhan.
■ LP . . . . .HMUSA 95
Heavy Metal America / Jun '87.

Kyuss

BLUES FOR THE RED SUN.
Tracks: Not Advised.
CD 370561340-2
MC 370561340-4
Elektra / Feb '93 / WEA.

DEMON CLEANER.
Tracks: Demon cleaner / Freedom run (CD1 only) / Day one (CD2 only).
7" . . . . .EKR 192
CD Single . . . . .EKR 192CD1
CD Single . . . . .EKR 192CD2
Elektra / Sep '94 / WEA.

SHY VALLEY.
Tracks: Not Advised.
CD 755961571-2
MC 755961571-4
Warner Bros. / Jun '94 / WEA.

L

L.A. Guns

Guitarist Tracii Guns quit band who bore his name, Guns N' Roses, to form own band in '87. Despite trio of modestly successful albums, energetic gigs and GN'R connection, band never broke big and split in '92. Guns turned side-project Killing Machine into permanent venture while singer Phil Lewis (ex-Girl) went on to Filthy Lucre.

BALLAD OF JAYNE.
Tracks: Ballad of Jayne / Kiss my love goodbye / Over the edge / Dirty love / My kookachoo.
■ 12" . . . . MERX 361
■ 7" . . . . MER 361
■ 7" P.Disc . . . . MERP 361
■ CD Single . . . . MERCD 361
Mercury / Dec '91.

COCKED AND LOADED.
Tracks: Letting go / Rip and tear / Never enough / Ballad of Jane / Give a little / 17 crash / Wheels of fire / Slap in the face / Sleazy come easy go / Malaria / Magdalaine / I'm addicted / Showdown (riot on sunset).
■ LP 838 592 1
■ CD 838 592 2
■ MC 838 592 4
Vertigo / Aug '89.

HOLLYWOOD VAMPIRES.
Tracks: Over the edge / Some lie 4 love / Kiss my love goodbye / Here it comes / Crystal eyes / Wild obsession / Dirty luv / My koo ka choo / It's over now / Snake eyes boogie / Ballad of Jayne / Big house.
■ LP 8496041
■ CD 8496042
■ MC 8496044
Mercury / Jan '92.

L.A. GUNS.
Tracks: No mercy / Sex action / One more reason / Electric gypsy / Nothing to lose / Bitch is back / Hollywood tease / One way ticket / Shoot for thrills / Down in the city.
■ LP . . . . VERH 55
MC . . . . VERHC 55
■ CD 834 144-2
Vertigo / Feb '88.

LOVE, PEACE AND GEESE.
Tracks: Not Advised.
VHS . . . . CFM 2704
Channel 5 / Oct '90 / Channel 5 Video / P.R.O. Video / Gold & Sons.

ONE MORE REASON.
Tracks: Not Advised.
VHS . . . . CFV 08332
Channel 5 / Jul '89 / Channel 5 Video / P.R.O. Video / Gold & Sons.

SOME LIE 4 LOVE.
Tracks: Some lie 4 love / Dirty luv (Only on 7" Single.) / Slap in the face (live) (Only on 12" and CD Single.) / Electric gypsy (live) (Only on 12" Single.) / Rip and tear (live) (Only on 10" Single.) / Sex action (live) (Only on 10" Single.) / Bitch is back (live) (Only on 10" and CD Single.) / Malaria (live) (Only on CD Single.).
■ 10" . . . . MEREP 358
■ 12" . . . . MERXP 358
■ 7" . . . . MER 358
■ CD Single . . . . MERCD 358
Mercury / Nov '91.

L7

All-girl quartet from LA who slotted neatly into early 90's grunge explosion by virtue of their short, punky songs and refusal to glam themselves up in the tradition of so many all-girl bands who preceded them. Instead of big harmonies and bigger hair, L7 sneered and rocked like a de-tuned version of The Ramones and, occasionally, Motorhead. Having started their recording career back in 1987 on Epitaph, they moved on to Seattle's Sub Pop label, before their potential attracted a major label deal in the shape of a Slash London Records contract.

ANDRES.
Tracks: Andres / Bomb / Interview (Only on CD single).
12" . . . . LASHX 48
7" . . . . LASH 48
CD Single . . . . LASCD 48
MC Single . . . . LASCS 48
Slash / Aug '94 / PolyGram.

BRICKS ARE HEAVY.
Tracks: Wargasm / Scrap / Pretend we're dead / Diet pill / Everglade / Slide / One more thing / Mr. Integrity / Monster / Shitlist / This ain't pleasure.
CD 8283072
LP 8283071
MC 8283074
Slash / May '92 / PolyGram.

EVERGLADE.
Tracks: Everglade.
■ 12" . . . . LASHXP 36
■ 7" . . . . LASH 36
■ CD Single . . . . LASHCD 36
Slash / May '92.

HUNGRY FOR STINK.
Tracks: Andres / Baggage / Can I run / Bomb / Questioning my sanity / Riding with a movie star / Stuck here again / Fuel my fire / Freak magnet / She has eyes / Shirley / Talk box.
CD 828531-2
LP 828531-1
MC 828531-4
Slash / Jul '94 / PolyGram.

L7.
Tracks: Not Advised.
CD . . . . E 864012
LP . . . . E 864011
MC . . . . E 864014
Epitaph / Jun '92 / Plastic Head.

PRETEND WE'RE DEAD.
Tracks: Pretend we're dead.
■ 12" . . . . LASHX 34
■ 7" . . . . LASH 34
■ CD Single . . . . LASCD 34
■ MC Single . . . . LASCS 34
Slash / Apr '92.
■ 7" . . . . LASH 42
■ CD Single . . . . LACDP 42
■ MC Single . . . . LACS 42
Slash / Nov '92.

SHOVE.
Tracks: Shove.
■ 7" . . . . EFA 08105
Sub Pop / Jan '91.

Laaz Rockit

ANNIHILATION PRINCIPLE.
Tracks: Mirror to madness / Chasin' Charlie / Fire in the hole / Shadow company / Holiday in Cambodia / Mob justice / Bad blood.
CD . . . . CDENV 521
■ LP . . . . ENVLP 521
■ MC . . . . TCENV 521
Enigma (EMI) / Mar '89.

EUROPEAN MELTDOWN.
Tracks: Not Advised.
■ VHS . . . . HEN 2194
Hendring Video / Feb '90.

HOLIDAY IN CAMBODIA.
Tracks: Holiday in Cambodia.
■ 12" . . . . RO 24361
■ CD Single . . . . RO 24361 CD
Roadracer / May '90.

KNOW YOUR ENEMY.
Tracks: Not Advised.
■ LP . . . . MFN 81
Music For Nations / Nov '87.

NO STRANGER TO DANGER.
Tracks: Not Advised.
■ LP 081866
Steamhammer (Germany) / '88.

Lag Wagon

TRASHED.
Tracks: Not Advised.
CD . . . . FAT 513-2
Fat Wreck Chords / Feb '94 / Plastic Head.

Last Crack

BURNING TIME.
Tracks: Not Advised.
LP . . . . RR 93301
MC . . . . RR 93304
■ CD . . . . RR 93302
Road Runner / May '91.

SINISTER FUNKHOUSE.
Tracks: Good morning from the funkhouse / Gush volcano crush / Blood brothers of the big black bear / Concrete slaughter dogs / Slicing steel / Saraboys cage / Last crack / Shelter / Terse / Thee abyas.
CD . . . . .RO 9501 2
■ LP . . . . RO 9501 1
MC . . . . RO 9501 4
Roadracer / '89 / Pinnacle.

Last Flight

DANCE TO THE MUSIC.
Tracks: Dance to the music / I'm ready.
■ 7" . . . . HEAVY 5
Heavy Metal / Mar '81.

Laughing Hyenas

CRAWL.
Tracks: Not Advised.
CD . . . . TG 102CD
LP . . . . TG 102
Touch & Go / Oct '92 / SRD.

HERE WE GO AGAIN.
Tracks: Here we go again / Candy.
■ 7" . . . . TNG 65
Tough & Go / Sep '90.

MERRY GO ROUND.
Tracks: Not Advised.
■ LP . . . . TGLP 25
Touch & Go / Sep '88.

Law

LAW, THE.
Tracks: For a little ride / Miss you in a heartbeat / Stone cold / Come save me (Julianne) / Laying down the law / Nature of the beast / Stone / Anything for you / Best of my love / Tough love / Missing you bad girl.
CD 7567821952
■ LP 7567821951
MC 7567821954
East West / Apr '91 / WEA.

Lawnmower Deth

BELLY.
Tracks: Somebody call me a taxi / Billy / I need to be my main / Squeeze / Do you wanna be a chuffed core / Buddy Holly never wrote a song called we're too punk / Up the junction / If it was grey you'd say it's black / Kids in America / March of the dweebs / Funny thing about it is / Purple haze.
CD . . . . MOSH 098CD
LP . . . . MOSH 098
MC . . . . MOSH 098MC
Earache / Oct '93 / Vital Distribution.

KIDS IN AMERICA.
Tracks: Kids in America.
■ CD Single . . . . MOSH 039CD
■ 12" . . . . MOSH 39 T
■ 7" 7MOSH 39
Earache / Jun '91.

OOH CRIKEY IT'S..
Tracks: Not Advised.
CD . . . . MOSH 25 CD
LP . . . . MOSH 25
MC . . . . MOSH 25 MC

Earache / Sep '90 / Vital Distribution.

QUACK EM ALL (see under Metal Duck).

RETURN OF THE FABULOUS METAL BOZO CLOWNS.
Tracks: Not Advised.
CD . . . . MOSH 072CD
LP . . . . MOSH 072
MC . . . . MOSH 072MC
Earache / Sep '92 / Vital Distribution.

Lazarus

CHEROKEE.
Tracks: Cherokee / Shaken not stirred / Met you too late / Big Mac.
■ CD Single . . . . SHAGCD 7003
Shagpile / Apr '92.

Lead Into Gold

AGE OF REASON.
Tracks: Not Advised.
CD . . . . WAX 116CD
LP . . . . WAX 116
Wax Trax / Aug '90 / SRD.
CD . . . . CDDVN 7
LP . . . . DVN 7
MC . . . . TDVN 7
Devotion / Mar '92 / Pinnacle.

Leather

SHOCK WAVES.
Tracks: All your neon / Shock waves / Something in this life / It's still in your eyes / Catastrophic hands / Battlefield of life / In a dream / Diamonds are for real / No place called home.
CD . . . . RO 9643-2
■ LP . . . . RO 9463 1
MC . . . . RO 9643-4
Roadracer / Jul '89 / Pinnacle.

Leatherface

CHERRY KNOWLE.
Tracks: Colorado Joe/Leningrad Vlad / Animal day / This land / Ghetto / Discipline / Postwar product of a fat man's wallet / Cabbage case / Right Reverand / Alright Jack / Sublime / Smile (your in a free and pleasant land) / Ghoulash / Heaven.
LP . . . . COX 017
Meantime / Feb '92 / Vital Distribution.

COMPACT AND BIJOU E.P.
Tracks: Not Advised.
■ CD Single . . . . HYPE 017CD
■ 10" . . . . HYPE 017T
Roughneck / Jul '92.

I WANT THE MOON.
Tracks: I want the moon.
■ 7" . . . . HYPE 014
Roughneck / Nov '91.

LAST, THE.
Tracks: Not Advised.
CD . . . . WIGCD 10
LP . . . . WIGLP 10
Domino (1) / Mar '94 / Pinnacle.

MINX.
Tracks: Not Advised.
CD . . . . NECKCD 011
LP . . . . NECKLP 011
MC . . . . NECKMC 011
Roughneck / May '93 / Pinnacle / RTM.

MUSH.
Tracks: Not Advised.
CD . . . . NECKCD 005
LP . . . . NECKLP 005
Roughneck / Sep '91 / Pinnacle / RTM.

NOT SUPERSTITIOUS.
Tracks: Not superstitious.
■ 12" . . . . HYPE 009 T
Roughneck / Aug '91.

WIN SOME, LOSE SOME.
Tracks: Win some, lose some / Boo da da boo / Discipline / Colarado Joe.
7" . . . . DUMP 018
Rugger Bugger / Feb '94 / Vital Distribution.

Leatherwolf

ENDANGERED SPECIES.
Tracks: Not Advised.
■ CD . . . . HMAXD 39
■ LP . . . . HMUSA 39
■ MC . . . . HMAMC 39
Heavy Metal America / Jul '85.

HIDEAWAY.
Tracks: Hide away / Too much / Rule the night (12" only).
■ 12" 12IS 416
■ 7" . . . . IS 416
■ 7" P.Disc . . . . ISP 416
■ CD Single . . . . CID 416
Island / Mar '89.
■ 12" . . . . ISS 416
Island / Mar '89.

LEATHERWOLF.
Tracks: Rise or fall / Calling / Share a dream / Cry out / Gypsies and thieves / Bad moon rising / Princess of love / Magical eyes / Rule the night.
■ CD . . . . CID 9889
■ LP . . . . ILPS 9889
■ MC . . . . ICT 9889
Island / May '88.
MC 842 862 4
MC . . . . ICM 2038
Island / '90 / PolyGram.

STREET READY.
Tracks: Wicked ways / Hideaway / Black knight / Way I feel / Too much / Street ready / Take a chance / Thunder / Lonely road / Spirits in the wind.
CD . . . . CID 9927
■ LP . . . . ILPS 9927
■ MC . . . . ICT 9927
Island / Mar '89.
MC 842 658 4
MC . . . . ICM 2037
Island / '90 / PolyGram.

Led Zeppelin

Eclipsed only by the Rolling Stones (whose album sales they exceeded), Led Zeppelin are among most successful rock bands of all-time. Highlights of oft-documented discography include: ten Top Ten albums; *Stairway To Heaven* (the most-played song on U.S. radio); fans' favourite *Physical Graffiti*; and *In Through The Out Door* - one of Zeppelin's least-acclaimed albums but nonetheless one credited with helping U.S. record industry out of recession in 1979. Unwavering interest after band's 1980 split eventually led to overhauling of their back catalogue in 1991, spearheaded by *Remasters* compilation. Pressure on vocalist Robert Plant and guitarist Jimmy Page to reunite finally bore fruit in 1994, although pair decline to revive Zeppelin name.

1972 INTERVIEW.
Tracks: Not Advised.
■ LP P.Disc . . . . RAMBLE ONE
Discussion / Nov '87.

1973 INTERVIEW.
Tracks: Not Advised.
CD . . . . RAMBLE 2CD
■ LP P.Disc . . . . RAMBLE 2
Discussion / Aug '88.

4 SYMBOLS.
Tracks: Black dog / Rock 'n' roll / Battle of Evermore / Stairway to heaven / Misty mountain hop / Four sticks / Going to California / When the levee breaks.
■ LP 2401 012
Atlantic / Nov '71.
■ MC K4 50008
Atlantic / '74.
CD 250 008
Atlantic / '83 / WEA.
■ LP . . . . K 50008
Atlantic / '88.
DCC 7567 815285
WEA / Jan '93 / WEA.
CD 756782638-2
MC 756782638-4
Warner Bros. / Jun '94 / WEA.

CHRIS TETLEY INTERVIEWS LED ZEPPELIN.
Tracks: Not Advised.
■ LP P.Disc . . . . CT 1004
Music & Media / Oct '87.

CODA.
Tracks: We're gonna groove / Poor Tom / I can't quit you baby / Walter's walk / Darlene / Ozone baby / Wearing and tearing / Bonzo's montreauz.
■ LP . . . . A 0051
■ MC . . . . A 0051 4
Swansong / Nov '82.
■ CD 790 051-2
Atlantic / Jul '87.
CD 756792444-2
MC 756792444-4
Atlantic / Aug '94 / WEA.

COMPLETE STUDIO RECORDINGS, THE.
Tracks: Good times bad times / Babe I'm gonna leave you / You shook me / Dazed and confused / Your time is gonna come / Black mountain side / Communication breakdown / I can't quit you baby / How many more times / Whole lotta love / What is and what should never be / Lemon song / Thank you / Heartbreaker / Living loving maid (she's just a woman) / Ramble on / Moby Dick / Bring it on home / Immigrant song / Friends / Celebration day / Since I've been loving you / Out on the tiles / Gallows pole / Tangerine / That's the way / Bron-y-aur stomp / Hats off to (Roy) Harper / Black dog / Rock and roll / Battle of evermore / Stairway to heaven / Misty mountain hop / Four sticks / Going to California / When the levee breaks / Song remains the same / Rain song / Over the hills and far away / Crunge / Dancing days / D'yer mak'er / No quarter / Ocean / Achilles last stand / For your life / Royal Orleans / Nobody's fault but mine / Candy store rock / Hots on for nowhere / Tea for one / Custard pie / Rover / In the time of dying / Houses of the holy / Trampled under foot / Kashmir / In the light / Bron-yr-aur / Down by the seaside / Ten years gone / Night flight / Wanton song / Boogie with Stu / Black country woman / Sick again / In the evening / South bound saurez / Fool in the rain / Hot dog / Carouselambra / All my love / I'm gonna crawl / We're gonna groove / Poor tom / Walter's walk / Ozone baby / Darlene / Bonzo's Montreux / Wearing and tearing / Baby come on home / Travelling riverside blues / White summer/Black mountain side / Hey hey what can I do.
CD Set 756782526-2
Atlantic / Apr '94 / WEA.

HOUSES OF THE HOLY.
Tracks: Song remains the same / Rain song / Over the hills and far away / Crunge / Dancing days / Yer mak'er / No quarter / Ocean.
■ LP . . . . K 50014
MC K4 50014
Atlantic / '74 / WEA.
CD 250 014
Swansong / '87 / WEA.
CD 191 30 2
Atlantic / '88 / WEA.
CD 756782639-2
MC 756782639-4
Warner Bros. / Jul '94 / WEA.

IN THROUGH THE OUT DOOR.
Tracks: In the evening / South bound saurez / Fool in the rain / Hot dog / Carouselambra / All my love / I'm gonna crawl.
■ MC SK4 59410
■ LP . . . . SSK 59410
Swansong / Aug '79.
■ CD . . . . SK 259410
Swansong / Jan '86.
CD 756792443-2
MC 756792443-4
Atlantic / Aug '94 / WEA.

LED ZEPPELIN.
Tracks: Good times bad times / Babe I'm gonna leave you / You shook me / Dazed and confused / Your time is gonna come / Black mountain side / Communication breakdown / I can't quit you baby / How many more times.
■ LP 588 171
Atlantic / Apr '69.
■ MC K4 40031
Atlantic / '74.
■ CD . . . . K 240031
Atlantic / Jan '87.
■ LP . . . . K 40031
Atlantic / '88.
CD 756782632-2
MC 756782632-4
Atlantic / Jun '94 / WEA.

LED ZEPPELIN 2.
Tracks: Whole lotta love / What is and what should be / Lemon song / Thank you / Heartbreaker / Livin' lovin' maid / (She's a woman) / Ramble on / Moby Dick / Bring it on home.
■ LP 588 198
Atlantic / Nov '69.

■ MC. K4 40037
Atlantic / '74.
■ CD. . . . . K 240037
Atlantic / Dec '86.
■ LP. K 40037
Atlantic / '88.
CD. 756782633-2
MC. 756782633-4
Atlantic / Jun '94 / WEA.

LED ZEPPELIN 3.
Tracks: Immigrant song / Friends / Celebration day /
Since I've been loving you / Out on the tiles /
Gallows pole / Tangerine / That's the way / Bron-y-
aur stomp / Hats off to (Roy) Harper.
■ LP. 2401 002
Atlantic / Nov '70.
■ LP. K 50002
■ MC. K4 50002
Atlantic / '74.
■ CD. . . . . K 250 002
Atlantic / Jan '87.
CD. 756782678-2
MC. 756782678-4
Warner Bros. / Aug '94 / WEA.

LED ZEPPELIN BOXED SET 2.
Tracks: Good times bad times / We're gonna groove
/ Night flight / That's the way / Baby come on home /
Lemon song / You shook me / Boogie with Stu /
Bron-y-Aur / Down by the seaside / Out on the tiles /
Black mountain side / Moby Dick / Sick again / Hot
dog / Carouselambra / South bound saurez /
Walter's walk / Darlene / Black Country woman /
How many more times / Rover / Four sticks / Hats off
to (Roy) Harper / I can't quit you baby / Hots on for
nowhere / Living loving maid (She's just a woman) /
Royal Orleans / Bonzo's Montreaux / Crunge / Bring
it home / Tea for one.
CD Set 7567824772
Atlantic / Sep '93 / WEA.

LED ZEPPELIN: INTERVIEW PICTURE DISC.
Tracks: Not Advised.
CD P.Disc. . . . . CBAK 4042
Baktabak / Apr '90 / Arabesque Ltd.

PHYSICAL GRAFFITI.
Tracks: Houses of the holy / Trampled under foot /
Kashmir / Custard pie / Rover / In my time of dying /
In the light / Bron-y-aur stomp / Down by the seaside
/ Ten years gone / Night flight / Wanton song /
Boogie with Stu / Back country woman / Sick again.
■ Double LP. . . . . SSK 89400
■ MC Set SK4 89400
Swansong / '75.
■ CD. . . . . SK 289400
Swansong / Jan '87.
CD. 756792442-2
MC. 756792442-4
Atlantic / Aug '94 / WEA.

PRESENCE.
Tracks: Achilles last stand / For your life / Royal
Orleans / Nobody's fault but mine / Candystore rock
/ Hots on for nowhere / Tea for one.
■ MC. SK4 59402
■ LP. . . . . SSK 59402
Swansong / Apr '76.
■ CD. . . . . SK 259402
Swansong / Jun '87.
CD. 756792439-2
MC. 756792439-4
Atlantic / Aug '94 / WEA.

REMASTERS (1) (1969 - 1980).
Tracks: Communication breakdown / Babe I'm gonna leave you / Good times, bad times / Dazed and
confused / Whole lotta love / Heartbreaker / Ramble
on / Immigrant song / Celebration day / Since I've
been loving you / Black dog / Rock 'n' roll / Battle of
Evermore / Misty mountain hop / Stairway to heaven
/ Song remains the same / Rain song / D'yer mak'er
/ No quarter / Houses of the holy / Kashmir / Tram-
pled underfoot / Nobody's fault but mine / Achilles
last stand / All my love / In the evening.
CD Set 7567 80415 2
■ LP Set. . . . . ZEP 1
MC Set . . . . ZEPC 1
Atlantic / Oct '90 / WEA.

REMASTERS (2).
Tracks: Whole lotta love / Heartbreaker / Communication breakdown / Babe I'm gonna leave you /
Dazed and confused / Ramble on / Your time is
gonna come / What is and what should never be /
Thank you / I can't quit you baby / Friends / Celebration day / Travelling riverside blues / Hey hey what
can I do / White summer/ Black mountain side /
Black dog / Over the hills and far away / Immigrant
song / Battle of the Evermore / Bron-y-aur stomp /
Tangerine / Going to California / Since I've been
loving you / D'yer mak'er / Gallows pole / Custard
pie / Misty mountain hop / Rock 'n' roll / Rain song /
Stairway to heaven / Kashmir / Trampled underfoot /
For your life / No quarter / Dancing days / When the
levee breaks / Song remains the same / Achilles last
stand / Ten years gone / Candy store rock / Moby
Dick / In my time of dying / In the evening / Ocean /
Ozone baby / Houses of the holy / Wearing and
tearing / Poor Tom / Nobody's fault but mine / Fool in
the rain / In the light / Wanton song / I'm gonna crawl
/ All my love.
CD Set 7567 821 44 2
■ LP Set. 7567 821 44 1
MC Set 7567 821 44 4
Atlantic / Oct '90 / WEA.

SONG REMAINS THE SAME, THE.
Tracks: Rock 'n' roll / Celebration day / Song re-
mains the same / Rain song / Dazed and confused /
No quarter / Stairway to heaven / Moby dick / Whole
lotta love.
MC Set SK4 89402
■ Double LP. . . . . SSK 89402
Swansong / Oct '76.
CD Set . . . . .SK 289402
Swansong / Feb '87 / WEA.

SONG REMAINS THE SAME, THE.
Tracks: Rock 'n' roll / Black dog / Since I've been
loving you / No quarter / Song remains the same /
Rain song / Dazed and confused / Stairway to hea-
ven / Moby Dick / Heartbreaker / Whole lotta love.
VHS . . . . PES 61389
Warner Home Video / Feb '86 / WEA / Hollywood
Nites / Gold & Sons / TBD.

STORY OF THE FILM "THE SONG RE-MAINS THE SAME" (Interview disc).
Tracks: Not Advised.
LP. . . . . BAK 6017
Baktabak / Dec '90 / Arabesque Ltd.
MC. . . . . MBAK 6017
Baktabak / Jan '92 / Arabesque Ltd.

Leeway

ADULT CRASH.
Tracks: Simple life / You / Make a move / 3 Wishes /
Withering heights / 10 Years / Silver tongue / Grip /
Roulaison / Clueless.
CD. . . . . CDVEST 4
Bulletproof / Mar '94 / Pinnacle.

BORN TO EXPIRE.
Tracks: Rise and fall / On the outside / Defy you /
Tools for war / Marathon / Catholic high school /
Mark and the squealer / Be loud / Enforcer / Born to
expire / Self defence / Unexpected.
CD. . . . . FILECD 257
■ LP. . . . . .FILER 257
MC. . . . . FILECT 257
Profile (USA) / Aug '89 / Pinnacle.

DESPERATE MEASURES.
Tracks: Not Advised.
CD. . . . . FILERCD 403
LP. . . . . .FILER 403
MC. . . . . FILERCT 403
Profile / Jul '91 / Vital Distribution.

Legal Weapon

TAKE OUT THE TRASH.
Tracks: Not Advised.
CD. . . . . TX 92772
LP. . . . . .TX 92771
Road Runner / Sep '91 / Pinnacle.

Legion Of Parasites

PRISON OF LIFE.
Tracks: Not Advised.
■ LP. . . . . THRASH 001
Thrash (USA) / Jul '85.

SAWN TO DUST.
Tracks: Not Advised.
■ LP. . . . . .STUDLP 3
Razor / Mar '88.

UNDESIRABLE GUESTS.
Tracks: Undesirable guests.
■ 12". . . . . .FIGHT 2
Fight Back / May '88.

Legs Diamond

CAPTURED LIVE.
Tracks: Not Advised.
CD. . . . . CDMFN 137
MC. . . . . .TMFN 137
Music For Nations / Jun '92 / Pinnacle.

LAND OF THE GUN.
Tracks: Not Advised.
MC. . . . . TMFN 59
Music For Nations / Mar '86 / Pinnacle.
■ LP. . . . . .MFN 59
Music For Nations / Mar '86.

OUT ON BAIL.
Tracks: Not Advised.
■ LP. . . . . MFN 52
MC. . . . . .TMFN 52
Music For Nations / Jun '85 / Pinnacle.

TOWN BAD GIRL.
Tracks: Not Advised.
CD. . . . . .CDZORRO 16
LP. . . . . ZORRO 16
MC. . . . . TZORRO 16
Metal Blade / Nov '90 / Pinnacle.

TURN TO STONE.
Tracks: Turn to stone / Twisted love / Right between
the eyes.
■ 12". . . . . 12 KUT 121
Music For Nations / Jun '86.

WISH.
Tracks: Not Advised.
CD. . . . . CDMFN 154
Under One Flag / Oct '93 / Pinnacle.

Lese Majesty

LESE MAJESTY.
Tracks: Not Advised.
■ LP. . . . . IW 1029
Iron Works (USA) / Aug '88.

Lethal

PROGRAMMED.
Tracks: Fire in your skin / Programmed / Plan of
peace / Another day / Arrival / What they've done /
Obscure the sky / Immune / Pray for me / Killing
machine.
CD. . . . . .CDZORRO 15
LP. . . . . ZORRO 15
Zorro / Nov '90 / Pinnacle.

Lethal Injection

MASS MURDER E.P.
Tracks: Not Advised.
7". . . . . MIND 006
Nuclear Blast / Jul '94 / Plastic Head.

Libido Boyz

CHILDHOOD MEMORIES.
Tracks: Childhood memories.
■ 7". . . . . .FST 008
First Strike / Oct '90.

HIDING AWAY.
Tracks: Not Advised.
■ LP. . . . . .FST 005
First Strike / Oct '89.

OPGU.
Tracks: Not Advised.
CD . . . . CDZORRO 42
LP . . . . ZORRO 42
MC . . . . TZORRO 42
Metal Blade / Jul '90 / Pinnacle.

Liege Lord

BURN TO MY TOUCH.
Tracks: Transgressor / Birds of prey / Cast out /
Portrait of despair / Black lit knights / Manic's mask /
Legend / Walking fire / Speed of sound.
■ LP . . . . RR 9625
Metal Blade / May '87.

FREEDOM'S RISE.
Tracks: Not Advised.
■ LP . . . . BD 004
Black Dragon / May '87.

MASTER CONTROL.
Tracks: Not Advised.
CD . . . . RR 95412
■ LP . . . . RR 95411
Road Runner / Nov '88.
CD 1995412
Metal Blade / Jan '89 / Pinnacle.

WARRIOR'S FAREWELL.
Tracks: Not Advised.
■ LP . . . . IW 1013
Iron Works (USA) / Jun '87.

Life Of Agony

RIVER RUNS RED.
Tracks: Not Advised.
CD . . . . RR 90432
LP . . . . RR 90431
Road Runner / Oct '93 / Pinnacle.

THIS TIME.
Tracks: This time.
CD Single . . . . RR 23733
Road Runner / May '94 / Pinnacle.

Life Sex & Death

SILENT MAJORITY, THE.
Tracks: Not Advised.
CD 7599269582
■ LP 7599269581
MC 7599269584
WEA / Aug '92 / WEA.

Lillian Axe

LOVE AND WAR.
Tracks: Not Advised.
■ CD . . . . DMCG 6060
■ LP . . . . MCG 6060
■ MC . . . . MCGC 6060
MCA / Sep '89.

POETIC JUSTICE.
Tracks: Not Advised.
CD . . . . CDMFN 131
LP . . . . MFN 131
MC . . . . TMFN 131
Music For Nations / Jul '92 / Pinnacle.

PSYCHOSCHIZOPHRENIA.
Tracks: Not Advised.
CD . . . . CDMFN 151
LP . . . . MFN 151
MC . . . . TMFN 151
Music For Nations / Sep '93 / Pinnacle.

Limbomaniacs

SHAKE IT.
Tracks: Shake it / Pavlov's frothing dogs.
■ 12" 6577936
■ 7" 6577937
■ CD Single 6577932
■ MC Single 6577934
In-Effect / Feb '92.

STINKY GROOVES.
Tracks: Butt funkin' / Maniac / Freestyle / Porno /
Shake it / That's the way / Toilet's flooded / Pavlov's
frothing dogs.
■ CD 4676142
■ LP 4676141
■ MC 4676144
Harder In Effect Than You / Aug '91.

Limelight

ASHES TO ASHES.
Tracks: Ashes to ashes / Knife in your back.
■ 7" . . . . FER 010
Future Earth / Oct '82.

I SHOULD HAVE KNOWN BETTER.
Tracks: I should have known better / Tell me why.
■ 7" . . . . UP 35779
United Artists / Jan '75.

LIMELIGHT.
Tracks: Going home / Knife in your back / Mamma (I
don't wanna lose you) / Man of colours / Metal man /
Walk on water / Don't look back.
■ LP . . . . FER 008
Future Earth / '80.

METAL MAN.
Tracks: Metal man / Hold me.
■ 7" . . . . SER 006
Future Rights / Jun '80.

Lion

DANGEROUS ATTRACTION.
Tracks: Not Advised.
■ LP . . . . BFZ 40797
Scotti Bros (USA) / Sep '87.

FATAL ATTRACTION.
Tracks: Armed and dangerous / Hard and heavy /
Never surrender / Death on legs / Powerlove / In the
name of love / After the fire / Shout it out.
■ CD 834 232-2
Polydor / Jan '88.

TROUBLE IN ANGEL CITY.
Tracks: Not Advised.
■ LP . . . . SLAM 5
Grand Slam (USA) / '89.
CD . . . . CDMFN 132
LP . . . . MFN 132
MC . . . . TMFN 132
Music For Nations / Jul '92 / Pinnacle.

Lionheart

DIE FOR LOVE.
Tracks: Die for love / Dangerous games.
■ 7" . . . . A 5001
Epic / Jan '85.

HOT TONIGHT.
Tracks: Wait for the night / Hot tonight / Die for love /
Towers of silver / Don't look back in anger / Night-
mare / Living in a dream / Another crazy dream /
Dangerous game.
■ LP . . . . EPC 26214
Epic / Jan '85.

Lions Breed

DAMN THE NIGHT.
Tracks: Not Advised.
■ LP . . . . ES 4008
Earthshaker (Germany) / Jun '85.

Lionsheart

LIONSHEART.
Tracks: Not Advised.
CD . . . . CDMFN 139
LP . . . . MFN 139
MC . . . . TMFN 139
Music For Nations / Jul '92 / Pinnacle.

Lionspride

BREAKING OUT.
Tracks: Not Advised.
■ LP . . . . SKULL 8336
MC . . . . TAPE 78336
Mausoleum / Oct '84 / Pinnacle.

Liquid Jesus

POUR IN THE SKY.
Tracks: Not Advised.
■ CD . . . . MCAD 10191
■ LP . . . . MCA 10191
■ MC . . . . MCAC 10191
MCA / Aug '91.

Little Angels

Little Angels released their mini album Too
Posh To Mosh in 1987 on the indie label
Powerstation, this earned them a deal with
Polydor where they went from strength to
strength, building up a solid fanbase despite being tagged unfashionable by many in
the media. Their third album Jam entered
the charts at No. 1 but it was to be the peak
of their short career. In the summer of 1994
they re-released their mini album and
signed off with a farewell tour of the U.K.
The band felt they had achieved all they
could, considering the inability of many,
more fashionable, Britsh rock bands to progress beyond domestic success it may well
have been a wise decision.

BAD OR JUST NO GOOD.
Tracks: Bad or just no good / Better than the rest /
Burning me / Reach for me.
■ 12" . . . . LAN 001
Little Angels / May '87.

BIG BAD EP.
Tracks: She's a little angel / Don't waste my time /
Better than the rest / Sex in cars.
■ 12" . . . . LTLEP 2
■ 7" . . . . LTL 2
■ CD Single . . . . LTLCD 2
Polydor / Feb '89.

BIG BAD VIDEO.
Tracks: She's a little angel / Kicking up dust / Young
gods / Radical your lover / Bone yard / Product of
the working class / Juvenile offender / That's my
kinda life / Don't pray for me / I ain't gonna cry.
VHS . . . . CFV 07852
Channel 5 / Feb '89 / Channel 5 Video / P.R.O. Video
/ Gold & Sons.
VHS 0838643
Polygram Music Video / Dec '91 / PolyGram.

BONEYARD.
Tracks: Boneyard / Fortunate son / Sweet love sedation / Jump the gun.
■ 12" P.Disc. . . . . LTLXP 8
Polydor / Feb '91.
■ 12" . . . . LTLX 8
■ 7" . . . . LTL 8
■ 7" P.Disc . . . . LTLXB 8
■ MC Single . . . . LTLCS 8
Polydor / Jan '91.

DO YOU WANNA RIOT.
Tracks: Do you wanna riot / Move in slow / Some
kind of alien (Available on 12" format only).
■ 10" . . . . LTLXV 3
■ 12" . . . . LTLX 3
■ 7" . . . . LTL 3
■ CD Single . . . . LTLCD 3
Polydor / Sep '89.

DON'T PREY FOR ME.
Tracks: Do you wanna riot / Kick hard / Big bad
world / Kicking up dust / Don't prey for me / Broken
wings of an angel / Bitter and twisted / Promises /
When I get out of here / No solution / Pleasure pyre.
CD 843 469-2
LP 843 469-1
MC 843 469-4
Polydor / Nov '89 / PolyGram.
CD 841 254-2
MC 841 254-4
■ LP 841 254-1
Polydor / Jun '90.

DON'T PREY FOR ME.
Tracks: Don't prey for me / Radical your lover / What
do you want (Available on 12" format.).
■ 12" . . . . LTLXP 4
■ 12" . . . . LTLX 4
■ 7" . . . . LTL 4
■ CD Single . . . . LTLCD 4
Polydor / Nov '89.
■ 7" . . . . LTLS 4
Polydor / Nov '89.

I AIN'T GONNA CRY.
Tracks: I ain't gonna cry.
■ 12" . . . . LTLX 11
■ 7" . . . . LTL 11
■ CD Single . . . . LTLCD 11
Polydor / Jul '91.

JAM.
Tracks: Way that I live / Too much too young /
Splendid isolation / Soap box / S.T.W. / Dont' confuse sex with love / Womankind / Eyes wide open /
Colour of love / I was not wrong / Sail away / Tired of
waiting for you (So tired) / Reprise/S.T.W. / She's a
little angel / Product of the working class (Grooved &
jammed) / I ain't gonna cry / Boneyard 1993 / Don't

■ DELETED

prey for me (Extended version) / Won't get fooled again.
CD. 517 642-2
Polygram / Jan '93 / PolyGram.
CD. 5176762
Polydor / Jan '93 / PolyGram.
DCC. 517 642-5
Polygram / Jan '93 / PolyGram.
MC. 5176764
Polydor / Jan '93 / PolyGram.
MC. 517 642-4
Polygram / Jan '93 / PolyGram.
■ LP. 5176761
Polydor / Jan '93.

JAM ON FILM.
Tracks: Little angels/Jam on file / Too much too young / Womankind / Way that I live / Don't confuse sex with love / Splendid isolation / Boneyard / Soapbox / Sail away / I was not wrong / Eyes wide open.
VHS 877763
Polygram Music Video / Nov '93 / PolyGram.

KICKING UP DUST.
Tracks: Kicking up dust / Kicking up dust (live) (12" only) / Sex in cars (12" Picture disc only.) / When I get out of here (12" Picture disc only.) / Pleasure pyre (CD single only.).
■ 7". . . . . LTL 5
■ 12". . . . . LTLX 5
■ 12" P.Disc. . . . . LTLXP 5
■ CD Single. . . . . LTLCD 5
■ MC Single. . . . . LTLCS 5
Polydor / Feb '90.
■ 7" Set. . . . . LTLB 5
Polydor / Feb '90.

LITTLE OF THE PAST.
Tracks: She's a little angel / Too much too young / Radical your lover / Womankind / Boneyard / Kickin' up dust / I ain't gonna cry / Sail away / Young Gods / Ninety in the shade / Product of the working class / Soapbox / First cut is the deepest / Ten miles high / I wanna be loved by you / Don't pray for me.
CD. 521936-2
MC. 521936-4
Polydor / Apr '94 / PolyGram.

NINETY IN THE SHADE.
Tracks: Ninety in the shade / England rocks / Big, bad world (Only on 12").
■ 12". . . . . LTLG 1
■ 12". . . . . LTLX 1
■ 7". . . . . LTL 1
Polydor / Sep '88.
■ 12" P.Disc. . . . . LTLXP 1
Polydor / Sep '88.

PRODUCT OF THE WORKING CLASS.
Tracks: Product of the working class.
■ 12". . . . . LTLX 9
■ 12" Remix. . . . . LTLXG 9
■ 7". . . . . LTL 9
■ CD Single. . . . . LTCDB 9
■ MC Single. . . . . LTLCS 9
Polydor / Apr '91.

RADICAL YOUR LOVER.
Tracks: Radical your lover.
■ 7". . . . . LTL 6
■ 7" Set. . . . . LTLB 6
■ MC Single. . . . . LTLCS 6
■ MC Single. . . . . LTLX 6
Polydor / Apr '90.

SAIL AWAY.
Tracks: Sail away / Mighty Quinn.
■ 7". . . . . LTLX 15
■ CD Single. . . . . LTLCD 15
■ CD Single. . . . . LTLDD 15
■ MC Single. . . . . LTCS 15
Polydor / Sep '93.

SHE'S A LITTLE ANGEL.
Tracks: She's a little angel / Down on my knees / She's a little angel (voodoo mix) (Only on 12" single.) / Sex in cars (live) (Only on limited edition 7" in tin.).
■ 12". . . . . LTLX 7
■ 7". . . . . LTLT 7
■ 7". . . . . LTL 7
■ MC Single. . . . . LTLCS 7
Polydor / Jul '90.

SOAPBOX.
Tracks: Soapbox.
■ 7". . . . . LTL 14
■ CD Single. . . . . LTLCD 14
■ MC Single. . . . . LTLCS 14
Polydor / May '93.

TEN MILES HIGH.
Tracks: Ten miles high / Hard times / Overrated (On 12 & first CD only) / Just one night (On 2nd CD only) / Too much too young (acoustic) (On 2nd CD only).
■ 12". . . . . LTLX 16
■ CD Single. . . . . LTDD 16
■ CD Single. . . . . LTLCD 16
■ CD Single. . . . . LTLDD 16
■ MC Single. . . . . LTLCS 16
Polydor / Mar '94.

TOO POSH TO MOSH.
Tracks: Not Advised.
■ LP. . . . . AMP 14
Powerstation / Nov '87.
CD. . . . . ESSCD 213
LP. . . . . ESSLP 213
MC. . . . . ESSMC 213
Essential / Jun '94 / Total / BMG.

YOUNG GODS.
Tracks: Back door man / Boneyard / Young Gods (Stand up stand up) / I ain't (Ain't) gonna cry / Wildside of life / Product of the working class / That's my kinda life / Juvenile offender / Love is a gun / Sweet love sedation / Smoke in my eyes / Natural born fighter / Feels like the world has come undone / Angels anthem.
CD. 847 846-2
■ LP. 847 846-1
MC. 847 846-4
Polydor / Feb '91 / PolyGram.

YOUNG GODS.
Tracks: Young gods.
■ 7". . . . . LTL 10
■ CD Single. . . . . LTLCD 10
■ MC Single. . . . . LTLCS 10
■ 12". . . . . LTLX 10
■ 12". . . . . LTLXB 10
Polydor / May '91.

Little Caesar

CHAIN OF FOOLS.
Tracks: Chain of fools.
■ 12". . . . . GEF 80T
■ 12" P.Disc. . . . . GEFTP 80
■ 7". . . . . GEF 80
■ CD Single. . . . . GEF 80CD
■ MC Single. . . . . GEF 80C
Geffen / Aug '90.

INFLUENCE.
Tracks: Stand up / You're mine / Turn my world around / Rum and coke / Ballad of Johnny / Ain't got it / Slow ride / Pray for me / Ridin' on / Piece of the action.
CD. . . . . DGCD 24472
■ LP. . . . . DGC 24472
■ MC. . . . . DGCC 24472
Geffen / May '92.

LITTLE CAESAR.
Tracks: Not Advised.
■ CD. 7599242882
■ LP. . . . . WX 352
■ MC. . . . . WX 352 C
WEA / Aug '90.
CD. . . . . DGLD 19128
MC. . . . . DGLC 19128
Geffen / May '92 / BMG.

WHOLE OF THE MOON.
Tracks: Whole of the moon.
■ CD Single. . . . . EAUCD 1
Rapid 9547 / Jun '90.
■ 7". . . . . EAU 1
■ 12". . . . . 12 EAU 1
Rapid 9547 / Sep '90.

Livgren, Kerry

SEEDS OF CHANGE.
Tracks: Just one way / Masks of the great deceiver / How can you live / Whiskey seed / To live for the king / Down to the core / Ground zero.
■ LP. . . . . NJZ 36567
Kirshner (USA) / '80.

Living Colour

One of the most succesful exponents of funk-metal along with Red Hot Chili Peppers and perhaps more importantly the first all black rock band to achieve commercial success. Their music, lyrics and appearance all challenged the stereotypes of 'black' and 'rock' music, the success they have had, considering the bigotry they faced from radio and television stations, the open hostility of some metal audiences and to some extent the press, is testament to their ability and commitment.

AUSLANDER.
Tracks: Auslander / Auslander (mix).
■ 12". 659173 6
■ 7". 659173 7
■ CD Single. 659173 2
Epic / Apr '93.

CULT OF PERSONALITY.
Tracks: Cult of personality / Open letter to a landlord / Middle man (live) (12" & CD single only.) / Should I stay or should I go (Not on 7") / What's your favourite colour.
■ 12". . . . . LCL T3
■ 7". . . . . LCL 3
■ CD Single. . . . . CDLCL 3
Epic / Sep '88.
■ 7". . . . . LCL B3
Epic / Sep '88.
■ 12". . . . . LCL P5
■ CD Single. . . . . CDLCL 5
Epic / May '89.
■ 12". . . . . LCL T5
■ 7". . . . . LCL 5
Epic / May '89.
■ 12". 6575356
■ 7". 6575357
■ CD Single. 6575352
■ MC Single. 6575354
Epic / Oct '91.

GLAMOUR BOYS.
Tracks: Glamour boys / Which way to America / Middleman (Only on 12" version.) / Rap track (conversation with Living Colour).
■ 12". . . . . LCL T2
■ 7". . . . . LCL G2
■ 7". . . . . LCL 2
■ 7" P.Disc. . . . . CTLCL 2
■ CD Single. . . . . CDLCL 2
Epic / Jul '88.

GLAMOUR BOYS (REMIX).
Tracks: Glamour boys / Cult of personality.
■ 12". . . . . LCL T6
■ 7". . . . . LCL 6
■ 7". . . . . LCL G6
■ CD Single. . . . . CDLCL 6
Epic / Sep '89.

LEAVE IT ALONE.
Tracks: Leave it alone / 17 Days / Ignorance is bliss (Live) / Middle man (Live) / T.V. News / Hemp (Full version).
■ 12". 658976 6
■ 7". 658976 7
■ CD Single. 658976 2
Epic / Feb '93.

LOVE REARS ITS UGLY HEAD.
Tracks: Love rears its ugly head (soul power mix) / Love rears its ugly head (album version).
■ 12". 6565936
■ 7". 6565937
CD P.Disc. 6565935
■ CD Single. 6565932
■ MC Single. 6565934
Epic / Jan '91.

MIDDLE MAN.
Tracks: Middle man / Desperate people / Funny vibe (Track available on 12" only.).
■ 12". . . . . LCL T1
■ 7". . . . . LCL 1
■ CD Single. . . . . CDLCL 1
Epic / May '88.
■ 7" P.Disc . . . . . LCL P1
Epic / May '88.

NOTHINGNESS.
Tracks: Nothingness / Nothingness (mix).
■ CD Single. 6593005
■ 7". 6593007
Columbia / Jun '93.

OPEN LETTER (TO A LANDLORD).
Tracks: Open letter (to a landlord) / Cult of personality (live) / Talkin' 'bout a revolution (live) (Only on 12" version.).
■ CD Single. . . . . CDLCL 4
■ 12". . . . . LCLT 4
■ 7". . . . . LCL 4
Epic / Feb '89.
■ 7". . . . . LCLQ 4
Epic / Feb '89.

PRIMER.
Tracks: Middle man / Cult of personality / Funny vibe / Broken hearts / Open a letter to a landlord / Glamour boys.
■ VHS. 490182
CMV Enterprises (Video) / Mar '90.

SOLACE OF YOU.
Tracks: Solace of you / Elvis is dead (Elvis is in the house mix) / Type (live) / Information overload (live) / Desperate people (live) / Solace of you (live).
- 12" 6569088
- 7" 6569087
- CD Single 6569089
- MC Single 6569084
Epic / Jun '91.
- 12" 6569085
Epic / Jun '91.

STAIN.
Tracks: Go away / Ignorance is bliss / Leave it alone / BL / Mind your own business / Auslander / Never satisfied / Nothingness / Postman / WTFF / This little pig / Hemp / Wall / T.V. News / Love rears it's ugly head (Live).
- CD 472856 2
- LP 472856 1
- MC 472856 4
Epic / Feb '93 / Sony.
- MiniDisc 472856 8
Epic / Feb '93 / Sony.

TIME TUNNEL.
Tracks: Funny vibe / Which way to America / Sailin' on / Desperate people / Pride / Middleman / Cult of personality / US National anthem / It's only rock 'n' roll / Love rears its ugly head / Times up / Information overload / Type (video) / Glamour boys / Fight the fight / Closing / What's your favourite colour.
- VHS 490602
Sony Music Video / '91 / Sony.

TIME'S UP.
Tracks: Time's up / History lesson / Pride / Love rears it's ugly head / New Jack theme / Someone like you / Elvis is dead / Type / Information overload / Under cover of darkness / Ology 1 / Fight the fight / Tag team partners / Solace of you / This is the life.
- CD 4669202
- MC 4669204
- LP 4669201
Epic / Mar '91.
- MiniDisc 466920-3
Epic / Feb '93 / Sony.

TYPE.
Tracks: Type (Only on 7") / Final Solution / Type (Album version) (Not on 7") / Should I stay or should I go / Middleman (live) (Only on 12") / Type (7"version) (Only on 12").
- 12" . . . . LCL GT7
- 7" . . . . LCL 7
- CD Single . . . . CD LCL 7
- MC Single . . . . LCLM 7
Epic / Aug '90.

VIVID.
Tracks: Cult of personality / I want to know / Middle man / Desperate people / Open letter (to a landlord) / Funny vibe / Memories can't wait / Broken hearts / Glamour boys / What's your favourite colour / Which way to America.
- CD 4607582
- LP 4607581
- MC 4607584
Epic / May '88.
- MiniDisc 460758-3
Epic / Apr '93 / Sony.

Living Death

BACK TO THE WEAPONS.
Tracks: Not Advised.
- LP . . . . AAARRG 002
Aaarrg / Jul '89.

LIVE.
Tracks: Not Advised.
- LP . . . . AAARRG 012
Aaarrg / Jul '89.

METAL REVOLUTION.
Tracks: Killing machine / Grippin' a heart / Rulers must come / Screaming from a chamber / Intro / Shadow of the dawn / Panic and hysteria / Road of destiny / Deep in Hell.
- LP . . . . ES 4012
Earthshaker (Germany) / Apr '86.

PROTECTED FROM REALITY.
Tracks: Not Advised.
- CD . . . . AAARRG 005CD
- LP . . . . AAARRG 005
Aaarrg / Jul '89.

VENGEANCE OF HELL.
Tracks: Not Advised.
- LP . . . . .SKULL 8360
Mausoleum / Oct '84.

WORLD NUEROSES.
Tracks: Not Advised.
- LP . . . . AAARRG 015
Aaarrg / Jul '89.

Lixx

LOOSE ON YOU.
Tracks: Not Advised.
- LP . . . . KICKASS 1
Blast Furnace / Jul '88.

Lizzy Borden

BEST OF LIZZY BORDEN.
Tracks: Not Advised.
- CD . . . . .CDMZORRO 72
Metal Blade / May '94 / Pinnacle.

LOVE YOU TO PIECES.
Tracks: Not Advised.
- LP . . . . RR 9771
Road Runner / Jun '85.

MASTER OF DISGUISE.
Tracks: Master of disguise / One false move / Love is a crime / Sins of the flesh / Phantoms never too young / Be one of us / Psychodrama / Waiting in the wings / Roll over and play dead / Under the rose / We got the power.
- CD . . . . RR 9454-2
- LP . . . . RR 9454-1
Road Runner / Aug '89.

ME AGAINST THE WORLD.
Tracks: Me against the world.
- 7" . . . . RR 5472
Road Runner / Oct '87.

MENACE TO SOCIETY.
Tracks: Not Advised.
- LP . . . . RR 9664
Road Runner / Oct '86.

MURDERESS METAL ROADSHOW, THE.
Tracks: Not Advised.
- LP . . . . RR 9702
Road Runner / Sep '86.

TERROR RISING.
Tracks: Not Advised.
- LP . . . . RR 9621
Road Runner / '89.

VISUAL LIES.
Tracks: Not Advised.
- CD . . . . RR 349592
Road Runner / Sep '87 / Pinnacle.
- LP . . . . RR 9592
Road Runner / Sep '87.

London

Formed in 1979, L.A. quartet London are best known for harbouring Nikki Sixx and Blackie Lawless, now leaders of Motley Crue and WASP, respectively. Founded by Lizzy Grey, now fronted by Nadir D'Priest, band released debut *Non-Stop Rock* in 1989 and have released two further albums to date.

DON'T CRY WOLF.
Tracks: Drop the bomb / Set me free / Hit and run lover / Under the gun / Oh darlin' / Fast as light / Put out the fire / Killing time / We want everything / For whome the bell tolls.
- LP . . . . AXISLP 1
Axis / May '87.

NON STOP ROCK.
Tracks: Not Advised.
- LP . . . . RR 9733
Road Runner / Nov '85.

PLAYA DEL ROCK.
Tracks: Not Advised.
- CD . . . . CDNUK 143
- MC . . . . ZCNUK 143
Noise / Jul '90.
- LP . . . . .NUK 143
Noise / Jun '90.

Lone Star

FIRING ON ALL SIX.
Tracks: Bells of Berlin / Ballad of crafty Jack / Time lays down / Hypnotic mover / Lovely Lubina / Seasons in your eyes / Rivers overflowing / All of us to all of you.
- LP . . . . CBS 82213
CBS / Sep '77.

LONE STAR.
Tracks: She said / Lonely soldier / Flying in the reel / Spaceships / New day / Million stars / Illusions.
- LP . . . . EPC 81545
Epic / Oct '76.
- CD . . . . .BGOCD 183
Beat Goes On / Apr '93 / Pinnacle.

LONE STAR AND THE SPROUT HEAD UPRISING (Lone Star & The Sprout Head Uprising).
Tracks: Not Advised.
- CD . . . . .AS 5032 CD
Antler / Sep '90 / Backs Distribution.

SEASONS IN YOUR EYES.
Tracks: Seasons in your eyes / Lovely Lubina.
- 7" . . . . CBS 5707
CBS / Oct '77.

Lord Crucifier

FOCUS OF LIFE.
Tracks: Not Advised.
- LP . . . . .VOV 670
- MC . . . . .VOV 670C
Metalworks / Jun '88.

Lost Breed

EVIL IN YOU AND ME, THE.
Tracks: Not Advised.
- CD . . . . HELL 023CD
Invisible / Jul '93 / Plastic Head.

SAVE YOURSELF.
Tracks: Circles / B.A.C. (What you fear) / Gears / Going strong / 472 C.I. of death / Lease on life / Chop / Dragon of chaos / You don't need to live / Tonga slut / Simulator / Up the hill.
- CD . . . . .H 0033-2
Hellhound / Aug '94 / Plastic Head.

Loud

D GENERATION.
Tracks: Not Advised.
- CD 847 168-2
- LP 847 168-1
- MC 847 168-4
Polydor / Nov '90 / PolyGram.
- CD . . . . WOLCD 1003
- LP . . . . WOL 1003
- MC . . . . WOLMC 1003
China / May '91 / Pinnacle.

D GENERATION.
Tracks: D Generation.
- 12" . . . . CHINX 25
- 7" . . . . CHINA 25
- CD Single . . . . CHICD 25
China / Aug '90.

EASY.
Tracks: Easy.
- 10" . . . . WOKX 2016
- 12" . . . . WOKT 2016
- 7" . . . . WOK 2016
- CD Single . . . . WOKCD 2016
China / Mar '92.

EXPLOSIVE.
Tracks: Explosive.
- 12" . . . . CHINX 29
- 12" P.Disc. . . . . CHIXP 29
- 7" . . . . CHINA 29
- CD Single . . . . CHICD 29
- MC Single . . . . CHICS 29
China / Oct '90.

MARY (SHE MADE ME).
Tracks: Mary (she made me).
- 12" . . . . WOKT 2022
- 7" . . . . WOK 2022
- CD Single . . . . WOKCD 2022
- MC Single . . . . WOKMC 2022
China / Jul '92.

PSYCHE 21.
Tracks: Not Advised.
- CD . . . . WOLCD 1026
- LP . . . . WOL 1026
- MC . . . . WOLMC 1026
China / Jun '92 / Pinnacle.

SEX 1991 EP.
Tracks: Not Advised.
- 10" . . . . WOKT 2002
- CD Single . . . . WOKCD 2002

■ EP .WOK 2002
China / May '91.

SONG FOR THE LONELY.
Tracks: Song for the lonely / Geist 2 / Massacre (Not available on 7" format).
■ 12" . . . . CHINX 33
■ 7" . . . . CHINA 33
■ CD Single . . . . CHICD 33
■ MC Single. . . . . CHICS 33
China / Jan '91.

Loudblast

CROSS THE THRESHOLD.
Tracks: Not Advised.
CD . . . . NO 2232
Modern Music / Nov '93 / Plastic Head.

Loudness

DISSOLUTION.
Tracks: Not Advised.
■ LP . . . . MFN 22
MC. . . . . TMFN 22
Music For Nations / Jun '85 / Pinnacle.

HURRICANE EYES.
Tracks: S.D.I. / This lonely heart / Rock 'n' roll gypsy / In my dreams / Take me home / Strike of the sword / Rock this way / In this world beyond / Hungry hunter / So lonely.
■ LP 790 619-1
MC 790 619-4
Atco / Aug '87 / WEA.

LET IT GO.
Tracks: Let it go / 1000 eyes / Ashes in the sky (Extra track on 12" version only).
■ 12" . . . . B 9498T
■ 7" . . . . B 9498
Atco / Oct '86.

LIGHTNING STRIKES.
Tracks: Let it go / Dark desire / 1000 eyes / Face to face / Who knows / Ashes in the sky / Black star oblivion / Street life dream / Complication.
CD 790 512-2
■ LP 790 512-1
Atlantic / Dec '86 / WEA.

ROADRACER.
Tracks: Roadracer / Shinkiro.
■ 12" . . . . 12 KUT 110
Music For Nations / Jun '84.

SOLDIER OF FORTUNE.
Tracks: Danger of love / You shook me / Demon disease / Soldier of fortune / 25 days from home / Faces in the fire / Red light shooter / Run for cover / Long after midnight / Lost without your love.
■ CD . . . . K 791283 2
■ LP . . . . K 791283 1
■ MC. . . . . K 791283 4
Atco / Sep '89.

THUNDER IN THE EAST.
Tracks: Not Advised.
■ LP . . . . MFN 38
Music For Nations / Mar '85.

Love/Hate

Hollywood-based quartet who were signed to Columbia on the strength of their adrenalin-rush live performances. Stars of the band were frontman Jizzy Pearl and bassist/songwriter Skid who formed an instant bond with UK audiences when they played here four times in the early 90's, promoting the infectious, short-sharp-shock tune-tactics on the albums *Blackout In The Red Room* and *Wasted In America*. Sadly, this success was not repeated back home and the band were dropped by Columbia; moving on to RCA for one album, *Let's Rumble* (with a new guitarist Darren Housholder). Since then they have reunited with original axeman Jon E Love and, together with ever-present drummer Joey Gold, are still looking to recapture lost ground.

BLACK OUT IN THE RED ROOM.
Tracks: Black out in the red room / Rock queen / Tumbleweed / Why do you think they call it dope / Fuel to run / One more round / She's an angel / Mary Jane / Straightjacket / Slutsy tipsy / Slave girl / Hell.
CD. 4663502
MC. 4663504
■ LP. 4663501
CBS / Apr '90.

BLACK OUT IN THE RED ROOM.
Tracks: Black out in the red room / Hell CA. POP 4 / Tinseltown / Slutsy tipsy.
■ 12" 6559176
■ 12" P.Disc. 6559175
■ 7" 6559177
■ CD Single 6559172
■ MC Single 6559174
CBS / Apr '90.

EVIL TWIN.
Tracks: Evil twin / Yucca man / I am the snake (Only on 12" and CD Single.) / Why do you think they call it dope (Live '91) (Only on 12" and CD Single).
■ 12" 6575965
■ 7" 6575967
■ CD Single 6575969
Columbia / Nov '91.

LET'S RUMBLE.
Tracks: Let's rumble / Spinning wheel / Boozor / Wrong side of the grape / Devil's squaw / Beer money / Here's to you / Sexical / Miracles / Flower.
CD. 7432115311-2
LP. 7432115311-1
MC. 7432115311-4
RCA / Jul '93 / BMG.

SHE'S AN ANGEL.
Tracks: She's an angel / One more round / One more round (live) (12" & CD single only) / Slave girl (live) (12" & CD single only).
■ 12" 6561126
■ 7" 6561127
■ CD Single 6561122
CBS / Jul '90.

WASTED IN AMERICA.
Tracks: Wasted in America / Spit / Miss America / Cream / Yucca man / Happy hour / Tranquilizer / Times up / Don't f**k with me / Don't be afraid / Social sidewinder / Evil twin.
CD. 4694532
MC. 4694534
■ LP. 4694531
Columbia / Feb '92.

WASTED IN AMERICA.
Tracks: Wasted in America / Castles from sand / Soul house tales (Not on 7".).
■ 12" 6578896
■ 7" 6578897
■ CD Single 6578892
Columbia / Mar '92.

Loverboy

BIG ONES.
Tracks: Working for the weekend / For you / Kid is hot tonite / Lovin' every minute of it / Lucky ones / This could be the night / Hot girls in love / Turn me loose / Too hot / Ain't looking for love / Notorious / Take me to the top.
■ LP 4660061
MC. 4660064
■ CD 4660062
CBS / Jan '90.

BREAK IT TO ME GENTLY.
Tracks: Break it to me gently / Read my lips / Working for the weekend (Only on 12" single.).
■ 12" 6514596
■ 7" 6514597
■ CD Single 6514592
CBS / Mar '88.
■ 12" Remix. 6514598
CBS / Mar '88.

GET LUCKY.
Tracks: Working for the weekend / When it's over / Jump / Gangs in the street / Emotional / Lucky ones / It's your life / Watch out / Take me to the top.
■ LP . . . . CBS 85402
MC. .40 85402
CBS / Feb '82 / Sony.
■ CD . . . . CD 85402
CBS / Jul '89.

HEAVEN IN YOUR EYES.
Tracks: Heaven in your eyes / Friday night / Loving every minute of it.
■ 12" 6501446
■ 7" 6501447
CBS / Jan '87.

HOT GIRLS IN LOVE.
Tracks: Hot girls in love / Meltdown.
■ 12" . . . . TA 3365
■ 7" . . . . A 3365
CBS / Jul '83.

KEEP IT UP.
Tracks: Not Advised.
MC. 40 25436
■ LP . . . . CBS 25436
CBS / Aug '83.
CD. 35 8P 27
Epic / '88 / Sony.

LOVERBOY.
Tracks: Kid is hot tonite / Turn me loose / Always on my mind / Lady of the 80's / Little girl / Prissy prissy / Teenage overdose / DOA / It don't matter.
■ LP . . . . CBS 84798
CBS / Mar '81.
■ CD . . . . CD 84698
CBS / '88.

LOVING EVERY MINUTE OF IT.
Tracks: Loving every minute of it / Steal the thunder / Friday night / This could be the night / Too much too soon / Lead a double life / Dangerous / Destination heartbreak / Bullet in the chamber.
■ LP . . . . CBS 26573
CBS / Nov '85.

NOTORIOUS.
Tracks: Notorious / Wild side.
■ 7" P.Disc 6510600
CBS / Oct '87.
■ 7" 6510607
CBS / Sep '87.
■ 12" 6510608
CBS / Oct '87.

QUEEN OF THE BROKEN HEARTS.
Tracks: Queen of the broken hearts / Change of a lifetime / Chain reaction / Lucky ones / Fantasy / On the loose.
■ 7" Set . . . . DA 3705
CBS / Nov '83.

THIS COULD BE THE NIGHT.
Tracks: This could be the night / It's your life.
■ 7" . . . . A 6950
CBS / Mar '86.

TURN ME LOOSE.
Tracks: Turn me loose / Prissy prissy.
■ 7" . . . . CBS 9557
CBS / Feb '81.
■ 7" . . . . A 1371
CBS / Feb '81.

WILDSIDE.
Tracks: Notorious / Walkin' on fire / Break it to me gently / Love will rise again / Can't get much better / Home town hero / Don't let go / That's where my money goes / Read my lips.
CD. 4600452
■ LP 4600451
■ MC. 4600454
CBS / Oct '87.

WORKING FOR THE WEEKEND.
Tracks: Working for the weekend / Emotional.
■ 7" . . . . CBS 1778
CBS / Jan '82.

Low Meato

LOW MEATO.
Tracks: Not Advised.
■ LP . . . . PIG 002
Metalworks / Nov '88.

Ludichrist

IMMACULATE DECEPTION.
Tracks: Not Advised.
■ LP . . . . WEBITE 34
We Bite / Oct '88.
CD. . . . . WB 3034-2
We Bite / Sep '93 / Plastic Head.

POWERTRIP.
Tracks: Not Advised.
■ LP . . . . WEBITE 35
We Bite / Oct '88.
■ LP 88561-8246-1
Combat Core (USA) / Sep '88.
CD. . . . . WEBITE 35CD
We Bite / Oct '88 / Plastic Head.

Lunachicks

BABYSITTERS ON ACID.
Tracks: Not Advised.
CD. . . . . BFFP 52CD
■ LP . . . . BFFP 52
■ MC. . . . . BFFP 52C
Blast First / Nov '89.

■ DELETED

BINGE & PURGE.
Tracks: Not Advised.
CD . . . . ELUNA 1CD
LP . . . . ELUNA 1
MC . . . . ELUNA 1C
Zuma / Mar '93 / SRD.

COMPLICATION.
Tracks: Complication.
■ 7" . . . . BFFP 055
Blast First / Apr '90.

GET OFF THE ROAD.
Tracks: Get off the road / Sugar luv.
■ 7" . . . . BFFP 44
Blast First / Apr '89.

Lung

CACTII.
Tracks: Not Advised.
CD . . . . YELLOWBIKE 003
Plastic Head / Jul '92 / Plastic Head.

LITANY.
Tracks: Litany / F**k generator.
■ 7" . . . . FATAL 002
Serial Killer / Jul '92.

SWING.
Tracks: Swing.
■ 7" . . . . SUR 715
Survival (1) / Sep '93.

THREE HEADS ON A PLATE.
Tracks: Paralysis / Elvis arsehole / Splinter / Mary's mother / Swing / Cot death baby / Slaughterhouse / Resuscitate / Johnny Favourite / Venus / Car crash / Exit / Compellor / Melonoma.
CD . . . . SUR 535CD
LP . . . . SUR 535
Survival (1) / Oct '93 / Vital Distribution.

Lynch, George

SACRED GROOVE.
Tracks: Memory Jack / Love power from the Mama head / Flesh and blood / We don't own this world / I will remember / Beast part 1 / Beast part 2 / Not necessary evil / Cry of the brave / Tierra del fuego.
CD 7559961422-2
MC 7559961422-4
Elektra / Aug '93 / WEA.

Lynch Mob

LYNCH MOB.
Tracks: Jungle of love / Tangled in the web / No good / Dream until tomorrow / Cold is the heart / Tie your mother down / Heaven is waiting / I want it / When darkness calls / Secret.
CD 75596132212
■ LP . . . . EKT 106
MC . . . . EKT 106C
Elektra / May '92 / WEA.

WICKED SENSATION.
Tracks: Wicked sensation / River of love / Sweet sister mercy / All I want / Hell child / She's evil but she's mine / Dance of the dogs / Rain / No bed of roses / Through these eyes / For a million years / Street fightin' man.
CD 7559609542
■ LP . . . . EKT 81
MC . . . . EKT 81 C
Elektra / Oct '90 / WEA.

Lynott, Phil

19.
Tracks: 19 / Day in the life of an old blues singer.
■ 12" . . . . POSPX 777
■ 7" . . . . POSP 777
Polydor / Nov '85.

DEAR MISS LONELY HEARTS.
Tracks: Dear Miss Lonely Hearts / Solo in Soho.
■ 7" . . . . SOLO 1
Vertigo / Apr '80.

KING'S CALL.
Tracks: King's call / Yellow pearl / Dear miss lonely hearts (Available on 12" only.).
■ 7" . . . . SOLO 2
Vertigo / Jun '80.
■ 12" . . . . LYN 112
■ 7" . . . . LYN 1
Vertigo / Jan '87.

OLD TOWN.
Tracks: Old town / Beat of the drum.
■ 7" . . . . SOLO 5

Vertigo / Sep '82.

OUT IN THE FIELDS (see under Moore, Gary).

PHILIP LYNOTT ALBUM, THE.
Tracks: Fatalistic attitude / Man's a fool / Old town / Cathleen / Growing up / Together / Little bit of water / Ode to liberty / Gino / Don't talk about me baby.
■ LP 6359 117
MC .7150 117
Vertigo / Oct '82 / PolyGram.
■ CD 8425642
Vertigo / Jul '90.

SOLO IN SOHO.
Tracks: Solo in soho / Kings call / Child lullaby / Tattoo / Dear Miss Lonely Hearts / Yellow pearl / Girls / Ode to a black man / Jamaican rum / Talk in 79 / So what / Turn the hands of time.
■ LP 9102 038
Vertigo / Apr '80.
■ LP . . . . .PRICE 88
■ MC . . . . .PRIMC 88
Vertigo / Sep '85.
CD 8425632
Vertigo / Jul '90 / PolyGram.

TOGETHER.
Tracks: Together / Somebody else's dream.
■ 12" . . . . SOLO 412
■ 7" . . . . SOLO 4
Vertigo / Jul '82.

YELLOW PEARL.
Tracks: Yellow pearl / Girls.
■ 7" . . . . SOLO 3
■ 12" . . . . SOLO 312
Vertigo / Dec '81.

Lynyrd Skynyrd

Founded at school in Florida, 1965, group's name was derived from teacher Leonard Skinner. 1973 debut *Pronounced Leh-nerd Skin-nerd* was produced by Al Kooper (ex-Blood, Sweat & Tears), also credited with discovering them. LP became smash after 1974 U.S. tour with The Who; closing track *Freebird* became rock classic. Group's career cut short by plane crash, killing leader Ronnie Van Zandt and three associates. Remaining members joined less successful Rossington Collins Band but greater recognition was afforded to 38 Special, led by Van Zandt's brother Donnie. Skynyrd reformed around another Van Zandt, Johnny, in 1987, although contractual dispute delayed remergence until 1991.

ANTHOLOGY - LYNYRD SKYNYRD.
Tracks: I ain't the one / Poison whiskey / Don't ask me no questions / Needle and spoon / Rool gypsy roll / Honky tonk night time man / Cheatin' woman / Made in the shade / Saturday night special (live) / Sweet home Alabama / Searching / Down south jukin / White dove / Freebird (live) / What's your name / One more time / Railroad song / Ballad of Curtis Loew / T for Texas (live) (Blue yodel no. 1).
MC . . . . .RAWTC 031
■ LP . . . . .RAWLP 031
Raw Power / Mar '87.

BEST OF THE REST.
Tracks: Not Advised.
■ MC . . . . MCLC 1834
MCA / Feb '91.

DEFINITIVE LYNYRD SKYNYRD, THE.
Tracks: Not Advised.
CD . . . . MCAD 310390
■ MC . . . . MCAC 310390
MCA / Feb '92.

DOUBLE TROUBLE.
Tracks: Double trouble / Roll, gypsy, roll.
■ 7" . . . . MCA 229
MCA / Feb '76.

DOWN SOUTH JUKIN'.
Tracks: Down south jukin' / That smell / Lend a helpin' hand / Call me the breeze.
■ EP . . . . .MCEP 101
MCA / Oct '78.

FREEBIRD.
Tracks: Freebird / Sweet home Alabama.
■ 12" . . . . .MCAT 251
■ 12" P.Disc. . . . . MCATP 251
MCA / Dec '83.
■ 12" . . . . .MCAT 1315
■ CD Single . . . . .DMCA 1315

■ 7" . . . . .MCA 1315
MCA / Jan '89.

FREEBIRD.
Tracks: Saturday night special / Whiskey rocker & roller / Working for MCA / I ain't the one / Sweet home Alabama / Ballad of curtis loew / Call me the breeze / Needle and spoon / Swamp music / Gimme 3 steps / Tuesday's gone / Freebird / Gimme back my bullets / What's your name / That smell / You got that right.
CD . . . . NTRCD 015
MC . . . . NTRC 015
Quality / Feb '94 / Pinnacle.

FREEBIRD (OLD GOLD).
Tracks: Freebird / Sweet home Alabama.
■ 7" . . . . .OG 9421
Old Gold / Jul '84.

GIMME BACK MY BULLETS.
Tracks: Gimme back my bullets / Every mother's son / Trust / Same old blues / Double trouble / Roll gypsy roll / Searching / Cry for the bad man.
■ LP . . . . .MCF 2744
MCA / Feb '76.
■ MC . . . . .MCLC 1653
■ LP . . . . .MCL 1653
MCA / Feb '82.
■ CD . . . . .DMCL 1653
MCA / May '90.
■ CD . . . . MCLD 19138
MCA / Jan '93.

GOLD AND PLATINUM (Very best of Lynyrd Skynyrd).
Tracks: Down south junkin' / Saturday night special / Gimme three steps / What's your name / You got that right / Gimme back my bullets / Sweet home Alabama / Freebird / That smell / On the hunt / I ain't the one / Whiskey rock and roller / Simple man / I know a little / Tuesday's gone / Comin' home.
■ Double LP . . . . MCDW 456
■ MC Set . . . . MCDC 456
MCA / Jul '82.
■ Double LP . . . . .MCSP 308
MCA / Feb '85.

I'VE NEVER BEEN YOUR FOOL.
Tracks: I've never been your fool / Gotta go.
■ 12" . . . . .MCAT 799
■ 7" . . . . MCA 799
MCA / Nov '82.

LAST REBEL, THE.
Tracks: Good lovin's hard to find / One thing / Can't take that away / Best things in life / Last rebel / Outta hell in my dodge / Kiss your freedom goodbye / South of heaven / Love don't always come easy / Born to run.
CD 756782447-2
MC 756782447-4
WEA / Feb '93 / WEA.

LEGEND, A.
Tracks: Georgia peaches / When you got good friends / Sweet little missy / Four walls of raiford / Simple man / Truck drivin' man / One in the sun / Mr. Banker / Take your time.
■ LP . . . . .MCF 3405
■ MC . . . . .MCFC 3405
MCA / Nov '87.

LYNYRD SKYNYRD.
Tracks: Smokestack lightnin' / Keeping the faith / Southern women / Pure and simple / I've seen enough / Backstreet crawler / Good thing / Money man / It's a killer / Mama (afraid to say goodbye) / End of the road.
CD 7567822582
■ LP 7567822581
MC 7567822584
East West / Jun '91 / WEA.

NUTHIN' FANCY.
Tracks: Made in the shade / Saturday night special / Cheatin' woman / I'm a country boy / On the hunt / Am I losin' / Whiskey rock a roller.
■ LP . . . . .MCF 2700
MCA / May '75.
■ MC . . . . .MCLC 1760
■ LP . . . . .MCL 1760
MCA / '83.
■ CD . . . . CMCAD 31003
MCA / Aug '87.
■ CD . . . . .DMCL 1760
MCA / '91.
CD . . . . MCLD 19074
■ MC . . . . MCLC 19074
MCA / Nov '92.

■ DELETED

NUTHIN' FANCY/GIVE ME BACK MY BULLETS.

Tracks: Saturday night special / Cheatin' woman / Railroad song / I'm a country boy / On the hunt / Am I losin' / Made in the shade / Whiskey rock and roller / Gimme back my bullets / Every mother's son / Trust / (I got the) same old blues / Double trouble / Roll gypsy roll / Searching / Cry for the bad man.
■ MC Set . . . . .MCA 2111
MCA / Sep '86.

ONE MORE FOR THE ROAD.

Tracks: Workin' for MCA / I ain't the one / Searching / Tuesdays gone / Saturday night special / Travellin' man / Whiskey rock and roller / Sweet home Alabama / Gimme three steps / Call me the breeze / T for Texas / Needle and spoon / Crossroads / Freebird.
■ Double LP. . . . . .MCSP 279
■ MC Set . . . . .MCSPC 279
MCA / Oct '76.
■ Double LP. . . . . .MCMD 7006
■ MC Set . . . . .MCMDC 7006
MCA / '91.
■ CD . . . . MCLD 19139
MCA / Nov '91.
CD Set . . . . MCLDD 19139
MC. . . . . MCLC 19139
MCA / Dec '92 / BMG.

PRONOUNCED LEH-NERD SKIN-NERD.

Tracks: I ain't the one / Tuesday's gone / Gimme three steps / Simple man / Things goin' on / Mississippi kid / Poison whiskey / Freebird.
■ LP . . . . MCL 1798
■ MC. . . . . MCLC 1798
MCA / Jun '84.
■ CD . . . . DMCL 1798
MCA / Jul '88.
CD . . . . MCLD 19072
MCA / Nov '91 / BMG.
■ MC. . . . . MCLC 19072
MCA / Oct '92.

PRONOUNCED LEH-NERD SKIN-NERD/ SECOND HELPING.

Tracks: I ain't the one / Tuesday's gone / Gimme three steps / Simple man / Things goin' on / Mississippi Alabama / I need you / Don't ask me no questions / Workin' for MCA / Ballad of Curtis Loew / Swamp music / Needle and spoon / Call me the breeze.
■ MC Set . . . . MCA 2 107
MCA (Twinpax Cassettes) / Sep '84.

SECOND HELPING.

Tracks: Sweet home Alabama / I need you / Don't ask me no questions / Workin' for MCA / Ballad of Curtis Loew / Swamp music / Needle and spoon / Call me the breeze.
■ LP . . . . MCL 1746
■ MC. . . . . MCLC 1746
MCA / '83.
■ CD. . . . . .MCAD 1686
MCA / '87.
■ LP . . . . FA 3194
■ MC. . . . . TCFA 3194
Fame / Oct '87.
■ CD . . . . DMCL 1746
MCA / Aug '89.
■ MC . . . . MCLC 19073
MCA / Nov '91.
CD . . . . MCLD 19073
MCA / Oct '92 / BMG.

SKYNYRD FIRST AND LAST.

Tracks: Not Advised.
■ LP . . . . .MCG 3529
MCA / Nov '78.
■ MC. . . . . MCLC 1627
■ LP . . . . MCL 1627
MCA / Aug '81.

SKYNYRDS INNYRDS.

Tracks: Not Advised.
CD . . . . .DMCG 6046

MC. . . . . MCGC 6046
■ LP . . . . .MCG 6046
MCA / Apr '89.

SOUTHERN BY THE GRACE OF GOD.

Tracks: Swamp music / Call me the breeze / Dixie / Comin' home / You got that right / What's your name / Gimme back my bullets / Sweet home Alabama.
■ Double LP. . . . . .MCMD 7004
■ CD. . . . . .DMCMD 7004
■ MC Set . . . . .MCMDC 7004
MCA / Apr '88.
■ CD . . . . MCLD 19010
■ MC. . . . . MCLC 19010
MCA / Apr '92.

STREET SURVIVORS.

Tracks: What's your name / That smell / One more time / I know a little / You got that right / I never dreamt / Honky tonk night time man / Ain't no good life.
■ LP . . . . .MCG 3525
MCA / Nov '77.
■ LP . . . . MCL 1694
■ MC. . . . . MCLC 1694
MCA / Jul '82.

VERY BEST OF LYNYRD SKYNYRD.

Tracks: Not Advised.
■ Double LP. . . . . .MCLD 624
■ MC Set . . . . .MCLDC 624
MCA / '91.
CD. . . . . MCLD 19140
MC. . . . . MCLC 19140
MCA / Jul '92 / BMG.

WHAT'S YOUR NAME.

Tracks: What's your name / I know a little.
■ 7" . . . . MCA 342
MCA / Jan '78.

M

M.C. 5

Short-lived Detroit quintet whose politicized stance and aggressive sound - captured on live, 1969 debut *Kick Out the Jams* - heavily influenced punkier end of hard rock. Tangential metal connection lies with guitarist Fred Smith, later husband of Blue Oyster Cult lyricist (and solo star) Patti Smith.

BABES IN ARMS.
Tracks: Shaking street / American ruse / Skunk (sonically speaking) / Tuttie fruttie / Poison / Gotta keep moving / Tonite / Kick out the jams / Sister / Future now / Gold / I can only give you everything / One of the guys / I just don't know / Looking at you.
■ CD . . . . DANCD 031
■ LP . . . . DANLP 031
Danceteria / Jun '92.

BACK IN THE U.S.A.
Tracks: Tutti frutti / Tonight / Teenage lust / Let me try / Looking at you / High school / Call me animal / American ruse / Shakin' street / Human being lawnmower / Back in the U.S.A.
■ LP . . . . K 50346
Atlantic / Feb '77.
CD .812271033-2
WEA / Mar '93 / WEA.

BLACK TO COMM.
Tracks: Not Advised.
CD . . . . RRCD 185
Reciever / May '94 / Total / BMG.

DO IT.
Tracks: Back in the U.S.A. / Kick out the jams / Tutti frutti / Rock 'n' roll pips.
CD . . . . YAK 5
Revenge (France) / Aug '88 / Pinnacle.

HIGH TIME.
Tracks: Not Advised.
CD 812271034-2
WEA / Mar '93 / WEA.

KICK OUT THE JAMS.
Tracks: Ramblin' rose / Kick out the jams / Come together / Rocket reducer No.62 / Borderline / Motor city is burning / I want you right now / Starship.
■ LP . . . . K 42027
Elektra.
CD 7559 740422
MC 7559 740424
Pickwick / Jan '93 / Pickwick.

LIVE IN DETROIT 68/69.
Tracks: Not Advised.
CD . . . . AU 50
Revenge (France) / Dec '88 / Pinnacle.

M.O.D.

DEVOLUTION.
Tracks: Not Advised.
CD . . . . .CDMFN 163
LP . . . . MFN 163
MC . . . . TMFN 163
Music For Nations / Jun '94 / Pinnacle.

GROSS MISCONDUCT.
Tracks: Not Advised.
MC . . . . N 0133 4
■ CD .CDNUK 133
■ LP . . . . .NUK 133
■ MC . . . . ZCNUK 133
Noise / Apr '89.

M.O.D.
Tracks: M.O.D.
■ 7" 6059233
Vertigo / Nov '79.

M.O.D. FOR U.S.A.
Tracks: Not Advised.
CD . . . . .CDMFN 126
LP . . . . MFN 126
MC . . . . TMFN 126
Music For Nations / Jul '91 / Pinnacle.

RHYTHM OF FEAR.
Tracks: Objection/Dead end / Get up and dance / Step by step / Rhymestein / Minute of courage /

Irresponsible / Override negative / I' the earth / Spy Vs. Spy / Intruder / Jive time Jimmy's revenge / Rally (NYC).
CD . . . . .CDMFN 145
LP . . . . MFN 145
MC . . . . TMFN 145
Megaforce / Nov '92 / Pinnacle.

SURFIN' M.O.D.
Tracks: Surfin' U.S.A. / Surf's up / Sgt. Drexall / Mr. Oofus.
■ CD Single . . . . RR 2452 2
■ EP . . . . RR 2452 1
Road Runner / Dec '88.

SURFIN' M.O.D.
Tracks: Not Advised.
■ LP . . . . CAROL 1359
Caroline (USA) / Aug '88.

U.S.A. FOR M.O.D.
Tracks: Not Advised.
■ LP . . . . CAROL 1344
Caroline (USA) / Sep '87.
CD .CAROLCD 1344
Caroline (USA) / Sep '87 / Pinnacle.
■ LP . . . . NUK 089
MC . . . . ZCNUK 089
Noise / Oct '89 / Pinnacle.

Macabre

GRIM REALITY.
Tracks: Not Advised.
■ LP . . . . SOL 18
Vinyl Solution / Oct '89.

SINISTER SLAUGHTER.
Tracks: Not Advised.
CD . . . . NB 070CD
LP . . . . NB 070
MC . . . . NB 070MC
Nuclear Blast / Jun '93 / Plastic Head.

MacAlpine, Tony

EDGE OF INSANITY.
Tracks: Not Advised.
■ LP . . . . RR 9706
■ MC . . . . RR 97064
Road Runner / Jun '86.
CD . . . . RR 349706
Road Runner / '89 / Pinnacle.

EYES OF THE WORLD.
Tracks: Not Advised.
■ LP 841 516 1
■ CD 841 516 2
■ MC 841 516 4
Vertigo / Apr '90.

FREEDOM TO FLY.
Tracks: Not Advised.
CD . . . . R 91572
Road Runner / Jul '92 / Pinnacle.

MAXIMUM SECURITY.
Tracks: Autumn lords / Hundreds of thousands / Tears of Sahara / Keys to the city / Time and the test / Kings cup / Sacred wonder / Etude 4 Opus 10 / Vision / Dreamstate / Porcelain doll.
■ CD 832 249 2
■ LP . . . . VERH 44
■ MC . . . . VERHC 44
Vertigo / Jun '87.

McBrain, Nicko

RHYTHM OF THE BEAST.
Tracks: Rhythm of the beast / Beehive boogie / McBrain damage.
■ 7" . . . . NICKO 1
■ 7" P.Disc . . . . NICKOPD 1
EMI / Jul '91.

Macc Lads

ALE HOUSE ROCK.
Tracks: Not Advised.
CD . . . . UPNOCD 1
MC . . . . UPNOMC 1
Dojo / May '94 / Castle Communications / BMG.

AN OFIFICE AND A GENITAL (Out - Takes 1986-1991).
Tracks: Eh up lets sup / Fat bastard / Baggy Anne / Head kicked in / Knutsford / No sheep til' buxton / Pie taster / I love Macc / Made of ale / Knock knock / Brevil brevil / Manfred Macc / Buenos aires '90 / Fellatio Nell, son / Two stroke Eddie / Even uglier women.
CD . . . . DOJOCD 141
Dojo / Feb '94 / Castle Communications / BMG.

BEER NECESSITIES, THE.
Tracks: Alcohol / Germans / Fallatio Nell, son / Desperate Dan / Grease stop / Apprentice dentist / Man in the boat / Newcy Brown / McCavity / Chester Zoo / Naughty boy / Mister Methane / More tea vicar / Two stroke Eddie / Animal testing / Don't fear the sweeper / Poodles.
■ CD . . . . HHCD 14
■ LP . . . . .HHLP 14
■ MC . . . . HH 14
Hectic House / Nov '90.
CD . . . . DOJOCD 158
MC . . . . DOJOMC 158
Dojo / May '94 / Castle Communications / BMG.

BEER, SEX, CHIPS AND GRAVY.
Tracks: Lads from Macc / Beer sex & chips 'n' gravy / Boddies / Sweaty Betty / England's glory / Blackpool / Miss Macclesfield / God's gift to women / Get weavin' / Now he's a pod / Nagasaki sauce / Saturday night / Buenos aires / Charlotte / Failure with girls / Do you love me / Dan's underpant / Twenty pints / Macc Lads party.
■ LP . . . . WKFMLP 56
FM Records / '85.
■ CD . . . . WKFMXD 110
FM Records / Aug '89.
■ MC . . . . HH 1
Hectic House / Aug '89.
CD . . . . .HHCD 110
Hectic House / '91.
CD . . . . DOJOCD 154
Dojo / Nov '93 / Castle Communications / BMG.
MC . . . . DOJOMC 154
Dojo / Nov '93 / Castle Communications / BMG.

BITTER, FIT CRACK.
Tracks: Barrel's round / Guess me weight / Uncle Knobby / Maid of ale / Dan's big log / Got to be Gordon's / Bitter, fit crack / Julie the schooly / Doctor doctor / Torremolinos / Al o'peesha.
■ LP . . . . WKFMLP 100
FM Records / Aug '87.
■ MC . . . . HH 7
FM Records / Aug '89.
■ CD . . . . WKFMXD 100
FM Records / Feb '91.
CD . . . . DOJOCD 155
Dojo / Nov '93 / Castle Communications / BMG.
MC . . . . DOJOMC 155
Dojo / Nov '93 / Castle Communications / BMG.

COME TO BRUM.
Tracks: Knock knock / Julie the schooly / Head kicked in / Twenty pints / Bitter fit crack / Bloik / Saturday night / Failure with girls / Fat bastard / No sheep 'til Buxton / Barrel's round / Jingle bells / God's gift to women / Sweaty Betty.
■ VHS . . . . MACC 2
Jettisoundz / Sep '89.
VHS . . . . HHV 4
Jettisoundz / Sep '91 / TBD / Visionary Communications.

EH UP!.
Tracks: Eh up.
■ 12" . . . . HH 1ST
■ 7" . . . . HH 1S
Hectic House / '86.

FROM BEER TO ETERNITY.
Tracks: Alton Towers / Geordie girl / No sheep 'til Buxton / All day drinking / Tab after tab / Lucy Lastic / My pub / Dead cat / Lady Muck / Gordon's revenge / Pie taster / Dan's round yer 'andbag / Ben Nevis / Fluffy pup / Stoppyback / Ugly women.
■ LP . . . . .HHLP 12
■ MC . . . . HH 12
■ CD . . . . HHCD 12
Hectic House / Sep '89.
CD . . . . DOJOCD 157

MC. DOJOMC 157
Dojo / May '94 / Castle Communications / BMG.

JINGLE BELLS.
Tracks: Jingle bells / Barrel's round.
■ 7″ . . . . VHF 42
FM Records / Nov '87.
■ 7″ . . . . RS 1
Renegade / Jan '90.

LIVE AT LEEDS (The Who?).
Tracks: Sweaty Betty / Ben Nevis / Bloink / Do you love me / God's gift to women / Charlotte / Blackpool / Lads from Macc / Now he's a poof / Doctor doctor / Julie the schooly / Guess me weight / Miss Macclesfield / Fat bastard / Get weavin' / Barrels' round / Dan's underpant.
■ CD . . . . WKFMXD 115
■ LP . . . . WKFMLP 115
■ MC. . . . . WKFMMC 115
FM Records / Aug '88.
■ MC. . . . . HH 10
Hectic House / Aug '88.
CD . . . . DOJOCD 161
MC. . . . . DOJOMC 161
Dojo / Mar '94 / Castle Communications / BMG.

ORIFICE AND A GENITAL.
Tracks: Not Advised.
MC. . . . . DOJOMC 141
Dojo / May '94 / Castle Communications / BMG.

PIE TASTER.
Tracks: Pie taster / No sheep till Buxton / Dan's underpants (live) (Extra track on 12″ version.).
■ MC Single. . . . . HH 9
FM Records / Apr '88.
■ 12″. . . . . 12 VHF 144
■ 7″ . . . . VHF 44
FM Records / Mar '88.

QUALITY OF MERSEY.
Tracks: 24 hours / Julie the schooly / Get weavin' / Nagasaki sauce / Geordie girl / Boddies / Lady Muck / Buenos Airies / Dan's underpants / Fluffy puppy / Lucy lastic / Guess me weight / Miss Macclesfield / Dead cat / Alton Towers / Head kicked in / Barrel's round / Blackpool / Macc Lads.
■ VHS . . . . MACC 3
ReVision / Nov '90.
VHS . . . . HHV 6
ReVision / Sep '91 / RTM / Pinnacle.

SEX PIES AND VIDEOTAPE.
Tracks: No sheep 'til Buxton / Alcohol / Eh up let's sup / Do you love me / Bitter fit crack / Failure with girls.
VHS 0843603
Polygram Music Video / May '92 / PolyGram.

THREE BEARS.
Tracks: Twenty pints / Now he's a poof / Eh up Macc Lads / Barrels round / Blackpool / Lads from Macc / Eh up lets sup / Knutsford / Charlotte / No sheep 'til Buxton.
■ VHS . . . . MACC 1
Jettisoundz / Apr '90.
VHS . . . . HHV 5
Jettisoundz / Sep '91 / TBD / Visionary Communications.

TURTLES HEADS.
Tracks: Not Advised.
CD . . . . HHCD 17
MC. . . . . HH 17
Hectic House / Sep '91 / Hectic House Records / Pinnacle.

TWENTY GOLDEN CRATES.
Tracks: No sheep til buxton / Sweaty Betty / Buenos airies 91 / Beer + sex + chip's 'n' gravey / Guess me weight / Made of ale / Ben Nevis / Blackpool / Dans underpant / Knock knock / Gordon's revenge / My pub / Charlotte / Dead cat / Boddies / Fluffy pup / Julie the schooly / Lady muck / Miss Macclesfield / Nagasaki sauce / Barrels round / Twenty pints (CD only) / Saturday night (CD only).
■ CD . . . . STR CD 015
■ LP . . . . STR LP 015
■ MC. . . . . STR MC 015
Street Link / Oct '92.
CD . . . . DOJOCD 115
MC. . . . . DOJOMC 115
Dojo / May '94 / Castle Communications / BMG.

Machine

MOVE IT.
Tracks: Move it / Man in the moon.
■ 7″ . . . . MWVS 008
In Crowd / Sep '87.

THERE BUT FOR THE GRACE OF GOD.
Tracks: There but for the grace of God / Get your body ready.

■ 12″. PC 1456
■ 7″ . . . . PB 1456
RCA / '79.

Machine Head

BURN MY EYES.
Tracks: Davidian / Old / Thousand eyes / None but my own / Rage to overcome / Death church / I'm your God now / Blood for blood / Nation on fire / Real eyes, realize, real lies / Block.
CD . . . . RR 90162
CD . . . . RR 90169
LP . . . . RR 90161
MC. . . . . RR 90164
Road Runner / Aug '94 / Pinnacle.

McKagan, Duff

BELIEVE IN ME.
Tracks: Believe in me / Man in the meadow / (Fucked up) Beyond belief / Could it be U / Just not there / Punk rock song / Majority / 10 Years / Swamp song / Trouble / Fuck you / Lonely tonite.
CD . . . . GED 24605
MC. . . . . GEC 24605
■ LP . . . . GEF 24605
Geffen / Sep '93.

BELIEVE IN ME.
Tracks: Not Advised.
■ CD Single. . . . . GED 21865
Geffen / Nov '93.

Mad Axeman

MAD AXEMAN.
Tracks: Not Advised.
■ LP . . . . .SKULL 8329
Mausoleum / May '85.

Mad Cow Disease

COSTERMONGERIN E.P.
Tracks: Jesus wants me for a vegetable / Body bag / Slop / Master of the universe.
■ 12″. . . . . .CATL 60016
■ CD Single . . . . .CATL 60012
■ MC Single . . . . .CATL 60014
Catalina / Sep '92.

GOAT LUNG (THE MEXICAN APPROACH).
Tracks: Brown / Sin song / Meat / Iron / Symptoms / Jesus wants me for a vegetable / Genital torture / Decomposition / Sky burial / Thrills & disease.
■ CD . . . . .CATL 10012
■ LP . . . . .CATL 10011
Catalina / May '93.

Mad Dog

MAD DOG.
Tracks: Falling / Johnny cyclops / It all comes down / Fortune favours the brave / Chill out / Shanghai Joe / Five bucks in New York city / Last great wilderness.
■ LP . . . . .STUDLP 1
Stud / Apr '87.

Mad Max

HEARTS ON FIRE.
Tracks: Hearts on fire.
■ 7″ . . . . RR 5475
Road Runner / Nov '87.

NIGHT OF PASSION.
Tracks: Burnin' the stage / Wait for the night / R I P / Drive through the slag / Wild and seventeen / Hearts of fire / Love loaded / Night of passion / Star crossed lovers / Fox on the run.
■ LP . . . . RR 9666
Road Runner / Jul '87.

ROLLIN' THUNDER.
Tracks: Not Advised.
■ LP . . . . RR 9838
Road Runner / Aug '84.

STORMCHILD.
Tracks: Not Advised.
■ LP . . . . RR 9763
Road Runner / Aug '85.

Mad Reign

SALUTE THE NEW FLAG.
Tracks: Salute the new flag.
■ EP . . . . IW 1010
Iron Works (USA) / Feb '87.

Madam X

HIGH IN HIGH SCHOOL.
Tracks: High in high school / Metal in my veins.
■ 7″ . . . . JET 7044
■ 7″ P.Disc . . . . .JETP 7044
Jet / Feb '85.

JUST THAT TYPE OF GIRL.
Tracks: Just that type of girl / Flirt.
■ 12″. . . . . A 9216 T
■ 7″ . . . . .A 9216
Atlantic / Nov '87.

MADAM X.
Tracks: Madam X / Just that type of girl / I'm weak for you / I wonder / Cherries in the snow / I want your body / Flirt / Marry me.
■ LP 781 774-1
MC. 781 774-4
Atlantic / Feb '88 / WEA.

MADAM X.
Tracks: Madam X.
■ 12″. . . . . .K 7817741 4
■ 7″ . . . . .K 7817741
Atlantic / Jan '88.

WE RESERVE THE RIGHT.
Tracks: Not Advised.
■ LP . . . . .JETLP 242
■ MC. . . . . .JETCA 242
Jet / Mar '85 / Sony / Total / BMG.

Maelstrom

MEGAMORPHISIS.
Tracks: Megamorphisis.
■ 7″ . . . . .TAANG 39
Taang / Nov '92.

STEP ONE.
Tracks: Not Advised.
CD . . . . EM 94072
LP . . . . EM 94071
Emergo / Dec '90 / Pinnacle.

Magnum

Formed in Birmingham in 1972, Magnum have achieved success through constant touring and have built themselves a loyal fanbase, initially described as pomp rock their first album *Kingdom Of Madness* sold solidly if unspectacularly on Jet Records, after illness and legal problems with Jet, Magnum were offered a career saving deal with FM Records the resulting album *On A Storyteller's Night* sold very well and led to a permanent deal with Polydor.

ANTHOLOGY - MAGNUM.
Tracks: In the beginning / Lords of chaos / Kingdom of madness / Bringer / Greta adventures / Firebird / Foolish heart / Stayin' alive / If I could live forever / Reborn (live) / Changes (live) / Walking the straight line / We all play the game / Spirit / Prise / Vicious companions / Word / Hit and run / So far away.
■ Double LP. . . . . .RAWLP 007
■ MC. . . . . .RAWTC 007
Raw Power / Apr '86.
■ CD . . . . .RAWCD 007
Raw Power / May '86.

ARCHIVE.
Tracks: Not Advised.
CD . . . . .JETCD 1005
LP . . . . .JETLP 1005
MC. . . . . .JETMC 1005
Jet / Apr '93 / Sony / Total / BMG.

BACK TO EARTH.
Tracks: Back to earth.
■ 7″ . . . . JET 7027
Jet / Sep '82.

BATTLE, THE.
Tracks: Not Advised.
■ CD 291003
Ariola Express / Nov '92.

CAPTURED LIVE.
Tracks: How far Jerusalem / Before first light / On a story tellers night / All England's eyes / Les morts dansant / Just like an army / Light burned out / Endless love / Two hearts / Soldier of the line / Kingdom of madness / Sacred heart.
CD . . . . .OPTMCD 004
MC. . . . . .OPTMC 004
Icon / May '93 / Pinnacle.

■ DELETED

CHANGES.
Tracks: Changes / Everybody needs.
■ 7" . . . . JET 155
Jet / Oct '79.
■ 7" . . . . JET 188
Jet / Jun '80.

CHASE THE DRAGON.
Tracks: Lights burned out / We will play the game / Teacher / Spirit / Soldier of the line / On the edge of the world / Walking the straight line / Sacred hour.
■ LP . . . . JETLP 235
MC. JETCA 235
Jet / Jun '84 / Sony / Total / BMG.
CD . . . . JETCD 004
Jet Caroline / Jan '87 / Sony.
■ CD . . . . WKFMXD 112
■ LP . . . . WKFMLP 112
■ MC. . . . . WKFMMC 112
FM Records / Jun '88.
■ LP P.Disc . . . . WKFMPD 112
FM Records / Oct '88

COLLECTION: MAGNUM.
Tracks: Not Advised.
CD. . . . . CCSCD 272
■ Double LP . . . . CCSLP 272
■ MC. . . . . CCSMC 272
Castle Collector Series / Oct '90.

DAY'S OF NO TRUST.
Tracks: Day's of no trust / Day's of no trust (ext.version) (Extra track on 12" and CD.) / Maybe tonight / Spirit, The (live) (Extra track on 12".) / Two hearts (live) / How far Jerusalem (live) (Track on CD only.).
■ 12" . . . . POSPX 910
■ 7" . . . . POSP 910
■ CD Single . . . . POCD 910
Polydor / Mar '88.

ELEVENTH HOUR, THE.
Tracks: Prize / Great disaster / Viscious companions / One night of passion / Word / Road to paradise.
■ LP . . . . JET LP 240
MC. . . . . JETCA 240
Jet / Jun '83 / Sony / Total / BMG.
CD . . . . JETCD 005
Jet / '88 / Sony / Total / BMG.
■ LP P.Disc . . . . WKFMPD 111
■ LP . . . . WKFMLP 111
■ MC. . . . . WKFMMC 111
FM Records / Jun '88.
■ CD . . . . WKFMXD 111
FM Records / Jun '88.

EVERYTHING YOU DO.
Tracks: Everything you do / Concrete kid.
■ 7" . . . . EPC 7366
Epic / '79.

FOUNDATION.
Tracks: Not Advised.
■ LP Set. . . . . WKFMBX 145
■ MC Set . . . . WKFMBXC 145
FM Records / Apr '90.
■ CD . . . . WKFMBXD 145
FM Records / Apr '90.

FROM MIDNIGHT TO L.A.
Tracks: Not Advised.
VHS . . . . CFM 2640
Channel 5 / Aug '90 / Channel 5 Video / P.R.O. Video / Gold & Sons.

GOODNIGHT L.A.
Tracks: Rockin' chair / Only a memory / Matter of survival / Heartbroke and busted / No way out / Born to be king / Mama / Reckless man / What kind of love is this / Shoot / Cry for you.
CD 843 568-2
■ LP 843 568-1
MC. 843 568-4
Polydor / Jul '90 / PolyGram.

HEARTBROKE AND BUSTED.
Tracks: Heartbroke and busted / Hanging tree.
■ 12" . . . . PZ 94
■ 7" . . . . PO 94
■ 7" P.Disc . . . . POP 94
■ CD Single . . . . PZCDT 94
■ MC Single . . . . POCS 94
Polydor / Aug '90.

INVASION-MAGNUM LIVE.
Tracks: Not Advised.
CD. . . . . RRCD 113
LP . . . . RRLP 113
MC. . . . . RRLC 113
Receiver / Jul '93 / Total / BMG / Grapevine Distribution.

IT MUST HAVE BEEN LOVE.
Tracks: It must have been love / Crying time / Lonely nights (live) / Just like an arrow (live) / Lights burned out (live).
■ 12" . . . . POSXB 930
■ 12" . . . . POSPX 930
■ 7" . . . . POSP 930
■ 7" . . . . POSPG 930
■ CD Single . . . . POCD 930
Polydor / Jun '88.

JUST LIKE AN ARROW.
Tracks: Just like an arrow / Two hearts.
■ 12" . . . . 12 VHF 4
■ 7" . . . . VHF 4
FM Records / Mar '85.

KEEPING THE NITE LITE BURNING.
Tracks: Not Advised.
CD. . . . . JETCD 1006
LP . . . . JETLP 1006
MC. . . . . JETMC 1006
Jet / Nov '93 / Sony / Total / BMG.

KINGDOM OF MADNESS.
Tracks: In the beginning / Baby rock me / Universe / Kingdom of madness / All that is real / Bringer / Invasion / Lords of chaos / All come together.
■ LP . . . . JETLP 210
■ MC. . . . . JETCA 210
Jet / Aug '78.
■ LP . . . . CLALP 126
■ MC. . . . . CLAMC 126
■ CD . . . . CLACD 126
Castle Classics / '86.
CD. . . . . JETCD 001
Jet / '88 / Sony / Total / BMG.
■ LP P.Disc . . . . WKFMPD 118
■ CD . . . . WKFMXD 118
■ LP . . . . WKFMLP 118
■ MC. . . . . WKFMMC 118
FM Records / Jan '89.

LIGHTS BURNED OUT.
Tracks: Lights burned out.
■ 7" . . . . JET 7020
Jet / Feb '82.

MAGNUM.
Tracks: Lights burned out / If I could live forever / Sacred hour.
■ CD Single CD3-7
Special Edition / '88.

MAGNUM - CD BOX SET.
Tracks: Not Advised.
■ CD Set. . . . . CLA BX 907
Castle Classics / Feb '92.

MAGNUM EP.
Tracks: Invasion / Kingdom of madness / All of my life / Great adventure.
■ EP . . . . JET 175
Jet / Mar '80.

MAGNUM II.
Tracks: Great adventure / Changes / Battle / If I could live forever / Reborn / So could the night / Foolish heart / Stayin' alive / Firebird / All of my life / In the beginning / Baby rock me / Universe / Kingdom of madness / All that is real / Bringer / Invasion / Lords of Chaos / All come together.
■ LP . . . . JETLP 222
■ MC. . . . . JETCA 222
Jet / Oct '79.
■ LP . . . . CLALP 125
Castle Classics / Mar '87.
■ MC. . . . . CLAMC 125
■ CD . . . . CLACD 125
Castle Classics / Mar '87.
CD. . . . . JETCD 002
Jet / '88 / Sony / Total / BMG.
■ LP P.Disc . . . . WKFMPD 119
■ CD . . . . WKFMXD 119
■ LP . . . . WKFMLP 119
■ MC. . . . . WKFMMC 119
FM Records / Jan '89.

MAGNUM LIVE.
Tracks: Not Advised.
VHS . . . . CFV 06372
Channel 5 / '88 / Channel 5 Video / P.R.O. Video / Gold & Sons.
VHS . . . . SPC 00152
Spectrum (1) / Oct '89 / PolyGram.

MARAUDER.
Tracks: If I could live forever / Battle / Foolish heart / In the beginning / Reborn / Changes / So could the night / Lords of chaos.
■ LP . . . . JETLP 230
■ MC. . . . . JETCA 230
Jet / May '80 / Sony / Total / BMG.
■ CD . . . . CLACD 124

■ LP . . . . CLALP 124
■ MC. . . . . CLAMC 124
Castle Classics / '86.

MIDNIGHT.
Tracks: Midnight / Backstreet kid.
■ 12" . . . . POSPX 833
■ 7" . . . . POSP 833
Polydor / Oct '86.

MIRADOR.
Tracks: Just like an arrow (Only on CD.) / Soldier of the line / Changes / Sacred hour / Great adventure / Lights burned out / In the beginning (Only on CD.) / How far Jerusalem (Only on CD.) / Spirit / Word / Prize (Only on CD.) / If I could live forever / Lords of chaos (Only on CD.) / Storyteller's night (Only on CD.).
CD MAGXD1
■ CD . . . . WKFMXD 106
■ LP . . . . WKFMLP 106
■ MC. . . . . WKFMMC 106
FM Records / Nov '87.
■ LP P.Disc . . . . WKFMPD 106
FM Records / May '88.

MUSIC AND MEDIA INTERVIEW PICTURE DISC.
Tracks: Not Advised.
■ LP P.Disc . . . . MM 1241
Music & Media / Feb '88.

NIGHTRIDING: MAGNUM.
Tracks: Invasion / Kingdom of madness / All of my life / Great adventure / Prize / Back to Earth / Firebird / Changes / Battle / Road to Paradise.
■ LP . . . . KNLP 10009
■ MC. . . . . KNMC 10009
Nightriding / Jul '88.
■ CD . . . . KNCD 10009
Nightriding / '89.

OH LONELY NIGHT.
Tracks: Oh lonely night / Le morts dansants (live) / Hold back your love (live).
■ 7" . . . . POSP 798
Polydor / Jun '86.
■ 12" . . . . POSPX 798
■ 7" . . . . POSPG 798
Polydor / Jun '86.

ON A STORYTELLER'S NIGHT.
Tracks: On a storyteller's night.
■ 12" . . . . 12 VHF 10
■ 7" . . . . VHF 10
FM Records / Jun '85.

ON A STORYTELLER'S NIGHT.
Tracks: Not Advised.
■ VHS . . . . HEN 2329
Hendring Video / Apr '91.

ON A STORYTELLER'S NIGHT.
Tracks: How far Jerusalem / Just like an arrow / Before first light / On a storytellers night / Les morts dansant / Endless love / Two hearts / Steal your heart / All England / Last dance.
CD . . . . WKFMXD 34
■ LP P.Disc . . . . WKFMPD 34
MC. . . . . WKFMMC 34
■ LP . . . . WKFMLP 34
FM Records / May '85.
■ LP . . . . PACK 1
FM Records / Feb '86.
■ LP P.Disc . . . . WKFMHP 34
FM Records / Jan '89.
■ LP . . . . WKFMGP 34
FM Records / May '90.
CD . . . . JETCD 1007
Jet / Jul '93 / Sony / Total / BMG.

ON THE WINGS OF HEAVEN.
Tracks: Back to earth (Live) / Vigilante / Wild swan / Start talking over / On a storytellers night (Live) / Needs a lot of love / Pray for the day / How far Jerusalem / One step away / Days of no trust / It must have been love / Don't wake the lion / Just like an arrow (Live) / Kingdom of madness / Sacred hour (Live).
VHS 041 698 2
Polygram Music Video / Jul '88 / PolyGram.
CD Video 080 388 1
Polygram Music Video / Oct '88 / PolyGram.
VHS . . . . CFV 08122
Channel 5 / Jun '89 / Channel 5 Video / P.R.O. Video / Gold & Sons.

ROCK ART.
Tracks: We all need to be loved / Hard hearted woman / Back in your arms again / Rock heavy / Tall ships / Tell tale eyes / Love's a stranger / Rain-a-bye baby / Just this side of heaven / I will decide myself / On Christmas Day.
CD . . . . CDEMD 1066

MC. . . . . TCEMD 1066
EMI / Jun '94 / EMI.

ROCKIN' CHAIR.
Tracks: Rockin' chair.
■ 12″. . . . . PZ 88
■ 7″. . . . . POG 88
■ 7″. . . . . PO 88
■ CD Single. . . . . PZCD 88
■ MC Single. . . . . POCS 88
Polydor / Jun '90.

SACRED HOUR,THE - LIVE.
Tracks: Not Advised.
VHS . . . . EV 1227
Embassy Home Video / Feb '86 / Sony.

SLEEP WALKING.
Tracks: Not Advised.
CD. CDMFN 143
LP. . . . . MFN 143
MC. . . . . TMFN 143
Music For Nations / Oct '92 / Pinnacle.

SPIRIT, THE.
Tracks: Introduction / Vigilante / Days of no trust / Mama / Need a lotta love / Pray for the day / Les morts dansants / Reckless man / How far Jerusalem / Spirit / On a storyteller's night / Rockin chair / Kingdom of madness / Sacred hour / When the world comes down.
CD. 5111692
■ Double LP. 5111691
■ MC Set 5111694
Polydor / Sep '91.

START TALKING LOVE.
Tracks: Start talking love / C'est la vie / Start talking love (extended remix) (Only on 12″ single.) / Back to earth (live) / On a storytellers night (live) (on 12″ and CD single only.) / Sacred hour (live) (Extra track available on CD single only.).
■ 12″. . . . . POSPX 920
■ 12″. . . . . POSXR 920
■ 7″. POSPG 920
■ CD Single. . . . . POCD 920
■ 7″. POSP 920
Polydor / Apr '88.

START TALKING LOVE (CD VIDEO).
Tracks: Start talking love.
CD Video 080 406 2
Polygram Music Video / Oct '88 / PolyGram.

SWEETS FOR MY SWEET.
Tracks: Sweets for my sweet / Movin' on.
■ 7″. CBS 2959
CBS / Jan '75.

UNCORKED - THE BEST OF MAGNUM.
Tracks: Not Advised.
CD. JETCD 1008
Jet / Jun '94 / Sony / Total / BMG.

VIGILANTE.
Tracks: Lonely nights / Need a lot of love / Sometime love / Midnight (you won't be sleeping) / Red on the highway / Holy rider / When the world comes down / Vigilante / Backstreet kid.
CD. 829 989-2
MC. POLDC 5198
■ LP. . . . . POLD 5198
Polydor / Oct '86.

VINTAGE MAGNUM/THE ELEVENTH HOUR.
Tracks: Back to earth / Hold back your love / Long days black nights / Lonesome star / Everybody needs / Changes (studio remix) / All of my life / Kingdom of madness / Invasion / Great adventure / Prize / Breakdown / Great disaster / Vicious companions / So far away / Hit and run / One night of passion / Word / Young and precious souls / Road to Paradise.
■ CD Set. . . . . TFOCD 1
That's Original / Apr '88.
■ Double LP. . . . . TFOLP 1
■ MC. . . . . TFOMC 1
That's Original / Apr '88.

WHEN THE WORLD COMES DOWN.
Tracks: Vigilante / When the world comes down.
■ 12″. . . . . POSPX 850
■ 7″. POSP 850
Polydor / Feb '87.

WINGS OF HEAVEN.
Tracks: Days of no trust / Wild swan / Start talking love / One step away / It must have been love / Different worlds / Pray for the day / Don't wake the lion (too old to die young).
■ LP P.Disc. . . . . POLDP 5221
Polydor / Dec '88.
CD. 835 277-2

MC. POLDC 5221
■ LP . . . . POLD 5221
Polydor / Mar '88.

Mahogany Rush

CHILD OF THE NOVELTY.
Tracks: Not Advised.
CD. . . . . REP 4029-WZ
Repertoire (Germany) / Aug '91 / Pinnacle.

DOUBLE LIVE.
Tracks: Not Advised.
CD. 874 614
■ Double LP. 784 612
Maze / May '89.

LIVE: MAHOGANY RUSH (Featuring Frank Marino).
Tracks: Not Advised.
■ LP . . . . CBS 82621
CBS / Mar '78.

LIVE: MAHOGANY RUSH & FRANK MARINO (see under Marino, Frank).

MAHOGANY RUSH 4 (see under Marino, Frank).

STRANGE UNIVERSE.
Tracks: Not Advised.
CD. . . . . REP 4028-WZ
Repertoire (Germany) / Aug '91 / Pinnacle.

WORLD ANTHEM (see under Marino, Frank).

Maineeaxe

GAME, THE.
Tracks: Game / No foolin'.
■ 7″. .OHM 8
Powerstation / Oct '84.

GIMME SOME GOLD.
Tracks: Not Advised.
■ LP .AMP 5
MC. .CAMP 5
Powerstation / Feb '85 / Powerstation Records.

GIMME YOUR LOVE.
Tracks: Gimme your love.
■ 12″. . . . . OHM 10T
Powerstation / Jan '85.

GONNA MAKE YOU ROCK.
Tracks: Gonna make you rock / Snatch.
■ 7″. . . . . .OHM 6
Powerstation / Jun '84.

HOUR OF THUNDER, THE.
Tracks: Not Advised.
■ LP . . . . AMP 007
Powerstation / Aug '86.

SHOUT IT OUT.
Tracks: Not Advised.
■ LP .AMP 3
Powerstation / Jun '84.

Malefice

LOTUS BLOSSOM.
Tracks: Not Advised.
LP .LF 011
Lost & Found / Apr '92 / Plastic Head.

Malevolent Creation

RETRIBUTION.
Tracks: Not Advised.
■ LP . . . . RC 91811
Road Runner / Jun '92.
CD. RC 91812
Road Runner / Jan '94 / Pinnacle.

STILLBORN.
Tracks: Not Advised.
CD. RR 90422
LP . . . . RR 90421
Road Runner / Oct '93 / Pinnacle.

TEN COMMANDMENTS, THE.
Tracks: Not Advised.
LP . . . . RC 93611
MC. RC 93614
Road Runner / Apr '91 / Pinnacle.
CD. RC 93612
Road Runner / Jan '94 / Pinnacle.

Malhavoc

PREMEDITATED MURDER.
Tracks: Not Advised.
■ CD . . . . .CDDVN 19
■ LP . . . . DVN 19
Devotion / Nov '92.

RELEASE, THE.
Tracks: Not Advised.
■ CD . . . . .CDDVN 11
■ LP . . . . DVN 11
■ MC . . . . .TDVN 11
N/A / Jun '92.

Malice

CRAZY IN THE NIGHT.
Tracks: Captive of light / Vice versa / Crazy in the night / Death or glory.
CD. RO 94452
■ LP . . . . RO 94451
Roadracer / Aug '89.

IN THE BEGINNING.
Tracks: Rockin' with you / Into the ground / Air attack / Stellar masters / Tarot dealer / Squeeze it dry / Hellrider / No haven for the raven / Unwanted / Godz of thunder.
■ LP 781 250-1
Atlantic / Oct '85.

LICENCED TO KILL.
Tracks: Not Advised.
■ LP . . . . K 781 714 1
MC. . . . . K 781 714 4
Atlantic / Mar '87 / WEA.

Malicious Onslaught

REBELLIOUS MAYHEM.
Tracks: Not Advised.
CD. . . . . BROO 1CD
LP . . . . BROO 1LP
MC. . . . . BROO 1MC
Brain Crusher / Nov '92 / Plastic Head.

Malmsteen, Yngwie

Self-proclaimed guitar genius, Malmsteem has been ridiculed for blatant Ritchie Blackmore influence. Latter demonstrated by first band Rising (title of Rainbow's second album) and union with Rainbow singers Graham Bonnet and Joe Lynn Turner in Alcatrazz and Rising Force, respectively. Malmsteem is an undeniably talented player, whose work is best heard on 1988 hit album Odyssey.

COLLECTION.
Tracks: Not Advised.
VHS 0849663
Polygram Music Video / Jun '92 / PolyGram.

ECLIPSE.
Tracks: Making love / Save our love / Devil in disguise / What do you want / Faultline / Eclipse / Bedroom eyes / Motherless child / Judas / Demon driver / See you in hell (don't be late).
■ LP 843 361-1
■ CD 843 361-2
■ MC 843 361-4
Polydor / Mar '90.

FIRE AND ICE.
Tracks: Not Advised.
CD. 7559611372
■ LP 7559611371
MC. 7559611374
Elektra / Feb '92 / WEA.

HEAVEN TONIGHT (Malmsteen, Yngwie & Rising Force).
Tracks: Heaven tonight / Riot in the dungeons / Rising force / Trilogy suite, Opus 5.
■ 12″. . . . . YJMX 1
■ 12″ P.Disc. . . . . YJMXP 1
■ 7″. YJM 1
■ 7″. . . . . YJMG 1
■ CD Single . . . . YJMCD 1
Polydor / Nov '88.

I SEE THE LIGHT TONIGHT.
Tracks: I see the light tonight / Far beyond the sun / I'm a viking.
■ 7″. 883 073-1
Polydor / Jun '85.

MAKING LOVE.
Tracks: Making love.
■ CD Single. . . . . PZCD 79

■ 12″. . . . . **PZ 79**
■ 7″. . . . . **PO 79**
Polydor / Apr '90.

MARCHING OUT (Malmsteen, Yngwie & Rising Force).
Tracks: Prelude / I'll see the light tonight / Don't let it end / Disciples of hell / I'm a viking / Overture 1383 / Anguish and fear / On the run again / Soldier without faith / Caught in the middle / Marching out.
CD. 825 733-2
■ LP . . . . POLD 5183
MC. . . . . POLDC 5183
Polydor / Aug '85 / PolyGram.

ODYSSEY (Malmsteen, Yngwie & Rising Force).
Tracks: Rising force / Hold on / Heaven tonight / Dreaming (tell me) / Bite the bullet / Riot in the dungeons / Deja vu / Crystal ball / Now is the time / Faster than the speed of light / Krakatau / Memories.
■ CD. 835 451-2
■ LP . . . . POLD 5224
■ MC. . . . . POLDC 5224
Polydor / May '88.

RISING FORCE.
Tracks: Black star / Far beyond the sun / Now your ships are burned / Evil eye / Icarus' dream suite / As above, so below / Little savage / Farewell.
■ LP 825 324-1
Verve / May '85.
CD. 825 324-2
Polydor / May '88 / PolyGram.

RISING FORCE LIVE '85.
Tracks: I'll see the light tonight / As above, so below / Don't let it end / Far beyond the sun / On the run again / Anguish and fear / I am a viking / Kree Nakoorie / Disciples of hell / Hiroshima mon amour / Black star / Jet to jet.
VHS . . . . CFV 03382
Channel 5 / Feb '89 / Channel 5 Video / P.R.O. Video / Gold & Sons.

SEVENTH SIGN.
Tracks: Never die / I don't know / Meant to be / Forever one / Hairtrigger / Brothers / Seventh sign / Bad blood / Prisoner of your love / Pyramid of cheops / Crash and burn / Sorrow.
CD. . . . . CDMFN 158
MC. . . . . TMFN 158
Music For Nations / Mar '94 / Pinnacle.

TRIAL BY FIRE (Live in Leningrad) (Malmsteen, Yngwie & Rising Force).
Tracks: Liar / Queen in love / Deja vu / Far beyond the sun / Heaven tonight / Dreaming (tell me) / You don't remember, I'll never forget / Guitar solo (Spasebo blues) / Black star / Spanish castle magic (edit version).
■ LP 839 726-1
■ MC. 839 726-4
■ CD. 839 726-2
Polydor / Oct '89.

TRIAL BY FIRE (Live in Leningrad) (Malmsteen, Yngwie & Rising Force).
Tracks: Rising force / Liar / Queen in love / Deja vu / You don't remember, I'll never forget / Crystal ball / Far beyond the sun / Dreaming (tell me) / Fury / Guitar solo / Heaven tonight / Riot in the dungeons / Black star / Spanish castle magic.
VHS . . . . CFV 08912
Channel 5 / Nov '89 / Channel 5 Video / P.R.O. Video / Gold & Sons.

TRILOGY.
Tracks: You don't remember, I'll never forget / Liar / Queen in love / Crying / Fury / Fire / Magic mirror / Dark ages / Trilogy suite, Opus 5.
CD. 831 073-2
■ LP . . . . POLD 5204
■ MC. . . . . POLDC 5204
Polydor / Nov '86.

Maltese Falcon

METAL RUSH.
Tracks: Not Advised.
■ LP . . . . RR 9824
Road Runner / Oct '84.

Mama's Boys

Talented Irish trio who have yet to achieve success they deserve; coming closest with 1985's *Power And Passion* album. Early '70s style has latterly been abandoned in favour of Foreigner-esque AOR; band having recruited a lead singer in 1987.

BELFAST CITY BLUES.
Tracks: Belfast city blues / Reach for the top.
■ 7″. .DT 015
Scoff / Apr '82.

GROWING UP THE HARD WAY.
Tracks: Not Advised.
■ LP .HIP 49
■ MC. . . . . HIPC 49
Jive / Nov '87.
■ CD. . . . . CHIP 49
Jive / Nov '87.

HARD 'N' LOUD.
Tracks: Hard 'n' loud.
■ 12″. . . . . JIVET 110
Jive / Nov '85.

HIGHER GROUND.
Tracks: Higher ground.
■ 12″. . . . . MBOY T1
■ 7″. . . . . MBOY 1
Jive / Jul '87.

IN THE HEAT OF THE NIGHT.
Tracks: In the heat of the night.
■ 7″. . . . . ION 1038
Albion / Oct '82.

LAUGH ABOUT IT (EP).
Tracks: Not Advised.
■ CD Single. . . . . .CDS 131103
CTM / Jun '92.

LIVE TONITE.
Tracks: Not Advised.
CD. . . . . .CDMFN 114
LP . . . . MFN 114
MC. . . . . .TMFN 114
Music For Nations / Apr '91 / Pinnacle.

MAMA WEER ALL CRAZEE NOW.
Tracks: Mama weer all crazee now.
■ 12″. .G 71
Jive / Aug '84.

MAMA'S BOYS.
Tracks: Not Advised.
■ LP .HIP 15
■ MC. . . . . HIPC 15
Jive / Jul '84.

MIDNIGHT PROMISES.
Tracks: Midnight promises / Lonely soul / High energy weekend (Only on 12″ single.).
■ 12″. 12SP 11
■ 7″. SP 11
Spartan / Jan '84.

NEEDLE IN THE GROOVE.
Tracks: Needle in the groove / Hard headed ways.
■ 12″. 12ION 1041
■ 7″. . . . . ION 1041
Albion / Jan '83.

NEEDLE IN THE GROOVE.
Tracks: Needle in the groove.
■ 7″ P.Disc . . . . JIVEP 96
■ 12″. . . . . JIVET 96
■ 7″. . . . . JIVE 96
Jive / May '85.

OFFICIAL BOOTLEG.
Tracks: Rock 'n' roll craze / Summertime / Without you / Demon / I'm leaving home / Belfast City blues / Hyland rock / Record machine.
■ LP . . . . UNKNOWN
Spartan / '81.

PLUG IT IN.
Tracks: In the heat of the night / Burning up / Needle in the groove / Reach for the top / Silence is out of fashion / Straight forward / Runaway dreams / Getting out / Belfast city blues.
■ LP . . . . ULTRA 1
Albion / Oct '82.
MC. . . . . CULTRA 1
Albion / Oct '82.
■ LP . . . . CLALP 111
■ MC. . . . . CLAMC 111
Castle Classics / Jul '86.

POWER AND PASSION.
Tracks: Hard 'n' loud / Straight forward, no looking back / Needle in the groove / Lettin' go / Run / Power and passion / Don't tell mama / Professor II / Let's get high.
■ LP .HIP 24
■ MC. . . . . HIPC 24
Jive / Mar '85.

RELATIVITY.
Tracks: Not Advised.
■ CD. . . . . CD 131003

■ MC. . . . . MC 131003
CTM / Jul '92.

TURN IT UP.
Tracks: Face to face / Loose living / Gentleman rogues / Lonely soul / Freedom fighters.
■ LP . . . . SPLP 001
Spartan / Oct '83.

WAITING FOR A MIRACLE.
Tracks: Waiting for a miracle / Lightning strikes.
■ 12″. . . . . JIVET 152
■ 7″. . . . . .JIVE 152
Jive / Sep '87.

Mammoth

ALL THE DAYS.
Tracks: All the days.
■ 12″. . . . . MOTH T2
■ 7″. . . . . MOTH 2
Jive / Jan '00.

CAN'T TAKE THE HURT.
Tracks: Can't take the hurt / None but the brave / Political animal.
■ 12″. . . . . MOTH T13
■ 7″. . . . . MOTH 3
Jive / Feb '89.
■ CD Single. . . . . MOTHCD 3
Jive / Feb '89.

FATMAN.
Tracks: Fat man / Political animal.
■ 12″. . . . . MOTH T1
■ 7″. . . . . MOTH 1
Jive / Jul '87.

MAMMOTH.
Tracks: All the days / Can't take the hurt / Dark star / Long time coming / Home from the storm / Fat man / 30 pieces of silver / Bet you wish / Bad times.
■ LP .HIP 56
■ MC. . . . . HIPC 56
■ CD. . . . . CHIP 56
Jive / Apr '89.

ROCK ME.
Tracks: Rock me / Rough 'n' ready.
■ 7″. . . . . .NEAT 42
Neat / Dec '84.

Mandator

PERFECT PROGENY.
Tracks: Not Advised.
CD. 841 716 2
LP 081 716 1
AM Music / Jan '90.

Mania

CHANGING TIMES.
Tracks: Prelude (intro) / Expulsion / Turn towards the light / No way back / Be strong / To the end of the world / Vision / Gambler / We don't need war / Violent time.
■ LP .NUK 139
■ MC. . . . . ZCNUK 139
■ CD. . . . . CDNUK 139
Noise / Oct '89.

WIZARD OF THE LOST KINGDOM.
Tracks: Not Advised.
■ Mini LP . . . . .NUK 127
Noise / Feb '89.

Manic Street Preachers

Welsh quartet who crossed over into metal after growing up as a more alternative pop/rock outfit. Deliberately controversial, they are much closer to latterday Sex Pistols than Iron Maiden although frontman James Dean Bradfield's songwriting has never been restricted by any genre limitations. Between elegantly wasted but at times alarmingly self destructive guitarist Richie, and alarmingly tall Sid Vicious-like bassist Nicky Wire, Bradfield fronts an engaging band who are just as likely to self-destruct next week as go on to achive megastardom. Never a dull moment on or offstage and, indeed, on their extremely colourful records.

FASTER.
Tracks: Faster / P.C.P. / Sculpture of man (Features on 10″ & CDS only.) / New art riot (In E minor) (Features on CDS only.).
■ 10″. 660447 0
■ 7″. 660447 7

■ CD Single. 660447 2
■ MC Single. 660447 4
Epic / May '94.

FROM DESPAIR TO WHERE.
Tracks: From despair to where / Hibernation / Spectators of suicide (On CD Single & 12" only) / Starlover (On CD Single only).
■ 12". .659337-6
■ CD Single. 659337-2
■ MC Single. 659337-4
Columbia / Jun '93.

GENERATION TERRORISTS.
Tracks: Slash 'n' burn / Nat West-Barclays-Midland-Lloyds / Born to end / Motorcycle emptiness / You love us / Love's sweet exile / Little baby nothing / Repeat (stars and stripes) / Tennessee / Another invented disease / Stay beautiful / So dead / Repeat (UK) / Spectators of suicide / Damn dog / Crucifix kiss / Methadone pretty / Condemned to rock 'n' roll.
CD. 4710602
CD P.Disc. 4710609
LP. 4710601
■ LP P.Disc. 4710600
MC. 4710604
Columbia / Jun '92 / Sony.
MiniDisc. 471060-3
Columbia / Feb '93 / Sony.

GOLD AGAINST THE SOUL.
Tracks: Sleepflower / From despair to where / La tristesse durera (scream to a sigh) / Yourself / Life becoming a landslide / Drug drug druggy / Roses in the hospital / Nostalgic pushead / Symphony of tourette / Gold against the soul.
MiniDisc. 474064-4
Columbia / Aug '93 / Sony.
CD. 4740642
LP. 4740641
MC. 4740644
Sony Music / Jun '93 / Sony.
■ LP P.Disc. 474064 9
Columbia / Jun '93.

HOLY BIBLE.
Tracks: Yes / Ifwhiteamericatoldthetruthforonedayit'sworldwouldfallapart / Of walking abortion / She is suffering / Archives of pain / Revol / 4st 7lb Mausoleum / Faster / This is yesterday / Die in the summertime / Intense humming of evil / PCP.
CD. 4774212
Columbia / Aug '94 / Sony.
CD P.Disc. 4774219
LP. 4774210
Epic / Aug '94 / Sony.
MC. 4774214
Columbia / Aug '94 / Sony.

LA TRISTESSE DURERA (SCREAM TO A SIGH).
Tracks: La tristesse durera (scream to a sigh) / Patrick Bateman / What's my name (live) (Available on CDS only) / Slash 'n' burn (live) (Available on CDS only) / Repeat (live) (Available on 12PD only) / Tennessee (Available on 12PD only).
■ 12" P.Disc. 659477 6
■ CD Single. 659477 2
■ MC Single. 659477 4
Columbia / Jul '93.

LIFE BECOMING A LANDSLIDE.
Tracks: Life becoming a landslide / Comfort comes / Are mothers saints (Available on CDS only.) / Charles Windsor (Available on CDS only.)
■ 12". .660070 6
■ 7". 660070 7
■ CD Single. 660070 2
■ MC Single. 660070 4
Columbia / Feb '94.

LITTLE BABY NOTHING.
Tracks: Little baby nothing / Never want again (Not on 658796-5) / Suicide alley (Not on 658796-5) / Dead yankee drawl (On 658796-2 only) / R.P.McMurphy (On 658796-5 only) / Tennessee (On 658796-5 only) / You love us (On 658796-5 only).
■ 7". 658796-7
■ CD Single. 658796-5
■ CD Single. 658796-2
■ MC Single. 658796-4
Columbia / Nov '92.

LOVE'S SWEET EXILE.
Tracks: Love's sweet exile / Repeat / Democracy coma (Only on 12" and CD single) / Stay beautiful (Only on CD single).
■ 12". .6575826
■ 7". 6575827
■ CD Single. 6575822
Columbia / Oct '91.

MOTORCYCLE EMPTINESS.
Tracks: Motorcycle emptiness / Bored out of my mind / Under my wheels (Only available on 12" and CD Single.) / Crucifix kiss (live) (Only available on CD Single.).
■ 12". .6580836
■ 7". 6580837
■ CD Single. 6580832
■ MC Single. 6580834
Columbia / Jun '92.

MOTOWN JUNK SINGLE.
Tracks: Motown junk single.
■ 12". .HVN 812
Heavenly / Jan '91.

NEW ART RIOT EP.
Tracks: Not Advised.
12". . . . . YUBB 004
CD Single. . . . . YUBB 004CD
Damaged Goods / Jul '94 / SRD.

ROSES IN THE HOSPITAL.
Tracks: Roses in the hospital / Roses in the hospital (mixes) (Available on 12 only) / Us against you (Not available on 12) / Donkeys (Not available on 12) / Wrote for luck (Available on CDS only).
■ 12". .659727 6
■ 7". 659727 7
■ CD Single. 659727 2
Columbia / Sep '93.

SLASH 'N' BURN.
Tracks: Slash 'n' burn / Motown junk / Ain't goin' down (12" & CD single only) / Sorrow 16 (CD single only).
■ 12". .6578736
■ 7". 6578737
■ MC Single. 6578734
■ CD Single. 6578732
Columbia / Mar '92.

STAY BEAUTIFUL.
Tracks: Stay beautiful / Soul Contamination.
■ 12". .6573376
■ 7". 6573377
■ CD Single. 6573372
Columbia / Jul '91.

THEME FROM M.A.S.H.(SUICIDE IS PAINLESS).
Tracks: Theme from M.A.S.H.(suicide is painless) / Everything I do (I do it for you) / Sleeping with the N.M.E. (On 12"/CDs only).
■ 12". .6583826
■ 7". 6583827
■ CD Single. 6583822
■ MC Single. 6583824
Columbia / Sep '92.

YOU LOVE US.
Tracks: You love us / Vision of dead desire / We her Majesty's prisoners (CD single only) / It's so easy (12" & CD single only).
■ 12". .HVN 1012
■ 7". . . . . .HVN 10
■ CD Single. . . . . .HVN 10CD
Heavenly / May '91.
■ 12". .6577246
■ 7". 6577247
■ MC Single. 6577244
■ CD Single. 6577242
Columbia / Jan '92.

Manilla Road

CIRCUS MAXIMUS.
Tracks: Not Advised.
CD. . . . . BDCD 53
Black Dragon / Oct '92.

MANILLA ROAD LIVE.
Tracks: Not Advised.
■ LP. . . . . BD 033
Black Dragon / Jun '88.

MYSTIFICATION.
Tracks: Not Advised.
■ LP. . . . . BD 024
Black Dragon / Jul '87.

Maninnya Blade

MERCHANTS IN METAL.
Tracks: Live life at speed / Fireborn / Bearer of the ring / Attila the hun / Raiders / Dance to evil / No pax Romana / Nosferatu / Voyage to Hades / Metal pride.
■ LP. . . . . .KILP 4005
Killerwatt / Oct '86.

Manitoba's Wild Kingdom

AND YOU.
Tracks: Party starts now / New York, New York / I want you tonite / Perfect high / Prototype / Haircut and attitude / DWI / Fired up / Had it coming / Speedball.
■ CD. .DMCG 6087
■ MC. .MCGC 6087
■ LP. . . . . .MCG 6087
MCA / May '90.

Mann, Geoff

I MAY SING GRACE.
Tracks: Not Advised.
LP. . . . . GRUB 4
Food For Thought / Oct '88 / Pinnacle.

IN ONE ERA.
Tracks: Picadilly Square / I wouldn't lie to you / Kingdom come / Afterwards / For God's sake / Green paper snow / My soul / Slow one / Creation / Dance / Gethsemane / Waves / Flowers.
CD. . . . . CYCL 004
Cyclops / Mar '94 / Pinnacle.

LOUD SYMBOLS.
Tracks: Not Advised.
CD. . . . . CDGRUB 15
LP. . . . . GRUB 15
MC. . . . . TGRUB 15
Food For Thought / Jul '91 / Pinnacle.

MINISTRY OF THE INTERIOR (Mann, Geoff Band).
Tracks: Not Advised.
CD. . . . . CDGRUB 21
LP. . . . . GRUB 21
MC. . . . . TGRUB 21
Food For Thought / Sep '91 / Pinnacle.

Manowar

Nobody except leader Joey DeMaio (bass) knows whether Manowar are merely putting on a front, but only false metal fans without a sense of humour would dare dispute the group's claim to be the kings of true metal. Their records are packed with all the archetypal heavy metal-isms ever invented (and a few known only to Manowar). In 1994 they were proud to regain their Guinness Book Of Records standing as The Loudest Band In The World. Guitarists, drummers and record deals have all come and gone but Manowar have remained proudly committed to heavy metal. What else would you expect from a band who were formed by Black Sabbath's former pyro technician (DeMaio), signed their recording contract in ink mixed with their own blood and are fronted by a singer Eric Adams whose muscles have got muscles?! Louder, faster, heavier, long may they reign.

ALL MEN PLAY ON 10.
Tracks: All men play on 10.
■ 12". .TEN 30-12
10 / Aug '84.

BATTLE HYMNS.
Tracks: Death tone / Metal daze / Fast taker / Shell shock / Battle hymns / Dark avenger / William's tale.
■ MC. .TC LBG 30349
■ LP. . . . . .LBG 30349
Liberty / Aug '82.

BLOW YOUR SPEAKERS.
Tracks: Blow your speakers / Violence and bloodshed.
■ 12". .B 9463 T
■ 7". . . . . .B 9463
Atlantic / May '87.

CHRIS TETLEY INTERVIEWS MANOWAR.
Tracks: Not Advised.
■ LP P.Disc. . . . . .CT 1009
Music & Media / Oct '87.

DEFENDER.
Tracks: Defender / Gloves of metal.
■ 12". .12 KUT 102
Music For Nations / Oct '83.

FIGHTING THE WORLD.
Tracks: Fighting the world / Blow your speakers / Carry on / Violence and bloodshed / Defender / Drums of doom / Holy war / Blackwind, fire and steel.
MC. 790 563-4
■ LP. 790 563-1

       ■ DELETED

Atlantic / Jan '87.
CD 790 563-2
Atlantic / Jul '88 / WEA.

HAIL TO ENGLAND.
Tracks: Blood of my enemies / Each dawn I die / Kill with power / Hail to England / Army of the immortals / Black arrows / Bridge of death.
■ LP . . . . MFN 19
MC. . . . . TMFN 19
Music For Nations / Feb '84 / Pinnacle.
CD . . . . CDMFN 19
Music For Nations / Dec '88 / Pinnacle.
CD . . . . GED 24539
Geffen / Nov '93 / BMG.

INTO GLORY RIDE.
Tracks: Warlord / Secret of steel / Gloves of metal / Gates of Valhalla / Hatred / Revelation (death's angel) / March for revenge / By the soldiers of death.
■ LP . . . . MFN 6
MC. . . . . TMFN 6
Music For Nations / Jul '83 / Pinnacle.
CD . . . . GED 24538
Geffen / Nov '93 / BMG.

METAL KINGS, THE.
Tracks: Wheels of fire / Kings of metal / Heart of steel / Sting of the bumblebee / Crown and the ring / Kingdom come / Hail and kill / Warriors prayer / Blood of the kings.
CD. . . . . K 781 930 2
■ LP . . . . K 781 930 1
MC. . . . . K 781 930 4
Atlantic / Nov '88 / WEA.

SECRETS OF STEEL.
Tracks: Not Advised.
■ CD Set. . . . . GED 24540
Geffen / Nov '93.

SIGN OF THE HAMMER.
Tracks: All men play on 10 / Animals / Thor / Mountains / Sign of the hammer / Oath / Thunderpick / Guyana (cult of the damned).
■ LP . . . . DIX 10
■ MC. . . . . CDIX 10
10 / Sep '84.
CD. . . . . XIDCD 21
■ MC. . . . . CXID 21
10 / Nov '90.

TRIUMPH OF STEEL.
Tracks: Achilles, agony and ecstacy in eight parts / Metal warriors / Ride the dragon / Spirit of the cherokee / Burning / Power of sword / Demon's whip / Master of the wind.
CD. 7567824232
■ LP 7567824231
MC. 7567824234
Atlantic / Oct '92 / WEA.

Mantas

WINDS OF CHANGE.
Tracks: Hurricane / Desperado / Sionara / Nowhere to hide / Deciever / Let it rock / King of the rings / Western days / Winds of change.
CD. . . . . NEATCD 1042
■ LP . . . . NEAT 1042
Neat / '88.
■ LP . . . . RR 95151
Road Runner / Oct '88.

Marcus

MARCUS.
Tracks: Black magic / Salmon ball / Kelly / Gypsy fever / Pillow stars / Highschool ladies / Streetcorner babies / Dream wheel / Rise unto falcon.
■ LP . . . . UALA 668 G
United Artists / '76.

Marillion

Self-confessed devotees of Yes and Pink Floyd, Marillion proved progressive rock could still be viable in '80s. Band headlined major UK tour even before release of debut album, *Script For A Jester's Tear*, in 1983. European success grew, peaking with *Kayleigh* single and *Misplaced Childhood* album, although Marillion have yet to 'crack' US. Association with metal community confirmed by appearance at 1986 'Monsters of Rock' festival. After one further album, charismatic frontman Fish acrimoniously quit for solo career. Against all expectations, band continued with Steve Hogarth, celebrating decade of success with *Singles Collection 1982-1992* compilation.

1982-1986 THE VIDEOS.
Tracks: Market Square heroes / He knows you know / Garden party / Assassing / Kayleigh / Lavender / Heart of Lothian / Lady Nina.
VHS . . . . MVP 99 1122 2
PMI / Jun '86 / EMI / Gold & Sons / TBD.

ALONE AGAIN IN THE LAP OF LUXURY.
Tracks: Alone again in the lap of luxury / Cover my eyes / Slainte Mhath / Uninvited guest / Living with the big lie / Space / River / Bridge.
■ CD Single . . . . CDEMS 318
■ CD Single . . . . CDEM 318
■ MC Single . . . . TCEM 318
■ 12" 12EMPD 318
EMI / May '94.

ASSASSING.
Tracks: Assassing / Cinderella search.
■ 7" . . . . .MARIL 2
■ 12" . . . . 12 MARIL 2
EMI / Apr '84.
■ 12" P.Disc. . . . . 12 MARILP 2
EMI / Apr '84.

B'SIDES THEMSELVES.
Tracks: Grendel / Charting the single / Market square heroes / Three boats down from the Candy / Cinderella search / Lady Nina / Freaks / Tux on / Margaret.
CD. . . . . CZ 39
■ LP . . . . EMS 1295
■ MC. TCEMS 1295
EMI / Jul '88.

BRAVE.
Tracks: Bridge / Living with the big lie / Runaway / Goodbye to all that / Wave / Mad / Opium den / Slide / Standing in the swing / Hard as love / Hollow man / Alone again in the lap of luxury / Now wash your hand / Paper lies / Brave / Great escape / Last of you / Falling from the moon / Made again.
CD. . . . . CDEMD 1054
■ LP . . . . EMD 1054
MC. . . . . TCEMD 1054
EMI / Feb '94 / EMI.

BRAVE (The Movie).
Tracks: Bridge / Living with the big lie / Runaway / Goodbye to all that (Part 3 - the opium den) / Good-bye to all that (Part 4 - the side) / Goodbye to all that (Part 5 - standing in the swing) / Hard as love / Hollow man / Alone again in the lap of luxury / I now wash your hands / Brave / Great escape (Part 1 - the last of you) / Great escape (Part 2 - fallin' from the moon).
VHS . . . . MVP 4912623
PMI / May '94 / EMI / Gold & Sons / TBD.

BRIEF ENCOUNTER.
Tracks: Lady Nina (live) / Freaks (live) / Kayleigh (live) / Fugazi (live) / Script for a jester's tears.

CLUTCHING AT STRAWS.
Tracks: Hotel hobbies / Warm wet circles / That time of the night / Going under / Just for the record / White Russian / Incommunicado / Torch song / Slainte Mhath / Sugar mice / Last straw.
■ CD . . . . CDEMD 1002
■ MC. TCEMC 3533
■ LP . . . . EMD 1002
EMI / Jun '87.
■ LP P.Disc . . . . EMDP 1002
EMI / Nov '87.
CD. . . . . CZ 214
■ LP . . . . ATAK 135
MC. . . . . TCATAK 135
EMI / '89 / EMI.

COVER MY EYES (PAIN AND HEAVEN).
Tracks: Cover my eyes (pain and heaven) / How can it hurt / Party (12" & CD single only).
■ 12" 12MARILP 13
■ 7" . . . . MARIL 13
■ CD Single . . . . CDMARIL 13
■ MC Single . . . . TCMARIL 13
EMI / May '91.

DRY LAND.
Tracks: Dry land / Holloway girl / After me / Substitute (Only on 12" Single.) / Waiting to happen (Only on 10" Single.) / Easter (Only on 10" and CD Single.) / Sugar mice (Only on 10" and CD Single.) / King of sunset town (Only on 12" Single.)
■ 10" 10MARIL 15
■ 12" P.Disc 12MARILPD 15
■ 7" . . . . MARIL 15
■ CD Single . . . . CDMARIL 15
EMI / Oct '91.

EASTER.
Tracks: Easter (7" edit) (Not on 12" & CD single.) / Release (Not on 12" Gatefold.) / Easter (12" edit) (12"

& CD single only.) / Uninvited guest (live) (12" & CD single only.).
■ 12" .12MARILG 12
■ 12" .12MARIL 12
■ 7" . . . . MARIL 12
■ 7" P.Disc . . . . MARILPD 12
■ CD Single . . . . CDMARIL 12
■ MC Single . . . . TCMARIL 12
EMI / Mar '90.

FREAKS 'LIVE'.
Tracks: Freaks (live) / Kayleigh (live) / Childhood's end (live) (CD single & 12" only.) / White feather (CD single & 12" only.).
■ 12" 12MARIL 9
■ 7" . . . . MARIL 9
■ 7" P.Disc . . . . MARILP 9
■ CD Single . . . . CDMARIL 9

FROM STOKE ROW TO IPANEMA (A Year in the Life June 89-July 90).
Tracks: Hooks in you / Uninvited guest / Eric / Kayleigh / Lavender / Easter / Ultimate gift / King of Sunset town / Holloway girl / Berlin / Season's end / Incommunicado.
VHS . . . . MVN 991 257 3
PMI / Nov '90 / EMI / Gold & Sons / TBD.

FUGAZI.
Tracks: Assassing / Punch and Judy / Jigsaw / Emerald lies / She chameleon / Incubus / Fugazi.
■ LP . . . . MRL 1
■ LP P.Disc . . . . MRLP 1
■ MC. TC MRL 1
EMI / Mar '84.
CD. . . . . CDFA 3196
■ LP . . . . FA 3196
MC. . . . . TCFA 3196
Fame / May '88 / EMI.
CD. . . . . CDEMC 3682
EMI / May '94 / EMI.

GARDEN PARTY.
Tracks: Garden party / Charting the single / Margaret.
■ 7" P.Disc . . . . EMIP 5393
■ 12" 12EMI 5393
■ 7" . . . . EMI 5393
EMI / Jun '83.

HE KNOWS YOU KNOW.
Tracks: He knows you know / Charting the single.
■ 7" . . . . EMI 5362
■ 12" 12EMI 5362
EMI / Jan '83.

HEART OF LOTHIAN.
Tracks: Heart of Lothian / Chelsea Monday / Live at Utrecht / Heart of Lothian (ext).
■ 12" . . . . 12 MARIL 5
■ 12" P.Disc. . . . . 12 MARILP 5
■ 7" . . . . MARIL 5
EMI / Nov '85.

HOLIDAYS IN EDEN.
Tracks: Splintering heart / Cover my eyes (pain and heaven) / Party / No one can / Holidays in Eden / Dry land / Waiting to happen / This town / Rakes's progress / 100 nights.
CD. . . . . CDEMD 1022
■ LP . . . . EMD 1022
■ MC. TCEMD 1022
EMI / Jun '91.

HOLLOW MAN, THE.
Tracks: Hollow man / Brave (Not available on CDS 1) / Marouette jam (Available on CDS 2 only) / Great escape (Available on CDS 1 only) / Last of you (Available on CDS 1 only) / Falling from the moon (Available on CDS 1 only) / Winter trees (Available on CDS 1 only).
■ 7" . . . . EM 307
■ CD Single . . . . CDEMS 307
■ CD Single . . . . CDEM 307
■ MC Single . . . . TCEM 307
EMI / Mar '94.

HOOKS IN YOU.
Tracks: Hooks in you / After me / Hooks in you (meaty mix) (12" & CD single only.).
■ 12" .12MARIL 10
■ 12" P.Disc. . . . . 12 MARILP 10
■ 7" . . . . MARIL 10
■ CD Single . . . . CDMARIL 10
■ MC Single . . . . TCMARIL 10
EMI / Aug '89.

INCOMMUNICADO.
Tracks: Incommunicado / Going under / Sugar mice.
■ 12" . . . . 12 MARIL 6
■ EP . . . . MARIL 6
EMI / May '87.

■ DELETED

INCOMMUNICADO.
Tracks: Incommunicado.
VHS . . . . MVW 99 0070 2
PMI / Aug '87 / EMI / Gold & Sons / TBD.

KAYLEIGH.
Tracks: Kayleigh / Lady Nina.
■ 7" P.Disc . . . . MARILP 3
■ 12" .12 MARIL 3
■ 7" . . . . .MARIL 3
EMI / May '85.
■ 12" P.Disc. . . . . 12 MARILP 3
EMI / May '85.

LAVENDER.
Tracks: Lavender.
■ 12" . . . . .12 MARIL 4
■ 7" . . . . .MARIL 4
EMI / Aug '85.

LIVE FROM LORELEY.
Tracks: Slainte Mhath / Assassing / Script for a
jester's tear / Incubus / Sugar mice / Hotel hobbies /
Warm wet circles / That time of the night / Kayleigh /
Lavender / Heart of Lothian / Last straw /
Incommunicado.
VHS . . . . MVN 99 1153 2
PMI / Nov '87 / EMI / Gold & Sons / TBD.

MARILLION: INTERVIEW PICTURE DISC.
Tracks: Not Advised.
LP P.Disc . . . . BAK 2021
Baktabak / Jul '87 / Arabesque Ltd.

MARKET SQUARE HEROES.
Tracks: Market square heroes.
■ 7" . . . . EMI 5351
■ 12" .12EMI 5351
EMI / Oct '82.

MISPLACED CHILDHOOD.
Tracks: Pseudo-silk kimono / Kayleigh / Lavender /
Bittersuite / Heart of Lothian / Waterhole / Lords of
the backstage / Blind curve / Childhood's end / White
feather.
■ LP . . . . MRL 2
MC. . . . . TC MRL 2
■ LP P.Disc . . . . MRLP 2
EMI / Jun '85.
■ CD . . . . CDP 746 160 2
EMI / Jun '85.
■ LP . . . . FA 3258
■ CD . . . . CDFA 3258
■ MC . . . . TCFA 3258
Fame / Aug '91.
CD . . . . CDEMC 3684
EMI / May '94 / EMI.

NO ONE CAN.
Tracks: No one can / Collection / Splintering heart
(live at Moles) (Only on CD single).
■ 7" . . . . MARIL 14
■ CD Single . . . . CDMARIL 14
■ MC Single. . . . . TCMARIL 14
EMI / Aug '91.

NO ONE CAN.
Tracks: No one can / Cover my eyes (pain and
heaven) / Sympathy (Only on 12" and CD single
(CDMARIL 17)) / Sugar mice (Only on CD single
(CDMARILS 17)).
■ 12" P.Disc 12MARILPD 17
■ 7" . . . . MARIL 17
■ CD Single . . . . CDMARIL 17
■ CD Single . . . . CDMARILS 17
EMI / Jun '92.

PUNCH AND JUDY.
Tracks: Punch and Judy / Market Square heroes /
Three boats down from candy.
■ 12" P.Disc. . . . . 12 MARILP 1
■ 12". . . . . .12 MARIL 1
■ 7" . . . . .MARIL 1
EMI / Jan '84.

REAL TO REEL.
Tracks: Assassing / Incubus / Cinderella search /
Emerald lies (Cassette & CD only) / Forgotten sons /
Garden party / Market Square heroes.
■ LP . . . . JEST 1
■ MC . . . . TCJEST 1
Fame / Nov '85.
■ CD . . . . CDFA 3142
Fame / Oct '87.

RECITAL OF THE SCRIPT.
Tracks: Not Advised.
VHS . . . . TVE 90 19542
PMI / '84 / EMI / Gold & Sons / TBD.
■ VHS . . . . MVP 99 1036 2
PMI / Oct '84.
VHS . . . . .MC 2057
Music Club Video / Mar '91 / Video Collection / Gold
& Sons / TBD.

SCRIPT FOR A JESTER'S TEAR.
Tracks: He knows, you know / Web / Garden party /
Chelsea Monday / Forgotten sons.
■ LP . . . . EMC 3429
MC. . . . . TCEMC 3429
EMI / Mar '83 / EMI.
■ LP P.Disc . . . . EMCP 3429
EMI / Jun '84.
CD. CDP 746 237 2
EMI / Feb '87 / EMI.
■ LP . . . . FA 3235
■ CD . . . . CDFA 3235
■ MC . . . . TCFA 3235
Fame / May '90.
CD. . . . . CDEMC 3683
EMI / May '94 / EMI.

SEASONS END.
Tracks: King of Sunset town / Easter / Uninvited
guest / Seasons end / Holloway girl / Berlin / After
me (Cassette & CD only) / Hooks in you / Space.
CD. . . . . CDEMD 1011
■ LP . . . . EMD 1011
■ MC . . . . TCEMD 1011
EMI / Aug '89.
■ LP P.Disc . . . . EMDPD 1011
EMI / Dec '89.

SINGLES COLLECTION 1982-1992, A.
Tracks: Cover my eyes (pain & heaven) / Kayleigh /
Easter / Warm wet circles / Uninvited guest / Assass-
ing / Hooks in you / Garden party / No one can /
Incommunicado / Dry land / Lavender / I will walk on
water / Sympathy.
CD. . . . . CDEMD 1033
■ LP . . . . EMD 1033
■ MC . . . . TCEMD 1033
EMI / May '92.

SIX OF ONE AND HALF A DOZEN OF THE OTHER.
Tracks: Sympathy / Cover my eyes (pain in heaven) /
No one can / Dryland / Hooks in you / Uninvited
guest / Easter / Warm wet circles / Incommunicado /
Kayleigh / Lavender / Assassing / Garden party / 4D
Man.
VHS . . . . MVP 4910053
PMI / Jun '92 / EMI / Gold & Sons / TBD.

SUGAR MICE.
Tracks: Sugar mice / Tux on.
■ 7" . . . . .MARIL 7
■ 12" .12 MARIL 7
■ 12" P.Disc. . . . . MARILP 7
■ 7" P.Disc . . . . MARILP 7
■ CD Single . . . . CDMARIL 7
EMI / Jul '87.

SYMPATHY.
Tracks: Sympathy / Kayleigh (live) / Dry land (live) / I
will walk on water.
■ 12" P.Disc. 12MARILPD 16
■ 7" . . . . MARIL 16
■ CD Single . . . . CDMARIL 16
■ CD Single . . . . CDMARILS 16
EMI / May '92.

THIEVING MAGPIE, THE (La Gazza Ladra).
Tracks: La gazza ladra / Slainte Mhath / He knows
you know / Chelsea Monday / Freaks / Jigsaw /
Punch and Judy / Sugar mice / Fugazi / Script for a
jester's tear / Incommunicado / White Russian /
Pseudo-silk kimono / Kayleigh / Lavender / Bitter
suite / Heart of Lothian / Waterhole / Lords of the
backstage / Blind curve / Childhood's end / White
feather.
CD Set . . . . CDMARIL 1
■ Double LP. . . . . .MARIL 1
■ MC Set . . . . TCMARIL 1
EMI / Nov '88.

UNINVITED GUEST.
Tracks: Uninvited guest / Uninvited guest (12" version) (12" & CD single only) / Bell in the sea.
■ 12" P.Disc. . . . . 12 MARILP 11
■ 12". 12MARIL 11
■ 7" . . . . MARIL 11
■ 7" P.Disc . . . . MARILPD 11
■ CD Single . . . . CDMARIL 11
■ MC Single. . . . . TCMARIL 11
EMI / Nov '89.

VIDEO EP: MARILLION.
Tracks: Not Advised.
VHS . . . . MVS 99 0008 2
PMI / Mar '84 / EMI / Gold & Sons / TBD.

WARM WET CIRCLES.
Tracks: Incommunicado (Live at Loreley) / White
Russian (Live at Loreley) / Warm wet circles.
■ CD Single . . . . CDMARIL 8
EMI / Nov '87.

■ 7" . . . . .MARIL 8
EMI / Nov '87.
■ 12" P.Disc. . . . . 12 MARILP 8
■ 12" .12 MARIL 8
EMI / Oct '87.

Marino

AFTER FOREVERS GONE.
Tracks: Northern sky (part 1) / Jasmine / El Salvador
/ Look into the sun / After forever's gone / Fishermen
(part II) / Borderline / Ian's garden / Did I say that /
Northern sky (part II) / Present light / Northern sky
(part III).
■ CD . . . . .WKFMCD 139
■ LP . . . . WKFMLP 139
■ MC . . . . WKFMMC 139
FM Records / Mar '90.

BLUES FOR LOVERS.
Tracks: Not Advised.
CD . . . . WKFMXD 167
■ LP . . . . WKFMLP 167
■ MC . . . . WKFMMC 167
FM Records / Mar '91.

ENDLESS ENIGMA, THE (A tribute to Salvador Dali).
Tracks: Galarina's strange enchantment / Salvador:
passion and fire / Anna Maria / Madonna of Port
Lligat / Gala mi armour / Midnight in Madrid /
Shades of Spanish sun / Impressions of Cadaques /
Endless enigma.
■ CD . . . . ESSCD 177
■ MC . . . . ESSMC 177
Essential / Feb '92.

Marino, Frank

JUGGERNAUT.
Tracks: Strange dreams / Midnight highway / Me-
mories of a hero / Free / Maybe it's true / Ditch
queen / For your love / Juggernaut.
■ LP . . . . CBS 85793
CBS / Sep '82.

MAHOGANY RUSH 4.
Tracks: Not Advised.
■ LP . . . . CBS 81417
CBS / Dec '77.

TALES OF THE UNEXPECTED.
Tracks: Sister change / All along the watchtower /
Norwegian wood / Tales of the unexpected / Down,
down, down / Door of illusion / Woman / Bottom of
the barrel.
■ LP . . . . CBS 83494
CBS / '79.

THERE'S NO GOOD IN GOODBYE.
Tracks: Not Advised.
■ LP 82567
CBS / '87.

WHAT'S NEXT.
Tracks: You got livin' / Finish line / Rock me baby /
Something's comin' our way / Roadhouse blues /
Loved by you / Rock'n'roll hall of fame / Mona.
■ LP . . . . CBS 8 3897
CBS / May '80.

WORLD ANTHEM.
Tracks: Not Advised.
■ LP . . . . CBS 8 1978
CBS / Jul '77.

YOU GOT LIVIN'.
Tracks: You got livin' / World anthem.
■ 7" . . . . CBS 8637
CBS / Jun '80.

Marionette

AVA DEMENTIA.
Tracks: Not Advised.
LP . . . . SHARP 048
Flicknife / Oct '90 / Pinnacle.

BLONDE SECRETS AND DARK BOMBSHELLS.
Tracks: Not Advised.
■ LP . . . . HMRLP 38
MC. . . . . HMRMC 38
Heavy Metal / Jul '85 / Sony / FM Revolver.

ON A NIGHT LIKE THIS.
Tracks: On a night like this.
■ 12" .12 VHF 12
FM Records / Jun '85.

Mars

78.
Tracks: Not Advised.
■ LP . . . . WSP 10
Widowspeak / Dec '86.

MARS LIVE.
Tracks: Not Advised.
CD . . . . CDSA 54025
Semantic / Feb '94 / Plastic Head.

METALDROME.
Tracks: Metaldrome.
■ EP . . . . A 31
Azra (USA) / Sep '87.

VENUS FLY TRAP.
Tracks: Not Advised.
LP . . . . DANLP 360
Danceteria / Apr '90.

Marsden, Bernie

AND ABOUT TIME TOO.
Tracks: You're the one / Song for Fran / Love made a fool of me / Here we go again / Still the same / Sad clown / Brief encounter / Are you ready / Head the ball.
■ LP . . . . PCS 7215
■ MC . . . . TCPCS 7215
Parlophone / May '81.

FRIDAY ROCK SHOWLIVE AT READING '82, THE.
Tracks: Not Advised.
CD . . . . FRSCD 007
Raw Fruit / May '92 / Pinnacle.

LOOK AT ME NOW.
Tracks: Look at me now / So far away / Who's foolin' who / Always love you so / Behind your dark eyes / Byblos shack / Thunder and lightnng / Can you do it / After all the madness.
MC . . . . TCPCS 7217
Parlophone / Aug '81 / EMI.
■ LP . . . . PCF 7217
Parlophone / Sep '81.
■ LP . . . . PCS 7217
Parlophone / Sep '81.

LOOK AT ME NOW.
Tracks: Look at me now / Always love you so.
■ 7" . . . . .R 6050
Parlophone / Jul '81.

SAD CLOWN.
Tracks: Sad clown / You and me.
■ 7" . . . . .R 6047
Parlophone / May '81.

THUNDER AND LIGHTNING.
Tracks: Thunder and lightning / Byblos shack.
■ 7" . . . . .R 6053
Parlophone / Jan '82.

Marseille

FRENCH WAY.
Tracks: French way / Cold steel.
■ 7" . . . . BON 1
Mountain / Mar '78.

KISS LIKE ROCK 'N' ROLL.
Tracks: Kiss like rock 'n' roll / Can can.
■ 7" . . . . TOP 39
Mountain / Jun '78.

KITES.
Tracks: Kites / Some like it hot.
■ 7" . . . . TOP 51
Mountain / Feb '80.

OVER AND OVER.
Tracks: Over and over / You're a woman / Can can.
■ 7" . . . . BON 2
Mountain / May '79.

TOUCH THE NIGHT.
Tracks: Not Advised.
■ LP . . . . ULTRA 3
Albion / Oct '84.

WALKING ON A HIGHWIRE.
Tracks: Walking on a highwire.
■ 7" . . . . WALK 1
Ultranoise / Sep '84.

Marshall Law

MARSHALL LAW.
Tracks: Armageddon / Under the hammer / Rock the nation / Marshall law / Hearts and thunder / Screaming / We're not / Feel it / System X / Future shock / When will it end.
■ CD . . . . .HMRXD 138
FM Records / Dec '89.
■ LP . . . . .HMRLP 138
■ MC . . . . .HMRMC 138
Heavy Metal / Dec '89.

POWER CRAZY.
Tracks: Power crazy.
■ 12" 12HM 172
■ CD Single . . . . HEAVYXD 172
Heavy Metal / Jul '91.

Martin, Eric

ERIC MARTIN.
Tracks: Not Advised.
■ LP . . . . MFN 57
Music For Nations / Dec '85.

INFORMATION.
Tracks: Information / I can't stop the fire.
■ 7" . . . . KUT 119
Music For Nations / Feb '86.

SUCKER FOR A PRETTY FACE.
Tracks: Sucker for a pretty face / Don't stop / Private live / Ten feet tall / Letting it out / Young at heart / Just another pretty boy / One more time / Catch me if you can / Love me.
■ LP 9602381
Elektra / Nov '83.

Marx, Richard

U.S. singer with two U.K. Top Ten albums to his credit, each of which spawned Top Ten single: *Right Here Waiting* from *Repeat Offender* and *Hazard* from *Rush Street*. Occasional tendency towards powerful AOR found outlet in Vixen, to whose debut album Marx contributed.

ANGELIA.
Tracks: Angelia (Not on 12".) / Right here waiting (edit) / Angelia (LP version) (12" only.) / Don't mean nothing (live) (CD single only.)
■ 12" 12MTG 74
■ 12" 12MT 74
■ 7" . . . . MT 74
■ CD Single . . . . CDMT 74
■ MC Single . . . . TCMT 74
EMI-Manhattan / Oct '89.

BEST OF RICHARD MARX, THE.
Tracks: Don't mean nothing / Should've known better / Endless Summer nights / Satisfied / Right here waiting / Angelia / Too late to say goodbye / Children of the night / Keep coming back / Hazard / Take this heart.
VHS . . . . MVP 4910423
Picture Music International(see PMI) / Nov '92 / EMI.

CHAINS AROUND MY HEART.
Tracks: Chains around my heart / Your world (7" only.) / I can't help falling in love with you (acoustic) (CD single only.) / Angelina (LP version) (CD single only.) / Wild life (CD single only.) / Chains around your heart (CHR mix) / Your world (LP version) / Should've known better / Living in the real world.
■ 7" . . . . .CL 676
■ CD Single . . . . CDCL 676
■ CD Single . . . . CDCLS 676
■ MC Single . . . . TCCL 676
EMI / Nov '92.

CHILDREN OF THE NIGHT.
Tracks: Children of the night (edit) (7" & cassingle only.) / Right here waiting (live) / Children of the night (LP version only.) (7" & CD single only.) / Real world (live) (12" & CD single only.) / Too late to say goodbye (live) (CD single only.).
■ 12" 12MT 84
■ 7" . . . . MT 84
■ CD Single . . . . CDMT 84
■ MC Single . . . . TCMT 84
EMI-Manhattan / Jun '90.

DON'T MEAN NOTHING.
Tracks: Don't mean nothing / Flame of love / Should've known better (Only on CD single.) / Endless Summer nights (edited version) (Only on CD single.).
■ 12" 12MT 26
■ 7" . . . . MT 26
EMI-Manhattan / Jul '87.
■ 12" P.Disc. 12MTP 26

■ CD Single . . . . CDMT 26
EMI-Manhattan / Jun '88.

ENDLESS SUMMER NIGHTS.
Tracks: Have mercy / Rhythm of life / Endless Summer nights / Hold on to the nights.
■ 12" 12MT 39
■ 7" . . . . MT 39
■ CD Single . . . . CDMT 39
EMI-Manhattan / Jun '88.
■ 12" Remix 12MTX 39
■ 7" P.Disc . . . . MTP 39
EMI-Manhattan / May '88.

ENDLESS SUMMER NIGHTS.
Tracks: Endless Summer nights (edited version) / Hold on to the nights (LP version) / Nothin' you can do about it (Live in Australia) (Not on 7" & cassingle.) / Hold on to the nights (LP edit) (7" & cassingle only.) / Real world (Live in Australia) (CD single only.)
■ 12" 12MTS 89
■ 12" 12MT 89
■ 7" . . . . MT 89
■ CD Single . . . . CDMT 89
■ MC Single . . . . TCMT 89
EMI-Manhattan / Aug '90.

HAZARD.
Tracks: Hazard / Keep coming back (CD single (1) only) / Thunder and lightning (CD single (1) only) / Endless Summer nights (CD single (1) only) / Right here waiting (Not on CD single (1)) / Too late to say goodbye (CD single (2) only) / Edge of a broken heart (live) (CD single (2) only).
■ 7" . . . . .CL 654
■ CD Single . . . . CDCL 654
■ MC Single . . . . TCCL 654
Capitol / Apr '92.
■ CD Single . . . . CDCLS 654
Capitol / May '92.

HOLD ON TO THE NIGHTS.
Tracks: Hold on to the nights / Lonely heart / Hold on to the nights (live edition) (on 12" only).
■ 12" 12MT 53
■ 7" . . . . MT 53
EMI-Manhattan / Aug '88.

HOLD ON TO THE NIGHTS.
Tracks: Endless Summer nights / Don't mean nothing / Hold on to the nights / Should've known better / Lulu / Rhythm of life / Living in the real world / Remember Manhattan / Have mercy.
VHS MVP99 1209 3
PMI / Feb '90 / EMI / Gold & Sons / TBD.

KEEP COMING BACK.
Tracks: Keep coming back / Superstar.
■ 12" 12CL 634
■ 7" . . . . CLS 634
■ CD Single . . . . CDCLS 634
■ MC Single . . . . TCCL 634
Capitol / Oct '91.

NOW AND FOREVER.
Tracks: Now and forever / Hazard (live) (Not available on CDS 1) / Whole world to save (Available on CDS 2 only) / Take this heart (live) (Available on CDS 1 only) / Miami 2017 (Available on CDS 1 only).
■ 7" . . . . .CL 703
■ CD Single . . . . CDCL 703
■ CD Single . . . . CDCLS 703
■ MC Single . . . . TCCL 703
EMI / Jan '94.

PAID VACATION.
Tracks: Way she loves me / One more try / Silent scream / Nothing to hide / Whole world to save / Soul motion / Now and forever / Goodbye / Hollywood / Heaven's waiting / Nothing left behind us / What you want / One man / Miami 2017 / Baby blues.
CD . . . . .CDESTU 2208
LP . . . . ESTU 2208
MC. . . . . .TCESTU 2208
EMI / Feb '94 / EMI.

REPEAT OFFENDER.
Tracks: Nothin' you can do about it / Satisfied / Angelia / Too late to say goodbye / Right here waiting / Heart on the line / Living in the real world / That was Lulu / Wait for the sunrise / Children of the night.
MC . . . . TCMTL 1043
■ LP . . . . MTL 1043
EMI-Manhattan / Apr '89.
CD . . . . CDMTL 1043
EMI-Manhattan / May '89 / EMI.
CD . . . . CDEST 2153
MC . . . . TCEST 2153
■ LP . . . . EST 2153
Capitol / Oct '91.
MiniDisc. 790380-3
Capitol / Feb '93 / EMI.

DCC. . . . . .DCCEST 2153
Capitol / Jan '93 / EMI.

RICHARD MARX.
Tracks: Should've known better / Don't mean nothing
/ Endless Summer nights / Lonely heart / Hold on to
the nights / Have mercy / Remember Manhattan /
Flame of love / Rhythm of life / Heaven only knows.
■ LP . . . . ST 53049
Capitol / Oct '87.
CD. . . . . CDMTL 1017
MC. . . . . TCMTL 1017
■ LP . . . . MTL 1017
EMI-Manhattan / Mar '88.
CD. . . . . CZ 397
■ LP . . . . ATAK 166
MC. . . . . TCATAK 166
EMI-Manhattan / Mar '91 / EMI.
CD. . . . . CDEST 2152
MC. . . . . TCEST 2152
■ LP . . . . EST 2152
Capitol / Oct '91.
MiniDisc. 746760-3
Capitol / Feb '93 / EMI.
DCC. DCCEST 2152
Capitol / Jan '93 / EMI.

RICHARD MARX CD BOX SET (Richard Marx/Repeat Offender/Rush Street).
Tracks: Should've known better / Don't mean nothing
/ Endless Summer nights / Lonely heart / Hold on to
the nights / Have mercy / Remember Manhattan /
Flame of love / Rhythm of life / Heaven only knows /
Nothin' you can do about it / Satisfied / Angelia / Too
late to say goodbye / Right here waiting / Heart on
the line / Living in the real world / If you don't want
my love / That was Lulu / Wait for the sunrise /
Children of the night / Playing with the night / Love
unemotional / Keep coming back / Take this heart /
Hazard / Hands in your pocket / Calling you / Super-
star / Street of pain / I get no sleep / Big boy now /
Chains around my heart / Your world.
■ CD Set. . . . . CDS 7806012
EMI / Oct '92.

RICHARD MARX VOL.1.
Tracks: Don't mean nothing / Should've known better
/ Endless Summer nights / Satisfied / Right here
waiting / Angelina / Too late to say goodbye.
■ VHS . . . . MVP 99 1241 3
PMI / Sep '90.

RIGHT HERE WAITING.
Tracks: Right here waiting (edit) (7" & cassingle
only.) / Hold on to the nights (live) / That was Lulu
(live) (Not on 7" & cassingle.) / Right here waiting
(Not on 7" & cassingle.) / Wild life (CD single only.).
■ 12". 12MT 72
■ 12". 12MTG 72
■ 7". . . . . MT 72
■ CD Single. . . . . CDMT 72
■ MC Single. . . . . TCMT 72
EMI-Manhattan / Aug '89.

RUSH STREET.
Tracks: Playing with fire / Love unemotional / Keep
coming back / Take this heart / Hazard / Hands in
your pocket / Calling you / Superstar / Street of pain
/ I get no sleep / Big boy now / Chains around my
heart / Your world.
CD. . . . . CDESTU 2158
MC. . . . . TCESTU 2158
■ LP . . . . ESTU 2158
Capitol / Nov '91.
MiniDisc. 795874-3
Capitol / Feb '93 / EMI.
DCC. DCCESTU 2158
Capitol / Jan '93 / EMI.

SATISFIED.
Tracks: Satisfied (LP version) (7" only.) / Should've
known better (live) / Satisfied (ext rock mix) (12"
only.) / Satisfied (single version).
■ 12". 12MT 64
■ 7". . . . . MT 64
■ CD Single. . . . . CDMT 64
EMI-Manhattan / Apr '89.
■ 7" P.Disc. . . . . MTP 64
EMI-Manhattan / May '89.

SHOULD'VE KNOWN BETTER.
Tracks: Should've known better / Rhythm of life /
Should've known better (ext. radio mix) (extra track
on 12" and CD Single.) / Have mercy (live version)
(extra track on CD Single.).
■ 12". 12MT 32
■ 12". 12MTS 32
■ 7". . . . . MT 32
EMI-Manhattan / Nov '87.
■ CD Single . . . . CDMT 32
EMI-Manhattan / Feb '88.

SILENT SCREAM.
Tracks: Silent scream / So into you (Only on 7" and
MCS.) / Another heaven (Features only on CDS.) /
Can't help falling in love (Features on CDS only.).
■ 7". . . . . CL 714
■ CD Single. . . . . CDCLS 714
■ MC Single. . . . . TCCL 714
EMI / Apr '94.
■ CD. . . . . CDCL 714
EMI / May '94.

TAKE THIS HEART.
Tracks: Take this heart / Hazard (Not on CD single
(2)) / Love unemotional (CD single (1) only) / Ride
with the idol (CD single (1) only) / Take it to the limit
(live) (CD single (2) only) / That was Lulu (live) (CD
single (2) only) / Rhythm of life (live) (CD single (2)
only).
■ 12". . . . . .TCCL 667
■ 7". . . . . CL 667
■ CD Single. . . . . CDCLS 667
■ CD Single. . . . . CDCL 667
Capitol / Aug '92.

TOO LATE TO SAY GOODBYE.
Tracks: Too late to say goodbye (7" edit) (Not on
12".) / Satisfied (live) / Too late to say goodbye (LP
version) (12" only.) / Endless Summer nights (12" &
CD single only.).
■ 12" P.Disc. 12MTP 80
■ 12". 12MT 80
■ 7". . . . . MT 80
■ 7". . . . . MTS 80
■ CD Single. . . . . CDMT 80
■ MC Single. . . . . TCMT 80
EMI-Manhattan / Mar '90.

WAY SHE LOVES ME.
Tracks: Way she loves me / Endless summer nights /
Teacher I need you (On 1st CD only) / Take it to the
limit (On 1st CD only) / (It looks like) I'm never gonna
fall in love again.
CD Single. . . . . CDCLS 721
CD Single. . . . . CDCL 721
MC Single. . . . . TCCL 721
EMI / Aug '94 / EMI.

Mas Optica

CHOOSE TO SEE MORE.
Tracks: Not Advised.
CD. . . . . IRS 972234
Rising Sun / Jun '94 / Plastic Head.

Masi

FIRE IN THE RAIN.
Tracks: Not Advised.
■ LP . . . . RR 9616
Road Runner / May '87.

VERTICAL INVADER.
Tracks: Instant army / Rhythm workers / Silver me-
mories / Dance of floda / Trapped in a warm feeling /
Rock of changes / Finn (she's so pink) / Quick
escape / Tribute to T.B. / Xperimental.
CD. . . . . CDZORRO 9
LP . . . . ZORRO 9
MC. . . . . TZORRO 9
Zorro / Jul '90 / Pinnacle.

Masi, Alex

ATTACK OF THE NEON SHARK.
Tracks: Under fire / Average green band / Twilight
passion / Toccata / Attack of the neon shark / DFWM
/ Cold sun / Wasted in the West / Alleys of Albion.
CD. . . . . RO 74702
■ LP . . . . RO 74701
Roadracer / May '89.

DOWNTOWN DREAMER.
Tracks: Not Advised.
■ LP . . . . RR 9543 1
Road Runner / '89.

Massacre

ENJOY THE VIOLENCE.
Tracks: Not Advised.
CD. . . . . SHARK 018 CD
LP . . . . SHARK 018
Shark / Mar '91 / Plastic Head.

FINAL HOLOCAUST.
Tracks: Not Advised.
CD. . . . . SHARK 014 CD
LP . . . . SHARK 014
Shark / Apr '90 / Plastic Head.

FROM BEYOND.
Tracks: Not Advised.
CD. . . . . MOSH 027 CD
LP . . . . MOSH 027
MC. . . . . MOSH 027 MC
Earache / Jul '91 / Vital Distribution.

INHUMAN CONDITIONS.
Tracks: Inhuman conditions.
■ 12". . . . . .MOSH 060T
■ CD Single. . . . . MOSH 060CD
Earache / Apr '92.

KILLING TIME.
Tracks: Not Advised.
CD. . . . . RECDEC 906
Rec Rec / Nov '93 / Plastic Head / SRD.

SECOND COMING, THE.
Tracks: Not Advised.
■ CD . . . . MOSH 27 CD
■ LP . . . . MOSH 27
■ MC. . . . . MOSH 27 MC
Earache / Sep '90.

Master

MASTER.
Tracks: Not Advised.
CD. . . . . NB 040
Nuclear Blast / Jan '91 / Plastic Head.

ON THE 7TH DAY GOD CREATED MASTER.
Tracks: Not Advised.
CD. . . . . NB 054CD
LP . . . . NB 054
Nuclear Blast / Feb '92 / Plastic Head.

THEY HAVE A HIT (Master & The Grandmaster).
Tracks: Not Advised.
LP . . . . KCR 138
Charlie's / Jan '89.

Masters Of Reality

CANDY SONG, THE.
Tracks: Candy song / Blue garden / Kill the king
(Available on 12" only.).
■ 12". DEFA 112
■ 7". . . . . DEFA 1
■ CD Single. . . . . DEFAC 1
American Recordings / Oct '89.

MASTERS OF REALITY.
Tracks: Theme for the scientist of the invisible /
Domino / Blue garden / Gettin high / Candy song /
Magical spell / Eyes of Texas / Sleep walkin / Lookin
to get rite / John Brown / Kill the King.
CD. 8384742
■ LP 8384741
MC. 8384744
American Recordings / May '89 / PolyGram.

SUNRISE ON SUFFERBUS.
Tracks: She got me (when she got her dress on) /
J.B. Witchdance / Jody sings / Rolling green / Ants in
the kitchen / V.H.V. / Bicycle / 100 years (of tears on
the wind) / T.U.S.A. / Tilt-a-whirl / Rabbit one /
Madonna / Gimme water / Moon in your pocket.
CD. 514947-2
LP 514947-1
MC. 514947-4
American Recordings / Jun '93 / PolyGram.

May, Brian

Revered Queen guitarist recorded *Star
Fleet Project* in 1983 during break in group's
activities. Credited to Brian May and
Friends - latter including Eddie Van Halen
and REO Speedwagon's Alan Gratzer - album was minor success. Following death of
Freddie Mercury and demise of Queen, May
launched solo career with hits *Too Much
Love Will Kill You* and *Driven By You*. His
metal credentials include penning anthemic
We Will Rock You, jamming with Def Leppard and performing on Rock-Aid Armenia's 1985 cover of *Smoke On The Water*.
Queen's heaviest album, *Sheer Heart Attack*, includes *Stone Cold Crazy* - later covered by Metallica.

BACK TO THE LIGHT.
Tracks: Dark / Back to the light / Love token /
Resurrection / Too much love will kill you / Driven by
you / Nothin' but blue / I'm scared / Last horizon /
Let your heart rule your head / Just one life / Rollin'
over.

CD. . . . . CDPCSD 123
MC. . . . . TCPCSD 123
■ LP . . . . PCSD 123
EMI / Oct '92.
■ CD. . . . . CDPCSDX 123
Parlophone / Jun '93.

BACK TO THE LIGHT.
Tracks: Back to the light / Nothin but blue (Guitar version) / Starfleet.
■ 7". . . . . .R 6329
■ CD Single. . . . . CDRX 6329
■ CD Single. . . . . CDR 6329
■ MC Single. . . . . TCR 6329
EMI / Nov '92.

DRIVEN BY YOU.
Tracks: Driven by you / Just one life.
■ 7". . . . . .R 6304
■ 12". 12R 6304
■ CD Single. . . . . CDR 6304
■ MC Single. . . . . TCR 6304
Parlophone / Nov '91.

LAST HORIZON.
Tracks: Last horizon.
■ 7". . . . . .R 6371
■ CD Single. . . . . CDRS 6371
■ CD Single. . . . . CDR 6371
■ MC Single. . . . . TCR 6371
Parlophone / Jan '94.

LIVE AT THE BRIXTON ACADEMY.
Tracks: Back to the light / Driven by you / Tie your mother down / Love token / Headlong / Love of my life / Let your heart rule your head / Too much love will kill you / Since you've been gone / Now I'm here / Guitar extravaganza / Resurrection / Last horizon / We will rock you / Hammer to fall.
CD. . . . . CDPCSD 150
LP. . . . . PCSD 150
MC. . . . . TCPCSD 150
Parlophone / Jan '94 / EMI.

LIVE AT THE BRIXTON ACADEMY.
Tracks: Back to the light / Driven by you / Tie your mother down / Love token / 39/Let your heart rule your head / Love of my life / Too much love will kill you / Since you've been gone / Now I'm here / Guitar extravaganza / Resurrection / Last horizon / We will rock you / Hammer to fall.
VHS. . . . . MVN 4911873
PMI / Jan '94 / EMI / Gold & Sons / TBD.

RESURRECTION (May, Brian & Cozy Powell).
Tracks: Resurrection / Love token / Too much love will kill you (live) / Driven by you two (Features on CDR 6351.) / Back to the light (Live version) (Features on CDR 6351.) / Tie your mother down (Live version) (Features on CDR 6351.).
■ 12" P.Disc. 12RPD 6351
■ CD Single. . . . . CDRS 6351
■ CD Single. . . . . CDR 6351
■ MC Single. . . . . TCR 6351
EMI / Jun '93.

STAR FLEET (May, Brian & Friends).
Tracks: Star fleet / Son of star fleet.
■ 7". EMI 5436
EMI / Nov '83.

STAR FLEET PROJECT (May, Brian & Friends).
Tracks: Not Advised.
■ MC. . . . . TCSFLT 1078061
■ Mini LP . . . . .SFLT 1078061
EMI / Dec '83.

TOO MUCH LOVE WILL KILL YOU.
Tracks: Too much love will kill you / I'm scared / Driven by you (CD's only. Featuring Cozy Powell & Neil Murray).
■ CD Single. . . . . CDRS 6320
■ 7". . . . . .R 6320
■ CD Single. . . . . CDR 6320
■ MC Single. . . . . TCR 6320
EMI / Sep '92.

May Linn

MAY LINN.
Tracks: Soldier / Joey don't care / In the shelter of the night / Breakout / Dangerous games / Backstreet life / Fit for fight / Long way from home.
CD. . . . . SHARK 007CD
■ LP. . . . . SHARK 007
Shark / Jun '88.

Mayhem

BLOOD RUSH.
Tracks: Blood rush / Addictive risk.
■ 12". . . . . .VIG 1T
■ 7". . . . . VIG 1
Vigilante / Mar '85.

DE MYSTERIIS DOM SATHANAS.
Tracks: Not Advised.
CD. . . . . ANTI-MOSH 006CD
LP. . . . . ANTI-MOSH 006
Deathlike Silence / Mar '94 / Plastic Head.

GENTLE MURDER.
Tracks: Gentle murder / Lie and clean / Clean cut.
■ 7". . . . . RIOT 24
■ 7". . . . . RIOT 13
Riot City / Nov '83.

LIVE IN LEIPZIG.
Tracks: Not Advised.
CD. . . . . .CDAV 004
LP. LPAV 004
Obscure Plasma / Apr '94 / Plastic Head.

Meanstreak

ROADKILL.
Tracks: Roadkill / Nostradamus / Lost stranger / Congregation / Searching forever / It seems to me / Warning.
CD. . . . . CDMFN 89
■ LP . . . . MFN 89
MC. . . . . TMFN 89
Music For Nations / Oct '88 / Pinnacle.

Meat Loaf

Meatloaf's inauspicious debut was album with *Hair* cast member Stoney in 1970. More productive partnership with Jim Steinman yielded *Bat Out Of Hell*. Released in 1978, it was massive success and is longest-charting album in UK history. Touring caused singer to lose voice; delaying follow-up until 1981. When it arrived, *Dead Ringer* yielded Top Five hit duet with Cher on *Dead Ringer For Love*. Without Steinman, Loaf consistently drew audiences and scored hit with *Modern Girl* in 1984, but had no record label by 1987. Revival of career followed renewed collaboration with Steinman on calculatedly-titled *Bat Out Of Hell II* and attendant number one single, *I'd Do Anything For Love*... Both topped 1993's best-seller lists.

12" TAPE: MEAT LOAF.
Tracks: Bat out of hell / Dead ringer for love / Read 'em and weep / If you really want to / Razor's edge.
MC. 4501314
Epic / Sep '86 / Sony.
CD. 4501312
Epic / Mar '93 / Sony.

ALL REVVED UP WITH NO PLACE TO GO.
Tracks: All revved up with no place to go.
■ 7". . . . . EPC 6797
Epic / '78.

BAD ATTITUDE.
Tracks: Bad attitude / Modern girl / Nowhere fast / Surf's up / Piece of the action / Jumping the gun / Cheatin' in your dreams / Don't leave your mark on me / Sailor to a siren.
■ LP 206619
■ MC. 406619
Arista / Oct '84.
■ CD 610187
Arista / Feb '85.
■ LP . . . . FA 3150
■ MC. . . . . FA 413 150 4
Fame / May '86.
■ CD 259049
Arista / Dec '93.

BAD ATTITUDE (LIVE).
Tracks: Not Advised.
VHS. . . . . .VVD 067
Virgin Vision / Gold & Sons / TBD.
VHS. 74321 19938-38
BMG Video / Apr '94 / BMG.

BAT OUT OF HELL.
Tracks: You took the words right out of my mouth / Heaven can wait / All revved up with no place to go / Two out of three ain't bad / Bat out of hell / For cryin' out loud / Paradise by the dashboard light / Praying for the end of time / Man and woman / Dead ringer for love.
■ LP . . . . EPC 82419

Epic / Jan '78.
CD. . . . . CD 82419
Epic / '83 / Sony.
■ CD P.Disc. 4677322
Epic / Dec '90.
CD. 40824192
■ LP 82419
MC. 40 82419
Epic / Jul '91 / Sony.

BAT OUT OF HELL.
Tracks: Bat out of hell / Heaven can wait.
■ 7" . . . . EPC 7018
Epic / Feb '79.
■ 7" . . . . RIS 41
■ 12". . . . . RIST 41
Arista / Oct '87.

BAT OUT OF HELL.
Tracks: Bat out of hell / Read 'em & weep / Rock 'n' roll dreams come through / Out of the frying pan (and into the fire) (On 12" only) / Lost boys & golden girls (On CD & cassette singles only).
■ 12". 660006 6
■ CD Single. 660006 2
■ CD Single. 660006 5
■ MC Single. 660006 4
Epic / Dec '93.

BAT OUT OF HELL (OLD GOLD).
Tracks: Bat out of hell / Dead ringer for love.
■ 7" . . . . .OG 9751
Old Gold / Jan '88.

BAT OUT OF HELL II: BACK IN HELL.
Tracks: I'd do anything for love (But I won't do that) / Life is a lemon and I want my money back / Rock 'n' roll dreams come through / It just won't quit / Out of the frying pan (and into the fire) / Objects in the rear view mirror may appear closer than they / Wasted youth / Everything louder than everything else / Good girls go to heaven (bad girls go everywhere) / Back into hell / Lost boys and golden girls.
CD. . . . . CDV 2710
LP. V 2710
MC. . . . . TCV 2710
Virgin / Aug '93 / EMI.

BAT OUT OF HELL/ HIT OUT OF HELL.
Tracks: Not Advised.
■ LP . . . . EPC ML 241
Epic / Aug '87.

BAT OUT OF HELL/DEADRINGER.
Tracks: Not Advised.
CD Set . . . . CDX82419 D
Epic / Feb '93 / Sony.

BLIND BEFORE I STOP.
Tracks: Execution day / Rock 'n' roll mercenaries / Getting away with murder / One more kiss (night of the soft parade) / Blind before I stop / Burning down / Standing on the outside / Masculine / Man and a woman / Special girl / Rock 'n' roll here.
■ LP 207741
■ MC. 407741
Arista / Sep '86.
■ CD 257741
Arista / Dec '93.

BLIND BEFORE I STOP.
Tracks: Blind before I stop.
■ 12". . . . . .RIST 3
■ 12". . . . . RIST 3R
■ 7". . . . . RIS 3
Arista / Feb '87.

CHRIS TETLEY INTERVIEWS MEATLOAF.
Tracks: Not Advised.
■ LP P.Disc. . . . . CT 1003
Music & Media / Oct '87.

COLLECTION, THE.
Tracks: Bat out of hell (Live) / Bad attitude / One more kiss (Night of the soft parade) / Execution day / Jumpin' the gun / Sailor to a siren / Modern girl (Live) / Special girl / Standing on the outside / Cheatin in your dreams / Masculine / Rock 'n' roll mercenaries.
CD. 74321 15218-2
MC. 74321 15218-4
Ariola Express / Sep '93 / BMG.

DEAD RINGER.
Tracks: Peel out / I'm gonna love her for both of us / More than you deserve / I'll kill you if you don't come back / Read 'em and weep / Nocturnal pleasure / Dead ringer for love / Everything is permitted.
■ LP . . . . EPC 83645
Epic / Sep '81.
■ LP . . . . EPC 32692
■ MC. 40 32692
Epic / Nov '85.

CD. . . . . CD 83645
Epic / Nov '87 / Sony.

DEAD RINGER FOR LOVE.
Tracks: Dead ringer for love / More than you deserve.
■ 7". . . . . EPCA 1697
Epic / Nov '81.

DEAD RINGER FOR LOVE (RE-RELEASE).
Tracks: Dead ringer for love / Heaven can wait / Bat out of hell (Only on 12" single).
■ 12". 6569826
■ 7". 6569827
■ CD Single. 6569822
■ MC Single. 6569824
Epic / Jun '91.

GETTING AWAY WITH MURDER.
Tracks: Getting away with murder / Scot free (remix) (On 10" only) / Rock 'n' roll hero.
■ 10". . . . . ARIST 10683
■ 12". . . . . ARIST 12683
■ 7". . . . . ARIST 683
■ 7" P.Disc. . . . . ARIST 683P
Arista / Nov '86.

GREATEST ORIGINAL HITS.
Tracks: Not Advised.
■ EP. . . . . EPCA 2621
Epic / Mar '83.

HITS OUT OF HELL.
Tracks: Bat out of hell / Read 'em and weep / Midnight at the lost and found / To out of three ain't bad / Dead ringer for love / Modern girl / I'm gonna love her for both of us / You took the words right out of my mouth (Hot Summer night) / Razor's edge / Paradise by the dashboard light.
■ LP. . . . . EPC 26156
MC. 40 26156
■ CD. . . . . CD 26156
Epic / Jan '85.
■ LP. 4504471
MC. 4504474
Epic / Mar '88 / Sony.
CD. 4504472
Epic / Mar '91 / Sony.
MiniDisc. . . . . MD 26156
Epic / Apr '93 / Sony.

HITS OUT OF HELL.
Tracks: Bat out of hell / Read 'em and weep / Two out of three ain't bad / Razor's edge / I'm gonna love her for both of us / If you really want to / You took the words right out of my mouth / Paradise by the dashboard light.
VHS. 323450
Cleveland City / Jan '86 / Grapevine Distribution / Sony / 3MV.
VHS. 498272
CMV Enterprises (Video) / Oct '89 / Sony.

I'D DO ANYTHING FOR LOVE (BUT I WONT' DO THAT).
Tracks: I'd do anything for love (But I won't do that) (Edit) / You took the words right out of my mouth (live) / Bat out of hell (Live).
■ 7". . . . . VS 1443
■ CD Single. . . . . VSCDT 1443
■ CD Single. . . . . VSCDG 1443
Virgin / Oct '93.

I'M GONNA LOVE HER FOR BOTH OF US.
Tracks: I'm gonna love her for both of us.
■ 7". . . . . EPCA 1580
Epic / Sep '81.

IF YOU REALLY WANT TO.
Tracks: If you really want to / Lost love / Keep driving.
■ 12". . . . . TA 3357
■ 7". . . . . A 3357
■ 7" P.Disc. . . . . WA 3357
Epic / Apr '83.

LIVE AT WEMBLEY.
Tracks: Not Advised.
VHS. . . . . .VFM 002
Videoform / Jan '84 / Gold & Sons.

LIVE: MEAT LOAF.
Tracks: Blind before I stop / Rock 'n' roll mercenaries / Took the words / Midnight at the lost and found / Modern girl / Paradise by the dashboard light / Two out of three ain't bad / Bat out of hell / Masculine (This track on cassette and CD only.) / Rock and roll medley (This track on cassette and CD only.)
CD. 258599
■ LP. 208599
MC. 408599
Arista / Oct '87 / BMG.

MEAT LOAF & FRIENDS.
Tracks: Not Advised.
CD. 472419-2
Sony Music / Sep '94 / Sony.

MEAT LOAF FEATURING STONEY & MEAT LOAF.
Tracks: Jimmy Bell / She waits by the window / It takes all kinds of people / Stone heart / Who is the leader of the people / What you see is what you get / Kiss me again / Sunshine / Jessica White / Lady be mine / Everything under the sun.
■ LP. . . . . PDL 2010
■ MC. . . . . CPDL 2010
Prodigal / Oct '81.
■ LP. . . . . ZL 72217
Motown / '86.

MEAT LOAF LIVE.
Tracks: Bat out of hell / You took the words right out of my mouth / Deadringer for love / All revved up and no place to go / I'm gonna love her for both of us / Promised land / Two out of three ain't bad / All revved up and no place to go (reprise).
VHS. . . . . .V 3320
Missing In Action / Nov '91 / Gold & Sons / TBD / Video Collection.
■ VHS. 791 217
BMG / Jan '92.

MIDNIGHT AT THE LOST AND FOUND.
Tracks: Razor's edge / Midnight at the Lost and found / Wolf at your door / Keep driving / Promised land / You never can be too sure about that girl / Priscilla / Don't you look at me like that / If you really want to / Fallen angel.
■ LP. . . . . EPC 25243
Epic / May '83.
MC. 4503604
■ LP. 4503601
Epic / Jan '87.

MIDNIGHT AT THE LOST AND FOUND.
Tracks: Midnight at the lost and found / Dead ringer.
■ 7". . . . . A 3748
■ 7" P.Disc. . . . . WA 3748
Epic / Sep '83.

MODERN GIRL.
Tracks: Modern girl / Take a number.
■ 12". . . . . ARIST 12585
■ 12" P.Disc. . . . . ARIPD 12585
■ 7". . . . . ARIST 585
Arista / Oct '84.

NOWHERE FAST.
Tracks: Nowhere fast / Clap your hands / Stand by me (Only on 12" single.).
■ 12". . . . . ARISG 600
■ 7". . . . . ARIST 600
■ 7" P.Disc. . . . . ARISD 600
Arista / Dec '84.

OBJECTS IN THE REAR VIEW MIRROR..
Tracks: Objects in the rear view mirror..
■ 7". . . . . VS 1492
■ CD Single. . . . . VSCDT 1492
■ MC Single. . . . . VSC 1492
Virgin / May '94.

PIECE OF THE ACTION.
Tracks: Piece of the action / Sailor to a siren / Bad attitude.
■ 12". . . . . ARIST 12603
■ 7". . . . . ARIST 603
■ 7" P.Disc. . . . . ARISD 603
Arista / Mar '85.

PRIMECUTS.
Tracks: Modern girl / Getting away with murder / Bat out of hell (Live) / Surfs up / Blind before I stop / Bad attitude / Jumpin' the gun / Two out of three ain't bad (live) / Paradise by the dashboard light (live) / Rock 'n' roll mercenaries.
CD. 260.363
■ LP. 210.363
MC. 410.363
RCA / Dec '89 / BMG.

RAZORS EDGE.
Tracks: Razor's edge / You can never be too sure about the girl.
■ 12". . . . . TA 3511
■ 7". . . . . A 3511
■ 7" P.Disc. . . . . WA 3511
Epic / Jun '83.
■ 12". . . . . TA 4080
■ 7". . . . . A 4080
Cleveland City / Jan '84.

READ 'EM AND WEEP.
Tracks: Read 'em and weep / Everything is permanent.

■ 7". . . . . EPCA 2012
Epic / Mar '82.

ROCK 'N' ROLL HERO.
Tracks: Modern girl / Rock 'n' roll mercenaries / Midnight at the lost and found (live) / Paradise by the dashboard light (live) / You took the words right out of my mouth (live) / Bat out of hell (Live) / Surf's up / Nowhere fast / Bad attitude / Rock 'n' roll hero / Piece of the action / Getting away with murder.
CD. . . . . PWKS 4121
MC. . . . . PWKMC 4121
Pickwick / Apr '94 / Pickwick.

ROCK 'N' ROLL MERCENARIES.
Tracks: Rock 'n' roll mercenaries / Revolutions per minute.
■ 12". . . . . ARIST 12666
■ 12" P.Disc. . . . . ARIST 12666 P
■ 7". . . . . .ARIST 666
Arista / Aug '86.
■ 12" P.Disc. . . . . ARIST 666 XP
■ 7" P.Disc. . . . . ARIST 666 P
Arista / Aug '86.

ROCK AND ROLL DREAMS COME THROUGH.
Tracks: Rock and roll dreams come through / Heaven can wait (live) / Paradise by the dashboard light (live).
■ 12". . . . . VSCDG 1479
■ 7". . . . . VSP 1479
■ CD Single. . . . . VSCDT 1479
■ MC Single. . . . . VSC 1479
Virgin / Dec '93.

SPECIAL GIRL.
Tracks: Special girl.
■ CD Single. . . . . RISCD 14
Arista / May '87.

TWO OUT OF THREE AIN'T BAD.
Tracks: Two out of three ain't bad / Midnight at the lost and found / I'm gonna lover her for both of us (12" & CD single only).
■ 7". . . . . EPC 6281
Epic / Aug '78.
■ 12". 6574916
■ 7". 6574917
■ CD Single. 6574912
■ MC Single. 6574914
Epic / Jun '92.

WHAT YOU SEE IS WHAT YOU GET.
Tracks: What you see is what you get / Way you do the things you do.
■ 7". . . . . PROD 10
Prodigal / Oct '81.

YOU TOOK THE WORDS RIGHT OUT OF MY MOUTH.
Tracks: You took the words right out of my mouth / Midnight at the lost and found.
■ 7". . . . . EPC 5980
Epic / May '78.

YOU TOOK THE WORDS RIGHT OUT OF MY MOUTH (OLD GOLD).
Tracks: You took the words right out of my mouth / Midnight at the lost and found.
■ 7". . . . . .OG 9865
Old Gold / Feb '89.

Meat Puppets

1.
Tracks: Not Advised.
CD. . . . . .SST 009 CD
LP. . . . . .SST 009
MC. . . . . .SST 009 C
SST / May '93 / Pinnacle.

HUEVOS.
Tracks: Not Advised.
■ LP. . . . . .SST 150
SST / Oct '87.
CD. . . . . .SST 150 CD
MC. . . . . .SST 150 C
SST / May '93 / Pinnacle.

I CAN'T BE COUNTED ON.
Tracks: I can't be counted on / Paradise.
■ 12". . . . . PSST 150
SST / Oct '87.

II.
Tracks: Not Advised.
CD. . . . . .SST 019 CD
LP. . . . . .SST 019
MC. . . . . .SST 019 C
SST / May '93 / Pinnacle.

■ DELETED

IN A CAR.
Tracks: In a car.
■ CD Single . . . . SST 044 CD
SST / Nov '88.
■ 7" . . . . SST 044
SST / Jul '89.
■ 10" . . . . SST 918
■ CD Single . . . . SST 044 C
SST / May '93.

MIRAGE.
Tracks: Not Advised.
CD . . . . SST 100 CD
SST / Jul '87 / Pinnacle.
■ LP . . . . SST 100 C
MC . . . . SST 100 C
SST / Jun '87 / Pinnacle.

MONSTERS.
Tracks: Not Advised.
CD . . . . SST 253 CD
■ LP . . . . SST 253
MC . . . . SST 253 C
SST / Oct '89 / Pinnacle.

NO STRINGS ATTACHED.
Tracks: Not Advised.
CD . . . . SST 265 CD
LP . . . . SST 265
MC . . . . SST 265 C
SST / May '93 / Pinnacle.

OUT MY WAY.
Tracks: Not Advised.
■ LP . . . . SST 049
SST / Sep '86.
CD . . . . SST 049 CD
SST / Sep '87 / Pinnacle.
MC . . . . SST 049 C
SST / May '93 / Pinnacle.

TOO HIGH TO DIE.
Tracks: Violet eyes / Never to be found / We don't exist / Severed Goddess head / Flaming heart / Shine / Backwater / Roof with a hole / Station / Things / Why / Evil love / Comin' down / Lake of fire.
CD 828484-2
LP 828484-1
MC 828484-4
London / Feb '94 / PolyGram.

UP ON THE SUN.
Tracks: Not Advised.
■ LP . . . . SST 039
SST / Apr '85.
CD . . . . SST 039 CD
SST / Aug '87 / Pinnacle.
MC . . . . SST 039 C
SST / May '93 / Pinnacle.

Meathook Seed

EMBEDDED.
Tracks: Famine sector / Furned grave / My infinity / Day of conceiving / Going to an image / Wilted remnant / Forgive / Focal point blur / Embedded / Visible shallow self / Sea of tranquility.
CD .MOSH 088CD
LP . . . . MOSH 088
MC .MOSH 088MC
Earache / Mar '93 / Vital Distribution.

Meatlocker

TRIANGLE OF PAIN.
Tracks: Not Advised.
CD . . . . SPV 56-141642
Progress Red / Sep '94 / Plastic Head.

Mega Mosh

DIFFERENT KIND OF MEAT, A.
Tracks: Not Advised.
CD . . . . PROPH 4CD
LP . . . . .PROPH 4LP
Prophecy / Nov '92 / Plastic Head.

Megadeth

Thrash four-piece formed by Dave Mustaine (guitar/vocals) as a vehicle for revenge after he was kicked out of Metallica in 1983. Time has tempered his motives (the bands have since made up) but not his determination and Megadeth's music has lost little of its spiteful aggression. Early line-ups were unstable, owing to Mustaine's volatile disposition and his dependance on drugs and alcohol. But following his drying-out (achieved around 1989), he has become infinitely mellower and the band is fast-approaching a democracy that actually gets

on socially, as well as professionally! Dave Ellefson (bass) has been alongside Mustaine through (and despite) everything and since the arrival of guitarist Marty Friedman and drummer Nick Menza (for 1990's Rust In Peace), the band have gone from strength to strength and look poised on the edge of Metallica-scaled success.

ANARCHY IN THE UK.
Tracks: Anarchy in the U.K. / Liar / 502 (Only on 12" single.).
■ 12" 12CL 480
■ 7" P.Disc . . . . CLP 480
■ 7" . . . . .CL 480
Capitol / Feb '88.

COUNTDOWN TO EXTINCTION.
Tracks: Skin o' my teeth / Symphony of destruction / Architecture of aggression / Foreclosure of a dream / Sweating bullets / This was my life / Countdown to extinction / High speed dirt / Psychotron / Captive honour / Ashes in your mouth.
CD . . . . .CDESTU 2175
■ LP . . . . ESTU 2175
MC . . . . .TCESTU 2175
Capitol / Jun '92 / EMI.
MiniDisc. 798531-3
Capitol / Feb '93 / EMI.

EXPOSURE OF A DREAM.
Tracks: Symphony of destruction / Foreclosure of a dream / Skin of my teeth / High speed dirt / Go to hell / Symphony of destruction (mix).
VHS . . . . MVR 4900053
Picture Music International(see PMI) / Nov '92 / EMI.

HANGAR 18.
Tracks: Hangar 18 (MJ12 edit) (Not on 12" & CD single.) / Conjuring, The (live) / Hangar 18 (12" & CD single only) / Hook in mouth (live) (12" & CD single only).
■ 12" .12CLG 604
■ 7" . . . . CLS 604
■ 7" P.Disc . . . . CLPD 604
■ CD Single . . . . CDCL 604
■ MC Single. . . . . TCCL 604
Capitol / Mar '91.

HOLY WARS..THE PUNISHMENT DUE.
Tracks: Holy wars..the punishment due / Lucretia (Not on 12" picture disc.) / Interview (edited) (12" gatefold & CD single only.) / Interview (12" picture disc.).
■ 12" .12CLP 588
■ 7" . . . . CLPD 588
■ 7" . . . . CLP 588
■ CD Single . . . . CDCL 588
■ MC Single. . . . . TCCL 588
Capitol / Sep '90.

KILLING IS MY BUSINESS AND BUSINESS IS GOOD.
Tracks: Last rites / Skin beneath the skin / These boots were made for walking / Rattle head / Looking down the cross / Mechanix.
■ LP . . . . MFN 46
Music For Nations / May '85.
CD . . . . CDMFN 46
Music For Nations / Aug '87 / Pinnacle.
■ Double LP . . . . MFN 46DM
■ LP P.Disc . . . . MFN 46P
MC . . . . TMFN 46
Music For Nations / May '88 / Pinnacle.

MARY JANE.
Tracks: Mary Jane / Hook in mouth / My last words (On 12" version only.).
■ 7" . . . . .CL 489
Capitol / Feb '88.
■ 7" P.Disc . . . . CLP 489
■ 12" 12CL 489
Capitol / May '88.

NO MORE MR. NICE GUY.
Tracks: No more Mr. Nice Guy / Different breed / Demon bell (The ballad of Horace Pinker) (12"'s & CD single only.).
■ 12" 12SBK 4
■ 12" P.Disc. 12SBKP 4
■ 7" . . . . SBK 4
■ 7" P.Disc . . . . SBKPD 4
■ CD Single . . . . CDSBK 4
■ MC Single . . . . TCSBK 4
SBK / Mar '91.

PEACE SELLS..BUT WHO'S BUYING.
Tracks: Wake up dead / Conjuring / Peace sells / Devil's Island / Good morning / Bad omen / I ain't superstitious / My last words / Black Friday.
■ LP . . . . EST 2022
Capitol / Nov '86.
■ LP P.Disc . . . . ESTP 2022
Capitol / Aug '88.

■ LP . . . . FA 3242
■ CD . . . . CDFA 3242
■ MC . . . . TCFA 3242
Fame / Oct '90.
CD. .CDEST 2022
EMI / Jul '94 / EMI.
MC. . . . . TC EST 2022
Capitol / Jul '94 / EMI.

RUST IN PEACE.
Tracks: Holy wars..the punishment due / Take no prisoners / Five magics / Poison was the cure / Lucretia / Tornado of souls / Dawn patrol / Rust in peace..Polaris.
■ LP P.Disc . . . . .ESTPD 2132
Capitol / Oct '90.
CD. .CDEST 2132
MC. .TCEST 2132
■ LP . . . . EST 2132
Capitol / Sep '90.

RUSTED PIECES.
Tracks: Peace sells / Wake up dead / In my darkest hour / Anarchy in the U.K. / Holy wars..the punishment due / Hangar 18.
VHS . . . . MVP 9912743
PMI / May '91 / EMI / Gold & Sons / TBD.

SKIN O' MY TEETH.
Tracks: Skin o' my teeth / Holy wars.the punishment due / High speed dirt (live) (CD & 10" only.) / Mustaine remarks on mega game (10" only.).
■ 10" 10CL 669
■ 7" . . . . CLP 669
■ CD Single . . . . CDCLS 669
■ CD Single . . . . CDCL 669
Capitol / Sep '92.

SO FAR SO GOOD SO WHAT.
Tracks: Into the lungs of hell / Set the world afire / Anarchy in the U.K. / Mary Jane / 502 / In my darkest hour / Liar / Hook in mouth.
CD . . . . .CDEST 2053
MC .TCEST 2053
■ LP P.Disc . . . . ESTP 2053
■ LP . . . . EST 2053
Capitol / Mar '88.

SWEATING BULLETS.
Tracks: Sweating bullets (Anxiety mix) / Ashes in your mouth (On CDCL 682 only.) / Countdown to extinction (Live 92') / Symphony of destruction (On CDCL 682 only.) / Ashes in your mouth (Live '92) (Features on 12" only.) / Symphony of destruction (mix).
■ 12" 12CL 682
■ CD Single . . . . CDCLX 682
■ CD Single . . . . CDCL 682
■ MC Single . . . . TCCL 682
EMI / Mar '93.

SYMPHONY OF DESTRUCTION.
Tracks: Symphony of destruction / Peace sells (live) (Only available on 7" Single.) / In my darkest hour (live) (Only available on 7"PD.) / Breakpoint (Only available on 12" and CD Single.) / Go to hell (Only available on 12" and CD single.).
■ 12" .12CLS 662
■ 7" . . . . CLS 662
■ 7" P.Disc . . . . CLPD 662
■ CD Single . . . . CDCL 662
Capitol / Jul '92.

WAKE UP DEAD.
Tracks: Wake up dead / Black Friday / Devils Island.
■ 12" 12CL 476
■ 7" . . . . .CL 476
Capitol / Dec '87.
■ 7" P.Disc . . . . CLP 476
EMI / Dec '87.

Mekong Delta

CLASSICS.
Tracks: Not Advised.
CD .ARG 270452
Aaarrg / Nov '93 / Plastic Head.

DANCES OF DEATH (AND OTHER WALKING SHADOWS).
Tracks: Not Advised.
CD .ARG 230343
LP . . . . .ARG 230341
MC .ARG 230342
Aaarrg / Dec '90 / Plastic Head.

FINISHED WITH THE DA.
Tracks: Not Advised.
■ LP . . . . GWLP 19
GWR / Dec '89.

MEKONG DELTA.
Tracks: Not Advised.
CD . . . . .AAARRG 004CD

■ LP . . . . AAAARRG 004
Aaarrg / '89.

MUSIC OF ERICH ZANN.
Tracks: Not Advised.
CD . . . . AAAARRG 011CD
■ LP . . . . AAAARRG 011
Aaarrg / '89.
■ LP . . . . GWLP 25
GWR / Dec '89.

PRINCIPLE OF DOUBT, THE.
Tracks: Not Advised.
CD . . . . AAAARRG 19CD
■ LP . . . . .AAAARRG 19
Aaarrg / May '89.

TOCCATA.
Tracks: Not Advised.
CD . . . . AAAARRG 017CD
■ LP . . . . AAAARRG 017
Aaarrg / '89.

VISIONS FUGITIVES.
Tracks: Not Advised.
CD . . . . CDVEST 19
Bulletproof / Jul '94 / Pinnacle.

Meliah Rage

KILL TO SURVIVE.
Tracks: Beginning of the end / Bates motel / Meliah rage / Deadly existence / Enter the darkness / Impalling doom / Pack.
■ LP 4632571
■ MC 4632574
Epic / Feb '89.
■ CD 4632572
Epic / Feb '89.

SOLITARY SOLITUDE.
Tracks: Solitary solitude / No mind / Decline of rule / Retaliation / Deliver me / Witching / Lost life / Swallow your soul / Razor ribbon.
MC 4666754
■ CD 4666752
■ LP 4666751
Epic / Jul '90.

Mellencamp, John

American singer, originally marketed as Johnny Cougar by team behind Rod Stewart. Gradual U.S. success exploded with 1982 American Fool album, which spawned three hits. One of latter, Jack And Diane, remains Mellencamp's biggest U.K. success, although his four albums from '87 to '93 all made Top 40. Work is frequently (unfavourably) compared with Bruce Springsteen, but Mellencamp is talented songwriter who deserves acclaim.

AIN'T EVEN DONE WITH THE NIGHT (Mellencamp, John Cougar).
Tracks: Ain't even done with the night / To M.G. whoever she may be.
■ 7" . . . . WEA 31
Riva / May '81.

AIN'T THAT AMERICA.
Tracks: Not Advised.
VHS . . . . CPV 06342
Channel 5 / Sep '87 / Channel 5 Video / P.R.O. Video / Gold & Sons.

AMERICAN FOOL (Mellencamp, John Cougar).
Tracks: Can you take it / Hurt so good / Jack and Diane / Hand to hold on to / Danger list / Can you fake it / Thundering hearts / China girl / Close enough / Weakest moments.
■ LP . . . . .RVLP 16
Riva / Nov '82.
CD . . . . RVCD 7501
Riva / Jan '85.
■ LP . . . . PRICE 85
MC . . . . PRIMC 85
Mercury / Sep '85 / PolyGram.
CD 814 993 2
Riva / '88.

AUTHORITY SONG.
Tracks: Authority song / Hurts so good / Thundering hearts (on 12" only).
■ 7" . . . . JCM 2
Riva / Feb '84.

BIG DADDY (Mellencamp, John Cougar).
Tracks: Big daddy of them all / To live / Martha say / Theo and weird Henry / Jackie Brown / Pop singer / Void in my heart / Mansions in heaven / Sometimes a great notion / Country gentleman / J.M.'s question.

■ LP 838 220 1
■ CD 838 220 2
■ MC 838 220 4
Mercury / May '89.

BIOGRAPHY, A (Cougar, Johnny).
Tracks: Born reckless / Factory / Night slumming / Taxi dancer / I need a lover / Alley of the angels / High C Cherrie / Where the sidewalk ends / Let them run your lives / Goodnight.
■ LP . . . . RVLP 6
MC . . . . RV 46
Riva.

CHECK IT OUT.
Tracks: Check it out / Check it out (live) (track on CD single.) / We are the people / Shama lama ding dong (Track on 12") / Pretty ballerina (track on 12" version.) / Pink houses (acoustic version).
■ 12" . . . . JCMX 10
■ 7" . . . . JCM 10
■ CD Single . . . . JCMCD 10
Mercury / Feb '88.

CHERRY BOMB.
Tracks: Cherry bomb.
■ 12" . . . . JCMX 9
■ 7" . . . . JCM 9
■ CD Single . . . . JCMCD 9
Mercury / Nov '87.

CHESTNUT STREET INCIDENT (Mellencamp, John Cougar).
Tracks: American dream / Oh, pretty woman / Jailhouse rock / Dream killin' town / Supergirl / Chestnut Street revisited / Good girls / Do you believe in magic / Twentieth Century Fox / Sad lady.
■ LP . . . . MML 602
MC . . . . MMK 602
Mainman / Oct '84.
CD . . . . CLACD 113
Castle Classics / '86 / BMG / Castle Communications.
■ LP . . . . CLALP 113
■ MC . . . . CLAMC 113
Castle Classics / May '86.

COLLECTION: JOHN COUGAR MELLENCAMP.
Tracks: American dream / Oh, pretty woman / Jailhouse rock / Dream killin' town / Supergirl / Chestnut Street revisited / Kid inside / Take what you want / Cheap shot / Side walks and street lights / R. gang / Good girls / Do you believe in magic / Twentieth Century Fox / Sad lady / Gearhead / Young genocides / Too young to live / Survive.
CD . . . . CCSCD 124
■ Double LP . . . . CCSLP 124
■ MC . . . . CCSMC 124
Castle Collector Series / Apr '86.

CRUMBLIN' DOWN.
Tracks: Crumblin' down / Golden gates.
■ 12" . . . . .JCM 112
■ 7" . . . . JCM 1
Riva / Nov '83.

DANCE NAKED.
Tracks: Not Advised.
CD 5224282
MC 5224284
Mercury / Jun '94 / PolyGram.

FACTORY (Cougar, Johnny).
Tracks: Factory / Alley of the angels.
■ 7" . . . . RIVA 16
Riva / May '78.

GET A LEG UP.
Tracks: Get a leg up / Whenever we wanted / Seventh son (Only on MC and CD single).
■ 12" . . . . .MERX 354
■ 7" . . . . MER 354
■ CD Single . . . . MERCD 354
■ MC Single . . . . MERMC 354
Mercury / Sep '91.

HAND TO HOLD ON TO (Mellencamp, John Cougar).
Tracks: Hand to hold on to / Hurts so good.
■ 12" . . . . .RIVA 38 T
■ 7" . . . . RIVA 38
Riva / Jan '83.

HOT NIGHT IN A COLD TOWN (Mellencamp, John Cougar).
Tracks: Hot night in a cold town / Tonight.
■ 7" . . . . RIVA 30
Riva / Feb '81.

HUMAN WHEELS.
Tracks: Not Advised.
CD 518008-2

MC 518008-4
Mercury / Sep '93 / PolyGram.

HURT SO GOOD (Mellencamp, John Cougar).
Tracks: Hurt so good / Close enough.
■ 7" . . . . RIVA 36
Riva / May '82.

I NEED A LOVER (Mellencamp, John Cougar).
Tracks: I need a lover / Born reckless.
■ 7" . . . . RIVA 14
Riva / Dec '79.

JACK AND DIANE (Mellencamp, John Cougar).
Tracks: Jack and Diane / Danger list / Need a lover.
■ 12" . . . . RIVA 37T
■ 7" . . . . RIVA 37
Riva / Sep '82.

JOHN COUGAR.
Tracks: Little night dancin' / Miami / Do you think that's fair / Welcome to Chinatown / Pray for me / Small paradise / Great midwest / I need a lover / Sugar Marie / Taxi dancer.
■ LP . . . . RVLP 9
MC . . . . RV 49
Riva.
CD 814 995 2
Riva / Jan '86.
■ LP . . . . PRICE 119
■ MC . . . . PRIMC 119
Mercury / Jun '88.

JOHN COUGAR MELLENCAMP.
Tracks: Not Advised.
VHS . . . . SPC 00142
Spectrum (1) / Oct '89 / PolyGram.

KID INSIDE, THE (Mellencamp, John Cougar).
Tracks: Kid inside / Take what you want / Cheap shot / Sidewalks and streetlights / R. Gang / American son / Gearhead / Young genocides / Too young to live / Survive.
MC . . . . CLAMC 112
■ LP . . . . CLALP 112
Castle Classics / May '86.
CD . . . . CLACD 112
Castle Classics / Nov '86 / BMG / Castle Communications.

LONELY OL' NIGHT.
Tracks: Lonely ol' night.
■ 12" . . . . JCMX 4
■ 7" . . . . JCM 4
Riva / Oct '85.

LONESOME JUBILEE, THE.
Tracks: Paper in fire / Down and out in paradise / Check it out / Real life / Cherry bomb / We are the people / Empty hands / Hard times for an honest man / Hot dogs and hamburgers / Rooty toot toot.
■ LP . . . . .MERH 109
■ CD 832 465-2
■ MC . . . . .MERHC 109
Mercury / Sep '87.

LOVE AND HAPPINESS.
Tracks: Love and happiness.
■ 12" . . . . MERX 362
■ 7" . . . . MER 362
■ CD Single . . . . MERCD 362
■ MC Single . . . . MERMC 362
Mercury / Feb '92.

MIAMI (Mellencamp, John Cougar).
Tracks: Miami / Do you think it's fair.
■ 7" . . . . RIVA 20
Riva / '79.

NOTHIN' MATTERS.
Tracks: Hot night in a cold town / Ain't even done with the night / Don't misunderstand me / This time / Make me feel / To M.G. / (Wherever she may be) tonight / Wild angel / Cheapshot.
■ LP . . . . .RVLP 10
MC . . . . RV 410
Riva.
CD 814 994 2
Riva / Jan '86.

NOW MORE THAN EVER (Mellencamp, John Cougar).
Tracks: Now more than ever.
■ 7" . . . . MER 368
■ CD . . . . .MERCD 368
■ MC . . . . .MERMC 368
Mercury / May '92.

■ DELETED

PAPER IN FIRE.
Tracks: Paper in fire / Never too old.
- 12″ . . . . JCMX 8
- 7″ . . . . JCM 8
Mercury / Sep '87.

PAPER IN FIRE (CD VIDEO).
Tracks: Paper in fire.
CD Video 080 212 2
Polygram Music Video / Sep '89 / PolyGram.

PINK HOUSES.
Tracks: Pink houses / Warmer place to sleep.
- 7″ . . . . JCM 3
Riva / Jun '84.

POP SINGER.
Tracks: Pop singer / JM's question / Like a rolling stone (live) / Check it out (live).
- 12″ . . . . JCM 1212
- 7″ . . . . JCM 12
- CD Single . . . . JCMCD 12
Mercury / May '89.

ROCK IN THE USA.
Tracks: Rock in the USA / Under the boardwalk.
- 12″ . . . . JCMX 6
- 7″ . . . . JCM 6
Riva / Apr '86.

ROOTY TOOT TOOT.
Tracks: Rooty toot toot / Check it out (live) / Pretty ballerina (On 12″ only).
- 12″ . . . . JCMX 11
- 7″ . . . . JCM 11
- CD Single . . . . JCMCD 11
Mercury / Jul '88.

SCARECROW.
Tracks: Rain on the scarecrow / Grandmas's theme / Small town / Minutes to memories / Lonely ol' night / Face of the nation / Justice and independence '85 / Between a laugh and a tear / Rumbleseat / You've got to stand for something / R.O.C.K. in the U.S.A. / Kind of fella I am.
CD 824 865 2
- LP . . . . .RIVH 2
- MC . . . . RIVHC 2
Riva / Nov '85.

SMALL TOWN.
Tracks: Small town.
- 12″ . . . . JCMX 5
- 7″ . . . . JCM 5
- 7″ Set . . . . JCMXD 5
- 7″ Set . . . . JCMDP 5
Riva / Jan '86.

THIS TIME (Mellencamp, John Cougar).
Tracks: This time / Don't misunderstand.
- 7″ . . . . RIVA 25
Riva / Oct '80.

UH-HUH.
Tracks: Crumblin' down / Pink houses / Authority song / Hurt so good / Thundering hearts / Warmer place to sleep.
CD 814 485 2
- LP . . . . .RIVL 1
MC . . . . RIVLC 1
Riva / Mar '84.

WHENEVER WE WANTED.
Tracks: Love and happiness / Now more than ever / I ain't never satisfied / Get a leg up / Crazy ones / Last chance / They're so tough / Melting pot / Whenever we wanted / Again tonight.
CD 5101512
MC 5101514
- LP 5101511
Mercury / Oct '91.
DCC 510 151-5
Mercury / Jan '93 / PolyGram.

Melvins

BULLHEAD.
Tracks: Not Advised.
CD .TUPCD 26
LP . . . . TUPLP 26
Tupelo / Jan '91 / Vital Distribution.

DALE CROVER.
Tracks: Dale crover.
- 12″ . . . . TUP 401
- CD Single . . . . TUP 402
- MC Single . . . . TUP 404
Tupelo / Aug '92.

EGG NOG.
Tracks: Egg nog.
- 10″ . . . . TUPEP 031
- CD Single . . . . TUPCD 031

- MC Single . . . . BR 284
Tupelo / Sep '91.

GLUEY PORCH TREATMENTS.
Tracks: Not Advised.
- LP . . . . VM 103
Alchemy.

HOUDINI.
Tracks: Hooch / Night goat / Lizzy / Going blind / Honey bucket / Hag me / Set me straight / Sky pup / Joan of arc / Teet / Copache / Pearl bomb / Spread eagle beagle.
CD 7567825322
MC 7567825324
Atlantic / Sep '93 / WEA.

JOE PRESTON.
Tracks: Joe Preston.
- 12″ . . . . TUP 411
- CD Single . . . . TUP 412
- MC Single . . . . TUP 414
Tupelo / Aug '92.

KING BUZZO.
Tracks: King buzzo.
- 12″ . . . . TUP 391
- CD Single . . . . TUP 392
- MC Single . . . . TUP 394
Tupelo / Aug '92.

LYSOL.
Tracks: Not Advised.
CD . . . . TUP 422
LP . . . . TUP 421
MC . . . . TUP 424
Tupelo / Nov '92 / Vital Distribution.

MELVINS: LIVE.
Tracks: Not Advised.
CD . . . . YCR 012CD
LP . . . . YCR 012
Your Choice / '92 / Plastic Head.

OZMA.
Tracks: Not Advised.
- LP . . . . TUPLP 007
Tupelo / Feb '90.

PRICK.
Tracks: Not Advised.
CD ARRCD53 333
LP ARR53 333
Amphetamine Reptile / Sep '94 / SRD.

Memento Mori

LIFE, DEATH AND OTHER MORBID TALES.
Tracks: Not Advised.
CD . . . . BM 051CD
LP . . . . BM 051LP
MC . . . . BM 051MC
Black Mark / Aug '94 / Plastic Head.

Mentors

UP THE DOSE.
Tracks: Kick it on down / Secretary hump / Couch test casting / S.F.C.C. / Up the dose / Hetrosexuals have the right to rock / Rock 'em and sock 'em / White trash women / Adultery / On the rag.
- LP . . . . RR 9657
Road Runner / Jan '87.

YOU AXED FOR IT.
Tracks: Not Advised.
- LP . . . . RR 9749
Road Runner / Sep '85.

Merciless

TREASURES WITHIN, THE.
Tracks: Not Advised.
CD .CDATV 26
LP . . . . ATV 26
Active / Jun '92 / Pinnacle.

VOMIT NAUSEA.
Tracks: Not Advised.
LP . . . . CCG 013
C.C.G. Underground / Nov '90 / Backs Distribution.

Mercy

WITCHBURNER.
Tracks: Not Advised.
CD .ERCD 921
Plastic Head / Jul '92 / Plastic Head.

Mercyful Fate

BEGINNING, THE.
Tracks: Not Advised.
CD . . . . RR 349603
- LP . . . . RR 9603
Road Runner / Nov '87.

BELLWITCH.
Tracks: Not Advised.
CD . . . . .CDMZORRO 78
Metal Blade / Jun '94 / Pinnacle.

BLACK FUNERAL.
Tracks: Black funeral / Black masses.
- 12″ . . . . 12 KUT 106
Music For Nations / Nov '83.

DON'T BREAK THE OATH.
Tracks: Not Advised.
- LP . . . . MFN 28
Music For Nations / Jul '84
CD . . . . RR 349835
- LP . . . . RR 9835
Road Runner / '89.

MELISSA.
Tracks: Not Advised.
- LP . . . . MFN 10
Music For Nations / Oct '83.
CD . . . . RR 349898
- LP . . . . RR 9898
Road Runner / '89.

MELISSA/DON'T BREAK THE OATH.
Tracks: Not Advised.
MC Set . . . . RR 49648
Road Runner / '89 / Pinnacle.

RETURN OF THE VAMPIRE.
Tracks: Not Advised.
CD . . . . RR 91842
- LP . . . . RR 91841
- MC . . . . RR 91844
Road Runner / May '92.

Mersinary

DEAD IS DEAD.
Tracks: Not Advised.
- LP . . . . IW 1027
Iron Works (USA) / Jun '88.

Messiah

CHOIR OF HORRORS.
Tracks: Not Advised.
CD .N 0183-2
LP . . . . .N 0183-1
MC .N 0183-4
Noise / '91 / Pinnacle.

EXTREME COLD WEATHER.
Tracks: Extreme cold weather / Enjoy yourself / Johannes Paul der Letzie / Mother Theresa / Hyperborea / Radetzky march: We hate to be in the. / Nero / Hymn To Abramelin / Messiah / Space invaders / Trashing madness / Golden dawn / Last inferno / Resurrection / Ole Perverus.
- LP . . . . CM 004
We Bite / Feb '88.

PSYCHOMORPHIA.
Tracks: Not Advised.
CD .N 0180-3
Mini LP . . . . .N 0180-5
Noise / '91 / Pinnacle.

ROTTEN PERISH.
Tracks: Not Advised.
CD .NO 1952
MC .NO 1954
Noise / Jul '92 / Pinnacle.

UNDERGROUND.
Tracks: Not Advised.
CD . . . . N 0244-2
Noise / Jun '94 / Pinnacle.

Messiah Force

LAST DAY, THE.
Tracks: Last day / Watch out / White night / Hero's saga / Third one / Call from the night / Spirit killer / Silent tyrant / Last day.
CD . . . . .BRMCD 022
- LP . . . . .BRMLP 022
Bold Reprive / Oct '88.

SEQUEL, THE.
Tracks: Sequel.
- 12″ .BRMT 021

■ 7" 7BRM 021
Bold Reprive / Oct '88.

Messiah Prophet

MASTER OF METAL.
Tracks: Hit and run / Master of the metal / For whom does the bell toll / Fear no evil / Heavy metal thunder / Friend / Battle cry / Voice that's calling.
■ LP . . . . .US 9
U.S. Metal / Jan '88.

Metal Church

BLESSING IN DISGUISE.
Tracks: Fake healer / Rest in pieces / Of unsound mind / Anthem to the estranged / Badlands / Spell can't be broken / It's a secret / Cannot tell a lie / Powers that be.
■ LP . . . . K 96087 1
■ MC . . . . K 96087 4
■ CD . . . . K 96087 2
WEA / Jan '89.

DARK, THE.
Tracks: Method of your madness / Watch the children play / Over my dead body / Dark / Psycho / Line of death / Burial at sea / Western alliance / Ton of bricks / Start the fire.
MC. 960 403-4
■ LP 960 493-1
Asylum / Nov '86.

HANGING IN THE BALANCE.
Tracks: Not Advised.
CD . . . . SPV 085-62170
SPV / May '94 / Plastic Head.

HUMAN FACTOR, THE.
Tracks: Human factor / Date with poverty / Final word / In mourning / In harm's way / In due time / Agent green / Flee from reality / Betrayed / Fight song.
CD 4678162
■ LP 4678161
■ MC. 4678164
Epic / Apr '91.

METAL CHURCH: INTERVIEW PICTURE DISC.
Tracks: Not Advised.
LP P.Disc . . . . BAK 2146
Baktabak / Oct '89 / Arabesque Ltd.

MUSIC AND MEDIA INTERVIEW PICTURE DISCS.
Tracks: Not Advised.
■ LP P.Disc . . . . MM 1255
Music & Media / Feb '88.

Metal Duck

AUTO DUCKO DESTRUCTO MONDO.
Tracks: Gore littoral / Duckulla assault / Drunk and a flirt / Smell of sex / To kill again / Gate of Asgard / Twilight zone / Rod, Jane and Freddy (part two) / Mean, green and pink / Well fu(n)ked up / In death / Apollyon communique.
CD . . . . CDMO 196
LP . . . . CMO 196
RKT / Oct '90.

QUACK EM ALL (Metal Duck & Lawn-mower Death).
Tracks: Not Advised.
■ LP . . . . CMO 192
CD . . . . CDMO 192
RKT / Oct '90.

Metal Messiah

HONOUR AMONG THIEVES.
Tracks: Intro / Mad dogs of war / Madman / Kiss of Nosferatu / Honour among thieves / Metal messiah / Curse of the king / Nightwing / Awakening.
LP . . . . CMO 195
RKT / Jul '90.

Metal Onslaught

CEASE TO EXIST.
Tracks: Waiting for death / Chester / Welcome to my hell / Redneck / Victims of the axe / Cease to exist / Run For Your Life / Death do us part / Buttf.k.
■ LP . . . . SHARK 003
Shark / Jan '88.

M 16

Metallica

Unquestionably the most popular (pure) heavy metal band on the planet in the mid 90's after a meteoric rise to stardom and just five albums. 1983 debut Kill 'Em All was raw thrash, but its successors, Ride The Lightning and (especially) Master Of Puppets, stand as classics, way above their contemporaries from San Francisco's now legendary Bay Area thrash scene. Lars Ulrich (drums), James Hetfield (guitar/vocals), Kirk Hammett (lead guitar) and Cliff Burton (bass) were set for major success until September 27, 1987, when Burton was killed as the Metallica tour bus crashed en route to Copenhagen. He enjoyed a huge cult following, and lesser bands would never have recovered. But Metallica grieved, then wisely and calmly replaced him with Jason Newsted (ex-Flotsam And Jetsam). The new quartet's first album together And Justice For All was flawed but strong and a hit single with One helped make the most of their new worldwide deal with Phonogram. An even stronger single, Enter Sandman, launched their eponymous fifth album in April 1989, since when their sales and reputation have soared all over the world. Band toured solidly from August 1991 to July 1993, playing arenas and stadiums, until few could touch them as a concert draw. In 1994 they went out and toured some more, just for fun and in no apparent hurry to make album number six, prefering to let fans digest the awesome multi-media Live Shit: Binge & Purge box set. But whatever Metallica do next, it's certain to be front page news and platinum selling.

2 OF ONE.
Tracks: Not Advised.
VHS . . . . CFV 08342
Channel 5 / May '89 / Channel 5 Video / P.R.O. Video / Gold & Sons.

AND JUSTICE FOR ALL.
Tracks: Blackened / Eye of the beholder / Shortest straw / Frayed ends of sanity / Dyes no evil / And justice for all / One / Harvester of sorrow / To live is to die.
CD 836 062-2
LP . . . . VERH 61
MC . . . . VERHC 61
Vertigo / Oct '88 / PolyGram.

CHRIS TETLEY INTERVIEWS METALLICA.
Tracks: Not Advised.
■ LP P.Disc . . . . CT 1008
Music & Media / Oct '87.

CLIFF 'EM ALL.
Tracks: Creeping death / Am I evil / Master of puppets / Whiplash / Four horsemen / Fade to black / Seek & destroy / Welcome home (Sanitarium) / For whom the bell tolls / No remorse / Metal militia.
VHS 041 666 2
Polygram Music Video / May '88 / PolyGram.
VHS . . . . CFV 08112
Channel 5 / '89 / Channel 5 Video / P.R.O. Video / Gold & Sons.

CREEPING DEATH.
Tracks: Creeping death / Am I evil / Blitzkrieg.
■ 12" . . . . 12 KUT 112
■ 12" P.Disc. P12KUT 112
Music For Nations / Nov '84.
■ 7" . . . . TKUT 112
Music For Nations / Nov '84.

END OF THE WORLD AS WE KNOW IT, THE (Interview Picture Disc).
Tracks: Not Advised.
LP . . . . BAK 6011
MC. . . . . MBAK 6011
Baktabak / Oct '90 / Arabesque Ltd.

ENTER SANDMAN.
Tracks: Enter sandman / Stone cold crazy / Holier than thou' (Only on 12" Single.).
■ 12" . . . . METBX 712
■ 12" . . . . METAL 712
■ 7" . . . . METAL 7
■ CD Single. . . . . METCD 7
Vertigo / Jul '91.

GARAGE DAYS REVISITED.
Tracks: Helpless / Small hours / Wait / Crash course in brain surgery / Last caress / Green hell.
CD 888 788 2
■ LP 888 788 1
MC. 888 788 4
Vertigo / May '90 / PolyGram.

GOOD, THE BAD AND THE LIVE (The 6 1/2 year anniversary 12" collection).
Tracks: Harvester of sorrow (live) / One (live) / Breadfan (live) / Jump in the fire / Creeping death / Five dollars ninety eight cents EP / Harvester of sorrow / One.
■ 12" 875 487 1
Vertigo / May '90.

HARVESTER OF SORROW.
Tracks: Harvester of sorrow / Breadfan / Prince.
■ 12" . . . . METAL 212
■ CD Single. . . . . METCD 2
Vertigo / Aug '88.

JUMP IN THE FIRE.
Tracks: Jump in the fire / Seek and destroy (live).
■ 12" . . . . 12 KUT 105
Music For Nations / Jan '84.
■ 7" P.Disc . . . . KUT 105P
■ MC Single. . . . . T12 KUT 105
Music For Nations / Mar '86.
■ 12" . . . . METAL 312
Vertigo / Jan '90.

KILL 'EM ALL.
Tracks: Hit the lights / Four horsemen / Motorbreath / Jump in the fire / Pulling teeth (Anesthesia) / Whiplash / Phantom lord / No remorse / Seek and destroy / Metal militia.
■ Double LP . . . . MFN 7DM
Music For Nations / Aug '86.
MC. . . . . TMFN 7
Music For Nations / Aug '86 / Pinnacle.
CD. . . . . CDMFN 7
Music For Nations / Apr '87 / Pinnacle.
■ LP . . . . MFN 7
Music For Nations / Apr '87.
CD 8381422
LP 8381421
MC. 8381424
Vertigo / May '89 / PolyGram.

LICK EM UP.
Tracks: Not Advised.
VHS . . . . UNKNOWN
Polygram Music Video / Jun '88 / PolyGram.

LIVE SHIT - BINGE AND PURGE.
Tracks: Not Advised.
■ CD Set. 5187250
Vertigo / Dec '93.

MASTER OF PUPPETS.
Tracks: Battery / Master of puppets / Thing that should not be / Welcome home (sanitarium) / Disposable heroes / Leper messiah / Orion / Damage Inc.
■ CD . . . . CDMFN 60
■ LP . . . . MFN 60
■ LP P.Disc . . . . MFN 60P
■ MC. . . . . TMFN 60
Music For Nations / Mar '86.
■ Double LP. . . . . MFN 60DM
Music For Nations / Dec '87.
CD. 8381412
LP 8381411
MC. 8381414
Vertigo / May '89 / PolyGram.

METALLICA (2).
Tracks: Enter sandmen / Sad but true / Holier than thou / Unforgiven / Wherever I may roam / Don't tread on me / Through the never / Nothing else matters / Of wolf and man / God that failed / My friend of misery / Struggle within.
CD 5100222
LP 5100221
MC. 5100224
Vertigo / Aug '91 / PolyGram.
DCC 510 022-5
Vertigo / Jan '93 / PolyGram.

METALLICA - NO LIFE TILL LEATHER.
Tracks: Creeping death / Am I evil / Blitzkrieg / Jump in the fire / Seek and destroy (live) / Phantom Lord (live).
CD. 8422192
MC. 8422194
Vertigo / Feb '90 / PolyGram.

METALLICA: INTERVIEW COMPACT DISC.
Tracks: Not Advised.
CD P.Disc. . . . . CBAK 4016
Baktabak / Nov '89 / Arabesque Ltd.

METALLICA: INTERVIEW COMPACT DISC II.
Tracks: Not Advised.
CD P.Disc. . . . . CBAK 4053
Baktabak / Apr '92 / Arabesque Ltd.

■ DELETED

METALLICA: INTERVIEW PICTURE DISC.
Tracks: Not Advised.
■ **LP P.Disc** . . . . **BAK 2066**
Baktabak / Sep '87 / Arabesque Ltd.

METALLICA: INTERVIEW PICTURE DISC (COLLECTION).
Tracks: Not Advised.
7" Set . . . . **BAKPAK 1015**
Baktabak / Dec '88 / Arabesque Ltd.

METALLICA: INTERVIEW PICTURE DISC VOL.2.
Tracks: Not Advised.
LP P.Disc . . . . **BAK 2163**
Baktabak / Jul '90 / Arabesque Ltd.

MUSIC AND MEDIA INTERVIEW PICTURE DISC.
Tracks: Not Advised.
■ **LP P.Disc** . . . . **MM 1253**
Music & Media / Feb '88.

NOTHING ELSE MATTERS.
Tracks: Nothing else matters / Enter sandman (live) / Harvester of sorrow (live) (Available on 12" and CD single only) / Nothing else matters (demo) (Available on 12" and CD single only).
■ **12"** . . . . **METAL 1012**
■ **7"** . . . . **METAL 10**
■ **MC Set** . . . . **METCD 10**
Vertigo / Apr '92.

ONE.
Tracks: One / Seek and destroy (live) (Not available on 12" and CD single) / For whom the bell tolls (On 12" and CD 5" only) / Welcome home (sanitarium) (On 12" and CD 5" only).
■ **10"** . . . . **METPD 5**
■ **12"** . . . . **METAL 512**
■ **12"** . . . . **METG 512**
■ **7"** . . . . **METAL 5**
■ **CD Single** . . . . **METCD 5**
Vertigo / Apr '89.

ONE.
Tracks: One / One (live) / One (demo).
■ **12"** . . . . **.858547-1**
■ **CD Single** . . . . **.858545-2**
■ **CD Single** . . . . **.858544-2**
Vertigo / Apr '94.

RIDE THE LIGHTNING.
Tracks: Fight fire with fire / Ride the lightning / For whom the bell tolls / Fade to black / Trapped under ice / Escape / Creeping death / Call of Ktulu.
MC . . . . **TMFN 27**
Music For Nations / Jul '84 / Pinnacle.
■ **LP P.Disc** . . . . **MFN 27P**
Music For Nations / Sep '86.
CD . . . . **CDMFN 27**
■ **LP** . . . . **MFN 27**
■ **Double LP** . . . . **MFN 27DM**
Music For Nations / '88.
CD **8384102**
LP **8384101**
MC **8384104**
Vertigo / May '89 / PolyGram.

SAD BUT TRUE.
Tracks: Sad but true.
■ **12"** . . . . **METAL 1112**
■ **7"** . . . . **METAL 11**
■ **CD Single** . . . . **METCD 11**
Vertigo / Feb '93.

SINGLES CD, THE.
Tracks: Not Advised.
CD . . . . **CD 12 KUTT**
Music For Nations / Nov '87 / Pinnacle.

UNFORGIVEN, THE.
Tracks: Unforgiven / Killing time / So what (Only on 12" single).
■ **12"** . . . . **METAL 812**
■ **7"** . . . . **METAL 8**
■ **CD Single** . . . . **METCD 8**
Vertigo / Oct '91.

WHEREVER I MAY ROAM.
Tracks: Not Advised.
■ **CD Single** . . . . **METCD 9**
Phonogram / Nov '92.

WHIPLASH.
Tracks: Whiplash.
■ **EP** **MRS04**
■ **7" P.Disc** **MRS04P**
Megaforce (USA) / Aug '87.

Mezzrow

THEN CAME THE KILLING.
Tracks: Then came the killing / Final holocaust / Distant death / Where death begins / Ancient terror / Frozen soul / Prevent necessary / Cross of torment.
CD . . . . **.CDATV 11**
LP . . . . **ATV 11**
Active / May '90 / Pinnacle.

Midas Touch

PRESAGE OF DESASTER.
Tracks: Forcibly incarcerated / Sinking censorship / When the boot comes down / True believers inc. / Sepulchral ephitaph / Lost paradise / Accessory before the fact / Terminal breath / Subhumanity / New beginning.
■ **CD** . . . . **.CDNUK 124**
■ **LP** . . . . **.NUK 124**
■ **MC** . . . . **ZCNUK 124**
Noise / Apr '89.

TOO MUCH LOVE TO SOON.
Tracks: Too much love too soon / Gotta get back to you.
■ **7"** . . . . **FUNK 3**
Champagne / May '81.

Mighty Force

DIVE.
Tracks: Dive.
■ **12"** . . . . **CUT 9012009**
Cut Deep / May '90.
■ **12"** . . . . **MOSH 34T**
■ **CD Single** . . . . **MOSH 34CD**
■ **MC Single** . . . . **MOSH 34MC**
Earache / Jan '93.

DUM DUM.
Tracks: Dum dum.
■ **12"** . . . . **.12KHZ 1**
Sub Bass / Apr '92.

HYPNOVEL.
Tracks: Not Advised.
CD . . . . **HZ 001CD**
■ **LP** . . . . **HZ 001**
■ **MC** . . . . **.HZ 001MC**
Sub Bass / Jun '92.

THRASHING A DEAD HOUSE.
Tracks: Thrashing a dead house.
■ **12"** . . . . **SUK 3**
Vinyl Drip / Nov '88.

Miller, Donnie

ONE OF THE BOYS.
Tracks: One of the boys / Normal guy (I want sex) / I can't stop flying / Me and you / Devil wears lingerie / Man said no / Blind man's buff / No time for running / You can't stop emotion / Welcome home.
CD **4658172**
■ **LP** **4658171**
MC **4658174**
Epic / Apr '90 / Sony.

Mind Funk

DROPPED.
Tracks: Goddess / Closer / Drowning / In the way eye / Zootiehead / Wisteria / Mama Moses and me / Il Ton butterfly / Hogwallow / Billy goat / Hollow.
CD . . . . **CDZAZ 3**
LP . . . . **ZAZ 3**
MC . . . . **TZAZ 3**
Megaforce / Apr '93 / Pinnacle.

MINDFUNK.
Tracks: Sugar ain't so sweet / Ride and drive / Bring it on / Big house / Burning / Fire / Blood runs red / Sister Blue / Woke up this morning / Innocence / Touch you.
■ **LP P.Disc** **4677900**
Epic / Jul '91.
■ **CD** **4677902**
■ **LP** **4677901**
■ **MC** **4677904**
Epic / Mar '91.

TOUCH YOU.
Tracks: Touch you / Bang time / Velvet Jane / Surprise touch.
■ **12"** **6576186**
■ **CD Single** **6576182**
Epic / Nov '91.

Mind Over 4

GODDESS, THE.
Tracks: Prayer for the dying / Goddess / 12 days of wind / Post / Gemini / Ice water steam / Autumn's here / Hell's bravest song / Airplanes.
■ **CD** . . . . **CARCD 9**
■ **LP** . . . . **CARLP 9**
■ **MC** . . . . **CARC 9**
Caroline / '90.

HALF WAY DOWN.
Tracks: Introduction/ Charged / Honor / Barriers & passages / Cycle of experience / Unknown peers / Faith / My name is nothing / Struggle / Conscience of nation / Then & now / Funny pocket / Coffee.
CD . . . . **CDRR 9072 2**
Road Runner / Apr '93 / Pinnacle.

OUT HERE.
Tracks: Not Advised.
■ **LP** **51005 1**
Triple XXX (USA) / Sep '87.

Mindstorm

BACK TO REALITY.
Tracks: Not Advised.
CD . . . . **PRD 70212**
LP . . . . **PRL 70211**
MC . . . . **PRC 70214**
Provogue / May '91 / Pinnacle.

LOVE GOES BLIND.
Tracks: Not Advised.
CD . . . . **PRS 10292**
Provogue / Sep '91 / Pinnacle.

MINDSTORM.
Tracks: Not Advised.
CD . . . . **PRD 70232**
LP . . . . **PRL 70231**
MC . . . . **PRC 70234**
Barricade / Feb '91 / Pinnacle.

Ministry

Al Jourgensen's Ministry first hit the map in 1982 with single *Cold Life*, released on independent Chicago label, Wax Trax. When song became hit, band were signed by Arista. Early releases were synth-pop affairs - band latterly renowned for crushing industrial metal and nerve-mangling live shows; the former best sampled on *Psalm 69: The Way To Succeed And The Way To Suck Eggs* album, which made U.K. Top 40 in 1992.

COLD LIFE.
Tracks: Cold life.
■ **12"** . . . . **SIT 17T**
Situation 2 / Mar '82.

DEATH BEFORE DISCO (Ministry & Celestial Symphony).
Tracks: Death before disco.
■ **12"** . . . . **.12MOMU 20**
■ **CD Single** . . . . **CDMOMU 20**
Mute / Sep '93.

I WANTED TO TELL HER.
Tracks: I wanted to tell her.
■ **12"** . . . . **ARIST 12533**
■ **7"** . . . . **.ARIST 533**
Arista / '83.

LAND OF RAPE AND HONEY.
Tracks: Stigmata / Missing / Deity / Golden dawn / Destruction / Land of rape and honey / You know what you are / Flashback / Abortive / Hizbollah (Only on CD.) / I prefer (Only on CD.).
CD . . . . **.925799 2**
■ **LP** . . . . **.925799 1**
■ **MC** . . . . **.925799 4**
WEA / Jan '89.
CD **7599257992**
WEA / Nov '92 / WEA.

LIVE - IN CASE YOU DIDN'T FEEL LIKE SHOWING UP.
Tracks: Not Advised.
VHS **7599381763**
WEA / Nov '92 / WEA.

LIVE - IN CASE YOU DIDN'T FEEL LIKE SHOWING UP.
Tracks: Missing / Deity / So what / Burning inside / Thieves / Stigmata.
CD **7599262662**
WEA / Nov '92 / WEA.

■ **DELETED**

MIND IS A TERRIBLE THING, THE.
Tracks: Thieves / Never believe / Breathe / Burning inside / Cannibal song / So what / Test / Dream song / Faith collapsing.
CD 7599260042
LP 7599260041
MC 7599260044
WEA / Mar '94 / WEA.

N.W.O.
Tracks: N.W.O.
■ 10" . . . . W 0125
■ CD Single . . . . W 0125CD
East West / Aug '92.

NATURE OF LOVE.
Tracks: Nature of love.
■ 12" . . . . WAXUK 009
Wax Trax / Oct '85.

PSALM 69.
Tracks: N.W.O. / Just one fix / TV II / Hero / Jesus built my hotrod / Scare crow / Psalm 69 / Corrosion / Grace.
CD 7599 26727-2
LP . . . . RX 481X
MC . . . . WX 481C
Warner Bros. / Jun '90 / WEA.

REVENGE.
Tracks: Revenge.
■ 12" . . . . ARIST 12549
■ 7" . . . . ARIST 549
Arista / '83.

TWITCH.
Tracks: Just like you / We believe / All day (remix) / Angel / Over the shoulder / My possession / Where you at now / Crash and burn / Twitch (version 11).
MC 925309 4
■ LP .925309 1
Sire / Apr '86.

WITH SYMPATHY.
Tracks: Not Advised.
CD . . . . ARCD 8016
Arista / '89 / BMG.

WORK FOR LOVE.
Tracks: Work for love / Do the etawa / I wanted to tell her / Say you're sorry / Here we go / Effigy / Revenge / She's got a cause / Should've known better.
■ LP .205306
■ MC .405306
Arista / Sep '83.
■ CD 255 306
Arista / Mar '93.

WORK FOR LOVE.
Tracks: Work for love / For love.
■ 7" . . . . .ARIST 510
Arista / Feb '83.
■ 12" . . . . ARIST 12510
Arista / Feb '83.

Minor Threat

COMPLETE DISCOGRAPHY.
Tracks: Not Advised.
CD . . . . DISCHORD 40
Dischord / Mar '90 / SRD.

LIVE AT BUFF HALL.
Tracks: Live at Buff hall.
■ 7" . . . . LF 002
Lost & Found / Apr '92.

MINOR THREAT.
Tracks: Not Advised.
LP . . . . DISCHORD 12
MC . . . . .DISCHORD 12C
Dischord / '88 / SRD.

MINOR THREAT.
Tracks: Not Advised.
VHS . . . . DISCHORD 27
Dischord / '85 / SRD.

OUT OF STEP.
Tracks: Not Advised.
■ LP . . . . DISCHORD 10
MC . . . . .DISCHORD 10C
Dischord / SRD.

SALAD DAYS.
Tracks: Salad days.
■ 7" . . . . DISCHORD 15
Dischord.

Minutemen

3 WAY TIE (FOR LAST).
Tracks: Not Advised.
■ LP . . . . SST 058
SST / Feb '86.
CD . . . . .SST 058 CD
SST / Feb '86 / Pinnacle.
MC . . . . .SST 058 C
SST / May '93 / Pinnacle.

BALLOT RESULT.
Tracks: Not Advised.
CD . . . . .SST 068 CD
LP . . . . SST 068
MC . . . . .SST 068 C
SST / May '93 / Pinnacle.

BUZZ OR HOWL UNDER THE IN-FLUENCE OF HEAT.
Tracks: Not Advised.
CD . . . . .SST 016 CD
LP . . . . SST 016
MC . . . . .SST 016 C
SST / May '93 / Pinnacle.

DOUBLE NICKELS ON THE DIME.
Tracks: Not Advised.
CD . . . . .SST 028 CD
SST / Oct '87 / Pinnacle.
LP . . . . SST 028
MC . . . . .SST 028 C
SST / May '93 / Pinnacle.

FAT.
Tracks: Not Advised.
CD . . . . .SST 214 CD
SST / Nov '88 / Pinnacle.

JOY.
Tracks: Joy.
■ 7" . . . . .SST 214
SST / Feb '90.
■ 10" . . . . .SST 923
■ MC Single . . . . .SST 214 C
SST / May '93.

PARANOID TIME (EP).
Tracks: Paranoid time.
■ 12" . . . . SST 2
SST / Mar '83.

POLITICS OF TIME.
Tracks: Not Advised.
CD . . . . .SST 277 CD
LP . . . . SST 277
MC . . . . .SST 277 C
SST / May '93 / Pinnacle.

POST-MERSH, VOL.1.
Tracks: Not Advised.
CD . . . . .SST 138 CD
MC . . . . .SST 138 C
SST / May '93 / Pinnacle.

POST-MERSH, VOL.2.
Tracks: Not Advised.
CD . . . . .SST 139 CD
MC . . . . .SST 139 C
SST / May '93 / Pinnacle.

POST-MERSH, VOL.3.
Tracks: Not Advised.
CD . . . . .SST 165 CD
MC . . . . .SST 165 C
SST / May '93 / Pinnacle.

PROJECT MERSH.
Tracks: Not Advised.
■ LP . . . . SST 034
SST / Jul '85.
CD . . . . .SST 034 CD
MC . . . . .SST 034 C
SST / May '93 / Pinnacle.

PUNCH LINE, THE.
Tracks: Not Advised.
CD . . . . .SST 004 CD
LP . . . . SST 004
MC . . . . .SST 004 C
SST / May '93 / Pinnacle.

TOUR SPIEL (LIVE EP).
Tracks: Not Advised.
■ EP . . . . REFLEX L
Homestead / Apr '85.

WHAT MAKES A MAN START FIRES.
Tracks: Not Advised.
CD . . . . .SST 014 CD
LP . . . . SST 014
MC . . . . .SST 014 C
SST / May '93 / Pinnacle.

Misfits

BEST OF THE MISFITS.
Tracks: Not Advised.
■ LP . . . . REVLP 74
Revolver / Jul '86.

BEWARE.
Tracks: Beware.
■ 7" . . . . PLP 9
Plan 9 / Jul '81.

DIE DIE MY DARLING.
Tracks: Die die my darling.
■ 12" . . . . .PL 903
Plan 9 / Nov '87.

EARTH AD/WOLF'S BLOOD.
Tracks: Not Advised.
LP . . . . AG 0024
Noise / Jul '91 / Pinnacle.

EVIL LIVE.
Tracks: Not Advised.
■ LP . . . . .PL 908
Caroline (USA) / Sep '87.
LP . . . . AGO 023
Noise / Jul '91 / Pinnacle.

EVIL/EARTH/WOLFS.
Tracks: Not Advised.
CD . . . . AGO 572
Noise / Jul '91 / Pinnacle.

MISFITS.
Tracks: Bullet / Horror business / Teenagers from Mars / Night of the living / Where eagles dare. Theme from / Vampira / Skulls / I turned into a martian / Eyes / Violent world / London dungeon / Ghoul's night out / Halloween / Die, die my darling / Mommy, can I go out and kill tonight.
CD . . . . .PL 9CD1
Plan 9 / May '88 / Pinnacle.

RAIN VOICES.
Tracks: Rain voices.
■ 12" . . . . MISFIT T 1
■ 7" . . . . MISFIT 1
Misfit / Dec '86.

WALK AMONG US.
Tracks: All hell breaks loose / Hatebreeders.
■ LP 925756 1
Ruby (USA) / Sep '88.

WOLFSBLOOD.
Tracks: Not Advised.
■ LP . . . . AG 024
Aggressive Rock Productions / Feb '84.

Mitchell, Kim

AKIMBO ALOGO.
Tracks: Go for soda / That's a man / All we are / Diary for rock 'n' roll man / Love ties / Feel it burn / Lager and ale / Rumour has it / Caroline / Called off.
■ LP . . . . .BRON 556
Bronze / Jun '85.

GO FOR SODA.
Tracks: Go for soda / Love ties.
■ 12" . . . . .BROX 192
■ 7" . . . . .BRO 192
Bronze / May '85.

ROCKLAND.
Tracks: Rockland wonderland / Lost lovers found / Rock 'n' roll duty / Tangle of love / Moodstreet / Crossroads / Expedition sailor / O mercy Louise / This dream / Great embrace.
CD . . . . K 781 963 2
■ LP 781 963-1
■ MC 781 963-4
Atlantic / Aug '89.

Molly Hatchet

BEATIN' THE ODDS.
Tracks: Beatin' the odds / Double talker / Rambler / Sailor / Dead and gone / Few and far between / Penthouse pauper / Get her back.
MC 40 84471
■ LP . . . . EPC 84471
Epic / Nov '80.
CD 40 32746
■ LP 32746
Prix D'Ami (France) / Sep '86.

BOUNTY HUNTER.
Tracks: Bounty hunter / Boogie no more / Flirtin' with disaster.
■ 12" . . . . EPC 12 8636

■ DELETED

7" . . . . EPC 8636
Epic / Jun '80.

DEED IS DONE, THE.
Tracks: Satisfied man / Backstabber / She does she does / Intro piece / Stone in your heart / Man on the run / Good smoke and whiskey / Heartbreak radio / I ain't got you / Straight shooter / Song for the children.
■ LP . . . . EPC 26213
■ MC .40 26213
Epic / Jan '85 / Sony.

DOUBLE TROUBLE LIVE.
Tracks: Whisky man / Bounty hunter / Gator country / Flirtin with disaster / Stone in your heart / Satisfied man / Bloody reunion / Boogie no more / Freebird / Walk on the side of the angels / Walk with you / Dreams I'll never see / Edge of sundown / Fall of the peacemakers / Beatin' the odds.
■ Double LP . . . . EPC 88670
■ MC Set 40 88670
Epic / Jan '86.

FLIRTIN' WITH DISASTER.
Tracks: Flirtin' with disaster / Gunsmoke.
■ 7" . . . . EPC 8221
Epic / Feb '80.

FLIRTING WITH DISASTER.
Tracks: Whiskey man / It's all over now / One man's pleasure / Jukin' city / Boogie no more / Flirtin' with disaster / Good rockin' / Gunsmoke / Long time / Let the good times roll.
■ LP . . . . EPC 83791
Epic / Oct '79.
CD . . . . CD 462940
CBS / Jul '89 / Sony.

MOLLY HATCHET.
Tracks: Bounty hunter / Gator country / Big apple / Creeper / Price you pay / Dreams I'll never see / I'll be running / Cheatin' woman / Trust your old friend.
■ LP . . . . EPC 83250
Epic / '79.

NO GUTS NO GLORY.
Tracks: What does it matter / Ain't even close / Sweet dixie / Fall of the peacemakers / What's it gonna take / Kinda like love / Under the gun / On the prowl / Both sides.
■ LP . . . . EPC 25244
MC .40 25244
Epic / Mar '83 / Sony.
■ LP . . . . EPC 32718
■ MC .40 32718
Epic / Feb '86.

SATISFIED MAN.
Tracks: Satisfied man / Straight shooter.
■ 12" . . . . TA 4848
■ 7" . . . . .A 4848
Epic / Jan '85.

TAKE NO PRISONERS.
Tracks: Bloody reunion / Respect me in the morning / Long tall Sally / Loss of control / All mine / Lady luck / Power play / Don't mess around / Don't leave me lonely / Dead giveaway.
■ LP . . . . EPC 85296
MC .40 85296
Epic / Dec '81 / Sony.

Monolith

SLEEP WITH THE DEAD.
Tracks: Sleep with the dead.
■ 7" . . . . CHTONIC 701
Cacophonus / Jun '93.

TALES OF THE MACABRE.
Tracks: Morbid curiosity / Sleep with the dead / Misery / Undead burial / Devoured from within / Locked in horror / Catalogue of carnage / Maceration.
CD . . . . SOL 036CD
LP .SOL 036
Vinyl Solution / Mar '93 / RTM / Pinnacle.

Monroe, Michael

DEAD, JAIL OR ROCK'N'ROLL.
Tracks: Dead, jail or rock'n'roll / Shakedown / Thrill me (On 12" singles and CD single only.).
■ 12" . . . . .VERXP 45
■ 12" . . . . .VERX 45
■ 7" . . . . VER 45
■ CD Single . . . . .VERCD 45
■ MC Single . . . . .VERMC 45
Vertigo / Nov '89.

MAN WITH NO EYES.
Tracks: Man with no eyes / Dead jail or rock 'n' roll / Love is thicker than blood (12" & CD single only.) / She's no angel (12" & CD single only.).
■ 12" . . . . .VERT 46
■ 12" . . . . .VERXC 46
■ 12" . . . . .VERX 46
■ 7" . . . . .VERP 46
■ 7" . . . . .VER 436
■ CD Single . . . . .VERCD 46
■ MC Single . . . . .VERMC 46
Vertigo / Feb '90.

NIGHTS ARE SO LONG.
Tracks: Not Advised.
CD .CD 1
Yahoo (Denmark) / '88 / Pinnacle.

NOT FAKIN' IT.
Tracks: Dead jail or rock'n'roll / While you were lookin' at me / She's no angel / All night with the lights on / Not fakin' it / Shakedown / Man with no eyes / Love is thicker than blood / Smokescreen / Thrill me.
■ CD 838 627 2
■ LP 838 627 1
■ MC 838 627 4
Mercury / Aug '89.

Monster Magnet

EVIL.
Tracks: Evil.
■ 12" . . . . GR 204
■ CD Single . . . . .GRCD 204
Glitterhouse / May '93.

SPINE OF GOD.
Tracks: Not Advised.
CD . . . . GR 0172
LP . . . . GR 0171
MC . . . . GR 0174
Glitterhouse / Jun '92 / SRD.

TWIN EARTH.
Tracks: Twin Earth.
■ 12" 580281-1
■ 7" 580280-7
■ CD Single 580281-2
A&M / Jun '93.

Montrose

First and most successful line-up of San Francisco's Montrose was assembled by top session guitarist, Ronnie Montrose. Eponymous 1974 debut is regarded among all-time best metal albums. Singer Sammy Hagar left for solo career in 1974 and later joined Van Halen. Final album, 1978's Open Fire was produced by Edgar Winter (with whom Ronnie Montrose once played), after which Montrose launched solo career. He also led group called Gamma, who produced three albums.

JUMP ON IT.
Tracks: Let's go / What are you waiting for / Tuft sedge / Music man / Jump on it / Rich man / Crazy for you / Merry go round.
■ LP . . . . K 56291
WEA.

MONTROSE.
Tracks: Rock the nations / Bad motor scooter / Space station No 5 / I don't want it / Good rockin' tonight / Rock candy / One thing on my mind / Make it last.
■ LP . . . . K 46276
WEA.

PAPER MONEY.
Tracks: Underground / Connection / Dreamer / Starliner / I got the fire / Spaceage sacrifice / We're going home / Paper money.
■ LP . . . . K 56069
WEA.

SPACE STATION NO. 5.
Tracks: Space station no. 5 / Good rockin' tonight.
■ 7" . . . . HM 9
Atlantic / Jun '80.

WARNER BROS PRESENT MONTROSE.
Tracks: Matriarch / All I need / Twenty flight back / Whaler / Dancin' feet / O lucky man / One and a half / Clown woman / Black train.
■ LP . . . . K 56170
WEA.

Montrose, Ronnie

DIVA STATION, A.
Tracks: Sorcerer / Weirding way / Choke Canyon / Stay with me / High and dry / Diva station / New kid in town / Little demon / Quid pro quo / Solitaire.
CD . . . . RR 9400 2
LP . . . . RR 9400 1
Road Runner / Apr '90 / Pinnacle.

MEAN.
Tracks: Not Advised.
■ LP . . . . ENIG 32641
Enigma (EMI) / Apr '87.

OPEN FIRE.
Tracks: Openers / Open fire / Mandolinia / Town without pity / Leo rising / Headsup / Rocky road / My little mystery / No beginning, no end.
■ LP . . . . BSK 3184
WEA / Nov '91.

SPEED OF SOUND.
Tracks: Mach 1 / Black box / Hyper thrust / Monolith / Zero G / Telstar / Sidewinder / Windsheer / VTOL / Outer marker in bound.
CD 3323 2
■ LP 3323 1
Enigma (EMI) / Apr '88.
■ LP . . . . GWLP 53
GWR / Aug '89.

TERRITORY.
Tracks: Catscan / I'm gonna be strong / Love you too / Odd man out / I spy / Territory / Synesthesia / Pentagon / Women of Ireland.
CD . . . . PJCD 88009
■ LP . . . . PJ 88009
MC . . . . PJC 88009
Passport Jazz (USA) / '87.

Moore, Gary

Irish guitarist/singer Moore began in Dublin band, Skid Row. 1973 solo debut did nothing and in '74 he joined Thin Lizzy, before period with Colosseum II. During break in latter's activities, Moore guested with Lizzy; then switched on permanent basis in '78, contributing to U.K. no. 2 album Black Rose. Sacked in 1979, Moore formed short-lived G Force. Solo career resumed in 1982 in metal vein, before fruitful musical switch with 1990's Still Got The Blues album . Other successes include U.K. hits Parisienne Walkways (1979) and Out In The Fields (1985). In 1994, Moore joined Ginger Baker and Jack Bruce for Cream-flavoured BBM project.

AFTER HOURS.
Tracks: Cold day in hell / Don't you like to me (I get evil) / Story of the blues / Since I met you baby / Separate ways / Only fool in town / Key to love / Jumpin' at shadows / Blues is alright / Hurt inside / Nothing's the same.
CD . . . . CDV 2684
■ LP . . . . V 2684
MC . . . . TCV 2684
Virgin / Mar '92 / EMI.
MiniDisc. . . . . MDV 2684
Virgin / Feb '93 / EMI.
DCC 462 558
Virgin / Jun '93.

AFTER THE WAR.
Tracks: After the war / Speak for yourself / Livin' on dreams / Led clones / Running from the storm / This thing called love / Ready for love / Blood of emeralds / Messiah will come again (Only on CD and MC.) / Dunluce (part 1) (Only on CD.) / Dunluce (part 2) (Only on CD.) / Dunluce (Only on MC.).
CD . . . . CDV 2575
■ LP . . . . V 2575
■ MC . . . . TCV 2575
Virgin / Dec '88.
MC . . . . OVEDC 335
■ LP . . . . OVED 335
Virgin / Sep '90.

AFTER THE WAR.
Tracks: After the war / This thing called love / Over the hills and far away (live) (on 12" only) / Emerald (on CD only) / Thunder rising (live) (on CD only).
■ 7" . . . . VS 1153
■ CD Single . . . . .VSCD 1153
Virgin / '88.
■ 12" . . . . VST 1153
Virgin / Dec '88.
■ 12" . . . . GMST 1
■ 7" . . . . GMSG 1
■ 7" . . . . GMS 1

■ CD Single . . . . GMSCD 1
Virgin / Jan '89.

ALWAYS GONNA LOVE YOU.
Tracks: Always gonna love you / Cold hearted.
■ 7" . . . . VS 528
Virgin / Sep '82.

AND THEN THE MAN SAID TO HIS..
Tracks: Not Advised.
■ LP Set 100 101
Accord / Sep '88.

ANTHOLOGY - GARY MOORE.
Tracks: Fanatical fascists / Don't believe a word /
Spirit / Run to your mama / Women in love / Rest in
peace / White knuckles / Back on the streets / Don't
let me be misunderstood / What would you rather
bee or a wasp / Dallas warhead (live) / Hurricane /
Bad news / I look at you / She's got you / Parisienne
walkways.
■ Double LP . . . . RAWLP 023
MC Set . . . . RAWTC 023
Raw Power / Sep '86 / Pinnacle.

BACK ON THE STREETS.
Tracks: Back on the streets / Don't believe a word /
Fanatical fascists / Flight of the snow goose / Hurri-
cane / Song for Donna / What would you rather bee
or a wasp / Parisienne walkways.
■ LP . . . . MCF 2853
MCA / Feb '79.
■ LP . . . . MCL 1622
■ CD . . . . DMCL 1622
■ MC . . . . MCLC 1622
MCA / Feb '91.
■ CD . . . . MCLD 19011
■ MC . . . . MCLC 19011
MCA / Apr '92.

BLUES ALIVE.
Tracks: Cold day in hell / Walking by myself / Story
of the blues / Oh pretty woman / Separate ways / Too
tired / Still got the blues / Since I met you baby / Sky
is crying / Further on up the road / King of the blues /
Parisienne walkways / Jumpin' at shadows.
CD . . . . CDVX 2716
LP . . . . V 2716
MC . . . . TCV 2716
Virgin / May '93 / EMI.

BLUES ALIVE.
Tracks: Not Advised.
VHS 4509924623
Warner Bros. / May '93 / WEA.

COLD DAY IN HELL.
Tracks: Cold day in hell.
■ CD Single . . . . VSD 1393
■ 7" . . . . VS 1393
■ MC Single . . . . VSC 1393
Virgin / Feb '92.

COLLECTION: GARY MOORE.
Tracks: Not Advised.
CD . . . . CCSCD 273
MC . . . . CCSMC 273
■ Double LP . . . . CCSLP 273
Castle Collector Series / Oct '90.

CORRIDORS OF POWER.
Tracks: Don't take me for a loser / Always gonna
love you / Wishing well / Gonna break my heart
again / Falling in love with you / End of the world /
Rockin' every night / Cold hearted / I can't wait until
tomorrow.
■ LP . . . . V 2245
■ LP . . . . OVED 210
■ MC . . . . OVEDC 210
Virgin / Oct '82.
CD . . . . CDV 2245
Virgin / Jul '85 / EMI.

DIRTY FINGERS.
Tracks: Hiroshima / Dirty fingers / Bad news / Don't
let me be misunderstood / Run to your Mama /
Nuclear attack / Kidnapped / Really gonna rock /
Lonely nights / Rest in peace.
■ LP . . . . JETLP 241
MC . . . . JETCA 241
Jet / Jun '84 / Sony / Total / BMG.
CD . . . . JETCD 007
Jet / Nov '86 / Sony / Total / BMG.
CD . . . . CLACD 131
■ LP . . . . CLALP 131
Castle Classics / '87.
■ MC . . . . CLAMC 131
Castle Classics / Apr '87.

DON'T LET ME BE MISUNDERSTOOD.
Tracks: Don't let me be misunderstood.
■ 7" . . . . JET 7043
Jet / Jun '84.

EMERALD AISLES.
Tracks: Not Advised.
■ VHS . . . . VVD 055
Virgin Vision / Jan '86.
VHS . . . . VVD 080
Virgin Vision / '88 / Gold & Sons / TBD.

EMPTY ROOMS.
Tracks: Empty rooms (summer 1985 version) (On all
versions) / Out of my system (NOT on CD) / Murder
in the skies (live) / Empty rooms (live) / Parisienne walkways (live) (On CD & double 7" set only) /
Empty rooms (long version) (On CD only).
■ 7" . . . . TEN 58
10 / Jul '85.
■ 7" Set . . . . TEND 58
10 / Jun '85.
■ CD Single . . . . CDT 35
10 / '88.

EVENING OF THE BLUES, AN (Moore, Gary & The Midnight Blues Band).
Tracks: Not Advised.
VHS . . . . VVD 872DP
Virgin Vision / Mar '91 / Gold & Sons / TBD.

FALLING IN LOVE WITH YOU.
Tracks: Falling in love with you.
■ 12" . . . . VS 564-12
■ 7" . . . . VS 564
Virgin / Feb '83.

FRIDAY ON MY MIND.
Tracks: Friday on my mind (On 7" only) / Reach for
the sky (live version) (On all versions) / Friday on my
mind (12" version) (On CD & 12" only) / Friday on my
mind (kool rap version) (On CD & 12" only) / Parisienne walkways (live) (On CD only).
■ 7" . . . . TEN 164
■ 12" . . . . TENT 164
■ 7" P.Disc . . . . TENP 164
■ CD Single . . . . KERRY 164
10 / Apr '87.

G-FORCE/LIVE AT THE MARQUEE.
Tracks: You / White knuckles / Rockin' and rollin' /
She's got you / I look at you / Because of your love /
You kissed me sweetly / Hot gossip / Woman's in
love / Dancin' / Back on the streets / Run to your
Mama / Parisienne walkways / Nuclear attack /
Dallas warhead.
■ CD Set . . . . TFOCD 2
That's Original / Mar '88.
■ Double LP . . . . TFOLP 2
■ MC . . . . TFOMC 2
That's Original / Mar '88.

GARY MOORE - CD BOX SET.
Tracks: Not Advised.
■ CD Set . . . . CLA BX 904
Castle Classics / Feb '92.

GARY MOORE CD BOX SET.
Tracks: Not Advised.
CD Set . . . . TPAK 18
Virgin / Nov '91 / EMI.

GARY MOORE E.P.
Tracks: Don't let me be misunderstood / Parisienne
walkways / White knuckles.
■ CD Single CD3-4
Special Edition / '88.

GARY MOORE: LIVE IN SWEDEN.
Tracks: Not Advised.
VHS . . . . VVD 249
Virgin Vision / '88 / Gold & Sons / TBD.

GRINDING STONE.
Tracks: Grinding stone / Time to heal / Sail across
the mountain / Energy dance / Spirit / Boogie my
way back home.
■ LP . . . . CBS 32699
■ MC 40 32699
CBS / Nov '85.
CD 4674492
■ LP 4674491
■ MC 4674494
CBS / Oct '90.

HOLD ON TO LOVE.
Tracks: Hold on to love / Devil in her heart / Law of
the jungle.
■ 12" . . . . TEN 13-12
■ 7" . . . . TEN 13
10 / Jan '84.

LED CLONES.
Tracks: Led clones.

LIVE AT THE MARQUEE.
Tracks: Back on the streets / Run to your mama /
Dancin' / She's got you / Parisienne walkways / You
/ Nuclear attack / Dallas warhead.
CD . . . . RAWCD 034
Raw Power / Jul '87 / Pinnacle.
■ LP . . . . RAWLP 034
MC . . . . RAWTC 034
Raw Power / Jun '87 / Pinnacle.
CD . . . . CLACD 211
■ LP . . . . CLALP 211
■ MC . . . . CLAMC 211
Castle Classics / Feb '91.

LIVIN' ON DREAMS.
Tracks: Livin' on dreams / Messiah will come again.
■ 12" . . . . VST 1219
■ 7" . . . . VS 1219
Virgin / Oct '89.

LONER, THE.
Tracks: Loner (On all versions) / Johnny Boy (On all
versions) / Loner, The (extended version) (Cassette
only) / Loner, The (live at Hammersmith Odeon) (12"
only).
■ 12" . . . . TENT 178
■ 7" . . . . TEN 178
■ MC Single . . . . TENC 178
10 / '87.

NIGHTRIDING: GARY MOORE (Golden decade of Gary Moore).
Tracks: Not Advised.
■ CD . . . . KNCD 10014
■ MC . . . . KNMC 10014
Nightriding / Aug '91.

NUCLEAR ATTACK.
Tracks: Nuclear attack.
■ 12" . . . . JET 12016
Jet / Oct '81.

NUCLEAR ATTACK - BEST OF.
Tracks: Not Advised.
■ LP 626265
Avenue (Germany) / Aug '88.

OH PRETTY WOMAN.
Tracks: Oh pretty woman / King of blues / Stumble
(Only on CD and 12" singles.).
■ 12" . . . . VSTP 1233
■ 12" . . . . VST 1233
■ 7" . . . . VS 1233
■ MC Single . . . . VSC 1233
■ CD Single . . . . VSCDT 1233
Virgin / Mar '90.

OUT IN THE FIELDS (Moore, Gary & Phil Lynott).
Tracks: Out in the fields / Military man / Still in love
with you (12" only).
■ 7" . . . . TEN 49
■ 12" . . . . TEN 49-12
10 / May '85.

OVER THE HILLS AND FAR AWAY.
Tracks: Over the hills and far away (NOT on CDT 16)
/ Crying in the shadows (On all versions) / Over the
hills and far away (extended) (On CD's & 12" only) /
Out in the fields (live) (On TENCD & TEND 134 only) /
All messed up (live) (On TEND, TENT & CDT 16 only.
Recorded at Milton Keynes).
■ 7" . . . . TEN 134
■ 12" . . . . TENT 134
10 / Dec '86.
■ 7" . . . . TENDJ 134
■ 7" . . . . TENG 134
■ 7" P.Disc . . . . TENP 134
■ CD Single . . . . TENCD 134
■ 7" Set . . . . TEND 134
10 / '88.

PARISIENNE WALKWAYS.
Tracks: Back on the streets / Fanatical fascists /
Don't believe a word / Spanish guitar / Parisienne
walkways / Put it this way / Desperado / Castles /
Fighting talk / Scorch.
■ LP . . . . MCL 1864
■ MC . . . . MCLC 1864
MCA / Nov '87.
■ CD . . . . DMCL 1864
MCA / May '90.
CD . . . . MCLD 19076
MCA / Nov '90 / BMG.
MC . . . . MCLC 19076
MCA / Oct '92 / BMG.

PARISIENNE WALKWAYS.
Tracks: Parisienne walkways / Fanatical fascists.
■ 7" . . . . MCA 419
MCA / Apr '79.

PARISIENNE WALKWAYS (LIVE).
Tracks: Parisienne walkways / Still got the blues / Since I met you baby (On VSCDT 1456 only.) / Key to love (On VSCDT 1456.) / Stop messin' around (On VSCDX 1456 only.) / You don't love me (On VSCDX 1456 only.).
- 7" . . . . VS 1456
- CD Single . . . . VSCDT 1456
- CD Single . . . . VSCDX 1456
- MC Single . . . . VSC 1456
Virgin / Apr '93.

Q-FORCE.
Tracks: Not Advised.
CD . . . . JETCD 006
Jet / Nov '86 / Sony / Total / BMG.

READY FOR LOVE.
Tracks: Ready for love / Wild frontier (live) / Loner, The (live) (on 12" only).
- 12" . . . . GMSTG 2
- 12" . . . . GMST 2
- 7" . . . . GMS 2
Virgin / Mar '89.
- CD Single . . . . GMSDX 2
- CD Single . . . . GMSCD 2
Virgin / Mar '89.

ROCKIN' EVERY NIGHT (Live in Japan).
Tracks: Rockin' every night / Wishing well / I can't wait until tomorrow / Nuclear attack / White knuckles / Rockin' and rollin' / Back on the streets / Sunset.
CD . . . . ZIDCD 1
- LP . . . . XID 1
- MC . . . . CXID 1
10 / Nov '86.
CD . . . . XIDCD 1
10 / Jun '88 / EMI.

RUN FOR COVER.
Tracks: Out in the fields / Reach for the sky / Run for cover / Military man / Empty rooms / Nothing to lose / Once in a lifetime / All messed up / Listen to your heartbeat / Out of my system (CD only).
- LP . . . . DIX 16
10 / Aug '85.
- MC . . . . CDIX 16
10 / Aug '85.
CD . . . . DIXCD 16
10 / Feb '86 / EMI.
MC . . . . OVEDC 274
- LP . . . . OVED 274
10 / '89.

SEPARATE WAYS.
Tracks: Separate ways (single) / Only Fool In Town / You don't love me (live) / Stumble / Further On up The Road (live With Albert Collins).
- 7" . . . . VS 1437
- CD . . . . VSCDX 1437
- CD . . . . VSCDT 1437
- MC Single . . . . VSC 1437
Virgin / Oct '92.

SHAPES OF THINGS.
Tracks: Shapes of things / Blinder.
- 12" . . . . TEN 19 12
- 7" . . . . TEN 19
10 / Mar '84.

SINCE I MET YOU BABY.
Tracks: Since I met you baby.
- 7" . . . . VS 1423
- CD Single . . . . VSCDG 1423
- CD Single . . . . VSCDT 1423
- MC Single . . . . VSC 1423
Virgin / Jul '92.

SPANISH GUITAR.
Tracks: Spanish guitar (2 pts).
- 7" . . . . MCA 534
MCA / Oct '79.

STILL GOT THE BLUES.
Tracks: Moving on / Oh pretty woman / Walking by myself / Still got the blues / Texas strut / All your love / Too tired / King of the blues / As the days go passing by / Midnight blues / That kind of woman / Stop messin' around.
CD . . . . CDV 2612
MC . . . . TCV 2612
- LP . . . . V 2612
Virgin / Mar '90.
CD . . . . PCDV 2612
Virgin / Feb '91 / EMI.
MiniDisc . . . . MDV 2612
Virgin / Feb '93 / EMI.

STILL GOT THE BLUES.
Tracks: Still got the blues (for you) / Left me with the blues / Still got the blues (for you) (full length) (Only on 12" single.) / Sky is crying (Only on 12" and CD singles.) / Further on up the road (Only on CD single

(VSCDT 1267)) / Mean cruel woman (Only on CD single (VSCDX 1267)).
- 12" . . . . VST 1267
- CD Single . . . . VSCDX 1267
- 7" . . . . VS 1267
- MC Single . . . . VSC 1267
- CD Single . . . . VSCDT 1267

STORY OF THE BLUES.
Tracks: Story of the blues / Movin' down the road / King of the blues (live) (Only on CD single (1)) / Midnight blues (live) (Only on CD single (2)).
- CD Single . . . . VSCDG 1412
- CD Single . . . . VSCDT 1412
- MC Single . . . . VSC 1412
- 7" . . . . VS 1412
Virgin / Apr '92.

TAKE A LITTLE TIME.
Tracks: Take a little time / Out in the fields / All messed up (live) / Thunder rising (live).
- 7" Set . . . . TEND 190
10 / Nov '87.

TOO TIRED.
Tracks: Too tired / Texas strut.
- CD Single . . . . VSCD 1306
- CD Single . . . . VSCDX 1306
- 12" . . . . VST 1306
- 7" . . . . VS 1306
- MC Single . . . . VSC 1306
Virgin / Nov '90.

VICTIMS OF THE FUTURE.
Tracks: Murder in the skies / All I want / Hold on to love / Law of the jungle / Victims of the future / Teenage idol / Shape of things to come / Empty rooms.
- LP . . . . OVED 206
- MC . . . . OVEDC 206
10 / Feb '84.
CD . . . . DIXCD 2
10 / Jun '88 / EMI.

VIDEO SINGLES: GARY MOORE.
Tracks: Not Advised.
VHS . . . . VVC 243
Virgin Vision / '88 / Gold & Sons / TBD.

WALKING BY MYSELF.
Tracks: Walking by myself / Still got the blues for you (live).
- 12" . . . . VST 1281
- 7" . . . . VS 1281
- CD Single . . . . VSCDT 1281
Virgin / Aug '90.

WALKWAYS.
Tracks: Not Advised.
CD 550 7382
MC 550 7384
Spectrum (1) / Sep '94 / PolyGram.

WE WANT MOORE.
Tracks: Murder in the skies / Shape of things to come / Victims of the future / Cold hearted / End of the world / Back on the streets / So far away / Empty rooms / Don't take me for a loser / Rockin' and rollin'.
- Double LP . . . . GMDL 1
- MC . . . . CGMDL 1
10 / Oct '84.
- CD Set . . . . GMDLD 1
MC . . . . OVEDC 410
10 / Apr '92 / EMI.

WHITE KNUCKLES.
Tracks: Nuclear attack / White knuckles / Rockin' and rollin' / Run to your mama (live) / You / Dirty fingers / Parisienne walkways (live) / Really gonna rock tonight / Hiroshima / You kissed me sweetly / Dancin' / Hot gossip / He's got you (live).
- LP . . . . RAWLP 006
Raw Power / Oct '85.
- MC . . . . RAWTC 006
Raw Power / Apr '86.
- CD . . . . RAWCD 006
Raw Power / Apr '86.

WILD FRONTIER.
Tracks: Over the hills and far away / Wild frontier / Take a little time / Loner / Friday on my mind / Strangers in the darkness / Thunder rising / Johnny boy / Wild frontier (12" version) (On CD only) / Over the hills and far away (12" version) (On CD only) / Crying in the shadows (On CD only).
CD . . . . DIXCD 56
10 / Feb '87 / EMI.
- LP . . . . DIX 56
- MC . . . . CDIX 56
10 / Feb '87.
- CD . . . . DIXPCD 56
10 / Jan '89.

WILD FRONTIER.
Tracks: Wild frontier (On all versions) / Run for cover (live version) (On all versions) / Wild version (extended version) (On 12" only) / Wild frontier (live) (On TEND & TENT 159 only) / Murder in the skies (live) (On TEND 159 only) / Over the hills and far away (On CD only) / Empty rooms (On CD only) / Out in the fields (On CD only) / Shapes of things (On CD only).
- 7" . . . . TEN 159
- CD Single . . . . KERRY 159
10 / Jul '87.
- 12" . . . . TENT 159
- 7" Set . . . . TEND 159
10 / Jul '87.

Moore, Vinnie

MIND'S EYE.
Tracks: In control / Saved by a miracle / Lifeforce / Mind's eye / Journey / Daydream / Hero without honour / N.N.Y. / Shadows of yesterday.
- LP . . . . RR 9635
Road Runner / Feb '87.
CD . . . . RR 349635
MC . . . . RR 96354
Road Runner / Feb '87 / Pinnacle.

TIME ODYSSEY.
Tracks: Not Advised.
- CD 834 634 2
- LP . . . . VERH 60
- MC . . . . VERHC 60
Vertigo / '88.

Morbid Angel

Florida-formed quartet whose debut, *Abominations of Desolation*, was scrapped by band itself (album finally appeared in '92). Dogged devotion to death inspired loyal live following. In '93, band released *Covenant* album; only their fourth after nearly a decade together. Involvement of Metallica producer Fleming Rasmussen, and deal with U.S. major Giant, suggests bright future for dark band.

ABOMINATIONS.
Tracks: Not Advised.
CD . . . . MOSH 048CD
LP . . . . MOSH 048
MC . . . . MOSH 048MC
Earache / Jan '93 / Vital Distribution.

ALTARS OF MADNESS.
Tracks: Visions from the darkside / Chapel of ghouls / Maze of torment / Damnation / Bleed for the devil.
CD . . . . MOSH 11 CD
LP . . . . MOSH 11
MC . . . . MOSH 11 MC
Earache / Sep '89 / Vital Distribution.
- LP P.Disc . . . . MOSH 11 P
Earache / Jul '90.

BLESSED ARE THE SICK.
Tracks: Not Advised.
CD . . . . MOSH 31CD
LP . . . . MOSH 31
MC . . . . MOSH 31MC
Earache / May '91 / Vital Distribution.

COVENANT.
Tracks: Rapture / Pain divine / World of shit / Vengeance is mine / Lion's den / Blood on my hands / Angel of disease / Sworn to black / Nar mattaru / God of emptiness.
CD . . . . MOSH 081CD
LP . . . . MOSH 081
MC . . . . MOSH 081MC
Earache / Jun '93 / Vital Distribution.

LAIBACH REMIXES.
Tracks: God of emptiness / Sworn to the black / Sworn to the black (Laibach remix) / God of emptiness (Laibach remixes).
12" . . . . MOSH 112T
CD Single . . . . MOSH 112CD
Earache / May '94 / Vital Distribution.

Morbid Saint

SPECTRUM OF DEATH.
Tracks: Not Advised.
CD . . . . GCI 89803
Plastic Head / Jun '92 / Plastic Head.

Mordred

ESSE QUAM VIDERI.
Tracks: Esse quam videri.
■ 12". . . . . N 01796
■ MC Single. . . . . N 01793
Noise / Jan '92.

EVERYDAY'S A HOLIDAY.
Tracks: Everyday's a holiday / Superfreak.
■ 7". . . . . .7 MORD 5
Noise / Jun '89.

FOOLS GAME.
Tracks: Not Advised.
CD. CDNUK 135
■ LP .NUK 135
MC. . . . . ZCNUK 135
Noise / May '89 / Pinnacle.

IN THIS LIFE.
Tracks: Esse quam videri / Downtown / Progress /
Killing time / Larger than life / High potence / Falling
away / Window / In this life / Strain.
CD. . . . . NO 159-2
LP . . . . NO 159-1
■ MC. NO 159-4
Noise / Feb '91.

NEXT ROOM, THE.
Tracks: Not Advised.
CD. . . . . .N 0211-2
Noise / Aug '94 / Pinnacle.

More

TRICKSTER.
Tracks: Trickster / Hey Joe.
■ 7". . . . . K 11744
Atlantic / Jul '82.

WARHEAD.
Tracks: Warhead / Fire / Soldier / Depression / Road
rocket / Lord of twilight / Way of the world / We are
the band / I have no answers.
■ LP . . . . K 50775
MC. K4 50775
Atlantic / Feb '81 / WEA.

WE ARE THE BAND.
Tracks: We are the band / Atomic rock.
■ 7". . . . . K 11561
Atlantic / Mar '81.

Morgana Lefay

SECRET DOCTRINE, THE.
Tracks: Not Advised.
CD. BMCD 42
Black Mark / May '94 / Plastic Head.

Morgoth

CURSED.
Tracks: Not Advised.
CD. CM 9719CD
LP . . . . .CM 9719
Century Media / '92 / Plastic Head.

ETERNAL FALL.
Tracks: Burnt identity / White gallery / Eternal sanc-
tify / Female infanticide / Pits of utumno.
CD. 8497082
MC. 0897114
Mini LP . . . . CM 97111
Century Media / Aug '90 / Plastic Head.

ODIUM.
Tracks: Not Advised.
CD. 8497492
LP 0897491
MC. 0897494
Century Media / Jun '93 / Plastic Head.

RESURRECTION ABSURD.
Tracks: Not Advised.
■ EP .CM 9708
Century Media / '92.

RESURRECTION, ETERNAL.
Tracks: Not Advised.
CD. CM 9708CD
MC. .CM 9708MC
Century Media / '92 / Plastic Head.

Morta Skuld

AS HUMANITY FADES.
Tracks: Unknown emotions / Century of ruins / Hu-
manity's lost / Awakening destiny / Paradise of the
masses / No world escapes / Different breeds /
Sanctuary denied / Relics / Sorrow fields / Through
obscurity (CD only) / In the shadows (CD only).
CD. DEAF 015CD
LP . . . . .DEAF 015
Deaf / Feb '94 / Vital Distribution.

DYING REMAINS.
Tracks: Lifeless (Instrumental) / Without sin / De-
voured fears / Dying remains / Useless to mankind /
Rotting ways / Withering seclusion / Hatred creation
/ Scarred / Consuming existence / Presumed dead
(Features on CD only).
■ CD . . . . DEAF 011CD
■ LP . . . . DEAF 011
Deaf / Feb '93.

Mortal Sin

EVERY DOG HAS IT'S DAY.
Tracks: Not Advised.
CD. .CDFLAG 61
LP . . . . .FLAG 61
MC. TFLAG 61
Music For Nations / Sep '91 / Pinnacle.

FACE OF DESPAIR.
Tracks: Martyrs of eternity / Infantry corps / Robbie
soles / Suspended animation / For richer for poorer /
Voyage of the disturbed / Terminal reward.
■ CD 8363702
■ LP 8363701
■ MC. 8363704
Vertigo / Mar '89.

FACE OF MAYHEM.
Tracks: Not Advised.
VHS . . . . CFV 10302
Channel 5 / Feb '90 / Channel 5 Video / P.R.O. Video
/ Gold & Sons.

I AM IMMORTAL.
Tracks: I am immortal / Lebanon (live) / Voyage of
the disturbed.
■ 12". . . . . .VERX 47
■ CD Single . . . . .VERCD 47
Vertigo / Jan '90.

MAYHEM DESTRUCTION.
Tracks: Not Advised.
MC. VERHC 48
■ LP . . . . VERH 48
Vertigo / Oct '87.

MAYHEMIC DESTRUCTION.
Tracks: Not Advised.
■ LP . . . . AJLP 1016
Mega Metal (Australia) / Sep '87.

Mortal Terror

L.P. (see under Generic).

Morticians

MORTAL MASSACRE.
Tracks: Mortal massacre.
■ 7". RR 018
Nuclear Blast / Sep '93.

SHE'S LIKE HEROIN.
Tracks: Not Advised.
■ LP .DIST 2
Distortion / '88.

Mortification

GRIND PLANETS.
Tracks: Not Advised.
VHS . . . . NBVID 002
Nuclear Blast / Jul '93 / Plastic Head.

MORTIFICATION.
Tracks: Not Advised.
CD. .NB 101CD
Nuclear Blast / Mar '94 / Plastic Head.

POST MOMENTARY AFFLICTION.
Tracks: Not Advised.
CD. . . . . NB 082
LP . . . . NBLP 082
MC. NBMC 082
Nuclear Blast / Nov '93 / Plastic Head.

Mortuary

BLACKENED IMAGES.
Tracks: Not Advised.
CD. .BR 003CD
LP . . . . BR 003LP
MC. BR 003MC
Brain Crusher / Nov '92 / Plastic Head.

REIGN OF DEAD.
Tracks: Reign of dead.
■ 7". TURBO 012
Turbo Music / Nov '92.

Mother

KEEPING UP WITH THE JONESES.
Tracks: Keeping up with the Joneses.
■ 7". GB 03
Nuclear Blast / Oct '92.

Mother Love Bone

Tragically short-lived Seattle band formed
after the demise of Green River and fronted
by Andrew Wood. Wood was killed by a
heroin overdose in 1990, just before the
release of the band's only album *Apple*.
Following the EP *Shine* (re-issued and re-
packaged with the album in 1992), *Apple*
promised much, but without their singer the
band could not continue. 1991's one-off al-
bum/project called *Temple Of The Dog* (a
tribute to Wood put together by Soundgarden's Chris Cornell) featured ex-Mother
Love Bone men Stone Gossard (guitar) and
Jeff Ament (bass), a pair who went on to
richly deserved success as members of
Pearl Jam.

APPLE.
Tracks: This is shangrila / Holy roller / Come bite the
apple / Heartshine / Man of golden words / Gentle
groove / Crown of thorns / Stardog champion / Bone
China / Stargazer / Captain hi-top / Capricorn sister /
Mr. Danny Boy.
CD. 843 191-2
■ LP 843 191-1
MC. 843 191-4
Polydor / Jul '90 / PolyGram.

Mother's Finest

FIRE.
Tracks: Give you all the love / Niggizz can't sing
rock'n'roll / My baby / Fly with me / Dontcha wanna
love me / Rain.
■ LP . . . . EPC 81595
Epic / Feb '77.

IRON AGE.
Tracks: Movin' on / Luv drug / Rock'n'roll 2 nite / U
turn me on / All the way / Evolution / Illusion / Time /
Gone with the rain / Earthling.
■ LP . . . . EPC 84924
Epic / Jul '81.

LOOKS COULD KILL.
Tracks: For your love / I'm 'n danger / Legs and
lipstick / Dream come true / Still over each other / I'll
never be the same / Brave and strong / Your wish is
my command / Cherish your lover / Heartbreaker /
Call me Mister (CD only) / Too serious (CD only).
■ CD . . . . CDEST 2114
■ LP . . . . EST 2114
■ MC. . . . . TCEST 2114
Capitol / Oct '89.

MOTHER FACTOR.
Tracks: Can't fight the feelin' / Tell me / Watch my
stylin' / Love changes / Don't wanna come back /
Give it up / Mr. Goodbar / I can't believe / More and
more.
■ LP . . . . EPC 83011
Epic / '79.

ONE MOTHER TO ANOTHER.
Tracks: Secret service / What kind of fool / Victory /
Love me too / Everybody needs somebody / Big shot
Romeo / What you do to me / In my baby's arms /
Some kind of madness / Take me to the middle (of
your luv).
■ LP . . . . EPC 25363
MC. 40 25363
Epic / Aug '83 / Sony.
■ LP . . . . EPC 25263
Epic / Aug '83.

Motley Crue

Founded in 1980, Motley Crue mixed punk and metal with highly successful results. An independent debut, *Too Fast For Love*, was followed by *Shout At The Devil* on Elektra. Extensive touring, and sensationalist press coverage, propelled Crue into the platinum league. The line-up remained constant — bassist Nikki Sixx, drummer Tommy Lee, guitarist Mick Mars and vocalist Vince Neil — until 1992, when Neil was replaced by John Corabi, ex-Scream. The band's turbulent career continued.

DECADE OF DECADENCE '81-'91.
Tracks: Live wire / Piece of your action / Shout at the devil / Looks that kill / Home sweet home / Smokin' in the boys room / Girls, girls, girls / Wild side / Dr. Feelgood / Kickstart my heart / Teaser / Rock 'n' roll junkie / Primal scream / Angela / Anarchy in the U.K.
CD 7659612042
MC . . . . EKT 95C
■ LP . . . . EKT 95
Elektra / Oct '91.

DECADE OF DECADENCE '81-'91.
Tracks: Not Advised.
VHS 8536401293
Warner Music Video / Apr '92 / WEA.

DECADENT DISCUSSION.
Tracks: Not Advised.
CD P.Disc . . . . CBAK 4031
MC . . . . MBAK 6038
Baktaba / Mar '92 / Arabesque Ltd.

DOCTOR FEELGOOD.
Tracks: Same old situation / Slice of your pie / Rattlesnake shake / Kick start my heart / Without you / Don't go away mad / She goes down / Sticky sweet / Time for a change / TNT / Dr. Feelgood / Terror in tinseltown.
CD 9608292
MC . . . . EKT 59 C
■ LP . . . . EKT 59
Elektra / Sep '89.

DOCTOR FEELGOOD.
Tracks: Dr. Feelgood / Sticky sweet.
■ 12" . . . . EKR 97T
■ 7" . . . . EKR 97X
■ 7" . . . . EKR 97
■ 7" P.Disc . . . . EKR 97P
■ CD Single . . . . EKR 97CD
■ MC Single . . . . EKR 97C
Elektra / Nov '89.

DR. FEELGOOD - THE VIDEOS.
Tracks: Not Advised.
VHS 7559401173
Warner Music Video / Feb '91 / WEA.

GIRLS, GIRLS, GIRLS.
Tracks: Girls, girls, girls / Sumthin' for nuthin' / Smokin' in the boys room (live) (Extra track on 12").
■ 7" . . . . EKR 59
■ 12" . . . . EKR 59 T
Elektra / Jul '87.

GIRLS, GIRLS, GIRLS.
Tracks: Wild side / Girls, girls, girls / Dancin' on glass / Bad boy boogie / Nona / Five years dead / All in the name of rock / Somethin' for nuthin' / All I need / Jailhouse rock (live).
CD 9607252
■ LP . . . . EKT 39
MC . . . . EKT 39 C
Elektra / Jun '87 / WEA.

HOOLIGAN'S HOLIDAY.
Tracks: Hooligan's holiday / Hooligan's holiday (mix) / Hypnotized (Available on CDS only).
■ 12" . . . . EKR 180T
■ 7" . . . . .EKR 180
■ CD Single . . . . EKR 180CD
■ CD Single . . . . EKR 180CDX
Elektra / Feb '94.

LOOKS THAT KILL.
Tracks: Looks that kill / Piece of your action.
■ 12" . . . . E 9756T
■ 7" . . . . E 9756
Elektra / Jul '84.

MISUNDERSTOOD.
Tracks: Misunderstood.
■ 12" . . . . EKR 183T
■ 7" . . . . EKR 183
■ CD Single . . . . EKR 183CD
■ MC Single . . . . EKR 183C
Elektra / May '94.

MOTLEY CRUE: INTERVIEW COLLECTION.
Tracks: Not Advised.
7" Set . . . . BAKPAK 1023
Baktabak / Aug '90 / Arabesque Ltd.

MOTLEY CRUE: INTERVIEW PICTURE DISC (1).
Tracks: Not Advised.
LP P.Disc . . . . BAK 2051
Baktabak / Jul '87 / Arabesque Ltd.

MOTLEY CRUE: INTERVIEW PICTURE DISC (2).
Tracks: Not Advised.
■ 12" P.Disc . . . . MOTLEY 1
Talkies / '87.

PRIMAL SCREAM.
Tracks: Primal scream.
■ 7" . . . . .EKR 133
■ CD Single . . . . EKR 133CD
■ MC Single . . . . EKR 133C
Elektra / Sep '91.

SHOUT AT THE DEVIL.
Tracks: In the beginning / Shout at the devil / Looks that kill / Bastard / Knock 'em dead kid / Danger / Too young to fall in love / Helter skelter / Red hot / Ten seconds 'til love / God bless the children of the beast.
■ LP 9602891
MC 9602894
Elektra / Sep '83 / WEA.
CD 9602892
Elektra / Jan '86 / WEA.

SMOKIN' IN THE BOYS ROOM.
Tracks: Smokin' in the boys room / Home sweet home / Shout at the devil (Only on 12" single.) / Use it or lose it.
■ 7" . . . . EKR 16
Elektra / Sep '84.
■ 12" . . . . E 9625T
■ 7" . . . . E 9625
Elektra / Aug '85.
■ 12" . . . . EKR 33 T
■ 7" . . . . EKR 33
Elektra / Jan '86.

THEATRE OF PAIN.
Tracks: City boy blues / Fight for your rights / Use it or lose it / Smokin' in the boys room / Louder than hell / Keep your eye on the money / Home sweet home / Tonight (we need a lover) / Save our souls / Raise your hands to rock.
■ LP . . . . EKT 8
■ MC . . . . EKT 8C
Elektra / Jul '85.
CD 9604182
Elektra / Jul '86 / WEA.

TIL DEATH US DO PART.
Tracks: Power to the music / Uncle Jack / Hooligan's holiday / Misunderstood / Loveshine / Poison apples / Hammered / 'Til death us do part / Welcome to the numb / Smoke the sky / Droppin like flies / Driftaway.
CD 755961534-2
LP 755961534-1
MC 755961534-4
WEA / Mar '94 / WEA.

TOO FAST FOR LOVE.
Tracks: Live wire / Come on and dance / Public enemy No. 1 / Merry go round / Take me to the top / Piece of your action / Starry eyes / Too fast for love / On with the show.
■ LP . . . . K 52425
Elektra / '82.
MC K4 52425
WEA / Feb '86 / WEA.

TOO YOUNG TO FALL IN LOVE (REMIX).
Tracks: Too young to fall in love / Take me to the top.
■ 12" . . . . E 9732T
■ 7" . . . . E 9732
Elektra / Oct '84.

UNCENSORED.
Tracks: Home sweet home / Smokin' in the boys room / Live wire / Looks that kill / Too young to fall in love.
VHS 9401043
WEA Music Video / '87 / WEA / Gold & Sons.

WITHOUT YOU.
Tracks: Without you / Livewire / Girls, girls, girls (12" single, CD single & cass-single only.) / All in the name of rock (12" single, CD single & cass-single only.).
■ 12" . . . . EKR 109 T
■ 7" . . . . .EKR 109
■ MC Single . . . . EKR 109 C
Elektra / Apr '90.
■ 7" P.Disc . . . . EKR 109P
Elektra / Apr '90.

YOU'RE ALL I NEED.
Tracks: You're all I need / Wild side / Home sweet home (On 12" only) / Looks that kill (On 12" only).
■ 12" . . . . .EKR 65T
■ 7" . . . . EKR 65
Elektra / Feb '88.

Motorhead

Formed in 1975 by ex-Hawkwind bassist, Ian 'Lemmy' Kilminster, Motorhead are one of the most successful metal acts in Britain. Considerable chart achievement has been coupled with a formidable live reputation. Debut eponymous LP reached top 50 in 1977. After gradually building a loyal following had first hit single with a cover of the Kingsmen's garage classic *Louie Louie* in 1978. *Overkill* LP and single were both hits in 1979. Motorhead's commercial peak was 1980-81, enjoying four top 20 singles including *Ace Of Spades*, the *Golden Years* EP and a duet with Girlschool on the *St. Valentine's Day Massacre* EP. Their *No Sleep 'Til Hammersmith* live LP entered the album charts at number one. Following 1982's *Iron Fist* LP, the group have had many personnel changes, but Motorhead with the enigmatic Lemmy at the helm have continued to record and tour with great success remaining seminal figures on the metal scene.

1916.
Tracks: One to sing the blues / I'm so bad (baby I don't care) / No voices in the sky / Going to Brazil / Nightmare/The dreamtime / Love me forever / Angel city / Make my day / Ramones / Shut you down / 1916.
CD P.Disc 4674819
■ LP P.Disc 4674810
Epic / Feb '91.
■ CD 4674812
■ LP 4674811
■ MC 4674814
Epic / Jan '91.

92 TOUR E.P.
Tracks: Hellraiser / You Better Run / Going To Brazil / Ramones.
■ 12" 658809-6
■ CD Single 658809-2
Epic / Nov '92.

ACE OF SPADES.
Tracks: Ace of spades / Bite the bullet / Chase is better than the catch / Dance / Fast and loose / Fire, fire / Hammer / Jailbait / Live to win / Love me like a reptile / Road crew / Shoot you in the back.
■ LP . . . . .BRON 531
MC . . . . .BRONC 531
Bronze / '85 / WEA.
CD . . . . LLMCD 3013
Legacy / Aug '87 / Sony.
CD . . . . CLACD 240
Castle Classics / Sep '91 / BMG / Castle Communications.

ACE OF SPADES.
Tracks: Ace of spades.
■ 7" . . . . BRO 106
Bronze / Nov '80.
■ MC Single . . . . .MCWGAF 101
■ 12" 12WGAF 101
■ CD P.Disc . . . . PDWGAF 101
■ CD Single . . . . CDWGAF 101
WGAF / Aug '93.

ACES HIGH.
Tracks: Not Advised.
CD 550 7242
MC 550 7244
Spectrum (1) / Aug '94 / PolyGram.

ALL THE ACES.
Tracks: Not Advised.
CD . . . . CTVCD 125
LP . . . . CTVLP 125
MC . . . . CTVMC 125
Castle / Oct '93 / BMG.

ANOTHER PERFECT DAY.
Tracks: Back at the funny farm / Shine / Dancing on your grave / Rock it / One track mind / Another perfect day / Marching off to war / I got mine / Tales of glory / Die you bastard.
■ LP . . . . .BRON 546
MC . . . . .BRONC 546
Bronze / May '83 / WEA.
■ LP . . . . CLALP 225
■ CD . . . . CLACD 225

■ MC. . . . . .CLAMC 225
Castle Classics / Feb '91.

ANOTHER PERFECT DAY/OVERKILL.
Tracks: Back at the funny farm / Shine / Dancing on your grave / Rock it / One track mind / Another perfect day / Marching off to war / I got mine / Tales of glory / Die you bastard / Overkill / Stay clean (I won't) pay your price / I'll be your sister / Capricorn / No class / Damage case / Tear ya down / Metropolis / Limb from limb.
■ **CD Set.** . . . . .TFOCD 8
That's Original / Mar '88.
■ **Double LP.** . . . . .TFOLP 8
That's Original / Mar '88.
■ **MC.** . . . . .TFOMC 8
That's Original / Mar '88.

ANTHOLOGY - MOTORHEAD.
Tracks: I got mine / Jailbait / Over the top / Step down / Dirty love / Ace of spades / Hoochie coochie man / Go to hell / Heart of stone / Louie Louie / Stone dead forever / Back at the funny farm / Chase is better than the catch / Turn you round again / Another perfect day / Capricorn / Lawman.
■ **LP.** . . . . .RAWLP 011
MC. . . . . .RAWTC 011
Raw Power / Apr '86 / Pinnacle.
■ **CD.** . . . . .RAWCD 011
Raw Power / Dec '86.

ANTHOLOGY - MOTORHEAD VOL 1.
Tracks: Not Advised.
CD. . . . . .LLMCD 3004
Legacy / '86 / Sony.

BEER DRINKERS AND HELL RAISERS.
Tracks: Beer drinkers and hell raisers / On patrol / I'm your witch doctor.
■ **7".** . . . . .SWT 61
Big Beat / Oct '80.

BEST OF MOTORHEAD.
Tracks: Not Advised.
■ **CD.** . . . . .CDAR 1014
■ **MC.** . . . . .ARLC 1014
Action Replay / Jun '90.

BEST OF MOTORHEAD (2).
Tracks: Not Advised.
LP. . . . . .RR 91251
MC. . . . . .RR 91254
■ **CD.** . . . . .RR 91252
Road Runner / Sep '92.

BEST OF MOTORHEAD, THE.
Tracks: Not Advised.
■ **VHS** . . . . .CMP 6072
Castle Music Pictures / Oct '91.

BEST OF THE REST.
Tracks: Not Advised.
■ **CD** . . . . .CDAR 1032
■ **MC** . . . . .ARLC 1032
Action Replay / Jun '93.

BIRTHDAY PARTY.
Tracks: Iron fist / Mean machine / On the road / We are the road crew / Hammer / Metropolis / Ace of spades / Steal your face / Nothing up my sleeve / Bite the bullet / Chase is better than the catch / No class / Killed by death (Only on CD.) / Bomber (Only on CD.) / Motorhead (Only on CD.).
CD. . . . . GWCD 101
LP. . . . . .GWLP 101
MC. . . . . .GWTC 101
GWR / Apr '90 / Pinnacle.
■ **CD** 106512
■ **LP** 106511
■ **MC** 106514
Musidisc / Dec '90.

BIRTHDAY PARTY.
Tracks: Iron fist / Stay clean / Hammer / Metropolis / Mean machine / On the road / Killed by death / Ace of spades / Steal your face / Nothing up my sleeve / We are the road crew / Bite the bullet / Chase is better than the catch / No class / Overkill / Bomber / Motorhead.
VHS . . . . .VVD 174
Virgin Vision / Oct '86 / Gold & Sons / TBD.

BLITZKREIG ON BIRMINGHAM.
Tracks: Not Advised.
CD. . . . . .RRCD 120
■ **LP** . . . . .RRLP 120
Receiver / Oct '89.

BOMBER.
Tracks: Dead men tell no tales / Lawman / Sweet revenge / Sharp shooter / Poison / Stone dead forever / All the aces / Step down / Talking head / Bomber.
■ **LP** . . . . .BRON 523
Bronze / Nov '79.

CD . . . . .LLMCD 3012
Legacy / Aug '87 / Sony.
CD. . . . . .CLACD 227
■ **LP** . . . . .CLALP 227
■ **MC** . . . . .CLAMC 227
Castle Classics / Apr '91.

BOMBER.
Tracks: Bomber / Over the top.
■ **7"** . . . . .BRO 85
Bronze / Dec '82.

BOMBER/ACE OF SPADES.
Tracks: Not Advised.
■ **Double LP.** . . . . .TFOLP 24
MC. . . . . .TFOMC 24
■ **CD Set.** . . . . .TFOCD 24
That's Original / Apr '90.

BORN TO LOSE.
Tracks: White lion fever / Leaving here / Train kept a rollin' / I'm your witch doctor / Lost Johnny / Keep us on the road / Vibrator / Watcher / Beer drinkers and hell raisers / Motorhead / Iron horse / City kids / Fools / On parole.
■ **LP** . . . . .DOJOLP 18
MC. . . . . .DOJOTC 18
Dojo / Apr '86 / Castle Communications / BMG.

CITY KIDS.
Tracks: Not Advised.
■ **LP** . . . . .PLP 28
■ **MC** . . . . .PMC 28
Platinum (W.Germany) / Oct '85.

COLLECTION: MOTORHEAD (Bear Trap).
Tracks: Motorhead / Overkill / Talking head / Rock it / Iron fist / I got mine / Steal your face / (We are) the road crew / Swaggletooth / Stay clean / Iron horse / One track mind / Speedfreak / Loser / (Don't need) religion / Stone dead forever / Sweet revenge / Capricorn / Love me like a reptile / Ace of spades.
CD. . . . . .CCSCD 237
■ **Double LP** . . . . .CCSLP 237
■ **MC** . . . . .CCSMC 237
Castle Collector Series / Mar '90.

DEAF FOREVER.
Tracks: Deaf forever / On the road.
■ **12"** . . . . .GWT 2
■ **7"** . . . . .GWR 2
GWR / Jul '86.

DEAF NOT BLIND.
Tracks: Not Advised.
VHS . . . . .VVD 052
Virgin Vision / Dec '84 / Gold & Sons / TBD.

DIRTY LOVE.
Tracks: Hump on your back / Dirty love / Love me like a reptile / Waltz of the vampire / Bastard / We are the road crew / Shoot you in the back / Dirty love (full version) / Fast and loose / Ace of spades (rare version) / Godzilla akimbo.
CD. . . . . .RRCD 123
■ **LP** . . . . .RRLP 123
Receiver / Jan '90.
MC. . . . . .RRLC 123
Receiver / Jul '93 / Total / BMG / Grapevine Distribution.

EAT THE RICH.
Tracks: Eat the rich / Cradle to the grave.
■ **7"** . . . . .GWR 6
GWR / Oct '87.
■ **12"** . . . . .RR 125468
Road Runner / '89.

EVERYTHING LOUDER THAN EVERY-THING ELSE.
Tracks: Metropolis / I'm so bad (baby I don't care) / Going to Brazil / Traitor / No voices in the sky / Power / Angel City / Love me forever / Ramones / Orgasmatron / Killed by death / Ace of spades.
VHS 490932
Sony Music Video / Jul '91 / Sony.

FROM THE VAULTS.
Tracks: Not Advised.
CD. . . . . .NEXCD 136
■ **LP** . . . . .NEXLP 136
■ **MC** . . . . .NEXMC 136
Sequel / Nov '90.

GOLDEN YEARS.
Tracks: Dead men tell no tales / Too late too long / Leaving here / Stone dead forever.
■ **12"** . . . . .BROX 92
■ **EP** . . . . .BRO 92
Bronze / May '80.

HEADBANGERS.
Tracks: Over the top / Ace of spades / Dirty love / I'm the doctor / Speed freak / Got to hell / Motorhead / Killed by death / Stone dead forever / No class / Tear ya down / Dancing on your grave / Die you bastard / Heart of stone / Like a nightmare / Iron house / Locomotive / Bomber / Law man / America.
CD. . . . . .ELITE 019CD
MC. . . . . .ELITE 019MC
Elite (Pickwick) / Oct '93 / Pickwick.

I GOT MINE.
Tracks: I got mine / Turn you round again.
■ **12"** . . . . .BROX 165
■ **7"** . . . . .BRO 165
Bronze / May '83.

IRON FIST.
Tracks: Iron fist / Heart of stone / I'm the doctor / Go to hell / Loser / Sex and outrage / America / Shut it down / Speed freak / (Don't let them) grind ya down / (Don't need) religion / Bang to rights.
■ **LP** . . . . .BRNA 539
Bronze / Apr '82.
■ **LP** . . . . .CLALP 123
■ **MC** . . . . .CLAMC 123
Castle Classics / Mar '87.
CD. . . . . .CLACD 123
Castle Classics / Mar '87 / BMG / Castle Communications.

IRON FIST.
Tracks: Iron fist / Remember me, I'm gone.
■ **7"** . . . . .BRO 146
Bronze / Apr '82.

KILLED BY DEATH.
Tracks: Killed by death / Under the knife.
■ **12"** . . . . .BROX 185
■ **12"** . . . . .BROP 185
■ **7"** . . . . .BRO 185
Bronze / Sep '84.

LIVE.
Tracks: Not Advised.
CD. . . . . .JHD 081
MC. . . . . .MCJHD 081
Tring / Mar '93 / Prism Leisure PLC / Midland Records.

LIVE 1983.
Tracks: Back to the funny farm / Tales of glory / Shoot you in the back / Marching off to war / Iron horse / Another perfect day / (Don't need) Religion / One track mind / Go to hell / America / Shine / Dancing on your grave / Rock it / I've got mine / Bite the bullet / Chase is better than the catch.
■ **CD** . . . . .STRCD 008
■ **MC** . . . . .STR MC 008
Street Link / Aug '92.
CD. . . . . .DOJOCD 108
Dojo / Feb '94 / Castle Communications / BMG.

LIVE AT BRIXTON '87.
Tracks: Doctor rock / Stay clean / Traitor / Metropolis / Dogs / Ace of spades / Stone deaf in the USA / Eat the rich / Built for speed / Rock'n'roll / Deaf forever / Just 'cos you got the power.
CD . . . . .RR 90092
LP . . . . .RR 90091
MC. . . . . .RR 90094
Road Runner / Mar '94 / Pinnacle.

LIVE JAILBAIT.
Tracks: Not Advised.
CD Set . . . . .RRDCD 005
LP Set. . . . . .RRLD 005
Receiver / Jul '93 / Total / BMG / Grapevine Distribution.

LOCK UP YOUR DAUGHTERS (Live in St.Albans).
Tracks: Motorhead / Leavin' here / Watcher / Louie Louie / Iron horse / Instrumental / I'll be your sister / Lost Johnny / Keep us on the road / Tear ya down / White line fever.
CD. . . . . .RRCD 130
■ **LP** . . . . .RRLP 130
MC. . . . . .RRMC 130
Receiver / Jul '93 / Total / BMG / Grapevine Distribution.

LOUIE LOUIE.
Tracks: Louie Louie / Tear ya down.
■ **7"** . . . . .BRO 60
Bronze / Sep '78.

MARCH OR DIE.
Tracks: Stand / Cat scratch fever / Bad religion / Jack the Ripper / I ain't no nice guy / Hellraiser / Asylum choir / Too good to be true / You better run / Name in vain / March or die.
■ **LP** 4717231

MC. 4717234
■ CD 4717232
Epic / Jul '92.
MiniDisc. 471723-3
Epic / Feb '93 / Sony.

MELTDOWN.
Tracks: Not Advised.
CD . . . . ESBCD 146
■ LP . . . . ESBLP 146
Essential / May '91.

MOTORHEAD.
Tracks: Motorhead / Vibrator / Lost Johnny / Iron horse / Born to lose / White line fever / Keep us on the road / Watcher / Train kept a rollin' / City kids / Beer drinkers and hell raisers / On parole / Intro / I'm your witch doctor.
■ LP . . . . WIK 2
MC. . . . . TC-CWK 3008
Chiswick Records / Sep '81 / Pinnacle.
CD . . . . CDWIK 2
Big Beat / Jun '88 / Pinnacle / Hot Shot / Jazz Music.
LP . . . . WIKM 2
Big Beat / Feb '91 / Pinnacle / Hot Shot / Jazz Music.

MOTORHEAD.
Tracks: Motorhead / City kids.
■ 7" P.Disc . . . . NSP 13
Chiswick Records / Feb '82.

MOTORHEAD (EP).
Tracks: Ace of spades / Bomber / Motorhead / Overkill.
■ CD Single CD3-10
Special Edition / '88.

MOTORHEAD (LIVE).
Tracks: Motorhead (live) / Over the top.
■ 12" P.Disc . . . . BROP 124
■ 7" . . . . BRO 124
Bronze / Jul '81.

MOTORHEAD - 4 CD BOXSET.
Tracks: Not Advised.
CD Set . . . . RRXCD 501
Reciever / Oct '93 / Total / BMG.

MOTORHEAD - CD BOX SET.
Tracks: Not Advised.
■ CD Set. . . . . .CLA BX 901
Castle Classics / Feb '92.

MUSIC AND MEDIA INTERVIEW PICTURE DISC.
Tracks: Not Advised.
■ LP P.Disc . . . . MM 1213
Music & Media / Feb '88.

NO CLASS.
Tracks: No class / Like a nightmare.
■ 7" . . . . BRO 78
Bronze / Jun '79.

NO REMORSE.
Tracks: Ace of spades / Motorhead / Jailbait / Stay clean / Too late / Killed by death / Bomber / Iron fist / Shine / Dancing on your grave / Metropolis / Snaggletooth / Overkill / Please don't touch / Stone dead forever / Like a nightmare / Emergency / Steal your face / Louie Louie / No class / Iron horse / We are the road crew / Leaving here / Locomotive.
■ LP . . . . PROLP 5
■ LP . . . . MOTOR 1
Bronze / Sep '84.
■ LP . . . . CLALP 121
MC. CLAMC 121
Castle Classics / Dec '86 / BMG / Castle Communications.
CD . . . . CLACD 121
Castle Classics / '88 / BMG / Castle Communications.

NO SLEEP AT ALL.
Tracks: Dr. Rock / Dogs / Built for speed / Deaf forever / Killed by death / Traitor / Ace of spades / Eat the rich / Just cos you got the power / Overkill.
■ CD . . . . GWCD 31
■ LP . . . . GWLP 31
■ MC. GWTC 31
GWR / Oct '88.
CD . . . . .RR 9514 2
■ LP .RR 9514 1
MC. .RR 9514 4
Road Runner / '89 / Pinnacle.

NO SLEEP TILL HAMMERSMITH.
Tracks: Ace of spades / Stay clean / Metropolis / Hammer / Iron horse / No class / Overkill / Road crew / Capricorn / Bomber / Motorhead.
■ LP .BRON 535
MC. .BRONC 535
Bronze / Jun '81 / WEA.
CD . . . . LLMCD 3014

Legacy / Aug '87 / Sony.
CD . . . . CLACD 179
MC. CLAMC 179
■ LP . . . . CLALP 179
Castle Classics / Feb '90.

ON PAROLE.
Tracks: Motorhead / On parole / Vibrator / Iron horse / Born to lose / City kids / Fools / Watcher / Leaving here / Lost Johnny.
■ LP . . . . LBR 1004
United Artists / Dec '79.
■ LP . . . . FA 3009
■ MC. TCFA 3009
Fame / May '82.
CD . . . . CDFA 3251
■ LP . . . . FA 3251
MC. TCFA 3251
Fame / Oct '90 / EMI.

ONE TO SING THE BLUES, THE.
Tracks: One to sing the blues / Dead man's hand / Eagle rock / Shut you down.
■ 7" 6565787
■ 7" 6565786
■ 7" P.Disc 6565780
■ CD Single 6565782
■ MC Single. 6565784
Epic / Dec '90.

ORGASMATRON.
Tracks: Not Advised.
■ CD .GWCD 1
■ LP .GWLP 1
■ MC. . . . . .GWTC 1
GWR / Aug '86.
CD . . . . RR 349677
■ LP . . . . RR 9677
MC. RR 49677
Road Runner / '89 / Pinnacle.
■ LP P.Disc . . . . .GWPD 1
GWR / Aug '89.
CD . . . . CLACD 283
Castle Classics / Apr '92 / BMG / Castle Communications.

OVERKILL.
Tracks: Overkill / Stay clean / Pay your price / I'll be your sister / Capricorn / No class / Damage case / Tear ya down / Metropolis / Limb from limb.
■ LP .BRON 515
Bronze / Mar '79.
CD . . . . LLMCD 3011
Legacy / Jul '87 / Sony.
CD . . . . CDFA 3236
■ LP . . . . FA 3236
MC. TCFA 3236
Fame / May '90 / EMI.
CD . . . . CLACD 178
■ LP . . . . CLALP 178
■ MC. CLAMC 178
Castle Classics / Feb '91.

OVERKILL.
Tracks: Overkill / Too late, too late.
■ 7" . . . . BRO 67
Bronze / Mar '79.

RECORDED LIVE.
Tracks: Not Advised.
■ LP 20041
MC. 40041
Astan (USA) / Nov '84.

ROCK 'N' ROLL.
Tracks: Not Advised.
■ CD .GWCD 14
■ LP .GWLP 14
■ MC. . . . . .GWTC 14
GWR / Aug '87.
CD . . . . RR 349594
■ LP . . . . RR 9594
MC. RR 4949 4
Road Runner / '89 / Pinnacle.
■ MC. . . . . .CLAMC 284
Castle / Mar '93.

SHINE.
Tracks: Shine / I'm your hoochie coochie man / (Don't need) religion.
■ 12" . . . . BRONX 167
■ 7" . . . . BRO 167
Bronze / Jul '83.

St. VALENTINES DAY MASSACRE (see under Headgirl (1)).

STAND BY YOUR MAN (see under Williams, Wendy O.).

TORONTO LIVE.
Tracks: Not Advised.
VHS 669750
Avatar / Oct '84 / C.M. Distribution.
VHS . . . . CASH 5037
Castle Hendring Video / Nov '89 / BMG / Gold & Sons / TBD.
■ VHS . . . . HEN 2312
Hendring Video / Oct '90.

WELCOME TO THE BEAR TRAP.
Tracks: Not Advised.

WHAT'S WORDS WORTH.
Tracks: Watcher / Iron horse / Born to lose / On parole / White line fever / Keep us on the road / Leaving here / I'm your witch doctor / Train kept a rollin' / City kids.
■ LP . . . . NED 2
■ MC. NEDC 2
Big Beat / Mar '83.
LP . . . . WIKM 49
Big Beat / Jan '90 / Pinnacle / Hot Shot / Jazz Music.

Mott The Hoople

At the time of their greatest success, this British band consisted of Dale Griffin, Ian Hunter, Mick Ralphs and Peter 'Overend' Watts. Formed in Herefordshire in 1969, Mott The Hoople built up a cult following with their powerful live shows. Early sales were disappointing, but they were persuaded not to split in 1972 by Mott fan, David Bowie. They recorded Bowie's *All The Young Dudes* which was a big Transatlantic hit. There then followed a string of successful releases, their biggest LP was *Mott*, in 1973. Ian Hunter penned their two 1973 Top 10 singles, *All The Way From Memphis* and *Roll Away The Stone*. Following their 1974 tour of America, which is documented in Hunter's *Diary Of A Rock 'n' Roll Star* book, the band acrimoniously disintergrated. Hunter continued to record with ex-Spiders From Mars guitarist, Mick Ronson who had joined Mott The Hoople only months earlier. The remainder of the band continued to record as Mott until 1976.

ALL THE WAY FROM MEMPHIS.
Tracks: Ballad of Mott the Hoople / One of the boys / Honaloochie boogie / All the young dudes / Sweet Jane / Hymn for the dudes / Violence / Crash Street kids / All the way from Memphis / Drivin's sister / Golden age of rock and roll / Roll away the stone.
MC. . . . . HSC 3055
■ LP . . . . SHM 3055
Hallmark / Mar '81.

ALL THE WAY FROM MEMPHIS.
Tracks: All the way from Memphis.
■ 7" . . . . CBS 1764
CBS / Sep '73.

ALL THE YOUNG DUDES.
Tracks: Not Advised.
■ LP . . . . CBS 65184
CBS / Sep '72.

ALL THE YOUNG DUDES.
Tracks: All the young dudes / Once bitten twice shy / Roll away the stone.
■ 7" 6581777
■ CD Single 6581772
Columbia / Jun '92.

ALL THE YOUNG DUDES.
Tracks: All the young dudes / One of the boys.
■ 7" . . . . CBS 8271
CBS / Aug '72.
. . . . .A 4581
CBS / Jul '84.

ALL THE YOUNG DUDES (OLD GOLD).
Tracks: All the young dudes / Roll away the stone.
7" . . . . .OG 9312
Old Gold / Mar '90 / Pickwick.

BALLAD OF MOTT: A RETROSPECTIVE, THE.
Tracks: Rock 'n' roll Queen / Walkin' with a mountain / Waterlow / Sweet Angeline / All the young dudes / Momma's little jewel / One of the boys / Sucker / Sweet Jane / Sea diver / Reach for love/After lights / Ballad of Mott The Hoople / Drivin' sister / Violence / Rose / I wish I was your mother / Honaloochie boogie / All the way from Memphis / Whizz kid / Hymn for the dudes / Golden age of rock'n'roll / Rest in peace / Marionette / Crash street kidds / Born late '58 / Roll away the stone / Where do you all come from / Henry & the H-bomb / Foxy foxy / Saturday

gigs / Lounge lizard / Through the looking glass / American pie.
CD Set . . . . CD 46973
Legacy / Nov '93 / Sony.

BRAIN CAPERS.
Tracks: Death may be your Santa Claus / Your own backyard / Darkness, darkness / Journey / Sweet Angeline / Second love / Moon upstairs / Wheel of the quivering meat conception.
■ **LP** . . . . ILPS 9178
Island / '74.

COLLECTION: MOTT THE HOOPLE (Mott The Hoople featuring Ian Hunter).
Tracks: Golden opportunity / All the way from Memphis / One of the boys / Roll away the stone / Sucker / You nearly did me in / Sweet Jane / All the young dudes / Crash Street kids / Stiff upper lip / Jerkin' crocus / Violence / Once bitten twice shy / Marionette / Drivin' sister / Rose / Hymn for the dudes / Saturday gigs / Where do you all come from.
■ **Double LP** . . . . CCSLP 174
■ **MC** . . . . CCSMC 174
Castle Collector Series / '88.
■ **CD** . . . . CCSCD 174
Castle Collector Series / Jan '94.

DRIVE ON.
Tracks: Not Advised.
■ **LP** . . . . CBS 69154
CBS / Oct '75.

FOXY FOXY.
Tracks: Foxy foxy / Trudi's song.
■ **7"** . . . . CBS 2439
CBS / Jun '74.

GOLDEN AGE OF ROCK AND ROLL.
Tracks: Golden age of rock and roll.
■ **7"** . . . . CBS 2177
CBS / Mar '74.

GREATEST HITS: MOTT THE HOOPLE.
Tracks: All the way from Memphis / Honaloochie boogie / Hymn for the dudes / Born late '58 / All the young dudes / Roll away the stone / Ballad of Mott the Hoople / Golden age of rock and roll / Foxy foxy / Saturday gigs.
■ **LP** . . . . CBS 32007
■ **MC** 40 32007
CBS / Jun '81.
CD . . . . CD 32007
CBS / Apr '89 / Sony.

HONALOOCHIE BOOGIE.
Tracks: Honaloochie boogie.
■ **7"** . . . . CBS 1530
CBS / Jun '73.

HOOPLE, THE.
Tracks: Not Advised.
■ **LP** . . . . CBS 69062
CBS / Apr '74.

LIVE.
Tracks: Not Advised.
■ **LP** . . . . CBS 69093
CBS / Nov '74.

MAD SHADOWS.
Tracks: Not Advised.
■ **LP** . . . . ILPS 9119
Island / Oct '70.

MONTE CARLO.
Tracks: Monte Carlo / Shout it all out.
■ **7"** . . . . CBS 3528
CBS / Aug '75.

MOTT.
Tracks: All the way from Memphis / Whizz kid / Hymn for the dudes / Honaloochie boogie / Violence / Drivin' sister / Ballad of Mott the Hoople / I'm a Cadillac / El camino dolo roso / I wish I was your mother.
■ **LP** . . . . CBS 69038
CBS / Sep '72.
■ **MC** . . . . CLAMC 138X
■ **CD** . . . . CLACD 138X
■ **LP** . . . . CLALP 138X
Castle Classics / '88.

MOTT THE HOOPLE.
Tracks: Dear Louise / Hot footin' / World cruise / Brother soul / 1,2,3,4, (Kickalong blues) / Wild in the streets.
■ **LP** . . . . ILPS 9108
Island / May '70.
CD . . . . SEACD 7
See For Miles / May '93 / Pinnacle.

MOTT THE HOOPLE/MAD SHADOWS.
Tracks: You really got me / At the crossroads / Laugh at me / Backsliding fearlessly / Rock 'n' roll Queen / Rabbit food and Toby time / Half moon bay / Wrath and roll / Thunderbuck ram / No wheels to ride / You are one of us / Walkin' with a mountain / I can feel / Threads of iron / When my minds gone.
CD . . . . EDCD 361
Demon / Jan '93 / Pinnacle / A.D.A. Distribution.

ROLL AWAY THE STONE.
Tracks: Roll away the stone.
■ **7"** . . . . CBS 1895
CBS / Nov '73.

SATURDAY GIG.
Tracks: Golden age of rock and roll.
■ **7"** . . . . CBS 2754
CBS / Nov '74.

WALKING WITH A MOUNTAIN (Best of 1969-1972).
Tracks: Rock'n'roll queen / At the crossroads / Thunderbuck ram / Whiskey woman / Waterlow / Moon upstairs / Second love / Road to Birmingham / Black scorpio (momma's little jewel) / You really got me / Walkin' with a mountain / No wheels to ride / Keep a knockin' / Midnight lady / Death may be your Santa Claus / Darkness darkness / Growing man blues / Black hills.
CD . . . . IMCD 87
Island / Jun '90 / PolyGram.

WILD LIFE.
Tracks: Not Advised.
■ **LP** . . . . ILPS 9144
Island / Apr '71.

Mountain

AVALANCHE.
Tracks: Whole lotta shakin' goin' on / Sister justice / Alisan / Swamp boy / Satisfaction / Thumb sucker / You better believe it / I love to see you fly / Back where I belong / Last of the sunshine days.
■ **LP** . . . . CLALP 136X
■ **MC** . . . . CLAMC 136X
■ **CD** . . . . CLACD 136X
Castle Classics / '87.

BEST OF MOUNTAIN.
Tracks: Never in my life / Taunta (Sammy's tune) / Nantucket sleighride / Roll over Beethoven / For Yasgur's farm / Animal trainer and the toa / Mississippi Queen / Kings Chorale / Boys in the band / Don't look around / Crossroader.
CD 4663352
CBS / Aug '90 / Sony.
MC 4663354
CBS / Oct '92 / Sony.

BEST OF MOUNTAIN.
Tracks: Not Advised.
CD . . . . BGOCD 33
■ **LP** . . . . BGOLP 33
MC . . . . BGOMC 33
Beat Goes On / '89 / Pinnacle.

CLIMBING.
Tracks: Not Advised.
CD . . . . BGOCD 112
LP . . . . BGOLP 112
MC . . . . BGOMC 112
Beat Goes On / Aug '91 / Pinnacle.

FLOWERS OF EVIL.
Tracks: Not Advised.
CD . . . . BGOCD 113
LP . . . . BGOLP 113
MC . . . . BGOMC 113
Beat Goes On / Aug '91 / Pinnacle.

GO FOR YOUR LIFE.
Tracks: Not Advised.
CD 290 14 032
Bellaphon / '86 / New Note.

NANTUCKET SLEIGHRIDE (Best of Mountain).
Tracks: Don't look around / You can't get away / Tired angels / My lady / Great train robbery / Taunta (Sammy's tune) / Nantucket sleighride / Animal trainer and the toad / Travellin' in the dark.
■ **LP** . . . . ILPS 9148
Island / Jun '71.
■ **LP** . . . . BGOLP 32
Beat Goes On / Dec '88.
CD . . . . BGOCD 32
■ **MC** . . . . BGOMC 32
Beat Goes On / Mar '89.

ROAD GOES ON FOREVER, THE.
Tracks: Not Advised.
■ **LP** . . . . ILPS 919█
Island / Jul '72.
CD . . . . BGOCD 11█
LP . . . . BGOLP 11█
MC . . . . BGOMC 11█
Beat Goes On / Aug '91 / Pinnacle.

Mournblade

EIN HELDENTRAUM (A heros dream).
Tracks: Ein heldentraum.
■ **12"** . . . . TVC 03█
Vanishing Tower / Dec '85.

LIVE FAST, DIE YOUNG.
Tracks: In the hall of the mountain king / Lolita / Blond, beautiful and dead / My baby left me / Voodoo / I love rock 'n' roll / I can't sleep / Kaw-liga / My gir█ / I went to see the gypsy / Big brown eyes.
■ **LP** . . . . GILP 333
G.I. / Jan '89.
■ **CD** . . . . GICD 333
G.I. / Nov '89 / Backs Distribution.

TIME'S RUNNING OUT.
Tracks: Not Advised.
■ **LP** . . . . SHARP 030
Flicknife / Jun '85.

Mox Nix

MOX NIX.
Tracks: Not Advised.
■ **LP** . . . . AXE 7023
Axe Killer / Jul '86.

Mr. Big

BUMP AHEAD.
Tracks: Colorado bulldog / Price you gotta pay / Promise her the moon / What's it gonna be / Wild world / Mr Gone / Whole world's gonna know / Nothing but love / Temperamental / Ain't seen love like that / Mr Big.
CD 7567824952
LP 7567824951
MC 7567824954
Atlantic / Sep '93 / WEA.

DRILL SONG, THE.
Tracks: Drill song / Road to ruin / Addicted to that rush / Strike to that rush.
■ **CD Single** . . . . A 7712CD
Atlantic / Apr '91.

GREEN TINTED SIXTIES MIND.
Tracks: Green tinted sixties mind.
■ **12"** . . . . A 7702T
■ **12" P.Disc** . . . . A 7702TP
■ **7"** . . . . A 7702
■ **CD Single** . . . . A 7702CD
Atlantic / May '91.

JUST TAKE MY HEART.
Tracks: Just take my heart / To be with you / Green tinted sixties mind.
■ **7"** . . . . A 7490
■ **CD Single** . . . . A 7490CD
■ **MC Single** . . . . A 7490C
East West / May '92.

LEAN INTO IT.
Tracks: Daddy / Brother / Lover / Little boy / Alive and kickin' / Green-tinted sixties mind / CDFF-Lucky this time / Voodoo kiss / Never say never / Just take my heart / My kinda woman / Little loo loose / Road to ruin / To be with you.
CD 7567822092
■ **LP** 7567822091
MC 7567822094
Atlantic / Apr '91 / WEA.

LEAN INTO IT.
Tracks: Not Advised.
VHS 8536502063
Warner Music Video / Oct '92 / WEA.

LIVE - MR BIG.
Tracks: Daddy, brother, lover, little boy (the electric drill song) / Alive and kickin' / Green tinted sixties mind / Just take my heart / Road to ruin / Lucky this time / Addicted to that rush / To be with you / 30 days in the hole / Shy baby / Baba O'Riley.
CD 7567805232
■ **LP** 7567805231
MC 7567805234
WEA / Nov '92 / WEA.

LIVE - MR BIG.
Tracks: Not Advised.
VHS 8536503343
WEA / Nov '92 / WEA.

MR BIG.
Tracks: Addicted to that rush / Wind me up / Merciless / Had enough / Blame it on my youth / Take a walk / Big love / How can you do what you do / Anything for you / Rock'n'roll over.
CD 781 990-2
■ LP 781 990-1
MC 781 990-4
Atlantic / Jul '89 / WEA.

TO BE WITH YOU.
Tracks: To be with you.
■ 7" . . . . .A 7514
■ CD Single . . . . A 7514CD
■ MC Single . . . . A 7514C
Atlantic / Feb '92.

WILD WORLD.
Tracks: Wild world / Temperamental.
■ 12" . . . . A 7310TP
■ 7" . . . . .A 7310
■ CD Single . . . . A 7310CD
■ MC Single . . . . A 7310C
Atlantic / Oct '93.

Mr. Big

U.S. quartet comprising trio of respected metal musicians and soul-inspired singer Eric Martin. After well-received debut on prestigious Atlantic label, follow-up *Lean Into It* made U.K. Top 30 in 1991. Group peaked in '92 when *To Be With You* single reached no. 3; this acoustic ballad was uncharacteristic of sound owing more to early '70s U.K. rock (Free, Humble Pie), but provided solid foundation for future.

EEE I'M ALRIGHT.
Tracks: Eee I'm alright / I ain't been a man.
■ 7" . . . . EPC 2464
Epic / Jul '74.

FEEL LIKE CALLING HOME.
Tracks: Feel like calling home.
■ 7" . . . . EMI 2610
EMI / May '77.

ROMEO.
Tracks: Romeo / Goodbye world.
■ 7" . . . . EMI 2567
EMI / Jan '77.

SENORA.
Tracks: Senora / Death boy.
■ 7" . . . . EMI 2819
EMI / Jun '78.

ZAMBIA.
Tracks: Zambia / Time base.
■ 7" . . . . EMI 2463
EMI / May '76.

Mr. Bungle

Mike Patton's pre-Faith No More band, which he revived as part-time venture in 1991. Sophistication of project can be gauged from slogan 'There's a tractor in my balls'. Eponymous album spent deservedly fleeting period in lower reaches of chart.

MR BUNGLE.
Tracks: Quote unquote / Slowy growing deaf / Squeeze me macaroni / Carousel / Egg / Stubb (a dub) / My ass is on fire / Girls of porn / Love is a fist / Dead goon.
CD 8282762
■ LP 8282761
MC 8282764
London / Sep '91 / PolyGram.

Mucky Pup

ACT OF FAITH.
Tracks: Not Advised.
CD . . . . CM 9731 CD
LP . . . . .CM 9731
MC . . . . CM 9731 MC
Century Media / Jul '92 / Plastic Head.

BOY IN A MAN'S WORLD, A.
Tracks: Not Advised.
CD . . . . RO 94752
■ LP . . . . RO 94751
Roadracer / May '89.

CAN'T YOU TAKE A JOKE?.
Tracks: Not Advised.
■ LP . . . . .RR 9553 1
Road Runner / '89.
CD . . . . RR 95532
Road Runner / Feb '93 / Pinnacle.

LEMONADE.
Tracks: Not Advised.
CD . . . . CM 77058
LP . . . . CM 77058-1
MC . . . . CM 77058-4
Century Media / Jan '94 / Plastic Head.

NOW.
Tracks: Hippies hate water / Three dead gophers / Jimmy's / Baby / She Quieffed / Feeling sick / Headbangers balls and 120 minutes / My hands, your neck / Face / Hotel Penitentiary / Mucky pumpin' beat / I know nobody / Walkin' with the devil / Yesterdays / To be lonely.
LP . . . . RO 93401
Roadracer / Nov '90 / Pinnacle.
CD . . . . RO 93402
Road Runner / Feb '93 / Pinnacle.

Mudhoney

Seattle's Mudhoney helped lay foundations of Grunge but are too unpolished to reap rewards. Released clutch of singles in late '80s, of which enduring classic is *Touch Me, I'm Sick*. Recent work on WEA has ironically failed to improve on minor chart success of Sub Pop-released 1991 album *Every Good Boy Deserves Fudge*.

ABSOLUTELY LIVE.
Tracks: Not Advised.
■ VHS K7 007
Studio K7 / Dec '91.

BOILED BEEF AND ROTTING TEETH.
Tracks: Not Advised.
■ CD . . . . TUPCD 009
Tupelo / Nov '89.

BURN IT CLEAN.
Tracks: Burn it clean.
■ 7" . . . . GR 0060
Glitterhouse / Aug '89.

EVERY GOOD BOY DESERVES FUDGE.
Tracks: Not Advised.
LP . . . . .SP 160
Sub Pop / Sep '91 / RTM.

FIVE DOLLAR BOB'S MOCK COOTER STEW.
Tracks: In the blood / No song II / Between me & you kid / Six two one / Make it now again / Deception pass / Underide.
CD 936245439-2
LP 936245439-1
MC 936245439-4
WEA / Oct '93 / WEA.

MUDHONEY.
Tracks: Not Advised.
LP . . . . GR 0069
Glitterhouse / Nov '89 / SRD.
MC . . . . SP 44A
Sub Pop / Jul '92 / RTM.

PIECE OF CAKE.
Tracks: No end in sight / Make it now / When in Rome / Suck you dry / Blinding sun / Thirteenth floor opening / Youth body expression explosion / I'm spun / Take me there / Living wreck / Let me let you down / Ritzville / Acetone.
CD 4509900732
MC 4509900734
WEA / Oct '92 / WEA.

SUCK YOU DRY.
Tracks: Suck you dry.
■ 12" . . . . W 0137T
■ 7" . . . . W 0137
■ CD Single . . . . W 0137CD
■ MC Single . . . . W 0137C
WEA / Oct '92.

SUPERFUZZ BUGMUFF.
Tracks: Not Advised.
LP . . . . GR 0034
Glitterhouse / Apr '89 / SRD.
■ LP . . . . EFA 4472
Glitterhouse / Feb '89.
MC . . . . SP 21A
Sub Pop / Jul '92 / RTM.

THIS GIFT.
Tracks: This gift.
■ 7" . . . . GR 0070
Glitterhouse / Nov '89.

THORN.
Tracks: Not Advised.
■ 12" . . . . GR 102
Glitterhouse / May '93.

TONIGHT (Mudhoney & Jimmie Dale Gilmore).
Tracks: Tonight.
7" . . . . .SP 124305
CD Single . . . . .SP 305305
Sub Pop / Apr '94 / RTM.

TOUCH ME I'M SICK (see under Sonic Youth).

YOU STUPID ASSHOLE.
Tracks: You stupid asshole / Knife.
■ 7" . . . . EFA 113527
Musical Tragedy / Jun '92.

YOU'RE GONE.
Tracks: You're gone.
■ 12" 12GR 0102
■ 7" . . . . GR 0102
Glitterhouse / Jul '90.

Mule

I'M HELL.
Tracks: I'm Hell.
■ 7" QS16
Quarter Stick / Nov '92.

MULE.
Tracks: Not Advised.
CD . . . . QS 15 CD
LP . . . . QS 15
Quarter Stick / Feb '93 / SRD.

Murder Inc.

CORPUSCLE.
Tracks: Corpuscle.
■ 12" . . . . 12 DVN 106
■ CD Single . . . . CDDVN 106
Devotion / Jun '92.

CORPUSCLE.
Tracks: Not Advised.
MC . . . . INV 016CS
Invisible / Jul '93 / Plastic Head.

MANIA.
Tracks: Not Advised.
■ 12" . . . . INV 014
Invisible / Jul '93.

MURDER INC.
Tracks: Not Advised.
CD . . . . INVCD 013
LP . . . . INV 013
Invisible / Feb '94 / Plastic Head.

MURDER INC.
Tracks: Supergrass / Murder Inc. / Mania / Hole in the wall / Uninvited guest / Gambit / Red black / Last of the urgents / Mrs. Whiskey name.
CD . . . . CDDVN 9
LP . . . . DVN 9
MC . . . . TDVN 9
Devotion / May '92 / Pinnacle.

Murphy's Law

BACK WITH A BONG.
Tracks: Not Advised.
CD . . . . FILECD 275
■ LP . . . . .FILER 275
MC . . . . FILECT 275
Profile (USA) / Aug '89 / Pinnacle.

BEST OF TIMES, THE.
Tracks: Not Advised.
LP . . . . RO 92401
MC . . . . RO 92404
■ CD . . . . RO 92402
Road Runner / Nov '91.

GOOD FOR NOW.
Tracks: Good for now.
7" . . . . .WB 2108
CD Single . . . . WB 2108-2
We Bite / Jun '94 / Plastic Head.

■ DELETED

Mutha's Day Out

LOCKED.
Tracks: Locked / Blank page (Available on CDS only.) / Willard (Available on CDS only.) / Through mine (Available on 10" only.) / I thirst (Available in 10" only.).
- 10" .10CHS 5007
- CD Single . . . . .CDCHS 5007
Chrysalis / Apr '94.

MY SOUL IS WET.
Tracks: Locked / My soul is wet / Green / What you see/We all bleed red / Dry water / Ding ding man / Get a clue / Blank page / Memories fade / Breakfast first please / Wait for me / Ugly.
CD .CDCHR 6061
LP . . . . CHR 6061
MC .TCCHR 6061
Chrysalis / May '94 / EMI.

MY SOUL IS WET.
Tracks: My soul is wet / Get a clue (Features on 10" only.) / Love is a hate situation (Features on 10" only.) / Mudpies (Features on CDS only.) / Idiot among us (Features on CDS only.).
10" .10CHS 5010
CD Single . . . . .CDCHS 5010
Chrysalis / Jun '94 / EMI.

Mutilation

AGGRESSION IN EFFECT.
Tracks: Not Advised.
CD Set . . . . .BR 002CD
LP Set . . . . .BRO 002LP
MC . . . . .BR 002MC
Brain Crusher / Nov '92 / Plastic Head.

My Dying Bride

AS THE FLOWER WITHERS.
Tracks: Not Advised.
CD . . . . .VILE 032CD
- LP . . . . VILE 032
- MC . . . . .VILE 032MC
Peaceville / May '92.

I AM THE BLOODY EARTH.
Tracks: I am the bloody earth / Transcending / Crown of sympathy.
12" . . . . VILE 044T
CD Single . . . . VILE 044TCD
Peaceville / Jan '94 / Vital Distribution / Pinnacle.

SYMPHONAIRE INFERNUS ET SPERA EMPYRIUM.
Tracks: Symphonaire infernus et spera empyrium.
- 12" .VILE 027T
- CD Single . . . . .VILE 027CD
Peaceville / Mar '92.

THRASH OF NAKED LIMBS, THE.
Tracks: Thrash of naked limbs / Le cerf malade / Gather me up forever.
- 12" .VILE 037T

- CD Single . . . . .VILE 037CD
Peaceville / Feb '93.

TURN LOOSE THE SWANS.
Tracks: Sear me MCMXC111 / Songless bird / Snow in my hand / Crown of sympathy / Turn loose the swans / Black God.
CD .VILE 039CD
LP . . . . VILE 039
MC . . . . .VILE 039MC
Peaceville / Oct '93 / Vital Distribution / Pinnacle.

My Little Funhouse

ADDICTED EP.
Tracks: Not Advised.
- 12" .GFST 24
- 7" . . . . GFS 24
- CD Single . . . . .GFSTD 24
BMG / Aug '92.

STANDUNDER.
Tracks: I want some of that / Destiny / Wishing well / L.S.D. / I know what I need / Catholic boy / Lonely / Anonymous / Been too long / raintown / Standunder.
CD . . . . GED 24497
- LP . . . . GEF 24497
- MC . . . . GEC 24497
Geffen / Nov '92.

WISHING WELL.
Tracks: Wishing well.
- 12" .GFST 48
- CD Single . . . . .GFSTD 48
Geffen / Jul '93.

My Sister's Machine

DIVA.
Tracks: Hands and feet / Pain / I hate you / Wasting time / Love at high speed / I'm sorry / Walk all over you / Sunday / Monster box / Diva.
CD . . . . CARCD 18
MC . . . . CARC 18
- LP .CARLP 18
Caroline / Apr '92.

WALL FLOWERS.
Tracks: Inside of me / Broken land / This is fear / Steamy swamp thang / Feed / Empty room / 16 Ways to go / Enemy / I slip away / Burn / Mockingbird / Cracking new ground.
CD 370561512-2
MC 370561512-4
WEA / Jul '93 / WEA.

Myles, Alannah

ALANNAH MYLES.
Tracks: Still got this thing / Black velvet / Lover of mine / If you want to / Who loves you / Rock this joint / Kick start my heart / Just one kiss / Make love.
CD 781 956-2
- LP 781 956-1

MC 781 956-
Atlantic / Nov '89 / WEA.

ALANNAH MYLES.
Tracks: Not Advised.
VHS 756750150
Warner Music Video / Jan '91 / WEA.

BLACK VELVET.
Tracks: Black velvet / If you want to / Who loves you
- 12" .A 8742TW
- CD Single . . . . .A 8742CD
- MC Single. . . . . .A 8742C
- 12" .A 8742T
- 7" . . . . .A 8742
Atlantic / Feb '90.

LOVE IS.
Tracks: Love is / Rock this joint / Hurry make love (Not on 7" single.).
- 12" .A 8918 T
- 7" . . . . .A 8918
- CD Single . . . . .A 8918 CD
- MC Single. . . . . .A 8918 MC
East West / May '90.

LOVER OF MINE.
Tracks: Lover of mine / Just one kiss.
- 12" .A 7872 TW
- 12" .A 7872 T
- 7" . . . . .A 7872
- CD Single . . . . .A 7872 CD
- MC Single. . . . . .A 7872 C
Atlantic / Aug '90.

ROCKING HORSE.
Tracks: Our world our times / Make me happy / Sonny say you will / Tumbleweed / Livin' on a memory / Song instead of a kiss / Love in the big town / Last time I saw William / Lies and rumours / Rocking horse.
CD .7567824022
MC .7567824024
WEA / Nov '92 / WEA.

SONG INSTEAD OF A KISS.
Tracks: Rockinghorse.
- 7" . . . . .A 7421
- CD Single . . . . .A 7421CD
- MC Single. . . . . .A 7421C
Atlantic / Oct '92.

Mythra

DEATH AND DESTINY.
Tracks: Death and destiny.
- 7" . . . . .GRM 16
Guardian / Oct '82.

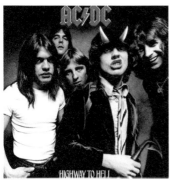

AC/DC – Highway to Hell

AC/DC – AC/DC Live

Bryan Adams – Reckless

Aerosmith – Pandora's Box

Aerosmith – Pump

Alice in Chains – Dirt

Plate 1

Black Crowes – The Southern Harmony &
Musical Companion

Black Sabbath – Paranoid

Bon Jovi – Slippery When Wet

Alice Cooper – Billion Dollar Babies

Coverdale Page

Cult – Sonic Temple

Deep Purple – Deep Purple in Rock

Def Leppard – Hysteria

Plate 2

Dof Loppard   Pyromania

Extromo   Extromo II Pornograffiti

Faith No More – The Real Thing

Foreigner – Foreigner 4

Guns N' Roses – Appetite for Destruction

Hanoi Rocks – Back to the Mystery City

Judas Priest – Screaming for Vengeance

Killing Joke – Pandemor

Plate 3

Kiss – Asylum

Kiss – Destroyer

L7 – Bricks are Heavy

Led Zeppelin – Led Zeppelin I

Led Zeppelin – Led Zeppelin IV

Love/Hate – Black Out In The Red Room

Lynyrd Skynyrd – Second Helping

M.C. 5 – Kick Out The Jams

Plate 4

Manic Street Preachers – Generation Terrorists

Mogadoth   Countdown To Extinction

Metallica – Master Of Puppets

Ministry – Psalm 69

Mother Love Bone – Apple

Mötley Crüe – Dr. Feelgood

Motörhead – Ace Of Spades

Naplam Death – Fear, Emptiness, Death

Plate 5

Nirvana – Nevermind

Ozzy Osbourne – Blizzard of Ozz

Pearl Jam – Vs

Robert Plant – Manic Nirvana

Queensrÿche – Operation: Mindcrime

Rainbow – Rising

Red Hot Chilli Peppers – BloodSugarSexMagik

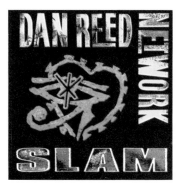

Dan Reed Network – Slam

Plate 6

Sex Pistols – Never Mind The Bollocks

Skid Row – Slave to the Grind

Soundgarden – Badmotorfinger

Temple Of The Dog

Therapy? – Troublegum

Thin Lizzy – Jailbreak

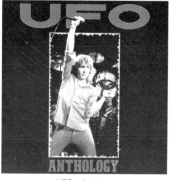

Thunder – Laughter On Judgement Day

UFO – Anthology

Plate 7

UFO – Lights Out

Van Halen – MCMLXXXIV

Whitesnake – Love Hunter

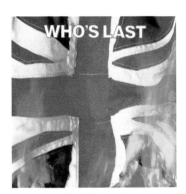

Who – Who's Last

Who – Who's Next

Wildhearts – Earth Vs The Wildhearts

Plate 8

N

Nailbomb

POINT BLANK.
Tracks: Not Advised.
CD . . . . RR 90552
LP . . . . RR 90551
MC . . . . RR 90554
Road Runner / Mar '94 / Pinnacle.

Naked Aggression

THEY CAN'T GET ME DOWN.
Tracks: They can't get me down.
■ 10" . . . . NANO 001
Neighbour Annoyer / Jun '93.

Naked Sun

NAKED SUN.
Tracks: Not Advised.
LP . . . . N 01812
LP . . . . N 01811
MC . . . . N 01814
Noise / Jan '92 / Pinnacle.

Naked Truth

BLACK.
Tracks: Black / Here lies America / I am he / Fight (Available on CD Single only).
■ 12" 658949 6
■ CD Single 658949 2
Sony Soho2 / Feb '93.

DEAD BETWEEN THE LINES.
Tracks: Read between the lines / Fight.
■ 10" 658429-0
■ 12" 658429-6
■ CD Single 658429-2
Sony Soho2 / Nov '92.

FIGHT.
Tracks: Door / Tormented world / Downtown / Lovejoy / Black / Read between the lines / I am he / Telepathy / Third eye spy / Red river.
CD 472981 2
LP 472981 1
MC 472981 4
Sony Soho2 / Mar '93 / Sony.

GREEN WITH RAGE.
Tracks: Pan American alive / King in my home (lovejoy) / Here lies America / Downtown / Blood flows / Harem scares.
MC 4961244
■ LP 4691241
Sony Soho2 / Nov '91.

Napalm

CRUEL TRANQUILITY.
Tracks: Mind melt / A.O.A. / Shake it off / Gag of steel / Devastation / Combat zone / Immoral society / Attack on America / Reanimate / Act of betrayal / Nightmare administrator / Practice what you preach / Kranked up and out.
CD 85-7565
■ LP 08-7563
Steamhammer (Germany) / Jun '89.

ZERO TO BLACK.
Tracks: Not Advised.
CD 847622
LP 087622
Steamhammer (Germany) / Nov '90 / Pinnacle.

Napalm Death

UK hardcore quintet, formed in 1982, who achieved notoriety five years later when they reinvented themselves with the debut album *Scum*. On it, the band, already at the quicker end of thrash metal, opted to play faster than ever before and almost faster then humanly possible. Coupled with virtually indistinguishable death metal vocals (originally by Lee Dorrian, now of Cathedral, latterly by Mark 'Barney' Greenaway), Napalm Death gained a reputation as one of the most extreme bands in the world. They cemented this with *From Enslavement To Obliteration* (1988) and *Harmony Corruption* (Barney's album debut). Since these, some have suggested famililarity has made the style seem less menacing in concert, but 1994's *Fear, Emptiness, Despair* proved they can still deliver on record.

DEATH BY MANIPULATION.
Tracks: Not Advised.
■ CD Set. . . . . MOSH 051CDL
Earache / Mar '92.
LP . . . . MOSH 051
MC .MOSH 051MC
Earache / Sep '92 / Vital Distribution.
CD . . . . MOSH 051CD
Earache / Sep '94 / Vital Distribution.

FEAR, EMPTINESS, DESPAIR.
Tracks: Twist the knife (slowly) / Hung / Remain nameless / Plague rages / More than meets the eye / Primed time / State of mind / Armageddon X 7 / Retching on the dirt / Fasting on deception / Throwaway.
CD . . . . .MOSH 109CD
LP . . . . MOSH 109
MC . . . . .MOSH 109MC
Earache / Mar '94 / Vital Distribution.

FROM ENSLAVEMENT TO OBLITERATION.
Tracks: Evolved as one / It's a M.A.N.'s world / Lucid fairytale / Private death / Unchallenged hate / Uncertainty blurs / Vision / Retreat to nowhere / Display to me / From enslavement / Blind to the truth / Emotional suffocation / Practice what you preach / Mentally murdered / Worlds apart.
LP . . . . MOSH 008
MC . . . . .MOSH 008MC
Earache / Oct '88 / Vital Distribution.
■ LP P.Disc . . . . .MOSH 008P
Earache / Jul '90.
CD . . . . MOSH 008CD
Earache / Sep '94 / Vital Distribution.

HARMONY CORRUPTION.
Tracks: Not Advised.
CD . . . . MOSH 019CD
Earache / Sep '94 / Vital Distribution.

HARMONY OF CORRUPTION.
Tracks: Not Advised.
CD . . . . MOSH 19 CD
LP . . . . MOSH 19
MC . . . . .MOSH 19 MC
Earache / Aug '90 / Vital Distribution.
■ LP P.Disc . . . . MOSH 19 P
Earache / Dec '90.

LIVE CORRUPTION.
Tracks: Not Advised.
VHS . . . . LFV 115
Fotodisk Video / Sep '90.

MASS APPEAL MADNESS.
Tracks: Mass appeal madness.
■ 7" 7MOSH 46
Earache / Jun '91.

MENTALLY MURDERED.
Tracks: Mentally murdered.
■ 12" . . . . MOSH 14 T
■ 7" . . . . MOSH 14
■ CD Single . . . . MOSH 14 CD
Earache / Aug '89.

MOVING TO AND FRO.
Tracks: Not Advised.
LP . . . . EFA 7202
LSD / Dec '88 / SRD.

NAPALM DEATH - TWO COMPLETE SESSIONS.
Tracks: Not Advised.
■ LP . . . . SFPSD 049
Strange Fruit / May '89.

NAZI PUNKS FUCK OFF.
Tracks: Nazi punks fuck off / Aryanisms / Nazi punks fuck off (live) / Contemptuous.
■ 7" 7MOSH 092
Earache / Jun '93.

PEEL SESSIONS.
Tracks: Not Advised.
CD . . . . SFRCD 120
Strange Fruit / Oct '93 / Pinnacle.

PEEL SESSIONS: NAPALM DEATH (13.9.87 - 8.3.88).
Tracks: Kill / Prison without walls / Dead part 1 / Deceiver / Lucid fairytale / In extremis / Extremis / Blind to the truty / Negative approach / Common enem6v / Obstinate direction / Life / You suffer pt 2 / Multi-national cooporations / Instinct of survival / Stigatised / Parasites / Moral crusade / Worlds apart / M.A.D. / Divine death / C. 9 / Control / Walls / Raging in hell / Conform or die / S.O.B.
CD . . . . SFPMCD 201
MC . . . . SFPMC 201
■ Mini LP . . . . SFPMA 201
Strange Fruit / '89.

PEEL SESSIONS: NAPALM DEATH.
Tracks: Not Advised.
■ 12" . . . . SFPS 049
Strange Fruit / May '88.
■ CD Single . . . . SFPSCD 049
■ MC Single. . . . . SFPSMC 049
Strange Fruit / Apr '89.

SCUM.
Tracks: Not Advised.
■ LP . . . . MOSH 003
Earache / Jun '87.
MC . . . . .MOSH 003MC
Earache / May '89 / Vital Distribution.
■ CD . . . . .MOSH 003CD
Earache / Sep '94.

SUFFER THE CHILDREN.
Tracks: Suffer the children.
■ 12" . . . . MOSH 24 T
■ 7" . . . . MOSH 24
■ CD Single . . . . MOSH 24 CD
Earache / Aug '90.

UTOPIA BANISHED.
Tracks: Not Advised.
LP . . . . MOSH 053
MC . . . . .MOSH 053MC
Earache / May '92 / Vital Distribution.
CD . . . . MOSH 053CD
Earache / Sep '94 / Vital Distribution.

WORLD KEEPS TURNING, THE.
Tracks: World keeps turning.
■ 12" . . . . .MOSH 065T
■ CD Single . . . . MOSH 065CD
Earache / Jul '92.

Narita

NARITA.
Tracks: Not Advised.
CD . . . . SHARK 022
Shark / Oct '92 / Plastic Head.

Nasty Idols

CRUEL INTENTION.
Tracks: Way ya walk / Cool way of living / American nights / Don't tear it down / Alive 'n' kickin' / House of rock and roll / B.I.T.C.H. / Can't get ya off my mind / Devil in disguise / Westcoast city rockers / Trashed and dirty / Can't get ya off my mind (2) (CD only).
CD . . . . BMCD 022
LP . . . . .BMLP 022
Black Mark / Apr '92 / Plastic Head.

Nasty Savage

ABSTRACT REALITY.
Tracks: Not Advised.
■ LP 722441
Metal Blade / Apr '88.
■ LP . . . . RR 95661
Road Runner / Feb '88.

INDULGENCE.
Tracks: Not Advised.
■ LP . . . . RR 9630
Road Runner / Mar '87.

INDULGENCE/ABSTRACT REALITY.
Tracks: Not Advised.
CD . . . . RR 9566 2
Road Runner / '89 / Pinnacle.

NASTY SAVAGE.
Tracks: Not Advised.
■ LP . . . . RR 9752
Road Runner / Sep 85.

NO MORE.
Tracks: No more / Heartbreak.
■ 7" . . . . DB 9149
■ 12" . . . . DBX 9149
Columbia (EMI) / Jul '87.

PENETRATION POINT.
Tracks: Welcome wagon / Irrational / Ritual submission / Powerslam / Sin eater / Penetration point / Puzzled / Horizertical / Family circus.
LP . . . . RO 94181
MC . . . . RO 94182
Roadracer / Jan '90 / Pinnacle.

Nausea

CRIMES AGAINST HUMANITY.
Tracks: Not Advised.
CD . . . . WRE 9182
LP . . . . WRE 9181
Wild Rags / Jan '92 / Plastic Head.

EXTINCTION.
Tracks: Not Advised.
LP . . . . SFLS 132
Selfless / Apr '93 / SRD.

Nazareth

Scottish rockers formed 1969, best remembered for 1973 album *Razamanaz* and hit revivals of Everlys' *Love Hurts*, Tomorrow's *My White Bicycle* and Joni Mitchell's *This Flight Tonight*. A popular U.S. concert draw in '70s, Nazareth are still active in '90s, albeit with microscopic success. Their *Hair Of The Dog* was revived by Guns N' Roses on *"The Spaghetti Incident?"*.

2 X S.
Tracks: Love leads to madness / Boys in the band / You love another / Gatecrash / Games / Back to the trenches / Dream on / Lonely in the night / Preservation / Take the rap / Mexico.
■ LP . . . . NIN 001
Nems International / Feb 83.
CD . . . . CLACD 217
Castle Classics / Feb '91 / BMG / Castle Communications.

20 GREATEST HITS: NAZARETH.
Tracks: Not Advised.
■ LP . . . . SAH 137
MC . . . . SAH 137C
Sahara / Jun 85.

ALIVE AND KICKING.
Tracks: Not Advised.
CD . . . . OPTMCD 009
MC . . . . OPTMC 009
Icon / May '93 / Pinnacle.

ANTHOLOGY - NAZARETH.
Tracks: Telegram (part 1) / On your way (part 2) / So you want to be a rock 'n' roll star (part 3) / Sound check (part 4) / Here we go again / Kentucky fried blues / Somebody to roll / Revenge is sweet / Beggars day / Expect no mercy / No mean city (parts 1 & 2) / Silver dollar forger (parts 1 & 2) / Cocaine (live) / Tush (live) / A-shapes of things B-Space safari / Turn on your receiver / Teenage nervous breakdown / Big boy / Go down fighting / Razamanaz / Vigilante man / Hair for the dog / Broken down angel / I want to do everything for you.
■ LP . . . . RAWLP 039
MC . . . . RAWTC 039
■ CD . . . . RAWCD 039
Raw Power / '88.
CD . . . . ESBCD 967
Essential / Oct '91 / Total / BMG.

BAD BAD BOY.
Tracks: Bad bad boy.
■ 7" . . . . MOON 9
Mooncrest / Jul 73.

BROKEN DOWN ANGEL.
Tracks: Broken down angel / Hair of the dog.
■ 7" . . . . MOON 1
Mooncrest / May 73.

CATCH, THE.
Tracks: Party down / Ruby Tuesday / Last exit Brooklyn / Moondance / Love of freedom / This month's messiah / You don't believe in us / Sweetheart tree / Road to nowhere.
■ LP . . . . VERL 20
MC. . . . . VERLC 20
Vertigo / Sep '84 / PolyGram.

CLOSE ENOUGH FOR ROCK AND ROLL.
Tracks: Not Advised.
■ LP . . . . SAH 126
Sahara / May 85.
CD . . . . CLACD 182
■ LP . . . . CLALP 182
Castle Classics / Aug '90.

DREAM ON.
Tracks: Dream on / Juicy Lucy.
■ 7" . . . . NES 103
Nems / Jun 83.

DRESSED TO KILL.
Tracks: Dressed to kill.
■ 7" . . . . NES 301
Nems / Mar 81.

EARLY YEARS, THE.
Tracks: Witchdoctor woman / Morning dew / King is dead / Called her name / Sad song / Woke up this morning / Broken down angel / Razamanaz / Bad bad boy / This flight tonight / Not faking it / Miss Misery / Changin' times / Jet lag / Shanghai'd in Shanghai / Shapes of things / Space safari.
CD . . . . EARL D2
Castle Classics / Aug '92 / BMG / Castle Communications.

EXERCISES.
Tracks: I will not be led / Cats eye, apple pie / In my time / Woke up this morning / Called her name / Fool about you / Love now you're gone / Madelaine / Sad song / 1692 (Glencoe massacre).
■ LP . . . . SAH 121
Sahara / May 85.
CD . . . . CLACD 220
Castle Classics / Feb '91 / BMG / Castle Communications.

EXPECT NO MERCY.
Tracks: This flight tonight / Dressed to kill / Love hurts / Whisky drinkin' woman / Razamanaz (live) / I want to (do everything for you) / Free wheeler / Broken down angel / Shanghai'D in Shanghai / Night woman / Hair of the dog / Alcatraz / Sold my soul / Shapes of things / Loved and lost / Expect no mercy.
MC. . . . . ELITE 022 MC
Pickwick / Oct '91 / Pickwick.
CD . . . . ELITE 022 CD
Pickwick / Aug '93 / Pickwick.

EXPECT NO MERCY.
Tracks: All the king's horses / Expect no mercy / Gimme what's mine / Gone dead train / Kentucky fried blues / New York broken toy / Place in your heart / Revenge is sweet / Shot me down.
■ LP . . . . TOPS 115
Castle Classics / Apr '80.
■ LP . . . . SAH 123
Castle Classics / May 85.
CD . . . . CLACD 187
■ LP . . . . CLALP 187
Castle Classics / Aug '90.

FOOL CIRCLE, THE.
Tracks: Dressed to kill / Another year / Moonlight eyes / Pop the silo / Let me be your leader / We are the people / Every young man's dream / Little part of you / Cocaine (live) / Victoria.
CD . . . . CLACD 214
■ LP . . . . CLALP 214
Castle Classics / Dec '90.

FROM THE VAULTS.
Tracks: Friends / If you see my baby / Hard living / Spinning top / Love hurts / Down / My white bicycle / Holy roller / Railroad boy / You're the violin / Good love / Razamanaz (Live) / Hair of the dog (Live) / Talkin' to one of the boys (Live) / Morning dew / Juicy Lucy / On the run.
CD . . . . NEMCD 639
Sequel / Mar '93 / Castle Communications / BMG / Hot Shot.

FULL CIRCLE, THE.
Tracks: Dress to kill / Another year / Moonlight eyes / Pop the silo / Let me be your leader / Victoria / We are the people / Every young man's dream / Little part of you / Cocaine (live).
■ LP . . . . NEL 6019
Nems / Feb 81.

GAMES.
Tracks: Games / You love another.
■ 7" . . . . NES 10?
Nems / Jan 83.

GONE DEAD TRAIN.
Tracks: Gone dead train / Greens / Desolation road
■ 7" . . . . NAZ 002
Mountain / Feb 78.

GREATEST HITS: NAZARETH.
Tracks: Razamanaz / Holly roller / Shanghaid in Shanghai / Love hurts / Turn on your receiver / Bad bad boy / This flight tonight / Broken down angel / Hair of the dog / Sunshine / My white bicycle / Woke up this morning.
■ LP . . . . TOPS 108
Mountain / Dec 75.
■ LP 9279 545
Mercury / Jul 81.
■ LP . . . . NEL 6022
MC. . . . . NEC 6022
Nems / Oct '82 / Pinnacle.
CD . . . . CLACD 149
MC . . . . CLAMC 149
■ LP . . . . CLALP 149
Castle Classics / Apr '89.

GREATEST HITS: NAZARETH.
Tracks: Not Advised.
CD . . . . BRCD 1392
■ MC. . . . . BRMC 1392
BR Music/BR Music (Holland) / Jun '94.

HAIR OF THE DOG.
Tracks: Hair of the dog / Miss Misery / Guilty / Changing times / Beggars day / Rose in the heather / Whisky drinking woman / Please don't ..
■ LP . . . . TOPS 107
Mountain / Apr '80.
■ LP . . . . SAH 124
Sahara / May 85.

HAIR OF THE DOG/ RAMPANT.
Tracks: Not Advised.
■ Double LP . . . . TFOLP 13
■ CD Set. . . . . TFOCD 13
■ MC Set . . . . TFOMC 13
That's Original / Jun '88.

HEARTS GROWN COLD.
Tracks: Hearts grown cold / Razamanaz / Hair of the dog / Talkin' to one of the boys.
■ 7" Set . . . . BSD 1
Nems / Jan 81.

HOLIDAY.
Tracks: Holiday / Talkin' 'bout love.
■ 7" . . . . TOP 50
Mountain / Feb '80.

HOLY ROLLER.
Tracks: Holy roller.
■ 7" . . . . TOP 3
Mountain / Nov 75.

HOT TRACKS.
Tracks: Love hurts / This flight tonight / Broken down angel / Hair of the dog.
■ EP . . . . NAZ 1
Mountain / Sep 77.

LIVE AND KICKING.
Tracks: Telegram / Razamanaz / I want to do everything for you / Boys in the band / Beggars day / Dream on / Cocaine / This month's messiah / This flight tonight / Love hurts / Hair of the dog / Teenage nervous breakdown / Ain't got you.

LOUD 'N' PROUD.
Tracks: Go down fighting / Not faking it / Turn on your receiver / Teenage nervous breakdown / Free wheeler / This flight tonight / Child in the sun / Ballad of Hollis Brown.
■ LP . . . . CREST 4
Mooncrest / Nov 73.
CD . . . . CLACD 174
Castle Classics / Dec '89 / BMG / Castle Communications.
■ LP . . . . CLALP 174
Castle Classics / Feb '90.

LOVE HURTS (EP).
Tracks: Love hurts / This flight tonight / Broken down angel / Hair of the dog.
■ 7" . . . . NAZ 001
Mountain / Sep 77.
■ EP . . . . HOT 1
Mountain / Jul '80.
■ 7" P.Disc . . . . NEP 2
Nems / Jan 83.

LOVE HURTS (OLD GOLD).
Tracks: Love hurts / Bad bad boy.
■ 7" . . . . OG 9803
Old Gold / Oct '88.

LOVE LEADS TO MADNESS.
Tracks: Love leads to madness.
■ 7" . . . . NES 101
Nems / Jul '82.

MALICE IN WONDERLAND.
Tracks: Holiday / Showdown at the border / Talkin' to one of the boys / Heart's grown cold / Fast cars / Big boy / Talkin' 'bout love / Fallen angel / Ship of dreams / Turning a new leaf.
■ LP . . . . TOPS 126
Mountain / Apr '80.
CD . . . . CLACD 181
■ LP . . . . CLALP 181
■ MC . . . . CLAMC 181
Castle Classics / Aug '90.

MAY THE SUNSHINE.
Tracks: May the sunshine / Expect no mercy.
■ 7" . . . . NAZ 003
Mountain / Jan '79.

MORNING DEW.
Tracks: Morning dew / Juicy Lucy.
■ 7" . . . . NES 302
Nems / Aug '81.

MY WHITE BICYCLE.
Tracks: My white bicycle.
■ 7" . . . . MOON 47
Mooncrest / Jun '75.

NAZARETH.
Tracks: Not Advised.
CD . . . . CLACD 286
Castle / Jun '92 / BMG.

NAZARETH (BBC Live in Concert).
Tracks: Not Advised.
CD . . . . WINCD 005
LP . . . . WINLP 005
MC . . . . WINMC 005
Windsong / Nov '91 / Pinnacle / A.D.A. Distribution.

NAZARETH.
Tracks: Not Advised.
■ LP . . . . TOPC 5001
Mountain / Apr '80.

NAZARETH (EP).
Tracks: This flight tonight / Broken down angel / Bad bad boy / Love hurts.
■ CD Single CD3-17
Special Edition / '88.

NAZARETH - CD BOX SET.
Tracks: Not Advised.
■ CD Set. . . . . CLA BX 908
Castle Classics / Feb '92.

NAZARETH: THE EARLY YEARS.
Tracks: Not Advised.
CD . . . . EARLCD 2
Dojo / Mar '92 / Castle Communications / BMG.

NO JIVE.
Tracks: Not Advised.
CD 36700102
MC 36700104
Silenz / Jul '92 / BMG.

NO MEAN CITY.
Tracks: Claim to fame / Just to get into it / May the sunshine / No mean city / Simple solutions / Star / Whatever you want babe / What's in it for me.
■ LP . . . . TOPS 123
Mountain / Feb '79.
■ LP . . . . SAH 120
Sahara / May '85.
CD . . . . CLACD 213
■ LP . . . . CLALP 213
Castle Classics / Dec '90.

PLACE IN YOUR HEART, A.
Tracks: Place in your heart / Kentucky fried blues.
■ 7" . . . . TOP 37
Mountain / May '78.

PLAY 'N' THE GAME.
Tracks: Somebody to roll / Down home girl / Flying / Waiting for the man / Born to love / I want to do everything for you / I don't want to go on without you / Wild honey / L.A. girls.
■ LP . . . . SAH 131
Sahara / May '85.
CD . . . . CLACD 219
Castle Classics / Feb '91 / BMG / Castle Communications.

RAMPANT.
Tracks: Not Advised.
■ LP . . . . CREST 15
Mooncrest / May '74.
■ LP . . . . TOPS 106
Mountain / Apr '80.
■ CD . . . . CLACD 242
Castle / Jun '92.

RAZAMANAZ.
Tracks: Razamanaz / Alcatraz / Vigilante man / Woke up this morning / Night woman / Bad bad boy / Sold my soul / Too bad, too sad / Broken down angel.
■ LP . . . . CREST 1
Mooncrest / May '73.
■ LP . . . . TOPS 104
Mountain / Apr '80.
■ LP . . . . NEL 6023
MC . . . . NEC 6023
Nems / Oct '82 / Pinnacle.
CD . . . . CLACD 173
Castle Classics / Dec '89 / BMG / Castle Communications.
■ LP . . . . CLALP 173
Castle Classics / Dec '89.

RAZAMANAZ.
Tracks: Not Advised.
■ VHS . . . . HEN 2247
Hendring Video / Apr '90.

RUBY TUESDAY.
Tracks: Ruby Tuesday.
■ 12" . . . . VERX 13
■ 7" . . . . VER 13
Vertigo / Sep '84.

SHANGHAI'D IN SHANGHAI.
Tracks: Shanghai'd in Shanghai.
■ 7" . . . . MOON 22
Mooncrest / Mar '74.

SINGLES COLLECTION, THE.
Tracks: Broken down angel / Bad bad boy / This flight tonight / My white bicycle / Out of time / Shanghai'd in Shanghai / Love hurts / Hair of the dog / Holy roller / Carry out feelings / You're the violin / Somebody to roll / I don't want to go on without you / Gone dead train / Place in your heart / May the sunshine / Star / Dressed to kill / Morning dew / Games / Love leads to madness.
CD . . . . CCSCD 280
■ Double LP . . . . CCSLP 280
■ MC . . . . CCSMC 280
Castle Collector Series / Dec '90.

SNAZ.
Tracks: Telegram / Razamanaz / I want to do everything for you / This flight tonight / Beggar's day / Every young man's dream / Heart's grown cold / Java blues / Cocaine / Big boy / So you want to be a rock 'n' roll star / Holiday / Let me be your leader / Dressed to kill / Hair of the dog / Expect no mercy / Shapes of things / Love hurts / Morning dew / Juicy Lucy / On your way.
■ LP . . . . NELD 102
Nems / Sep '81.
CD . . . . CLACD 130
Castle Classics / Jul '87 / BMG / Castle Communications.
■ MC . . . . CLAMC 130
■ LP . . . . CLALP 130
Castle Classics / Jul '87.

SOMEBODY TO ROLL.
Tracks: Somebody to roll / Vancouver shakedown.
■ 7" . . . . TOP 22
Mountain / Jan '77.

SOUND ELIXIR.
Tracks: All nite radio / Milk and honey / Whippin' boy / Rain on the window / Back room boy / Why don't you read the book / I ran / Rags to riches / Local still / Where are you now.
■ LP . . . . SAH 130
Sahara / May '85.
CD . . . . CLACD 218
Castle Classics / Feb '91 / BMG / Castle Communications.

STAR.
Tracks: Star / Born to love.
■ 7" . . . . TOP 45
Mountain / Jul '79.

THIS FLIGHT TONIGHT.
Tracks: This flight tonight.
■ 7" . . . . MOON 14
Mooncrest / Oct '73.

THIS FLIGHT TONIGHT (OLD GOLD).
Tracks: This flight tonight / Broken down angel.
■ 7" . . . . OG 9801
Old Gold / Oct '88.

WHATEVER YOU WANT BABE.
Tracks: Whatever you want babe / Telegram.
■ 7" . . . . MAS 4
Mountain / Apr '79.

Necrodeath

FRAGMENTS OF INSANITY.
Tracks: Not Advised.
■ LP . . . . MET 114
Metal Master / May '89.

Necromantia

CROSSING THE FIERY PATH.
Tracks: Not Advised.
CD . . . . OPCD 021
Osmose / Feb '94 / Plastic Head.

Necronomicon

DEVILS TONGUE, THE.
Tracks: Not Advised.
CD 15 197
MC 79 071
Laserlight / Aug '91 / TBD / BMG / Target.

NECRONOMICON.
Tracks: Not Advised.
■ LP 805269
Scratch (Germany) / Jun '87.

Necrony

NECRONYCISM.
Tracks: Not Advised.
CD . . . . SPV 065-57722
Poserslaughter / Jun '94 / Plastic Head.

Necrophobic

NOCTURNAL SILENCE.
Tracks: Not Advised.
CD . . . . BMCD 40
Black Mark / Aug '93 / Plastic Head.

Necrosanct

INCARNATE.
Tracks: Ritual acts / Inevitable demise / Undeath dead dying / Abhorrence / Incarnate / Necronomicon / Exiternity / Restless dead / Solace / Ominous despair / Oblivion seed.
CD . . . . BMCD 021
LP . . . . BMLP 021
MC . . . . BMCT 021
Black Mark / Apr '92 / Plastic Head.

Neighbour Hoods

HOODWINKED.
Tracks: Hangin' / Roxanne / King of the rats / Hate zone / Evil Knievel / Love holiday / Hoodwinked / Anything / Sea of memories / Southern girls / Nancy.
CD . . . . EM 9462-2
MC . . . . EMC 9462
Emergo / Nov '90 / Pinnacle.

PURE AND EASY.
Tracks: Pure and easy.
■ 7" . . . . EM 5505
Road Runner / Oct '87.

REPTILE MEN, THE.
Tracks: Not Advised.
■ LP . . . . EM 9626
Emergo / May '87.

Neil, Vince

EXPOSED.
Tracks: Look in her eyes / Sister of pain / Can't have your cake / Edge / Can't change me / Fine, fine wine / Living is a luxury / You're invited but your friend can't come / Gettin' hard / Forever.
CD 936245260-2
LP 936245260-1
MC 936245260-4
Warner Bros. / Apr '93 / WEA.

Nelson

AFTER THE RAIN.
Tracks: Can't live without your love and affection / After the rain / More than ever / Fill you up / Bits and pieces / I can hardly wait / Tracy's song / Only time will tell / (It's just) desire / Interlude / Everywhere I go / Will you love me.
■ LP . . . . WX 394
■ CD 759924902
■ MC . . . . WX 394C
Geffen / Nov '90.
■ CD . . . . DGCD 24290
■ LP . . . . DGC 24290
■ MC . . . . DGCC 24290
Geffen / Aug '91.
■ LP . . . . GEF 24290
■ CD . . . . GEFD 24290
■ MC . . . . GEFC 24290
Geffen / May '91.

AFTER THE RAIN.
Tracks: After the rain / It's just desire / Be still (Not available on 7" format.) / Won't walk away (Not available on 7" format.).
■ 12" .GEF 86T
■ 7" . . . . GEF 86
■ CD Single . . . . .GEF 86CD
■ MC Single . . . . GEF 86C
Geffen / Jan '91.

AFTER THE RAIN.
Tracks: Not Advised.
VHS . . . . .GEFV 39501
Geffen Video / '91 / BMG.

CAN'T LIVE WITHOUT YOU.
Tracks: Can't live without you.
■ 12" . . . . GEF 82 T
■ 7" . . . . GEF 82
■ CD Single . . . . GEF 82 CD
■ MC Single . . . . GEF 82 C
Geffen / Sep '90.

Nembrionic Hammerdeath

NEMBRIONIC HAMMERDEATH/CONSOLATION SPLIT ALBUM (Nembrionic Hammerdeath & Consolation).
Tracks: Not Advised.
CD . . . . D 00027
Displeased Records / Mar '94 / Plastic Head.

Nemesis

DAY OF RETRIBUTION, THE.
Tracks: Not Advised.
LP . . . . ATV 15
Active / Jan '90 / Pinnacle.

I WANT YOUR SEX.
Tracks: I want your sex.
■ 12" . . . . PROFT 341
■ CD Single . . . . PROFTCD 341
Profile / Sep '91.

MUNCHIES FOR YOUR BASS.
Tracks: Not Advised.
CD . . . . FILERCD 411
LP . . . . FILER 411
MC . . . . FILERCT 411
Profile / Jul '91 / Vital Distribution.

TEMPLE OF BOOM.
Tracks: Temple of boom / Nemesis on the premises / Deep up on it / Cantfiguritout / Big, The, the bad, the bass / Get ya flow on / Str8jackin' / Hard from birth / Parkin' lot on Dixon / Go Ron C / Brand new team / Cloud 7.
CD . . . . FILECD 441
LP . . . . FILER 441
MC . . . . FILECT 441
Profile / Jun '93 / Vital Distribution.

TO HELL AND BACK.
Tracks: Not Advised.
LP .FILER 283
Profile (USA) / Apr '90 / Pinnacle.

Neurosis

ENEMY OF THE SUN.
Tracks: Not Advised.
CD . . . . .VIRUS 134CD
LP . . . . VIRUS 134
Alternative Tentacles / Oct '93 / RTM / Pinnacle.

NEUROSIS: LIVE.
Tracks: Not Advised.
LP . . . . .YCR 014
Your Choice / Jun '92 / Plastic Head.

PAIN OF MIND.
Tracks: Not Advised.
■ LP . . . . VM 105
Alchemy / Apr '88.
■ MC . . . . VM 105C
Alchemy / Apr '88 / Pinnacle.
CD . . . . VIRUSCD 146
LP . . . . VIRUS 146
Alternative Tentacles / May '94 / RTM / Pinnacle.

Nevada Beach

NEVADA BEACH.
Tracks: Not Advised.
LP . . . . ZORRO 2
Metal Blade / Jul '90 / Pinnacle.

ZERO DAY.
Tracks: Not Advised.
CD .CDZORRO 13
LP . . . . ZORRO 13
MC . . . . TZORRO 13
Zorro / Sep '90 / Pinnacle.

New England

DON'T EVER WANNA LOSE YA.
Tracks: Don't ever wanna lose ya / Encore.
■ 7" . . . . INF 113
Infinity / Aug '79.

YOU CAN'T KEEP LIVING THIS WAY.
Tracks: Suicide / Real live mind / Money / Nine / Communication breakdown / We R 4 U2 / No zone / War / Love.
■ LP . . . . STR LP 014
Street Link / Oct '92.
CD . . . . STRCD 014
Street Link / Oct '92 / BMG.

New York Dolls

Glam-Punk rock group formed 1971 by Johnny Thunders (d. 23/4/91) Rick Rivets, Arthur Kane, Billy Murcia (d 6/11/72) and David Johansen. Sylvain Sylvain replaced Rivets and Jerry Nolan (d. 14/1/92) replaced Billy Murcia after an early UK tour. The New York Dolls' brand of trashy R & B rock was derivative of the Stones, M.C. 5 and early 60's girl groups. Eponymous debut LP was produced by Todd Rundgren and won critical appraisal but sold modestly. The aptly titled *Too Much Too Soon*, fared worse and the band were dropped by Mercury. The New York Dolls were briefly managed by Malcolm McLaren, but even he couldn't save the band from disintergrating in 1977. Johansen and Thunders subsequently launched successful solo careers, but the influence that the New York Dolls had on punk and beyond is unquestionable.

AFTER THE STORM (New York Dolls & The Original Pistols).
Tracks: Not Advised.
■ LP . . . . RRLP 102
Receiver / Jul '90.
CD .RRCD 102
Receiver / Jul '93 / Total / BMG / Grapevine Distribution.

BACK IN THE U.S.A.
Tracks: Not Advised.
CD .RRCD 163
■ LP . . . . RRLP 163
Receiver / Oct '92.

IN NYC 1975.
Tracks: Not Advised.
CD .RRCD 173
Receiver / Jul '93 / Total / BMG / Grapevine Distribution.

JET BOY.
Tracks: Jet boy / Babylon / Who are the mystery grils.
■ 7" 6160 008
Mercury / Jun '77.

LIPSTICK KILLERS.
Tracks: Bad girl / Looking for a kiss / Don't start me talking / Don't mess with cupid / Human being / Personality crisis / Pills / Jet boy / Frankenstein.
MC . . . . A 104
Reach Out International / '83 / Reach Out Int. Records / Windsong International Ltd.
■ CD . . . . DANCD 038
Danceteria / May '90.

LP . . . . DANLP 038
Danceteria / May '90.

LOOKING FOR A KISS.
Tracks: Looking for a kiss.
■ 12" . . . . DOLLS 12002CV
Dolls / '87.

NEW YOK DOLLS, THE.
Tracks: Personality crisis / Looking for a kiss / Vietnamese baby / Lonely planet boy / Frankenstein / Trash / Bad girl / Subway train / Pills / Private world / Jet boy.
■ LP 6336280
Mercury / '73.

NEW YORK DOLLS, THE.
Tracks: Babylon / Bad detective / Bad girl / Chatterbox / Don't start me to talkin' / Frankenstein / Human being / It's too late / Jet boy / Lonely planet boy / Looking for a kiss / Personality crisis / Pills / Private world / Puss 'n' boots / Showdown / Stranded in the jungle / Subway train / Trash / Vietnamese baby / Who are the mystery girls.
■ MC Set . . . . PRIDC 12
■ Double LP . . . . PRID 12
Mercury / Apr '86.

PERSONALITY CRISIS.
Tracks: Personality crisis.
■ 12" . . . . DOLLS 12001CV
Dolls / '87.

PERSONALITY CRISIS.
Tracks: Personality crisis / Looking for a kiss / Bad girl / Subway train.
■ 12" . . . . SEA 3
■ CD Single . . . . SEACD 3
See For Miles / Jul '90.

PERSONALITY CRISIS EP.
Tracks: Personality crisis / Subway train / Bad girl / Looking for a kiss.
■ 12" . . . . ERA 013/12
Kamera / Feb '86.

PILLS.
Tracks: Pills.
■ 7" .NYD 1
Fan Club / Oct '84.

RED PATENT LEATHER.
Tracks: Girls / Downtown / Pirate love / Personality crisis / Pills / Something else / Daddy rollin' stone / Dizzy Miss Lizzy.
■ LP .FC 007
Fan Club / Sep '84.
■ CD . . . . FC 007 CD
Fan Club / Oct '88.
CD .422253
New Rose / May '94 / Pinnacle / Topic Records / Direct Distribution.

SEVEN DAY WEEKEND.
Tracks: Seven day weekend / Frankenstein / Mystery girls / Showdown / Back in the U.S.A. / Endless party / Jet boy / It's too late / Bad detective / Lonely planet boy / Subway train / Private world / Trash / Human being / Don't start me talking / Hoochie coochie man / Great big kiss / Vietnamese baby / Babylon.
CD . . . . .RRCD 163
Reciever / Jul '93 / Total / BMG.

STRANDED IN THE JUNGLE.
Tracks: Stranded in the jungle / Who are the mystery girls.
■ 7" 6052615
Mercury / Jun '74.

TOO MUCH TOO SOON.
Tracks: Not Advised.
■ LP .6463 064
Mercury / May '81.

Niagara

NOW OR NEVER.
Tracks: Fallen angel / Walking / I will be there / Take my hand / Now or never / I should be stronger / No conversation / You belong to me / Secret lover / Live on the line.
■ LP . . . . KILP 4006
Killerwatt / '88.

RELIGION.
Tracks: Le ciel s'est dechire / Chemin de croix / Au dela de la riviere / Psychotrope / L'ame des vandales / Ma vie est un serpent au coeur froid / J'ai vu / Pendant que les champs brulent / Chien rouge / La vie est peut etre belle / Pardon a mes ennemis.
■ CD 843 446-2
■ LP 843 446-1
■ MC 843 446-4
Polydor / Jul '90.

Night Ranger

BIG LIFE.
Tracks: Big life / Color of your smile / Love is standing near / Rain comes crashing down / Secret of my success / Carry on / Better let it go / I know tonight / Hearts away.
- CD . . . . DMCF 3362
- LP . . . . MCF 3362
- MC . . . . MCFC 3362
MCA / Apr '87.

COLOUR OF YOUR SMILE.
Tracks: Colour of your smile / Girls will like it / When you close your eyes (live) / Don't tell me you love me (live).
- 12" . . . . MCAT 1125
- 7" . . . . MCA 1125
MCA / Apr '87.

DAWN PATROL.
Tracks: Don't tell me you love me / Sing me away / At night she sleeps / Call my name / Eddie's comin' out tonight / Can't find me a thrill / Young girl in love / Play rough / Penny / Night ranger.
- LP . . . . EPC 25301
- MC 40 25301
Epic / Mar '83 / Sony.

DON'T TELL ME YOU LOVE ME.
Tracks: Don't tell me you love me / Night ranger.
- 7" .EP A 3210
Epic / Mar '83.

GREATEST HITS: NIGHT RANGER.
Tracks: You can still rock in America / Goodbye / Sister Christian / Secret of my success / Rumours in the air / Sing me away / When you close your eyes / Sentimental street / Restless kind / Eddie's comin' out tonight.
- LP .MCG 6055
- MC . . . . MCGC 6055
- CD . . . . DMCG 6055
MCA / Jul '89.

MIDNIGHT MADNESS.
Tracks: Rock in America / Rumours in the air / Why does love have to change / Sister Christian / Touch of madness / Passion play / When you close your eyes / Chippin' away / Let him run.
- LP . . . . EPC 25845
- MC 40 25846
Epic / Jan '84 / Sony.
- CD . . . . DIDX 54
- LP . . . . MCF 3209
- MC . . . . MCFC 3209
MCA / Jul '84.

NIGHT RANGER.
Tracks: Not Advised.
- CD . . . . DMCA 112
MCA.

SECRET OF MY SUCCESS, THE.
Tracks: Secret of my success / Carry on / Sister Christian (live) (Extra track on 12").
- 12" . . . . MCAT 1163
- 7" . . . . MCA 1163
MCA / Jun '87.

SENTIMENTAL STREET.
Tracks: Sentimental street / Night machine.
- 12" . . . . .MCAT 973
- 7" . . . . MCA 973
MCA / May '85.

SEVEN WISHES.
Tracks: Not Advised.
- LP . . . . MCF 3278
- MC . . . . MCFC 3278
MCA / Jun '85.

SISTER CHRISTIAN.
Tracks: Sister Christian / Chippin' away
- 7" . . . . MCA 881
MCA / Jun '84.

Nightmare

CHILDREN OF THE NIGHT.
Tracks: Kung fu, karate and tai kwando / Dr. Voodoo / Children of the night / Boogi bogi man / I wanna be a monster in a movie / Drac's back / Young dead heroes / Fly angel fly / Evolution / Video nasties / Schizo psycho homicidal maniac / Cellar / Witch woman / Dance of death.
- LP . . . . RTLP 003
Zarg / Mar '87.

EVOLUTION.
Tracks: Evolution / Ruth Ellis.
- 7" . . . . PV 37
PVK / Apr '80.

I WANNA BE A MONSTER IN A MOVIE.
Tracks: I wanna be a monster in a movie / Boogi bogi man.
- 7" . . . . RTLS 011
Swoop / '86.

I WANNA BE SHOT.
Tracks: I wanna be shot / Ruth Ellis.
- 7" .PVK 119
PVK / '87.

NEW ORLEANS.
Tracks: New Orleans / Drac's back.
- 7" . . . . RTL 001
Swoop / Jan '83.

POWER OF THE UNIVERSE.
Tracks: Not Advised.
- LP . . . . EBON 30
Ebony (Pinnacle) / Apr '85.

Nightshade

DEAD OF NIGHT.
Tracks: Not Advised.
- CD . . . . .CDMFN 122
- LP . . . . MFN 122
- MC . . . . .TMFN 122
Music For Nations / Sep '90 / Pinnacle.

Nightwing

BARREL OF PAIN.
Tracks: Barrel of pain.
- 7" . . . . OVS 1209
Ovation / Jul '80.

NIGHT OF MYSTERY.
Tracks: Night of mystery / Dressed to kill.
- 7" . . . . GULS 77
Gull / Feb '84.

NIGHT OF THE MYSTERY ALIVE ALIVE.
Tracks: Not Advised.
- LP . . . . GULP 1043
Gull / Jun '85.

STAND UP AND BE COUNTED.
Tracks: Not Advised.
- 7" P.Disc . . . . GULP 1038
Gull / Jul '85.

STRANGERS ARE WELCOME.
Tracks: Strangers are welcome / Games to play / Devil walks behind you / Cell.
- 7" Set . . . . GULS 80
Gull / Jun '85.

TREADING WATER.
Tracks: Treading water / Call your name / Barrel of pain.
- 12" . . . . GULS 7512
- 7" . . . . GULS 75
Gull / Jun '85.

Nihilist

BIG DOG E.P.
Tracks: Not Advised.
CD Single . . . . BD 003CD
Big Dog Productions / Aug '94 / Plastic Head.

Nine Inch Nails

An industrial flavoured, progressive, electronic Metal mutant act fronted and, effectively, consisting of Trent Reznor. He claims it's more than a one-man show but it certainly couldn't exist without him. Nine Inch Nails debuted in 1990 with the anthemic *Head Like A Hole* (from the album *Pretty Hate Machine*), one of the songs which introduced the then-newly-christened Industrial Metal genre to a worldwide audience. 1992's low-key follow-up *Broken* (a mini-album) further stretched the boundaries of what Metal music could encompass - as did Reznor's masterstroke of having the whole thing remixed and re-released as *Fixed*. 1994 saw NIN's best moment yet in the form of Downward Spiral and the way ahead for Reznor ought to be onwards and upwards.

BROKEN.
Tracks: Pinion / Wish / Last / Help me I am in hell / Happiness in slavery / Gave up / Physical / Suck.
CD . . . . IMCD 8004
LP . . . . .ILPM 8004
MC . . . . ICM 8004
Island / Oct '92 / PolyGram.

CLOSER.
Tracks: Closer / Closer (Mixes) / Heresy (On ISX/CIDX only) / March of the fuckheads (On ISX/CIDX only) / Memorablia (On ISX/CIDX only).
- 12" . . . . 12 ISX 596
- 12" . . . . 12 IS 596
- CD Single . . . . CIDX 596
- CD Single . . . . CID 596
Island / May '94.

DOWN IN IT.
Tracks: Down in it / Terrible lie.
- 12" 12IS 482
- CD Single . . . . CID 482
Island / Nov '90.

DOWNWARD SPIRAL, THE.
Tracks: Mr. Self destruct / Piggy / Heresy / March of the pigs / Closer / Ruiner / Becoming / I do not want this / Big man with a gun / Warm place / Eraser / Reptile / Downward spiral / Hurt.
CD . . . . CID 8012
LP Set . . . . .ILPSD 8012
MC . . . . .ICT 8012
Island / Mar '94 / PolyGram.

FIXED.
Tracks: Gave up / Wish / Happiness in slavery / Throw this away / First fuck / Screaming slave.
CD . . . . IMCD 8005
LP . . . . .ILPM 8005
MC . . . . ICM 8005
Island / Dec '92 / PolyGram.

HEAD LIKE A HOLE.
Tracks: Head like a hole.
- 10" . . . . 10 ISP 484
- 12" . . . . 12 IS 484
- CD Single . . . . CID 484
- 7" . . . . IS 484
Island / Aug '91.

MARCH OF THE PIGS.
Tracks: March of the pigs / Violent fluid (Not on CIDX 592) / All the pigs, all lined up (On CID 592/12IS 592 only) / Big man with a gun (On CID 592 only) / Underneath the skin (On CIDX 592 only) / Reptilian (On CIDX 592 only).
- 12" 12IS 592
- 7" . . . . IS 592
- CD Single . . . . CIDX 592
- CD Single . . . . CID 592
Island / Mar '94.

PRETTY HATE MACHINE.
Tracks: Head like a hole / Terrible lie / Down in it / Santified / Something I can never have / Kinda I want to / Sin / That's what I get / Only time / Ringfinger.
CD . . . . CID 9973
LP . . . . .ILPS 9973
MC . . . . .ICT 9973
Island / Sep '91 / PolyGram.

SIN.
Tracks: Sin / Get down make love.
- 12" . . . . 12 IS 508
- CD Single . . . . CID 508
- 7" . . . . IS 508
- MC Single . . . . CIS 508
Island / Oct '91.

Nirvana

Although tragically ended by the suicide of Kurt Cobain in February 1994, the story of Nirvana nonetheless contains some of the greatest successes in popular music in the 90's. Formed by Cobain (guitar and vocals) in 1988 as an escape from an unhappy childhood and the chance to play a bit of very heavy punk - "like if Cheap Trick were to have a lot of distortion on their guitars" - Nirvana were quickly signed to Seattle's Sub Pop label and came to the attention of a worldwide audience thank's to their impressive 1989 debut album *Bleach*. Geffen were first in the queue to sign them to a major deal. They had their faith repaid with dividends so handsome it was almost embarrassing, come the release of the *Smells Like Teen Spirit* single and its parent album *Nevermind* in 1991: As sales of the latter rose (now close to 10 million), the always fragile and unstable Cobain began to recoil against the pressures his sudden success and popularity put upon him. Bandmates Krist Novoselic (bass) and Dave Grohl (drums) coped better but 1993's *In Utero* was strained and the band appeared to have split even before Cobain's death. Their legacy is plain to see: generations of Metal fans excited by loud guitars and theatrics

---

suddenly realised that music just as exciting could be played by guys who dressed just like they did, led by a singer who wrote songs about real life rather than traditional Metal fictions and fantasies. Metal would never be the same again.

ALL APOLOGIES.
Tracks: All apologies.
- 12" . . . . .GFST 65
- 7" . . . . GFS 66
- CD Single . . . . .GFSTD 66
- MC Single . . . . .GFSC 66
Geffen / Dec '93.

BLEACH.
Tracks: Not Advised.
- CD . . . . TUPCD 006
- LP . . . . TUPLP 006
- MC . . . . TUPMC 006
Tupelo / Jan '92.

BLEACH.
Tracks: Blew / Floyd the barber / About a girl / School / Love Buzz / Paper cuts / Negative creep / Scoff / Swap meet / Mr. Moustache / Sifting / Big cheese (Available on MC & CD only) / Downer (Only available on CD).
CD . . . . .GEFD 24433
- LP . . . . GEF 24433
MC . . . . .GEFC 24433
Geffen / Aug '92 / BMG.

BLEW.
Tracks: Blew.
- 7" . . . . TUPEP 8
- CD Single . . . . TUPCD 8
Tupelo / Dec '89.

COME AS YOU ARE.
Tracks: Come as you are.
- 12" . . . . DGCT 7
- 7" . . . . DGCS 7
- CD Single . . . . DGCTD 7
- MC Single . . . . DGCTP 7
MCA / Mar '92.

HEART SHAPED BOX.
Tracks: Heart shaped box / Milk it / Marigold.
- 12" . . . . .GFST 54
- 7" . . . . GFS 54
- CD Single . . . . .GFSTD 54
- MC Single . . . . .GFSC 54
Geffen / Aug '93.

IN BLOOM.
Tracks: In bloom.
- 12" . . . . .GFSTP 34
- 7" . . . . GFS 34
- CD Single . . . . .GFSTD 34
- MC Single . . . . .GFSC 34
BMG / Nov '92.

IN UTERO.
Tracks: Serve the servants / Scentless apprentice / Heart shaped box / Rape me / Frances Farmer will have her revenge on Seattle / Dumb / Very ape / Milk it / Penny royal tea / Radio friendly unit shifter / Tourrets / All apologies / Gallons of rubbing alcohol flow through the strip (Features on CD only).
CD . . . . GED 24536
LP . . . . GEF 24536
MC . . . . GEC 24536
Geffen / Sep '93 / BMG.

INCESTICIDE.
Tracks: Dive / Sliver / Been a son / Turnaround / Molly's lips / Son of a gun / (New wave) Polly / Beeswax / Downer / Mexican seafood / Hairspray queen / Aero zepplin / Big long now / Aneurysm.
CD . . . . GED 24504
- LP . . . . GEF 24504
MC . . . . GEC 24504
Geffen / Dec '92 / BMG.

LITHIUM.
Tracks: Lithium.
- CD Single . . . . DGCSD 9
- 12" . . . . DGCTP 9
- 7" . . . . DGCS 9
- MC Single . . . . DGCSC 9
Geffen / Aug '92.

LOVE BUZZ.
Tracks: Nirvana.
- 7" . . . . .SP 023
Sub Pop / '88.

NEVERMIND.
Tracks: Smells like teen spirit / In bloom / Come as you are / Breed / Lithium / Polly / Territorial pissings / Drain you / Lounge act / Stay away / On a plain / Something in the way.

CD . . . . .DGCD 244258
- LP . . . . DGC 244425
MC . . . . DGCC 244425
Geffen / Aug '91 / BMG.
DCC . . . . DGCX 244425
Geffen / Jan '93 / BMG.

OH THE GUILT/PUSS (Nirvana & Jesus Lizard).
Tracks: Oh the guilt / Puss.
- 7" . . . . TG 83
- CD Single . . . . TG 83CD
Touch & Go / Feb '93.

SLIVER.
Tracks: Sliver / Dive / About a girl (live) (Only on 12" and CD Single).
- 7" . . . . TUP 25
- 12" . . . . TUPEP 25
- CD Single . . . . .TUPCD 25
Tupelo / Jan '91.

SMELLS LIKE TEEN SPIRIT.
Tracks: Smells like teen spirit.
- 12" . . . . DGCT 5
- 7" . . . . DGCS 5
- CD Single . . . . DGCTD 5
Geffen / Nov '91.

No Means No

BLOBS VOL.1.
Tracks: Not Advised.
- LP . . . . WD 009
Plastic Head / Jan '92 / Plastic Head.

DAY EVERYTHING BECAME ISOLATED AND DESTROYED, THE.
Tracks: Not Advised.
CD Set . . . . .VIRUS 62/63CD
Alternative Tentacles / Jan '89 / RTM / Pinnacle.

DAY EVERYTHING BECAME NOTHING, THE.
Tracks: Day everything became nothing.
- 12" . . . . VIRUS 062
Alternative Tentacles / Apr '88.

MAMA.
Tracks: Not Advised.
CD .WRONG 001CD
MC . . . . .WRONG 001C
Wrong / Nov '92 / SRD.

MANIC DEPRESSION.
Tracks: Manic depression / Power of positive thinking.
- CD Single . . . . VIRUS 81 CD
Alternative Tentacles / Apr '90.
- 12" . . . . VIRUS 81
Alternative Tentacles / Mar '90.

SEX MAD.
Tracks: Sex mad / Dad / Obsessed / No f.. / She beast / Dead Bob / Long days / Metronome / Revenge / Self pity.
- LP . . . . VIRUS 56
Alternative Tentacles / Jan '88.

SKY IS FALLING, THE (see under Biafra, Jello).

SMALL PARTS ISOLATED AND DESTROYED.
Tracks: Not Advised.
- CD . . . . VIRUS 63CD
- LP . . . . VIRUS 63
Alternative Tentacles / '88.

WHY DO THEY CALL ME MR. HAPPY.
Tracks: Not Advised.
CD . . . . VIRUS 123 CD
LP . . . . VIRUS 123
Alternative Tentacles / May '93 / RTM / Pinnacle.

WRONG.
Tracks: Not Advised.
MC .VIRUS 077MC
Alternative Tentacles / Dec '89 / RTM / Pinnacle.
CD . . . . .VIRUS 077CD
- LP . . . . VIRUS 077
Alternative Tentacles / Oct '89.

No Sweat

HEART AND SOUL.
Tracks: Heart and soul / Diamond rough (Available on 12" and CD single format only) / Walk on by / Tear down the walls (Available on CD single format only.)
- 7" Set . . . . LONB 274
- 12" . . . . LONX 274

- 7" . . . . .LON 274
- CD Single . . . . .LONCD 274
- MC Single . . . . .LONCS 274
London / Sep '90.

NO SWEAT.
Tracks: Heart and soul / Shake / Stay / On the edge / Waters Flow / Tear down the walls / Generation / Lean on me / Stranger / Mover.
CD 828 206 2
- LP 828 206 1
MC 828 206 4
London / May '92 / PolyGram.

ON THE EDGE.
Tracks: On the edge / Just for a day / Storm into the sea (12" & CD single only) / Lean on me (CD single only.)
- 12" . . . . LONX 270
- 7" . . . . .LON 270
- 7" P.Disc . . . . LONPD 270
- CD Single . . . . .LONCD 270
- MC Single . . . . .LONCS 270
London / Jul '90.

TEAR DOWN THE WALLS.
Tracks: Tear down the walls / Ride on by.
- 12" . . . . LONX 257
- 7" . . . . .LON 257
- CD Single . . . . .LONCD 257
- MC Single . . . . .LONCS 257
London / May '90.

TEAR DOWN THE WALLS.
Tracks: Tear down the walls (Not on 12".) / On the edge (Not on 7" EP.) / Sweet nothing blues (Not on 7" EP.) / Tear down the walls (Full length remix) (12" only.) / Lean on me (7" EP only.) / Diamond rough (7" EP only.) / Ball and chain (7" EP only.)
- 12" . . . . LONX 288
- 7" . . . . .LON 288
- CD Single . . . . .LONCD 288
- EP . . . . LONB 288
- MC Single . . . . .LONCS 288
London / Jan '91.

Nocturnal Emissions

BEFEHLOSNOTSTAND.
Tracks: Not Advised.
- LP . . . . SR 5
Sterile / '84.
CD . . . . DV 22
Dark Vinyl / Nov '93 / Plastic Head.

CHAOS.
Tracks: Not Advised.
- LP . . . . CFC LP 2
Cause For Concern / Aug '84.

DEATHDAY.
Tracks: Not Advised.
MC . . . . .SRC 003
Sterile / May '85.

DROWNING IN A SEA OF BLISS.
Tracks: Not Advised.
- LP . . . . SR 4
Sterile / '84.

NO SACRIFICE.
Tracks: No sacrifice.
- 12" . . . . .SR 6
Sterile / Sep '84.

SHAKE THOSE CHAINS, RATTLE THOSE CAGES.
Tracks: Shake those chains rattle those cages (Live at the ICA.)
- LP . . . . SR 009
MC . . . . .SRC 009
Sterile / Jan '86.

SONGS OF LOVE AND REVOLUTION.
Tracks: Not Advised.
- LP . . . . SR 7
Sterile / Jun '85.
CD . . . . DVO 19CD
Dark Vinyl / Sep '93 / Plastic Head.

SPIRIT FLESH.
Tracks: Not Advised.
- LP . . . . EARTH 004
Earthly Delights / Aug '88.

STONEFACE.
Tracks: Not Advised.
CD 841101
LP 081100
Parade Amoureuse / Jan '90.

TISSUE OF LIES.
Tracks: Not Advised.
■ LP . . . . EMISS 001
Sterile / '84.

WORLD IS MY WOMB, THE.
Tracks: Not Advised.
■ LP . . . . EARTH 002
Earthly Delights / Jun '87.

Nocturnus

KEY, THE.
Tracks: Not Advised.
■ LP P.Disc . . . . MOSH 23 P
Earache / Dec '90.
CD . . . . MOSH 23 CD
LP . . . . MOSH 23
MC . . . . MOSH 23 MC
Earache / Sep '90 / Vital Distribution.

POSSESS THE PRIEST.
Tracks: Possess the priest.
7" . . . . DEAD 02EP
Morbid Sounds / Jul '94 / Plastic Head.

THRESHOLDS.
Tracks: Not Advised.
CD . . . . MOSH 055CD
LP . . . . MOSH 055
MC . . . . MOSH 055MC
Earache / Apr '92 / Vital Distribution.

NOFX

10 YEARS OF FUCKING UP.
Tracks: Not Advised.
VHS . . . . NOFXVID 1
Nuclear Blast / Apr '94 / Plastic Head.

LIBERAL ANIMATION.
Tracks: Not Advised.
CD . . . . E 86417 2
MC . . . . E 86417 4
Epitaph / Nov '92 / Plastic Head.

LONGEST LINE.
Tracks: Not Advised.
CD . . . . FAT 503CD
Fat Wreck Chords / Nov '92 / Plastic Head.

PUNK IN DRUBLIC.
Tracks: Not Advised.
CD . . . . E 864352
LP . . . . E 864351
MC . . . . E 864354
Epitaph / Jun '94 / Plastic Head.

RIBBED.
Tracks: Not Advised.
CD . . . . E 864102
LP . . . . E 864101
MC . . . . E 864104
Epitaph / Nov '92 / Plastic Head.

S & M AIRLINES.
Tracks: Not Advised.
CD . . . . E 86405CD
LP . . . . E 864054LP
MC . . . . E 86405MC
Epitaph / Nov '92 / Plastic Head.

WHITE TRASH.
Tracks: Not Advised.
CD . . . . E 864182
LP . . . . E 86418
MC . . . . E 864184
Epitaph / Jun '93 / Plastic Head.

Nonoyesno

DEPSHIT ARKANSAS.
Tracks: Not Advised.
CD . . . . NB 094-2
LP . . . . NB 094
MC . . . . NB 094-4
Nuclear Blast / Feb '94 / Plastic Head.

NONOYESNO: LIVE.
Tracks: Not Advised.
LP . . . . YCR 011
Your Choice / '92 / Plastic Head.

Norum, John

LOVE IS MEANT.
Tracks: Love is meant / In chase of the wind / Don't believe a word / Love is meant (extended mix).
■ 12" 6514936
■ 7" 6514937
Epic / Mar '88.

TOTAL CONTROL.
Tracks: Let me love you / Love is meant / Too many hearts / Someone else here / Eternal flame / Back on the streets / Blind / Law of life / We'll do what it takes together / In chase of the wind.
■ LP 4602031
■ CD 4602032
■ MC 4602034
Epic / Mar '88.

Nosferatu

DIVA.
Tracks: diva / Diva (scarlet mix) / Wiccaman / Her heaven (angelic mix) (12" only) / Arabian heat (MCS only).
■ 12" . . . . POSSTX 004
■ MC Single. . . . . POSSC 004
Possession / Sep '92.

INSIDE THE DEVIL.
Tracks: Inside the devil / Away / Inside the devil (clubmix) / Crystal ring (Features on CDS only).
■ 12" . . . . POSSTX 005
■ CD Single . . . . POSSCDS 005
Possession / Apr '93.

LEGEND.
Tracks: Not Advised.
CD . . . . CLEO 1016-2
Cleopatra / Mar '94 / Plastic Head / Pinnacle.

RISE.
Tracks: Gathering / Rise / Dark angel / Her heaven / Lucy is red / Lament (CD only) / Alone / Vampyres cry / Crysania (CD only) / Siren / Away / Close.
CD . . . . POSSCD 006
LP . . . . POSSTX 006
Possession / May '93 / Vital Distribution.

SAVAGE KISS.
Tracks: Savage kiss / Keeper / Time of legends (On CD single only).
■ 12" . . . . POSSTX 007
■ CD Single . . . . POSSCDS 007
Possession / Nov '93.

VAMPYRES CRY.
Tracks: Vampyres cry / Abominations (Only on 12" single) / Crystal ring (Only on 12" single) / Pictures of betrayal (Only on MC single) / Crysania (Only on MC single).
■ 12" . . . . POSSTX 003
■ MC Single . . . . POSSC 003
Possession / Mar '92.

Not Fragile

WHO DARES WINS.
Tracks: Not Advised.
■ LP . . . . OTH 13
Metalother / Jul '88.
MC . . . . OTH 13C
Metalother / Jul '88 / Backs Distribution.

Notorious

SWALK, THE.
Tracks: Swalk / Eyes of the world.
■ 7" . . . . BYZ 1
Bronze / Nov '90.

Nova, Aldo

ALDO NOVA.
Tracks: Fantasy / Hot love / It's too late / Ball and chain / Heart to heart / Foolin' yourself / Under the gun / You're my love / Can't stop lovin' you / See the light.
■ LP . . . . PRT 85287
Portrait / Jun '82.

BLOOD ON THE BRICKS.
Tracks: Blood on the bricks / Medicine man / Bang bang / Someday / Young love / Modern world / This ain't love / Hey Ronnie (Veronica's song) / Touch of madness / Bright lights.
■ LP 8485131
■ CD 8485132
■ MC 8485134
Mercury / Jun '91.

FANTASY.
Tracks: Fantasy / Under the gun.
■ 7" . . . . A 2081
Portrait / May '82.

HOLD BACK THE NIGHT.
Tracks: Hold back the night / Heart to heart / Monkey on my back / Hot love.
■ 12" . . . . TA 4189

■ 12" . . . . DA 4189
■ 7" . . . . A 4189
Portrait / Jan '84.

MONKEY ON MY BACK.
Tracks: Monkey on my back / Armageddon.
■ 7" . . . . A 3926
Portrait / Nov '83.

SUBJECT.
Tracks: Subject's theme / Armageddon (Race cars) / Monkey on your back / Hey operator / Cry baby cry / Victim of a broken heart / Africa (primal love) / Hold back the night / Always be mine / All night long / Was suite / Prelude to paradise / Paradise.
■ LP . . . . PRT 25482
MC .40 25482
Portrait / Nov '83 / Sony.

TWITCH.
Tracks: Tonite (lift me up) / Rumours of you / Surrender / Your heart / If looks could kill / Heartless / Long hot summer / Fallen angel / Stay / Lay your love on me / Twitch.
■ LP . . . . PRT 26440
MC .40 26440
Portrait / Nov '85 / Sony.

Nuclear Assault

BRAIN DEATH.
Tracks: Brain death / Final flight / Demolition.
■ 12" . . . . 12 FLAG 102
Under One Flag / Jan '87.

FIGHT TO BE FREE.
Tracks: Fight to be free / Equal rights / Stand up.
■ 12" . . . . 12 FLAG 105
■ MC Single. . . . . FLAG 105C
Under One Flag / Aug '88.

GAME OVER.
Tracks: LSD / Cold steel / Betrayal / Radiation sickness / Hang the Pope / After the holocaust / Mr. Softee theme / Stranded in Hell / Nuclear war / My America / Vengeance / Brain death.
■ LP . . . . FLAG 5
Under One Flag / Nov '86.
CD . . . . CDFLAG 5
Under One Flag / Aug '87 / Pinnacle.
MC . . . . TFLAG 5
Under One Flag / Aug '87 / Pinnacle.

GOOD TIMES BAD TIMES.
Tracks: Good times bad times / Hang the Pope (Live) / Lesbians / My America / Happy days.
■ 12" . . . . 12 FLAG 107
Under One Flag / Jul '89.

HANDLE WITH CARE.
Tracks: Not Advised.
CD . . . . CDFLAG 35
■ LP .FLAG 35
MC . . . . TFLAG 35
Under One Flag / Sep '89 / Pinnacle.

HANDLE WITH CARE EUROPEAN TOUR '89.
Tracks: Not Advised.
VHS . . . . LFV 104
Fotodisk Video / May '90.

LIVE AT HAMMERSMITH.
Tracks: Not Advised.
LP . . . . RO 91671
■ CD . . . . RO 91672
Road Runner / May '92.

OUT OF ORDER.
Tracks: Not Advised.
CD . . . . CDFLAG 64
LP . . . . FLAG 64
MC . . . . TFLAG 64
Music For Nations / Sep '91 / Pinnacle.

PLAGUE, THE.
Tracks: Game over / Nightmares / Buttf**k / Justice / Plague / Cross of iron.
■ LP . . . . MFLAG 13
Under One Flag / Jul '87.
MC . . . . TMFLAG 13
Under One Flag / Jul '87 / Pinnacle.

RADIATION SICKNESS.
Tracks: Betrayal / Stranded in hell / Nuclear war / Buttf**k / Justice / My America / Radiation sickness / After the holocaust / Hang the pope / Lesbians / Vengeance.
■ VHS .JE 185
Jettisoundz / Dec '88.

SOMETHING WICKED.
Tracks: Something wicked / Another violent end / Behind glass walls / Chaos / Forge / No time / To

serve man / Madness descends / Poetic justice / Art / Other end.
CD . . . . ALTGOCD 003
Alter Ego / Apr '93 / Vital Distribution.

SURVIVE.
Tracks: Brainwashed / Great depression / Equal rights / Good times bad times / Survive / Wired / Technology.
■ LP . . . . .FLAG 21
Under One Flag / Jul '88.
■ LP P.Disc . . . . FLAG 21P
Under One Flag / Oct '88.
CD . . . . CDFLAG 21
MC . . . . TFLAG 21
Under One Flag / Jul '88 / Pinnacle.

Nuclear Death

CARRION OF WORDS.
Tracks: Not Advised.
CD . . . . WRE 9172
LP . . . . WRE 9171
Wild Rags / Jan '92 / Plastic Head.

Nuclear Valdez

(SHARE A LITTLE) SHELTER.
Tracks: (Share a little) shelter / Summer (acoustic version) / If I knew then (Only on 12" single).
■ 12" 6579016
■ 7" 6575417
■ CD Single 6575419
Epic / Apr '92.

DREAM ANOTHER DREAM.
Tracks: Will / (Share a little) shelter / I think I fell / Dream another dream / Aragon / Dance where the bullets fly / Eve '91 / Without words / Sense her all around / Oba lube.
■ CD 4686822
■ LP 4686821
■ MC 4686824
Epic / Jun '92.

I AM I.
Tracks: Summer / Hope / Trace the thunder / If I knew then / Unsung hero / Strength / Eve / Apache / Run through the fields / Where do we go from here / Rising sun.
■ LP 4659801
MC 4659804
■ CD 4659802
Epic / Apr '90.

SUMMER.
Tracks: Summer / Summer (Acoustic version) / Rising sun.
■ 12" 6559118
■ 7" 6559117
■ CD Single 6559112
■ MC Single 6559114
Epic / Apr '90.

Nudeswirl

NUDESWIRL.
Tracks: Not Advised.
CD . . . . CDZAZ 1
LP . . . . ZAZ 1
Megaforce (USA) / Feb '93 / Pinnacle.

Nugent, Ted

Originator of phrase "If it's too loud, you're too old", Nugent obtained first guitar aged eight. In 1965 he joined Amboy Dukes, who scored U.S. hit with *Journey To The Center Of The Mind*. Assumed leadership of band and became popular concert draw in early '70s. Group billing dropped in '75; Nugent's more successful solo career peaked with 1977's *Cat Scratch Fever* (no. 17 in U.S. and his only Top 30 success in U.K.). Subsequent waning fortunes revived in 1989 by formation of Damn Yankees with Tommy Shaw, ex-Styx. Despite softer AOR sound, Nugent remains outspoken champion of own talents.

ANTHOLOGY - TED NUGENT.
Tracks: Flesh and blood / Weekend warriors / Workin' hard, playin' hard / Snakeskin cowboys / Motor city madness / Scream dream / Come and get it / Smoke screen / Stormtroopin' / Stranglehold / Cat scratch fever / Dog eat dog / Turn it up / Hard as nails / Death by misadventure / State of shock / Where have you been all my life / I love you so I told you a lie / Out of control / Live it up.
MC Set . . . . RAWTC 026
■ Double LP . . . . RAWLP 026

Raw Power / Sep '86.
■ MC . . . . CCSMC 282
■ CD . . . . CCSCD 282
Castle Collector Series / Feb '91.

CALL OF THE WILD.
Tracks: Call of the wild / Sweet revenge / Pony express / Ain't it the truth / Renegade / Rot gut / Below the belt / Cannon balls.
CD . . . . EDCD 278
LP . . . . ED 278
Edsel / Oct '89.

CALL OF THE WILD/ TOOTH FANG (Nugent, Ted & Amboy Dukes).
Tracks: Call of the wild / Sweet revenge / Pony express / Ain't it the truth / Renegade / Rot gut / Below the belt / Cannon balls / Lady luck / Living in the woods / Hibernation / Free flight / Maybellene / Great white buffalo / Sacha / No holds barred.
■ Double LP . . . . K 69202
Discreet (USA) / Feb '77.

CAT SCRATCH FEVER.
Tracks: Cat scratch fever / Wang dang sweet poontang / Death by misadventure / Live it up / Home bound / Workin' hard, playin hard / Sweet Sally / Thousand knives / Fist fightin' son of a gun / Out of control.
■ LP . . . . EPC 82010
■ MC 40 82010
Epic / Jun '77.
■ CD . . . . CD 32252
CBS / Jul '89.

CAT SCRATCH FEVER.
Tracks: Cat scratch fever / Thousand nights.
■ 7" . . . . EPC 5482
Epic / Jul '77.

DOUBLE LIVE GONZO.
Tracks: Not Advised.
■ Double LP . . . . EPC 88282
Epic / Mar '78.

FLESH AND BLOOD.
Tracks: Flesh and blood / Motor city madness.
■ 12" 12 8640
■ 7" . . . . EPC 8640
Epic / Jun '80.

FREE FOR ALL.
Tracks: Free for all / Dog eat dog / Writing on the wall / Turn it up / Together / Street rats / Hammer down / Light my way / I love you so I told you a lie.
■ LP . . . . EPC 81397
Epic / Oct '76.
■ LP . . . . EPC 32065
MC 40 32065
Epic / Jan '84 / Sony.

GREAT GONZOS, THE BEST OF TED NUGENT.
Tracks: Cat scratch fever / Just what the doctor ordered / Free for all / Dog eat dog / Motor city madness / Paralysed / Stranglehold / Baby please don't go / Wango tango / Wang dang sweet poontang.
■ LP . . . . EPC 85408
Epic / Jan '82.
CD . . . . EK 37667
Epic / '88 / Sony.

HOME BOUND.
Tracks: Home bound.
■ 7" . . . . EPC 5945
Epic / Feb '78.

IF YOU CAN'T LICK 'EM, LICK 'EM.
Tracks: Can't live with 'em / She drives me crazy / If you can't lick 'em lick 'em / Skin tight / Funlover / Spread your wings / Harder they come (the harder I get) / Separate the men from the boys, please / Bite the hand / That's the story of love.
■ CD 255385 2
■ LP . . . . K 255385 1
■ MC . . . . K 255385 4
WEA / Feb '88.

INTENSITIES-(IN 10 CITIES).
Tracks: Put up or shut up / Spontaneous combustion / My love is like a tyre iron / I am a predator / Heads will roll / Flying lip lock / Land of a thousand dances / TNT overture / I take no prisoners.
■ LP . . . . EPC 84917
MC 40 84917
Epic / Apr '81 / Sony.

JOURNEYS AND MIGRATIONS.
Tracks: Not Advised.
■ Double LP . . . . MRD 5008
Mainstream / Feb '83.

LITTLE MISS DANGEROUS.
Tracks: High heels in motion / Strangers / Little Miss Dangerous / Savage dancer / Crazy ladies / When your body talks / My little red book / take me away / Angry young man / Painkiller.
■ MC 255388 4
■ CD 252388 2
■ LP 252388 1
WEA / Nov '86.

MARRIAGE AND ON THE ROCKS (Nugent, Ted & Amboy Dukes).
Tracks: Not Advised.
■ Double LP 2664 344
Polydor / Jun '77.

ON THE EDGE.
Tracks: Dr. Slingshot / Night time / You talk sunshine, I breathe fire / Scottish tea / Good natured Emma / Prodigal man / Missionary Mary / St. Philip's friend / Journey to the centre of the mind / Flight of the byrd / Baby please don't go / Inside the outside / Loaded for bear / On the edge.
CD . . . . CDTB 097
MC . . . . THBC 097
Thunderbolt / '91 / TBD / Jazz Music.

OUT OF CONTROL.
Tracks: Not Advised.
CD Set . . . . CD 47039
MC 4047039
Epic / May '94 / Sony.

OVER THE TOP.
Tracks: Down on Philips escalator / Surrender to your kings / Gimme love / For his namesake / I'll prove I'm right / Conclusion/Journey / To the centre of the mind / Migration / Lovely lady / Mississippi murderer / Let's go get stoned / It's not true / Ivory castles / Colours / Over the top.
CD . . . . CDTB 120
MC . . . . THBC 120
Thunderbolt / May '91 / TBD / Jazz Music.

PENETRATOR.
Tracks: Tied up in love / Draw the line / Knocking at your door / Don't you want my love / Go down fighting / Thunderthighs / No man's land / Blame it on the night / Lean mean r'n'r machine / Take me home.
■ LP 780 125-1
Epic / '84.

SCREAM DREAM.
Tracks: Wango tango / Scream dream / Hard as nails / I gotta move / Violent love / Flesh and blood / Spit it out / Come and get it / Terminus Eldora / Don't cry.
■ LP . . . . EPC 86111
Epic / Jun '80.

STATE OF SHOCK.
Tracks: Paralysed / Take it or leave it / Alone / It doesn't matter / State of shock / I want to tell you / Satisfied / Bite down hard / Snake charmer / Saddle sore / Put up or shut up / Spontaneous combustion / My love is like a tire iron / Jailbait / I am a predator / Heads will roll / Lip rock / Land of a thousand dances / T.N.T overture / Take no prisoners.
■ LP . . . . EPC 86092
■ MC 40 86092
Epic / Jun '79.

STORM TROOPIN'.
Tracks: Storm troopin' / Hey baby.
■ 7" . . . . EPC 3900
Epic / Feb '77.

TED NUGENT.
Tracks: No, no, no / Bound and gagged / Habitual offender / Fightin' words / Good and ready / Ebony / Don't push me / Can't stop me now / We're gonna rock tonight / Tail gunner.
■ LP 32028
CBS / '81.
■ LP . . . . K 50898
WEA / Aug '82.

TIED UP IN LOVE.
Tracks: Tied up in love / Lean mean r'n'r machine.
■ 7" . . . . A 9705
Atlantic / Feb '84.

TOOTH FANG AND CLAW.
Tracks: Lady luck / Living in the woods / Hibernation / Free flight / Maybellene / Great white buffalo / Sasha / No holds barred.
CD . . . . EDCD 295
■ LP . . . . ED 295
Edsel / Oct '89.

WEEKEND WARRIORS.
Tracks: Not Advised.
■ LP . . . . EPC 83036
Epic / Jan '78.

WHIPLASH BASH.
Tracks: Not Advised.
■ VHS . . . . HEN 2279
Hendring Video / Oct '90.

Nutz

SICK AND TIRED.
Tracks: Sick & tired / Wallbanger.

■ 7" . . . . AMS 7272
A&M / Jan '77.

Nymphs

NYMPHS, THE.
Tracks: Not Advised.
■ CD . . . . DGCD 24366
■ LP . . . . DGC 24366

■ MC . . . . DGCC 24366
Geffen / Feb '92.

PRACTICAL GUIDE TO ASTRAL PRO-JECTION, A.
Tracks: Imitating angels / Alright / Cum 'n' get it / Wasting my days / Highway.
■ CD . . . . DGCTD 8
■ LP . . . . DGCT 8
■ MC . . . . DGCTC 8
Geffen / Jun '92.

O.L.D.

LO FLUX TUBE.
Tracks: Not Advised.
CD . . . . MOSH 041CD
■ LP . . . . MOSH 041
■ MC . . . . MOSH 041MC
Earache / Oct '91.

Obituary

Five-strong band from Florida (like so many others in the genre) who (unlike many of the others) have made consistently strong records by evolving their sound and refusing to be staightjacketed by the original 'Death Metal blue print' They formed in 1985 (when they were known as Xecutioner) and established themselves with the classic *Slowly We Rot* in 1988. Come 1994's *World Demise* - featuring brothers John and Don Tardy (vocals and drums respectively), Trevor Peres (guitar), Allen West (guitars) and Frank Watkins (bass) - Obituary even looked set to move away from Death Metal altogether although they still weren't prepared to make John Tardy's deathly grunts any easier to decipher by including a lyric sheet!

CAUSE OF DEATH.
Tracks: Infected / Chopped in half / Dying / Cause of death / Turned inside out / Bodybag / Circle of the tyrants / Find the arise / Memories remain.
CD . . . . RO 93072
LP . . . . RO 93071
MC . . . . RO 93074
Roadracer / Sep '90 / Pinnacle.

END COMPLETE, THE.
Tracks: Not Advised.
CD . . . . RC 92012
LP . . . . RC 92011
MC . . . . RC 92014
Road Runner / Apr '92 / Pinnacle.

SLOWLY WE ROT.
Tracks: Not Advised.
CD . . . . RO 94892
■ LP . . . . RO 94891
MC . . . . RO 94894
Roadracer / May '89 / Pinnacle.

WORLD DEMISE.
Tracks: Not Advised.
CD . . . . RR 89955
CD . . . . RR 89952
LP . . . . RR 89951
MC . . . . RR 89954
Road Runner / Sep '94 / Pinnacle.

Oblivion

FROM THIS DAY FORWARD.
Tracks: Not Advised.
■ CD . . . . CDATV 14
■ LP . . . . ATV 14
Active / Oct '90.

Obsessed

CHURCH WITHIN, THE.
Tracks: To protect and to serve / Field of hours / Streamlined / Blind lightning / Neatz brigade / World apart / Skybone / Streetside / Climate of despair / Mourning / Touch of everything / Decimation / Living rain.
CD 476504 2
LP 476504 1
MC 476504 4
Columbia / Apr '94 / Sony.

LUNAR WOMB.
Tracks: Not Advised.
CD . . . . H 0015-2
Hellhound / Jan '92 / Plastic Head.

OBSESSED, THE.
Tracks: Tombstone highway / Way she fly / Forever midnight / Ground out / Fear child / Freedom / Red disaster / Inner turmoil / River of soul.

■ CD . . . . HELLCD 008
■ LP .HELLLP 008
Hellhound / Mar '92.

Obsession

METHODS OF MADNESS.
Tracks: Not Advised.
■ LP 3262 1
Enigma (EMI) / Oct '87.

WITHOUT YOU.
Tracks: Without you.
■ 12" . . . . .12 ALMY 53
■ CD Single . . . . CDALMY 53
Almighty / Mar '94.

Obus

PODEROSO COMOEL TRUENO.
Tracks: Not Advised.
■ LP . . . . SKULL 8343
Mausoleum / Oct '84.

Occult

INTERSINCARNAEL.
Tracks: Intersincarnael.
■ 7" . . . . THRO 16
Thrash / Nov '92.

PREPARE TO MEET THY DOOM.
Tracks: Not Advised.
CD . . . . FDN 2010
Foundation 2000 / Jun '94 / Plastic Head.

Offender

FIGHT BACK.
Tracks: Fight back.
■ 7" . . . . BC 1657
Bitzcore / '89.

TREVOR'S TROUSERS.
Tracks: Trevor's trousers.
■ 7" . . . . P 25
■ 12" . . . . PX 25
Power / Mar '90.

WAIT FOR ME.
Tracks: Wait for me / Trevor's trousers (slop out mix).
■ 12" . . . . PX 25
■ 7" . . . . P 25
Release / Sep '89.

WE MUST REBEL.
Tracks: Not Advised.
■ LP . . . . BC 1656
Bitzcore / '89.

Offspring

COME OUT AND PLAY.
Tracks: Come out and play.
12" . . . . EPUK 001
CD Single . . . . EPUKCD 001
MC Single . . . . EPUKMC 001
Epitaph / Aug '94 / Plastic Head.

IGNITION.
Tracks: Not Advised.
CD . . . . E 864242
LP . . . . E 864241
MC . . . . E 86424-4
Epitaph / Nov '92 / Plastic Head.

SMASH.
Tracks: Not Advised.
CD . . . . E 864321-2
LP . . . . E 864321
MC . . . . E 864321-4
Epitaph / May '94 / Plastic Head.

Old People Are Mad

TRUST.
Tracks: Trust.
■ 7" . . . . WRINK 888
Wrinkley / Feb '85.

Omen

BATTLE CRY.
Tracks: Not Advised.
■ LP . . . . RR 9818
Road Runner / Sep '84.

CURSE, THE.
Tracks: Not Advised.
■ LP . . . . RR 9661
Road Runner / '87.

ESCAPE TO NOWHERE.
Tracks: It's not easy / Radar love / Escape to nowhere / Cry for the morning / Thorn in your flesh / Poisoned / Nomads / King of the hill / No way out.
CD . . . . RR 95442
■ LP . . . . RR 95441
Road Runner / Nov '88.

NIGHTMARES.
Tracks: Not Advised.
■ LP . . . . RR 9617
Road Runner / Jun '86.

SATISFACTION.
Tracks: Satisfaction.
■ 12" . . . . DEBTX 3065
■ 7" . . . . DEBT 3065
Debut (1) / Mar '89.

WARNING OF DANGER.
Tracks: Not Advised.
■ LP . . . . RR 9738
Road Runner / Nov '85.

Only Child

ONLY CHILD.
Tracks: Not Advised.
CD . . . . CDVAG 002
■ LP . . . . LPVAG 002
MC . . . . CASSVAG 002
Savage / Oct '88 / Pinnacle / Sony.

SAVE A PLACE IN MY HEART.
Tracks: Save a place in my heart / Shot heard around the world.
■ 7" 7VAG 002
Savage / Oct '88.

Only Living Witnesses

PRONE MORTAL FORM.
Tracks: Not Advised.
CD . . . . CM 849743-2
MC . . . . CM 849743-4
Century Media / Oct '93 / Plastic Head.
CD . . . . CM 77072-2
Century Media / Jun '94 / Plastic Head.

Onslaught

FORCE, THE.
Tracks: Not Advised.
■ LP . . . . FLAG 1
Under One Flag / Apr '86.
MC . . . . TFLAG 1
Under One Flag / Apr '86 / Pinnacle.
CD . . . . CDFLAG 1
Under One Flag / Dec '88 / Pinnacle.

IN SEARCH OF SANITY.
Tracks: Asylum / Shellshock / Let there be rock / Welcome to dying / In search of sanity / Lightning war / Blood upon the ice / Powerplay.
■ CD 828 142 2
■ MC 828 142 4
■ LP 828 142 1
London / Apr '89.

LET THERE BE ROCK.
Tracks: Let there be rock / Shellshock / Metal forces (on 12" only).
■ 12" . . . . 12 FLAG 103
Under One Flag / Oct '87.
■ 12" . . . . LONX 224
■ 7" . . . . LON 224
■ 12" . . . . LONXP 224
■ 7" . . . . LONB 224
■ CD Single . . . . LONCD 224
London / Apr '89.

MY GENERATION.
Tracks: My generation / Angel of mercy.
■ 7″ . . . . 69 D 17
Creative Reality / May '85.

POWER FROM HELL.
Tracks: Damnation / Onslaught (Power from hell) / Thermo neuclear devastation / Skullcrusher 1 / Lord of evil / Death metal / Angels of death / Devil's legion / Street meets steel / Skullcrusher 2 / Witch hunt / Mighty empress.
■ LP . . . . GURT 2
Children Of The Revolution / Jun '85.
■ LP . . . . FLAG 7
Under One Flag / Mar '87.

SHELL SHOCK.
Tracks: Shellshock / Confused / H-eyes.
■ 12″ . . . . LONX 215
London / Dec '88.

WELCOME TO DYING.
Tracks: Welcome to dying / Nice 'n' sleazy / Atomic punk (Only on 12″ single.).
■ 12″ . . . . LONX 198
■ 7″ . . . . .LON 198
London / Jul '89.

Ophthalamia

JOURNEY INTO DARKNESS, A.
Tracks: Not Advised.
CD . . . . CDAV 003
Avant Garde / May '94 / Plastic Head.

Optimum Wound Profile

LOWEST COMMON DOMINATOR.
Tracks: Drain / Tranqhead / Ego crotch / Downmouth / Blindfold / Incision / Responsibility / Skin / Melt / Damage / Crave (Excerpt).
CD . . . . RR 91272
■ LP . . . . RR 91271
Road Runner / Oct '92.

SILVER OR LEAD.
Tracks: One head two eyes / Nazilover / Twisted / Crotch metal orgasm / Plato O Plomo / Slavetrade / Verfall / Sidewinder / Doghead / Exorcise / Lubricator / Modus Operandi.
CD . . . . RR 90402
LP . . . . RR 90401
Road Runner / Sep '93 / Pinnacle.

Oral

SEX.
Tracks: Not Advised.
■ LP . . . . QUEST 6
Conquest / Sep '85.

Orange

MADBRINGER.
Tracks: Honey let me feel your pussy / Get away / Don't stop I'm stoned again / Release / Madbringer / Got to be / Blood lips / Your eyes call me back to Tokyo / Let the child be born.
■ LP .2121 344
TRB (Yugoslavia) / Jun '84.

Order From Chaos

EVOLUTIONARY ELEMENT.
Tracks: Evolutionary element.
■ 12″ . . . . PUMP(T) 3
Box 52 / Mar '91.

STILLBIRTH MACHINE.
Tracks: Not Advised.
CD . . . . WRR 030
Wild Rags / Aug '93 / Plastic Head.
CD . . . . DEC 006
Decapitated / Apr '94 / Plastic Head.

Organization

FREE BURNING.
Tracks: Not Advised.
CD . . . . CDVEST 23
Bulletproof / Jul '94 / Pinnacle.

ORGANIZATION, THE.
Tracks: Not Advised.
CD . . . . IRS 986972
IRS (Holland) / Nov '93 / Pinnacle.

Osbourne, Ozzy

Fired by Black Sabbath in 1979, Osbourne embarked on a successful, solo career in 1980. First two albums boasted now-legendary guitarist Randy Rhoads, and made Osbourne a superstar. Reputation as exciting performer guaranteed fanatical audiences, particularly in the U.S. Career has been dogged by controversy: death of Rhoads in plane crash, addiction and notorious incident where Osbourne bit head off live dove. Performed with Sabbath at Live Aid, but subsequent reunions have proved abortive.

BARK AT THE MOON.
Tracks: Rock 'n' roll rebel / Bark at the moon / You're no different / Now you see it (now you don't) / Forever / So tired / Waiting for darkness / Spiders.
■ LP . . . . EPC 25739
Epic / Dec '83.
■ LP . . . . EPC 32780
Epic / Apr '86.
■ LP 32780
CBS / Apr '86.
■ MC 40 32780
Epic / Apr '86.
CD . . . . ZK 38987
CBS / Aug '88 / Sony.
CD . . . . CD 32780
Epic / Oct '88 / Sony.

BARK AT THE MOON.
Tracks: Bark at the moon / One up the B side / Slow down.
■ 12″ . . . . TA 3915
■ 7″ .A 3915
Epic / Nov '83.

BARK AT THE MOON.
Tracks: Not Advised.
■ VHS . . . . HEN 2249
Hendring Video / Jun '90.
VHS 041 329 2
Polygram / Jun '92 / PolyGram.

BARK AT THE MOON/THE ULTIMATE SIN/NO REST FOR THE WICKED.
Tracks: Not Advised.
CD Set 4683342
CBS / '91 / Sony.

BLIZZARD OF OZ.
Tracks: I don't know / Crazy train / Goodbye to romance / Dee / Suicide solution / Mr. Crowley / No bone movies / Revelation (mother earth) / Steal away (the night).
■ LP . . . . JETLP 234
Jet / Sep '80.
CD . . . . CD 234
Jet / Jul '86 / Sony / Total / BMG.
MC 4504534
■ LP 4504531
CBS / '87.
CD . . . . CD 84700
CD . . . . CD 65299
CBS / Nov '87 / Sony.

CHANGES.
Tracks: Changes / Changes (live) / No more tears (On CD single only) / Desire (On CD single only).
■ CD Single 659340-2
■ 12″ P.Disc 659340-6
Epic / Jun '93.

CHRIS TETLEY INTERVIEWS OZZY OSBOURNE.
Tracks: Not Advised.
■ LP P.Disc . . . . CT 1010
Music & Media / Oct '87.

CLOSE MY EYES FOREVER (see under Ford, Lita).

CRAZY TRAIN.
Tracks: Crazy train.
■ 7″ . . . . JET 197
Jet / Sep '80.
■ 12″ 6509436
■ 7″ 6509437
Epic / Jun '87.

DIARY OF A MADMAN.
Tracks: Over the mountain / Flying high again / You can't kill rock and roll / Believer / Little dolls / Tonight / S.A.T.O / Diary of a madman.
■ LP . . . . JETLP 237
MC . . . . JETCA 237
Jet / Nov '81 / Sony / Total / BMG.
CD . . . . JETCD 237

Jet / May '87 / Sony / Total / BMG.
CD 4630862
MC 4630864
■ LP 4630861
Epic / Apr '91.

DON'T BLAME ME.
Tracks: Not Advised.
VHS .491032
Sony Music Video / Jan '92 / Sony.

FLYING HIGH AGAIN.
Tracks: Flying high again / I don't know.
■ 7″ . . . . .JET 12107
Jet / Oct '81.

JUST SAY OZZY.
Tracks: Miracle man / Bloodbath in paradise / Shot in the dark / Tattooed dancer / Sweet leaf / War pigs.
MC 4659404
■ CD 4659402
■ LP 4659401
Epic / Mar '90.

LIVE & LOUD.
Tracks: Intro / Paranoid / I don't want to change the world / Desire / Mr. Crowley / I don't know / Road to nowhere / Flying high again / Guitar solo / Suicide solution / Goodbye to romance / Shot in the dark / No more tears / Miracle man / Drum solo / War pigs / Bark at the moon / Mama, I'm coming home / Crazy train / Black Sabbath / Changes.
MC 4737984
■ MiniDisc 4737988
■ CD 4737982
Epic / Jun '93.

MAMA, I'M COMING HOME.
Tracks: Mama, I'm coming home / Time after time (Only on 12″ Single.) / Goodbye to romance (Only on 12″ Single.) / Don't blame me / Ozzy on the Steve Wright Show (Only on CD Single.).
■ 12″ 6576178
■ 7″ 6576177
■ CD Single 6576179
Epic / Nov '91.

MIRACLE MAN.
Tracks: Miracle man / Crazy babies / Liar (Only on 12″ & CD single.)
■ 12″ 6530636
■ 7″ 6530630
■ CD Single 6530632
Epic / Oct '88.
■ 12″ Remix 6530638
■ 7″ P.Disc 6530639
Epic / Oct '88.

MR. CROWLEY.
Tracks: Mr. Crowley / You said it all / Suicide solution (On 12″ only).
■ 12″ . . . . .JET 12-7003
■ 7″ . . . . JET 7003
Jet / Nov '80.

MUSIC AND MEDIA INTERVIEW PICTURE DISC.
Tracks: Not Advised.
■ LP P.Disc . . . . MM 1201
Music & Media / Feb '88.

NO MORE TEARS.
Tracks: No more tears / S.I.N. / Party with the animals.
■ 12″ 6574406
■ CD Single 6574402
■ 7″ 6574407
Epic / Sep '91.
■ MC Single 6574408
Epic / Sep '91.

NO MORE TEARS.
Tracks: Mr. Tinkertrain / I don't want to change the world / Mama, I'm coming home / Desire / No more tears / S.I.N / Hellraiser / Time after time / Zombie stomp / A.V.H. / Road to nowhere.
CD 4678592
■ LP 4678591
MC 4678594
Epic / Oct '91 / Sony.
MiniDisc 467859-3
Epic / Feb '93 / Sony.

NO REST FOR THE WICKED.
Tracks: Miracle man / Devil's daughter (Holy war) / Crazy babies / Breakin' all the rules / Bloodbath in paradise / Fire in the sky / Tattooed dancer / Demon alcohol.
■ LP 4625811
Epic / Oct '88.

■ DELETED

CD. 4625812
MC. 4625814
Epic / May '94 / Sony.

OVER THE MOUNTAIN.
Tracks: Over the mountain / I don't know.
■ 12". . . . . .JET 12017
■ 7". JET 7017
Jet / Dec '81.

OZZY OSBOURNE: INTERVIEW PICTURE DISC.
Tracks: Not Advised.
LP P.Disc. . . . . BAK 2053
Baktabak / Jul '87 / Arabesque Ltd.

SHOT IN THE DARK.
Tracks: Shot in the dark / Rock 'n' roll rebel.
■ 12". TA 6859
■ 7". . . . . .QA 6859
■ 7". . . . . .A 6859
Epic / Jan '86.

SO TIRED.
Tracks: So tired / Forever / Waiting for darkness (On 12" only) / Paranoid (On 12" only).
■ 12". TA 4260
■ 7" Set. . . . . DA 4260
CBS / Mar '84.
■ 12" P.Disc. . . . . .WA 4460
■ 7". . . . . .A 4460
Epic / Mar '84.

SYMPTOM OF THE UNIVERSE.
Tracks: Symptom of the universe nib / Iron man / Children of the grave.
■ 12" P.Disc. . . . . .JETP 7030
■ 7". . . . . JET 12030
Jet / Dec '82.

TALK OF THE DEVIL.
Tracks: Symptom of the Universe / Snow blind / Black Sabbath / Fairies wear boots / War pigs / Wizard / N.I.B / Sweatleaf / Never say die / Sabbath bloody Sabbath / Iron man / Children of the grave / Paranoid.
■ Double LP. . . . . JETDP 401
Jet / Dec '82.
■ Double LP. 4511241
■ MC Set. 4511244
Epic / Sep '87.
■ CD. 4511242
Epic / Jun '89.
■ CD. . . . . CCSCD 296
■ MC. . . . . .CCSMC 296
Castle Classics / Jul '91.

TRIBUTE (Osbourne, Ozzy & Randy Rhodes).
Tracks: I don't know / Crazy train / Believer / Mr. Crowley / Flying high again / Revelation (mother earth) / Steal away (the night) / Suicide solution / Iron man / Children of the grave / Paranoid / Goodbye to romance / No bone movies / Dee (Randy Rhodes studio out-takes).
■ LP. 4504751
MC. 4504754
Epic / May '87 / Sony.
CD. 4504752
Epic / May '87 / Sony.

TRUST ME THE INTERVIEW.
Tracks: Not Advised.
CD P.Disc. . . . . CBAK 4062
Baktabak / Feb '94 / Arabesque Ltd.

ULTIMATE OZZY, THE.
Tracks: Not Advised.
VHS. . . . . .VVD 183
Virgin Vision / May '87 / Gold & Sons / TBD.

ULTIMATE SIN.
Tracks: Ultimate sin / Secret loser / Never know why / Thank God for the bomb / Never / Lightning strikes / Killer of giants / Fool like you / Shot in the dark.
■ LP P.Disc. . . . . .EPC 11 26404
Epic / Aug '86.
■ LP. . . . . EPC 26404
Epic / Feb '86.
CD. CD 26404
Epic / Jul '86 / Sony.

CD. .462496 2
■ LP. 462496 1
MC. .462496 4
Epic / Feb '89 / Sony.

ULTIMATE SIN.
Tracks: Ultimate sin / Lightning strikes.
■ 7". . . . . .A 7311
Epic / Jul '86.

ULTIMATE SIN (SINGLE).
Tracks: Ultimate sin / Bark at the moon / Mr. Crowley / Diary of a madman.
■ 12". 6528756
■ CD Single. 6528752
Epic / Jul '88.

WICKED VIDEOS.
Tracks: Not Advised.
VHS. 490082
CIC Video / '88 / Sony / Pickwick / TBD / Gold & Sons.

Osmium

RISE UP.
Tracks: Not Advised.
CD. DMCD 1032
LP. DMLP 1032
Demi-Monde / Feb '92 / RTM / Pinnacle.

Ostrogoth

DON'T POINT YOUR FINGER.
Tracks: Not Advised.
■ LP. . . . . .SKULL 8374
Mausoleum / Jul '85.

ECSTASY AND DANGER.
Tracks: Not Advised.
■ LP. . . . . .SKULL 8319
Mausoleum / Mar '84.
MC. . . . . .TAPE 78319
Mausoleum / May '84 / Pinnacle.

FEELING OF FURY.
Tracks: Not Advised.
■ LP. . . . . ULT 331804
Ultraprime / Dec '87.

FULL MOONS EYES.
Tracks: Full moons eyes / Heroes museum / Paris by night / Rock fever.
■ 12". . . . . .BONE 128310
Mausoleum / Aug '84.

Outrage

SPIT.
Tracks: Not Advised.
CD. 450994308-2
MC. 450994308-4
WEA / Feb '94 / WEA.

THEME FROM OUTRAGE.
Tracks: Not Advised.
■ 12". . . . . JB 015
■ CD Single. . . . . JB 015CD
Boys Own / Dec '93.

Outside Edge

HEARTBEAT AWAY.
Tracks: Heartbeat away / Out of my head / Soldier boy (Extra track on 12" version only).
■ 7". . . . . TEN 92
■ 12". . . . . .TEN 92-12
10 / Mar '86.

RUNNING HOT.
Tracks: Heartbeat away / Wait / Louella / Don't be a hero / Running hot / Don't leave me tonight / You / Heartbreaker / Hold on.
■ LP. . . . . DIX 24
■ MC. . . . . .CDIX 24
10 / May '86.

Over Kill

FEEL THE FIRE.
Tracks: Not Advised.
■ CD. . . . . .CDNUK 035
■ LP. . . . . NUK 035
Noise / Oct '89.
CD. . . . . .CDMFN 127
LP. MFN 127
MC. . . . . .TMFN 127
Music For Nations / Oct '92 / Pinnacle.

FUCK YOU.
Tracks: Fu** you.
■ 12". . . . . 12 FLAG 104
Under One Flag / Jul '87.

HELL'S GETTING HOTTER.
Tracks: Not Advised.
■ 7". . . . . .SST 008
SST / May '93.

HORRORSCOPE.
Tracks: Coma / Infectious / Blood money / Thanx for nothin' / Bare bones / Horrorscope / New machine / Frankenstein / Live young die free / Nice day.. for a funeral / Solitude.
CD. 7567822832
■ LP. 7567822831
MC. 7567822834
East West / Aug '91 / WEA.

I HEAR BLACK.
Tracks: Dreaming in Columbian / I hear black / World of hurt / Feed my head / Shades of grey / Spiritual void / Ghost dance / Weight of the world / Ignorance & innocence / Undying / Just like you.
CD. 756782476-2
MC. 756782476-4
Atlantic / Apr '93 / WEA.

TAKING OVER.
Tracks: Deny the cross / Wreckin' crew / Fear his name / Use your head / Fatal if swallowed / Power-surge / In union we stand / Electro-violence / Over-kill II.
MC. 781 735-4
■ LP. 781 735-1
Atlantic / Apr '87.
■ CD. . . . . .CDNUK 069
■ LP. . . . . NUK 069
■ MC. . . . . .ZCNUK 069
Noise / Oct '89.

TRIUMPH OF WILL.
Tracks: Not Advised.
■ LP. . . . . .SST 038
SST / Sep '85.
CD. . . . . .SST 038 CD
SST / Oct '93 / Pinnacle.

UNDER THE INFLUENCE.
Tracks: Shred / Never say never / Hello from the gutter / Mad gone world / Brainfade / Drunken wisdom / End of the line / Head first / Overkill III.
CD. 781 865-2
■ LP. . . . . K 781 865 1
MC. . . . . .K 781 865 4
Atlantic / Jun '88 / WEA.

YEARS OF DECAY.
Tracks: Not Advised.
CD. K7 82045 2
■ LP. K7 82045 1
MC. K7 82045 4
Megaforce / Nov '89 / Pinnacle.

Oz

ROLL THE DICE.
Tracks: Not Advised.
CD. BMCD 11
LP. BMLP 11
MC. . . . . .BMCT 11
Black Mark / '92 / Plastic Head.

P

Pagan

PAGAN.
Tracks: Not Advised.
CD . . . . CDUS 18
LP . . . . US 18
U.S. Metal / Sep '90 / Vital Distribution.

Pagan Babies

NFXT
Tracks: Not Advised.
■ LP . . . . HR 9545 1
Hawker / '89.

Page, Jimmy

Experienced session guitarist Page formed Led Zeppelin from ashes of Yardbirds. After end of Zeppelin, Page kept low-profile; producing soundtrack, *Death Wish II*, guesting at ARMS charity gigs and sharing leadership of The Firm with Free singer Paul Rodgers. *Outrider* album, Page's first solo venture since 1965 single *She Just Satisfies*, met muted reception. Tentative efforts to reform Zeppelin came to nothing, Page teaming up instead with Whitesnake's David Coverdale for 1993 *Coverdale Page* album.

1972 INTERVIEW (2).
Tracks: Not Advised.
■ 12" . . . . RAMBLE 3
■ 12" P.Disc . . . . RAMBLE 3P
Wax / Jun '89.

1972 INTERVIEW PART 2.
Tracks: Not Advised.
■ LP . . . . RAMBLE 4
Discussion / Sep '89.

COVERDALE PAGE (see under Coverdale-Page).

JAM SESSION (Page, Jimmy, Sonny Boy Williamson & Brian Auger).
Tracks: Don't send me no flowers / I see a man downstairs / She was so dumb / Walking little girl / How old are you / It's a bloody life / Getting out of town.
■ LP . . . . CR 30193
Charly / Jan '82.

NO INTRODUCTION NECESSARY (Page, Jimmy & Friends).
Tracks: Lovin' up a storm / Everything I do is wrong / Think it over / Boll weevil song / Livin' lovin' wreck / One long kiss / Dixie fried / Down the line / Fabulous / Breathless / Rave on / Lonely weekends / Burn up.
■ LP . . . . THBL 007
MC . . . . THBC 007
Thunderbolt / Sep '84 / TBD / Jazz Music.
CD . . . . CDTB 007
Magnum Music / Apr '93 / Magnum Music Group / TBD.

OUTRIDER.
Tracks: Wasting my time / Wanna make love / Writes of winter / Only one / Liquid mercury / Hummingbird / Emerald eyes / Prison blues / Blues anthem.
CD 9241882
MC . . . . WX 155C
■ LP . . . . WX 155
Geffen / Jun '88.
■ CD . . . . GEFD 24188
■ MC . . . . GEFC 24188
Geffen / Aug '91.

SESSION MAN.
Tracks: Not Advised.
LP . . . . AIP 10041
AIP / Jan '90.
CD . . . . AIP 10041CD
AIP / May '90.

SESSION MAN VOL 2.
Tracks: Not Advised.
CD . . . . AIP 10053CD
LP . . . . AIP 10053
AIP / Jul '90.

SMOKE AND FIRE.
Tracks: Wailing sounds / 'Cause I love you / Flashing lights / Gutty guitar / Would you believe / Smoke and fire / Thumping beat / Union Jack car / One for you baby / L-O-N-D-O-N / Brightest lights / Baby come back.
■ LP . . . . THBL 2.022
MC . . . . THBC 2.022
Thunderbolt / May '85 / TBD / Jazz Music.
CD . . . . CDTB 2.022
Thunderbolt / '86 / TBD / Jazz Music.

WASTING MY TIME.
Tracks: Wasting my time / Writes of winter.
■ 7" . . . . GEF 41
Geffen / Jun '88.

Paice, Ashton, Lord

MALICE IN WONDERLAND.
Tracks: Ghost story / Remember the good times / Arabella / Silas and Jerome / Dance with me, baby / On the road again / Again / Sneaky Private Lee / I'm gonna stop drinking / Malice in Wonderland.
■ LP 2482 485
Polydor / Nov '80.

Pain

PAIN.
Tracks: Not Advised.
■ LP . . . . N 0039
Noise / Jun '86.

Painkiller

BURIED SECRETS.
Tracks: Not Advised.
CD . . . . MOSH 062 CD
LP . . . . MOSH 062
MC . . . . MOSH 062 MC
Earache / Oct '92 / Vital Distribution.

GUTS OF A VIRGIN.
Tracks: Not Advised.
CD . . . . MOSH 045 CD
LP . . . . MOSH 045
■ MC . . . . MOSH 045 MC
Earache / Sep '91.

Pallas

ARRIVE ALIVE.
Tracks: Heart attack / Crown of thorns / Queen of the deep / Ripper.
■ LP . . . . CKLP 002
Cool King / Feb '83.

ARRIVE ALIVE.
Tracks: Arrive alive / Stranger.
■ 7" . . . . GWS 1
Granite Wax / Jun '82.

EYES IN THE NIGHT.
Tracks: Eyes in the night / East West.
■ 7" P.Disc . . . . PLSP 1
■ 12" . . . . 12 PLS 1
■ 7" . . . . PLS 1
EMI / Jan '84.

KNIGHTMOVES TO WEDGE.
Tracks: Not Advised.
CD . . . . CENCD 002
Centaur / Oct '93 / Pinnacle / Harmonia Mundi (UK).

PARIS IS BURNING.
Tracks: Paris is burning / Hammer falls / Stranger on the edge of time.
■ 12" . . . . 12 CK 010
■ 7" . . . . CK 010
Cool King / Apr '83.

SENTINEL.
Tracks: Not Advised.
CD . . . . CENCD 001
Centaur / Oct '93 / Pinnacle / Harmonia Mundi (UK).

SENTINEL, THE.
Tracks: Eyes in the night / Cut and run / Rise and fall / Shock treatment / Art of infinity / Atlantis.
■ MC . . . . TCSHSP 240012
■ LP . . . . SHSP 2400121
Harvest / Feb '84.

SHOCK TREATMENT.
Tracks: Shock treatment / March on Atlantis.
■ 12" . . . . 12 PLS 2
■ 7" . . . . PLS 2
Harvest / Mar '84.

STRANGERS.
Tracks: Strangers / Nightmare / Sanctuary.
■ 12" . . . . 12 PLS 3
■ 12" P.Disc . . . . 12 PLSP 3
■ 7" . . . . PLS 3
Harvest / Apr '85.

THROWING STONES AT THE WINDOW.
Tracks: Cut and run / Crown of thorns (available on 12" version only.) / Throwing stones at the window.
■ 12" . . . . 12 PLS 4
■ 7" . . . . PLS 4
Harvest / Jan '86.

WEDGE, THE.
Tracks: Dance through the fire / Throwing stones at the wind / Win or lose / Executioner (Bernie Goetz a gun) / Million miles away, A (imagination) / Ratracing / Just a memory.
■ LP . . . . SHVL 850
■ MC . . . . TCSHVL 850
Harvest / Feb '86.

WIN OR LOSE.
Tracks: Just a memory / Win or lose.
■ 12" 12PLS 5
■ 7" . . . . PLS 5
EMI / Apr '86.

Pandemonium

HOLE IN THE SKY.
Tracks: Not Advised.
■ LP . . . . RR 9727
Road Runner / Nov '85.

KILL, THE.
Tracks: Not Advised.
■ LP . . . . RR 95371
Road Runner / Aug '88.

Pandora's Box

GOOD GIRLS GO TO HEAVEN (BAD GIRLS GO EVERYWHERE.
Tracks: Good girls go to Heaven (bad girls go everywhere) / Requiem metal / Pray lewd / Pandora's house: room by room (Only on 12" and CD single.).
■ 12" . . . . VST 1227
■ 7" . . . . VS 1227
■ CD Single . . . . VSCD 1227
Virgin / Feb '90.

IT'S ALL COMING BACK TO ME NOW.
Tracks: It's all coming back to me now (Only on 7", MC and 12" single (VSTX 1216) / I've been dreaming up a storm lately (Not on 12" single (VSTX 1216)) / Pray lewd (Only on 12" (VST 1216) and CD singles) / Teenager in love (video prologue) (Only on 12" VSTX 1216).
■ 12" . . . . VST 1216
■ 7" . . . . VS 1216
■ 12" . . . . VSTX 1216
■ CD Single . . . . VSCDX 1216
■ CD Single . . . . VSCD 1216
■ MC Single . . . . VSC 1216
Virgin / Sep '89.

ORIGINAL SIN.
Tracks: Invocation / Original sin (the natives are restless tonight) / Twentieth century fox / Safe sex (when it comes 2 loving U) / Good girls go to heaven (bad girls go everywhere) / Requiem metal / I've been dreaming up a storm lately / It's all coming back to me now / Opening of the box / Want ad / My little red book / It just won't quit / Pray lewd / Future ain't what it used to be.

CD . . . . CDV 2605
■ LP . . . . V 2605
■ MC. . . . . TCV 2605
Virgin / Sep '89.

SAFE SEX (When It Comes 2 Loving U).
Tracks: Safe sex (When it comes 2 loving u).
■ 12". . . . . VST 1275
■ 7". VS 1275
Virgin / Jun '90.

Panic

EPIDEMIC.
Tracks: Not Advised.
CD . . . . CDZORRO 24
LP . . . . ZORRO 24
MC. . . . . TZORRO 24
Metal Blade / Jul '91 / Pinnacle.

FACT.
Tracks: Die tryin' / Close my eyes and jump / Burn
one / Nonchalance / Two things (XYZ) / Hit and
dragged / Rotator / Gone bad / Hell no fuck yes /
Think about it.
CD . . . . CDZORR 060
Metal Blade / May '93 / Pinnacle.

Pantera

Conceived as sub-Kiss U.S. glam outfit,
Pantera reinvented themselves with 1988's
Power Metal album. Fronted by mighty god
of Phil Anselmo, band became hardcore-
tinged metallers, whose '94 album Far
Beyond Driven blasted in at top of U.S.
charts. Pantera look set to be one of this
decade's greatest metal bands.

COWBOYS FROM HELL.
Tracks: Cowboys from hell / Primal concrete sledge /
Psycho holiday / Cemetery gates / Shattered / Medi-
cine man / Sleep / Heresy / Domination / Clash with
reality / Message in blood / Art of shredding.
CD 7567913722
■ LP 7567913721
MC. 7567913724
East West / Jul '90 / WEA.

COWBOYS FROM HELL.
Tracks: Not Advised.
VHS 8536503143
Warner Music Video / Oct '92 / WEA.

FAR BEYOND DRIVEN.
Tracks: Strength beyond strength / Becoming / 5
minutes alone / I'm broken / Good friends and a
bottle of Pils / Hard lines, sunken cheeks / Slaugh-
tered / 25 years / Shedding skin / Use my third arm /
Throes of rejection / Planet caravan.
CD .756792302-2
CD .756792375-2
LP .756792374-1
LP .756792302-1
MC. 756792302-4
Atco / Mar '94 / WEA.

FIVE MINUTES ALONE.
Tracks: Five minutes alone / Badge.
■ 7". .A 8293
Atlantic / May '94.

I'M BROKEN.
Tracks: I'm broken / Mouth of war / Slaughtered.
■ 12". B 5932T
■ CD Single . . . . B 5932CD2
■ CD Single . . . . B 5932CD1
Atco / Mar '94.

POWER METAL.
Tracks: Not Advised.
■ LP . . . . MMR 1988
Metal Magic (USA) / May '88.

VULGAR DISPLAY OF POWER, A.
Tracks: Mouth of war / New level / Walk / Fucking
hostile / This love / Rise / No good for no one / Live
in a hole / Regular people / By demons be driven /
Hollow.
CD 7567917522
■ LP 7567917581
MC. 7567917584
Atco / Feb '92 / WEA.

VULGAR VIDEO.
Tracks: Not Advised.
VHS 853650345-3
Atco / Jan '94 / WEA.

WALK.
Tracks: Walk / No good (attack the radical).
■ 12". . . . . B 6076T
■ CD Single . . . . B 6076CDX

■ CD Single . . . . B 6076CD
Atco / Feb '93.

Panzer

SALVESE QUIEN PUEDA.
Tracks: Not Advised.
■ LP . . . . .SKULL 8342
Mausoleum / Aug '84.

Paradise Lost

GOTHIC.
Tracks: Not Advised.
CD . . . . VILE 026CD
■ MC. . . . . VILE 26MC
Peaceville / Apr '91.
■ LP . . . . VILE 26
Peaceville / Apr '91.

GOTHIC E.P.
Tracks: Gothic (Mix) / Rotting misery (Doom dub) /
Breeding fear (Demolition dub) / Painless (Mix).
CD Single . . . . VILE 041CD
Peaceville / Jul '94 / Vital Distribution / Pinnacle.

HARMONY BREAKS.
Tracks: Oesolate / Mortals watch the day / Joys of
the emptiness / Gothic / Your hand in mine / Pity the
sadness / Shallow seasons / As I die (promo) / Pity
the sadness (promo) / True belief (promo) / Embers
fire (promo) / Outro (Sweetness).
VHS . . . . VFN 13
Video For Nations / Aug '94 / Pinnacle.

ICON.
Tracks: Not Advised.
CD . . . . CDMFN 152DG
CD . . . . CDMFN 152
LP . . . . MFN 152
MC. TMFN 152
Music For Nations / Sep '93 / Pinnacle.

IN DUB.
Tracks: In dub.
■ 12". . . . . VILE 019T
Peaceville / Apr '90.

LIVE DEATH.
Tracks: Deadly inner sense / Frozen illusion / Breed-
ing fear / Paradise lost / Our saviour / Rotting misery
/ Internal torment.
■ VHS . . . . .JE 204
Jettisoundz / Jun '90.

PARADISE LOST.
Tracks: Intro / Deadly inner sense / Paradise lost /
Our saviour / Rotting misery / Frozen illusion /
Breeding fear / Lost paradise.
CD . . . . VILE 17 CD
■ MC. . . . . VILE 17 MC
Peaceville / Apr '90.
LP . . . . VILE 17
Peaceville / Apr '90 / Vital Distribution / Pinnacle.

SEALS THE SENSE EP.
Tracks: Not Advised.
12". 12KUT 157
CD Single . . . . CDKUT 157
Music For Nations / Feb '94 / Pinnacle.

SHADES OF GOD.
Tracks: Not Advised.
CD . . . . CDMFN 135
LP . . . . MFN 135
MC. TMFN 135
Music For Nations / Jun '92 / Pinnacle.

Paradox

HERESY.
Tracks: Not Advised.
CD . . . . RO 95062
■ LP . . . . RO 95061
Roadracer / Dec '89.

PRODUCT OF IMAGINATION.
Tracks: Not Advised.
■ LP . . . . RR 9593
Road Runner / Nov '87.
CD .RO 9593-2
Roadracer / Apr '89 / Pinnacle.

Parasite

PARASITE.
Tracks: Not Advised.
■ LP . . . . SWORDLP 003
Music For Nations / Feb '85.

Pariah

BLAZE OF OBSCURITY.
Tracks: Missionary of mercy / Puppet regime / Can-
ary / Retaliate / Hypochondriac / Enemy within.
CD .857595
■ LP 087594
Steamhammer (Germany) / Jun '89.

KINDRED, THE.
Tracks: Not Advised.
CD .857528
■ LP 087526
Steamhammer (Germany) / '89.

TAKE AND WALK.
Tracks: Not Advised.
■ LP 20002
Mushroom (Australia) / Feb '89.

Parr, John

JOHN PARR.
Tracks: Magical / Naughty naughty / Love grammar /
Treat me a like an animal / She's gonna love you to
death / Revenge / Heartbreaker / Somebody stole
my thunder / Don't leave your mark on me / St.
Elmo's fire.
CD 826 384-2
■ LP . . . . LONLP 12
■ MC. . . . . LONC 12
London / Oct '85.

MAN WITH A VISION.
Tracks: Man with a vision.
■ 12". 12KUT 144
■ 7". . . . . .KUT 144
■ CD Single . . . . CDKUT 144
Music For Nations / Feb '92.

MAN WITH A VISION.
Tracks: Not Advised.
CD . . . . CDMFN 129
LP . . . . MFN 129
MC. TMFN 129
Music For Nations / Jan '93 / Pinnacle.

NAUGHTY NAUGHTY.
Tracks: Naughty naughty / Revenge / Everything
they say is true (Extra track on 12" version only.)
■ 12". . . . . LONX 80
■ 7". LON 80
London / Jan '86.

RESTLESS HEART.
Tracks: Restless heart.
■ 12". 12TX 2
■ 7". 7TX 2
■ CD Single . . . . CDTX 2
Trax / Sep '88.

RUNNING THE ENDLESS MILE.
Tracks: Two hearts / Don't worry 'bout me / King of
lies / Running the endless mile / Don't leave your
mark on me / Scratch / Do it again / Blame it on the
radio / Story still remains the same / Steal you away.
■ LP . . . . .LONLP 23
MC. LONC 23
London / Oct '86 / PolyGram.
CD 830 401 2
London / Oct '86 / PolyGram.

TWO HEARTS.
Tracks: Two hearts / Two hearts (version) / Somebody stole my thunder (Extra track on 12" version
only.).
■ 12". . . . . LONX 100
■ 7". LON 100
London / Sep '86.

Partners In Crime

HOLD ON.
Tracks: Hold on / She's got eyes for you.
■ 12". . . . . TX 4803
■ 7". . . . . .A 4803
Epic / Oct '84.

HOLLYWOOD DREAM.
Tracks: Hollywood dream / She's got eyes for you.
■ 12". . . . . TX 6170
■ 7". . . . . .A 6170
Epic / Apr '85.

MIRACLES.
Tracks: Miracles.
■ 7". . . . . .A 5040
Epic / Jan '85.

ORGANISED CRIME.
Tracks: Hollywood dreams / Miracles / Fools / Hold
on / Gypsy tricks / Heat of the night / No way out of

■ DELETED

here / I can't forget / What does it take / She's got eyes.
■ **LP** . . . . **EPC 26356**
Epic / Jun '85.

Paw

COULDN'T KNOW.
Tracks: Couldn't know / Bridge / Dragline.
■ **7"** 580344-7
■ **CD Single** 580345-2
■ **MC Single** 580345-4
A&M / Jul '93.

DRAGLINE.
Tracks: Gasoline / Sleeping bag / Jessie / Bridge / Couldn't know / Pansy / Lolita / Dragline / Veronica / One more bottle / Sugarcane / Hard pig.
CD. 540 065-2
MC. 540 065-4
A&M / Mar '94 / PolyGram.

JESSIE.
Tracks: Gasoline (Not on 12") / Jessie / Slow burn (On CDs only) / Bridge (On CDs only) / Pansy (On 12" only) / Sleeping bag (On 12" only).
■ **12"** 5802931
■ **CD Single** 5802932
A&M / May '93.
■ **12"** 580561-1
■ **7"** 580560-7
■ **CD Single** 580561-2
■ **MC Single** 580560-4
A&M / Mar '94.

Pearl Jam

Founder members Jeff Ament (bass), Stone Gossard (guitar) and Mike McCready (guitar) were working on what became the *Temple Of The Dog* album (a tribute to the recently deceased Mother Love Bone singer Andrew Wood) when in October 1990 they auditioned singer Eddie Vedder. Vedder, recommended to them by ex-Red Hot Chili Peppers drummer Jack Irons, fitted in straight away and Pearl Jam were born. Although at this stage they were named Mookie Blaycock after New Jersey Jets basketball player, they were rechristened Pearl Jam (after a hallucinogenic preserve made by Vedder's grandmother, Pearl!) come the release of their groundbreaking debut album, 10. It was bursting with mellow-sounding songs delivered in a full-on rock mode and like Nirvana's *Nevermind* before it, found a huge audience - including metal fans looking for something new and vital. Follow-up *V's* came within spitting distance of selling a million in its first week of release and broke the previous world record for such sales. But Pearl Jam aren't interested in records like that, only records full of intense and well-reasoned songs.

ALIVE.
Tracks: Alive / Once / Wash (Only on 12" and CD Single.).
■ **12"** 6575726
■ **CD Single** 6575722
■ **MC Single** 6575724
Epic / Feb '92.

DAUGHTER.
Tracks: Daughter / Blood / Yellow Ledbetter (On CD single & 12" only).
■ **12"** 660020 6
■ **7"** 660020 7
■ **CD Single** 660029 2
■ **MC Single** 660020 4
Epic / Dec '93.

DISSIDENT.
Tracks: Dissident / Rearviewmirror (Live) / Release (Live) / Even flow (Live) / Dissident (Live) (Features on 660441 5 CDS only.) / Why go (Live) (Features on CDS 660441 5 only.) / Deep (Live) (Features on CDS 660441 5 only.).
■ **7"** 660441 7
■ **CD Single** 660441 5
■ **CD Single** 660441 2
Epic / May '94.

EVEN FLOW.
Tracks: Even flow (new version) / Oceans.
■ **7"** 6578577
■ **CD Single** 6578572
■ **MC Single** 6578574
Epic / Apr '92.

GO.
Tracks: Go / Elderly woman behind the counter in a small town / Alone / Animal (live).

■ **12"** 659795 6
■ **CD Single** 659795 2
Epic / Oct '93.

JEREMY.
Tracks: Jeremy / Alive.
■ **MC Single** 658258 4
■ **12"** 6582586
■ **7"** 6582587
■ **CD Single** 6582582
Epic / Sep '92.

PEARL JAM.
Tracks: Go / Animal / Daughter / Glorified G / Dissident / W.M.A. / Blood / Rear view mirror / Rats / Elderly woman behind the counter in a small town / Leash / Indifference.
CD. 474549 2
LP. 474549 1
MC. 474549 4
MiniDisc. 474549 8
Epic / Oct '93 / Sony.

TEN.
Tracks: Once / Even flow / Alive / Why go / Black / Jeremy / Oceans / Porch / Garden / Deep / Release / Master/Slave.
CD. 468884 5
Epic / Dec '92 / Sony.
CD. 4688842
LP. 4688841
MC. 4688844
Epic / Feb '92 / Sony.
■ **LP P.Disc**. 4688840
Epic / Mar '92.
MiniDisc. 468884-3
Epic / Feb '93 / Sony.

Pell, Axel Rudi

BALLADS, THE.
Tracks: Not Advised.
CD. . . . . SPV 084-76642
Steamhammer (Germany) / Jul '93 / Pinnacle.

BETWEEN THE WALLS.
Tracks: Not Advised.
CD. SPV084-76822
Nosferatu / Jun '94 / Plastic Head.

Pentagram

DAY OF RECKONING.
Tracks: Day of reckoning / Broken vows / Madman / When the screams come / Burning saviour / Evil seed / Wartime.
■ **LP** . . . . **FLAME 6**
Firebird / Jun '87.
CD. . . . . VILE 040CD
LP. . . . . VILE 040
Peaceville / Aug '93 / Vital Distribution / Pinnacle.

PENTAGRAM.
Tracks: Not Advised.
■ **LP** . . . . **DEVIL 4**
Pentagram / Jul '85.

RELENTLESS.
Tracks: Death row / All your sins / Sign of the wolf / Ghoul / Relentless / Run my course / Sinister / Deist / You're lost, I'm free / Dying world / 20 Buck spin.
CD. . . . . VILE 038CD
LP. . . . . VILE 038
Peaceville / Apr '93 / Vital Distribution / Pinnacle.

Perry, Joe

LET THE MUSIC DO THE TALKING (Joe Perry Project).
Tracks: Let the music do the talking / Conflict of interest / Discount dogs / Shooting star / Break song / Rockin' train / Mist is rising / Ready on the firing line / Life at a glance.
■ **LP** . . . . **CBS 84213**
CBS / Jul '80.

ONCE A ROCKER, ALWAYS A ROCKER (Perry, Joe Project).
Tracks: Once a rocker, always a rocker / Black velvet pants / Woman in chains / Guns West / Crossfire / Adrianna / King of the Kings / Get it on (bang a gong) / Walk with me Sally / Never wanna stop.
■ **LP** . . . . MCF 3205
■ **MC** . . . . MCFC 3205
MCA / Jan '84.

Persian Risk

RIDIN' HIGH.
Tracks: Riding high / Hurt you.
■ **7"** . . . . .NEAT 24
Neat / Mar '83.

RISE UP.
Tracks: Not Advised.
■ **LP** . . . . .METALLP 2
Razor / May '86.

TOO DIFFERENT, TWO PEOPLE.
Tracks: Too different, two people / Dark tower / Sky's falling down.
■ **12"** . . . . 12 RA 3
Zebra (1) / Jul '84.

Pestilence

CONSUMING IMPULSE.
Tracks: Not Advised.
■ **LP** . . . . RO 94211
Roadracer / Dec '89.
MC. . . . . RO 94214
Road Runner / Dec '89 / Pinnacle.
CD. . . . . RO 94212
Roadracer / Jan '94 / Pinnacle.

MALLEUS MALEFICARUM.
Tracks: Malleus Maleficarum / Subordinate to the domination / Commandments / Bacterial surgery / Osculum inflame / Parricade / Extreme unction / Chemo therapy / Cycle of existance / Systematic instruction.
■ **LP** . . . . RR 95191
■ **LP** . . . . RR 95192
Road Runner / Oct '88.

SPHERES.
Tracks: Mind reflections / Multiple beings / Level of perception / Aurian eyes / Soul search / Personal energy / Voices from within / Spheres / Changing perspective / Phileas / Demise of time.
CD. . . . . CD RR 9081 2
LP. . . . . .RR LP 9081 1
MC. . . . . MC RR 9081 4
Road Runner / Aug '93 / Pinnacle.

TESTIMONY OF THE ANCIENTS.
Tracks: Not Advised.
MC. . . . . RC 92854
■ **LP**. . . . . RC 92851
Road Runner / Sep '91.
CD. . . . . RC 92852
Road Runner / Jan '94 / Pinnacle.

Pet Hate

BAD PUBLICITY.
Tracks: I'm not the one / Girls grow up too fast / Cry of the wild / Street fighting man / She's got the action.
■ **LP** . . . . HMRLP 23 W
MC. . . . . HMRMC 23
Heavy Metal / Dec '84 / Sony / FM Revolver.
■ **LP** . . . . HMRLP 23
Heavy Metal / Dec '85.

BLOWN OUT AGAIN.
Tracks: Blown out again.
■ **12"** . . . . EARFITS 1
Trapper / Mar '84.

BRIDE WORE RED, THE.
Tracks: Bride wore red / Moya's comim' out / How can I carry on / Love me madly / Wanting you / Caught (red handed) / Party's over / Roll away the stone / First kiss / Real good time.
■ **LP** . . . . HMRLP 17
MC. . . . . HMRMC 17
Heavy Metal / Apr '84 / Sony / FM Revolver.

GIRLS GROW UP TOO FAST.
Tracks: Girls grow up too fast.
■ **7"** . . . . VHF 8
Fobik / Apr '85.

ROLL AWAY THE STONE.
Tracks: Roll away the stone.
■ **12"** . . . . 12 VHF 2
FM Records / Jul '84.

Petra

BACK TO THE STREET.
Tracks: Not Advised.
CD. . . . . SRCD 2073
■ **LP** . . . . SR R 2073
MC. . . . . SR C 2073
Star Song / Jan '87 / Word Records (UK) / Sony.

BEAT THE SYSTEM.
Tracks: Not Advised.
CD . . . . .SS D 8057
Star Song / Word Records (UK) / Sony.
■ LP . . . . .SR R 2057
MC . . . . .SR C 2057
Star Song / '85 / Word Records (UK) / Sony.

CAPTURED IN TIME AND SPACE.
Tracks: Not Advised.
■ LP . . . . .SR R 2065
MC . . . . .SR C 2065
Star Song / Aug '86 / Word Records (UK) / Sony.

CAPTURED IN TIME AND SPACE.
Tracks: Not Advised.
VHS . . . . .MV 5025
Word (UK) / Jul '89 / Word Records (UK) / Sony.

MORE POWER TO YA.
Tracks: Not Advised.
MC . . . . SR C 397
■ LP . . . . SR R 397
Star Song / '83.

NEVER SAY DIE.
Tracks: Not Advised.
CD . . . . .SS D 8016
Star Song / Word Records (UK) / Sony.
■ LP . . . . .SR R 357
MC . . . . .SR C 357
Star Song / '82 / Word Records (UK) / Sony.

NOT OF THIS WORLD.
Tracks: Not Advised.
CD . . . . .SS D 8050
Star Song / Word Records (UK) / Sony.
■ LP . . . . .SR R 418
MC . . . . .SR C 418
Star Song / '83 / Word Records (UK) / Sony.

ON FIRE.
Tracks: Not Advised.
CD . . . . .SS D 8106
■ LP . . . . .SS R 8106
MC . . . . .SS C 8106
Star Song / '87 / Word Records (UK) / Sony.

PETRA PRAISE (the rock cries out).
Tracks: Not Advised.
CD . . . . DAYCD 4184
Dayspring / Dec '89 / Word Records (UK) / Sony.
■ LP . . . . .DAY R 4184
MC . . . . .DAY C 4184
Dayspring / Nov '89 / Word Records (UK) / Sony.

THIS MEANS WAR!.
Tracks: Not Advised.
CD . . . . .SS D 8084
■ LP . . . . .SR R 8084
MC . . . . .SR C 8084
Star Song / Sep '87 / Word Records (UK) / Sony.

WASHES WHITER THAN SNOW.
Tracks: Not Advised.
■ LP . . . . .SR R 327
■ MC . . . . .SR C 327
Star Song / '79.

Phantom

DEAD OR ALIVE.
Tracks: Dead or alive / Under the gun / Punish the sinner / Stand / Black widow / Take me down slow / Dead of night / Turbo-charged.
MC . . . . NRC 14
New Renaissance(USA) / Nov '87 / Pinnacle.
■ LP . . . . NRR 14
New Renaissance(USA) / Nov '87.
■ LP . . . . US 12
U.S. Metal / Mar '88.
CD . . . . CDUS 12
U.S. Metal / May '88 / Vital Distribution.

PHANTOM.
Tracks: Not Advised.
CD . . . . SHARK 023CD
LP . . . . SHARK 023
Shark / Jan '92 / Plastic Head.

Phantom Blue

Founded in Los Angeles, 1988, by guitarists Michelle Meldrum and Nicole Couch. 1989 debut attracted rave reviews but scant sales; belated follow-up *Built To Perform* emerged in 1993. Producers involved with band include Marty Friedman, who joined Megadeth in 1990, and Don Dokken, of Dokken.

BUILT TO PERFORM.
Tracks: Not Advised.
CD . . . . RR 90272
LP . . . . RR 90271
MC . . . . RR 90274
Road Runner / Oct '93 / Pinnacle.

PHANTOM BLUE.
Tracks: Not Advised.
CD . . . . .RR 9469 2
■ LP . . . . .RR 9469 1
■ MC . . . . .RR 9469 4
Road Runner / Jun '89.

Phenomena

DANCE WITH THE DEVIL.
Tracks: Dance with the devil / Hell on wings.
■ 12" . . . . .BROX 193
■ 7" . . . . BRO 193
Bronze / Jun '85.

Phillips, Simon

PROTOCOL.
Tracks: Streetwise / Protocol / V8 / Red rocks / Slofunk / Wall Street.
■ LP . . . . .GRUB 10 M
MC . . . . GRUB 10 MD
Food For Thought / Dec '88 / Pinnacle.
CD . . . . GRUB 10 MCD
Food For Thought / Dec '88 / Pinnacle.

Picture

DIAMOND DREAMER.
Tracks: Lady lightning / Night hunter / Hot lovin' / Diamond dreamer / Message from hell / You're all alone / Lousy lady / Hangmen / Get me rock and roll / You're touching me.
■ LP 6350 065
Back Door / Dec '83.

ETERNAL DARK.
Tracks: Not Advised.
■ LP . . . . .CAL 217
MC . . . . .CAC 217
Carrere / Jul '85 / WEA.

HEAVY METAL EARS.
Tracks: Not Advised.
■ LP 6530 058
Philips (Holland) / Feb '82.

MARATHON.
Tracks: Breakaway / Vampire of the new age / Money / Desperate call / I'm on my way / S.O.S. / Get out of my sight / We just can't lose / Don't keep me waiting.
■ LP . . . . .CAL 228
Carrere / Mar '88.

NIGHT HUNTER.
Tracks: Lady lightning / Night hunter / Hot lovin' / Diamond dreamer / Message from hell / You're all alone / Lousy lady / Hangmen / Get me rock and roll / You're touching me.
■ LP . . . . .CAL 146
MC . . . . .CAC 146
Carrere / Jul '83 / WEA.

Pigface

FOOK.
Tracks: Not Advised.
CD . . . . .CDDVN 18
LP . . . . DVN 18
MC . . . . .TDVN 18
Music For Nations / Oct '92 / Pinnacle.

GLITCH.
Tracks: Not Advised.
VHS . . . . VFN 7
Video For Nations / Jul '92 / Pinnacle.

GUB.
Tracks: Not Advised.
CD . . . . CDDVN 2
LP . . . . DVN 2
MC . . . . .TDVN 2
Devotion / Sep '91 / Pinnacle.

GUB.
Tracks: Tapeworm / Bushmaster / Cylinder head world / Point blank / Suck / Symphony for taps / Greenhouse / Little sisters / Tailor made / War ich nicht immer ein guter junge / Blood and sand / Weightless.
CD . . . . CDGRAM 47
LP . . . . GRAM 47
MC . . . . .GRAMC 47
Anagram / Feb '91 / Pinnacle.

LEAN JUICY PORK.
Tracks: Not Advised.
CD . . . . INV 012-2
LP . . . . INV 012
Invisible / Jul '93 / Plastic Head.

NOTES FROM THEE UNDERGROUND.
Tracks: Ashole / Divebomber / Your own you own / Fuck it up / Hagseed / Chickasaw / Empathy / Magazine / Think / Trivial scene / Slut/Blood/Pain / Psalm springs eternal / Steamroller / Your music is garbage.
CD . . . . .CDDVN 29
Devotion / May '94 / Pinnacle.

SPOON BREAKFAST.
Tracks: Spoon breakfast.
■ 12" . . . . INV 008
Invisible / Jul '93.

TRUTH WILL OUT.
Tracks: Not Advised.
CD . . . . .CDDVN 25
Devotion / Jan '94 / Pinnacle.

WELCOME TO MEXICO..ASSHOLE.
Tracks: Not Advised.
CD . . . . CDTDVN 3
LP . . . . DVN 3
MC . . . . .TDVN 3
Devotion / Nov '91 / Pinnacle.

Piledriver

METAL INQUISITION.
Tracks: Metal inquisition / Sex with Satan / Sodomize the deed / Witch hunt / Pile driver / Human sacrifice / Alien rape.
■ LP . . . . .RR 9762
Road Runner / Sep '85.

STAY UGLY.
Tracks: Not Advised.
CD . . . . RR 9701
Road Runner / Jul '86.

Pink Cream 69

49 DEGREES/8 DEGREES.
Tracks: Talk to the moon (long version 91) / Where the eagle learns to fly (acoustic 91) / Detroit Rock City (live studio jam 91) / Ballerina (acoustic remake 91) / Everybody's somebody (remixed demo version 88) / White men do reggae (live version 90) / Greetings.
■ CD 4694912
■ MC 4694911
Epic / Mar '92.

Pink Fairies

Evolving in 1969 from underground group Deviants, Pink Fairies enjoy cult following but 1972's *What A Bunch Of Sweeties* album (U.K. no. 48) remains sole commercial success. Often associated with Hawkwind, who poached Fairies' Paul Rudolph in 1975. Main claim to metal fame is harbouring of future Motorhead guitarist Larry Wallis.

BEST OF THE PINK FAIRIES, THE.
Tracks: Snake / City kids / Wargirl / Portobello shuffle / Heavenly man / Do it / Pigs of uranus / Well well well / Chromium plating / I went up I went down / Say you love me / Street urchin.
CD 8438942
MC 8438944
Polydor / Oct '90 / PolyGram.

KILL EM 'N EAT' EM.
Tracks: Broken statue / Fear of love / Undercover of confusion / Waiting for the ice cream to melt / Taking LSD / White girls on amphetamine / Seeing double / Fool about you / Bad attitude / I might be lying.
■ LP . . . . .FIEND 105
Demon / Oct '87.
CD . . . . .FIENDCD 105
Demon / Oct '90 / Pinnacle / A.D.A. Distribution.

■ DELETED

LIVE AT THE ROUNDHOUSE.
Tracks: City kids / Waiting for the man / Lucille / Uncle Harry's last freakout / Going down.
■ LP . . . . WIK 14
Big Beat / Jul '82.
CD . . . . CDWIK 965
Big Beat / Jul '91 / Pinnacle / Hot Shot / Jazz Music.

NEVER NEVER LAND.
Tracks: Not Advised.
■ LP 2383 045
Polydor / '74.

POLICE CAR.
Tracks: Police car.
■ CD Single . . . . TRUCKCDEP 1
Terrapin Truckin' / Mar '94.

PREVIOUSLY UNRELEASED.
Tracks: As long as the price is right / Waiting for the lightning to strike / Can't find the lady / No second chance / Talk of the devil / I think it's coming back again.
■ LP . . . . NED 9
Big Beat / Oct '84.

WHAT A BUNCH OF SWEETIES.
Tracks: Prologue / Right on fight on / Portobello shuffle / Marilyn pigs of Uranus / Walk don't run / I went up, I went down / X ray / I saw her standing there.
■ LP 2383 132
Polydor / '74.

Pink Floyd

From their psychedelic beginnings, Pink Floyd's image was based on spectacular live shows and intricate, often instrumental music. Their 1973 classic, *Dark Side Of The Moon*, paved the way for a succession of multi-million sellers, notably *The Wall*, in 1979. The latter yielded a chart-topping single *Another Brick In The Wall*, a film and a series of legendary concerts. The band survived the loss of chief songwriters, Syd Barrett (fired in 1968) and Roger Waters (quit in 1985), both of whom embarked on relatively successful solo careers. Now led by guitarist Dave Gilmour, Floyd continue to enjoy massive album and ticket sales around the world.

ANIMALS.
Tracks: Pigs on the wing (part one) / Dogs / Pigs (three different ones) / Sheep / Pigs on the wing (part two).
■ LP . . . . SHVL 815
■ LP Q4SHVL 815
■ MC . . . . TCSHVL 815
Harvest / Feb '77.
■ CD . . . . CDP 746 128 2
Harvest / Jul '86.
CD . . . . CDEMD 1060
MC . . . . TCEMD 1060
EMI / Aug '94 / EMI.

ANOTHER BRICK IN THE WALL.
Tracks: Another brick in the wall.
■ 7" . . . . HAR 5194
Harvest / Nov '79.

ARNOLD LAYNE.
Tracks: Arnold Layne.
■ 7" . . . . DB 8156
Columbia (EMI) / Mar '67.

ATOM HEART MOTHER.
Tracks: Rise and shine / Sunny side up / Morning glory / Remergence / Father's shout / Breast milky / Mother fore / Funky dung / Mind your throats please / If / Summer '68 / Fat old sun / Alan's psychedelic breakfast.
■ LP . . . . SHVL 781
MC . . . . TCSHVL 781
Harvest / Jun '74 / EMI.
CD . . . . CDP 746 381 2
Harvest / Mar '87 / EMI.

COLLECTION OF GREAT DANCE SONGS, A.
Tracks: One of these days / Money / Another brick in the wall (part 2) / Wish you were here / Shine on you crazy diamond / Sheep.

■ LP . . . . SHVL 822
Harvest / Dec '81.
■ LP . . . . FA 3144
MC . . . . TCFA 3144
Fame / Nov '85 / EMI.
CD . . . . CDP 790 732 2
EMI / Nov '88 / EMI.

COLLECTION: PINK FLOYD.
Tracks: Not Advised.
CD 32DP 363
CBS / '88 / Sony.

DARK SIDE OF THE MOON.
Tracks: Speak to me / Breath in the air / On the run / Time / Great gig in the sky / Money / Us and them / Any colour you like / Brain damage / Eclipse.
■ LP . . . . SHVL 804
■ MC . . . . TCSHVL 804
Harvest / Mar '73.
■ CD . . . . CDSHVL 804
Harvest / Aug '84.
■ CD . . . . CDDSOM 20
EMI / Mar '93.
CD . . . . CDEMD 1064
MC . . . . TCEMD 1064
EMI / Aug '94 / EMI.

DELICATE SOUND OF THUNDER.
Tracks: Shine of you crazy diamond / Learning to fly / Yet another movie / round and 'round / Sorrow / Dogs of war / On the turning away / One of these days / Timed / Wish you were here / Us and them (Cassette & CD only.) / Money (Album & CD only.) / Another brick in the wall (part 2) / Comfortably numb / Run like hell.
CD Set . . . . CDEQ 5009
■ Double LP . . . . EQ 5009
MC Set . . . . TCEQ 5009
EMI / Nov '88 / EMI.

DELICATE SOUND OF THUNDER.
Tracks: Shine on you crazy diamond / Sorrow / One of these days / On the run / One the turning away / Wish you were here / One slip / Signs of life / Learning to fly / Dogs of war / Us and them / Time / Great gig in the sky / Comfortably numb / Run like hell / Shine on you crazy diamond (reprise).
VHS . . . . MVN 99 1186 3
PMI / Jun '89 / EMI / Gold & Sons / TBD.
VCD . . . . PMCD 4912752
PMI / Jul '94 / EMI / Gold & Sons / TBD.

DIVISION BELL, THE.
Tracks: Cluster one / What do you want from me / Poles apart / Marooned / Great day for freedom / Wearing the inside out / Take it back / Coming back to life / Keep talking / Lost for words / High hopes.
CD . . . . CDEMD 1055
LP . . . . EMD 1055
MC . . . . TCEMD 1055
EMI / Apr '94 / EMI.
MiniDisc . . . . MDEMD 1055
EMI / Sep '94 / EMI.

FINAL CUT, THE.
Tracks: Postwar dream / Your possible / One of the few / Hero's return / Gunner's dream / Paranoid eyes / Get your filthy hands off my desert / Fletcher memorial home / Southampton dock / Final cut / Not now John / Two suns in the desert.
■ LP . . . . SHPF 1983
MC . . . . TCSHPF 1983
Harvest / Mar '83 / EMI.
CD . . . . CDP 746 129 2
Harvest / Jun '86 / EMI.

LA CARRERA PANAMERICANA.
Tracks: Run like hell / Pan Am shuffle / Yet another movie / Sorrow / Signs of life / Country theme / Mexico '78 / Big theme / One slip / Small theme / Carrera slow blues.
■ VHS . . . . MVN 9913453
PMI / Mar '92.
VHS . . . . MC 2134
Music Club / Mar '94 / Gold & Sons / TBD / Video Collection / C.M. Distribution.

LEARNING TO FLY.
Tracks: One slip (Edited version) / Terminal frost (LP version) / Terminal frost (dyol version) / Learning to fly.
■ CD Single . . . . CDEM 26
EMI / Aug '87.

LIVE AT POMPEII.
Tracks: Careful with that axe Eugene / Saucerful of secrets / One of these days I'm going to cut you inot little pieces / Set the controls for the heart of the sun / Mademoiselle nobs.
VHS . . . . CFV 05182

Channel 5 / '88 / Channel 5 Video / P.R.O. Video / Gold & Sons.
VHS . . . . .PM 0010
Channel 5 / Aug '88 / Channel 5 Video / P.R.O. Video / Gold & Sons.
Laser Disc 080 730 1
Polygram Music Video / Nov '89 / PolyGram.
VHS . . . . CFV 10422
Channel 5 / Mar '90 / Channel 5 Video / P.R.O. Video / Gold & Sons.

LONDON 66-67.
Tracks: Not Advised.
VHS . . . . PFV 1
See For Miles / Sep '94 / Pinnacle.

MEDDLE.
Tracks: One of these days / Pillow of winds / Fearless (Interpolating) / San Tropez / Seamus / Echoes.
■ LP . . . . ATAK 35
■ LP . . . . SHVL 795
■ MC . . . . TOATAK 33
■ MC . . . . TCSHVL 795
Harvest / Nov '71.
■ CD . . . . CDP 746 034 2
Harvest / Aug '84.
CD . . . . CDEMD 1061
MC . . . . TCEMD 1061
EMI / Aug '94 / EMI.

MOMENTARY LAPSE OF REASON, A.
Tracks: Signs of life / Learning to fly / Dogs of war / One slip / On the turning away / Yet another movie / round and 'round / New machine (part 1) / Terminal frost / New machine (part 2) / Sorrow.
CD . . . . CDEMD 1003
MC . . . . TCEMD 1003
■ LP . . . . EMD 1003
EMI / Sep '87.
■ LP . . . . EMDS 1003
EMI / Mar '88.

MOMENTARY LASPE OF REASON, A.
Tracks: Signs of life / Learning to fly / Dogs of war / One slip / On the turning away / Yet another movie / round and 'round / New machine (part 1) / Terminal frost / New machine (part 2).

MONEY.
Tracks: Money / Let there be more light.
■ 12" . . . . 12 HAR 5217
Harvest / Dec '81.

NICE PAIR, A.
Tracks: Astronomy domine / Lucifer Sam / Matilda mother / Flaming / Take up thy stethoscope and walk / Interstellar overdrive / Gnome / Chapter 24 / Scarecrow / Bike / Let there be more light / Remember a day / Set the controls for the heart of the sun / Corporal Clegg / Saucerful of secrets / See-saw / Jugband blues.
MC TC2EXE 1013
Harvest / Feb '74 / EMI.
■ Double LP. . . . . .SHDW 403
Harvest / Jan '74.

NOT NOW JOHN.
Tracks: Not now John / Heroes return.
■ 12" . . . . 12 HAR 5224
■ 7" . . . . HAR 5224
Harvest / May '83.

OBSCURED BY CLOUDS.
Tracks: Obscured by clouds / When you're in / Burning bridges / Gold it's in / Wots..uh the deal / Mudmen / Childhood's end / Free four / Stay / Absolutely curtains.
MC . . . . TCSHSP 4020
■ LP . . . . SHSP 4020
Harvest / Jun '72.
CD . . . . CDP 746 385 2
EMI / Mar '87 / EMI.

ON THE TURNING AWAY.
Tracks: On the turning away (Live) / Run like hell (live) (Recorded live at Atlanta, November 5th, 1987) / On the turning away / On the turning away (album version).
■ 12" 12EMP 34
■ 12" 12EM 34
■ 7" . . . . EM 34
■ 7" . . . . EMP 34
■ CD Single . . . . CDEM 34
EMI / Dec '87.

ONE SLIP.
Tracks: One slip / Terminal frost / Dogs of war "live" (Extra track available on 12" only.)
■ 12" 12EMP 52
■ 7" . . . . EMG 52
■ CD Single . . . . CDEM 52
EMI / Jun '88.
■ 7" . . . . EM 52
EMI / May '88.

■ 12" **12EM 52**
EMI / Jun '88.

PINK FLOYD: INTERVIEW COLLECTION.
Tracks: Not Advised.
■ 7" Set . . . . **BAKPAK 1022**
Baktabak / Jun '90.

PINK FLOYD: INTERVIEW PICTURE DISC.
Tracks: Not Advised.
LP P.Disc . . . . **BAK 2028**
Baktabak / Apr '87 / Arabesque Ltd.
CD P.Disc . . . . **CBAK 4013**
Baktabak / Apr '88 / Arabesque Ltd.

PIPER AT THE GATES OF DAWN, THE.
Tracks: Astronomy domine / Lucifer Sam / Matilda mother / Flaming / Pow r toc h / Take up thy stethoscope and walk / Interstellar overdrive / Gnome / Chapter 24 / Scarecrow / Bike.
■ LP . . . . **SCX 6157**
Columbia (EMI) / Aug '67.
■ LP . . . . **FA 3065**
■ MC . . . . **TCFA 3065**
Fame / May '83.
CD . . . . **CDP 746 384 2**
EMI / Jan '87 / EMI.

RELICS.
Tracks: Arnold Layne / Interslellar overdrive / See Emily play / Remember a day / Paintbox / Julia dream / Careful with that axe, Eugene / Cirrus minor / Nile song / Bidin' my time / Bike.
■ LP . . . . **SRS 5071**
Starline (EMI) / Aug '71.
■ LP . . . . **MFP 50397**
MC . . . . **TCMFP 50397**
MFP / Dec '78 / EMI.

SAUCERFUL OF SECRETS, A.
Tracks: Let there be more light / Remember a day / Set the controls for the heart of the sun / Corporal Clegg / Saucerful of secrets / See-saw / Jugband blues.
■ LP . . . . **SCX 6258**
■ MC . . . . **TC SCX 6258**
Columbia (EMI) / Jun '85.
■ LP . . . . **FA 3163**
■ MC . . . . **TCFA 3163**
Fame / Aug '86.
■ CD . . . . **CDP 746 383 2**
EMI / Jan '87.
CD . . . . **CDEMD 1063**
MC . . . . **TCEMD 1063**
EMI / Aug '94 / EMI.

SEE EMILY PLAY.
Tracks: See Emily play / Scarecrow.
■ 7" . . . . **DB 8214**
Columbia (EMI) / Jun '67.

SHINE ON.
Tracks: Not Advised.
CD Set . . . . **PFBOX 1**
EMI / Nov '92 / EMI.

TAKE IT BACK.
Tracks: Take it back / Astronomy domine.
■ 7" . . . . **EM 309**
■ CD Single . . . . **CDEM 309**
■ CD Single . . . . **CDEMS 309**
■ MC Single . . . . **TCEM 309**
EMI / May '94.

THERE'S SOMEBODY OUT THERE (Interview album).
Tracks: Not Advised.
■ LP . . . . **BAK 6003**
MC . . . . **MBAK 6003**
Baktabak / Jun '89 / Arabesque Ltd.

TONITE, LET'S ALL MAKE LOVE IN LONDON.
Tracks: Not Advised.
CD . . . . **SFM 2**
See For Miles / Oct '93 / Pinnacle.

TONITE, LET'S MAKE LOVE IN LONDON.
Tracks: Tonite, let's make love in London.
■ 7" . . . . **SEA 4**
■ CD Single . . . . **SEACD 4**
See For Miles / Sep '91.

UMMAGUMMA.
Tracks: Astronomy domine / Careful with that axe, Eugene / Set the controls for the heart of the sun / Saucerful of secrets / Sysyphus (parts 1-4) / Grantchester meadows / Several species of small furry animals gathered together.. / Narrow way / Grand Vizier's garden party.
■ MC Set **TC2SHDW 4501**
EMI / Aug '71.
■ Double LP . . . . **SHDW 1**

EMI / Dec '79.
CD Set . . . . **CDS 746 404 8**
EMI / Mar '87 / EMI.

VIDEO EP: PINK FLOYD.
Tracks: Not Advised.
■ VHS . . . . **MVS 99 0003 2**
PMI / '86.
VHS . . . . **.PM 8010**
Video Collection / '88 / Gold & Sons / Video Collection / TBD.

WHEN THE TIGERS BROKE FREE.
Tracks: When the tigers broke free / Bring the boys back home.
■ 7" . . . . **HAR 5222**
Harvest / Jul '82.

WISH YOU WERE HERE.
Tracks: Shine on you crazy diamond (Parts 1-9) / Welcome to the machine / Have a cigar / Wish you were here.
■ CD . . . . **CDP 7460352**
■ MC . . . . **TCSHVL 814**
■ LP . . . . **SHVL 814**
Harvest / May '92.
CD . . . . **CDEMD 1062**
MC . . . . **TCEMD 1062**
EMI / Aug '94 / EMI.

Pitch Shifter

DESENSITIZED.
Tracks: Lesson one / Diable / Ephemerol / Triad / To die is to gain / (A higher form of) killing / Lesson two / Cathode / N/A / Gatherer of data / N.C.M. / Routine.
CD . . . . **MOSH 075CD**
LP . . . . **MOSH 075**
MC . . . . **MOSH 075MC**
Earache / Oct '93 / Vital Distribution.

INDUSTRIAL.
Tracks: Not Advised.
CD . . . . **DEAF 5CD**
LP . . . . **DEAF 5**
■ MC . . . . **DEAF 5MC**
Deaf / Feb '91.

SUBMIT.
Tracks: Not Advised.
CD . . . . **MOSH 066CD**
LP . . . . **MOSH 066**
MC . . . . **MOSH 066MC**
Earache / Apr '92 / Vital Distribution.

Plant, Robert

Following demise of Led Zeppelin in 1980, Plant embarked on solo career. First two albums, *Pictures At Eleven* and *Principal Of Moments* buoyed by, respectively, Zeppelin's reputation and hit single *Big Log*. Refusal to capitalise on hard rock reputation led to part-time venture Honeydrippers, a '50s-style band, and two, less successful, solo albums. Spurred by resurgence of interest in Zeppelin, Plant returned to style that made him famous on excellent *Manic Nirvana* and *Fate Of Nations*.

29 PALMS.
Tracks: 29 palms.
■ 7" . . . . **FATE 1**
■ CD Single . . . . **FATEX 1**
■ MC Single . . . . **FATEM 1**
Fontana / May '93.

BIG LOG.
Tracks: Big log / Messin' with the Mekon.
■ 12" . . . . **B 9848 T**
■ 7" . . . . **B 9848**
WEA / Jul '83.

BURNING DOWN ONE SIDE.
Tracks: Burning down one side / Moonlight.
■ 12" . . . . **SSK 19249 T**
■ 7" . . . . **SSK 19429**
Swansong / Sep '82.

FATE OF NATIONS.
Tracks: Calling to you / Down to the sea / Come into my life / I believe / 29 Palms / Memory song (Hello, hello) / If I were a carpenter / Colours of a shade / Promised land / Greatest gift / Great spirit / Network news.
CD **514 867-2**
DCC **514 867-5**
LP **514 867-1**
MC **514 867-4**
Fontana / May '93 / PolyGram.

HEAVEN KNOWS.
Tracks: Heaven knows / Walking toward paradise.
■ 12" . . . . **A 9373 T**
■ 7" . . . .**A 9373**
Es Paranza / Jan '88.

HURTING KIND (I'VE GOT MY EYES ON YOU).
Tracks: Hurting kind (I've got my eyes on you).
■ 12" . . . . **A 8985 T**
■ 7" . . . . **A 8985**
WEA / Apr '90.

I BELIEVE.
Tracks: I believe.
■ 7" . . . . **FATE 2**
■ CD Single . . . . **FATEX 2**
■ MC Single . . . . **FATEM 2**
Fontana / Jun '93.

IF I WERE A CARPENTER.
Tracks: If I were a carpenter / I believe (Not on 8580712) / Tall cool one (Not on 8580732) / Going to California (On 8580732).
■ 7" . . . . **FATE 4**
■ CD Single **8580732**
■ CD Single **8580712**
■ MC Single **8580704**
Phonogram / Nov '93.

IN THE MOOD.
Tracks: In the mood / Pledge pin.
■ 7" . . . . **PLANT 2**
Es Paranza / Nov '83.
■ 12" . . . . **B 6970 T**
Es Paranza / Nov '83.

LITTLE BY LITTLE.
Tracks: Little by little.
■ 12" . . . . **B 9621 T**
■ 7" . . . . **B 9621**
Es Paranza / Aug '85.

LONG TIME COMING.
Tracks: Long time coming / I've got a secret.
■ 7" . . . . **CBS 2858**
CBS / Jul '67.

MANIC NIRVANA.
Tracks: Hurting kind (I've got my eyes on you) / S S S and Q / Nirvana / Your ma said you cried in your sleep / Liars dance / Big love / I cried / Tie dye on the highway / Anniversary / Watching you.
CD **7567913362**
CD . . . . **WX 339CD**
■ MC . . . . **WX 339C**
Atlantic / Mar '90.

NOW AND ZEN.
Tracks: Heaven knows / Dance on my own / Tall cool one / Way I feel / Helen of Troy / Billy's revenge / Ship of fools / Why / White, clean and neat.
CD **790 863-2**
■ LP . . . . **WX 149**
MC . . . . **WX 149C**
Es Paranza / Feb '88 / WEA.

PICTURES AT ELEVEN.
Tracks: Burning down one side / Moonlight in Samosa / Pledge pin / Slow dancer / Worse than Detroit / Fat lip / Like I've never been gone / Mystery title.
MC **SK4 59418**
■ LP . . . . **SSK 59418**
Swansong / Jul '82.
CD . . . . **SK 259418**
Swansong / '86 / WEA.

PINK AND BLACK.
Tracks: Pink and black / Trouble your money.
■ 12" . . . . **B 9640 T**
■ 7" . . . . **B 9640**
Es Paranza / May '85.

PRINCIPAL OF MOMENTS.
Tracks: Other arms / In the mood / Messin' with the Mekon / Wreckless love / Through with the two step / Horizontal departure / Big log / Stranger here than over there.
CD **790101 2**
WEA / Jul '83 / WEA.
■ LP **790101 1**
MC **790101 4**
Es Paranza / Jul '83 / WEA.

ROBERT PLANT.
Tracks: Heaven knows / Big log / Little by little / In the mood / Tall cool one.
VHS **750121-3**
WEA Music Video / Jan '89 / WEA / Gold & Sons.

ROBERT PLANT: INTERVIEW PICTURE DISC.

Tracks: Not Advised.
LP P.Disc . . . . BAK 2097
Baktabak / Apr '88 / Arabesque Ltd.

SHAKEN 'N' STIRRED.

Tracks: Hip to hoo / Kallalou / Too loud / Trouble your money / Pink and black / Little by little / Doo doo a do do / Easily lead / Sixes and sevens.
MC 790265 4
■ LP 790265 1
Es Paranza / Jun '85.
CD 790265 2
WEA / Jun '85 / WEA.

SHIP OF FOOLS.

Tracks: Ship of fools / Helen of Troy / Heaven knows (live) (Only on 12") / Dimples (live) (Only on CD single).
■ 7" . . . . .A 9281
■ CD Single . . . . A 9281 CD
■ 12" . . . . A 9281 T
Atlantic / Sep '88.

TALL COOL ONE.

Tracks: Tall cool one / White, clean and neat.
■ 12" . . . . A 9348 T
■ 7" . . . . .A 9348
Atlantic / May '88.

YOUR MA SAID YOU CRIED IN YOUR SLEEP LAST NIGHT.

Tracks: Your ma said you cried in your sleep last night / She said.
■ 12" . . . . A 8945 T
■ 7" . . . . .A 8945
■ CD Single . . . . A 8945 CD
■ MC Single. . . . . A 8945 C
East West / Jun '90.

Plasmatics

Plasmatics emerged from New York in 1979 and split by 1984. Singer Wendy O. Williams' on-stage antics attracted attention of fans and police; misgivings about detonation of car led GLC to ban act from London in 1980. After split, Williams and bassist Jean Beauvoir enjoyed minor solo success, both aided by collaboration with Kiss.

BUTCHER BABY.

Tracks: Butcher baby.
■ 12" . . . . BUYIT 76
■ 7" . . . . BUY 76
Stiff / Jun '80.

COUP D'ETAT.

Tracks: Put your love in me / Stop / Rock 'n' roll / Lightning breaks / No class / Mistress of taboo / Country fairs / Path of glory / Just like on TV / Damned.
■ LP .EST 12237
Capitol / Nov '82.
■ LP . . . . REV LP 78
MC . . . . REV MC 78
Revolver / '86 / FM Revolver / Sony.

MONKEY SUIT.

Tracks: Monkey suit / Squirm.
■ 7" . . . . BUY 91
Stiff / Sep '80.

NEW HOPE FOR THE WRETCHED.

Tracks: Tight black pants / Monkey suit / Living dead / Test tube babies / Won't you / Concrete shoes / Squirm (live) / Want you baby / Dream lover / Sometimes / Corruption / Butcher baby.
■ LP . . . . .SEEZ 24
Stiff / Sep '80.
CD . . . . .DOJOCD 74
Dojo / Feb '94 / Castle Communications / BMG.
CD . . . . .STIFFCD 16
Disky / Jan '94 / TBD.

VALLEY OF 84 + METAL PRIESTESS.

Tracks: Not Advised.
CD . . . . PVCCD 8929
■ LP . . . . PVC 8929
MC . . . . PVCC 8929
PVC (USA) / '87.

Point Blank

ON A ROLL.

Tracks: On a roll / I just want to know / Love on fire / Don't look now / Great white line / Let her go / Gone Hollywood / Take me up.
■ LP . . . . MCF 3141
■ MC . . . . MCFC 3141
MCA / Jun '82.

Poison

LA glam metal legends formed in 1983 who became famous for the way they looked (back-combed hair, make-up and outfits that looked like an explosion in a Liquorice All-sorts factory) as how they sounded. Their 1986 debut album *Look What The Cat Dragged In* was, however, a classic of its kind featuring Bret Michaels (vocals), CC Deville (guitar), Bobby Dall (bass) and Rikki Rocket (drums) posin' and poutin' for all they were worth. The image mellowed with time and come the early 90's the band were having a serious rethink in the wake of their waning popularity and the change of musical fashions. They (briefly) replaced CC with Ritchie Kotzens for the more "Adult" *Native Tongue* but fell on hard times. Come 1994, Kotzen had left, Bret only just survived a serious motorbike accident and their future looked uncertain.

7 DAYS LIVE.

Tracks: Scream / Strike up the band / Ride the wind / Good love / Body talk / Something to believe in / Stand / Fallen angel / Look what the cat dragged in / Until you suffer some (Fire and ice) / 7 days over you / Unskinny bop / Every rose has its thorn / Nothin' but a good time.
VHS . . . . MVP 4911523
PMI / Nov '93 / EMI / Gold & Sons / TBD.

CRY TOUGH.

Tracks: Cry tough.
■ 12" . . . . 12 KUT 127
■ 7" . . . . .KUT 127
Music For Nations / Aug '87.

EVERY ROSE HAS ITS THORN.

Tracks: Every rose has its thorn.
■ 12" 12CLG 520
■ 7" . . . . CLS 520
■ 7" P.Disc . . . . CLP 520
■ 12" 12CL 520
■ 7" . . . . CL 520
Capitol / Jan '89.
■ CD Single . . . . CDCL 520
Capitol / Jan '89.

FALLEN ANGEL.

Tracks: Fallen angel / Bad to be good / Open up and say ... interview (12" only).
■ 12" 12CL 500
■ 7" .CL 500
■ 7" . . . . CLS 500
■ 12" P.Disc. 12CLP 500
Capitol / Oct '88.

FLESH AND BLOOD.

Tracks: Strange days of uncle Jack / Valley of lost souls / (Flesh and blood) sacrifice / Swampjuice (soul-o) / Unskinny bop / Let it play / Life goes on / Come hell or high water / Ride the wind / Don't give up an inch / Something to believe in / Ball and chain / Life loves a tragedy / Poor boy blues.
CD . . . . .CDEST 2126
■ LP . . . . EST 2126
■ MC . . . . TCEST 2126
Capitol / Jul '90.
MiniDisc 791813-8
Capitol / Apr '93 / EMI.

FLESH, BLOOD AND VIDEOTAPE.

Tracks: Unskinny bop / Ride the wind / Something to believe in / Life goes on / (Flesh and blood) sacrifice.
VHS . . . . MVR 9901003
PMI / Nov '91 / EMI / Gold & Sons / TBD.

LOOK WHAT THE CAT DRAGGED IN.

Tracks: Cry tough / I want action / I won't forget you / Play dirty / Look what the cat dragged in / Talk dirty to me / Want some, need some / Blame it on you / No. 1 bad boy / Let me go to the show.
CD . . . . .CDMFN 69
■ LP . . . . MFN 69
■ LP P.Disc . . . . MFN 69P
Music For Nations / Oct '86.
■ MC . . . . TMFN 69
Music For Nations / Oct '86.
■ LP . . . . ATAK 162
MC . . . . TCATAK 162
■ LP . . . . CMP 1003
Capitol / Nov '90.
■ CD . . . . CDFA 3281
Fame / Oct '92.
CD . . . . CDCMP 1003
MC . . . . TCCMP 1003
Capitol / Jul '94 / EMI.

NATIVE TONGUE.

Tracks: Native tongue / Scream / Stand / Stay alive / Until you suffer some (Fire and Ice) / Body talk / Bring it home / 7 Days over you / Richie's acoustic

thang / Ain't that the truth / Theatre of the soul / Strike up the band / Ride child ride / Blind faith / Bastard son of a thousand blues.
CD . . . . .CDESTU 2190
■ LP . . . . ESTU 2190
■ MC . . . . .TCESTU 2190
Capitol / Feb '93.

NOTHIN' BUT A GOOD TIME.

Tracks: Nothin' but a good time / Look but you can't touch / Livin' for the minute.
■ 12" 12CL 486
■ 7" .CL 486
■ 7" P.Disc . . . . CLP 486
Capitol / Apr '88.
■ 12" 12CLG 486
■ 7" . . . . CLZ 486
Capitol / Apr '88.

NOTHIN' BUT A GOOD TIME.

Tracks: Nothin' but a good time / Livin' for the minute / Look what the cat dragged in (12" & CD single only).
■ CD Single . . . . CDCL 539
■ 12" 12CL 539
■ 12" P.Disc 12CLPD 539
■ 7" .CL 539
■ MC Single . . . . TCCL 539
■ 7" . . . . CLX 539
Capitol / Jul '89.
■ 12" 12CLG 539
Capitol / Jul '89.

OPEN UP AND SAY AHH.

Tracks: Love on the rocks / Nothin' but a good time / Back to the rocking horse / Good love / Tearin' down the walls / Look but you can't touch / Fallen angel / Every rose has it's thorn / Your mama don't dance / Bad to be good.
■ LP . . . . EST 2059
■ LP P.Disc . . . . ESTP 2059
Capitol / May '88.
MiniDisc. 748493-3
Capitol / Feb '93 / EMI.
CD . . . . .CDEST 2059
MC. . . . . .TCEST 2059
Capitol / Feb '94 / EMI.

POISON INTERVIEW 86.

Tracks: Not Advised.
■ 10" . . . . POISON 10
■ 7" P.Disc . . . . POISON 7P
Wax / Jul '89.

POISON: INTERVIEW PICTURE DISC.

Tracks: Not Advised.
LP P.Disc . . . . BAK 2047
Baktabak / Jun '87 / Arabesque Ltd.
CD P.Disc . . . . CBAK 4036
Baktabak / Jun '90 / Arabesque Ltd.

SIGHT FOR SORE EARS, A.

Tracks: Cry tough / I want action / Talk dirty to me / I won't forget you / Nothin' but a good time / Fallen angel / Every rose has its thorn / Your mama don't dance.
VHS MVP99 1208 3
PMI / Feb '90 / EMI / Gold & Sons / TBD.

SO TELL ME WHY.

Tracks: So tell me why / Unskinny bop (live) / Ride the wind (live) (Only on 12" and CD single).
■ 12" 12CL 640
■ 7" .CL 640
■ CD P.Disc . . . . CDCLP 640
Capitol / Nov '91.

SOMETHING TO BELIEVE IN.

Tracks: Something to believe in / Ball and chain (Not on gatefold.) / Poison - interview (Bret Michaels on album 'Flesh & Blood', track by track. CDsingle & 10".) / Look what the cat dragged in (Gatefold only.) / Your mama don't dance (Gatefold only.) / Every rose has it's thorn (Gatefold only.)
■ 12" 12CLG 594
■ 10" 10CL 594
■ 7" .CL 594
■ CD Single . . . . CDCL 594
■ MC Single . . . . TCCL 594
Capitol / Oct '90.

STAND.

Tracks: Stand / Native tongue/ Scream / Whip comes down (Available on CD Single only.) / Stand (LP Version) (Available on LP only.)
■ 7" .CLG 679
■ CD Single . . . . CDCL 679
■ MC Single . . . . TCCL 679
EMI / Feb '93.

SWALLOW THIS - LIVE.

Tracks: Intro / Look what the cat dragged in / Look but you can't touch / Good love / I want action / Something to believe in / Poor boy blues / Unskinny

bop / Every rose has it's thorn / Fallen angel / Your mama don't dance / Nothin' but a good time / Talk dirty to me / So tell me why / Souls on fire / Only time will tell / No more lookin' back (Poison jazz).
■ Double LP . . . . ESTU 2159
■ CD . . . . CDESTU 2159
■ MC . . . . TCESTU 2159
Capitol / Oct '91.

SWAMPJUICE (SOUL-O).
Tracks: Swampjuice (soul-O) / Unskinny bop / Valley of lost souls / Poor boy blues (Picture disc & CD single only.).
■ 12" 12CL 582
■ 12" P.Disc. 12CLPD 582
■ 7" . . . . CL 582
■ CD Single . . . . CDCL 582
■ MC Single . . . . TCCL 582
Capitol / Jun '90.

TALK DIRTY TO ME.
Tracks: Talk dirty to me / Want some, need some / Poison interview.
■ 12" . . . . 12 KUT 125
■ 7" . . . . KUT 125
■ 7" P.Disc P12KUT 125
Music For Nations / May '87.

UNTIL YOU SUFFER SOME (FIRE AND ICE).
Tracks: Until you suffer some (fire and ice) / Bastard song of a thousand blues / Stand (On CDs only.) / Until you suffer some (fire and ice)(ice mix) (On CDs only).
■ 12" 12CLP 685
■ 7" . . . . CLPD 685
■ CD Single . . . . CDCL 685
■ MC Single . . . . TCCL 685
EMI / Apr '93.

YOUR MAMA DON'T DANCE.
Tracks: Your mama don't dance / Tearin' down the walls / Love on the rocks.
■ 12" 12CLB 523
■ 7" . . . . CLS 523
■ 12" 12CL 523
■ 7" . . . . CL 523
■ CD Single . . . . CDCL 523
Capitol / Apr '89.

Poison Idea

DUTCH COURAGE.
Tracks: Not Advised.
CD . . . . BC 1667CD
LP . . . . BC 1667
Bitzcore / Jan '92 / Plastic Head.

FEEL THE DARKNESS.
Tracks: Not Advised.
MC. . . . . SOL 25 C
Vinyl Solution / Feb '91 / RTM / Pinnacle.

KINGS OF PUNK.
Tracks: Not Advised.
■ LP 0012-10
Pusmort.
CD . . . . TG 9284 2
LP . . . . TG 9284 1
Road Runner / Sep '91 / Pinnacle.

PAJAMA PARTY.
Tracks: Kick out the jams / Vietnamese baby / We got the beat / Motorhead / Endless sleep / Laudy Miss. Clawdy / Jailhouse rock / Flamethrower love / New rose / Doctor, doctor / Up front / Harder they come / Green onions.
CD . . . . SOLO 34 CD
LP . . . . SOLO 34
MC . . . . SOLO 34 MC
Vinyl Solution / Aug '92 / RTM / Pinnacle.

POISON IDEA.
Tracks: Not Advised.
■ LP . . . . FACE 6
In Your Face / Jul '89.

RECORD COLLECTORS ARE PRETENTIOUS ASSHOLES.
Tracks: Not Advised.
Mini LP . . . . BC 1658
Bitzcore / '89 / Plastic Head.
CD . . . . TG 9299 2
Mini LP . . . . TG 9299 1
Road Runner / Sep '91 / Pinnacle.

WAR ALL THE TIME.
Tracks: Temple / Romantic self destruction / Push the button / Ritual chicken / Nothing is final / Motorhead / Hot time / Steel rule / Typical / Murderer / Marked for life.
MC. . . . . VM 106 C
Alchemy / Nov '87 / Pinnacle.

■ LP . . . . VM 106
Alchemy / Nov '87.
■ CD . . . . SOLD 40
■ MC . . . . SOLC 40
Vinyl Solution / Oct '93.
CD . . . . SOL 40CD
LP . . . . SOL 40
Vinyl Solution / Sep '94 / RTM / Pinnacle.

Poland, Chris

RETURN TO METALOPOLIS.
Tracks: Not Advised.
CD . . . . RR 9348-2
LP . . . . RR 9348-1
LP . . . . RR 9348-4
Road Runner / Sep '90 / Pinnacle.

Porno For Pyros

In September '91, Perry Farrell split Jane's Addiction, oversaw development of Lollapalooza festival and enthusiastically pursued narcotic nirvana. He also found time to create new group with guitarist Peter DiStefano, Jane's drummer Steve Perkins and Thelonious Monster bassist Martyn LeNoble. Porno For Pyros' 1993 debut charted higher than any Addiction album, despite indiscernible musical development.

PETS.
Tracks: Pets / Tonight.
■ 12" . . . . W 0177TP
■ 7" . . . . W 0177
■ CD Single . . . . W 0177CDX
■ MC Single . . . . W 0177C
Warner Bros. / May '93.

PORNO FOR PYROS.
Tracks: Sadness / Porno for pyros / Meija / Cursed female / Cursed male / Pets / Bad shit / Packin' 25 / Black girlfriend / Blood rag / Orgasm.
CD 936245228-2
MC 936245228-4
Warner Bros. / Apr '93 / WEA.

Possessed

BEYOND THE GATES.
Tracks: Heretic / Tribulation / March to die / Phantasm / No will to live / Beyond the gates / Beast of the Apocalypse / Seance / Restless dead / Dog fight.
■ LP . . . . FLAG 3
Under One Flag / Nov '86.
CD . . . . CDFLAG 3
Under One Flag / Aug '87 / Pinnacle.

EYES OF HORROR, THE.
Tracks: Not Advised.
■ LP . . . . MFLAG 16
Under One Flag / Jun '87.

SEVEN CHURCHES.
Tracks: Exorcist / Burning in hell / Seven churches / Holy hell / Fallen angel / Pentagram / Evil warriors / Satan's curse / Twisted minds / Death metal.
■ LP . . . . RR 9757
Road Runner / Dec '85.
■ CD . . . . RO 9757-2
Roadracer / Apr '89.

Post Mortem

AGAINST ALL ODDS.
Tracks: Against all odds.
■ EP . . . . FM 006
Flowmotion / Aug '84.

CORONER'S OFFICE.
Tracks: Not Advised.
■ LP . . . . NRR 11
New Renaissance(USA) / Aug '87.
MC. . . . . NRC 11
New Renaissance(USA) / Aug '87 / Pinnacle.

MISSING LINK.
Tracks: Not Advised.
■ LP . . . . NRR 19
New Renaissance(USA) / Sep '87.
MC. . . . . NRC 19
New Renaissance(USA) / Sep '87 / Pinnacle.

POST MORTEM.
Tracks: Post mortem.
■ EP . . . . POST 1
Lightbeat / May '83.

Potential Threat

BRAINWASHED.
Tracks: Brainwashed.
■ 7" . . . . COR 6
Children Of The Revolution / Apr '85.

DEMAND AN ALTERNATIVE.
Tracks: Not Advised.
■ LP . . . . MORT 24
Mortarhate / May '88.

WHAT'S SO GREAT ABOUT BRITAIN.
Tracks: What's so great about Britain.
■ EP . . . . HOOT 7
Out Of Town / Jun '82.

Powell, Cozy

Journeyman drummer, variously associated with Jeff Beck, MSG, Gary Moore, Rainbow, Black Sabbath, Robert Plant, ELP and Whitesnake. Scored three solo hits in '73/'74, of which biggest was Dance With The Devil (U.K. no. 3). and returned to charts in 1980 with Over The Top album (U.K. no. 34). Most recently spotted in Brian May's band.

DANCE WITH THE DEVIL.
Tracks: Dance with the devil / Man in black / Nanana.
■ 7" . . . . RAK 165
RAK / Dec '73.
■ 7" G45 30
EMI Golden 45's / Jul '84.
■ CD Single . . . . OG 6177
Pickwick / Sep '92.

DRUMS ARE BACK, THE.
Tracks: Drums are back / Ride to win / I wanna hear you shout / Light in the sky/Return of the 7 / Battle hymn / Legend of the glass mountain / Cryin' / Classical gas / Somewhere in time / Rocket.
■ MC . . . . TCODN 1008
■ CD . . . . CDODN 1008
EMI (Odeon) / Aug '92.

FORCEFIELD III (see under Bonnet, Graham).

LONER.
Tracks: Loner / El Sid.
■ 7" . . . . ARO 205
Ariola / Feb '80.

MAN IN BLACK.
Tracks: Man in black.
■ 7" . . . . RAK 173
RAK / May '74.

NA NA NA.
Tracks: Na na na.
■ 7" . . . . RAK 180
RAK / Aug '74.

OCTOPUSS.
Tracks: Up on the downs / 633 squadron / Title track / Big country / Formula one / Princetown / Dartmoor / Rattler.
MC. POLDC 5093
Polydor / Apr '83 / PolyGram.
■ LP . . . . POLD 5093
Polydor / May '83.

OVER THE TOP.
Tracks: Theme one / Killer / Heidi goes to town / El sid / Sweet poison / Loner / Over the top.
■ LP . . . . ARL 5036
Ariola / Jan '80.
■ LP . . . . FA 3056
MC. . . . . TCFA 3056
Fame / Jan '83 / EMI.

SOONER OR LATER.
Tracks: Sooner or later / 633 squadron / Cat moves / Blister / Right side / Formula one / Hot rock / Prince town / Living a lie / Dartmoore / Jekyll and Hyde / Rattler.
CD . . . . ELITE 018CDP
MC. . . . . ELITE 018MCP
Elite (Pickwick) / Aug '91 / Pickwick.

SOONER OR LATER.
Tracks: Sooner or later / Blister.
■ 7" . . . . POSP 328
Polydor / Sep '81.

THEME ONE.
Tracks: Theme one.
■ 7" . . . . ARO 189
Ariola / Nov '79.

■ DELETED

TILT.
Tracks: Right side / Jekyll and Hyde / Sooner or later / Living a lie / Cat moves / Sunset / Blister / Hot rock.
■ LP . . . . POLD 5047
Polydor / Sep '81.

Power Station

COMMUNICATION.
Tracks: Communication / Murderess.
■ 12" 12R 6114
■ 7" .R 6114
Parlophone / Oct '85.

GET IT ON.
Tracks: Get it on.
■ 12" 12R 6096
■ 7" .R 6096
Parlophone / Apr '85.

POWER STATION.
Tracks: Some like it hot / Murderess / Lonely tonight / Communication / Get it on / Go to zero / Harvest for the world / Still in your heart.
■ LP . . . . POST 1
■ LP . . . . EJ 2402971
■ MC . . . . .TCPOST 1
■ MC . . . . .EJ 240297
Parlophone / Apr '85.
CD . . . . .CDP 746127 2
EMI / Jul '85 / EMI.
CD . . . . CDFA 3206
MC . . . . TCFA 3206
■ LP . . . . FA 3206
Fame / Sep '88.
CD . . . . CDPRG 1011
■ MC . . . . TCPRG 1011
Parlophone / Aug '93.

SOME LIKE IT HOT.
Tracks: Some like it hot / Heat is on.
■ 12" P.Disc. 12RP 6091
Parlophone / Apr '85.
■ 12" 12R 6091
Parlophone / Feb '85.
■ 7" .R 6091
Parlophone / Feb '85.
■ 7" P.Disc . . . . RP 6091
Parlophone / Mar '85.

VIDEO EP: POWER STATION.
Tracks: Some like it hot / Communication / Get it on.
■ VHS . . . . MVR 99 0044 2
■ VHS . . . . MVP 99 0044 2
PMI / Jun '86.
VHS . . . . MC 2031
Music Club Video / '88 / Video Collection / Gold & Sons / TBD.

Powerhouse

NIGHTLIFE/LOVIN' MACHINE.
Tracks: Not Advised.
CD . . . . PRD 70182
Provogue / Nov '90 / Pinnacle.

POWERHOUSE.
Tracks: Not Advised.
■ LP 40 1003
Ambush (Belgium) / Jun '86.

Powerlord

AWAKENING, THE.
Tracks: Masters of death / Malice / Silent terror / Invasion of the Lords / Merciless Titans / Powerlord.
CD . . . . .SHARK 008 CD
Shark / Jun '88 / Plastic Head.
■ LP . . . . .SHARK 008
Shark / Jun '88.

Powersurge

POWERSURGE.
Tracks: Not Advised.
CD . . . . RR 93112
LP . . . . RR 93111
MC . . . . RR 93114
Road Runner / Jul '91 / Pinnacle.

Praying Mantis

ALL DAY AND ALL OF THE NIGHT.
Tracks: All day and all of the night / Beads of ebony.
■ 7" . . . . .ARIST 397
Arista / Mar '81.

CAPTURED CITY.
Tracks: Captured city / Johnny cool / Ripper (On 12" only).
■ 12" 12HAR 5201

■ 7" . . . . HAR 5201
Harvest / Feb '80.

CHEATED.
Tracks: Cheated / 30 pieces of silver / Free live single / Flirting with suicide / Panic in the streets.
■ EP . . . . .ARIST 378
Arista / '82.

CRY FOR THE NEW WORLD, A.
Tracks: Not Advised.
CD . . . . CDFLAG 80
Under One Flag / Sep '93 / Pinnacle.

PRAYING MANTIS.
Tracks: Praying Mantis / High roller.
■ 7" . . . . GEMS 36
Gem (2) / Jul '80.

PREDATOR IN DISGUISE.
Tracks: Can't see the angels / She's hot / This time girl / Time slipping away / Listen what your heart says / Still want you / Horn / Battle royal / Only you / Borderline / Can't wait forever.
CD . . . . CDFLAG 77
Under One Flag / Feb '93 / Pinnacle.

TELL ME THE NIGHTMARE'S WRONG.
Tracks: Tell me the nightmare's wrong / Turn the tables / Question of time.
■ 7" . . . . JET 7026
Jet / Sep '82.

TIME TELLS NO LIES.
Tracks: Cheated / All day and all of the night / Running for tomorrow / Rich city kids / Lovers to the grave / Panic in the streets / Beads of ebony / Flirting with suicide / Children of the earth.
■ LP . . . . SPART 1153
Arista / May '81.

Preacher

HARDCORE DEMO SERIES.
Tracks: Not Advised.
■ LP . . . . WRR 004
Wild Rags / Nov '88.

Precious Metal

MOVIN' MOUNTAINS.
Tracks: Movin' mountains.
■ 7" 7VAG 001
Savage / Sep '88.

PRECIOUS METAL.
Tracks: Not Advised.
■ LP . . . . MCF 3069
MCA / Jun '80.

STAND UP AND SHOUT.
Tracks: Stand up and shout / Sweet sweet.
■ 7" 7VAG 902
Savage / Jan '89.

THAT KIND OF GIRL.
Tracks: Not Advised.
CD . . . . .CDVAG 001
■ LP . . . . .LPVAG 001
MC . . . . .CASSVAG 001
Savage / Aug '88 / Pinnacle / Sony.

Predator

PREDATOR.
Tracks: Not Advised.
■ LP . . . . RR 9714
Road Runner / Apr '86.

PUNK MAN.
Tracks: Punk man / Paper boy song.
■ 7" . . . . SOL 1
Bust / Apr '78.

Pretty Boy Floyd

LEATHER BOYZ WITH ELECTRIC TOYS.
Tracks: Not Advised.
■ CD . . . . .DMCG 6076
■ LP . . . . .MCG 6076
■ MC . . . . .MCGC 6076
MCA / Nov '89.

ROCK AND ROLL (IS GONNA SET THE NIGHT ON FIRE).
Tracks: Rock and roll (is gonna set the night on fire) / Toast of the town / Rock and roll outlaws (Available on 12" format).
■ 12" . . . . MCATB 1393
■ 12" . . . . MCAT 1393
■ 7" . . . . MCA 1393
■ CD Single . . . . .DMCAP 1393

■ CD Single . . . . DMCAT 1393
MCA / Jan '90.

Pretty Maids

FUTURE WORLD.
Tracks: Future world / Loud 'n' proud / Love games / Yellow rain / Rodeo / We came to rock / Needles in the dark / Eye of the storm / Long way to go.
■ LP 4502811
■ MC 4502814
Epic / May '87.

LOVE GAMES.
Tracks: Love games / Needles in the dark / Yellow rain (Extra track on 12" only).
■ 12" 6504378
■ 7" 6504377
Epic / May '87.

PRETTY MAIDS.
Tracks: Not Advised.
■ LP . . . . CULP 1
Bullet / Oct '83.

RED HOT AND HEAVY.
Tracks: Fortuna / Back to back / Red hot and heavy / Waitin' for the time / Cold killer / Battle of pride / Night danger / Place in the night / Queen of dreams / Little darlin'.
■ LP . . . . PC 26207
■ MC 40 26207
Epic / Jun '85.

Pride & Glory

PRIDE AND GLORY.
Tracks: Not Advised.
CD . . . . GED 24703
MC . . . . GEC 24703
Geffen / May '94 / BMG.

Primus

CHEESY HOME VIDEO.
Tracks: Not Advised.
VHS 8536503123
East West / Jun '92 / WEA.

FRIZZLE FRY.
Tracks: To defy the laws of tradition / Too many puppies / Frizzle fry / You can't kill Michael Malloy / Pudding time / Spaghetti western / To defy / Ground hog's day / Mr. Know it all / John the fisherman / Toys go winding down / Sathington Willoby / Harold of the rocks.
CD . . . . CARCD 10
LP . . . . CARLP 10
MC . . . . CARC 10
Caroline / Jul '90 / Caroline International / EMI.

PORK SODA.
Tracks: Pork chop's little ditty / My name is mud / Welcome to this world / Bob / Dmv / Ol' diamond back sturgeon / Nature boy / Wounded knee / Pork soda / Pressman / Mr. Krinkle / Air is getting slippery / Hamburger train / Hail santa.
CD 756792257-2
MC 756792257-4
Interscope / Apr '93 / WEA.

RIDDLES ARE ABOUND TONIGHT (Sausage).
Tracks: Not Advised.
CD 654492361-2
MC 654492361-4
Interscope / Apr '94 / WEA.

SAILING THE SEAS OF CHEESE.
Tracks: Seas of cheese / Here come the bastards / Sgt. Baker / American life / Jerry was a race car driver / Eleven / Is it luck / Grandad's little ditty / Tommy the cat / Sathington waltz / Those damned blue-collar tweekers / Fish on (fisherman chronicles, chapter II) / Los bastardos.
CD 7567916592
■ LP 7567916591
MC 7567916594
East West / May '91 / WEA.

SUCK ON THIS.
Tracks: John the fisherman / Groundhog's day / Heckler / Pressman / Jellikit / Tommy the cat / Pudding time / Harold of the rocks / Frizzle fry.
CD 7567918332
■ LP 7567918331
MC 7567918334
Interscope / Apr '92 / WEA.

■ DELETED

Princess Pang

PRINCESS PANG.
Tracks: Not Advised.
CD. . . . . .RO 9471-2
■ LP . . . . .RO 9471-1
MC. . . . . .RO 9471-4
Roadracer / Aug '89 / Pinnacle.

Prism

ARMAGEDDON.
Tracks: Coming home / Jealousy / Virginia / You walked away again / Take it or leave it / Armageddon / Night to remember / Mirror man.
■ LP . . . . .EST 12051
Capitol / May '80.

DON'T LET HIM KNOW.
Tracks: Don't let him know / Wings of your love.
■ 7". . . . . .CL 238
Capitol / Mar '82.

SMALL CHANGE.
Tracks: Don't let him know / Turn on your radar / Hole in paradise / Rain / When will I see you again / Heart and soul / When love goes wrong / In the jailhouse now / Wings of your love.
■ LP . . . . .EST 12184
Capitol / May '82.

SPACESHIP SUPERSTAR.
Tracks: Spaceship superstar / Julie.
■ 7" . . . . INT 543
EMI International / Jan '78.

TAKE ME TO THE KAPTIN.
Tracks: Take me to the Kaptin / It's over.
■ 7" . . . . INT 559
EMI International / Jun '78.

TURN ON YOUR RADAR.
Tracks: Turn on your radar / When love goes wrong.
■ 7". . . . . .CL 246
Capitol / May '82.

YOU WALKED AWAY AGAIN.
Tracks: You walked away again / N-n-n-no.
■ 7" . . . . CL 16132
Capitol / Mar '80.

YOUNG AND RESTLESS.
Tracks: American music / Young and restless / Satellite / Party lime / Acid rain / Here comes another world / Visitor / Deception / Hideaway / Runnin' for cover.
■ LP . . . . .EST 12072
Capitol / Jul '80.

Private Lives

BECAUSE YOU'RE YOUNG.
Tracks: Because you're young / Because you're young (part 2).
■ 12". . . . . .CHS 122564
■ 7" . . . . CHS 2564
Chrysalis / Feb '82.

BREAK THE CHAINS.
Tracks: Break the chains / You've got to win.
■ 12". 12PRIV 1
■ 7" . . . . .PRIV 1
EMI / Sep '83.

FROM A RIVER TO A SEA.
Tracks: From a river to a sea / Because you're young.
■ 12". 12PRIV 3
■ 7" . . . . .PRIV 3
EMI / '84.

LIVING IN A WORLD (TURNED UPSIDE DOWN).
Tracks: Living in a world turned upside down / Break up.
■ 12". 12PRIV 2
■ 7" . . . . .PRIV 2
EMI / Feb '84.

MEMORY OF YOUR NAME.
Tracks: Memory of your name / Swim away / Stranger the love.
■ 12". . . . . .CHS 122628
■ 7" . . . . CHS 2628
Chrysalis / '82.

PREJUDICE AND PRIDE.
Tracks: From a river to a sea / No chance you'll pay / Living in a world / Stop / God only knows / Break the chains / Don't wanna cry / Win / Break the whole thing down / Prejudice and pride.
■ LP . . . . .LIV 1
MC. . . . . .TCLIV 1

EMI / Jul '84 / EMI.
■ LP .EJ2401361
Parlophone / Jul '84.

WHERE DO I GO.
Tracks: Where do I go / On the road.
■ 7" . . . . K 18303
WEA / Aug '80.

Pro-Pain

FOUL TASTE OF FREEDOM.
Tracks: Not Advised.
CD. . . . . RR 90682
LP . . . . RR 90681
MC. . . . . RR 90684
Road Runner / Apr '93 / Pinnacle.

TRUTH HURTS.
Tracks: Make war (Not love) / Bad blood / Truth hurts / Put the lights out / Denial / Let sleeping dogs lie / One man army / Down in the dumps / Beast is back / Switchblade knife / Death on the dancefloor (Features on MC only.) / Pound for pound (Features on MC only.) / Foul taste of freedom (Features on MC only.).
CD. . . . . RR 89852
LP . . . . RR 89851
MC. . . . . RR 89854
Road Runner / Aug '94 / Pinnacle.

Prong

New York hardcore trio whose profile has risen steadily since independent 1987 debut *Primitive Origins*. Sixth album, 1994's *Cleansing*, expanded musical range but not audience.

BEG TO DIFFER.
Tracks: For dear life / Steady decline / Beg to differ / Lost and found / You fear / Intermenstrual DSB / Right to nothing / Prime cut / Just the same / Take it in hand.
■ LP 4663751
■ CD 4663752
■ MC. .4663754
Epic / Apr '90.

CLEANSING.
Tracks: Another worldly device / Whose fist is this anyway / Snap your fingers, snap your neck / Cutrate / Broken peace / One outnumbered / Out of this misery / No question / Not of this earth / Home rule / Sublime / Test.
CD. 474796 2
LP 474796 1
MC. 474796 4
Epic / Feb '94 / Sony.

FORCE FED.
Tracks: Not Advised.
■ LP . . . . SPT 2
■ MC. . . . . SPT 2C
Spigot / Apr '88 / SRD.

PEEL SESSIONS: PRONG (22.1.89).
Tracks: Defiant / Decay / Senseless abuse / In my view.
■ 12". SFPS 078
■ CD Single . . . . SFPSCD 078
■ MC Single. . . . . .SFPSC 078
Strange Fruit / Jul '90.

PRIMITIVE ORIGINS.
Tracks: Disbelief / Watching / Cling to life / Denial / Dreams like that / In my view / Climate control / Persecution.
■ LP . . . . SPT 1
Spigot / Oct '87.

PROVE YOU WRONG.
Tracks: Irrelevant thoughts / Unconditional / Positively blind / Prove you wrong / Hell if I could / Pointless / Contradictions / Torn between / Brainwave / Territorial rites / Get a grip (on yourself) / Shouldn't have bothered / No way to deny it.
■ CD 4689452
■ LP 4689451
■ MC. .4689454
Epic / Oct '91.

SNAP YOUR FINGERS, SNAP YOUR NECK.
Tracks: Snap your fingers / Snap your fingers (mixes) / Another worldly device / Prove you wrong / Beg to differ / Snap your fingers, snap your neck (mixes).
12". . . . . .DRA 660069
CD Single. . . . . .DRA 660062
Dragnet / Feb '94 / SRD.
12". .660069-8
CD Single. 660069-5

CD Single. 660069-2
Epic / Jun '94 / Sony.

WHOSE FIST IS THIS ANYWAY (EP).
Tracks: Prove you wrong / Hell if I could (EP & CD single only) / (Get a) grip (on yourself) (EP & CD single only) / Irrelevant thoughts (12" special only) / Talk talk (12" special only).
■ CD Single 6580002
■ 12" 6580028
■ EP 6580026
Epic / Apr '92.

Prophet

CYCLE OF THE MOON.
Tracks: Not Advised.
■ LP . . . . K 781822-1
MC. K 781822-4
Megaforce / '88 / Pinnacle.

SOUND OF A BREAKING HEART.
Tracks: Sound of a breaking heart / Asylum / Hard lovin' man (On 12" only).
■ 12" . . . . A 9082 T
■ 7" . . . . .A 9082
Atlantic / May '88.

Prophets Of Doom

ACCESS TO WISDOM.
Tracks: Not Advised.
■ LP . . . . .VOV 672
Metalworks / May '89.

Psychosis

SQUIRM.
Tracks: Not Advised.
CD. MASSCD 018
Massacre / Nov '93 / Plastic Head.

Psychotic Waltz

INTO THE EVERFLOW.
Tracks: Not Advised.
CD. . . . . DCD 9205
Dream Circle / Jul '93 / Plastic Head.

MOSQUITO.
Tracks: Not Advised.
CD. CDVEST 27
Bulletproof / Sep '94 / Pinnacle.

SOCIAL GRACE, A.
Tracks: Social grace.
CD. 972202
■ LP 942202
FM Records / May '91.

Psychotic Youth

BE IN THE SUN.
Tracks: Not Advised.
CD. . . . . RA 91792
Road Runner / Mar '92 / Pinnacle.

Puncture

PUNCTURE.
Tracks: Not Advised.
CD. CDVEST 29
Bulletproof / Aug '94 / Pinnacle.

Pungent Stench

BEEN CAUGHT BUTTERING.
Tracks: Not Advised.
CD. .NB 052CD
■ LP . . . . NB 052
MC. .NB 052C
Revolver / Jan '92 / FM Revolver / Sony.

CLUB MONDO BIZARRE.
Tracks: Not Advised.
CD. .NB 079CD
LP . . . . NB 079
MC. .NB 079C
Nuclear Blast / Mar '94 / Plastic Head.

DIRTY RHYMES AND PYSCOTRONIC.
Tracks: Not Advised.
CD. .NB 078CD
LP . . . . NB 078
MC. .NB 078MC
Nuclear Blast / Jun '93 / Plastic Head.

FOR GOD YOUR SOUL.
Tracks: Not Advised.
CD. 842973

LP 082973
Nuclear Blast / Aug '90 / Plastic Head.

PUNGENT STENCH.
Tracks: Not Advised.
LP 082 932
Nuclear Blast / Aug '89 / Plastic Head.

SPLIT LP (Pungent Stench & Disharmonic Orchestra).
Tracks: Not Advised.
LP . . . . NB 019
Nuclear Blast / Dec '90 / Plastic Head.

VIDEO LA MUERTE.
Tracks: Not Advised.
VHS . . . . NB 092VID
Nuclear Blast / Aug '93 / Plastic Head.

Pursuit Of Happiness

LOVE JUNK.
Tracks: Hard to laugh / She's so young / Walking in the woods / Looking for girls / Tree of knowledge / Ten fingers / Consciousness raising / Beautiful white / Man's best friend / Killed by love.
■ LP . . . . CHR 1675
■ CD . . . . CCD 1675
■ MC. ZCHR 1675
Chrysalis / Mar '89.

ONE SIDED STORY.
Tracks: Not Advised.
■ LP . . . . CHR 1757
■ CD . . . . CCD 1757
■ MC. ZCHR 1757
Chrysalis / Jun '90.

SHE'S SO YOUNG.
Tracks: She's so young.
■ 12". . . . . .CHS 123370
■ 7" . . . . CHS 3370
■ CD Single. . . . . POHCD 1
Chrysalis / Jun '89.

Purtenance

MEMBER OF IMMORTAL DAMNATION.
Tracks: Not Advised.
CD. . . . . DL 011CD
LP . . . . .DL 011
Drowned / Jun '93 / Plastic Head.

Pussy Galore

CORPSE LOVE.
Tracks: Not Advised.
CD. . . . . HUT 013CD
Hut / Feb '92 / EMI.

DIAL 'M' FOR MOTHERFUCKER.
Tracks: Understand me / SM57 / Kicked out / Sold = Sex / Undertaker / DWDA / Dick Johnson / 1 Hour late / Eat me / Waxhead / Wait a minute / Evil eye / ADWD 2 / Hang on / Penetration of a centrefold (Available on CD only.) / Handshake (Available on CD only.) / Adolescent wet dream (Available on CD only.) / Sweet little Hi-Fi (Available on CD only.) / Brick (Available on CD only.) / Renegade (Available on CD only.).
■ MC . . . . INCMC 001
Product Inc. / May '89.
CD . . . . INCCD 001
LP . . . . .INCLP 001
Product Inc. / Jun '94 / Vital Distribution.

GROOVY HATE FUCK.
Tracks: Not Advised.
■ LP . . . . .SUK 001
Vinyl Drip / Feb '89.

HISTORIA DELLA MUSICA-ROCK.
Tracks: Not Advised.
CD. . . . . ROUGHCD 149
LP .ROUGH 149
MC. . . . . .ROUGHC 149
Rough Trade / Apr '90 / Pinnacle.

MAXIMUM PENETRATION.
Tracks: Watusi pussy / Pig sweat / White noise / Just wanna die / Nothing can bring me down / Biker rock loser / Constant pain / Pussy stomp / New York City 1999 / C*nt tease / When I get off / Get out / Pretty fuck look / Trashcan oildrum / Die bitch / Spinout / Kill yourself / No count / Fu** you man / Alright.
■ VHS .JE 192
Jettisoundz / Jun '89.

RIGHT NOW.
Tracks: Not Advised.
■ LP 33PROD 19
Product Inc. / Sep '87.
CD. . . . . .PRODCD 19
Product Inc. / Feb '88 / Vital Distribution.

SUGAR SHIT SHARP.
Tracks: Yu gung / Adolescent wet dream / Brick / Handshake / Sweet little hi-fi / Renegade.
■ LP . . . . M PROD 15
MO. M PRODC 15
Product Inc. / Oct '88 / Vital Distribution.

Putrid Offal

EXULCERATION.
Tracks: Not Advised.
CD. .CDAB 002
Adipocre / Feb '94 / Plastic Head.

Pyogenesis

WAVES OF EROTASIA.
Tracks: Waves of erotasia.
CD Single. . . . . NB 106-2
Nuclear Blast / Apr '94 / Plastic Head.

Pyrexia

SERMON OF MOCKERY.
Tracks: Not Advised.
CD. . . . . DC 017
Drowned / Apr '94 / Plastic Head.

Q

Q5

STEEL THE LIGHT.
Tracks: Not Advised.
■ LP . . . . MFN 39
MC. . . . . TMFN 39
Music For Nations / Mar '85 / Pinnacle.

STEEL THE LIGHT.
Tracks: Steel the light / That's alright with you.
■ 12" . . . . 12 KUT 115
Music For Nations / May '05.

WHEN THE MIRROR CRACKS.
Tracks: Not Advised.
■ LP . . . . MFN 64
MC. . . . . TMFN 64
Music For Nations / Sep '86 / Pinnacle.
CD . . . . CDMFN 64
Music For Nations / Dec '87 / Pinnacle.

Quartz

AGAINST ALL ODDS.
Tracks: Tell me why / Too hot to handle / Buried alive / Avalon / Just another man / Madman / Hard road / Wake / Silver wheels / Love em & run / (It's) Hell, livin' without you.
■ LP . . . . HMRLP 9
Heavy Metal / Jun '83.

BEYOND THE CLOUDS.
Tracks: Beyond the clouds / For Geromine.
■ 7" 7NL 25797
Pye International / Oct '78.

QUARTZ-LIVE.
Tracks: Street fighting lady / Good times / Mainline rider / Belinda / Count Dracula / Around and around / Roll over Beethoven.
■ LP . . . . MOGO 4007
Logo / Jul '80.

SATAN'S SERENADE.
Tracks: Satan's serenade / Bloody fool.
■ 12" . . . . GOT 387
■ 7" . . . . GO 387
Logo / Jun '80.

STAND UP AND FIGHT.
Tracks: Stand up and fight / Charlie Snow.
■ 7" . . . . MCA 661
MCA / Jan '81.

STOKING UP THE FIRES OF HELL.
Tracks: Stroking up the fires of hell / Circles.
■ 7" . . . . MCA 642
MCA / Aug '80.

TELL ME WHY.
Tracks: Tell me why / Streetwalker.
■ 7" . . . . HEAVY 17
Heavy Metal / Dec '83.

Queen

Second only to Beatles as U.K.'s most successful act, Queen retained stable line-up for nearly 30 years: singer Freddie Mercury, guitarist Brian May, drummer Roger Taylor and bassist Jon Deacon. Career distinguished by record-breaking chart runs - notably classic single *Bohemian Rhapsody* and 1981 *Greatest Hits* album; innovative videos; hits in numerous styles from metal to disco; and huge international audiences, particularly in wake of triumphant Live Aid performance. Mercury's death in 1991 robbed music world of one of its best-loved figures and bands. Remaining members staged star-studded tribute show in 1992, featuring Guns N' Roses, Def Leppard, Metallica and Extreme.

ANOTHER ONE BITES THE DUST.
Tracks: Another one bites the dust / Dragon attack.
■ 7" . . . . EMI 5102
EMI / Aug '80.

ANOTHER ONE BITES THE DUST.
Tracks: Another one bites the dust / Dragon attack / Las palabras de amor (the words of love).

■ CD Single . . . . QUEENCD 8
EMI / Nov '88.

BACK CHAT.
Tracks: Back chat / Staying power.
■ 12" 12EMI 5325
■ 7" . . . . EMI 5325
EMI / Jul '82.

BODY LANGUAGE.
Tracks: Body language / Life is real (song for Lennon).
■ 7" . . . . EMI 5293
EMI / May '82.

BOHEMIAN RHAPSODY.
Tracks: Bohemian rhapsody / I'm in love with my car.
■ 7" . . . . EMI 2375
EMI / Oct '75.

BOHEMIAN RHAPSODY.
Tracks: Bohemian rhapsody / I'm in love with my car / You're my best friend.
■ CD Single . . . . QUEENCD 3
EMI / Nov '88.

BOHEMIAN RHAPSODY (1991 REISSUE).
Tracks: Bohemian rhapsody / These are the days of our lives.
■ 7" . . . . QUEEN 20
■ CD Single . . . . CDQUEEN 20
■ MC Single . . . . TCQUEEN 20
Parlophone / Dec '91.

BOHEMIAN RHAPSODY (VIDEO SINGLE).
Tracks: Bohemian rhapsody / Crazy little thing called love.
VHS . . . . PM 0022
Gold Rushes / May '87 / Gold & Sons.

BOX OF FLIX.
Tracks: Not Advised.
VHS . . . . MVB 9913243
PMI / Nov '91 / EMI / Gold & Sons / TBD.

BREAKTHRU.
Tracks: Breakthru / Stealin' / Breakthru (12" version) (12" & CD single only.).
■ 12" 12QUEEN 11
■ 7" . . . . QUEENLH 11
■ 7" . . . . QUEEN 11
■ 7" P.Disc . . . . QUEENPD 11
■ CD Single . . . . CDQUEEN 11
■ MC Single . . . . TCQUEEN 11
Parlophone / Jun '89.

COMPLETE WORKS.
Tracks: Not Advised.
■ LP Set . . . . QB 1
■ LP Set . . . . QBX 1
EMI / Dec '85.

CRAZY LITTLE THING CALLED LOVE.
Tracks: Crazy little thing called love / Spread your wings (live).
■ 7" . . . . EMI 5001
EMI / Oct '79.
■ 12" 05263317
EMI (Germany) / May '88.

CRAZY LITTLE THING CALLED LOVE.
Tracks: Crazy little thing called love / Spread your wings / Flash.
■ CD Single . . . . QUEENCD 2
EMI / Nov '88.

DAY AT THE RACES, A.
Tracks: Long away / Millionaire waltz / You and I / Somebody to love / White man / Good old-fashioned lover boy / Drowse / Teo torriate / Tie your mother down / You take my breath away.
■ LP . . . . EMTC 104
■ MC . . . . TCEMTC 104
EMI / Jan '77.
CD . . . . CDP 746 051 2
EMI / '84 / EMI.
CD . . . . CZ 105
EMI / Jun '88 / EMI.
CD . . . . CDPCSD 131
Parlophone / Sep '93 / EMI.

DON'T STOP ME NOW.
Tracks: Don't stop me now / In only seven days.
■ 7" . . . . EMI 2910
EMI / Feb '79.

FAT BOTTOMED GIRLS.
Tracks: Bicycle race / Fat bottomed girls.
■ 7" . . . . EMI 2870
EMI / Oct '78.

FLASH.
Tracks: Flash / Football fight.
■ 7" . . . . EMI 5126
EMI / Dec '80.

FRIENDS WILL BE FRIENDS.
Tracks: Friends will be friends / Seven seas of Rhye.
■ 7" P.Disc . . . . QUEENP 8
■ 12" . . . . 12 QUEEN 8
■ 7" . . . . QUEEN 8
EMI / Jun '86.

GAME, THE.
Tracks: Play the game / Dragon attack / Another one bites the dust / Need your loving tonight / Crazy little thing called love / Rock it (prime jive) / Don't try suicide / Sweet sister / Coming soon / Save me.
MC . . . . TCEMA 795
EMI / Jul '80 / EMI.
■ LP . . . . EMA 795
EMI / Jun '80.
CD . . . . CZ 104
EMI / Jun '88 / EMI.
CD . . . . CDPCSD 134
MC . . . . TCPCSD 134
Parlophone / Feb '94 / EMI.

GREATEST FLIX.
Tracks: Bohemian rhapsody / Another one bites the dust / Killer queen / Fat bottomed girls / Bicycle race / Don't stop me now / Save me / Crazy little thing called love / Somebody to love / Now I'm here / Play the game / Flash / We will rock you / We are the champions / Spread your wings / Tie your mother down / You're my best friend / Love of my life.
VHS . . . . MVP 99 1011 2
PMI / Oct '84 / EMI / Gold & Sons / TBD.

GREATEST FLIX II.
Tracks: Not Advised.
VHS . . . . VC 4112
Video Collection / Nov '91 / Gold & Sons / Video Collection / TBD.

GREATEST FLIX: I & II.
Tracks: Killer Queen / Bohemian rhapsody / You're my best friend / Somebody to love / Tie your mother down / We are the champions / We will rock you / Spread your wings / Bicycle race / Fat bottomed girls / Don't stop me now / Love of my life / Crazy little thing called love / Save me / Play the game / Another one bites the dust / It's a kind of magic / Under pressure / Flash / Radio ga ga / I want it all / I want to break free / Innuendo / It's a hard life / Breakthru / Who wants to live forever / Headlong / Miracle / I'm going slightly mad / Invisible man / Hammer to fall / Friends will be friends / Show must go on / One vision.
VCD . . . . PMCD 4912712
PMI / Jul '94 / EMI / Gold & Sons / TBD.

GREATEST HITS: QUEEN.
Tracks: Bohemian rhapsody / Another one bites the dust / Killer queen / Fat bottomed girls / Bicycle race / You're my best friend / Don't stop me now / Save me / Crazy little thing called love / Now I'm here / Good old-fashioned lover boy / Play the game / Flash / Seven seas of Rhye / We will rock you / We are the champions / Somebody to love.
■ LP . . . . EMC 3350
EMI / Nov '80.
■ LP . . . . EMTV 30
MC. . . . . TCEMTV 30
EMI / Oct '81 / EMI.
CD . . . . CDEMTV 30
CD . . . . CDP 746 033 2
EMI / Sep '84 / EMI.
CD . . . . CDPCSD 141
MC . . . . TCPCSD 141
Parlophone / Jun '94 / EMI.

■ DELETED

HAMMER TO FALL.
Tracks: Hammer to fall / Tear it up.
■ 7″		QUEEN 4
■ 12″		12 QUEEN 4

EMI / Sep '84.

HEADLONG.
Tracks: Headlong (12″ Picture disc only.) / All God's people / Mad the swine (On CD single & 12″s only.) / Headlong (Album version) (Only on 12″ Picture Disc (Limited edition)).
■ 12″		12QUEEN 18
■ 12″ P.Disc.		12QUEENPD 18
■ 7″		QUEEN 18
■ CD Single		CDQUEEN 18
■ MC Single.		TCQUEEN 18

EMI / May '91.

HOT SPACE.
Tracks: Staying power / Dancer / Back chat / Body language / Action this day / Put out the fire / Life is real (song for Lennon) / Calling all girls / Las palabras de amor (the words of love) / Cool cat / Under pressure.
MC.		TCEMA 797
■ LP		EMA 797

EMI / May '82.
■ CD		CZ 101

EMI / Jun '88.
■ CD		CDFA 3228
■ LP		FA 3228
■ MC		TCFA 3228

Fame / Aug '89.
CD		CDPCSD 135
MC.		TCPCSD 135

Parlophone / Feb '94 / EMI.

I WANT IT ALL.
Tracks: I want it all / Hang on in there / I want it all (album version) (Not on 7″.)
■ 12″		12QUEEN 10
■ 7″		QUEEN 10
■ CD Single		CDQUEEN 10
■ MC Single.		TCQUEEN 10

Parlophone / May '89.

I WANT TO BREAK FREE.
Tracks: I want to break free / Machines (or Back to humans) / I want to break free (extended version) (Available on 12″ only).
■ 7″		QUEEN 2
■ 12″		12 QUEEN 2

EMI / Apr '84.

I WANT TO BREAK FREE.
Tracks: I want to break free / Machines (or Back to humans) / It's a hard life.
■ CD Single.		QUEENCD 11

EMI / Nov '88.

I'M GOING SLIGHTLY MAD.
Tracks: I'm going slightly mad / Hitman / Lost opportunity (CD single & 12″ gatefold only.)
■ 12″		12QUEENG 17
■ 7″		QUEEN 17
■ 7″ P.Disc		QUEENPD 17
■ MC Single.		TCQUEEN 17
■ CD Single.		CDQUEEN 17

Parlophone / Mar '91.

INNUENDO.
Tracks: Innuendo / Bijou / Under pressure (Not on 7″ or cassingle.).
■ 12″		12QUEEN 16
■ 12″ P.Disc.		12QUEENPD 16
■ 7″		QUEEN 16
■ CD Single		CDQUEEN 16
■ MC Single.		TCQUEEN 16

Parlophone / Jan '91.

INNUENDO.
Tracks: Innuendo / I'm going slightly mad (edit) (LP only.) / I'm going slightly mad (Cassette and CD only.) / Headlong / I can't live with you / Ride the wild wind / All God's people / These are the days of our lives / Delilah / Don't try so hard (edit) (LP only.) / Don't try so hard (Cassette & CD only.) / Hitman, The (edit) (LP only.) / Hitman (Cassette & CD only.) / Bijou (edit) (LP only.) / Bijou (Cassette & CD only.) / Show must go on.
CD		CDPCSD 115
■ LP		PCSD 115
MC.		TCPCSD 115

Parlophone / Feb '91 / EMI.

INTERVIEW COLLECTION, THE.
Tracks: Not Advised.
CD P.Disc.		CBAK 4957

Baktabak / Feb '94 / Arabesque Ltd.

INVISIBLE MAN, THE.
Tracks: Invisible man / Hijack my heart.
■ 12″		12QUEENX 12
■ 12″		12QUEEN 12

■ 7″		QUEEN 12
■ 7″		QUEENX 12
■ CD Single.		CDQUEEN 12
■ MC Single.		TCQUEEN 12

Parlophone / Aug '89.

IT'S A HARD LIFE.
Tracks: It's a hard life / Is this the world we created.
■ 12″ P.Disc.		12 QUEENP 3
■ 12″		12 QUEEN 3

EMI / Aug '84.
■ 7″		QUEEN 3

EMI / Jul '84.

JAZZ.
Tracks: Mustapha / Fat bottomed girls / Jealousy / Bicycle race / If you can't beat them / Let me entertain you / Dead on time / In only seven days / Dreamers ball / Fun it / Leaving home ain't easy / Don't stop me now / More of that jazz.
■ LP		ATAK 24
MC.		TCATAK 24
■ LP		EMA 788
■ MC		TCEMA 788

EMI / Nov '78.
■ CD		CZ 103

EMI / Jun '88.
CD		CDPCSD 133
MC.		TCPCSD 133

Parlophone / Feb '94 / EMI.

KEEP YOURSELF ALIVE.
Tracks: Keep yourself alive / Son and daughter.
■ 7″		EMI 2036

EMI / Jul '73.

KILLER QUEEN.
Tracks: Killer queen / Flick of the wrist.
■ 7″		EMI 2229

EMI / Oct '74.

KILLER QUEEN.
Tracks: Killer queen / Flick of the wrist / Brighton rock.
■ CD Single		QUEENCD 2

EMI / Nov '88.

KIND OF MAGIC, A.
Tracks: Princes of the universe / Kind of magic / One year of love / Pain is so close to pleasure / Friends will be friends / Who wants to live forever / Gimme the prize / Don't lose your head / One vision / Friends will be friends will be friends.. (Available on CD only) / Forever (Available on CD only).
■ LP		EU 3509
MC.		TCEU 3509

EMI / Jun '86 / EMI.
CD		CDP 746 267 2

EMI / Jun '88 / EMI.

KIND OF MAGIC, A.
Tracks: Kind of magic / Dozen red roses for my darling / One vision.
■ CD Single.		QUEENCD 12

EMI / Nov '88.

KIND OF MAGIC, A.
Tracks: Kind of magic / Don't lose your head (instrumental) / Kind of magic, A (extended version) (12″ only.) / Dozen red roses for my darling.
■ 12″ P.Disc.		12 QUEENT 7
■ 12″		12 QUEEN 7
■ 7″		QUEEN 7

EMI / Mar '86.

KIND OF MAGIC, A (VIDEO SINGLE).
Tracks: Kind of magic / Who wants to live forever.
■ VHS		MVW 99 0059 2

PMI / Oct '86.

LAS PALABRAS DE AMOR (THE WORDS OF LOVE).
Tracks: Las palabras de amor (the words of love) / Cool cat.
■ 7″		EMI 5316

EMI / Jun '82.

LIVE AT WEMBLEY '86.
Tracks: One vision / Tie your mother down / In the lap of the Gods / Seven seas of Thye / Tear it up / Kind of magic / Under pressure / Another one bites the dust / Who wants to live forever / I want to break free / Impromptu / Brighton rock solo / Now I'm here / Love of my life / Is this the world we created / (You're so square) baby I don't care / Hello Mary Lou (Goodbye heart) / Tuttie frutti / Gimme some lovin' / Bohemian rhapsody / Hammer to fall / Crazy little

thing called love / Big spender / Radio ga ga / We will rock you / Friends will be friends / We are the champions / God save the Queen.
CD Set		CDPCSP 7251
■ Double LP		PCSP 7251
MC Set		TCPCSP 7251

Parlophone / Jun '92 / EMI.

LIVE IN BUDAPEST.
Tracks: Kind of magic / One vision / Tie your mother down / In the lap of the gods..revisited / Seven seas of Rhye / Tear it up / Under pressure / Who wants to live forever / I want to break free / Now I'm here / Love of my life / Tavaski Szel (Hungarian folk song) / Is this the world we created / Tutti frutti / Bohemian rhapsody / Hammer to fall / Crazy little thing called love / Radio ga ga / We will rock you / Friends will be friends / We are the champions / God save the Queen.
■ VHS		MVN 99 1146 2

PMI / Feb '87.
CD Video		080 510 1

Polygram Music Video / Oct '88 / PolyGram.

LIVE IN RIO.
Tracks: Not Advised.
■ VHS		MVP 99 1079 2

PMI / May '85.

LIVE KILLERS.
Tracks: We will rock you / Let me entertain you / Death on two legs / Killer queen / Bicycle race / I'm in love with my car / Get down make love / You're my best friend / Now I'm here / Dreamers ball / Love of my life / '39 / Keep yourself alive / Don't stop me now / Spread your wings / Brighton rock / Bohemian rhapsody / Tie your mother down / Sheer heart attack / We are the champions / God save the Queen.
■ Double LP		EMSP 330
■ MC Set		TC2EMSP 330

EMI / Jun '79.
CD Set		CZD 107

EMI / Jun '88.
CD		CDPCSD 138
MC.		TCPCSD 138

Parlophone / Apr '94 / EMI.

LIVE MAGIC.
Tracks: One vision / Tie your mother down / Seven seas of Rhye / Another one bites the dust / I want to break free / Is this the world we created / Bohemian rhapsody / Hammer to fall / Radio ga ga / We will rock you / Friends will be friends / We are the champions / God save the Queen / Kind of magic / Under pressure.
MC.		TCEMC 3519
■ LP		EMC 3519

EMI / Dec '86.
CD		CDP 746 413 2

EMI / Jan '87 / EMI.

LOVE OF MY LIFE (LIVE).
Tracks: Love of my life (live) / Now I'm here (live).
■ 7″		EMI 2959

EMI / Jul '79.

MAGIC YEARS - THE COMPLETE SET.
Tracks: Not Advised.
VHS		MVB 99 1157 2

PMI / Dec '87 / EMI / Gold & Sons / TBD.

MAGIC YEARS VOL.1.
Tracks: Not Advised.
VHS		MVP 99 1154 2

PMI / Nov '87 / EMI / Gold & Sons / TBD.

MAGIC YEARS VOL.2.
Tracks: Not Advised.
VHS		MVP 99 1155 2

PMI / Nov '87 / EMI / Gold & Sons / TBD.

MAGIC YEARS VOL.3.
Tracks: Not Advised.
VHS		MVP 99 1156 2

PMI / Nov '87 / EMI / Gold & Sons / TBD.

MESSAGE FROM THE PALACE (Interview picture disc).
Tracks: Not Advised.
LP		BAK 6014

Baktabak / Sep '90 / Arabesque Ltd.
MC.		MBAK 6014

Baktabak / Jun '91 / Arabesque Ltd.

MIRACLE, THE.
Tracks: Party / Khashoggi's ship / Miracle / I want it all / Invisible man / Breakthru / Rain must fall / Scandal / My baby does me / Was it all worth it /

Hang on in there (Available on CD only) / Chinese torture (Available on CD only).

CD. CDPCSD 107
■ LP . . . . PCSD 107
■ MC. . . . . TCPCSD 107
Parlophone / May '89.

MIRACLE, THE.
Tracks: Miracle / Stone cold crazy (live) (Live from The Rainbow, London 1974.) / My melancholy blues (live) (Live from Houston, Texas 1977. 12" & CD single only.).

■ 7" . . . . .QUEEN 15
■ 12" 12QUEEN 15
■ 12" 12QUEENP 15
■ CD Single . . . . CDQUEEN 15
■ MC Single . . . . TCQUEEN 15
■ Special . . . . .QUEENH 15
Parlophone / Nov '89.

MIRACLE, THE (VIDEO EP).
Tracks: I want it all / Breakthru / Invisible man / Scandal.

■ VHS . . . . MVL 9900843
PMI / Dec '89.

MUSIC AND MEDIA INTERVIEW PICTURE DISC.
Tracks: Not Advised.

■ LP P.Disc . . . . MM 1218
Music & Media / Feb '88.

NEWS OF THE WORLD.
Tracks: We will rock you / We are the champions / Sheer heart attack / All dead all dead / Spread your wings / Fight from the inside / Get down make love / Sleeping on the sidewalk / Who needs you / It's late / My melancholy blues.

■ MC. . . . . TCEMA 784
■ LP . . . . EMA 784
EMI / Nov '77.
■ CD . . . . CZ 102
EMI / Jun '88.
CD. CDPCSD 132
MC. TCPCSD 132
Parlophone / Sep '93 / EMI.

NIGHT AT THE OPERA, A.
Tracks: Death on two legs / Lazing on a Sunday afternoon / I'm your best friend / I'm in love with my car / Sweet lady / Seaside rendezvous / Good company / '39 / Prophet's song / Love of my life / Bohemian rhapsody / God save the Queen.

■ LP .EMTC 103
EMI / Dec '75.
■ MC. . . . . TCEMTC 103
EMI / Jan '76.
CD . . . . CDP 746 050 2
EMI / '84 / EMI.
■ CD . . . . CZ 106
EMI / Jun '88.
CD. CDPCSD 130
Parlophone / Jul '93 / EMI.

NOW I'M HERE.
Tracks: Now I'm here / Lily of the valley.

■ 7" . . . . EMI 2256
EMI / Jan '75.

ONE VISION.
Tracks: One vision / Blurred vision.

■ 12" . . . . 12 QUEEN 6
■ 7" . . . . QUEEN 6
■ 7" . . . . EMI 5535
EMI / Nov '85.

PHOTO SESSION.
Tracks: Not Advised.

CD Set . . . . .QU 2
UFO / Nov '92 / Pinnacle.

PLAY THE GAME.
Tracks: Play the game / Human body.

■ 7" . . . . EMI 5076
EMI / Jun '80.

QUEEN.
Tracks: Keep yourself alive / Doing alright / Great King Rat / My fairy King / Liar / Night comes down / Modern times rock 'n' roll / Son and daughter / Jesus / Seven seas of Rhye.

■ LP .EMC 3006
EMI / Mar '74.
■ LP . . . . FA 3040
Fame / Aug '82.
■ MC. TCFA 3040
Fame / Nov '86.
■ CD . . . . CDP 746 204 2
Fame / Nov '86.
■ CD . . . . CDFA 3040
Fame / May '88.
CD. CDPCSD 139
MC. TCPCSD 139
Parlophone / Apr '94 / EMI.

QUEEN AT THE BEEB.
Tracks: My fairy King / Keep yourself alive / Doing alright / Liar / Ogre battle / Great King Rat / Modern times rock 'n' roll / Son and daughter.

CD. BOJCD 001
■ LP . . . . BOJLP 001
■ MC. . . . . BOJMC 001
Band Of Joy / Dec '89.

QUEEN AT WEMBLEY.
Tracks: One vision / Tie your mother down / In the lap of the gods / Seven seas of Rhye / Yea yea yea (Freddie ad-libs with audience) / Under pressure / Another one bites the dust / Who wants to live forever / I want to break free / Is this the world we created / Tutti frutti / Bohemian rhapsody / Hammer to fall / Crazy little thing called love / Radio Ga Ga / We will rock you / Friends will be friends / We are the champions / National anthem.

VHS . . . . MVP 99 1259 3
PMI / Jun '92 / EMI / Gold & Sons / TBD.

QUEEN GREATEST HITS 2.
Tracks: Kind of magic / Under pressure / I want it all / I want to break free / Innuendo / Breakthrou' / Who wants to live forever / Headlong / Miracle / I'm going slightly mad / Invisible man / Hammer to fall / Friends will be friends / Show must go on.

CD. CDPMTV 2
■ Double LP. . . . . PMTV 2
MC. TCPMTV 2
Parlophone / Oct '91 / EMI.

QUEEN GREATEST HITS I & II.
Tracks: Bohemian rhapsody / Another one bites the dust / Killer Queen / Fat bottomed girls / Bicycle race / You're my best friend / Don't stop me now / Save me / Crazy little thing called love / Somebody to love / Now I'm here / Good old fashioned lover boy / Play the game / Flash / Seven seas of Rhye / We will rock you / We are the champions / Kind of magic / Under pressure / Radio ga ga / I want to break free / Innuendo / It's a hard life / Breakthru / Who wants to live forever / Headlong / I'm going slightly mad / Invisible man / Hammer to fall / friends will be friends / Show must go on / One vision.

■ LP Set. . . . . GHBOX 1
Parlophone / Nov '92.

QUEEN II.
Tracks: Procession / Father to son / White Queen (as it began) / Some day one day / Loser in the end / Ogre battle / Fairy feller's master-stroke / Nevermore / March of the black Queen / Funny how love is / Seven seas of Rhye.

■ LP . . . . EMA 767
EMI / Mar '74.
■ LP . . . . FA 3099
■ MC. TCFA 3099
Fame / Apr '84.
■ CD . . . . CDP 746 205 2
Fame / Nov '86.
■ CD . . . . CDFA 3099
Fame / May '88.
CD. CDPCSD 140
MC. TCPCSD 140
Parlophone / Apr '94 / EMI.

QUEEN LIVE IN BUDAPEST.
Tracks: Not Advised.

VHS .MC 2138
Video Collection / Sep '94 / Gold & Sons / Video Collection / TBD.

QUEEN'S FIRST EP.
Tracks: Good old-fashioned lover boy / Death on two legs / Tenement funster / White Queen (as it began).

■ EP . . . . EMI 2623
EMI / Jun '77.
■ CD Single . . . . QUEENCD 5
EMI / Nov '88.

QUEEN: INTERVIEW COLLECTION.
Tracks: Not Advised.

7" Set . . . . BAKPAK 1021
Baktabak / Jun '90 / Arabesque Ltd.

QUEEN: INTERVIEW COMPACT DISC.
Tracks: Not Advised.

CD P.Disc. . . . . CBAK 4022
Baktabak / Nov '89 / Arabesque Ltd.

QUEEN: INTERVIEW PICTURE DISC.
Tracks: Not Advised.

LP P.Disc. . . . . BAK 2014
Baktabak / Jul '87 / Arabesque Ltd.

RADIO GA GA.
Tracks: Radio ga ga / I go crazy / Radio ga ga (extended version) (Available on 12" only) / Radio ga ga (instrumental) (Available on 12" only).

■ 12" . . . . 12 QUEEN 1

RADIO GA GA.
■ 7" . . . . QUEEN 1
EMI / Jan '84.

RADIO GA GA.
Tracks: Radio ga ga / I go crazy / Hammer to fall.

■ CD Single . . . . QUEENCD 10
EMI / Nov '88.

RARE LIVE.
Tracks: I want it all / Crazy little thing called love / Liar / Another one bites the dust / Big spender / Jailhouse rock / Stupid cupid / My melancholy blues / Hammer to fall / Killer queen / We will rock you / Somebody to love / Tie your mother down / Keep yourself alive / Love of my life / Stone cold crazy / Radio ga ga / You take my breath away / Sheer heart attack / We are the champions.

VHS . . . . MVP 99 1189 3
PMI / Aug '89 / EMI / Gold & Sons / TBD.

SAVE ME.
Tracks: Save me / Let me entertain you (live).

■ 7" . . . . EMI 5022
EMI / Feb '80.

SCANDAL.
Tracks: Scandal / My life has been saved / Scandal (12" version) (12" & CD single only.).

■ 12" 12QUEEN 14
■ 7" . . . . .QUEENP 14
■ 7" . . . . QUEEN 14
■ CD Single . . . . CDQUEEN 14
■ MC Single . . . . TCQUEEN 14
■ Special 12QUEENS 14
Parlophone / Oct '89.

SEVEN SEAS OF RHYE.
Tracks: Seven seas of Rhye / See what a fool I've been.

■ 7" . . . . EMI 2121
EMI / Mar '74.

SEVEN SEAS OF RHYE.
Tracks: Seven seas of Rhye / See what a fool I've been / Funny how love is.

■ CD Single . . . . QUEENCD 1
EMI / Nov '88.

SHEER HEART ATTACK.
Tracks: Brighton rock / Tenement funster / Flick of the wrist / Lily of the valley / Now I'm here / In the lap of the gods / Stone cold crazy / Bring back that Leroy Brown / She makes me (stormtrooper in stilettos) / In the lap of the gods..revisited / Killer queen / Dear friends / Misfire.

■ MC. . . . . TCEMC 3061
■ LP .EMC 3061
EMI / Nov '74.
CD . . . . CDP 746 052 2
EMI / '84 / EMI.
CD. CDPCSD 129
Parlophone / Jul '93 / EMI.

SHOW MUST GO ON, THE.
Tracks: Show must go on / Keep yourself alive / Queen talks (Only on 12" and CD single) / Body language (Only on CD single).

■ MC Single . . . . TCQUEEN 19
Parlophone / Nov '91.
■ 12" 12QUEENSG 19
■ CD Single . . . . CDQUEEN 19
■ 7" . . . . .QUEEN 19
Parlophone / Oct '91.

SOMEBODY TO LOVE.
Tracks: Somebody to love / White man.

■ 7" . . . . EMI 2565
EMI / Oct '76.

SOMEBODY TO LOVE.
Tracks: Somebody to love / White man / Tie your mother down.

■ CD Single . . . . QUEENCD 4
EMI / Nov '88.

SPREAD YOUR WINGS.
Tracks: Spread your wings / Sheer heart attack

■ 7" . . . . EMI 2757
EMI / Feb '78.

THANK GOD IT'S CHRISTMAS.
Tracks: Thank God it's Christmas / Man on the prowl (Available on 7" only) / Keep passing the open windows (Available on 7" only) / Man on the prowl (extended version) (Available on 12" only) / Keep passing the open windows (extended version) (Available on 12" only).

■ 12" . . . . 12 QUEEN 5

■ DELETED

■ 7″ . . . . QUEEN 5
EMI / Nov '84.

TIE YOUR MOTHER DOWN.
Tracks: Tie your mother down / You and I.
■ 7″ . . . . EMI 2593
EMI / Mar '77.

TWELVE INCH COLLECTION (Telstar Box Set).
Tracks: Bohemian rhapsody / Radio ga ga / Machines (or back to humans) (instrumental) / I want to break free / It's a hard life / Hammer to fall / Man on the prowl / Kind of magic / Pain is so close to pleasure / Breakthru' / Invisible man / Show must go on.
CD . . . . .CDQTEL 0001
MC . . . . .TCQTEL 0001
Parlophone / Jun '92 / EMI.

UNDER PRESSURE (Queen & David Bowie).
Tracks: Under pressure / Soul brother.
■ 7″ . . . . EMI 5250
EMI / Nov '81.

UNDER PRESSURE (Queen & David Bowie).
Tracks: Under pressure / Soul brother / Body language.
■ CD Single . . . . QUEENCD 9
EMI / Nov '88.

WE ARE THE CHAMPIONS.
Tracks: We are the champions / We will rock you.
■ 7″ . . . . EMI 2708
EMI / Oct '77.

WE ARE THE CHAMPIONS.
Tracks: We are the champions / We will rock you / Fat bottomed girls.
■ CD Single . . . . QUEENCD 6
EMI / Nov '88.

WE WILL ROCK YOU.
Tracks: Tie your mother down / Bohemian rhapsody / We will rock you / Under pressure / God save the Queen / We are the champions / Love of my life / Dragon attack / Now I'm here / Save me / Get down make love / I'm in love with my car / Killer queen / Somebody to love / Play the game / Let me entertain you / Sheer heart attack / Another one bites the dust / Keep yourself alive / Crazy little thing called love.
VHS 888 6122 3
Peppermint Music / Sep '84.
VHS . . . . VC 4012
Video Collection / May '87 / Gold & Sons / Video Collection / TBD.
VHS . . . . .MC 2032
Music Club Video / Sep '89 / Video Collection / Gold & Sons / TBD.

WORKS (VIDEO EP), THE.
Tracks: Radio ga ga / I want to break free / It's a hard life / Hammer to fall.
■ VHS . . . . MVS 99 0010 2
PMI / Nov '84.
■ VHS . . . . MVT 99 0010 2
PMI / Oct '84.

WORKS, THE.
Tracks: Radio ga ga / Tear it up / It's a hard life / Man on the prowl / Machines (or Back to humans) / I want to break free / Keep passing the open windows / Hammer to fall / Is this the world we created.
CD . . . . CDP 746 016 2
EMI / Apr '84 / EMI.
■ LP . . . . .WORK 1
MC . . . . .TC WORK 1
EMI / Feb '84 / EMI.
CD . . . . .CDPCSD 136
MC . . . . .TCPCSD 136
Parlophone / Feb '94 / EMI.

YOU'RE MY BEST FRIEND.
Tracks: You're my best friend / '39.
■ 7″ . . . . EMI 2494
EMI / Jul '76.
■ 7″ . . . . .G 45 1
EMI Golden 45's / Mar '84.

Queensryche

Seattle band who have occasionally been compared to Judas Priest (due mainly to singer Geoff Tate's Rob Halford-esque upper register) but who can reasonably lay claim to be truly unique. The band - whose line-up is completed by Chris DeGarmo (guitar), Michael Wilton (guitar), Eddie Jackson (bass), Scott Rockenfield (drums) - overcame some peculiar choices of image in their early years (notably around the time

of 1985's *Rage For Order*) to turn a healthy cult following into a worldwide fanbase with classic *Operation: mindcrime* in 1988. The album was a truly awesome record, that they've wisely chosen to sidestep rather than attempt to overtake. As such, 1990's follow up *Empire* was a much mellower affair which sold as well nonetheless.

BEST I CAN.
Tracks: Best I can / I dream in infrared (Cassingle only).
■ 10″ 10MT 97
■ CD Single . . . . CDMT 97
EMI-Manhattan / Jul '91.
■ 7″ . . . . MT 97
■ MC Single . . . . TCMT 97
EMI-Manhattan / Jun '91.

BUILDING EMPIRES.
Tracks: Nightrider / Prophesy (live) / Gonna get close to you / Eyes of a stranger (Unseen version) / Empire / Best I can / Silent Lucidity / Jet city woman / Another rainy night (Unseen version) / Another rainy night / Anybody listening / Resistence (Live) / Walk in the shadows (Live) / Thin line, The (Live) / Take hold of the flame (Live) / Lady wore black, The (Live) / Silent Lucidity (Live) / I will remember (From MTV's Unplugged) / Della Brown (From MTV's Unplugged).
VHS . . . . MVN 4910953
PMI / Feb '93 / EMI / Gold & Sons / TBD.

EMPIRE.
Tracks: Best I can / Thin line / Jet city woman / Della Brown / Another rainy night (without you) / Empire / Resistgance / Silent lucidity / Hand on heart / One and only / Anybody listening.
CD . . . . CDMTL 1058
MC . . . . TCMTL 1058
■ Double LP . . . . MTL 1058
EMI-Manhattan / Sep '90.

EMPIRE.
Tracks: Empire / Scarborough Fair / Prophecy (Not on 7″).
■ 7″ P.Disc . . . . MTPD 90
■ 12″ 12MT 90
■ 7″ . . . . MT 90
■ CD Single . . . . CDMT 90
EMI-Manhattan / Sep '90.

EYES OF A STRANGER.
Tracks: Eyes of a stranger / Queen of the Reich / Walk in the shadows (12″ only.) / Take hold of the flame (12″ only.) / Prophecy.
■ CD Single . . . . CDMT 65
■ 12″ 12MT 65
■ 12″ 12MTG 65
■ 7″ . . . . MT 65
EMI-Manhattan / Apr '89.

GONNA GET CLOSE TO YOU.
Tracks: Gonna get close to you / Prophecy / Queen of the Reich (On 7″ set only) / Deliverance (On 7″ set only).
■ 7″ . . . . EA 22
■ 7″ Set . . . . EAD 22
EMI-America / Aug '86.

JET CITY WOMAN.
Tracks: Jet city woman / Empire (live) (Not on CD single) / Walk in the shadows (Only on 12″ and CD single) / Queen of the Reich (Only on CD single).
■ 12″ 12MTS 98
■ 7″ . . . . MT 98
■ 7″ P.Disc . . . . MTPD 98
■ CD Single . . . . CDMT 98
EMI-America / Aug '91.

LIVE IN TOKYO.
Tracks: Nightrider / Prophecy / Deliverance / Child of fire / Lady wore black / Warning / Queen of the Reich.
■ VHS . . . . MVP 99 1075 2
PMI / Mar '85.

OPERATION LIVE CRIME.
Tracks: I remember now / Anarchy-x / Revolution calling / Operation: Mindcrime / Speak / Spreading the disease / Mission / Suite sister Mary / Needle lies / Electric requiem / Breaking the silence / I don't believe in love / Waiting for 22 / My empty room / Eyes of a stranger.
VHS . . . . MVB 9913213
PMI / Nov '91 / EMI / Gold & Sons / TBD.
VHS . . . . MVP 4911383
PMI / Sep '93 / EMI / Gold & Sons / TBD.

OPERATION: MINDCRIME.
Tracks: I remember now / Anarchy X / Revolution calling / Operation: Mindcrime / Speak / Spreading the disease / Mission / Suite sister Mary / Needle

lies / Electric requiem / Breaking the silence / I don't believe in love / Waiting for 22 / My empty room / Eyes of a stranger.
MC . . . . TCMTL 1023
■ CD . . . . CDMTL 1023
■ LP . . . . MTL 1023
EMI-Manhattan / May '88.

OVERSEEING THE OPERATION (Excerpts from "Operation: Mindcrime").
Tracks: I remember now / Revolution calling / Operation: Mindcrime / Breaking the silence / Eyes of a stranger / Suite Sister Mary.
■ 10″ . . . . 10 QR 1
EMI-Manhattan / Oct '88.

QUEEN OF THE REICH.
Tracks: Queen of the Reich / Nightrider / Blinded / Lady wore black.
■ 12″ . . . . .12 EA 162
EMI-America / Sep '83.

QUEENSRYCHE: INTERVIEW PICTURE DISC.
Tracks: Not Advised.
LP P.Disc . . . . BAK 2124
Baktabak / '90 / Arabesque Ltd.

RAGE FOR ORDER.
Tracks: Walk in the shadows / I dream in infrared / Whisper / Gonna get close to you / Killing words / Surgical strike / Neue regal / Chemical youth (We are rebellion) / London / Screaming in digital / I will remember.
■ LP . . . . AML 3105
EMI-America / Jul '86.
■ CD . . . . CDP 746 330 2
EMI-America / Jan '87.
CD . . . . .CDAML 3105
MC . . . . .TCAML 3105
EMI-America / Aug '91 / EMI.

SILENT LUCIDITY.
Tracks: Silent lucidity / Mission, The (live) / Della Brown (CD single only.).
■ 7″ Set . . . . MTS 94
■ 12″ 12MTP 94
■ 7″ . . . . MT 94
■ CD Single . . . . CDMT 94
■ MC Single . . . . TCMT 94
EMI-Manhattan / Apr '91.

SILENT LUCIDITY.
Tracks: Silent lucidity / Eyes of a stranger (CD single (1) only) / Operation: Mindcrime (CD single (1) only) / Suite sister Mary (CD single (2) only) / Last time in Paris (CD single (2) & 12″ picture disc only) / I don't believe in love (7″ only) / Take hold of the flame (12″ picture disc only).
■ 12″ 12MTPD 104
■ 7″ . . . . MT 104
■ CD Single . . . . CDMTS 104
■ CD Single . . . . .CDMT 104
EMI-Manhattan / Sep '92.

TAKE HOLD OF THE FLAME.
Tracks: Take hold of the flame / Nightrider.
■ 7″ . . . . EA 183
EMI-America / Oct '84.

VIDEO MIND CRIME.
Tracks: Remember now / Anarchy X / Revolution calling / Operation / Mindcrime / Speak / Breaking the silence / I don't believe in love / Waiting for 22 / Eyes of a stranger.
■ VHS . . . . MVP 9911990
PMI / Nov '89.

WARNING, THE.
Tracks: Warning / En force / Deliverance / No sanctuary / NM 156 / Take hold of the flame / Before the storm / Child of fire / Roads to madness.
MC . . . . TCATAK 108
EMI-America / Sep '84 / EMI.
■ LP . . . . .QY 1
EMI / Sep '84.
CD . . . . CDP 746 557 2
EMI / Feb '87 / EMI.

Quick Change

CIRCUS OF DEATH.
Tracks: Will you die / Show no mercy / Sea witch / Circus of death / Injected / What's next / Sludge / A.T.L. / Leave it to the beaver / Battle your fear / Death games / Plowed.
CD . . . . .RR 950 32
■ LP . . . . .RR 950 31
Road Runner / Feb '89.

■ DELETED

Quicksand

QUICKSAND E.P.
Tracks: Not Advised.
■ 7" . . . . REVEL 018
■ CD Single . . . . REVEL 018 CD
■ MC Single . . . . REVEL 018 MC
Revelation / Apr '92.

Quiet Riot

L.A. quartet enjoyed success in 1983 with *Metal Health* album and cover of Slade's *Cum On Feel The Noize*. First two albums, released in 1977/'78, featured Randy Rhoads, later Ozzy Osbourne's guitarist; later line-up included future Whitesnake and WASP personnel. Declining fortunes prompted group to disband in late '80s.

BAD BOYS.
Tracks: Bad boys / Metal health / Slick black Cadillac.
■ 12" . . . . TA 4250
■ 7" . . . . A 4250
Epic / Mar '84.

CONDITION CRITICAL.
Tracks: Sign of the times / Mama weer all crazee now / Party all night / Stomp your hands, clap your feet / Winners take all / Condition critical / Scream and shout / Red alert / Bad boy / Born to rock.
■ LP . . . . EPC 26075
Epic / Aug '84.
CD . . . . CD 26075
Epic / '88 / Sony.

CUM ON FEEL THE NOIZE.
Tracks: Cum on feel the noize / Run for cover.
■ 7" . . . . A 3616
Epic / Aug '83.

MAMA WEER ALL CRAZEE NOW.
Tracks: Mama weer all crazee now / Bad boy / Love's a bitch.
■ 12" . . . . TA 4572
■ 7" . . . . A 4572
Epic / Aug '84.

METAL HEALTH.
Tracks: Metal health / Cum on feel the noize / Don't wanna let you go / Slick black cadillac / Love's a bitch / Breathless / Run for cover / Battle axe / Let's get crazy / Thunderbird.
■ LP . . . . EPC 25322
Epic / Jun '83.
■ LP 4500841
MC 4500844
Epic / Jan '87 / Sony.
■ CD . . . . CD 25322
Epic / '88.

METAL HEALTH.
Tracks: Metal health / Cum on feel the noize.
■ 12" . . . . TA 3968
■ 7" . . . . A 3968
Epic / Dec '83.

POWER AND GROOVE.
Tracks: Stay with me tonight / Calling the shots / Run to you / I'm king of the hill / Joker / Lunar obsession / Don't wanna be your fool / Coppin' a feel / In a rush / Empty promises.
CD 4628962
■ LP 4628961
■ MC 4628964
Epic / Nov '88.

QUIET RIOT 3.
Tracks: Main attraction / Wild and the young / Twilight hotel / Down and dirty / Rise or fall / Put up or shut up / Still of the night / Pump / Slave to love / Helping hand / Bass care.
■ LP . . . . EPC 26945
■ MC 40 26945
Epic / Aug '86.
■ CD . . . . CD 26945
Epic / Aug '86.

RANDY RHOADS YEARS, THE.
Tracks: Not Advised.
CD 812271445-2
Atlantic / Feb '94 / WEA.

WILD AND THE YOUNG.
Tracks: Wild and the young / Rise or fall.
■ 12" . . . . TA 7280
■ 7" . . . . A 7280
Epic / Sep '86.

WILD, YOUNG AND CRAZEE.
Tracks: Metal health / Cum on feel the noize / Love's a bitch / Mama weer all crazee now / Winner takes all / Condition critical / Bad boy / Main attraction / Wild and the young / Put up or shut up / Slave to love / Let's get crazy.
■ LP . . . . RAWLP 033
MC. . . . . RAWTC 033
Raw Power / May '87 / Pinnacle.

WINNERS TAKE ALL.
Tracks: Winners take all / Red alert.
■ 7" . . . . A 4806
Epic / Oct '84.

Quireboys

Formed in Newcastle, 1984, Quireboys became heroes of club scene; aided by manager Sharon Osbourne - wife and manager of Ozzy. Signed to EMI, band scored hits with *Hey You*, *I Don't Love You Anymore* and debut album *A Bit Of What You Fancy* in 1990, but took four years to release follow-up - by which time U.K. metal scene had passed them by. Among usurpers of band's Best Newcomers title were Wildhearts, formed by ex-Quireboy Ginger.

7 O'CLOCK.
Tracks: 7 o'clock / Pretty girls / How do you feel (Not on 7".).
■ CD Single . . . . CDR 6230
■ 12" 12R 6230
■ 7" . . . . R 6230
■ MC Single . . . . TCR 6230
■ 7" P.Disc . . . . RPD 6230
Parlophone / Oct '89.

BIT OF WHAT YOU FANCY, A.
Tracks: Seven o'clock / Whippin' boy / Man on the loose / I don't love you anymore / Hey you / Long time comin' / Sex party.
VHS MVR99 0085 3
PMI / Feb '90 / EMI / Gold & Sons / TBD.

BITTER SWEET AND TWISTED.
Tracks: Tramps and thieves / Can't get through / Ain't love blind / King of New York / White trash blues / Sweet little girl / Wild wild wild / Take no revenge / Can't park here / Ode to you (baby just walk) / Hates to please / Last time.
■ CD . . . . CDPCSD 120
■ LP . . . . PCSD 120
■ MC . . . . TCPCSD 120
Parlophone / Mar '93.

BITTER, SWEET & LIVE (AT THE TOWN & COUNTRY).
Tracks: Tramps and thieves / Can't park here / Mislead / White trash blues / Roses and rings / Don't bite the hand / King of New York / Hey you / Ode to you / Debbie / Whipping boy / Take no revenge / Sweet Mary Ann / My saint Jude / Man on the loose / Sex party / 7 o'clock / I don't love you anymore / Long time coming.
VHS . . . . MVP 4911053
PMI / Mar '93 / EMI / Gold & Sons / TBD.

BROTHER LOUIE.
Tracks: Brother Louie / Tramps and thieves (Live) / I don't love you anymore (Live) / Hey you (Live) / Sweet Mary Ann (Live) / Can't get through.
■ 12" 12RP 6335
■ CD Single . . . . CDRS 6335
■ MC Single . . . . TCR 6335
EMI / Feb '93.

FROM TOOTING TO BARKING.
Tracks: Not Advised.
CD . . . . ESSCD 222
Essential / Sep '94 / Total / BMG.

HEY YOU.
Tracks: Hey you / Sex party / Hoochie coochie man (live) (12" & CD single only.).
■ 12" 12RP 6241
■ CD Single . . . . CDR 6241
■ 12" 12R 6241
■ 7" . . . . RG 6241
■ 7" . . . . R 6241
■ MC Single . . . . TCR 6241
Parlophone / Dec '89.

I DON'T LOVE YOU ANYMORE.
Tracks: I don't love you anymore / Mayfair (original version) / Hey you (live) (Not on 7"'s or Cassingle.).
■ 7" P.Disc . . . . RP 6248

CD Single . . . . CDR 6248
■ 12" 12R 6248
■ 12" 12RP 6248
■ 7" . . . . R 6248
■ 7" . . . . RG 6248
■ 7" P.Disc . . . . RPD 6248
■ MC Single . . . . TCR 6248
Parlophone / Mar '90.

LITTLE BIT OF WHAT YOU FANCY, A.
Tracks: 7 o'clock / Man on the loose / Whippin' boy / Sex party / Sweet Mary Ann / I don't love you anymore / Hey you / Misled / Long time comin' / Roses and rings / There she goes again / Take me home.
■ LP . . . . PCS 7335
Parlophone / Jan '90.
■ CD . . . . .CDPCSX 7335
■ LP . . . . PCSX 7335
■ MC . . . . TCPCSX 7335
Parlophone / Oct '90.
■ CD . . . . CDPCS 7335
■ MC . . . . TCPCS 7335
Parlophone / Oct '90.

LIVE: QUIREBOYS (Recorded Around The World).
Tracks: Hey you / Sex party / Whipping boy / Sweet Mary Ann / Heartbreaker / I don't love you anymore / Hold on I'm coming / There she goes again.
CD . . . . CDPRG 1002
■ LP . . . . PRG 1002
MC. . . . . TCPRG 1002
Parlophone / Nov '90 / EMI.

MAYFAIR.
Tracks: Mayfair / Misled / Man on the loose (12" single only.).
■ 12" . . . . SUR 12 043
■ 7" . . . . .SUR 043
Survival (1) / May '88.

MINI CD.
Tracks: Not Advised.
CD . . . . SURCD 014
Survival (1) / Sep '91 / Vital Distribution.

QUIREBOYS: INTERVIEW PICTURE DISC.
Tracks: Not Advised.
LP P.Disc . . . . BAK 2166
Baktabak / Jun '90 / Arabesque Ltd.

THERE SHE GOES AGAIN.
Tracks: There she goes again / How do ya feel / Sex party (12" only.).
■ 7" P.Disc . . . . .PDSUR 46
Survival (2) / Dec '88.
■ 7" . . . . SUR 46
■ 12" . . . . .SURT 46
Survival (2) / Oct '88.

THERE SHE GOES AGAIN.
Tracks: There she goes again / Misled / Heartbreaker (live) (12" gatefold & CD single only.).
■ 12" 12RG 6267
■ 7" . . . . R 6267
■ 7" P.Disc . . . . RPD 6267
■ CD Single . . . . CDR 6267
■ MC Single . . . . TCR 6267
Parlophone / Sep '90.

TRAMPS AND THIEVES.
Tracks: Tramps and thieves / Ain't love blind / Wild wild wild (12" only) / Can't park here (12" only) / Pleasure and pain (CDs only) / Hold on I'm coming (live) (On CDRS 6323 only) / Heartbreaker (live) (On CDRS 6323).
■ 12" . . . . 12 RS 6323
■ 7" . . . . RS 6323
■ CD . . . . CDR 6323
■ CD Single . . . . CDRS 6323
EMI / Sep '92.

Quorthon

QUORTHON.
Tracks: Not Advised.
CD . . . . BMCD 666-9
LP . . . . .BMLP 666-9
MC. . . . . BMMC 666-9
Black Mark / May '94 / Plastic Head.

R

R.I.P.

GIVE ME THOUGHT.
Tracks: Not Advised.
■ LP . . . . HM 01
Soundscape (USA) / Sep '87.

R.P.L.A.

ABSOLUTE QUEEN OF POP, THE.
Tracks: Absolute Queen of pop / Bad thing coming / Broken down & stranded (On CD single only).
■ 12" . . . . 12 RPLA 4
■ 7" . . . . RPLA 4
■ CD Single . . . . CDRPLA 4
EMI / Sep '89.

CITY OF ANGELS.
Tracks: City of angels / Made of stars / Sunset and vine (Only on 12" and CD single) / Leather sequined hot pants (bison mix) (Only on CD single).
■ 12" 12RPLA 2
■ 7" . . . . RPLA 2
■ CD Single . . . . CDRPLA 2
■ MC Single . . . . TCRPLA 2
EMI / Aug '91.

LAST NIGHT A DRAG QUEEN SAVED YOUR LIFE.
Tracks: Last night a drag queen saved your life (Mixes) / Metal Queen hijack (Mixes).
■ MC Single . . . . TCRPLA 3
■ 12" 12RPLA 3
■ 7" . . . . RPLA 3
■ CD Single . . . . CDRPLA 3
EMI / Aug '93.

METAL QUEEN HIJACK.
Tracks: Absolute Queen of pop / City of angels / Loving you is a dirty job (but somebody's got to do it) / Unnatural woman / Bomb and the gun / Uk rock city / Something to live and breathe by / Vagabond sister / Hair of the dog that bit me / Hold back the storm.
CD . . . . CDEMC 3617
LP . . . . EMC 3617
MC . . . . TCEMC 3617
EMI / Jan '92 / EMI.
CD . . . . RPLACD 1
LP . . . . RPLALP 1
MC . . . . RPLATC 1
EMI / Nov '93 / EMI.

UNNATURAL WOMAN.
Tracks: Unnatural woman (Not on 12") / Girl from Baton Rouge (Cassingle only) / Monster sexuality (12" & CD single only).
■ 12" 12RPLA 1
■ 7" . . . . RPLA 1
■ CD Single . . . . CDRPLA 1
■ MC Single . . . . TCRPLA 1
EMI / May '91.

Rabin, Trevor

CAN'T LOOK AWAY.
Tracks: Can't look away / Sorrow (your heart) / Promises / Eyes of love / Hold on to me / I miss you now / Something to hold on to / Cover up / Etoile noir / I didn't think it would last / Sludge / Cape.
CD 9607812
■ LP . . . . EKT 58
MC . . . . .EKT 58C
Elektra / Jul '89 / WEA.

FACE TO FACE.
Tracks: I'll take the weight / Don't you ever lose / I'm old enough / Wanderer / You / Now / Ripper / Candy's bar / Always the last one.
■ LP . . . . CHR 1221
MC . . . . ZCHR 1221
Chrysalis / '86 / EMI.

SOMETHING TO HOLD ON TO.
Tracks: Something to hold on to / I miss you now.
■ 7" . . . . EKR 94
Elektra / Oct '89.

TAKE ME TO A PARTY.
Tracks: Take me to a party / Looking for a lady.
■ 7" . . . . CHS 2508
Chrysalis / Mar '81.

TREVOR RABIN.
Tracks: Getting to know you / Finding me a way back home / All I want is your love / Live a bit / Fantasy / Stay with me / Red desert / Painted picture / Love life.
■ LP . . . . CHR 1196
■ MC . . . . ZCHR 1196
Chrysalis / '83.

WOLF.
Tracks: Open ended / Heard you cry / Wolf / Do ya want me / Stop turn / Lost in love / Looking for a lady / Pain / Take me to a party / She's easy / Long Island sound.
■ LP . . . . CHR 1293
■ MC . . . . ZCHR 1293
Chrysalis / Feb '81.

Racer X

EXTREME VOLUME.
Tracks: Not Advised.
CD . . . . RR 9530 2
■ LP . . . . RR 9530 1
Road Runner / '88.

LIVE EXTREME VOL.2.
Tracks: Not Advised.
CD . . . . RR 91422
Road Runner / Jan '94 / Pinnacle.

SECOND HEAT.
Tracks: Not Advised.
CD . . . . RR 349601
Road Runner / Dec '87 / Pinnacle.
■ LP . . . . RR 9601
Road Runner / Nov '87.

STREET LETHAL (Racer X, with Paul Gilbert).
Tracks: Frenzy / Street lethal / Into the night / Blow-in' up the radio / Hotter than fire / On the loose / Loud and clear / Y.R.O. / Dangerous love / Getaway / Rock it.
■ LP . . . . RR 9705
Road Runner / Sep '86.
CD . . . . RO 97052
Roadracer / Mar '90 / Pinnacle.

Rage

Rage's career has been fraught with problems. In 1987, following two acclaimed albums, bassist/vocalist 'Peavey' Wagner laid band to rest in face of insurmountable personnel problems. Rage returned with 1988's more mature *Perfect Man* album; but, despite new proficiency, have yet to make mark outside homeland Germany.

BEYOND THE WALL.
Tracks: Not Advised.
CD . . . . .NO 2023
Noise / Nov '92 / Pinnacle.

EXECUTION GUARANTEED.
Tracks: Not Advised.
■ CD . . . . CDNUK 073
■ LP .NUK 073
■ MC . . . . ZCNUK 073
Noise / Oct '89.

EXTENDED POWER.
Tracks: Not Advised.
■ CD . . . . NO 1693
■ LP . . . . NO 1695
Noise / May '91.

INVISIBLE HORIZONS.
Tracks: Invisible horizons.
■ 12" .12RAGE 6
Noise / Sep '89.

LOOKING FOR YOU.
Tracks: Looking for you / Come on now / Great balls of fire (Extra track on 12" version only) / Hallelujah I love her so (Extra track on 12" version only).
■ 12" . . . . BIG RAGE 1
Noise / May '86.
■ 7" . . . . RAGE 1
Noise / May '86.

MISSING LINK.
Tracks: Not Advised.
CD . . . . .NO 2172
LP . . . . .NO 2171
Noise / Aug '93 / Pinnacle.

PERFECT MAN.
Tracks: Don't fear the winter / Death in the afternoon / Pilgrim's path / Time and place / Round trip / Between the lines / Wasteland / In the darkest hour / Animal instinct / Perfect man / Sinister thinking / Supersonic hydromatic.
CD . . . . .N 0112-3
■ LP . . . . .N 0112
MC . . . . .N 0112-2
Noise / May '88 / Pinnacle.

REFLECTIONS OF A SHADOW.
Tracks: Introduction (a bit more green) / That's hu-man bondage / True face in everyone / Flowers that fade in my hand / Reflections of a shadow / Can't get out / Waiting for the moon / Saddle the wind / Dust / Nobody knows.
■ CD . . . . CDNUK 160
■ LP .NUK 160
■ MC . . . . ZCNUK 160
Noise / Dec '90.

REIGN OF FEAR.
Tracks: Not Advised.
■ CD . . . . CDNUK 038
■ LP .NUK 038
Noise / Oct '89.

SECRETS IN A WEIRD WORLD.
Tracks: Not Advised.
■ CD . . . . CDNUK 137
■ LP .NUK 137
■ MC . . . . ZCNUK 137
Noise / Sep '89.

TRAPPED.
Tracks: Shame on you / Solitary man / Enough is enough / Medicine / Questions / Take me to the water / Power and greed / Body talks / Not forever / Beyond the wall of sleep / Baby I'm your nightmare / Fast as a shark / Difference.
CD . . . . NO 189-2
LP . . . . NO 189-1
MC . . . . NO 189-4
Noise / Apr '92 / Pinnacle.

VIDEO LINK.
Tracks: Shame on you / Don't fear the winter / Certain days / Suicide / Refuge / Baby I'm your nightmare / Down by law / Firestorm / Nevermore / soundmix in Florida / Solitary man / Enough is enough / Invisible horizons.
VHS . . . . NV 0020
Noise / Jan '94 / Pinnacle.

Rage

BOOTLIGGERS.
Tracks: Bootliggers / Roll the dice.
■ 7" . . . . .CAR 199
Carrere / Jul '81.

MONEY.
Tracks: Money / Thank that woman.
■ 7" . . . . .CAR 159
Carrere / Sep '80.

NEVER BEFORE.
Tracks: Never before / Rock fever.
■ 7" . . . . .CAR 291
Carrere / Oct '83.

NICE 'N' DIRTY.
Tracks: American radio stations / Wasted years / Woman / Heartbreaker / Silver & gold / Long way from home / Only child / Blame it on the night / Wild cat woman / Ready to go.
■ LP . . . . CAL 138
MC . . . . .CAC 138
Carrere / Jun '82 / WEA.

OUT OF CONTROL.
Tracks: Out of control / What have I done wrong / She's on fire / Roll the dice / Fallen idol / Money / I didn't want to leave / Rage / Thank that woman.
■ LP . . . . CAL 124

■ DELETED

R 1

MC. . . . . .CAC 124
Carrere / Mar '81 / WEA.

OUT OF CONTROL.
Tracks: Out of control / Double dealer.
■ 7" .CAR 182
Carrere / Mar '81.

RUN FOR THE NIGHT.
Tracks: Cry from a hill / Fantasy / Can't say no / Light years / Ladykiller / No prisoners / Run for the night / Badlands / Never before / Rock fever.
■ LP .CAL 149
MC. . . . . .CAC 149
Carrere / Oct '83 / WEA.

WOMAN.
Tracks: Woman.
■ 7" .CAR 240
Carrere / Jul '82.

Rage Against The Machine

L.A. quartet formed in 1991 and promptly won support slots with likes of Public Enemy and Porno For Pyros. Having declined offer from Madonna's Maverick label, they signed to Epic for eponymous 1993 debut. Album was instant success with audience too young to spot Jane's Addiction steals, and RATM embarked on year of headlining appearances. Political sophistication of band members has yet to translate onto releases, epitomised by 1993's most notorious lyric: "Fuck you, I won't do what you tell me!"

BULLET IN THE HEAD.
Tracks: Bullet in the head / Settle for nothing (Live) / Bullet in the head (mix).
■ 12" 659258 6
■ 7" .659258 7
■ CD Single 659258 2
Epic / Apr '93.

KILLING IN THE NAME.
Tracks: Killing in the name / Clear the lane (On 7" & 12" only) / Darkness of greed (On 12" & CDS only).
■ 12" 658492 6
■ 7" .658492 7
■ CD Single 658492 2
Epic / Feb '93.

RAGE AGAINST THE MACHINE.
Tracks: Bombtrack / Killing in the name / Take the power back / Settle for nothing / Bullet in the head / Know your enemy / Wake up / Fistful of steel / Township rebelion / Freedom.
CD . . . . .EPC 472224 2
LP 4722241
MC. .4722244
Epic / Mar '93 / Sony.
MiniDisc. 472224 8
Epic / Oct '93 / Sony.

Raging Slab

ASSMASTER.
Tracks: Mr. Lucky / Rocks off is rocks off.
■ LP . . . . BOR 12011
Buy Our (USA) / Sep '88.

RAGING SLAB.
Tracks: Don't dog me / Jaynde / Sorry's all I got / Waiting for the potion / Get off my jollies / Shiny mama / Geronimo / Bent for silver / When love comes loose / Dig a hole / San Loco.
■ CD . . . . PD 90396
■ LP . . . . PL 90396
RCA / Feb '90.
■ MC. . . . . PK 90396
RCA / Feb '90.

TAKE A HOLD.
Tracks: Take a hold / Move that thang / Weatherman.
■ CD Single 858 437-2
American Recordings / May '94.

Railway

CLIMAX.
Tracks: Not Advised.
■ LP . . . . RR 9667
Road Runner / Jul '87.

RAILWAY.
Tracks: Hell soldiers / Heavy metal fever / Nightrider.
■ LP . . . . RR 9821
Road Runner / Jan '85.

RAILWAY 2.
Tracks: Not Advised.
■ LP . . . . RR 9760
Road Runner / Feb '86.

Rainbow

Ex-Deep Purple guitarist Ritchie Blackmore took personnel from U.S. band Elf to create Rainbow; eponymous debut was released in 1975. First of myriad personnel changes saw Blackmore sack entire band except singer Ronnie James Dio, who lasted until 1979 before leaving for Black Sabbath. New line-up, boasting ex-Marbles singer Graham Bonnet and Purple bassist Roger Glover, scored two U.K. Top 10 hits and headlined first Castle Donington 'Monsters of rock' festival. Yet another line-up produced most successful single I Surrender, which reached no. 3. Dissatisfied with attempts to assemble perfect line-up and crack U.S. market, Blackmore split group in 1984 and returned to Purple.

ALL NIGHT LONG.
Tracks: All night long / Weiss heim.
■ 7" . . . . POSP 104
Polydor / Feb '80.

BENT OUT OF SHAPE.
Tracks: Stranded / Can't let you go / Fool for the night / Fire dance / Anybody there / Desperate heart / Street of dreams / Drinking with the devil / Snowman / Make your move.
■ LP . . . . POLD 5116
Polydor / Sep '83.
■ CD 815 305-2
Polydor / Sep '83.

BEST OF RAINBOW.
Tracks: All night long / Man on the silver mountain / Can't happen here / Lost in Hollywood / Since you've been gone / Stargazer / Catch the rainbow / Kill the king / Sixteenth century greensleeves / I surrender / Long live rock 'n' roll / Eyes of the world / Starstruck / Light in the black / Mistreated.
■ Double LP . . . . POLDV 2
MC Set . . . . PODVC 2
Polydor / Oct '81 / PolyGram.
CD Set 800 074-2
Polydor / '83 / PolyGram.
■ Double LP 800 074-1
MC Set 800 074-4
Polydor / Mar '91 / PolyGram.

CAN'T HAPPEN HERE.
Tracks: Can't happen here / Jealous lover.
■ 7" . . . . POSP 251
Polydor / Jun '81.

CAN'T LET YOU GO.
Tracks: Can't let you go / All night long (live).
■ 7" . . . . POSP 654
Polydor / Nov '83.

DIFFICULT TO CURE.
Tracks: I surrender / Spotlight kid / No release / Magic / Vielleicht das nachster zeit (Maybe next time.) / Can't happen here / Freedom fighter / Midtown tunnel vision / Difficult to cure.
■ LP . . . . POLD 5036
Polydor / Feb '81.
■ MC Set 3574 141
Polydor / Feb '83.
CD 800 018-2
■ LP . . . . SPELP 76
Polydor / Aug '84.
■ MC. . . . . SPEMC 76
Polydor / Aug '84.

DOWN TO EARTH.
Tracks: All night long / Eyes of the world / No time to lose / Making love / Since you've been gone / Love's no friend / Danger zone / Lost in Hollywood.
■ LP . . . . POLD 5023
Polydor / Aug '79.
■ LP . . . . SPELP 69
MC. . . . . SPEMC 69
Polydor / Apr '84 / PolyGram.
CD 823 705-2
Polydor / Dec '86 / PolyGram.

FINAL CUT, THE.
Tracks: Spotlight kid / Death Alley driver / I surrender / All night long / Can't happen here / Difficult to cure / Can't let you go / Stone cold / Street of dreams / Power / Since you've been gone.
VHS 041 385 2
Polygram Music Video / Jun '86 / PolyGram.
VHS . . . . CFV 02652
Channel 5 / Nov '87 / Channel 5 Video / P.R.O. Video / Gold & Sons.

FINYL VINYL.
Tracks: Spotlight kid / I surrender / Miss Mistreated / Jealous lover / Can't happen here / Tearin' out m heart / Since you've been gone / Bad girl / Difficult t cure / Stone cold / Power / Long live rock 'n' roll Weiss heim / Man on the silver mountain.
CD Set 827 987-
■ Double LP . . . . PODV
■ MC Set . . . . PODVC
Polydor / Feb '86.

I SURRENDER.
Tracks: I surrender / Veilleicht das nachester zeit.
■ 7" . . . . POSP 221
Polydor / Jan '81.

KILL THE KING.
Tracks: Kill the king / Man on the silver mountain Mistreated.
■ 7" 2066 84
Polydor / Sep '77.

L.A. CONNECTION.
Tracks: L.A. connection / Lady of the lake.
■ 7" 2066 96
Polydor / Sep '78.
■ 7" . . . . POSP 274
Polydor / Jul '81.

LIVE BETWEEN THE EYES.
Tracks: Spotlight kid / Miss Mistreated / Power / Stone cold / Can't happen here / Ode to joy / Smoke on the water / Long live rock 'n' roll / Tearin' out my heart / All night long.
VHS . . . . CFV 00262
Channel 5 / '88 / Channel 5 Video / P.R.O. Video / Gold & Sons.

LIVE IN GERMANY 1976.
Tracks: Kill the king / Mistreated / Sixteenth century greensleeves / Catch the rainbow / Man on the silver mountain / Stargazer / Still I'm sad / Do you close your eyes.
CD Set . . . . DPVSOPCD 155
■ Double LP . . . . DPVSOPLP 155
MC Set . . . . DPVSOPMC 155
Connoisseur Collection / Oct '90 / Pinnacle.

LONG LIVE ROCK 'N' ROLL.
Tracks: Long live rock 'n' roll / Lady of the lake / L.A. connection / Gates of Babylon / Sensitive to light / Kill the King / Shed / Rainbow eyes.
■ LP . . . . POLD 5002
Polydor / May '78.
■ LP . . . . SPELP 34
■ MC. . . . . SPEMC 34
Polydor / Aug '83.

LONG LIVE ROCK 'N' ROLL.
Tracks: Long live rock 'n' roll / Sensitive to light.
■ 7" 2066 913
Polydor / Apr '78.
■ 7" . . . . POSP 276
Polydor / Jul '81.

ON STAGE.
Tracks: Kill the king / Man on the silver mountain / Blues / Starstruck / Catch the Rainbow / Mistreated / 16th century Greensleeves / Still I'm sad.
■ Double LP . . . . SPDLP 6
Polydor / Jul '77.
CD 823 656-2
Polydor / Nov '86 / PolyGram.

RAINBOW RISING.
Tracks: Tarot woman / Run with the wolf / Starstruck / Do you close your eyes / Stargazer / Light in the black.
■ LP 2490 137
Polydor / Jun '76.
■ LP . . . . SPELP 35
■ MC. . . . . SPEMC 35
Oyster / Aug '83.
CD 823 655-2
Polydor / Nov '86 / PolyGram.

RITCHIE BLACKMORE'S RAINBOW.
Tracks: Man on the silver mountain / Self portrait / Black sheep of the family / Catch the rainbow / Snake charmer / Temple of the king / If you don't like rock'n'roll / 16th century greensleeves / Still I'm sad.
■ LP . . . . .OYA 2001
Oyster / Sep '75.
■ LP 2490 141
Polydor / Aug '81.
■ LP . . . . .SPELP 7
■ MC. . . . . SPEMC 7
Oyster / Aug '83.
■ CD 825 089-2
Polydor / '88.

■ DELETED

SINCE YOU'VE BEEN GONE.
Tracks: Since you've been gone / Bad girl.
■ 7" . . . . **POSP 70**
Polydor / Sep '79.

SINCE YOU'VE BEEN GONE (OLD GOLD).
Tracks: Since you've been gone / All night long.
■ 7" . . . . **OG 9772**
Old Gold / Feb '88.

STONE COLD.
Tracks: Stone cold / Rock fever.
■ 7" . . . . **POSP 421**
Polydor / Apr '82.

STRAIGHT BETWEEN THE EYES.
Tracks: Death Alley driver / Stone cold / Bring on the night / Tite squeeze / Tearin' out my heart / Power / Miss Mistreated / Rock fever / Eyes on fire.
■ LP . . . . **POLD 5056**
Polydor / Apr '82
■ CD **800 028-2**
Polydor / '83.
CD **521709-2**
Polydor / Apr '94 / PolyGram.

STREET OF DREAMS.
Tracks: Street of dreams / Anybody there.
■ 12" . . . . **POSPX 631**
■ 7" . . . . **POSP 631**
■ 7" P.Disc . . . . **POSPP 631**
Polydor / Aug '83.

Ram Jam

BLACK BETTY.
Tracks: Black Betty / Keep your hands on the wheel (CBS release only) / I should have known (Epic release only).
■ 7" . . . . **EPC 5492**
Epic / Sep '77.
■ 7" . . . . **A 4585**
CBS / Jul '84.

BLACK BETTY (2).
Tracks: Black Betty (rough 'n ready remix) / Black Betty (original version) / Black Betty (rough 'n ready remix edit).
■ MC Single. **6554304**
Epic / Feb '90.
■ 12" **6554306**
■ 7" **6554307**
■ CD Single **6554302**
Epic / Jan '90.

BLACK BETTY (OLD GOLD).
Tracks: Black Betty / Race with the devil.
■ 7" . . . . **OG 9193**
Old Gold / Jul '82.

FREETOWN.
Tracks: Freetown / Do what.
■ 7" . . . . **JAM 001**
White Line / Sep '81.

KEEP YOUR HANDS ON THE WHEEL.
Tracks: Keep your hands on the wheel / Right on the money.
■ 7" . . . . **EPC 5806**
Epic / Dec '77.

Ramones

New York punks formed in 1974 - Joey, Johnny, Dee Dee and Tommy (replaced by Marky in 1977) - released a succession of classic LP's in the late 70's. *Ramones, Ramones leave home*, and *Rocket to Russia* typified their non-stop blitzkrieg approach to the two minute pop song and were hugely influential on the emerging UK punk scene. Their exhilarating live set was captured on 1979's *It's alive*. Phil Spector produced *End of the century* in 1980 which included their biggest hit, a cover of the Ronettes' *Baby I love you*. 1993's *Acid Eaters* was the band's 13th LP - is evidence of the Ramones' durable appeal.

'LOCO' LIVES.
Tracks: Good, the bad, the ugly / Durango 95 / Teenage lobotomy / Psycho therapy / Blitzkreig bop / Rock 'n' roll radio / I believe in miracles / Gimme gimme shock treatment / Rock and roll high school / I wanna be sedated / KKK took my baby away / I wanna live / Bonzo goes to Bitberg / Too touch to die / Sheena is a punk rocker / Rockaway beach / Pet Sematary / Don't bust my chops / Palisades park / Mama's boy / Animal boy / War hog / Surfin' bird / Cretin hop / I don't wanna walk around with you / Today your love, tomorrow the world / Pinhead /

Someday put something in my drink / Beat on the brat / Judy is a punk / Chinese rocks / Love kills / Ignorance is bliss.
CD . . . . **CCD 1901**
■ LP . . . . **CHR 1901**
■ MC . . . . **ZCHR 1901**
Chrysalis / Oct '91.

ACID EATERS.
Tracks: Journey to the centre of the mind / Substitute / Out of time / Shape of things to come / When I was young / 7 and 7 is / My back pages / Can't seem to make you mine / Have you ever seen the rain / I can't control myself / Surf city.
CD . . . . **CDCHR 6052**
LP . . . . **CHR 6052**
MC . . . . **TCCHR 6052**
Chrysalis / Nov '93 / EMI.

ALL THE STUFF.
Tracks: Blitzkrieg bop / Beat on the brat / Judy is a punk / Now I wanna sniff some glue / Don't go down the basement / Loudmouth / Havana affair / 53rd and 3rd / I don't wanna walk around with you / I wanna be sedated / Glad to see you go / I remember you / Sheena is a punk rocker / Pinhead / Swallow my pride / California sun / I wanna be your boyfriend / You're gonna kill that girl / Babysitter / Listen to my heart / Let's dance / Today your love, tomorrow the world / I can't be / Gimme gimme shock treatment / Oh oh I love her so / Suzy is a headbanger / Now I wanna be a good boy / What's your game / Commando / Chainsaw / You should never have opened that door / California sun (live).
CD **759926204**
■ LP **759926201**
MC **759926202**
Sire / Aug '90 / WEA.

ANIMAL BOY.
Tracks: Somebody put something in my drink / Animal boy / Love kills / Ape man hop / She belongs to me / Crummy stuff / Bonzo goes to Bitburg / Metal hell / Eat that rat / Freak of nature / Hair of the dog / Something to believe in.
■ LP . . . . **BEGA 70**
MC . . . . **BEGC 70**
Beggars Banquet / Jul '86 / WEA / RTM / Pinnacle.

BABY I LOVE YOU.
Tracks: Baby I love you / Don't come close.
■ 7" . . . . **SIR 4031**
Sire / Jan '80.
■ MC Single. . . . . **SPC 6**
WEA / Apr '81.

BLITZ KRIEG BOP.
Tracks: Blitz krieg bop / Havana affair.
■ 7" **6078 601**
Sire / Jul '76.

BONZO GOES TO BITBURG.
Tracks: Bonzo goes to Bitburg / Daytime dilemma / Go home Ann (on 12" only).
■ 12" . . . . **BEG 140T**
■ 7" . . . . **BEG 140**
Beggars Banquet / Jun '85.

BRAIN DRAIN.
Tracks: I believe in miracles / Punishment fits the crime / Pet Semetary / Merry Christmas / Learn to listen / Zero zero UFO / All screwed up / Can't get you outta my mind / Ignorance is bliss.
CD . . . . **CCD 1725**
■ LP . . . . **CHR 1725**
Chrysalis / Jul '89.
■ MC . . . . **ZCHR 1725**
Chrysalis / Aug '92.

CHASING THE NIGHT.
Tracks: Chasing the night / Howlin' at the moon / Smash you / Street fighting.
■ 12" . . . . **BEG 128TP**
Beggars Banquet / Mar '85.

CRUMMY STUFF.
Tracks: Crummy stuff / She belongs to me / I don't want to live this life (Track on 12" only).
■ 12" . . . . **BEG 167T**
Beggars Banquet / Jul '86.

DO YOU REMEMBER ROCK'N'ROLL RADIO.
Tracks: Do you remember rock 'n' roll radio / I want you around.
■ 7" . . . . **SIR 4037**
Sire / Apr '80.

DO YOU WANNA DANCE?.
Tracks: Do you wanna dance / Long way back to Germany / Cretin hop.
■ 7" **6078615**
Sire / Apr '78.

DON'T COME CLOSE.
Tracks: Don't come close / I don't want you.
■ 7" . . . . **SRE 1031**
Sire / Sep '78.

END OF THE CENTURY.
Tracks: Do you remember rock 'n' roll radio / I'm affected / Danny says / Chinese rocks / Return of Jackie and Judy / Let's go baby / Baby I love you / I can't make it on time / This ain't Havanna.
MC . . . . **SRC 6077**
Sire / Jan '80 / WEA.
■ LP . . . . **SRK 6077**
Sire / May '88.
CD **E59927429-2**
Sire / Mar '94 / WEA.

HALFWAY TO SANITY.
Tracks: Wanna live / Bop 'till you drop / Garden of serenity / Weasel face / Go lil' Camaro go / I know better now / Death of me / I lost my mind / Real cool time / I'm not Jesus / Bye bye baby / Worm man.
CD . . . . **BEGA 89 CD**
Beggars Banquet / Dec '87 / WEA / RTM / Pinnacle.
■ LP . . . . **BEGA 89**
MC . . . . **BEGC 89**
Beggars Banquet / Sep '87 / WEA / RTM / Pinnacle.

HOWLING AT THE MOON (SHA LA LA).
Tracks: Howlin' at the moon (sha la la) / Chasing the night / Smash you / Street fighting.
■ 12" . . . . **BEG 128T**
■ 7" . . . . **BEG 128**
Beggars Banquet / Jan '85.
■ 7" Set . . . . **BEG 128D**
Beggars Banquet / Mar '85.

I JUST WANT TO HAVE SOMETHING TO DO.
Tracks: I just want to have something to do / Here today gone tomorrow / I wanna be your boyfriend.
■ 7" . . . . **SREP 1**
WEA / Dec '80.

I WANNA BE SEDATED.
Tracks: I wanna be sedated / Return of Jackie and Judy.
■ 7" . . . . **RSO 70**
RSO / Jan '81.

I WANNA LIVE.
Tracks: I wanna live / Merry Christmas (I don't want to fight tonight).
■ 12" . . . . **BEG 201 T**
■ 7" . . . . **BEG 201**
Beggars Banquet / Nov '87.

IT'S ALIVE.
Tracks: Rockaway beach / Teenage labotomy / Blitz-krieg bop / I wanna be well / Glad to see you go / Gimme gimme shock treatment / You're gonna kill that girl / I don't care / Sheena is a punk rocker / Havana affair / Commando / Here today gone tomor-row / Surfin' bird / Cretin hop / Listen to my heart / California sun / I don't wanna walk around with you / Pinhead / Suzy is a headbanger / Let's dance / Oh oh I lover her so / Now I wanna sniff some glue / We're a happy family.
■ MC . . . . **SRC 26074**
■ Double LP . . . . **SRK 26074**
Sire / Jun '79.

LEAVE HOME.
Tracks: Glad to see you go / Gimme gimme shock treatment / I remember you / Oh oh I love her so / Carbona not glue / Suzy is a headbanger / Pinhead / Now I wanna be a good boy / Shallow my pride / What's your game / California sun / Commando / You're gonna kill that girl / You should never have opened that door.
■ LP . . . . **SR 6031**
Sire / Sep '78.
■ LP . . . . **MAU 602**
Mau Mau / Sep '87.

PET SEMETARY.
Tracks: Pet semetary / All screwed up / Zero zero UFO (Available on 12" format only.).
■ 12" . . . . **CHS 123423**
■ 7" . . . . **CHS 3423**
Chrysalis / Nov '89.

PLEASANT DREAMS.
Tracks: We want the airwaves / All's quiet on the eastern front / KKK took my baby away / Don't go / You sound like you're sick / It's not my place / She's a sensation / 7-11 / You didn't mean anything to me / Come on now / This business is killing me / Sitting in my room.
MC . . . . **SRC 3571**
Sire / Jul '81 / WEA.

■ LP . . . . SRK 3571
Sire / May '88.
CD .759923571-2
Sire / Mar '94 / WEA.

POISON HEART.
Tracks: Poison heart / Chinese rocks (12" only.) /
Sheena is a punk rocker (12"and Cdsingle only.) /
Rockaway beach (12" and CD single only.) / Censor-
shit (7" only) / Rock 'n' roll radio.
■ 12" . . . . 12 CHSS 3917
■ 7" . . . . CHS 3917
■ CD Single . . . . CDCHSS 3917
Chrysalis / Nov '92.

RAMONES MANIA.
Tracks: I wanna be sedated / Teenage lobotomy / Do
you remember rock 'n' roll radio / Gimme gimme
shock treatment / Beat on the brat / Sheena is a punk
rocker / I wanna live / Pinhead / Blitzkrieg bop /
Cretin hop / Rockaway beach / Commando / I wanna
be your boyfriend / Mamma's boy / Bop 'till you drop
/ We're a happy family / Bonzo goes to Bitburg /
Outsider / Psycho therapy / Wart hog / Animal boy /
Needles and pins / Howlin' at the moon / Somebody
put something in my drink / We want the airwaves /
Chinese rocks / I just want to have something to do /
KKK took my baby away / Indian giver / Rock 'n' roll
high school.
CD .925709 2
■ Double LP 925709 1
MC .925709 4
Sire / Jun '88 / WEA.

RAMONES, THE.
Tracks: Blitzkrieg bop / Beat on the brat / Judy is a
punk / I wanna be your boyfriend / Chain saw / Now,
I wanna sniff some glue / I don't wanna go down in
the basement / Loud mouth / Havana affair / Listen
to my heart / 53rd and 3rd / Let's dance / I don't
wanna walk around with you / Today your love,
tomorrow the world.
■ LP . . . . SR 6020
Sire / Sep '87.

REAL COOL TIME.
Tracks: Real cool time / Life goes on / Indian giver.
■ 12" .BEG 198T
■ 7" . . . . BEG 198
Beggars Banquet / Sep '87.

ROAD TO RUIN.
Tracks: I just want to have something to do / I wanted
everything / Don't come close / I don't want you /
Needles and pins / I'm against it / I wanna be
sedated / Go mental / Questionnably / She's the one /
Bad brain / It's a long way back.
■ LP . . . . SRK 6063
Sire / Sep '78.

ROCK 'N' ROLL HIGH SCHOOL.
Tracks: Rock 'n' roll high school / Blitzkrieg bop /
Sheena is a punk rocker.
■ 7" . . . . SIR 4021
Sire / Sep '79.

ROCKET TO RUSSIA.
Tracks: Cretin' hop / Rockaway beach / Here today,
gone tomorrow / Locket loe / Don't care / Sheena is
a punk rocker / We're a happy family / Teenage
lobotomy / Do you wanna dance / I wanna be well / I
can't give you anything / Ramona / Surfin' bird / Why
is it always this way / Cretin hop / Locket love.
■ LP 9102 255
Sire / Dec '77.
■ LP . . . . SR 6042
■ MC 7222 102
Sire / Sep '78.

SHE'S A SENSATION.
Tracks: She's a sensation / All's quiet on the Eastern
Front.
■ 7" . . . . SIR 4052
Sire / Oct '81.

SHE'S THE ONE.
Tracks: She's the one / I wanna be sedated.
■ 7" . . . . SIR 4009
Sire / Jan '79.

SHEENA IS A PUNK ROCKER.
Tracks: Sheena is a punk rocker.
■ 7" . . . . RAM 001
Sire / May '77.

**SHEENA IS A PUNK ROCKER (OLD
GOLD).**
Tracks: Sheena is a punk rocker / Baby I love you.
■ 7" . . . . OG 9909
Old Gold / '89.

SOMETHING TO BELIEVE IN.
Tracks: Something to believe in / Somebody put
something in my drink / Can't say anything nice.

■ 12" . . . . BEG 157T
■ 7" . . . . BEG 157
Beggars Banquet / May '86.

SUBTERRANEAN JUNGLE.
Tracks: Little bit o' soul / I need your love / Outsider /
What'd ya do / Highest trails above / Somebody like
me / Psycho therapy / Time has come today / My
kind of a girl / In the park / Time bomb / Everytime I
eat vegetables.
■ LP . . . . W 3800
Sire / May '83.
CD .759923800-2
Sire / Mar '94 / WEA.

SWALLOW MY PRIDE.
Tracks: Swallow my pride / Pinhead / Let's dance.
■ 7" 6078 607
Sire / Aug '77.

TIME HAS COME TODAY.
Tracks: Time has come today / Psycho therapy /
Baby I love you (on 12" only) / Don't come close (on
12" only).
■ 12" . . . . W 9606T
■ 7" . . . . W 9606
Sire / Jun '83.

TOO TOUGH TO DIE.
Tracks: Mama's boy / I'm not afraid of life / Too
tough to die / Durango 95 / Wart hog / Danger zone /
Chasing the night / Howling at the moon / Daytime
dilemma / Planet earth 1988 / Human kind / Endless
vacation / No go.
■ LP . . . . BEGA 59
MC . . . . BEGC 59
Beggars Banquet / Jan '85 / WEA / RTM / Pinnacle.

WE WANT THE AIRWAVES.
Tracks: We want the airwaves / You sound like your
sick.
■ 7" . . . . SIR 4051
Sire / Jul '81.

Rancid Hell Spawn

AXE HERO.
Tracks: Not Advised.
CD . . . . STUNCH 6
Wrench / Sep '93 / SRD.

FESTERING PUS.
Tracks: Festering pus.
■ 7" . . . . STUNCH 001
Wrench / Dec '88.

RANCID HELL SPAWN.
Tracks: Siamese sextuplets / Bicycle shed girls /
Sixteen cans of Stella / Botulism babies / Waste not
want more / Farm night / Fifteen seconds fame /
Cancerous cowboys / Ketchup boys / Sledgehammer
job / Homunculus stumps / Monstrous man / Football
special to Grimsby / Drinking myself to death / Eye in
my stomach / Scalpel party / Jumpin' Jack flash /
Going down to Croydon / Emphysema Eddie / Shane
MacGowan's brain / Dirt city / Washout / Great
expectations / Sex in a butchers' shop.
■ LP . . . . STUNCH 002
Wrench / Sep '89.

Rapscallion

CHAMELEON DROOL.
Tracks: Not Advised.
CD .CDZORRO 41
LP . . . . ZORRO 41
MC .TZORRO 41
Metal Blade / Jul '90 / Pinnacle.

Rarebell, Herman

HERMAN ZE GERMAN.
Tracks: Not Advised.
■ LP . . . . WKFMLP 80
MC . . . . WKFMMC 80
FM Records / Mar '87 / FM Revolver / Sony.

NIP IN THE BUD.
Tracks: Messing around / Two timer / Havin' a good
time / Rock your balls / Triangle / Slob / Junk junk /
Do it / Pancake / I'll say goodbye.
■ LP . . . . SHSP 4118
Harvest / Nov '81.

ROCK YOUR ALL.
Tracks: Rock your all / Pancake.
■ 7" . . . . HAR 5218
Harvest / Jan '82.

Ratos De Paraos

ANARKOPHOBIA.
Tracks: Not Advised.
CD . . . . RO 9326
LP . . . . RO 9326
MC . . . . RO 9326
Road Runner / Apr '91 / Pinnacle.

BRASIL.
Tracks: Not Advised.
CD . . . . RO 94242
■ LP . . . . RO 94241
Roadracer / Dec '89.

Ratt

DANCIN' UNDER COVER.
Tracks: Dance / Body talk / Take a chance / Looking
for love / Seventh avenue / Drive me crazy / Slip of
the lip / One good lover / Enough is enough / It
doesn't matter.
CD 781 683-2
■ LP 781 683-1
■ MC 781 683-4
Atlantic / Oct '86.

DETONATOR.
Tracks: Intro to shame / Shame, shame, shame /
Lovin' you's a dirty job / Scratch that itch / One step
away / Hard time / Heads I win, tails you lose / All or
nothing / Can't wait on love / Givin' yourself away /
Top secret.
CD 7567821272
■ LP 7567821271
■ MC 7567821274
Atlantic / Sep '90 / WEA.

DETONATOR VIDEOACTION.
Tracks: Not Advised.
VHS 8536501603
Warner Music Video / Oct '92 / WEA.

INVASION OF YOUR PRIVACY.
Tracks: You're in love / Never use love / Lay it down
/ Give it all / Closer to my heart / Between the eyes /
What you give me is what you get / Gome me on the
line / You should know by now / Dangerous but
worth the risk.
CD 781 257-2
MC 781 257-4
■ LP 781 257-1
Atlantic / Jun '85.

LAY IT DOWN.
Tracks: Lay it down / Got me on the line.
■ 12" . . . . A 9546 T
■ 7" . . . . .A 9546
Atlantic / Jun '85.

LOVIN' YOU'S A DIRTY JOB.
Tracks: Lovin' you's a dirty job / What's it gonna be.
■ 12" . . . . A 7844 T
■ 7" . . . . .A 7844
■ CD Single . . . . A 7844 CD
■ MC Single . . . . A 7844 MC
Atlantic / Oct '90.

OUT OF THE CELLAR.
Tracks: Wanted man / You're in the money / round
and 'round / In your direction / She wants money /
Lack of communication / Back for more / Morning
after / I'm insane / Scene of the crime.
■ LP 780 143-1
■ MC 780 143-4
Atlantic / Apr '84.
CD 780 143-2
Atlantic / '88 / WEA.

RATT.
Tracks: Sweet cheater / You think you're tough / U
got it / Tell the world / Back for more / Walking the
dog.
■ LP . . . . MFN 2
Music For Nations / Jun '83.
■ LP 790245 1
■ MC .790245 4
Time Coast / Sep '86.

RATT 'N' ROLL.
Tracks: Tell the world / You think you're tough /
round and 'round / Wanted man / Back for more /
Lack of communication / Lay it down / You're in love
/ Slip of the lip / Dance / Body talk / Way cool JR. / I
want a woman / Lovin' you's a dirty job / Shame,
shame, shame / Givin' yourself away / One step
away / Heads I win tails you lose / Nobody rides for
free.
CD 7567822602
■ LP 7567822601
MC 7567822604
East West / Sep '91 / WEA.

■ DELETED

RATT: INTERVIEW PICTURE DISC.
Tracks: Not Advised.
■ LP P.Disc . . . . BAK 2092
Baktabak / Apr '88 / Arabesque Ltd.

RATT: THE VIDEO.
Tracks: Not Advised.
VHS 750 101-3
Atlantic / Jun '86 / WEA.

REACH FOR THE SKY.
Tracks: What I'm after / Chain reaction / City to city /
I want a woman / No surprise / Don't bite the hand
that feeds / Bottom line / What's it gonna be / No one
can stop you now / Way cool JR / I want to love you
tonight.
■ CD 781 929-2
■ LP 781 929-1
■ MC 781 929-4
Atlantic / Oct '88.

ROUND AND AROUND.
Tracks: round and 'round / You think you're tough /
Sweet cheater.
■ 7" . . . . A 9693
Atlantic / Sep '84.
■ 12" . . . . A 9573T
■ 7" . . . . A 9573
Atlantic / Mar '85.

YOU'RE IN LOVE.
Tracks: You're in love / Between the eyes.
■ 7" . . . . A 9502
Atlantic / Jan '86.

Rattlesnake Kiss

RATTLESNAKE KISS.
Tracks: Railroad / Sad Suzie / Angel / Alright by me /
Nothing this good (could be real) / Wake up / Taste it
/ Don't make it right / All to me (that I was to you) /
Kiss this.
CD . . . . SOV 106CD
MC . . . . SOV 106TC
Sovereign Music / '92 / TBD / ACD Trading Ltd. /
Target Sales & Marketing.

SAD SUZIE.
Tracks: Sad suzie / Wake up / Drive / Railroad
return, The (acoustic).
■ CD Single . . . . SOV 105CD
Sovereign Music / '92.

Ravage

WRECKING BALL.
Tracks: Not Advised.
■ LP . . . . RR 9672
Road Runner / Jan '87.

Raven

ALL FOR ONE.
Tracks: Take control / Mind over metal / Sledgeham-
mer rock / All for one / Run silent, run deep / Hung
drawn and quartered / Break the chain / Take it
away / Seek and destroy / Athletic rock.
CD . . . . NEATCD 1011
■ LP . . . . NEAT 1011
MC . . . . NEATC 1011
Neat / '85 / Grapevine Distribution.

BORN TO BE WILD.
Tracks: Born to be wild / Inquisitor.
■ 12" . . . . NEAT 29 12
■ 7" . . . . NEAT 29
■ 7" P.Disc . . . . NEAT 29P
Neat / Aug '83.

BREAK THE CHAIN.
Tracks: Break the chain / Ballad of Marshall Stack.
■ 7" . . . . NEAT 23
Neat / Mar '83.

CRASH BANG WALLOP (EP).
Tracks: Crash bang wallop / Firepower / Run them
down / Rock hard.
■ 12" . . . . NEAT 15 12
Neat / Oct '82.

DEVIL'S CARRION, THE.
Tracks: Hard ride / Bring the hammer down / Inquisi-
tor / All for one / Hellraiser / Action (Medley) / Live
at the inferno / Crash, bang, wallop / Ballad of
Marshall Stack / Crazy world / Rock until you drop /
Don't need your money / Hell patrol / Rock hard /
Faster than the speed of light / Wiped out / Break the
chain / Read all about it / Firepower / Athletic rock /
Run silent, run deep.
■ Double LP . . . . RAWLP 003
MC . . . . RAWTC 003
Raw Power / Apr '86 / Pinnacle.

DON'T NEED YOUR MONEY.
Tracks: Don't need your money / Wiped out.
■ 7" . . . . NEAT 06
Neat / Aug '80.

GIMME SOME LOVIN'.
Tracks: Gimme some lovin' / One on.
■ 7" . . . . A 9453
Atlantic / Feb '86.

HARD RIDE.
Tracks: Hard ride / Crazy world.
■ 7" . . . . NEAT 11
Neat / Nov '81.

LIFE'S A BITCH.
Tracks: Savage and the hungry / Pick your window /
Life's a bitch / Never forgive / Iron league / On the
wings of an eagle / Overload / You're a liar / Fuel to
the fire / Only the strong survive / Juggernaut /
Playing with the razor / Finger on the trigger (extra
track on cassette only.).
■ LP 781 734-1
MC 781 734-4
Atlantic / Apr '87 / WEA.

LIVE AT THE INFERNO.
Tracks: I don't need your money / Break the chain /
Hell patrol / Live at the inferno / Crazy world / Let it
rip / I.G.A.R.B.O. / Wiped out / Fire power / All for
one / Forbidden planet / Star war / Tyrant of the
airways / Run silent, run deep / Take control / Mind
over metal / Crash bang wallop / Rock until you drop
/ Faster than the speed of light.
■ Double LP . . . . NEAT 1020
Neat / May '85.
■ Double LP . . . . RR 9808
Road Runner / '88.

NOTHING EXCEEDS LIKE EXCESS.
Tracks: Not Advised.
CD . . . . CDFLAG 28
■ LP . . . . FLAG 28
MC . . . . TFLAG 28
Under One Flag / Aug '89 / Pinnacle.

PACK IS BACK, THE.
Tracks: Pack is back / Gimme some lovin' / Screa-
min' down the house / Young blood / Hyperactive /
Rock dogs / Don't let it die / Get into your car / All I
want / Nightmare ride.
MC 781 629-4
■ LP 781 629-1
Atlantic / Mar '86.

PRAY FOR THE SUN.
Tracks: Pray for the sun / On and on / Bottom line.
■ 12" . . . . RAVEN 1T
Atlantic / Mar '85.

ROCK UNTIL YOU DROP.
Tracks: Hard ride / Hell patrol / Don't need your
money / Over the top / 39-40 / For the future / Rock
until you drop / Nobody's hero / Hellraiser / Action /
Lambs to the slaughter / Tyrant of the airways.
■ LP . . . . NEAT 1001
■ LP P.Disc . . . . NEATP 1001
■ MC . . . . NEATC 1001
Neat / May '85.
CD . . . . RC 93872
LP . . . . RC 93871
Road Runner / Jul '90 / Pinnacle.

STAY HARD.
Tracks: Stay hard / When the going gets tough / On
and on / Get it right / Restless child / Power & the
glory / Pray for the sun / Hard ride / Extract the
action / Bottom line.
■ LP 7812411
Atlantic / May '85.

WIPED OUT.
Tracks: Faster than the speed of light / Bring the
hammer down / Fire power / Read all about it / To
the limit / To the top / Battle zone / Live at the
inferno / Star war / UXB / 20/21 / Hold back the fire /
Chain saw.
■ LP . . . . NEAT 1004
Neat / May '85.

Razor

CUSTOM KILLING.
Tracks: Not Advised.
■ LP . . . . FPL 3042
Fist Fight (USA) / Sep '87.

EVIL INVADERS.
Tracks: Nowhere fast / Legacy of doom / Iron ham-
mer / Cut throat / Tortured skull / Cross me fool / Evil
invaders / Instant death / Speed merchants /
Thrashdance.
■ LP . . . . RR 9732

Road Runner / Dec '85.
CD . . . . RO 97322
Roadracer / May '89 / Pinnacle.

EXECUTIONER'S SONG.
Tracks: Not Advised.
■ LP . . . . RR 9778
Road Runner / Jun '85.

MALICIOUS INTENT.
Tracks: Not Advised.
■ LP . . . . RR 9698
Road Runner / Aug '86.

VIOLENT RESTITUTION.
Tracks: Not Advised.
CD 857 571
■ LP 087 569
Steamhammer (Germany) / '89.

Razor Baby

TOO HOT TO HANDLE.
Tracks: Danger / Rock this place / Downtown / Outta
hand sister / Move me / Too hot to handle / Got me
running / Low down and dirty.
■ LP . . . . HMUSA 102
■ MC . . . . HMAMC 102
Heavy Metal America / Aug '88.
CD . . . . HMAXD 102
Heavy Metal America / Aug '89 / FM Revolver / Sony.

Re-Animator

CONDEMNED TO ETERNITY.
Tracks: Don't eat the yellow snow / St. Alphonzo's
pancake breakfast / Cosmik debris / Apostrophe /
Stink foot / I'm the slime / 50/50 / Dinah moe hum /
Nanook rubs it / Father O'Blivion / Excentrifugal forz
/ Uncle Remus / Camarillo brillo / Dirty love / Zomby
woof / Montana.
CD . . . . CDFLAG 37
■ LP . . . . FLAG 37
MC . . . . TFLAG 37
Under One Flag / Oct '89 / Pinnacle.

DENY REALITY.
Tracks: Deny reality / Fatal descent / Re-animator /
Follow the masses / O.P.C. / D.U.A.F.
■ LP . . . . MFLAG 32
Under One Flag / Feb '89.

LAUGHING.
Tracks: Not Advised.
CD . . . . CDFLAG 53
LP . . . . FLAG 53
MC . . . . TFLAG 53
Under One Flag / Feb '91 / Pinnacle.

THAT WAS THEN, THIS IS NOW.
Tracks: Take me away / 2 CV / Cold sweat / Hope /
Last laugh / Kick back / Listen up / Sunshine times /
That was then.This is now / D.U.A.F. (Features on CD
only.).
CD . . . . CDFLAG 67
LP . . . . FLAG 67
MC . . . . TFLAG 67
Under One Flag / Oct '92 / Pinnacle.

Reactor

REVELATION.
Tracks: Not Advised.
CD 1MF 37700332
Invisible / Jul '93 / Plastic Head.

Realm

ENDLESS WAR.
Tracks: Not Advised.
CD . . . . RO 9509 2
■ LP . . . . RO 9509 1
Roadracer / Dec '88.

SUICIETY.
Tracks: Not Advised.
CD . . . . RO 94062
LP . . . . RO 94061
MC . . . . RO 94064
Roadracer / Oct '90 / Pinnacle.

Recipients Of Death

FINAL CONFLICT.
Tracks: Not Advised.
CD . . . . WRE 905CD
LP . . . . WRE 905
Wild Rags / Sep '91 / Plastic Head.

Red Dogs

RED DOGS.
Tracks: Not Advised.

■ CD	LUSCD 5
■ LP	LUSLP 5
■ MC	LUSMC 5

Episode / Jul '90 / Grapevine Distribution.

SWEET LITTLE RUBY.
Tracks: Sweet little Ruby / Help me on my way / Take you away / Heartbeat.

■ CD Single	12 LUSCD 3
■ 12"	12 LUS 3

Castle / Dec '89.

■ 7"	7 LUS 3

Castle / Dec '89.

WORKING LATE.
Tracks: Pays to be pretty / Working late / Lessons in love / Baby's so fine / Get ready / River / Sweet little Ruby / Help me on my way / I shall be released / I wanna dance.

■ CD	ESSCD 179
■ MC	ESSMC 179

Essential / Jul '92.

WRONG SIDE OF TOWN, THE.
Tracks: Not Advised.

■ CD	LUSMCD 6
■ LP	LUSMLP 6

Razor / Jul '91.

Red Hot Chili Peppers

Formed in Los Angeles in 1983 when singer Anthony Keidis joined up with Flea (bass, born Michael Balzary), Hillel Slovak (guitar) and Jack Irons (drums) and the quartet changed their name from What Is This? The question in their former moniker has never accurately been answered as the Chilis' musical style has twisted and turned in all directions, often at the same time. Funk Metal is perhaps the most widely accepted description, but with a healthy dash of Hendrix-flavoured 60's groove. The band have not had had an easy road to the top, losing Slovak to heroin in between *Uplift Mofo Party Plan* and *Mothers Milk*, although eventual success with *Bloodsugarsexmagik* album was on multi-million scale. Present line-up looks more stable with drummer Chad Smith and ex-Jane's Addiction guitarist Dave Navarro.

ABBEY ROAD EP, THE.
Tracks: Backwoods / Catholic school girls rule (on 12" version only) / Hollywood (Africa) / True men don't kill Coyotes.

■ EP	MT 41
■ 12"	12MT 41

EMI-Manhattan / May '88.

BLOOD SUGAR SEX MAGIK.
Tracks: Power of equality / If you have to ask / Breaking the girl / Funky monks / Suck my kiss / I could have lied / Mellowship slinky in B major / Righteous and the wicked / Give it away / Blood sugar sex magik / Under the bridge / Naked in the rain / Apache rose peacock / Greeting song / My lovely man / Sir psycho sexy / They're red hot.

■ CD	7599266812
■ LP	WX 441
■ MC	WX 441C

WEA / Oct '91 / WEA.

■ MiniDisc	759926681-8

Warner Bros. / Apr '93 / WEA.

BREAKING THE GIRL.
Tracks: Breaking the girl.

■ 12"	W 0126T
■ 7"	W 0126
■ CD Single	W 0126CD
■ CD Single	W 0126CDX
■ MC Single	W 0126C

WEA / Aug '92.

FIGHT LIKE A BRAVE.
Tracks: Fight like a brave (mofo mix) / Fight like a brave (knucklehead mix) / Fight like a brave (LP version) / Fire.

■ 12"	12EA 241
■ 7"	EA 241

EMI-America / Jan '88.

■ 12" P.Disc.	12EAP 241

EMI-America / Jan '88.

FREAKY STYLEY.
Tracks: Jungle man / Hollywood (Africa) / American ghost dance / If you want me to stay / Nevermind / Freaky styley / Blackeyed blonde / Brothers cup / Battle ship / Lovin' and touchin' / Catholic school

girls rule / Sex rap / Thirty dirty birds / Yertle the turtle.

CD	CDMTL 1057
■ LP	MTL 1057
MC	TCMTL 1057

EMI-Manhattan / Aug '90 / EMI.

GIVE IT AWAY.
Tracks: Give it away / Give it away (mixes) / Soul to squeeze.

■ 12"	W 0225T
■ CD Single	W 0225CD1
■ CD Single	W 0225CD2
■ MC Single	W 0225C

Warner Bros. / Jan '94.

HIGHER GROUND.
Tracks: Higher ground (CD single only.) / Politician (mini rap) (12" only.) / Higher ground (Munchkin mix) / Higher ground (dub mix) (12" only.) / Mommy, where's daddy / Millionaires against hunger (Not on 12").

■ 7"	MT 75
■ CD Single	CDMT 75
■ 12"	12MT 75

EMI-Manhattan / Nov '89.

■ 12" Remix	12MTX 75

EMI-Manhattan / Nov '89.

HIGHER GROUND.
Tracks: Higher ground (7" & Cassingle only.) / Fight like a brave (LP version) / Higher ground (munchkin mix) (Special only.) / Out in L.A. (Special & CD single only.) / Higher ground (Daddy O mix) (Picture disc only.) / Behind the sun (LP version) (CD single only.).

■ 12" P.Disc.	12MTPD 88
■ 7"	MT 88
■ CD Single	CDMT 88
■ MC Single.	TCMT 88

EMI-Manhattan / Aug '90.

HOLLYWOOD.
Tracks: Hollywood / Never mind.

■ 12"	12EA 205
■ 7"	EA 205

EMI-America / Sep '85.

KNOCK ME DOWN.
Tracks: Knock me down / Punk rock classic / Pretty little ditty (7" & Picture Disc only.) / Special secret song inside (12" only.) / Magic Johnson (12" & CD single only.) / Jungle man (Avaliable on CD single only.).

■ 7" P.Disc	MTPD 70
■ 12"	12MT 70
■ 7"	MT 70
■ CD Single	CDMT 70

EMI-Manhattan / Aug '89.

MOTHER'S MILK.
Tracks: Good time boys / Higher ground / Subway to Venus / Magic Johnson / Nobody weird like me / Knock me down / Taste the pain / Stone cold bush / Fire / Pretty little ditty / Punk rock classic / Sexy Mexican maid / Johnny kick a hole in the sky.

CD	CDMTL 1046
■ LP	MTL 1046
MC	TCMTL 1046

EMI-Manhattan / Aug '89 / EMI.

POSITIVE MENTAL OCTOPUS.
Tracks: Taste the pain / Higher ground / Knock me down / Fight like a brave / Fire / Jungle man / Catholic school girls rule / True men don't kill coyotes.

VHS	MVR 9900923

PMI / Mar '91 / EMI / Gold & Sons / TBD.

PSYCHEDELIC SEXFUNK - LIVE FROM HEAVEN.
Tracks: Stone cold bush / Good time boys / Sexy Mexican maid / Magic Johnson / Pretty little ditty / Knock me down / Special secret song / Subway to Venus / Never mind.

VHS	MVP 99 1237 3

PMI / Sep '90 / EMI / Gold & Sons / TBD.

RED HOT CHILI PEPPERS.
Tracks: True men don't kill coyotes / Baby appeal / Buckle down / Get up and jump / Why don't you love me / Green heaven / Mommy, where's daddy / Out in L.A. / Police helicopter / You always sing / Grand pappy du plenty.

■ LP	MTL 1056
■ CD	CDMTL 1056
■ MC	TCMTL 1056

EMI-Manhattan / Aug '90.

CD	CDFA 3297
MC	TCFA 3297

Fame / May '93 / EMI.

TASTE THE PAIN.
Tracks: Taste the pain (Not on special.) / Show me your soul / If you want me to stay (12" only.) / Castles

made of sand (Special only.) / Never mind (12" & CD single only.) / Taste the pain (LP version) (Special & CD single only.).

■ 10"	10MT 85
■ 12"	12MTX 85
■ 7"	MT 85
■ MC Single	TCMT 85
■ CD Single	CDMT 85

EMI-Manhattan / Jun '90.

UNDER THE BRIDGE.
Tracks: Under the bridge / Suck my kiss / Fela's cock (On CDs only) / Sikamikanico (On CDXs only).

■ 7"	W 0237
■ CD Single	W 0237CD
■ CD Single	W 0237CDX
■ MC Single	W 0237C

Warner Bros. / Apr '94.

UPLIFT MOFO PARTY PLAN.
Tracks: Fight like a brave / Funky crime / Me and my friends / Backwoods / Skinny sweaty man / Behind the sun / Subterranean homesick blues / Special secret song inside / No chump love sucker / Walkin' on down the road / Love trilogy / Organic anti-beat box band.

CD	CDAML 3125
■ LP	AML 3125
MC	TCAML 3125

EMI-America / Aug '90 / EMI.

WHAT HITS.
Tracks: Higher ground / Fight like a brave / Behind the sun / Me and my friends / Backwoods / True men don't kill coyotes / Fire / Get up and jump / Knock me down / Under the bridge / Show me your soul / If you want me to stay / Hollywood (Africa) / Jungle man / Brothers cup / Taste the pain / Catholic school girls rule / Johnny kick a hole in the sky.

CD	CDMTL 1071
■ LP	MTL 1071
MC	TCMTL 1071

EMI-America / Oct '92 / EMI.

WHAT HITS - THE VIDEO.
Tracks: Not Advised.

VHS	MVP 4910493

Picture Music International(see PMI) / Oct '92 / EMI.

Redd Kross

BORN INNOCENT.
Tracks: Not Advised.

LP	46091L

Frontier / Jul '91 / Vital Distribution.

JIMMY'S FANTASY.
Tracks: Jimmy's fantasy.

■ 12"	WAY 1511
■ CD Single	WAY 1533

Quicksilver / Aug '93.

NEUROTICA.
Tracks: Neurotica / Play my song / Frosted flake / Janus, Jeanie and George Harrison / Love is you / Peach kelli pop / McKenzie / Ballad of a love doll / What they say / Gandhi is dead (I'm the cartoon man) / Beautiful bye byes.

■ LP	ZL 71427X
■ MC	ZK 71427X

Big Time Records / Sep '87.

SWITCHBLADE SISTER.
Tracks: Switchblade sister.

■ 7"	WAY 1011
■ CD Single	WAY 1033

This Way Up / Jun '93.

THIRD EYE.
Tracks: Faith healer / Annie's gone / I don't know how to be your friend / Shonen knife / Bubblegum factory / Where I am today / Zira (call out my name) / Love is not love / 1976 / Debbie & Kim / Elephant flares.

CD	7567821482
MC	7567821484

East West / Apr '91 / WEA.

TRANCE.
Tracks: Trance / Byrds and fleas / Huge wonder (Only available on CD Single.).

■ 7"	TWANG 014
■ CD Single	TWANG 014CD

Seminal Twang / Jun '92.

VISIONARY.
Tracks: Visionary / It won't be long.

■ 10"	WAY 2788
■ CD Single	WAY 2733

This Way Up / Dec '93.

YESTERDAY ONCE MORE/SUPERSTAR (Redd Kross & Sonic Youth).
Tracks: Yesterday once more / Superstar.
7" 580792-7
CD Single 580792-2
MC Single 580792-4
A&M / Aug '94 / PolyGram.

Reed, Dan

BABY NOW I (Reed, Dan Network).
Tracks: Baby now I / Thy will be done / Stronger than steel (Only on 10" and CD Single.) / Living with a stranger (Only on 10" Single.).
■ 10" . . . . .MERX 352
■ 7" . . . . MER 352
■ CD Single . . . . .MERCD 352
■ MC Single. . . . . .MERMC 352
Mercury / Sep '91.

COME BACK BABY (Reed, Dan Network).
Tracks: Come back baby.
■ 12" . . . . DRN 2T
■ CD Single . . . . DRNCD 2
■ 12" .DRNSP 212
■ 7" . . . . .DRNPB 2
■ 7" . . . . DRN 2
■ MC Single. . . . . .DRNMC 2
Mercury / Jan '90.

DAN REED NETWORK (Reed, Dan Network).
Tracks: World has a heart too / Resurrect / Get to you / Baby don't fade / Ritual / Human / Forgot to make her mine / Halfway round the world / Tamin' the wild nights / Rock you all night long / I'm so sorry.
■ LP 834 309-1
■ MC. 834 309-4
■ CD 834 309-2
Mercury / Nov '88.

GET TO YOU (Reed, Dan Network).
Tracks: Get to you (12" mix) (Only on 12" version & CD single.) / Forgot to make her mine / Get to you (album mix) (Only on CD single.) / Halfway round the world (LP version) (Only on the CD single.).
■ CD Single . . . . .MERCD 269
■ 12" . . . . .MERX 269
■ 7" . . . . MER 269
Mercury / Oct '88.

HEAT, THE (Reed, Dan Network).
Tracks: Baby now I / Blame it on the moon / Mix it up / Heat / Let it go / Love don't work that way / Money / Chill out / Life is sex / Salt of joy / Take my hand / Lonley sun / Thy will be done / Wake up.
CD. 848855-1
■ LP 848855-1
■ MC. .848855-4
Mercury / Jul '91.

LOVER (Reed, Dan Network).
Tracks: Lover / Money / Ritual (extended Dido Slam mix) (Only on 12" and CD single).
■ 12" . . . . .DRN 512
■ 12" . . . . .DRNG 512
■ 7" . . . . DRN 5
■ CD Single . . . . DRNCD 5
■ MC Single. . . . . .DRNMC 5
Mercury / Aug '90.

MIX IT UP (Reed, Dan Network).
Tracks: Mix it up / Heat / Slavery (On 10" only.) / Lonely sun (On 12" & CD only.).
■ 12" . . . . .MERX 345
■ 7" . . . . MER 345
■ CD Single . . . . .MERCD 345
■ 10" . . . . .MERXP 345
Mercury / Jul '91.

RAINBOW CHILD (Reed, Dan Network).
Tracks: Rainbow child / You can leave your hat on / Ritual (12" and CD single only.) / Tamin' the wild nights (Only on CD single.).
■ 12" .DRNPC 312
■ 12" .DRN 312
■ 7" . . . . .DRNG 3
■ 7" . . . . DRN 3
■ CD Single . . . . .DRNCD 3
Mercury / Mar '90.

SLAM (Reed, Dan Network).
Tracks: Make it easy / Slam / Tiger in a dress / Rainbow child / Doin' the love thing / Stronger than steel / Cruise together / Under my skin / Lover / I'm lonely / Please stay / Come back baby / All my lovin' / Seven Sisters Road.
■ LP 838 868 1
■ CD 838 868 2
■ MC. 838 868 4
Mercury / Oct '89.

STARDATE 1990 (Reed, Dan Network).
Tracks: Stardate 1990 / Rainbow child (live) / Without you (Only on 12" and CD single.) / Come to me (Only on 12" and CD single.).
■ 12" . . . . .DRN 412
■ 12" .DRNG 412
■ 7" . . . . DRN 4
■ CD Single . . . . DRNCD 4
■ MC Single. . . . . .DRNMC 4
Mercury / Jul '90.

TIGER IN A DRESS (Reed, Dan Network).
Tracks: Tiger in a dress / Affection / Seven Sisters Road (Available on 12" only) / Get to you (Available on CD and MC single only).
■ 12" . . . . .DRN 112
■ 7" . . . . DRN 1
■ CD Single . . . . DRNCD 1
■ MC Single. . . . . .DRNMC 1
Mercury / Sep '89.

Renegade

LOST ANGELS.
Tracks: Not Advised.
CD. 15 392
MC. 79 392
Laserlight / Aug '91 / TBD / BMG / Target.

REO Speedwagon

Formed in 1967 in Illinois and named after make of fire engine, REO were led by guitarist Gary Richrath. After eponymous 1971 debut, singer Terry Luttrell was replaced by Kevin Cronin, himself replaced after *R.E.O. T.W.O.* by Mike Murphy. Cronin returned in '75, his country-tinged singing distinguishing Richrath's songs. Slow but steady success peaked with 1980's *Hi Infidelity*, which reached no. 1 in U.S., 6 in U.K. and hung around both charts for months; spawning biggest international hit *Keep On Lovin' You*. Later releases more infrequent and less successful.

6 TRACK HITS.
Tracks: Only the strong survive / Meet me on the mountain / Shakin' it loose / In your letter / I need you tonight / Roll with the changes.
■ EP 7SR 5049
MC. 7SC 5049
Scoop 33 / Aug '84.

BEST FOOT FORWARD.
Tracks: Roll with the changes / Take it on the run / Don't let him go / Live every moment / Keep on loving you / Back on the road again / Wherever you're goin' (it's alright) / Can't fight this feeling / Shakin' it loose / Time for me to fly / Keep pushin' / I wish you were there.
■ LP . . . . EPC 26640
MC. 40 26640
Epic / Nov '85 / Sony.
CD. 4686032
■ MC 4686034
Epic / Oct '91.

CAN'T FIGHT THIS FEELING.
Tracks: Can't fight this feeling / Keep on loving you / Rock 'n' roll star.
■ 12" . . . . TA 4880
■ 7" . . . . .A 4880
Epic / Mar '85.

DECADE OF ROCK & ROLL.
Tracks: Sophisticated lady / Music man / Golden country / Son of a poor man / Lost in a dream / Reelin' / Keep pushin' / Our time is gonna come / Breakaway / Lightning / Like you do / Flying turkey trot / 157 Riverside Avenue / Ridin' the storm out / Roll with the changes / Time for me to fly / Say you love me or say goodnight / Only the strong survive / Back on the road again.
■ Double LP. . . . . EPC 22131
Epic / Jun '82.

EARTH, A SMALL MAN, HIS DOG AND A CHICKEN, A.
Tracks: Love is a rock / Heart survives / Live it up / All heaven broke loose / Love in the future / Halfway / Love to hate / You won't see me / Can't lie to my heart / L.I.A.R. / Go for broke.
■ CD 4670132
■ LP 4670131
■ MC. 4670134
Epic / Sep '90.

GOOD TROUBLE.
Tracks: Keep the fire burning / Sweet time / Girl with the heart of gold / Every now and then / I'll follow

you / Key / Back in my heart again / Let's be-bop / Stillness of the night / Good trouble.
■ LP . . . . EPC 85789
Epic / Jul '82.
■ LP . . . . EPC 32789
Epic / '86.

HERE WITH ME.
Tracks: Here with me / Wherever you're goin' (it's alright)
■ 12" 6516466
■ 7" 6516467
■ CD Single 6516462
Epic / Sep '88.

HI-INFIDELITY.
Tracks: Don't let him go / Keep on loving you / Follow my heart / In your letter / Take it on the run / Tough guys / Out of season / Shakin' it loose / Someone tonight / I wish you were there.
■ LP . . . . EPC 84700
Epic / Apr '81.
■ LP . . . . EPC 32538
Epic / Nov '84.
CD. . . . . .CD CBS 847 00
CBS / '88 / Sony.

HITS, THE.
Tracks: I don't want to lose you / Here with me / Roll with the changes / Keep on loving you / That ain't love / Take it on the run / Don't let him go / Can't fight this feeling / Keep pushin' / In my dreams / Time for me to fly / Ridin' the storm out.
CD. 4608562
■ LP 4608561
MC. 4608564
Epic / May '88 / Sony.

IN MY DREAMS.
Tracks: In my dreams / Over the edge.
■ 7" 6510407
Epic / Nov '87.

IN YOUR LETTER.
Tracks: In your letter / Shakin' it loose.
■ 7" . . . . EPCA 1562
Epic / Oct '81.

KEEP ON LOVING YOU.
Tracks: Keep on loving you / Time for me to fly.
■ 7" . . . . EPC 9544
Epic / Apr '81.

KEEP THE FIRE BURNING.
Tracks: Keep the fire burning / I'll follow you.
■ 7" . . . . EPCA 2495
Epic / Jul '82.

KEY, THE.
Tracks: Key / Let's be-bop.
■ 7" . . . . EPCA 2889
Epic / Oct '82.

LIFE AS WE KNOW IT.
Tracks: New way to love / That ain't love / In my dreams / One too many girlfriends / Variety tonight / Screams and whispers / Can't get you out of my heart / Over the edge / Accidents can happen / Tired of getting nowhere.
■ LP 4503801
MC. 4503804
Epic / Apr '87 / Sony.
■ CD 4503802
CBS / Apr '87.

LIVE EVERY MOMENT.
Tracks: Live every moment / Gotta feel more.
■ 7" . . . . .A 6466
Epic / Sep '85.

NINE LIVES.
Tracks: Heavy on your love / Drop it / Only the strong survive / Easy money / Rock 'n' roll music / Take me / I need you tonight / Meet me on the mountains / Back on the road again.
■ LP . . . . EPC 83647
Epic / Aug '79.

ONE LONELY NIGHT.
Tracks: One lonely night / Wheels are turning.
■ 12" . . . . TA 6225
■ 7" . . . . .A 6225
Epic / May '85.

ONLY THE STRONG SURVIVE.
Tracks: Only the strong survive / Meet me on the mountain.
■ 7" . . . . EPC 7918
Epic / Oct '79.
■ 7" . . . . EPC 8903
Epic / Aug '80.

REO GRANDE.
Tracks: Not Advised.
CD.................... CD 26640
Epic / May '87 / Sony.

REO SPEEDWAGON.
Tracks: Not Advised.
■ LP.................... CBS 32096
CBS / Dec '81.
CD.................... 9829672
MC.................... 9829674
Pickwick/Sony Collector's Choice / Jun '93 / Pickwick / Pinnacle.

REO SPEEDWAGON.
Tracks: Not Advised.
VHS....................706150
Fox Video / '88.

REO SPEEDWAGON.
Tracks: Gypsy woman's passion / 157 Riverside Avenue / Antiestablishment man / Lay me down / Sophisticated lady / Five men were killed today / Prison women / Dead at last.
■ LP.................... EPC 64813
Epic / Jul '72.

ROLL WITH THE CHANGES.
Tracks: Roll with the changes / Unidentified tuna trot.
■ 7"..................... EPC 6415
Epic / Jun '78.

SECOND DECADE OF ROCK AND ROLL 1981 TO 1991, THE.
Tracks: Don't let him go / Tough guys / Take it on the run / Shakin' it loose / Keep the fire burnin' / Roll with the changes / I dowanna know / Can't fight this feeling / Live every moment / That ain't love / One too many girlfriends / Variety tonight / Back on the road again / Keep on loving you 89 / Love is a rock / All heaven broke loose / L.I.A.R. / Live it up.
■ CD..................... 4689582
■ MC..................... 4689584
Epic / Nov '91.

SWEET TIME.
Tracks: Sweet time / Stillness of the night.
■ 7"..................... EPCA 2715
Epic / Sep '82.

TAKE IT ON THE RUN.
Tracks: Take it on the run / Someone tonight.
■ 7".....................EPC A 1207
Epic / Jun '81.

THAT AIN'T LOVE.
Tracks: That ain't love / Accidents can happen.
■ 7"..................... 6503907
Epic / Mar '87.

WHEELS ARE TURNIN'.
Tracks: I do'wanna know / One lonely night / Thru the window / Rock and roll star / Live every moment / Can't fight this feeling / Gotta feel more / Break his spell / Wheels are turning.
■ LP..................... EPC 26137
MC.....................40 26137
■ CD..................... CD 26137
Epic / '84.

WHEELS ARE TURNIN'.
Tracks: Not Advised.
VHS.....................VVD 185
Virgin Vision / '87 / Gold & Sons / TBD.

WHEREVER YOU'RE GOING.
Tracks: Wherever you're going / Shakin' it loose.
■ 7".....................A 6673
Epic / Oct '85.

YOU CAN TUNE A PIANO.
Tracks: Not Advised.
■ LP..................... EPC 32115
Epic / Oct '82.

YOU GET WHAT YOU PLAY FOR.
Tracks: Like you do / Lay me down / Any kind of love / Being kind (can hurt someone sometimes) / Keep pushin' / Only a summer love / Son of a poor man / I believe our time is gonna come (flying turkey trot) / Gary's guitar solo / 157 Riverside Avenue / Ridin' the storm out / Music man / Little Queenie / Golden country.
■ Double LP.............. EPC 88265
Epic / Aug '87.

Repulsion

HORRIFIED.
Tracks: Stench of burning death / Acid bath / Radiation sickness / Splattered cadavers / Festering boils / Eaten alive / Slaughter of the innocent / Pestilent decay / Decomposed.
CD.................... NECRO 2CD
■ LP.................... NECRO 2
Necrosis / Jul '89.

HORRIFIED.
Tracks: Not Advised.
CD.................... RR 6063CD
MC.................... RR 6063MC
Relapse / Jun '93 / Plastic Head.

Resistant Militia

HARDCORE DEMO SERIES.
Tracks: Not Advised.
■ LP.................... WRR 003
Wild Rags / Nov '88.

Revelation

NEVER COMES SILENCE.
Tracks: Not Advised.
CD.................... HELL 020CD
Hellhound / Dec '92 / Plastic Head.

SALVATION'S ANSWER.
Tracks: Not Advised.
CD....................RISE 006CD
LP.................... RISE 006
■ MC.................... RISE 006MC
Rise / Mar '92.

Revolting Cocks

BEERS, STEERS AND QUEERS.
Tracks: Beers, steers and queers.
■ 12".................... WAX 149
Wax Trax / Apr '91.

BEERS, STEERS AND QUEERS.
Tracks: Not Advised.
CD.................... WAX 063 CD
LP.................... WAX 063 LP
MC.................... WAX 063 MC
Wax Trax / May '90 / SRD.
CD.................... DVNCD 4
LP.................... DVN 4
MC.................... DVNT 4
Devotion / Feb '92 / Pinnacle.

BEERS, STEERS AND QUEERS (REMIXES).
Tracks: Beers, steers and queers.
■ 12"....................12DVN 105
Devotion / Feb '92.

BIG SEXY LAND.
Tracks: Not Advised.
CD....................WAX 017CD
■ LP....................WAXUK 017
Wax Trax / '88.
CD.................... CDDVN 6
LP.................... DVN 6
MC.................... TDVN 6
Devotion / Mar '92 / Pinnacle.

CRACKIN' UP.
Tracks: Crackin' up.
12"....................12DVN 112
CD Single.............. CDDVN 112
Devotion / May '94 / Pinnacle.

DO YA THINK I'M SEXY.
Tracks: Do ya think I'm sexy.
■ 12"....................12 DVN 111
■ CD Single............. CDDVN 111
Devotion / Aug '93.

LINGER FICK'EM GOOD.
Tracks: Not Advised.
CD....................CDDVN 22
LP.................... DVN 22
MC....................TDVN 22
Devotion / Sep '93 / Pinnacle.

NO DEVOTION.
Tracks: No devotion / Attack ships / On Fire.
■ 12"....................WAXUK 011
Wax Trax / Feb '86.

PHYSICAL.
Tracks: Not Advised.
CD.................... WAX 086 CD
Wax Trax / '89 / SRD.

STAINLESS STEEL PROVIDERS.
Tracks: Stainless steel providers / At the top.
■ 12".................... WAX 042
Wax Trax / Mar '89.

YOU GODDAMNED SON OF A BITCH.
Tracks: Not Advised.
CD....................WAXCD 037
■ LP....................WAXUK 037
Wax Trax / May '88.
CD.................... CDDVN 8
LP.................... DVN 8
MC.................... TDVN 8
Devotion / Apr '92 / Pinnacle.

YOU GODDAMNED SON OF A BITCH.
Tracks: Not Advised.
VHS.................... WAXUK 037 V
Wax Trax / Jun '88 / SRD.
VHS.................... VFN 8
Video For Nations / Apr '92 / Pinnacle.

YOU OFTEN FORGET.
Tracks: You often forget.
■ 12"....................WAXUK 022
Wax Trax / Feb '87.

Rhino Buckett

GET USED TO IT.
Tracks: Beat to death like a dog / No friend of mine / Hey there / Devil sent you / This ain't heaven / She's a screamer / Bar time / Burn the world / Ride with yourself / Scratch 'n' sniff / Stomp.
CD.................... 7599269572
■ LP.................... 7599269571
MC.................... 7599269574
Sire / Jul '92 / WEA.

RHINO BUCKET.
Tracks: One night stand / Beg for your love / Train ride / Going down tonight / Even the sun goes down / Blood on the cross / Shot down / I'd rather go insane / Inside/Outside / Ride the rhino.
CD.................... 7599263172
MC.................... 7599263174
■ LP.................... 7599263171
WEA / Sep '90.

Riff Raff

VINYL FUTURES.
Tracks: Nina / Shades of blue / Treat me right / I ain't gonna run anymore / Mary lou / My, my / Love in vain / Heroes / Time riff / Hall of mirrors.
■ LP.................... K 50819
Atco / Jul '81.

YOU WANNA DANCE.
Tracks: You wanna dance.
■ 12"....................TT 122020
20/20 / Sep '88.

Riggs

RIGGS.
Tracks: Ready or not / One night affairs / Over and over / Take it off / Depending on love / Girls on the loose / Christine / Don't walk away / Too strong.
■ LP.................... K 99197
Full Moon (USA) / May '82.

Righteous Pigs

LIVE AND LEARN.
Tracks: Not Advised.
LP.................... NB 12
Nuclear Blast / Jul '89 / Plastic Head.

STRESS RELATED.
Tracks: Not Advised.
LP.................... NB 035
Nuclear Blast / Dec '90 / Plastic Head.

Rio

ATLANTIC RADIO.
Tracks: Atlantic radio.
■ 12".................... 12 KUT 123
■ 7".................... KUT 123
Music For Nations / Jul '86.

BORDERLAND.
Tracks: Not Advised.
■ LP.................... MFN 53
MC.................... TMFN 53
Music For Nations / Sep '85 / Pinnacle.

I DON'T WANNA BE THE FOOL.
Tracks: I don't wanna be the fool.
■ 12".................... 12 KUT 118

■ DELETED

■ 7″ .KUT 118
Music For Nations / Sep '85.

SEX CRIMES.
Tracks: Pay for love / Under pressure / Atlantic radio / High school love / Guilty / When the walls come down / Danger zone / Sex crimes / Dirty movies / Bad blood.
■ LP . . . . MFN 65
Music For Nations / Sep '86.

Riot

BORN IN AMERICA.
Tracks: Not Advised.
■ LP . . . . SLAM 6
Grand Slam (USA) / '89.

FIRE DOWN UNDER.
Tracks: Swords and tequila / Fire down under / Feel the same / Outlaw / Don't bring me down / Don't hold back / Altar of the king / No lies / Run for your life / Flashbacks.
■ LP . . . . K 52315
Elektra / Sep '81.

NARITA.
Tracks: Waiting for the taking / 49er / Kick down the wall / Narita / Here we come again / Do it up / Hot for love / White rock / Born to be wild / Road racin'.
■ LP . . . . .EST 12081
Capitol / May '80.

NIGHTBREAKER.
Tracks: Not Advised.
CD . . . . SPV 084 62222
Rising Sun / Jun '94 / Plastic Head.

OUTLAW.
Tracks: Outlaw / Rock city.
■ 7″ . . . . K 12565
Elektra / Oct '81.

PRIVILEGE OF POWER.
Tracks: On your knees / Metal soldiers / Runaway / Killer / Dance of death / Storming the gates of hell / Maryanne / Little Miss Death / Black leather and glitter steel / Race with the devil on a Spanish highway.
■ LP 4664861
■ CD 4664862
■ MC 4664864
Epic / May '90.

RESTLESS BREED.
Tracks: Restless breed / Hard lovin' man / CIA / When I was young / Loved by you / Loneshark / Over to you / Showdown / Dream away / Violent crimes.
■ LP . . . . K 52398
Elektra / Jul '82.

RIOT LIVE.
Tracks: Not Advised.
CD . . . . .CDZORRO 55
Metal Blade / Jul '92 / Pinnacle.

ROCK CITY.
Tracks: Desperation / Warrior / Rock city / Overdrive / Angel / Tokyo rose / Heart of fire / Gypsy queen / This is what I get.
■ LP . . . . ARL 5007
Ariola / '78.
CD . . . . .CDMZORRO 54
CD . . . . .CDMZORR 055
Metal Blade / Feb '93 / Pinnacle.

THUNDERSTEEL.
Tracks: Thundersteel / Fight or fall / Sign of the crimson storm / Flight of the warrior / On wings of eagles / Johnny's back / Bloodstreets / Run for your life / Buried alive (tell-tale heart).
■ CD 4609762
■ LP 460976 1
■ MC 4609764
Epic / Sep '88.

Ripcord

DEFIANCE OF POWER.
Tracks: Not Advised.
■ LP . . . . ACHE 05
Manic Ears / Jun '87.

POETIC JUSTICE.
Tracks: Not Advised.
■ LP . . . . .RAGE 001
Raging / May '89.

RIPCORD: LIVE.
Tracks: Not Advised.
LP .YCR 002
Your Choice / '92 / Plastic Head.

Ripping Corpse

DREAMING WITH THE DEAD.
Tracks: Dreaming with the dead.
CD . . . . .CDFLAG 57
LP .FLAG 57
MC . . . . TFLAG 57
Music For Nations / Jun '91 / Pinnacle.

SPLATTERED REMAINS.
Tracks: Splattered remains.
LP . . . . CCG 006
C.C.G. Underground / Mar '90 / Backs Distribution.

Risk

BACK TO THE FUTURE.
Tracks: Not Advised.
■ LP . . . . PHZA 20
Unicorn Records / Jun '88.

BITTER SWEET.
Tracks: Not Advised.
■ LP . . . . PHZA 25
Unicorn Records / Dec '88.

DIRTY SURFACES.
Tracks: Not Advised.
CD 0876234
LP 0876231
MC 8476232
Steamhammer (Germany) / Aug '90 / Pinnacle.

HELL'S ANIMALS.
Tracks: Monkey business / Perfect kill / Dead or alive / Secret of our destiny / Sicilian showdown / Torture and pain / Mindshock / Megalomania / Russian nights / Epilogue.
CD 85-7593
■ LP 08-7592
Steamhammer (Germany) / Jun '89.

OUT AND ABOUT (Risk and the Threads).
Tracks: Not Advised.
■ MC . . . . PHZC 16
Unicorn Records / May '88.

STATE OF THE UNION.
Tracks: State of the union.
■ 12″ 12PHZ 42
Unicorn Records / Jul '89.

Roadhouse

ALL JOIN HANDS.
Tracks: All join hands / Straight for your heart / More that I want (Only on 12″ and CD Single).
■ 12″ . . . . .VERX 56
■ 7″ . . . . VER 56
■ CD Single . . . . .VERCD 56
Vertigo / Jul '91.

HELL CAN WAIT.
Tracks: Hell can wait / Loving you / Jackson high (Not on 7″) / More than I want (Not on 7″).
■ 12″ P.Disc. . . . . .VERP 57
■ 7″ . . . . VER 57
■ CD Single . . . . .VERCD 57
Vertigo / Jan '92.

ROADHOUSE.
Tracks: All join hands / Time / Tower of love / Loving you / Little love / Hell can wait / One heart / New horizon / Desperation calling / Stranger in your eyes.
■ LP 510 078 1
■ CD 510 0782
■ MC 510 078 4
Vertigo / Jan '92.

TOWER OF LOVE.
Tracks: Tower of love / Can't take the credit for it / Freight train (Only on 12″ and CD single).
■ CD Single . . . . .VERCD 55
■ 12″ . . . . .VERX 55
■ 7″ . . . . VER 55
Vertigo / May '91.

TOWER OF LOVE.
Tracks: Tower of love / I can't take the credit for it / Freight train (acoustic) (Only on 12″ Single).
■ 12″ . . . . .VERX 59
■ 7″ . . . . VER 59
Vertigo / Oct '91.

Roberts, Kane

KANE ROBERTS.
Tracks: Rock doll / Women on the edge of love / Triple X / Gorilla / Outlaw / If this is heaven / Out for blood / Pull pull / Too much (for anyone to touch) / Tears of fire / Strong arm needs a stronger heart.
■ LP . . . . IMCA 5787
■ MC . . . . .IMCAC 5787
MCA / Oct '87.

SAINTS AND SINNERS.
Tracks: Not Advised.
■ CD . . . . DGCD 24320
■ LP . . . . DGC 24320
■ MC . . . . DGCC 24320
Geffen / Apr '87.

Rock City Angels

YOUNG MAN'S BLUES.
Tracks: Deep inside my heart / Hard to hold / Mary / Our little secret / Damned don't cry / Wild tiger / These arms of mine / Rumblefish / Boy from Hell's kitchen / Liza Jo / Beyond Babylon / Hush child / Ya gotta swear / Rough'n'tumble / South of the border.
■ CD 9241932
■ Double LP . . . . WX 204
■ MC . . . . WX 204C
Geffen / Sep '88.

Rock Goddess

HEAVY METAL ROCK'N'ROLL.
Tracks: Heavy metal rock'n'roll / Satisfied the crucified.
■ 12″ . . . . .AMSX 8263
A&M / Nov '82.

HELL HATH NO FURY.
Tracks: Hold me down / No more / Gotta let your hair down / Don't want your love / In the night / Visitors are here / I've seen it all before / You've got fire / It will never change / God be with you.
■ LP . . . . AMLX 68560
■ MC . . . . CXM 68560
A&M / Oct '83.

I DIDN'T KNOW I LOVED YOU TILL I SAW YOU ROCK'N'ROLL.
Tracks: I didn't know I loved you till I saw you rock'n'roll / Hell hath no fury.
■ 12″ . . . . AMX 185
■ 7″ . . . . AMS 185
A&M / Mar '84.

MY ANGEL.
Tracks: My angel / In the heat of the night.
■ 12″ . . . . .AMSX 8311
■ 7″ . . . . .AMS 8311
A&M / Feb '83.

ROCK GODDESS.
Tracks: Heartache / Back to you / Love lingers still / To be betrayed / Take your love away / My angel / Satisfied then crucified / Start running / One way love / Make my night / Heavy metal rock 'n' roll.
■ LP . . . . AMLH 68554
■ MC . . . . CAM 68554
A&M / Mar '83.

YOUNG & FREE.
Tracks: Not Advised.
CD . . . . .CDTB 155
Magnum Music / Jul '94 / Magnum Music Group / TBD.

Rockett, Garth

IAN GILLAN'S GARTH ROCKETT & THE MOONSHINERS STO (Rockett, Garth & The Moonshiners).
Tracks: Not Advised.
CD . . . . .ROHACD 3
■ LP P.Disc . . . . .ROHALP 3
MC . . . . .ROHAMC 3
EMI / Feb '90 / EMI.

LIVE AT THE RITZ '89 (Rockett, Garth & The Moonshiners).
Tracks: Not Advised.
VHS . . . . .LFV 103
Fotodisk Video / Aug '90.

Rockhead

CHELSEA ROSE.
Tracks: Chelsea rose / Sleepwalk / Angelfire (Angelfire available on CDS only).
■ 12″ 12CHELS 1
■ CD Single . . . . .CDCHELS 1
EMI / Jun '93.

■ DELETED

ROCKHEAD.
Tracks: Bed of roses / Chelsea rose / Heartland / Lovehunter / Death do us part / Warchild / Sleepwalk / Hell's back door / Hard rain / Angelfire / Webhead / Baby wild / House of cards.
LP . . . . EMC 3649
■ CD . . . . CDEMC 3649
■ MC . . . . TCEMC 3649
EMI / Mar '93.

Rodgers, Paul

CUT LOOSE.
Tracks: Fragile / Cut loose / Live in peace / Sweet sensation / Rising sun / Boogie mama / Morning after the night before / Northwinds / Superstar woman / Talking guitar blues.
■ LP 780 121-1
■ MC 780 121-4
Atlantic / Nov '83.

CUT LOOSE.
Tracks: Cut loose / Talking guitar blues.
■ 7" . . . . A 9749
Atlantic / Nov '84.

MUDDY WATER BLUES.
Tracks: Muddy water blues / Hunter (Rocdp 1 only) / Stone free / Nature of the beast (Rocdp 1 only) / Little wing (Rogcd 1 only).
■ CD Single . . . . ROCDP 1
■ CD Single . . . . ROGCD 1
London / Jan '94.

MUDDY WATER BLUES.
Tracks: Not Advised.
CD 828424-2
MC 828424-4
London / Jun '93 / PolyGram.

Rods

HEAVIER THAN THOU.
Tracks: Heavier than thou / Make me a believer / Angels never run / Crossfire / I'm gonna rock / She's trouble / Born to rock / Chains of love / Communication breakdown / Fool for your love / Cold sweat and love / Music man.
■ LP . . . . ZEB 9
Zebra (1) / Jan '87.

LET THEM EAT METAL.
Tracks: Not Advised.
■ LP . . . . MFN 29
Music For Nations / Jul '84.

POWER LOVER.
Tracks: Power lover / Nothing going on in the city.
■ 12" . . . . ARIST 12457
Arista / Feb '82.
■ 7" . . . . ARIST 457
Arista / Feb '82.

RODS LIVE, THE.
Tracks: Not Advised.
■ LP . . . . MFN 16
MC . . . . TMFN 16
Music For Nations / Jan '84 / Pinnacle.

RODS, THE.
Tracks: Power lover / Crank it up / Hungry for some love / Music man / Woman / Nothing going on in the city / Get ready to rock'n'roll / Ace in the hole / Rock hard / Roll with the night.
■ LP . . . . SPART 1182
Arista / Sep '81.

TOO HOT TO STOP.
Tracks: Too hot to stop / Power lover.
■ 12" . . . . ARIST 12484
■ 7" . . . . ARIST 484
Arista / '82.

WILD DOGS.
Tracks: Too hot to stop / Waiting for tomorrow / Violation / Burned by love / Wild dogs / You keep me hangin' on / Rockin' 'n' rollin' again / End of the line / No sweet talk / Honey / Night lives to rock.
MC . . . . TCART 1196
■ LP . . . . SPART 1196
Arista / Jul '82.

Rogue Male

ALL OVER YOU.
Tracks: All over you / Real me.
■ 12" . . . . 12 KUT 114
Music For Nations / May '85.

ANIMAL MAN.
Tracks: Progress / L.U.S.T. / Take no shit / You're on fire / Real me / Animal man / Belfast / Job centre / Low rider / Passing.

■ LP . . . . MFN 68
Music For Nations / Jul '86.

BELFAST.
Tracks: Belfast / Rough tough (pretty too) / Take no shit.
■ 12" . . . . 12 KUT 122
Music For Nations / Jul '86.

FIRST VISIT.
Tracks: Not Advised.
■ LP . . . . MFN 40
Music For Nations / May '85.

Rollin' Thunder

HOWL.
Tracks: Atlantic to Pacific / B.A.R.B. / Pink and greens / Going South / Bloodstained legends / Shadow fall / Immortal soul / Street of lost causes / Once.
■ LP . . . . SHARP 039
Flicknife / Apr '87.

LONESOME.
Tracks: Not Advised.
■ LP . . . . NICK 002
Hell's Kitchen / Feb '86.

TOO LOOSE.
Tracks: Too loose.
■ 7" . . . . NICK 001
Hell's Kitchen / Jul '85.

Rollins Band

LIAR.
Tracks: Liar.
7" 7432121305-7
CD Single 7432121305-2
MC Single 7432121305-4
Imago / Aug '94 / BMG.

LIFE TIME.
Tracks: Not Advised.
CD 986977
Intercord / Jan '94 / Pinnacle / C.M. Distribution.

WEIGHT.
Tracks: Disconnect / Fool / Icon / Civilised / Divine objects of hatred / Liar / Step back / Wrong man / Volume / Tired / Alien blueprint / Shine.
CD 72787 21034-23
LP 72787 21034-16
MC 72787 21034-47
Imago / Apr '94 / BMG.

Rollins, Henry

Henry Rollins formed own band after five years with L.A. hardcore outfit and pivotal influence on Kurt Cobain, Black Flag. Success grew such that '94 album *Weight* debuted within whisker of U.K. Top 20 - not bad for resolutely uncommercial jazz/blues/hardcore cocktail. Rollins is also known as book publisher, spoken-word performer, fitness freak and actor.

BIG UGLY MOUTH.
Tracks: Not Advised.
CD . . . . QS 9CD
Quarter Stick / Jul '92 / SRD.

BOXED LIFE, THE (Spoken Word Performances Parts 1 & 2).
Tracks: Bone tired / Airplanes / Airport courtesy phone / Jet lag / Hating someone's guts, part 1 / Funny guy / Love in Venice / Strength, part 1 / Strength, part 2 / Odd ball / Hating someone's guts, part 2 / Blues / Big knowledge / Good advice / Vacation in England / Condos / Trade secrets / I know you / Odd ball gets a big laugh.
CD 7278721009-2
■ MC 7278721009-4
Imago / Jan '93.

DEEP THROAT BOX SET.
Tracks: Not Advised.
CD Set . . . . QS 13CD
Quarter Stick / Jul '92 / SRD.

DO IT (Rollins, Henry Band).
Tracks: Not Advised.
CD . . . . TXH 013
Texas Hotel / Apr '89 / Pinnacle.
CD 986978
Intercord / Jan '94 / Pinnacle / C.M. Distribution.

END OF SILENCE, THE (Rollins, Henry Band).
Tracks: Low self opinion / Grip / Tearing / You didn't need / Almost real / Obscene / What do you do / Blues jam / Another life / Just like you.
■ CD . . . . PD 90641
MC . . . . PK 90641
■ LP . . . . PL 90641
Imago / Mar '92.

HARD VOLUME.
Tracks: Not Advised.
CD . . . . SERV 010CD
■ LP . . . . SERV 010LP
World Service / Nov '89.
CD 986979
Intercord / Jan '94 / Pinnacle / C.M. Distribution.

HOT ANIMAL MACHINE.
Tracks: Not Advised.
■ LP . . . . SAVE 024
Fundamental / Aug '87.
CD . . . . SAVE 024CD
Fundamental / Oct '88 / Plastic Head.
CD 986976
Intercord / Jan '94 / Pinnacle / C.M. Distribution.

HUMAN BUTT.
Tracks: Not Advised.
CD . . . . QS 12CD
Quarter Stick / Jul '92 / SRD.

LIFETIME (Rollins, Henry Band).
Tracks: Burned beyond recognition / What am I doing here / 1,000 times beyond / Lovely / Wreckage / Gun in mouth blues / You look at you / If you're alive / Turned out.
CD . . . . SAVE 065CD
■ LP . . . . SAVE 065
Fundamental / Sep '88.

LIVE AT MCCABES.
Tracks: Not Advised.
CD . . . . QS 11CD
Quarter Stick / Jul '92 / SRD.

LIVE-HENRY ROLLINS & GORE (Rollins, Henry & Gore).
Tracks: Not Advised.
■ LP . . . . EKSAKT 034
Eksakt (Holland) / Oct '87.

READINGS - SWITZERLAND.
Tracks: Not Advised.
MC . . . . ACTIONK 001
Various / '89.

SWEAT BOX.
Tracks: Not Advised.
■ LP Set . . . . TXH 015
Texas Hotel / Apr '89.
CD . . . . QS 10CD
Quarter Stick / Jul '92 / SRD.

TALKING FROM THE BOX.
Tracks: Not Advised.
VHS 727872100934
BMG Video / Feb '93 / BMG.

TEARING (Rollins, Henry Band).
Tracks: Tearing / Earache My Eye (live) / Ghost Rider / (There'll Be No) Next Time (Live).
■ 7" 72787 250187
■ CD Single 72787 250188
■ 12" 72787 250181
Imago / Sep '92.

TURNED ON - LIVE IN VIENNA, AUSTRIA (Rollins, Henry Band).
Tracks: Not Advised.
LP . . . . EFA 16178401
Quarter Stick / Dec '90 / SRD.

Romeo's Daughter

ATTRACTED TO THE ANIMAL.
Tracks: Attracted to the animal.
■ 12" . . . . 12 KUT 155
■ CD Single . . . . CDKUT 155
Music For Nations / Jun '93.

DELECTABLE.
Tracks: Not Advised.
CD . . . . CDMFN 153
LP . . . . MFN 153
MC . . . . TMFN 153
Music For Nations / Oct '93 / Pinnacle.

DON'T BREAK MY HEART.
Tracks: Don't break my heart.
■ 12" . . . . JIVET 186
■ 7" . . . . JIVE 186
Jive / Oct '88.

■ DELETED

HEAVEN IN THE BACK SEAT.
Tracks: Heaven in the back seat.
■ 12" . . . . JIVET 208
■ 7" . . . . JIVEX 208
■ 7" . . . . JIVE 208
■ CD Single . . . . JIVECD 208
Jive / Apr '90.

I CRY MYSELF TO SLEEP.
Tracks: I cry myself to sleep at night.
■ 12" . . . . JIVET 194
■ 7" . . . . JIVE 194
■ CD Single . . . . JIVECD 194
Jive / Feb '89.

ROMEO'S DAUGHTER.
Tracks: Heaven in the back seat / I cry myself to sleep at night / Hymn (look through golden eyes) / Inside out / Colour you a smile / Don't break my heart / Wild child / Velvet tongue / I like what I see.
CD . . . . CHIP 69
■ LP . . . . HIP 69
■ MC . . . . HIPC 69
Jive / Mar '89.

Ronson, Mick

Guitarist on five David Bowie albums - including the heaviest, *Man Who Sold the World* - Ronson graduated to Mott the Hoople in '73, then went solo in '74. *Slaughter On Tenth Avenue* made U.K. Top Ten but subsequent career was more low-key: played with Dylan and periodically reunited with Mott mainman Ian Hunter. He died from cancer on April 29, '93, inspiring tributes from both old employers and younger fans, latter ranging from Joe Elliot to Morrissey.

BILLY PORTER.
Tracks: Billy Porter / Slaughter on 10th Avenue.
■ 7" . . . . RCA 2482
RCA / Feb '77.
■ 7" . . . . GOLD 546
RCA Golden Grooves / May '82.

COMPILATION.
Tracks: Not Advised.
CD . . . . GY 003
Trident / Mar '94 / Pinnacle.

DON'T LOOK DOWN (Ronson, Mick & Joe Elliott).
Tracks: Don't look down / Mick Ronson - Slaughter on 10th Avenue / Billy Porter (Not available on MCS) / Love me tender (Not available on MCS).
■ 12" 660358 6
■ CD Single 660358 2
■ MC Single 660358 4
Epic / May '94.

HEAVEN AND HULL.
Tracks: Don't look down / Like a rolling stone / When the world falls down / Trouble with me / Life's a river / You and me / Colour me / Take a long line / Midnight love / All the young dudes.
CD 474742 2
LP 474742 1
MC 474742 4
Epic / May '94 / Sony.

ONLY AFTER DARK.
Tracks: Love me tender / Growing up and I'm fine / Only after dark / Music is lethal / I'm the one / Pleasure man / Hey Ma get Papa / Slaughter in 10th Avenue / Leave my heart alone (Live B side) / Love me tender (Live) / Slaughter on 10th Avenue (Live) / Billy Porter / Empty bed (Oi me no andrei) / White light/White heat / Play don't worry / Hazy days / Girl can't help it / Empty bed (Oi me no andrei) / Woman / Seven days (B'side) / Stone love / I'd rather be me.
CD Set . . . . GY 003
Humbug / Aug '94 / Pinnacle.

PLAY DON'T WORRY.
Tracks: Billy Porter / Angel No. 9 / This is for you / White light / Play don't worry / Hazy days / Girl can't help it / Empty bed (Io me ne andrei) / Woman.
■ LP APL1 0681
RCA / Mar '75.

SLAUGHTER ON TENTH AVENUE.
Tracks: Love me tender / Growing up and I'm fine / Only after dark / Music is lethal / I'm the one / Pleasure man (medley) / Slaughter on 10th Avenue.
■ LP APL1 0353
RCA / Mar '74.

Rose Tattoo

ANGRY METAL.
Tracks: Not Advised.
LP . . . . REP 2010
MC . . . . REP 2010-SX
Repertoire (Germany) / Aug '91 / Pinnacle.

ASSAULT AND BATTERY.
Tracks: Out of this place / All the lessons / Let it go / Assault & battery / Magnum maid / Rock 'n' roll is king / Manzil madness / Chinese Dunkirk / Sidewalk Sally / Suicide city.
■ LP . . . . CAL 127
■ MC . . . . CAC 127
Carrere / Sep '81.
CD . . . . STRCD 003
LP . . . . STRLP 003
Link / Aug '90 / ACD Trading Ltd.
CD . . . . REP 4011-WZ
Repertoire (Germany) / Aug '91 / Pinnacle.

ASSAULT AND BATTERY.
Tracks: Assault & battery / Astra wally.
■ 7" . . . . CAR 220
Carrere / Dec '81.

BAD BOY FOR LOVE.
Tracks: Bad boy for love / Tramp.
■ 7" . . . . CAR 191
Carrere / May '81.

BEST OF ROSE TATTOO, THE.
Tracks: Rock 'n' roll outlaw / Remedy / Nice boys / One of the boys / Bad boy for love / Butcher and fast Eddy / Manzil madness / All the lessons / Assault & battery / Rock 'n' roll is king / Branded / Scarred for life / It's gonna work itself out / We can't be beaten / Southern stars / I wish / Death or glory / Saturdays rage / Freedoms flame.
CD . . . . STR CD 024
Street Link / Oct '92 / BMG.

IT'S GONNA WORK ITSELF OUT.
Tracks: It's gonna work itself out / Fightin' sons.
■ 7" . . . . CAR 263
Carrere / Mar '83.

ROCK 'N' ROLL IS KING.
Tracks: Rock 'n' roll is king / If I had you first.
■ 7" . . . . CAR 210
Carrere / Oct '81.

ROCK 'N' ROLL OUTLAW.
Tracks: Rock 'n' roll outlaw / Remedy.
■ 7" . . . . CAR 200
Carrere / Jul '81.

ROCK 'N' ROLL OUTLAWS.
Tracks: Rock 'n' roll outlaw / Nice boys / Butcher and fast Eddy / One of the boys / Remedy / Bad boy for love / T.V. / Stuck on you / Tramp / Astra wally.
■ LP . . . . CAL 125
■ MC . . . . CAC 125
Carrere / Apr '81.
CD . . . . STRCD 002
LP . . . . STRLP 002
MC . . . . STRMC 002
Link / Aug '90 / ACD Trading Ltd.
CD . . . . REP 4010-WZ
LP . . . . REP 2024
MC . . . . REP 2024-TS
Repertoire (Germany) / Aug '91 / Pinnacle.

ROSE TATTOO.
Tracks: Not Advised.
CD . . . . REP 4103-WZ
Repertoire (Germany) / Aug '91 / Pinnacle.

SCARRED FOR LIFE.
Tracks: Scarred for life / We can't be beaten / Juice on the loose / Who's got the cash / Branded Texas / It's gonna work itself out / Sydney girls / Dead set / Revenge.
■ LP . . . . CAL 144
■ MC . . . . CAC 144
Carrere / Nov '82.
CD . . . . STRCD 004
LP . . . . STRLP 004
MC . . . . STRMC 004
Link / Aug '90 / ACD Trading Ltd.
CD . . . . REP 4049-WZ
LP . . . . REP 2049
MC . . . . REP 2049-TS
Repertoire (Germany) / Aug '91 / Pinnacle.

SOUTHERN STARS.
Tracks: Southern stars / Let us live / Freedom's flame / I wish / Saturday's rage / Death or glory / Pirate song / You've been told / No secrets / Radio said rock 'n' roll is dead.
CD . . . . STRCD 005
LP . . . . STRLP 005
Link / Aug '90 / ACD Trading Ltd.

CD . . . . REP 4050-WZ
LP . . . . REP 2050
MC . . . . REP 2020-TS
Repertoire (Germany) / Aug '91 / Pinnacle.

Rosicrucian

NO CAUSE FOR CELEBRATION.
Tracks: Not Advised.
CD . . . . BMCD 57
Black Mark / Aug '94 / Plastic Head.

SILENCE.
Tracks: Column of grey / Way of all flesh / Within the silence / Esoteric traditions / Autocratic faith / Nothing but something remains / Aren't you bored enough / Back in the habit / Defy the oppression / Do you know who you're crucifying.
CD . . . . BMCD 025
MC . . . . .BMCT 025
Black Mark / Oct '92 / Plastic Head.

Rosy Vista

YOU BETTER BELIEVE IT.
Tracks: Not Advised.
Mini LP . . . . N 0033
Noise / Feb '86 / Pinnacle.

Roth, David Lee

When once asked about his role in Van Halen, David (then Daaaaave) answered immediately: "I hesitate to use the word 'guru', but..". He was indeed a guru. A one off, a living legend: the most outrageous of all Heavy Metal frontmen. He left Van Halen in 1985, bouncing back with a couple of more-of-the-same (much more) solo records in the shape of the *Crazy From The Heat* EP and 1986 album *Eat Em And Smile*. Since then he has - unfortunately - toned down his outrageous persona and attempted to concentrate more on the music. One commendable last fling (with guitar wizard Steve Vai in tow) on *Skyscraper* was followed by the lacklustre *A Little Ain't Enough* and the lacking-in-lots-of-things *Your Filthy Little Mouth*. The future is worrying.

CALIFORNIA GIRLS.
Tracks: California girls / Just a gigolo / I ain't got nobody / Yankie rose (12" & CD single only.)
■ 7" . . . . W 9102
WEA / Feb '85.
■ CD Single . . . . W 7650 CD
■ 12" . . . . W 7650T
■ 7" . . . . W 7650
WEA / Nov '88.

CRAZY FROM THE HEAT.
Tracks: Easy Street / Just a gigolo / I ain't got nobody / California girls / Coconut grove.
■ LP 925222 1
MC 925222 4
WEA / Feb '85 / WEA.

DAMN GOOD.
Tracks: Damn good / Stand up.
■ 7" . . . . W 7753
WEA / Aug '88.
■ 12" . . . . W 7753 T
WEA / Aug '88.

DAVID LEE ROTH.
Tracks: Not Advised.
VHS . . . . K 938126 3
WEA Music Video / '87 / WEA / Gold & Sons.

EAT 'EM AND SMILE.
Tracks: Yankee rose / Shy boy / I'm easy / Ladies' nite in Buffalo / Goin' crazy / Tobacco Road / Elephant gun / Big trouble / Bump and grind / That's life.
CD 925470 2
■ LP . . . . WX 56
■ MC . . . . WX 56 C
WEA / Aug '86.

JUST A GIGOLO.
Tracks: Just a gigolo.
■ 7" . . . . W 9040
WEA / Apr '85.

JUST LIKE PARADISE.
Tracks: Just like paradise / Bottom line.
■ 12" . . . . W 8119T
■ 7" . . . . W 8119
WEA / Feb '88.

LI'L AIN'T ENOUGH, A.
Tracks: Li'l ain't enough / Tell the truth.
■ 12".................................W 0002T
■ 7"..................................W 0002
■ CD Single.........................W 0002CD
■ MC Single.........................W 0002C
WEA / Dec '90.

LITTLE AIN'T ENOUGH, A.
Tracks: Little ain't enough / Shoot it / Lady luck / Hammerhead shark / Tell the truth / Baby's on fire / 40 below / Sensible shoes / Last call / Dogtown shuffle / It's showtime / Drop in the bucket.
CD...............................7599264772
■ LP.................................WX 403
■ MC.................................WX 403 C
WEA / Jan '91.

NIGHT LIFE.
Tracks: Night life / Jump / Panama (On CDs only).
■ 7"..................................W 0249
■ CD Single........................W 0249CD
■ CD Single.......................W 0249CDX
■ MC Single........................W 0249C
WEA / May '94.

SENSIBLE SHOES.
Tracks: Sensible shoes / Li'l ain't enough, S.
■ 7" P.Disc...........................W 0016
WEA / Mar '91.

SHE'S MY MACHINE.
Tracks: She's my machine / Mississippi power / Land's edge / Yo breath' it.
■ 7"..................................W 0229
■ CD Single.......................W 0229CD2
■ CD Single.......................W 0229CD1
■ MC Single........................W 0229C
Warner Bros. / Feb '94.

SKYSCRAPER.
Tracks: Hot dog and a shake / Stand up / Hina / Perfect timing / Two fools a minute / Knucklebones / Just like paradise / Bottom line / Skyscraper / Damn good / California girls (Only on re-released issue.) / Just a gigolo (Only on re-released issue.)
■ CD...............................925671 2
■ LP.................................WX 140
■ MC.................................WX 140C
WEA / Feb '88.
CD.................................925824 2
■ LP.................................WX 236
MC.................................WX 236C
WEA / Jan '89 / WEA.

YANKEE ROSE.
Tracks: Yankee rose / Shy boy / Easy Street (Extra track available on 12" version only.)
■ 7"..................................W 8656
■ 12"...............................W 8656T
WEA / Jul '86.

YOUR FILTHY LITTLE MOUTH.
Tracks: She's my machine / Everybody's got the monkey / Big train / Experience / Little luck / Cheatin' heart cafe / Hey, you never know / No big 'ting / You're breathin' it / Your filthy little mouth / Land's edge / Night life / Sunburn.
CD.............................936245391-2
LP.............................936245391-1
MC.............................936245391-4
Warner Bros. / Mar '94 / WEA.

Roth, Uli John

BEYOND THE ASTRAL SKIES (Roth, Uli John & Electric Sun).
Tracks: Night the master comes / What is love / Why / I'll be there / Return / Ice breaker / I'm a river / Angel of peace / Eleison / Son of sky / Homesick blues / East of Mississippi.
■ LP..................................ROTH 1
MC................................TC ROTH 1
EMI / Jan '85 / EMI.

NIGHT THE MASTER COMES (Roth, Uli John & Electric Sun).
Tracks: Night the master comes / Return.
■ 7"................................EMI 5511
EMI / Jan '85.

ULI JOHN ROTH'S ELECTRIC SUN.
Tracks: Not Advised.
■ CD.............................METALCD 123
Razor / Jul '88.

Rotting Christ

PASSAGE TO ARCTURO.
Tracks: Not Advised.
CD..................................DEC 003
Decapitated / Nov '93 / Plastic Head.

Rottrevore

INIQUITOUS.
Tracks: Not Advised.
CD...................................DC 016
Drowned / Apr '94 / Plastic Head.

Roughneck

FORCE 10 FROM NAVARONE.
Tracks: Force 10 from Navarone / Jack off / Force 10 from Navarone (extended version) (Only on 12" version.)
■ 12"..............................12 MNG 709
■ 7"................................MNG 709
Mango / May '89.

Rox

DDDDDANCE.
Tracks: DDDDDance / You don't know what I caught.
■ 7"..............................EPC A 1212
Epic / May '81.

HOT LOVE IN THE CITY.
Tracks: Hot love in the city.
■ 7"................................ROX 100
Teentees / Aug '82.

KRAZY KUTS.
Tracks: Krazy kuts.
■ 12".............................12 KUT 103
Music For Nations / Sep '83.

VIOLENT BREED.
Tracks: Not Advised.
■ LP.................................MFN 11
Music For Nations / Oct '83.

Rox Diamond

ROX DIAMOND.
Tracks: Not Advised.
CD.................................CDATV 25
LP...................................ATV 25
Active / Jul '92 / Pinnacle.

Roxx Gang

SCRATCH MY BACK.
Tracks: Scratch my back / I need your sex / Red rose (Only on 12" single.)
■ 12".................................VUST 4
■ 7"..................................VUS 4
Virgin America / Oct '89.

THINGS YOU'VE NEVER DONE BEFORE.
Tracks: Scratch my back / No easy way out / Race with the devil / Red rose / Live fast die young / Too cool for school / Ball'n'chain / Fastest gun in town / Nine lives / Need your sex.
■ CD................................CDVUS 4
■ LP................................VUSLP 4
■ MC...............................VUSMC 4
Virgin America / Sep '89.

Rubicon

CRAZED.
Tracks: Crazed.
■ CD Single.........................BBQ 4CD
■ 12"...............................BBQ 4T
Beggars Banquet / Jul '92.

I COULD SHOW YOU LOVE.
Tracks: I could show you love.
■ 12".............................12 PRES 200
■ 7"...............................PRES 200
Preset / Mar '88.

Runaways

AND NOW..THE RUNAWAYS.
Tracks: Saturday night special / Eight days a week / Mama weer all crazee now / I'm a million / Right now / Take over / My buddy and me / Little lost girls / Black leather / Saturday nite special.
■ LP..................................ARED 3
■ MC................................CARED 3
Cherry Red / Jul '79.
CD..............................CDMGRAM 63
Cherry Red / Jun '93 / Pinnacle.

BORN TO BE BAD.
Tracks: Not Advised.
CD...............................FM 1004CD
Marilyn / Jul '92 / RTM / Pinnacle.
LP.................................USM 1004
Marilyn / Jul '94 / RTM / Pinnacle.

FLAMING SCHOOLGIRLS (Runaways & Cherie Currie).
Tracks: Introduction / Strawberry fields forever / C'mon / Hollywood cruisin' / Blackmail / Is it day or night / Here comes the sun / Hollywood dream / Don't abuse me / I love playin' with fire / Secrets.
■ LP...................................ARED 9
Cherry Red / '82.

QUEENS OF NOISE.
Tracks: Not Advised.
■ LP................................9100 032
Mercury / Feb '77.

RIGHT NOW.
Tracks: Right now / Black leather.
■ 7"................................CHERRY 8
Cherry Red / Aug '79.

RUNAWAYS.
Tracks: School days / Wait for me / Wasted / Don't go away / Waiting for the night / Blackmail / You drive me wild / I love playin' with fire / Born to be bad / Take it or leave it.
■ LP.................................MERB 12
MC.................................MERBC 12
Mercury / Jan '76 / PolyGram.

WAITIN' FOR THE NIGHT.
Tracks: Not Advised.
■ LP................................9100 047
Mercury / Dec '77.

YOUNG AND FAST.
Tracks: Not Advised.
■ LP.................................ST 72866
Allegiance (USA) / Oct '87.

Runestaff

DO IT.
Tracks: Do it / Ruenstaff.
■ 7"..................................VHF 17
FM Records / Oct '85.

ROAD TO RUIN.
Tracks: Road to ruin.
■ 7"...................................VHF 5
FM Records / Mar '85.

RUNESTAFF.
Tracks: Do it / Whatever you want from me / Time's running out / Road to ruin / Runestaff / Last time / Games you play / Last chances.
■ LP...............................HMRLP 26
MC...............................HMRMC 26
Heavy Metal / Feb '85 / Sony / FM Revolver.

Running Wild
Influenced by punk and NWOBHM, Running Wild recorded first demo in 1981. Distinguished by pirate-style image and eccentric frontman Rock'n'Rolf, band topped chart in homeland Germany with debut album Gates Of Purgatory. Best regarded album is 1987's Under Jolly Roger.

BAD TO THE BONE.
Tracks: Bad to the bone / Battle of Waterloo / March on (Not on 7".)
■ 12"...............................12EM 116
■ 7"................................EM 116
■ CD Single........................CDEM 116
Noise (EMI) / Nov '89.

BLAZIN' STONE.
Tracks: Not Advised.
■ CD.................................NO 1712
■ LP.................................NO 1711
■ MC.................................NO 1714
Noise / May '91.

BRANDED AND EXILED.
Tracks: Not Advised.
■ CD..............................CDNUK 030
■ LP...............................NUK 030
Noise / Oct '89.

DEATH OR GLORY.
Tracks: Riding the storm / Renegade / Evilution / Running blood / Highland glory (the eternal flight) / Marooned / Bad to the bone / Tortuga bay / Death or glory / Battle of Waterloo / March on (CD only.)
■ CD..............................CDEMC 3568
■ LP..............................EMC 3568
■ MC.............................TCEMC 3568
Noise (EMI) / Feb '90.

■ DELETED

DEATH OR GLORY TOUR.
Tracks: Not Advised.
VHS . . . . NFV 109
Fotodisk Video / May '90.

FIRST YEARS OF PIRACY, THE.
Tracks: Not Advised.
CD N01842
LP N01841
MC. N01844
Noise / Jan '92 / Pinnacle.

GATES TO PURGATORY.
Tracks: Not Advised.
■ CD . . . . CDNUK 012
■ LP . . . . .NUK 012
Noise / Oct '89.

PORT ROYAL.
Tracks: Not Advised.
■ CD . . . . CDNUK 122
■ LP . . . . .NUK 122
■ MC. . . . . ZCNUK 122
Noise / Oct '89.

READY FOR BOARDING.
Tracks: Not Advised.
■ LP . . . . .NUK 108
MC. . . . . ZCNUK 108
Noise / Oct '89 / Pinnacle.

UNDER JOLLY ROGER.
Tracks: Not Advised.
■ CD . . . . CDNUK 062
■ LP . . . . .NUK 062
■ MC. . . . . ZCNUK 062
Noise / Oct '89.

WALPURGIS NIGHT.
Tracks: Not Advised.
■ 12" . . . . UNKNOWN
Noise / '84.

Rush

Canadian trio formed in 1969 by bassist/vocalist Geddy Lee, guitarist Alex Lifeson, and drummer John Rutsey. Latter promptly replaced by Neil Peart, who assumed chief songwriting role. Regarded by critics as Led Zeppelin copyists, band developed own identity, based on complex lyrics and lengthy suites of music; culminating in *2112* album. Critical hostility escalated, with ill-founded accusations of fascism, but could not keep pace with growing popularity. At one point tipped to be 'the next Pink Floyd', after band's mid-'80s lay-off, Rush have instead maintained position just outside mainstream. They are a prolific albums band, touring when mood takes them.

2112.
Tracks: Lessons / Passage to Bangkok / Something for nothing / Tears / Twilight zone / 2112 overture / Temples of syrinx / Discover / Presentation / Oracle / Dream / Soliloquy / Grand finale.
■ LP . . . . PRICE 79
MC. . . . . PRIMC 79
Mercury / Jan '85 / PolyGram.
CD 822 545-2
Mercury / Apr '87 / PolyGram.

ALL THE WORLD'S A STAGE.
Tracks: Anthem / Bastille day / By Tor and the snow dog / At the tobes of Hades / Across the styx / Of the battle / Epilogue / Fly by night / In the mood / In the end / Lakeside park / Something for nothing / 2112 overture / Temples of syrinx / Presentation / Soliloquy / Grand finale / What you're doing / Working man / Finding my way.
■ Double LP. . . . . .PRID 1
■ MC Set . . . . PRIDC 1
Mercury / Sep '84.
CD 822 552-2
Mercury / Apr '87 / PolyGram.

ARCHIVES.
Tracks: Not Advised.
■ LP Set. 6641799
Mercury / '78.

BIG MONEY, THE.
Tracks: Big money / Territories / Red sector A.
■ 7" . . . . RUSH 12
Vertigo / Oct '85.

BIG MONEY, THE (CD VIDEO).
Tracks: Not Advised.
CD Video 080 084 2
Polygram Music Video / Sep '89 / PolyGram.

BODY ELECTRIC, THE.
Tracks: Body electric.
■ 10" . . . . RUSH 1110
■ 7" . . . . RUSH 11
Vertigo / Apr '84.

CARESS OF STEEL.
Tracks: Bastille day / Fountain of Lamneth / In the valley / Didacts and narpets / No one at the bridge / Panacea / Bacchus plateau / Fountain / I think I'm going bald / Lakeside park / Necromancer / Into the darkness / Under the shadow / Return of the Prince.
■ LP . . . . PRICE 20
■ MC. . . . . PRIMC 20
Mercury / Jun '83.
CD 822 543-2
Mercury / Apr '87 / PolyGram.

CHRONICLES.
Tracks: Finding my way / Fly by night / Bastille day / 2112 overture / Temples of syrinx / Farewell to kings / Trees / Freewill / Tom Sawyer / Limelight / Subvisions / Distant early warning / Big money / Force ten / Mystic rhythms (live) / Working man / Anthem / Lakeside Park / What you're doing (live) / Closer to the heart / La villa strangiato / Spirit of radio / Red Barchetta / Passage to Bangkok / New world man / Red sector A / Manhattan Project / Time stand still / Show don't tell.
CD Set 8389362
■ LP Set. 8389363
MC Set 8389364
Vertigo / Sep '90 / PolyGram.

CHRONICLES.
Tracks: Closer to the heart / Trees / Limelight / Tom Sawyer / Red barchetta / Subdivisions / Distant early warning / Red sector a / Big money / Mystic rhythms / Times stands still / Lock and key.
VHS . . . . CFM 02764
PMV / Apr '91 / PolyGram.

CLOSER TO THE HEART.
Tracks: Closer to the heart / Trees.
■ 7" . . . . RUSH 7
Mercury / Feb '78.

COUNTERPART.
Tracks: Animate / Stick it out / Cut to the chase / Nobody's hero / Between sun and moon / Alien shore / Speed of love / Double agent / Leave that thing alone / Cold fire / Everyday glory.
CD 756782528-2
LP 756782528-1
MC. .756782528-4
WEA / Oct '93 / WEA.

EXIT STAGE LEFT.
Tracks: Limelight / Tom Sawyer / Trees / Xanadu / Red Barchetta / Freewill / Closer to the heart / YYZ / By-Tor and the snow dog / In the end / In the mood / 2112 finale.
VHS . . . . CFV 05072
Channel 5 / '88 / Channel 5 Video / P.R.O. Video / Gold & Sons.

EXIT..STAGE LEFT.
Tracks: Spirit of radio / Red barchetta / YYZ / Passage to Bangkok / Closer to the heart / Beneath, between and behind / Jacob's ladder / Broon's bane / Trees / Xanadu / Freewill / Tom Sawyer / La villa strangiato.
■ Double LP. 6619 053
■ MC Set .7558 053
Mercury / Nov '81.
CD 822 551-2
Mercury / Apr '87 / PolyGram.

FAREWELL TO KINGS, A.
Tracks: Farewell to Kings / Xanadu / Closer to the heart / Cinderella man / Madrigal / Cygnus X - 1.
■ LP 9100 042
Mercury / Oct '77.
■ LP . . . . PRICE 92
■ MC. . . . . PRIMC 92
Vertigo / Apr '86.
CD 822 546-2
Mercury / Apr '87 / PolyGram.

FLY BY NIGHT.
Tracks: Anthem / Beneath, between and behind / Best I can / By Tor and the snow dog / At the tobes of hades / Across the styx / Of the battle / Epilogue / Fly by night / In the end / Making memories / Rivendell.
■ LP . . . . PRICE 19
MC. . . . . PRIMC 19
Mercury / Jun '83 / PolyGram.
CD 822 542-2
Mercury / Apr '87 / PolyGram.

GHOST OF A CHANCE.
Tracks: Ghost of a chance / Dreamline / Chain lightning (Only on 12" single) / Red tide (Only on 12" single).

■ 7" . . . . .A 7491
■ CD Single. . . . . A 7491 CD
Atlantic / Apr '92.

GRACE UNDER PRESSURE.
Tracks: Distant early warning / After image / Red sector / Enemy within, An / Body electric / Kid gloves / Red lenses / Between the wheels.
CD 818 476 2
■ LP . . . . VERH 12
MC. . . . . .VERHC 12
Vertigo / Apr '84 / PolyGram.

GRACE UNDER PRESSURE.
Tracks: Not Advised.
VHS . . . . CFV 07352
Channel 5 / Jun '88 / Channel 5 Video / P.R.O. Video / Gold & Sons.

HEMISPHERES.
Tracks: Not Advised.
■ IP 9100 069
Mercury / Nov '78.
■ LP . . . . .GR 8303
Gramavision / Feb '84.
CD 822 547-2
■ LP 822 547-1
Mercury / Apr '87.
■ LP . . . . PRICE 118
■ MC. . . . . PRIMC 118
Vertigo / Mar '88.

HOLD YOUR FIRE.
Tracks: Force team / Time stands still / Open secrets / Prime mover / Lock and key / Tai Shan / High water.
■ LP . . . . VERH 47
■ MC. . . . . .VERHC 47
Vertigo / Oct '87.
CD 832 464 2
Vertigo / '88 / PolyGram.

MOVING PICTURES.
Tracks: Tom Sawyer / Red Barchetta / YYZ / Limelight / Camera / Witch hunt / (Part III of Fear) / Vital signs.
MC. 7141 160
Mercury / Feb '81 / PolyGram.
■ LP 6337 160
Mercury / Feb '82.
CD 800 048-2
Mercury / '83 / PolyGram.

NEW WORLD MAN.
Tracks: New world man / Countdown.
■ 7" . . . . RUSH 8
Mercury / Sep '82.
■ 12" . . . . RUSH 1012
■ 7" . . . . RUSH 10
■ 7" P.Disc . . . . .RUSHP 10
Mercury / Jun '83.

PERMANENT WAVES.
Tracks: Spirit of radio / Freewill / Jacob's ladder / Entre nous / Different strings / Natural science.
CD 822 548-2
■ LP 9100 071
MC. 7142 720
Mercury / Jan '80 / PolyGram.

POWER WINDOWS.
Tracks: Big money / Grand design / Manhattan Project / Marathon / Territories / Middletown dreams / Emotion detector / Mystic rhythms.
CD 826 098-2
■ LP . . . . VERH 31
■ MC. . . . . .VERHC 31
Vertigo / Nov '85.

PRESTO.
Tracks: Show, don't tell / Chain lightning / Pass / War paint / Scars / Presto / Super conductor / Anagram (for mongo) / Red tide / Hand over fist / Available light.
CD 782 040-2
■ LP . . . . WX 327
■ MC. . . . . WX 327 C
Atlantic / Dec '89.

PRIME MOVER.
Tracks: Prime mover / Distant early warning / Distant early warning (live) (Track on Ltd. Ed. 12".) / New world man (Track on Ltd. Ed. 12").
■ 12" . . . . RUSH 1412
■ 12" Remix. . . . . RUSHR 1412
■ 7" . . . . RUSH 14
■ 7" . . . . .RUSHR 14
■ CD Single. . . . . .RUSHCD 14
Vertigo / Apr '88.

ROLL THE BONES.
Tracks: Dreamline / Bravado / Roll the bones / Face up / Where's my thing / Big wheel / Heresay / Ghost of a chance / Neurotica / You bet your life.

CD 7567822932
■ LP . . . . WX 436
MC . . . . WX 436 C
Atlantic / Sep '91 / WEA.

RUSH.
Tracks: Before and after / Finding my way / Here again / In the mood / Need some love / Take a friend / What you're doing / Working man.
■ LP . . . . PRICE 18
■ MC . . . . PRIMC 18
Mercury / Jun '83.
CD 822 541-2
Mercury / Apr '87 / PolyGram.

RUSH ARCHIVES.
Tracks: Not Advised.
■ MC 7649 103
Mercury / Jun '78.

RUSH THROUGH TIME.
Tracks: Fly by night / Making memories / Bastille day / Something for nothing / Cinderella man / Anthem / 2112 (Overture) / 2112 (The temples of syrinx) / Twilight zone / Best I can / Closer to the heart / In the end.
■ LP 6337 171
MC 7141 171
Mercury / Sep '81 / PolyGram.

RUSH: INTERVIEW PICTURE DISC.
Tracks: Not Advised.
LP P.Disc . . . . BAK 2083
Baktabak / Dec '87 / Arabesque Ltd.
CD P.Disc . . . . CBAK 4055
Baktabak / Apr '92 / Arabesque Ltd.

SHOW OF HANDS, A.
Tracks: Big money / Subdivisions / Marathon / Turn the page / Manhattan project / Mission / Distant early warning / Mystic rhythms / Witch hunt / Rhythm

method (Neil Peart drum solo.) / Force ten / Time stands still / Red sector / Closer to the heart.
CD 846 346-2
■ Double LP 836 346-1
■ MC 836 346-4
Vertigo / Jan '89.

SHOW OF HANDS, A.
Tracks: Big money / Subdivisions / Marathon / Turn the page / Manhattan project / Mission / Distant early warning / Mystic rhythms / Witch hunt / Rhythm method (Neil Peart drum solo.) / Force ten / Time stands still / Red sector.
VHS . . . . CFV 07812
Channel 5 / Feb '89 / Channel 5 Video / P.R.O. Video / Gold & Sons.

SIGNALS.
Tracks: Subdivisions / Analog kid / Chemistry / Digital man / Weapon / New world man / Losing it / Countdown.
■ LP 6337 243
MC 7141 243
Mercury / Sep '82 / PolyGram.
CD 810 002-2
Mercury / '83 / PolyGram.

SPIRIT OF THE RADIO.
Tracks: Spirit of the radio / Trees / Working man (Only on 12" single.).
■ 12" . . . . .RADIO 12
■ 7" . . . . .RADIO 7
Mercury / Feb '80.

SPIRIT OF THE RADIO (OLD GOLD).
Tracks: Spirit of the radio / Closer to the heart.
■ 7" . . . . .OG 9767
Old Gold / Feb '88.

SUBDIVISIONS.
Tracks: Subdivisions.
■ 7" . . . . RUSH 9
Mercury / Oct '82.

THRU' THE CAMERA'S EYE.
Tracks: Not Advised.
VHS . . . . CFV 06332
Channel 5 / Nov '87 / Channel 5 Video / P.R.O. Video / Gold & Sons.
VHS . . . . SPC 00132
Spectrum (1) / Oct '89 / PolyGram.

TIME STAND STILL.
Tracks: Time stands still / Force ten / Enemy within (live) (extra track on 12" only.) / Witchhunt (live) (Extra track on 12" only).
■ 12" . . . . RUSH 1312
■ 7" . . . . RUSH 13
■ 7" P.Disc . . . . RUSHP 1312
Vertigo / Oct '87.

TOM SAWYER (LIVE).
Tracks: Tom Sawyer.
■ 12" . . . . EXIT 12
■ 7" . . . . EXIT 7
Mercury / Oct '81.

VITAL SIGNS.
Tracks: Vital signs / Passage to Bangkok.
■ 12" . . . . VITAL 12
■ 7" . . . . VITAL 7
Mercury / Mar '81.

Ruthless

METAL WITHOUT MERCY.
Tracks: Not Advised.
■ EP . . . . IW 1004
Iron Works (USA) / Jan '86.

■ DELETED

S

S.A.D.O.

CIRCLE OF FRIENDS.
Tracks: Not Advised.
■ LP .NUK 091
■ MC . . . . .ZCNUK 091
Noise / Oct '89.

DIRTY FANTASY.
Tracks: Not Advised.
■ CD . . . . .CDNUK 115
■ LP .NUK 115
Noise / Aug '88.
■ MC . . . . .ZCNUK 115
Noise / Aug '88.

SENSITIVE.
Tracks: Talk about me / Just married / Women and whiskey / Dear Miss J / Every time / Bad lovin / Time out / Love lies / Run baby run.
■ CD . . . . .CDNUK 147
■ LP .NUK 147
■ MC . . . . .ZCNUK 147
Noise / Feb '90.

S.D.I.

SATANS DEFLORATION.
Tracks: Not Advised.
■ LP .805035
Scratch (Germany) / Feb '87.

SIGN OF THE WICKED.
Tracks: Not Advised.
CD 15 390
MC 79 390
Laserlight / Aug '91 / TBD / BMG / Target.

S.N.F.U.

SOMETHING GREEN AND LEAFY THIS WAY COMES.
Tracks: Not Advised.
CD . . . . E 86430CD
LP . . . . E 86430
MC . . . . E 86430MC
Epitaph / Dec '93 / Plastic Head.

S.O.B.

THRASH NIGHT.
Tracks: Not Advised.
LP . . . . RISE 002
Rise / Feb '90 / Pinnacle.

WHAT'S THE TRUTH.
Tracks: Not Advised.
CD . . . . RISE 4 CD
LP . . . . .RISE 4
MC . . . . RISE 4 MC
Rise / Dec '90 / Pinnacle.

YOU MAKE ME WONDER.
Tracks: Make me wonder / Corporation buzz.
■ 12" .RTT 219
■ 7" . . . . .RT 219
Rough Trade / Sep '89.

S.O.D.

LIVE AT BUDOKAN.
Tracks: Not Advised.
CD . . . . .CDMFN 144
LP . . . . .MFN 144
MC . . . . .TMFN 144
Music For Nations / Sep '92 / Pinnacle.

LIVE AT BUDOKAN.
Tracks: Not Advised.
VHS . . . . VFN 10
Video For Nations / Jul '93 / Pinnacle.

SPEAK ENGLISH OR DIE.
Tracks: Not Advised.
■ LP . . . . RR 9725
Road Runner / Dec '85.
■ MC . . . . RR 97254
Road Runner / Oct '89.
■ CD . . . . RR 349725
Road Runner / Oct '89.

Sabbat

English quintet formed in 1985, Sabbat were briefly Britain's Brightest Hopes in European-dominated thrash scene. Despite distinctive, Pagan-flavoured theatrics and enthusiastic support from U.K. press, Sabbat never fulfilled potential and split in '91 after *Mourning Has Broken* album. Singer Martin Walkyier formed Skyclad.

DREAMWEAVER.
Tracks: Not Advised.
■ CD . . . . .CDNUK 132
■ LP .NUK 132
■ MC . . . . .ZCNUK 132
Noise / May '89.

HISTORY OF A TIME TO COME.
Tracks: Cautionary tale / Hosanna in excelsis / Behind the crooked cross / Horned is the hunter / For an eye / For those who died / Dead man's robe / Church bizarre.
■ LP .NUK 098
■ MC . . . . .ZCNUK 098
Noise / Mar '88.
■ CD . . . . .CDNUK 098
Noise / Nov '89.

LIVE - THE END OF THE BEGINNING.
Tracks: Not Advised.
VHS . . . . .NFV 111
Fotodisk Video / Jul '90.

MOURNING HAS BROKEN.
Tracks: Demise of history / Paint the world black / Voice of time / Without a trace / Theological void / Dumbstruck / Dreamscape / Mourning has broken.
■ CD . . . . .NO 1622
■ LP . . . . .NO 1621
■ MC . . . . .NO 1624
Noise / Mar '91.

Sabotage

BEHIND ENEMY LINES.
Tracks: Not Advised.
■ LP . . . . TE 2001
Trans Euro / Mar '87.

SABOTAGE.
Tracks: Not Advised.
■ LP . . . . TE 2002
Trans Euro / Jun '88.

Sabre

HIDDEN VISIONS.
Tracks: Not Advised.
■ EP . . . . .MSQ 8703
Masque / Jun '88.

MIRACLE MAN.
Tracks: On the loose / Miracle man.
■ 7" . . . . .NEAT 23
Neat / Jun '83.

Sabu

ANGELINE.
Tracks: Angeline / Shake, rattle & roll.
■ 7" . . . . VHF 25
FM Records / Oct '85.

HEARTBREAK.
Tracks: Not Advised.
■ CD . . . . HMAXD 36
■ LP . . . . HMUSA 36
■ MC . . . . HMAMC 36
Heavy Metal America / '89.

Sacred Alien

LEGENDS.
Tracks: Legends / Sittin' in the front row.
■ 7" . . . . .SAD 001X
Neon / Mar '84.

Sacred Child

SACRED CHILD.
Tracks: Not Advised.
■ LP . . . . BD 034
Black Dragon / Jun '88.

Sacred Denial

EXHUMED.
Tracks: Not Advised.
LP 102 942
Nuclear Blast / '89 / Plastic Head.

EXTRA STRENGTH.
Tracks: Not Advised.
LP 102 941
Nuclear Blast / '89 / Plastic Head.

NORTH OF THE ORDER.
Tracks: Not Advised.
■ LP SD003
Forefront (USA) / Aug '87.

SIFTING THROUGH THE WRECKAGE.
Tracks: Sifting through the wreckage / When I sleep / Brothers inventions / Some curiosity / Conquer / No way / Take a look around / Violent affection.
LP . . . . NB 101
Nuclear Blast / Nov '88 / Plastic Head.
CD .082955
Nuclear Blast / '90 / Plastic Head.

Sacred Reich

ALIVE AT THE DYNAMO.
Tracks: Not Advised.
■ CD . . . . RO 94312
■ LP . . . . RO 94311
Roadracer / Oct '89.

AMERICAN WAY, THE.
Tracks: Love ... hate / Crimes against humanity / I don't know / State of emergency / American way / Way it is / Flavors.
CD . . . . RO 93922
■ LP . . . . RO 93921
■ MC . . . . RO 93924
Roadracer / May '90.
CD R093925
Road Runner / Jun '91 / Pinnacle.

IGNORANCE.
Tracks: Death squad / Victim of demise / Layed to rest / Ignorance / No believers / Violent solutions / Rest in peace / Sacred Reich / Administrative decisions.
■ LP . . . . RR 9578
Road Runner / Nov '87.
CD . . . . .RR 9578 2
Road Runner / '89 / Pinnacle.
CD . . . . .CDZORRO 30
LP . . . . ZORRO 30
MC . . . . TZORRO 30
Music For Nations / Sep '91 / Pinnacle.

IGNORANCE/SURF NICARAGUA.
Tracks: Not Advised.
MC . . . . RR 95784
Road Runner / Oct '89 / Pinnacle.

SURF NICARAGUA.
Tracks: Not Advised.
CD . . . . .RR 9512 2
■ LP . . . . RR 9512 1
Road Runner / Dec '88.
CD . . . . .CDZORRO 47
MC . . . . .TMZORRO 47
Music For Nations / Aug '92 / Pinnacle.

Sacrifice

APOCALYPSE INSIDE.
Tracks: My eyes see red / Apocalypse inside / Flesh / Salvation / Beneath what you see / Incarcerated / Ruins of the old / Lose / Freedom Slave.
CD . . . . .CDZORRO 62
Metal Blade / Jul '93 / Pinnacle.

Sacrifice

FORWARD TO TERMINATION.
Tracks: Not Advised.
■ LP . . . . RR 9595
Road Runner / '89.

TORMENT IN FIRE.
Tracks: Not Advised.
■ LP . . . . RR 9697
Road Runner / Oct '86.

Sacrilege

BEYOND THE REALMS OF MADNESS.
Tracks: Lifeline / At death's door / Sacred / Out of sight out of mind.
■ LP . . . . GURT 4
COR / Apr '88.
CD . . . . CORECD 8
LP . . . . CORE 8
Metalcore / Nov '91 / Pinnacle.

TURN BACK TRILOBITE.
Tracks: Not Advised.
CD . . . . CDFLAG 29
■ LP . . . . .FLAG 29
Under One Flag / Jan '89.

WITHIN THE PROPHECY.
Tracks: Not Advised.
■ LP . . . . .FLAG 15
Under One Flag / Aug '87.
MC . . . . TFLAG 15
Under One Flag / Aug '89 / Pinnacle.

Sacrilege B.C.

PARTY WITH GOD.
Tracks: Not Advised.
■ LP . . . . VM 102
MC . . . . VM 102C
Alchemy / Pinnacle.

TOO COOL TO PRAY.
Tracks: Not Advised.
■ LP . . . . GWLP 47
GWR / Aug '89.

Sacrosanct

TRAGIC INTENSE.
Tracks: Not Advised.
CD 1MF 37700322
Invisible / Jul '93 / Plastic Head.

Sadus

CHEMICAL EXPOSURE.
Tracks: Not Advised.
LP . . . . RO 92591
MC . . . . RO 92594
■ CD . . . . RO 92592
Road Runner / Nov '91.

SWALLOWED IN BLACK.
Tracks: Not Advised.
LP . . . . RO 93681
MC . . . . RO 93684
■ CD . . . . RO 93682
Roadracer / Oct '90.

Saga

BEGINNERS GUIDE TO THROWING SHAPES.
Tracks: How do I look / Starting all over / Shape / Odd man out / Nineties / Scarecrow / As I am / Waiting in the wings / Giant.
■ LP 210367
BMG / '89.

BEHAVIOUR.
Tracks: Listen to your heart / Take a chance / What do I know / Misbehaviour / Nine lives of Miss Midi / You and the night / Out of the shadows / Easy way out / Promises / Here I am (goodbye) / Once upon a time.
MC 40 26579
■ LP . . . . PRT 26579
Portrait / Sep '85.

CAREFUL WHERE YOU STEP.
Tracks: Careful where you step / How long / Take it or leave it.
■ 12" . . . . POSPX 228
■ 7" . . . . POSP 228
Polydor / Feb '81.

FLYER.
Tracks: Flyer / Writing.
■ 12" . . . . TA 3817

■ 7" . . . . .A 3817
Epic / Oct '83.

HEADS OR TAILS.
Tracks: Flyer / Catwalk / Sound of strangers / Writing / Intermission / Social orphan / Vendetta / Scratching the surface / Pitchman.
■ LP . . . . PRT 25740
Portrait / Nov '83.
CD 815 410-2
Polydor / '88 / PolyGram.

IMAGES AT TWILIGHT.
Tracks: It's time / See them smile / Slow motion / You're not alone / Take it or leave it / Images / Hot to cold / Mouse in a maze.
■ LP 2391 437
Polydor / Aug '80.
CD 825 254-2
Polydor / '88 / PolyGram.

IN TRANSIT.
Tracks: Not Advised.
CD 800 100-2
Polydor / '88 / PolyGram.

IT'S TIME.
Tracks: It's time / Mouse in a maze.
■ 7" 2095246
Polydor / Sep '80.

ON THE LOOSE.
Tracks: On the loose / Framed.
■ 7" . . . . PRT A 2958
Portrait / Jan '83.

SAGA.
Tracks: How long / Humble stance / Climbing the ladder / Will it be you (chapter four) / Perfectionist / Give 'em the money / Ice nice / Tired world (chapter six).
■ LP 2424175
Polydor / '78.

SCRATCHING THE SURFACE.
Tracks: Scratching the surface / Sound of strangers.
■ 12" . . . . TA 4067
■ 7" . . . . .A 4067
Portrait / Jan '84.

SILENT KNIGHT.
Tracks: Don't be late / What's it gonna be / Time to go / Compromise / Too much to lose / Help me out / Someone should / Careful where you step.
■ LP 237 416 6
Polydor / Dec '80.
CD 821 934-2
Polydor / '88 / PolyGram.

TAKE A CHANCE.
Tracks: Take a chance / You and the night.
■ 12" . . . . TX 6840
■ 7" . . . . .A 6840
Portrait / Jan '86.

WHAT DO I KNOW.
Tracks: What do I know / Easy way out.
■ 12" . . . . TX 6515
■ 7" . . . . .A 6515
CBS / Sep '85.

WIND HIM UP.
Tracks: Wind him up / Amnesia.
■ 7" . . . . PRT A 3053
Portrait / Mar '83.

WORLDS APART.
Tracks: On the loose / Wind him up / Amnesia / Framed / Time's up / Interview / No regrets / Conversations / No stranger.
■ LP . . . . PRT 25054
Portrait / Feb '83.
CD 821 479-2
Polydor / '88 / PolyGram.

Saigon Kick

FIELDS OF RAPE.
Tracks: One step closer / Space oddity / Water / Torture / Fields of rape / I love you / Sgt. Steve / My heart / On and on / Way / Sentimental girl / Close to you / When you were mine / Reprise.
CD 756792300-2
MC 756792300-4
WEA / Oct '93 / WEA.

LIZARD, THE.
Tracks: Cruelty / Hostile youth / Feel the same way / Freedom / God of 42nd Street / My dog / Peppermint tribe / Love is on the way / Lizard / All alright / Sleep / All I want / Body bags / Miss Jones / World goes round / Chanel.
CD 7567921582
■ LP 7567921581

MC 7567921584
Atlantic / Jan '92 / WEA.

LOVE IS ON THE WAY.
Tracks: All I want (Only to be found on MCS, CDS & 7".) / Hostile youth (Only to be found on 12".).
■ 12" .A 7451T
■ 7" . . . . .A 7451
■ CD Single . . . . A 7451CD
■ MC Single. . . . . A 7451C
Atlantic / Oct '92.

SAIGON KICK.
Tracks: New world / What you say / What do you do / Suzy / Colours / Coming home / Love of God / Down by the ocean / Acid rain / My life / Month of Sundays / Ugly / Come take me now / I.C.U.
CD 7567916342
■ LP 7567916341
MC 7567916344
East West / Apr '91 / WEA.

Salas, Steve

HARDER THEY COME, THE (Salas, Steve Colourcode).
Tracks: Stand up / Caught in the middle of it / Two bullets and a gun / Over and over again / Indian chief / Blind / Just like that / Harder they come / Baby walk on / Cover me.
■ LP . . . . ILPS 9963
■ CD . . . . CID 9963
■ MC .ICT 9963
Island / May '90.

HARDER THEY COME, THE (Salas, Steve Colourcode).
Tracks: Harder they come / Blind / Indian chief.
■ 12" . . . . 12 IS 459
Island / Jul '90.
■ 7" . . . . IS 459
■ CD Single . . . . CID 459
Island / Oct '90.

Salty Dog

EVERY DOG HAS IT'S DAY.
Tracks: Not Advised.
CD 7599242702
■ LP 7599242701
MC 7599242704
Geffen / Feb '90 / BMG.
■ CD . . . . .GEFD 24270
■ MC . . . . .GEFC 24270
Geffen / Aug '91.

Samael

BLOOD RITUAL.
Tracks: Not Advised.
CD .84 97374
LP .08 97371
MC .08 97344
Century Media / Dec '92 / Plastic Head.

CEREMONY OF OPPOSITES.
Tracks: Not Advised.
CD . . . . CM 77064CD
LP . . . . CM 77064
MC . . . . CM 77064C
Century Media / Mar '94 / Plastic Head.

Sambora, Richie

BALLAD OF YOUTH.
Tracks: Ballad of youth / Father time / Wind cries Mary (Only on 12" and CD Single).
■ 12" . . . . .MERX 350
■ 7" . . . . MER 350
■ CD Single . . . . .MERCD 350
■ MC Single . . . . .MERMC 350
Mercury / Aug '91.

STRANGER IN THIS TOWN.
Tracks: Rest in peace / Church of desire / Stranger in this town / Ballad of youth / One light burning / Mr. Bluesman / Rosie / River of love / Father time / Answer.
CD 8488952
MC 8488984
■ LP 8488951
Phonogram / Sep '91.

Samhain

NOVEMBER-COMING-FIRE.
Tracks: Diabolos '88 / In my grip / Mother of mercy / Birthright / To walk the night / Let the day begin / Halloween II / November's fire / Kiss of steel / Unbridled / Human pony girl.

■ DELETED

■ LP . . . . REVLP 82
Revolver / Aug '86.

Samson

Briefly regarded as standard-bearers for New Wave of British Heavy Metal, Samson are best-remembered for once numbering future Iron Maiden alumni Bruce Dickinson and Clive Burr, and Mel Gaynor (later of Simple Minds), among their ranks. Formed in 1979 by guitarist Paul Samson, band's only notable chart success came with *Head On* album, U.K. no. 34 in 1980. After split in early '80s, Samson plodded on with short-lived Empire, then solo career.

1988.
Tracks: Not Advised.
■ CD . . . . PIPCD 054
Great Expectations / Jul '93.

AND THERE IT IS.
Tracks: Not Advised.
■ LP . . . . METALPM 126
Metal Masters / Sep '88.

ARE YOU READY.
Tracks: Are you ready / Front page news / La Grange.
■ 12" . . . . POSPX 670
■ 7" . . . . POSP 670
■ 7" P.Disc . . . . POPP 670
Polydor / Feb '84.

BEFORE THE STORM.
Tracks: Danger zone / Stealing away / Red skies / I'll be round / Test of time / Life on the run / Turn out the lights / Losing my grip / Young idea.
■ LP . . . . POLS 1077
Polydor / '83.

BICEPS OF STEEL.
Tracks: Hard times / Vice versa.
VHS . . . . MMGVE 001
MMG Video / '87 / TBD.

DON'T GET MAD GET EVEN.
Tracks: Are you ready / Love hungry / Burning up / Fight goes on / Don't get mad get even / Into the valley / Bite on the bullet / Dr. Ice / Front page news / Leaving love (behind).
■ LP . . . . POLD 5132
Polydor / Apr '84.

FIGHT GOES ON.
Tracks: Fight goes on / Riding with the angels / Vice versa (Available on 12" only).
■ 12" . . . . POSPX 680
■ 7" . . . . POSP 680
Polydor / Apr '84.

HARD TIMES.
Tracks: Hard times / Angel with a machine gun.
■ 7" . . . . GEMS 38
Gem (2) / Aug '80.

HEAD ON.
Tracks: Hard times / Take it like a man / Vice versa / Manwatcher / Too close to rock / Thunderburst / Hammerhead / Hunted / Take me to your leader / Walking out on you.
■ LP . . . . GEMLP 108
Gem (2) / Jul '80.
CD . . . . REP 4037-WZ
LP . . . . REP 2015
Repertoire (Germany) / Aug '91 / Pinnacle.

HEAD TACTICS (Samson & Bruce Dickinson).
Tracks: Vice versa / Earth mother / Losing my grip / Take it like a man / Once bitten / Go to hell / Hard times / Nice girl / Too close to rock / Walking out on you.
■ MC. . . . . TCEST 2006
■ LP . . . . EST 2006
Capitol / Mar '86.

LAST RITES.
Tracks: Mr. rock 'n' roll / Big brother / Koz / Leavin' you / It's not easy as it seems / Telephone / Wrong side of time / Primrose shuffle / I wish I was the saddle of a schoolgirl's bike / Inside out.
■ LP . . . . THBL 015
Thunderbolt / Sep '84.

LIFE ON THE RUN.
Tracks: Life on the run.
■ 7" . . . . POSP 519
■ 7" Set . . . . POSPG 519
Polydor / Oct '82.

LIVE AT READING '81.
Tracks: Not Advised.
CD . . . . FRSCD 001
LP . . . . FRSLP 001
MC. . . . . FRSMC 001
Raw Fruit / Dec '90 / Pinnacle.
CD . . . . REP 4040-WP
LP . . . . REP 2040
MC. . . . . REP 2040-TT
Repertoire (Germany) / Aug '91 / Pinnacle.

LOSING MY GRIP.
Tracks: Losing my grip.
■ 12" . . . . POSPX 471
■ 7" P.Disc . . . . POSPP 471
■ 12" P.Disc . . . . POSPPX 471
Polydor / Jun '82.

MR. ROCK 'N' ROLL.
Tracks: Mr. Rock 'n' roll / Driving music.
■ 7" . . . . LIG 553
Lightning / Mar '79.

PILLARS OF ROCK.
Tracks: Danger zone / Stealing away / Red skies / Losing my grip / Running out of time / Drivin' with zz / Young idea / Test of time / Leaving love (behind) / Fight goes on / Don't get mad get even / Dr. Ice / Front page news / Bite on the bullet / Into the valley / Tomorrow or yesterday / Mr. rock 'n' roll / Love hungry.
LP . . . . VSOPLP 151
■ CD . . . . VSOPCD 151
■ MC. . . . . VSOPMC 151
Connoisseur Collection / Oct '90.

RED SKIES.
Tracks: Red skies / Living, loving, lying.
■ 12" . . . . POSPX 554
■ 7" . . . . POSP 554
■ 7" P.Disc . . . . POSPP 554
Polydor / Mar '83.

REFUGEE.
Tracks: Good to see you / Turn on the lights / Room 109 / Look to the future / Too late / Silver screen / Can't live without your love / Love this time / State of emergency / Someone to turn to / Samurai sunset.
CD . . . . GMGCD 001
LP . . . . GMGLP 001
MC. . . . . GMGMC 001
Communique / Jul '90 / Plastic Head.

RIDIN' WITH THE ANGELS.
Tracks: Ridin' with the angels / Little big man.
■ 7" . . . . RCA 67
RCA / May '81.

SAMSON.
Tracks: Not Advised.
CD . . . . .CMGCD 008
Communique / Aug '93 / Plastic Head.

SHOCK TACTICS.
Tracks: Not Advised.
■ LP . . . . RCALP 5031
MC. . . . . RCAK 5031
RCA / May '81 / BMG.
CD . . . . REP 4038-WZ
LP . . . . REP 2016
MC. . . . . REP 2016-TS
Repertoire (Germany) / Aug '91 / Pinnacle.

SURVIVORS.
Tracks: It's not as easy as it seems / I wish I was the saddle of a school girl / Big brother / Tomorrow or yesterday / Koz / Six foot under / Wrong side of time / Mr. rock 'n' roll / Primrose shuffle / Telephone / Leavin' you.
■ LP . . . . THBL 001
MC. . . . . THBC 001
Thunderbolt / Jun '84 / TBD / Jazz Music.
CD . . . . REP 4039-WZ
LP . . . . REP 2039
MC. . . . . REP 2039-TS
Repertoire (Germany) / Aug '91 / Pinnacle.

TELEPHONE.
Tracks: Telephone / Leavin' you.
■ 7" . . . . LIG 547
Lightning / Oct '78.

THANK YOU AND GOODNIGHT.
Tracks: Not Advised.
■ LP . . . . METALP 102
Metal Masters / Mar '85.

VICE VERSA.
Tracks: Vice versa / Hammerhead.
■ 7" . . . . GEMS 34
Gem (2) / Jun '80.
■ 7" . . . . EMI 5061
EMI / May '80.

VICE VERSA (Samson & Bruce Dickinson).
Tracks: Vice versa / Losing my grip.
■ 12" 12CL 395
■ 7" . . . . CL 395
Capitol / Feb '86.

Samson, Paul

JOINT FORCES.
Tracks: Burning emotion / No turning back / Russians / Tales of the fury / Reach out to love / Chosen few / Tramp / Power of love / Tell me.
■ LP . . . . RAWLP 018
MC. . . . . RAWTC 018
Raw Power / May '86 / Pinnacle.

Sanctuary

INTO THE MIRROR BLACK.
Tracks: Future tense / Taste revenge / Long since dark / Epitaph / Eden lies obscured / Mirror black / Seasons of destruction / One more murder / Communion.
MC. 4658764
■ CD 4658762
■ LP 4658761
Epic / Apr '90.

PRICE TO PAY.
Tracks: Not Advised.
MC. SANC 1
Vision / Feb '85 / SRD.

REFUGE DENIED.
Tracks: Battle angels / Termination force / Die for my sins / Soldiers of steel / Sanctuary / White rabbit / Ascension to destiny / Third war / Veil of disguise.
CD 4608112
■ MC. 4608114
■ LP 4608111
Epic / Apr '88.

Santers

GUITAR ALLEY.
Tracks: Not Advised.
■ LP . . . . HMUSA 3
Heavy Metal America / Jun '84.

RACING TIME.
Tracks: Mistreatin' heart / Mystical eyes / Still I am / Dog without a home / Road to Morocco / Two against the world / Backstreets / Winter freeze / Hard time lovin' you / Racing time.
■ LP . . . . HMILP 4
Heavy Metal / Dec '82.

SANTE FE.
Tracks: Not Advised.
■ LP . . . . BSS 326
Tank / Nov '79.

Saracen

CHANGE OF HEART.
Tracks: We have arrived / Love on sight / Julie / Seabird / Meet me at midnight / Jekyll and Hyde / Cheating / Face in the crowd / Hot love / Bridge of tears.
■ LP . . . . NEAT 1016
Neat / Jan '85.

HEROES, SAINTS AND FOOLS.
Tracks: Crusader / Rock of ages / No more lonely nights / Horsemen of the Apocalypse / Heroes, saints and fools / Dolphin ride / Ready to fly.
■ LP . . . . MPRGR 492
Decca / Apr '82.

NO MORE LONELY NIGHTS.
Tracks: No more lonely nights / Rock of ages.
■ 7" .SARI 1
Nucleus / May '82.

WE HAVE ARRIVED.
Tracks: We have arrived / Face in the crowd.
■ 7" .NEAT 30
Neat / Aug '83.

Saraya

LOVE HAS TAKEN IT'S TOLL.
Tracks: Love has taken it's toll / Running out of time.
■ 12" 889 293 1
■ 7" 889 292-7
Polydor / Jul '89.

SARAYA.
Tracks: Love has taken it's toll / Healing touch / Get U ready / Gypsy child / One night away / Alsace

---

■ DELETED

S 3

Lorraine / Runnin' out of time / Back to the bullet / Fire to burn / St. Christopher medal / Drop the bomb.
■ LP 837 764-1
■ CD 837 764-2
■ MC 837 764-4
Polydor / Jul '89.

SEDUCER.
Tracks: Seducer.
■ CD Single . . . . PZCD 149
■ 7" . . . . PO 149
■ 12" . . . . PZ 149
Polydor / Jun '91.

WHEN THE BLACKBIRD SINGS.
Tracks: Queen of Sheba / Bring back the light / Hitchin a ride / When you see me again / Tear down the wall / Seducer / When the blackbird sings / Lions den / In the shade of the sun / White highway / New world.
CD 849 087-2
■ LP 849 087-1
MC 849 087-4
Polydor / May '91 / PolyGram.

Sarcofago

LAWS OF SCOURGE.
Tracks: Not Advised.
CD . . . . CDFLAG 66
MC . . . . TFLAG 66
■ LP . . . . FLAG 66
Music For Nations / Apr '92.

ROTTING.
Tracks: Not Advised.
CD . . . . CDFLAG 52
MC . . . . TFLAG 52
Under One Flag / Oct '89 / Pinnacle.
LP . . . . FLAG 52
Under One Flag / Oct '89 / Pinnacle.

Sargent

LIVING IN THE FAST LANE.
Tracks: Not Advised.
■ LP . . . . AMP 10
Powerstation / Sep '86.

SGT.
Tracks: Not Advised.
■ LP . . . . SKULL 8367
Mausoleum / Apr '85.

Sarkoma

COMPLETELY DIFFERENT.
Tracks: Not Advised.
CD . . . . GC 189805
Recommended / Jul '92 / Impetus Records / ReR Megacorp.

INTERGRITY.
Tracks: Not Advised.
CD . . . . CDVEST 16
Bulletproof / Jun '94 / Pinnacle.

Satan

COURT IN THE ACT.
Tracks: Into the fire / Trial by fire / Blades of steel / No turning back / Broken treaties / Break free / Hunt you down / Ritual / Dark side of innocence / Alone in the dock.
■ LP . . . . NEAT 1012
Neat / Jan '85.

INTO THE FUTURE.
Tracks: Not Advised.
■ Double LP 601 898
Steamhammer (Germany) / '89.

KISS OF DEATH.
Tracks: Kiss of death / Heads will roll.
■ 7" . . . . GRC 145
Guardian / Sep '82.

SUSPENDED SENTENCE.
Tracks: Not Advised.
■ LP 081 837
Steamhammer (Germany) / '89.

SUSPENDED SENTENCE/INTO THE FUTURE.
Tracks: Not Advised.
CD 851 819
Steamhammer (Germany) / '89 / Pinnacle.

Satanic Rites

LIVE TO RIDE.
Tracks: Live to ride / Hit and run.
■ 7" . . . . HEAVY 8
Heavy Metal / Sep '81.

NO USE CRYING.
Tracks: Not Advised.
■ LP . . . . CHUB 002
Chub / Nov '87.

Sator

HEADQUAKE.
Tracks: Slug it out / We're right you're wrong / I wanna go home / Bound to be good / I'd rather drink than talk / Skyscraper / Turnpike / No time tomorrow / Heyday / Someone got shot / Haywire / Down / Outro.
CD 9031764522
■ LP 9031764521
MC 9031764524
Magnet / Aug '92 / WEA.

Satriani, Joe

Satriani made name as San Francisco guitar teacher; pupils including Kirk Hammett (later of Metallica) and Steve Vai. Wider acceptance followed 1987 album *Surfing With The Alien* and successor *Flying In A Blue Dream*, peaking with *Extremist* (U.K. no. 13) in 1992. Played with Deep Purple in '94.

ALWAYS WITH YOU, ALWAYS WITH ME.
Tracks: Always with you, always with me.
■ 7" . . . . YUM 112
Music For Nations / Jun '88.

BIG BAD MOON.
Tracks: Big bad moon / Day at the beach.
■ 7" . . . . YUM 118
Food For Thought / May '90.

DREAMING 11.
Tracks: Crush of love / Ice nine / Memories / Hordes of locusts.
■ LP . . . . YUMT 114
Food For Thought / Dec '88.
CD 473604 2
MC 473604 4
Relativity / May '93 / Sony.

EXTREMIST, THE.
Tracks: Friends / Extremist / War / Cryin' / Rubina's blue sky happiness / Summer song / Tears in the rain / Why / Motorcycle driver / New blues.
CD 4716722
■ LP 4716721
MC 4716724
Epic / Aug '92 / Sony.
MiniDisc. 471672-8
Relativity / Apr '93 / Sony.

FLYING IN A BLUE DREAM.
Tracks: Flying in a blue dream / Mystical potato head groove thing / Can't slow down / Headless / Strange / I believe / One big rush / Big bad moon / Feeling / Phone call / Day at the beach / Back to Shalla-bal / Ride / Forgotten, The (Part one) / Forgotten, The (Part two) / Bells of Lal, The (Part one) / Bells of Lal, The (Part two) / Into the light.
CD . . . . CDGRUB 14
■ LP . . . . GRUB 14
MC . . . . TGRUB 14
Food For Thought / Nov '89 / Pinnacle.
CD . . . . CDGRUB 14X
LP . . . . GRUB 14X
MC . . . . TGRUB 14X
Food For Thought / Feb '93 / Pinnacle.
CD 465995 2
MC 465995 4
Relativity / May '93 / Sony.

NOT OF THIS EARTH.
Tracks: Not of this Earth / Snake / Rubina / Memories / Brother John / Enigmatic / Driving at night / Hordes of locusts / New day / Headless horseman.
■ LP . . . . GRUB 7
Food For Thought / Feb '87.
CD . . . . CDGRUB 7
MC . . . . TGRUB 7
Food For Thought / Sep '88 / Pinnacle.
CD . . . . CDGRUB 7X
LP . . . . GRUB 7X
MC . . . . TGRUB 7X
Food For Thought / Feb '93 / Pinnacle.
CD 462972 2
MC 462972 4
Relativity / May '93 / Sony.

SATCH E.P., THE.
Tracks: Not Advised.
■ 12" 6589536
■ CD Single 6589532
Relativity / Feb '93.

SURFING WITH THE ALIEN.
Tracks: Surfing with the alien / Ice 9 / Crushing day / Always with you, always with me / Satch boogie / Hill of the skull / Circles / Lords of Karma / Midnight / Echo.
CD . . . . CDGRUB 8
Food For Thought / Oct '87 / Pinnacle.
■ LP . . . . GRUB 8
MC . . . . TGRUB 8
Food For Thought / '89 / Pinnacle.
CD . . . . CDGRUB 8X
LP . . . . GRUB 8X
MC . . . . TGRUB 8X
Food For Thought / Feb '93 / Pinnacle.
CD 462973 2
MC 462973 4
Relativity / May '93 / Sony.

TIME MACHINE.
Tracks: Time machine / Mighty turtle head / All alone / Banana mango (2) / Thinking of you / Crazy / Speed of light / Baroque / Dweller on the threshold / Banana mango / Dreaming / I am become death / Saying goodbye / Woodstock jam / Satch boogie / Summer song / Flying in a blue dream / Cryin' / Crush of love / Tears in the rain / Always with you, always with me / Big bad moon / Surfing with the alien / Rubina / Circles / Drum solo / Lords of karma / Echo.
CD 474515 2
LP 474515 1
MC 474515 4
Relativity / Oct '93 / Sony.

Savage

HYPERACTIVE.
Tracks: We got the edge / Eye for an eye / Hard on your heels / Blind hunger / Gonna tear ya heart out / Runnin' scared / Stevie's vengeance / Cardiac / All set to sing / Keep it on ice / She don't need you.
■ LP . . . . ZEB 4
MC . . . . CZEB 4
Zebra (1) / Jun '85 / Pinnacle.

LOOSE 'N' LETHAL.
Tracks: Not Advised.
■ LP . . . . EBON 12
Ebony (Pinnacle) / Nov '83.

ONLY YOU.
Tracks: Only you / Turn around.
■ 12" . . . . CART 350
■ 7" . . . . CAR 350
Carrere / Nov '84.

WE GOT THE EDGE.
Tracks: We got the edge / Running scared / She don't need you.
■ 12" . . . . 12 RA 4
Zebra (1) / Nov '84.

Savage Steel

BEGINS WITH A NIGHTMARE.
Tracks: Not Advised.
■ LP . . . . NRR 17
MC . . . . NRC 17
New Renaissance(USA) / Nov '87 / Pinnacle.

SAVAGE STEEL.
Tracks: Not Advised.
LP 084615
Maze / '90.

Savatage

DUNGEONS ARE CALLING, THE.
Tracks: Not Advised.
CD . . . . CDMFN 42
■ LP . . . . MFN 42
Music For Nations / Mar '85.

EDGE OF THORNS.
Tracks: Edge of thorns / He carves his stone / Lights out / Skraggy's tomb / Labyrinths / Follow me / Exit music / Degrees of sanity / Conversation piece / All that I bleed / Damien / Miles away / Sleep.
CD 756782488-2
MC 756782488-4
Atlantic / Mar '93 / WEA.

FIGHT FOR THE ROCK.
Tracks: Fight for the rock / Out on the streets / Crying for love / Day after day / Edge of midnight / Hyde / Lady in disguise / She's only rock 'n' roll / Wishing well / Red light paradise.

■ DELETED

■ LP 781 634-1
MC. 781 634-2
Atlantic / May '86 / WEA.

GUTTER BALLET.
Tracks: Of rage and war / Temptation revelation / Silk and steel / Hounds / Mentally yours / Gutter ballet / When the crowds are gone / She's in love / Unholy / Summer's rain.
CD . . . . K 782 008 2
■ LP . . . . K 782 008 1
MC. K 782 008 4
Atlantic / Jan '90 / WEA.

HALL OF THE MOUNTAIN KING.
Tracks: 24 hours ago / Beyond the doors of dark / Legion / Strange wings / Prelude to madness / Hall of the mountain king / Price you pay / White witch / Last down / Devastation.
MC. K 781 775 4
■ LP . . . . K 781 775 1
Atlantic / Sep '87.

HANDFUL OF RAIN.
Tracks: Not Advised.
CD . . . . CDVEST 32
Bulletproof / Aug '94 / Pinnacle.

POWER OF THE NIGHT.
Tracks: Power of the night / Unusual / Warriors / Necrophilia / Washed out / Hard for love / Fountain of youth / Skull session / Stuck on you / In the dream.
■ LP 781 247-1
Atlantic / Aug '85.

SIRENS.
Tracks: Sirens / Holocaust / I believe / Rage / On the run / Twisted little sister / Living for the night / Scream murder / Out on the streets.
CD . . . . CDMFN 48
■ LP . . . . MFN 48
Music For Nations / Sep '85.

STREETS.
Tracks: Streets / Jesus saves / Tonight he grins again / Strange reality / Little too far / You're alive / Sammy and Tex / Can you hear me now / New York City don't mean nothing / Ghost in the ruins / Agony and ecstacy / Heal my soul / Somewhere in time / Believe.
CD 7567823202
■ LP 7567823201
MC. 7567823204
WEA / Oct '91 / WEA.

STREETS: A ROCK OPERA.
Tracks: Not Advised.
CD 75678282012
■ LP 75678282011
MC. 75678282014
Atlantic / Nov '91 / WEA.

Saxon

Saxon formed in 1977 in Yorkshire; focal point was singer Biff Byford. Scored impressive 15 chart singles between 1980-'88, of which biggest were *And The Bands Played On* (no. 12 in 1981) and *747 (Strangers In The Night)* (no. 13 in 1980). Album achievements included three Top 10 hits, highest being *Wheels Of Steel* (no. 5 in 1980). However, Saxon failed to emulate U.S. success of fellow New Wave of British Heavy Metal pack-leaders - Iron Maiden and Def Leppard - and were reduced to club act in '90s, though they retain loyal European following. Original drummer Pete Gill joined Motorhead in 1983.

747 (STRANGERS IN THE NIGHT).
Tracks: 747 (strangers in the night).
■ 7" . . . . CAR 151
Carrere / Jun '80.

AND THE BANDS PLAYED ON.
Tracks: And the bands played on.
■ 7" . . . . CAR 180
Carrere / Apr '81.

AND THE BANDS PLAYED ON (OLD GOLD).
Tracks: And the bands played on / 747 (strangers in the night) / Never surrender.
■ CD Single . . . . OG 6181
Pickwick / Oct '92.

ANTHOLOGY.
Tracks: Stallions of the highway / Battle cry / Backs to the wall / Sixth form girls / Heavy metal thunder / Midnight rider / Out of control / Power and the glory / Warrior / Just let me rock / Rock city / Machine gun / Freeway mad / Wheels of steel / Midas touch / Suzie hold on / Still fit to boogie.

■ CD . . . . CCSCD 315
Castle / Jan '94.

ANTHOLOGY: SAXON.
Tracks: Rockin' again / Rock 'n' roll gypsy / Stallions of the highway / Battle cry / Party 'til you puke / Backs to the wall / Sixth form girls / Heavy metal thunder / Midnight rider / Out of control / Power and the glory / Warrior / Just let me rock / Rock city / Machine gun / Freeway mad / Wheels of steel / Midas touch / Suzie hold up / Still fit to boogie.
■ Double LP . . . . RAWLP 038
MC. . . . . RAWTC 038
■ CD . . . . RAWCD 038
Raw Power / Oct '88.

BACK ON THE STREETS.
Tracks: Power and the glory / Backs to the wall / Watching the sky / Midnight rider / Never surrender / Princess of the night / Motorcycle man / 747 (Strangers in the night) / Wheels of steel / Nightmare / Back on the streets / Rock 'n' roll gypsy / Broken heroes / Devil rides out / Party 'til you puke / Rock the nations / Waiting for the night / Ride like the wind / I can't wait anymore / We are the strong.
CD . . . . VSOPCD 147
■ Double LP . . . . VSOPLP 147
MC. . . . . VSOPMC 147
Connoisseur Collection / Jan '90 / Pinnacle.

BACK ON THE STREETS.
Tracks: Back on the streets / Live fast, die young.
■ 12" 12RA 6103
■ 12" 12R 6103
■ 7" . . . . R 6103
Parlophone / Jul '85.

BACKS TO THE WALL.
Tracks: Backs to the wall / Militia guard.
■ 7" . . . . CAR 129
Carrere / Jul '80.
■ 7" . . . . HM 6
Carrere / Jun '80.

BEST OF SAXON.
Tracks: Eagle has landed / Ride like the wind / Crusader / Rainbow theme/Frozen rainbow / Midas touch / Denim and leather / Broken heroes / Dallas 1 p.m. / 747 (strangers in the night) (live) / Princess of the night (live) / And the band played on (CD only.) / Never surrender (CD only.) / This town rocks (CD only.) / Strong arm of the law (live) (CD only.) / Heavy metal thunder (live) (CD only.).
CD . . . . CDEMS 1390
■ LP . . . . EMS 1390
■ MC. . . . . TCEMS 1390
EMI / Mar '91.

BIG TEASER.
Tracks: Big teaser.
■ LP . . . . CAL 200
MC. CAC 200
Carrere / Mar '85 / WEA.
■ LP . . . . ATAK 59
MC. . . . . TCATAK 59
Parlophone / Jan '86 / EMI.

BIG TEASER.
Tracks: Big teaser / Rainbow theme.
■ 7" . . . . HM 5
Carrere / Jun '80.

CRUSADER.
Tracks: Crusader prelude / Crusader / Little bit of what you fancy / Sailing to America / Set me free / Just let me rock / Bad boys (like to rock 'n' roll) / Do it all for you / Rock city / Run for your lives.
■ LP . . . . EMS 1168
■ MC. . . . . TCEMS 1168
EMI / May '86.
CD 817 849 2
Carrere / '88 / WEA.

DENIM AND LEATHER.
Tracks: Princess of the night / Never surrender / Out of control / Rough and ready / Play it loud / And the bands played on / Midnight rider / Fire in the sky / Denim and leather.
■ LP . . . . CAL 128
Carrere / Oct '81.
■ LP . . . . EMS 1163
EMI / Mar '86.
■ LP . . . . FA 3175
■ MC. . . . . TCFA 3175
Fame / May '87.
■ CD . . . . CDFA 3175
Fame / Oct '87.

DESTINY.
Tracks: Ride like the wind / Where the lightning strikes / I can't wait anymore / Calm before the storm / S.O.S. / Song for Emma / For whom the bell tolls / We are strong / Jericho siren / Red alert.
■ LP . . . . EMC 3543

■ CD . . . . CDEMC 3543
■ MC. . . . . TCEMC 3543
EMI / Mar '88.

DO IT ALL FOR YOU.
Tracks: Do it all for you / Just let me rock.
■ 12" . . . . CART 323
■ 7" . . . . CAR 323
Carrere / May '84.

EAGLE HAS LANDED, THE.
Tracks: 747 (Strangers in the night) / Princess of the night / Strong arm of the law / Heavy metal thunder / 20,000 ft / Wheels of steel / Never surrender / Fire in the sky / Machine gun / Rock the nations / Motorcycle man.
■ LP . . . . CAL 137
Carrere / Sep '82.
■ LP . . . . ATAK 74
MC. . . . . TCATAK 74
■ LP . . . . EMS 1166
■ MC. . . . . TCEMS 1166
EMI / May '86.
CD . . . . CZ 210
EMI / Jul '89 / EMI.

FLIPHITS (4 TRACK CASSETTE EP).
Tracks: 47 (Strangers in the night) / And the bands played on / Never surrender / Princess of the night.
MC. RCXK 013
Carrere / Jul '83 / WEA.

FOREVER FREE.
Tracks: Not Advised.
CD . . . . WARCD 10
LP . . . . WARLP 10
MC. . . . . WARMC 10
Warhammer / May '93 / Grapevine Distribution.

GREATEST HITS LIVE: SAXON.
Tracks: Opening theme / Heavy metal thunder / Rock & roll gypsy / And the bands played on / Twenty thousand feet / Ride like the wind / Motor cycle man / 747 (Strangers in the night) / See the light shinin' / Frozen rainbow / Princess of the night / Wheels of steel / Denim & leather / Crusader / Rockin' again / Back on the streets again.
CD . . . . ESSCD 132
MC Set . . . . ESDMC 132
■ Double LP . . . . ESDLP 132
Essential / Sep '90.

GREATEST HITS LIVE: SAXON.
Tracks: Opening theme / Heavy metal thunder / Rock 'n' roll gypsy / And the bands played on / Twenty thousand feet / Ride like the wind / Motor cycle man / 747 (strangers in the night) / See the light shinin' / Frozen rainbow / Strong arm of the law / Princess of the night / Wheels of steel / Denim & leather / Crusader / Rockin' again / Back on the streets again.
■ VHS . . . . CMP 7009
Castle Music Pictures / Sep '90.

I CAN'T WAIT ANYMORE.
Tracks: I can't wait anymore / Broken heroes / Gonna shout.
■ 12" 12EM 54
■ 7" . . . . EMS 54
■ 7" . . . . EM 54
EMI / Apr '88.

INNOCENCE IS NO EXCUSE.
Tracks: Rockin' again / Call of the wild / Back on the streets / Devil rides out / Rock 'n' roll gypsy / Broken heroes / Gonna shout / Everybody up / Raise some hell / Give it everything you've got.
■ LP . . . . SAXON 2
■ LP P.Disc . . . . SAXONP 2
MC. . . . . TCSAXON 2
Parlophone / Sep '85 / EMI.

LIVE INNOCENCE.
Tracks: Not Advised.
■ VHS . . . . MVP 99 1098 2
PMI / Jan '86.
VHS . . . . MC 2024
Music Club Video / Jun '89 / Video Collection / Gold & Sons / TBD.

MUSIC AND MEDIA INTERVIEW PICTURE DISC.
Tracks: Not Advised
■ LP P.Disc . . . . MM 1243
Music & Media / Feb '88.

NEVER SURRENDER.
Tracks: Never surrender / 20,000 ft.
■ 7" . . . . CAR 204
Carrere / Jul '81.

NIGHTMARE.
Tracks: Nightmare / Midas touch.
■ 12" . . . . CART 284
■ 7" . . . . CAR 284

■ 7" P.Disc . . . . CARP 284
Carrere / Jul '83.

NORTHERN LADY.
Tracks: Everybody up (live in Madrid) / Dallas 1pm (live in Madrid) (12" only.).
■ 12". 12EMI 5593
■ 7" . . . . EMI 5593
EMI / Jan '87.

POWER AND THE GLORY.
Tracks: Power and the glory / Redline / Warrior / Nightmare / This town rocks / Watching the sky / Midas touch / Eagle has landed.
■ LP . . . . CAL 147
MC. . . . . .CAC 147
Carrere / Mar '83 / WEA.
■ LP . . . . ATAK 75
MC. . . . . TCATAK 75
■ LP . . . . EMS 1167
■ MC . . . . TCEMS 1167
EMI / May '86.
CD 811 529-2
Polydor / '88 / PolyGram.
■ CD . . . . CZ 209
EMI / Jul '89.

POWER AND THE GLORY.
Tracks: Power and the glory / See the light shining.
■ 12". SAXONT 1
■ 7". . . . . SAXON 1
■ 7" P.Disc . . . . SAXON P 1
Carrere / Apr '83.

POWER AND THE GLORY (The Video Anthology).
Tracks: Nightmare / Suzy hold on / Just let me rock / Rockin' again / Back on the streets / Power and the glory / Broken heroes / Everybody up / Northern lady / Rock the nations / Waiting for the night / Rock 'n' roll gypsy / Ride like the wind / I can't wait anymore.
■ VHS . . . . MVP 99 1178 3
PMI / Feb '89.

PRINCESS OF THE NIGHT.
Tracks: Princess of the night / Fire in the sky.
■ 7" . . . . .CAR 208
Carrere / Oct '81.

RIDE LIKE THE WIND.
Tracks: Ride like the wind / Red alert / Rock the nations (Live at Hammersmith.) / Back on the streets (live).
■ 12". 12EM 43
■ 7" . . . . EM 43
■ 7" P.Disc . . . . EMP 43
■ CD Single . . . . CDEM 43
EMI / Feb '88.

ROCK 'N' ROLL GYPSIES.
Tracks: Power and the glory / And the bands played on / Rock the nations / Dallas, 1 p.m. / Broken heroes / Battle cry / Rock'n'roll gypsies / Northern lady / I can't wait anymore / This town rocks / Eagle has landed (Only on CD.) / Just let me rock (Only on CD.).
CD . . . . CDENV 535
■ LP . . . . ENVLP 535
■ MC . . . . TCENV 535
Enigma (EMI) / Aug '89.
■ LP . . . . RR 94161
MC. . . . . RR 94164
■ CD . . . . RR 94162
Road Runner / Dec '89.

ROCK 'N' ROLL GYPSY.
Tracks: Rock 'n' roll gypsy / Krakatoa / Medley, The: Heavy metal thunder (Available on 12" version only) / Stand up and be counted (Available on 12" version only) / Taking your chances (Available on 12" version only) / Warrior (Available on 12" version only).
■ 12". 12R 6112
■ 7" . . . . .R 6112
■ 7" P.Disc . . . . RP 6112
Parlophone / '86.

ROCK THE NATIONS.
Tracks: Rock the nations / Battle cry / Waiting for the night / We came here to rock / You ain't no angel / Running hot / Party 'til you puke / Empty promises / Motorcycle man / Northern lady.
■ LP . . . . EMC 3515
■ MC . . . . TCEMC 3515
CD . . . . CZ 38
EMI / Feb '88 / EMI.

ROCK THE NATIONS.
Tracks: Rock the nations.
■ 12". 12EMI 5587
■ 12" P.Disc 12EMIP 5587
■ 7" . . . . EMI 5587
■ 7" P.Disc . . . . EMIP 5587
EMI / '86.

SAILING TO AMERICA.
Tracks: Sailing to America / Little bit of what you fancy.
■ 12". CART 6301
■ 7" . . . . .CAR 301
Carrere / Jan '84.

SAXON.
Tracks: Rainbow theme / Frozen rainbow / Big teaser / Judgement day / Stallions of the highway / Backs to the wall / Still fit to boogie / Millie Guard.
■ LP . . . . .CAL 110
Carrere / '77.
■ LP . . . . EMS 1161
■ MC . . . . TCEMS 1161
Capitol / Jan '86.

SAXON LIVE.
Tracks: Not Advised.
VHS . . . . SPC 00042
Spectrum (1) / Oct '89 / PolyGram.

SOLID BALL OF ROCK, A.
Tracks: Solid ball of rock / Altar of the gods / Requiem (we will remember) / Lights in the sky / I just can't get enough / Baptism of fire / Ain't gonna take it / I'm on fire / Overture in B / Minor refugee / Bavarian beaver / Crash dive.
■ LP . . . . LPVIR 4
■ CD . . . . CDVIR 4
■ MC . . . . MCVIR 4
Virgin / Jan '91.

STRONG ARM METAL.
Tracks: Not Advised.
■ LP . . . . .CAL 212
■ MC .CAC 212
Carrere / Dec '84 / WEA.
■ LP . . . . ATAK 58
MC. . . . . TCTAK 58
Parlophone / Jan '86 / EMI.
CD 823 680-2
Carrere / '88 / WEA.

STRONG ARM OF THE LAW.
Tracks: Heavy metal thunder / To hell and back again / Strong arm of the law / Taking your chances / 20,000 Ft. / Hungry years / Sixth form girls / Dallas 1 p.m.
■ LP . . . . .CAL 120
Carrere / Nov '80.
■ LP . . . . EMS 1162
EMI / Mar '86.
■ LP . . . . FA 3176
■ MC . . . . TCFA 3176
Fame / May '87.

STRONG ARM OF THE LAW.
Tracks: Strong arm of the law / Taking your chances.
■ 12". CAR 170
■ 7" . . . . .CAR 170
Carrere / Nov '80.

SUZY HOLD ON.
Tracks: Suzy hold on.
■ 12". CAR 165T
■ 7" . . . . .CAR 165
Carrere / Sep '80.

WAITING FOR THE NIGHT.
Tracks: Waiting for the train (extended version) / Chase the fade.
■ 12". 12EMI 5575
■ 7" . . . . EMI 5575
EMI / '86.

WE WILL REMEMBER.
Tracks: We will remember / Alter of the gods.
■ 12". DINST 105
■ 7" . . . . DINS 105
■ 7" P.Disc . . . . DINSY 105
■ CD Single . . . . DINSD 105
Virgin / Jun '91.

WHEELS OF STEEL.
Tracks: Motorcycle man / Stand up and be counted / 747 (strangers in the night) / Freeway mad / See the light shining / Fighting gang / Suzi hold on / Machine gun / Wheels of steel.
■ LP . . . . .CAL 115
Carrere / Apr '80.
■ LP . . . . FA 41 3143 1
MC. . . . . FA 41 3143 4
Fame / '85 / EMI.

WHEELS OF STEEL.
Tracks: Wheels of steel / Stand up and be counted (On CAR 143 only) / 747 (On SPC 8 only).
■ 7" . . . . .CAR 143
Carrere / Mar '80.
■ 7" . . . . SPC 8
WEA / Apr '81.

Scanner

HYPERTRACE.
Tracks: Not Advised.
■ CD . . . . CDNUK 111
■ LP . . . . .NUK 111
■ MC. ZCNUK 111
Noise / Oct '80.

TERMINAL EARTH.
Tracks: Law / Not alone / Wonder / Buy or die / Touch the light / Terminal earth / From the dust of ages / Challenge.
■ CD . . . . CDNUK 141
■ LP . . . . .NUK 141
■ MC. ZCNUK 141
Noise / Feb '90.

Scarab

ROCK NIGHT.
Tracks: Rock night / Wicked woman.
■ 7" . . . . HEADBANGER 1
Inferno (1) / Aug '80.

Scat Opera

ABOUT TIME.
Tracks: Not Advised.
CD . . . . CDMFN 111
LP . . . . MFN 111
MC. . . . . TMFN 111
Music For Nations / Feb '91 / Pinnacle.

FOUR GONE CONFUSION.
Tracks: Not Advised.
CD . . . . CDMFN 140
LP . . . . MFN 140
MC. . . . . TMFN 140
Music For Nations / Oct '92 / Pinnacle.

Scatterbrain

MINDUS INTELLECTUALIS.
Tracks: Write that hit / Beer muscles / Everybody does it / Funny thing / How could I love you / Dead man blues / Down with the ship.
CD . . . . CDMVEST 33
Bulletproof / Jul '94 / Pinnacle.

MOUNTAINS GO RHYTHMIC.
Tracks: Not Advised.
■ LP . . . . .IRMG 11
Irmgardz / Jul '85.

SCAMBOOGERY.
Tracks: Big fun / Fine line / Tastes just like chicken / Grandma's house of babes / Sonata [8]X11 (rondo alla turca) / Bartender / Scamboogery / Swiss army girl / Logic / Down the road (rock 'n' roll ain't pretty).
CD 7559612242
■ LP 7559612241
MC. 7559612244
WEA / Nov '91 / WEA.

Schenker, Michael

Notoriously unreliable '70s guitar hero who debuted in Scorpions and played major role in UFO's success. Jammed with Joe Perry-less Aerosmith in late '79, but then formed Michael Schenker Group. Success in early '80s peaked with live album One Night At Budokan (U.K. no. 5, 1982) and ground to halt after endless line-up changes. Group resurfaced as MSG (M now standing for singer McAuley, Robin) in '87, but scaled-down fortunes (including mildly-acclaimed acoustic tour of U.S.) also dwindled away and Schenker was last heard sniffing around UFO reunion.

ANYTIME (Schenker, Michael Group).
Tracks: What we need / Anytime (LP version) (12" & CD single only.).
■ 12". 12EM 127
■ 12" P.Disc. 12EMPD 127
■ 7" . . . . EM 127
■ CD Single . . . . CDEM 127
■ MC Single. . . . . TCEM 127
EMI / Jan '90.

ARMED AND READY (Schenker, Michael Group).
Tracks: Armed and ready / Bijou pleasurette.
■ 7" . . . . CHS 2455
Chrysalis / Aug '80.

■ DELETED

ASSAULT ATTACK (Schenker, Michael Group).
Tracks: Assault attack / Rock you to the ground / Dancer / Samurai / Desert song / Broken promises / Searching for a reason / Ulcer.
■ LP . . . . CHR 1393
MC. . . . . ZCHR 1393
Chrysalis / Nov '82 / EMI.

BBC LIVE IN CONCERT (Schenker, Michael Group).
Tracks: Armed and ready / Cry for the nations / Mad axeman / But I want more / Heavy blues / Instrumental guitar / Let sleeping dogs lie / Lost horizons / Doctor doctor.
CD . . . . WINCD 043
Windsong / Sep '93 / Pinnacle / A.D.A. Distribution.

BEST OF MICHAEL SCHENKER GROUP, THE (Schenker, Michael Group).
Tracks: Armed and ready / Cry for the nations / Victim of illusion / Into the arena (Overture) / Are you ready to rock / Attack of the mad axeman / On and on / Assault attack / Dancer / Searching for a reason / Desert song / Rock my nights away / Captain Nemo / Let sleeping dogs lie / Bijou pleasurette / Lost horizons.
CD . . . . MCCD 160
MC. . . . . .MCTC 160
Music Club / May '94 / Gold & Sons / TBD / Video Collection / C.M. Distribution.

BUILT TO DESTROY (Schenker, Michael Group).
Tracks: Rock my nights away / I'm gonna make you mine / Dogs of war / Systems failing / Captain Nemo / Still love that little devil / Red sky / Time waits for no one / Walk the stage.
MC. . . . . ZCHR 1441
■ LP P.Disc . . . . CHRP 1441
Chrysalis / '83.
■ LP . . . . CHR 1441
Chrysalis / '86.

COLLECTION: M.S.G. (Schenker, Michael Group).
Tracks: Armed and ready / Lost horizons / Buou pleasurette / Ready to rock / Let sleeping dogs lie / But I want more / Into the arena / Never trust a stranger / Dancer / Desert songs / Broken promises / Rock my nights away / Captain Nemo / Walk the stage.
CD . . . . CCSCD 294
MC. . . . . CCSMC 294
Castle / Jul '91 / BMG.

CRY FROM THE NATIONS (Schenker, Michael Group).
Tracks: Cry from the nations / Armed and ready (live) / Into the arena (live).
■ 7" . . . . CHS 2471
■ 12" . . . . .CHS 122471
Chrysalis / Nov '80.

DANCER (Schenker, Michael Group).
Tracks: Dancer / Girl from uptown.
■ 12" . . . . .CHS 122636
■ 7" . . . . CHS 2636
Chrysalis / Aug '82.

ESSENTIAL MICHAEL SCHENKER GROUP (Schenker, Michael Group).
Tracks: Armed and ready / Cry for the nations / Bijou pleasurette / Into the arena / Attack of the mad axeman / On and on / Never trust a stranger / Assault attack / Rock you to the ground / Captain Nemo / Rock will never die / Still love that little devil / Don't take it out on me.
■ MC . . . . TCCHR 1949
■ CD . . . . CDCHR 1949
Chrysalis / Oct '92.

GIMME YOUR LOVE (Schenker, Michael Group).
Tracks: Gimme your love / Rock 'till you're crazy.
■ 12" 12EM 30
■ 12" P.Disc 12EMP 30
■ 7" . . . . EM 30
EMI / Oct '87.

LOVE IS NOT A GAME (Schenker, Michael Group).
Tracks: Love is not a game / Get out.
■ 12" 12EM 40
■ 12" Remix 12EMS 40
■ 7" . . . . EM 40
EMI / Jan '88.

MICHAEL SCHENKER GROUP (Schenker, Michael Group).
Tracks: Armed and ready / Cry from the nations / Victim of illusion / Bijou pleasurette / Feels like a

good thing / Into the arena / Looking out from nowhere / Tales of mystery / Lost horizons.
■ LP . . . . CHR 1302
■ MC. . . . . ZCHR 1302
Chrysalis / Oct '80.
■ LP 41 3105 1
MC. 41 3105 4
Fame / Jun '84 / EMI.

MSG (Schenker, Michael Group).
Tracks: Eve / Paradise / When I'm gone / This broken heart / We believe in love / Crazy / Invincible / What happens to me / Lonely nights / This night is gonna last forever / Nightmare.
■ LP . . . . EUSLP 3
■ CD . . . . CDP 798 487 2
■ MC. . . . . EUSMC 3
EMI-Electrola (Germany) / Feb '92.

ONE NIGHT AT BUDOKAN (Schenker, Michael Group).
Tracks: Armed and ready / Cry from the nations / Attack of the mad axeman / Axeman / But I want more / Victim of illusion / Into the arena / On and on / Never trust a stranger / Let sleeping dogs lie / Courvoisier concerto / Lost horizons / Doctor doctor / Are you ready to rock.
■ Double LP . . . . CTY 1375
■ MC Set . . . . ZCTY 1375
Chrysalis / Mar '82.
■ CD Set. . . . . CCD 1375
Chrysalis / Sep '91.

PERFECT TIMING (Schenker, Michael Group).
Tracks: Gimme your love / Here today / Don't stop me now / No time for losers / Follow the night / Get out / Love is not a game / Time / I don't wanna lose / Rock 'till you're crazy.
■ CD . . . . CDEMC 3539
■ LP . . . . EMC 3539
■ MC. . . . . TCEMC 3539
EMI / Oct '87.

PORTFOLIO (Schenker, Michael Group).
Tracks: Doctor doctor / Rock bottom / Rock will never die / Armed and ready / Ready to rock / Assault attack / Ulcer / Attack of the mad axeman / I'm a loser / Reasons to love / Too hot to handle / Only you can rock me / Lights out / Arbory hill / Love drive / Searching for a reason / Rock my nights away / Captain Nemo.
■ CD . . . . MPCD 1598
■ LP . . . . CNW 1
■ MC. . . . . ZCNW 1
Chrysalis / Jul '87.

READY TO ROCK (Schenker, Michael Group).
Tracks: Ready to rock / Attack of the mad axeman.
■ 7" . . . . CHS 2541
Chrysalis / Sep '81.

ROCK WILL NEVER DIE.
Tracks: Captain Nemo / Rock my nights away / Are you ready to rock / Attack of the mad axeman / Into the arena / Courvoisier concerto / Dream on (rock will never die) / Desert song / I'm gonna make you mine / Armed and ready / Doctor doctor.
■ VHS . . . . HEN 2013
Hendring Video / Oct '84.
VHS . . . . CVHS 5028
Chrysalis Music Video / '88 / EMI.

ROCK WILL NEVER DIE (Schenker, Michael Group).
Tracks: Captain Nemo / Rock my nights away / Are you ready to rock / Attack of the mad axeman / Into the arena / Rock will never die / Desert song / I'm gonna make you mine / Doctor doctor.
■ MC . . . . ZCUX 1470
Chrysalis / Apr '84.
■ LP . . . . CUX 1470
Chrysalis / Jun '84.

SAVE YOURSELF (Schenker, Michael Group).
Tracks: Save yourself / Bad boys / Anytime / Get down to bizness / Shadow of the night / What we need / I am your radio / There has to be another way (instrumental) / This is my heart / Destiny / Take me back (Not on album.).
CD . . . . CDEMC 3567
■ LP . . . . EMC 3567
■ MC. . . . . TCEMC 3567
EMI / Oct '89.

STORY OF MICHAEL SCHENKER, THE.
Tracks: Doctor doctor / Natural thing / Lights out / Coast to coast / Love drive / Armed and ready / Into the arena / Ready to rock / Desert song / Gimme

your love / Time / Anytime / Save yourself / Nightmare / When I'm gone (acoustic version) / Only you can rock me (unplugged).
CD . . . . CDCHR 6071
Chrysalis / Apr '94 / EMI.

SOUNDS OF COMING.
Tracks: Not Advised.
CD . . . . AVRCD 008
Nosferatu / Jun '94 / Plastic Head.

SLASH & BURN.
Tracks: Not Advised.
CD .CDDVN 23
■ LP . . . . DVN 23
Devotion / Sep '93.

SUBURBAN MINDS.
Tracks: Not Advised.
CD . . . . HY 391009CD
Hyperion / Nov '92 / Select Distribution.

WE ARE THE PEOPLE.
Tracks: Not Advised.
■ LP . . . . RR 95021
Road Runner / Dec '88.

COLOSSUS.
Tracks: Endless / Crimson seed / Blackout / Sky is loaded / Nothing hunger / Beyond / Little angel / White irises blind / Scorpionic / Night ash black / Sunstroke.
CD . . . . MOSH 091CD
LP . . . . MOSH 091
MC. . . . . MOSH 091MC
Earache / Jun '93 / Vital Distribution.

DELIVERANCE.
Tracks: Deliverance.
■ 12" . . . . MOSH 078 T
■ CD Single . . . . MOSH 078 CD
Earache / Oct '92.

EVANESCENCE.
Tracks: Silver rain fell / Light trap / Falling / Automata / Days passed / Dreamspace / Exodus / Night tide / End / Slumber.
CD . . . . MOSH 113CD
LP Set . . . . MOSH 113
Earache / Jun '94 / Vital Distribution.

LICK FOREVER DOG.
Tracks: Lick forever dog.
■ 12" . . . . MOSH 061T
■ CD Single . . . . MOSH 061CD
Earache / Mar '92.

SILVER RAIN FELL.
Tracks: Silver rain fell (Album version) / Silver rain fell (Meat beat manifesto remix).
12" . . . . MOSH 122T
Earache / Aug '94 / Vital Distribution.

VAE SOLIS.
Tracks: Not Advised.
CD . . . . MOSH 054CD
Double LP . . . . MOSH 054
MC. . . . . .MOSH 054MC
Earache / Apr '92 / Vital Distribution.

WHITE IRISES BLIND.
Tracks: White irises blind / White irises blind (mix) / Black ash dub / Drained / Host of scorpion.
■ 10" . . . . MOSH 093T
■ CD Single . . . . MOSH 093CD
Earache / Apr '93.

Original, 1971 line-up of Germany's most successful metal band included Schenker brothers Rudy and Michael. Latter left for UFO and was replaced by Hendrix-fixated Uli Jon Roth. Fronted by Klaus Meine, Scorpions were especially popular in Japan, hence live *Tokyo Tapes*. Signed to EMI in 1979, subsequent *Lovedrive* (featuring new guitarist Matthias Jabs and brief return of Michael Schenker) was first charting album in U.K.; major U.S. success followed. Band were natural choice for Roger Waters' star-studded 1990 performance of *The Wall* in

Berlin. Biggest success achieved by international 1991 hit single *Wind Of Change* (U.K. no. 2).

ACTION.
Tracks: I'm goin' mad / It all depends / Leave me / In search of the peace mind / Inheritance / Action / Lonesome crow.
■ **LP** 0040 150
Brain (Germany) / May '80.

ALL NIGHT LONG.
Tracks: All night long / Flying to the rainbow / Speedy's coming / In trance.
■ **12"** . . . . PC 9402
RCA / Nov '79.

ANIMAL MAGNETISM.
Tracks: Make it real / Don't make no promises (your body can't keep) / Hold me tight / 20th century man / Lady starlight / Falling in love / Only a man / Zoo / Animal magnetism.
■ **LP** . . . . SHSP 4113
Harvest / Mar '80.
■ **LP** . . . . ATAK 48
■ **MC** . . . . TCATAK 48
Harvest / May '80.
■ **MC** . . . . TCSHSP 4113
Harvest / Aug '85.
CD . . . . CDFA 3217
■ **LP** . . . . FA 3217
MC . . . . TCFA 3217
Fame / May '89 / EMI.

BELIEVE IN LOVE.
Tracks: Believe in love / Love on the run / Believe in love (LP version) (On 12" only.).
■ **12"** . . . . 12 HAR 5241
■ **7"** . . . . HAR 5241
Harvest / Aug '88.

BEST OF ROCKERS 'N' BALLADS.
Tracks: Rock you like a hurricane / Can't explain / Rhythm of love / Big city nights / Lovedrive / Is there anybody there / Holiday / Still loving you / No one like you / Blackout / Another piece of meat / You give me all I need / Hey you / Zoo / China white.
CD . . . . CDFA 3262
MC . . . . TCFA 3262
Fame / Oct '91 / EMI.

BEST OF THE SCORPIONS.
Tracks: Steam rock fever / Pictured life / Robot man / Back stage queen / Speedy's coming / Hellcat / He's a woman she's a man / In trance / Dark lady / Sails of Charon / Virgin killer.
■ **LP** . . . . RCALP 3035
■ **MC** . . . . RCAK 3035
■ **CD** . . . . PD 70082
RCA / Sep '81.
CD . . . . ND 74006
■ **LP** . . . . NL 74006
■ **MC** . . . . NK 74006
RCA / Feb '89.

BEST OF THE SCORPIONS VOL.2.
Tracks: Top of the bill / They need a million / Longing for fire / Catch your train / Speedy's coming (live) / Crying days / All night long (live) / This is my song / Sun in my hand / Well burn the sky (live).
CD . . . . ND 74517
■ **LP** . . . . NL 74517
■ **MC** . . . . NK 74517
RCA / Feb '90.

BIG CITY NIGHTS.
Tracks: Big city nights / Bad boys running wild.
■ **12"** . . . . 12 HAR 5231
■ **12" P.Disc.** . . . . 12 HARP 5231
■ **7"** . . . . HAR 5231
Harvest / Oct '84.

BLACKOUT.
Tracks: Blackout / Can't live without you / You give me all I need / Now / Dynamite / Arizona / China white / When the smoke is going down.
■ **LP** . . . . SHVL 823
Harvest / Apr '82.
■ **LP** . . . . FA 3126
MC . . . . TCFA 3126
Fame / May '85 / EMI.
CD 814 981 2
Mercury / '88 / PolyGram.
CD . . . . CDFA 3126
Fame / Nov '88 / EMI.

CAN'T LIVE WITHOUT YOU.
Tracks: Can't live without you / Always somewhere.
■ **7"** . . . . HAR 5221
Harvest / Jul '82.

CRAZY WORLD.
Tracks: Tease me please me / To be with you in heaven / Restless night / Kicks after six / Money and

fame / Don't believe her / Wind of change / Lust or love / Hit between the eyes / Send me an angel.
CD 846908 2
MC 846908 4
■ **LP** 846908 1
Vertigo / Nov '90.
DCC 846 908-5
Mercury / Jan '93 / PolyGram.

CRAZY WORLD TOUR (Berlin 1991).
Tracks: Lust or love / Hit between the eyes / Crazy world / Zoo / Big city nights / Rock you like a hurricane / Wind of change / Tease me please me / Don't believe her / Send me an angel.
VHS 0836203
Polygram Music Video / '91 / PolyGram.

DON'T BELIEVE HER.
Tracks: Don't believe her / Kicks after six / Big city holiday (live).
■ **MC Single.** . . . . VERMC 52
■ **12"** .VERXG 52
■ **12"** . . . . .VERX 52
■ **7"** . . . . VER 52
■ **CD Single** . . . . .VERCD 52
Vertigo / Dec '90.

FACE THE HEAT.
Tracks: Alien nation / No pain no gain / Someone to touch / Under the same sun / Taxman woman / Unholy alliance / Woman / Hate to be nice / Ship of fools / Nightmare avenue.
CD 5182802
MC 5182804
■ **LP** 5182801
Mercury / Sep '93.

FIRST STING VIDEO EP.
Tracks: Not Advised.
■ **VHS** . . . . MVS 99 0037 2
PMI / Apr '85.
VHS . . . . .MC 2063
Music Club Video / Mar '91 / Video Collection / Gold & Sons / TBD.

FLY TO THE RAINBOW.
Tracks: Speedy's coming / They need a million / Drifting sun / Fly, people fly / This is my song / Fly away / Fly to the rainbow.
■ **LP** . . . . RS 1023
RCA / '79.
■ **LP** . . . . NL 70084
■ **MC** . . . . NK 70084
RCA / Oct '85.
■ **CD** . . . . ND 70084
RCA / Apr '88.

GOLD BALLADS.
Tracks: Still loving you / Holiday / Always somewhere / When the smoke is going down / Lady starlight.

GOLD ROCK.
Tracks: Not Advised.
■ **LP** 0040 016
Brain (Germany) / Nov '77.

HOT & HARD.
Tracks: Top of the bill / Drifting sun / Sun in my hand / Longing for fire / Catch your train / Virgin killer / Hell cat / Polar nights / I've got to be free / Riot of your times / He's a woman, she's a man / Steam rock fever / Suspender love (Live) / Hound dog (Live) / Long tall Sally (Live) / Fly to the rainbow.
CD 74321 15119-2
RCA / Sep '93 / BMG.

HOT AND HEAVY.
Tracks: He's a woman - she's a man / Speedy's coming / Catch your train / Dark lady / Far away / Steamrock fever / Riot of our time / Robot man / Polar nights / I've got to be free.
■ **CD** . . . . ND 70672
RCA / Feb '90.

HOT AND SLOW (Best Of The Ballads).
Tracks: In trance / Life's like a river / Yellow raven / Born to touch your feeling / In search for the peace of mind (live) / Far away / In your park / Crying days / Fly people fly / We'll burn the sky (live) / Living and dying / Kojo notsuki (live).
CD . . . . ND 75029
MC . . . . NK 75029
RCA / Dec '91 / BMG.

HURRICANE ROCK.
Tracks: Fly to the rainbow / Speedy's coming / In trance / Robot man / Polar nights / We'll burn the sky / Steamrock fever / He's a woman, she's a man / Another piece of meat / Coast to coast / Love drive / Zoo / Blackout / Can't live without you / When the smoke is going down / Dynamite / Rock you like a hurricane / Still loving you / Coming home / Rhythm of love.

CD . . . . VSOPCD 156
■ **LP** . . . . VSOPLP 156
■ **MC** . . . . VSOPMC 156
Connoisseur Collection / Dec '90 / Pinnacle.

IN TRANCE.
Tracks: Dark lady / In trance / Life's like a river / Top of the bill / Living and dying / Robot man / Evening wind / Sun in my hand / Longing for fire / Night lights.
■ **LP** . . . . .RS 1039
RCA / '79.
■ **LP** . . . . .INTS 5251
RCA / Aug '83.
MC . . . . NK 70028
■ **LP** . . . . NL 70028
RCA / '84.
■ **CD** . . . . ND 70028
RCA / Feb '90.

INTERVIEW, THE.
Tracks: Not Advised.
CD P.Disc. . . . . CBAK 4066
Baktabak / Feb '94 / Arabesque Ltd.

IS THERE ANYBODY THERE.
Tracks: Is there anybody there / Another piece of meat.
■ **12"** .12HAR 5185
■ **7"** . . . . HAR 5185
Harvest / May '79.

LONESOME CROW.
Tracks: I'm going mad / It all depends / Leave me / In search of peace of the peace of mind / Inheritance / Action / Lonesome.
■ **LP P.Disc** . . . . HMIPD 2
Heavy Metal / Nov '82.
■ **LP** . . . . .HMILP 2
Heavy Metal / '83.
MC . . . . HMIMC 2
Heavy Metal / Jul '85 / Sony / FM Revolver.
CD 825 739-2
Braun / '88.
CD . . . . METALMCD 124
LP . . . . METALPS 114
MC . . . . METALK 121
Razor / Jul '91 / Grapevine Distribution.
■ **LP** . . . . HM1 LP 2
FM Records / Oct '92.

LOVE AT FIRST STING.
Tracks: Bad boys running wild / Rock you like a hurricane / I'm leaving you / Coming home / Same thrill / Big city nights / As soon as the good times roll / Crossfire / Still loving you.
CD . . . . CDP 746 025 2
■ **LP** . . . . ATAK 69
MC . . . . TCATAK 69
Harvest / Feb '84 / EMI.
■ **LP** . . . . SHSP 2400071
Harvest (Germany) / Nov '87.
CD . . . . CDFA 3224
■ **LP** . . . . FA 3224
■ **MC** . . . . TCFA 3224
Fame / Aug '89.

LOVEDRIVE.
Tracks: Loving you Sunday morning / Another piece of meat / Always somewhere / Coast to coast / Can't get enough / Is there anybody there / Lovedrive / Holiday.
■ **LP** . . . . FA 3080
■ **LP** . . . . FA 4130801
Fame / Sep '83.
■ **LP** . . . . SHSP 4097
■ **MC** . . . . TCSHSP 4097
Harvest / Sep '83.
CD . . . . CDFA 3080
Fame / Nov '88 / EMI.

LOVEDRIVE.
Tracks: Lovedrive.
■ **7"** . . . . HAR 5188
Harvest / Aug '79.

MAKE IT REAL.
Tracks: Make it real / Don't make no promises.
■ **7"** . . . . HAR 5206
Harvest / May '80.

NO ONE LIKE YOU.
Tracks: No one like you / Zoo.
■ **7"** . . . . HAR 5219
Harvest / Apr '82.
■ **7"** . . . . HAR 5237
Harvest / Jun '85.

PASSION RULES THE GAME.
Tracks: Passion rules the game / Every minute everyday / Is there anybody there (CD single & 12" only).
■ **7"** . . . . HARS 5242
■ **12" P.Disc.** . . . . HARP 5242

■ DELETED

Harvest / Feb '89.
- ■ 12″ . . . . 12 HAR 5242
- ■ CD Single . . . . CDHAR 5242

Harvest / Jan '89.
- ■ 7″ . . . . HAR 5242

Harvest / Feb '89.
- ■ 12″ . . . . 12 HARG 5242

Harvest / Jan '89.

RHYTHM OF LOVE.
Tracks: Rhythm of love / We let it rock (you let it roll) / Love on the run (rough mix version) (Track on 12″ version only).
- ■ 12″ P.Disc. . . . . HARP 5240
- ■ 7″ Set . . . . HARX 5240
- ■ 12″ . . . . 12 HAR 5240
- ■ 7″ . . . . HAR 5240

Harvest / May '88.

ROCK GALAXY.
Tracks: Speedy's coming / They need a million / Drifting sun / Fly people fly / This is my song / Far away / Fly to the rainbow / Dark lady / In trance / Life's like a river / Top of the bill / Living and dying / Robot man / Evening wind / Sun in my hand / Longing for fire / Night lights.

ROCK YOU LIKE A HURRICANE.
Tracks: Rock you like a hurricane / Coming home.
- ■ 7″ . . . . HAR 5225

Harvest / Feb '84.

ROCKERS 'N' BALLADS.
Tracks: Rock you like a hurricane / Can't explain / Rhythm of love / Big city nights / Lovedrive / Is there anybody there / Holiday / Still loving you / No one like you / Blackout / Another piece of meat / You give me all I need / Hey you / Zoo / China white.
- CD . . . . CDEMD 1014
- MC . . . . TCEMD 1014
- ■ LP . . . . EMD 1014

Harvest / Nov '89.

SAVAGE AMUSEMENT.
Tracks: Don't stop at the top / Rhythm of love / Passion rules the game / Media overkill / Walking on the edge / We let it rock (you let it roll) / Every minute everyday / Love on the run / Believe in love.
- ■ LP . . . . SHSP 4125
- ■ MC . . . . TCSHSP 4125
- ■ CD . . . . .CDSHSP 4125

Harvest / May '88.

SCORPIONS CD SET.
Tracks: Countdown / Coming home / Blackout / Bad boys running wild / Loving you Sunday morning / Make it real / Big city nights / Coast to coast / Holiday / Still loving you / Rock you like a hurricane / Can't live without you / Zoo / No one like you / Dynamite / Don't stop at the top / Rhythm of love / Passion rules the game / Media overkill / Walking on the edge / We let it rock (you let it roll) / Every minute of the day / Love on the run / Believe in love / Can't explain / Lovedrive / Is there anybody there / Another piece of meat / You give me all I need / Hey you / China white.
- CD Set . . . . CDS 7979632

EMI / Oct '91 / EMI.

SCORPIONS: INTERVIEW PICTURE DISC.
Tracks: Not Advised.
- LP P.Disc . . . . BAK 2101

Baktabak / Aug '88 / Arabesque Ltd.

SEND ME AN ANGEL.
Tracks: Send me an angel / Wind of change / Tease me, please me (live) (Only on 12″ and CD Single.) / Lust or love (live) (Only on 12″ and CD Single.)
- ■ 12″ . . . . VERXP 60
- ■ 7″ . . . . VER 60
- ■ CD Single . . . . VERCD 60
- ■ MC Single. . . . . VERMC 60

Vertigo / Nov '91.

STILL LOVING YOU.
Tracks: Still loving you / Holiday / Big city nights (on 12″ only).
- ■ 12″ . . . . 12 HAR 5232
- ■ 7″ . . . . HAR 5232

Harvest / Mar '85.

STILL LOVING YOU.
Tracks: Believe in love / Born to touch your feelings / Lady Starlight / Is there anybody there / Walking on the edge / When the smoke is going down / Always somewhere / Holiday / Still loving you.
- ■ CD . . . . CDEMC 3586
- ■ LP . . . . EMC 3586
- ■ MC . . . . TCEMC 3586

Harvest / Nov '90.
- ■ LP . . . . EMD 1031
- ■ CD . . . . CDEMD 1031

- ■ MC. . . . . TCEMD 1031

EMI / Feb '92.

TAKEN BY FORCE.
Tracks: Steamrock fever / We'll burn the sky / I've got to be free / Riot of your time / Sails of Charon / Your light / He's a woman, She's a man / Born to touch your feelings.
- ■ LP . . . . PL 28309
- ■ MC . . . . PK 28309

RCA / '79.
- ■ LP . . . . RCALP 3024
- ■ MC . . . . RCAK 3024

RCA / Sep '81.
- ■ LP . . . . NL 70081
- ■ MC . . . . NK 70081
- ■ CD . . . . ND 70081

RCA / Oct '88.

TO RUSSIA WITH LOVE AND OTHER SAVAGE AMUSEMENTS (Live).
Tracks: Blackout / Rhythm of love / Holiday / Believe in love / Zoo / Walking on the edge / Long tall Sally / Don't stop at the top / Rock you like a hurricane / Media overkill / Passion rules the game / We let it rock (you let it roll).
- VHS . . . . MVP 99 1176 3

PMI / Feb '89 / EMI / Gold & Sons / TBD.

TOKYO TAPES.
Tracks: All night long / Pictured life / Backstage queen / Polar nights / In trance / We'll burn the sky / Suspender love / In search of the peace of the mind / Fly to the rainbow.
- ■ Double LP. . . . . NL 28331

RCA / Feb '79.
- ■ CD Set. . . . . PD 70008
- ■ Double LP . . . . NL 70008
- ■ MC Set . . . . NK 70008

RCA / '84.

UNDER THE SAME SUN.
Tracks: Under the same sun / Ship of fools / Partners in crime.
- ■ 12″. . . . . .MERX 395
- ■ CD Single . . . . MERCD 395
- ■ CD Single . . . . MRCDS 395
- ■ MC Single. . . . . MERMC 395

Mercury / Oct '93.

VIRGIN KILLER.
Tracks: Pictured life / Catch your train / Backstage Queen / Virgin killer / Hell cat / Crying days / Polar nights / Yellow raven.
- ■ LP . . . . .PPL 14225

RCA / Feb '77.
- ■ CD . . . . ND 70031
- ■ LP . . . . NL 70031

RCA / Apr '88.

WIND OF CHANGE.
Tracks: Wind of change.
- ■ 12″ . . . . .VERX 54
- ■ 7″ . . . . VER 54
- ■ CD Single . . . . VERCD 54
- ■ MC Single. . . . . VERMC 54

Vertigo / Mar '91.

WIND OF CHANGE.
Tracks: Wind of change / Restless nights / Hit between the eyes (Only on 12″ Single.) / Blackout (live) (Only on 12″ and CD Single.) / To be with you in heaven (Only on CD Single.).
- ■ 12″ . . . . .VERX 58
- ■ 7″ . . . . VER 58
- ■ CD Single . . . . VERCD 58
- ■ MC Single. . . . . VERMC 58

Vertigo / Sep '91.

WORLD WIDE LIVE.
Tracks: Countdown / Coming home / Blackout / Bad boys running wild / Loving you sunday morning / Make it real / Big city nights / Coast to coast / Holiday / Still loving you / Rock you like a hurricane / Can't live without you / Zoo / No-one like you / Dynamite.
- ■ Double LP. . . . . SCORP 1
- MC Set . . . . TCSCORP 1
- ■ Double LP . . . . EN 2403433
- ■ MC Set . . . . EN 2403435

Harvest / Jun '85.
- ■ CD Set. . . . . CDP 746 155 2

Harvest / Feb '86.

WORLD WIDE LIVE.
Tracks: Not Advised.
- VHS . . . . MVP 99 1113 2

PMI / Dec '85 / EMI / Gold & Sons / TBD

ZOO, THE.
Tracks: Zoo / Holiday.
- ■ 7″ . . . . HAR 5212

Harvest / Sep '80.

Scott, Bon

EARLY YEARS (Scott, Bon & The Valentines).
Tracks: To know you is to love you / She said / Everyday I have to cry / I can't dance with you / Peculiar hole in the sky / Love makes sweet music / I can hear raindrops / Why me / Sooky Sooky.
- ■ LP C5-520
- ■ MC. C5K-520

C5 / '88 / Pinnacle.
- ■ CD . . . . SEECD 247

See For Miles / '88.
- CD. C5CD-520

See For Miles / Sep '91 / Pinnacle.

HISTORICAL DOCUMENT (Scott, Bon & The Spectors).
Tracks: Not Advised.
- CD . . . . SEACD 6

See For Miles / Oct '92 / Pinnacle.

SEASONS OF CHANGE 1968-72.
Tracks: Not Advised.
- ■ LP . . . . .RVLP 33

Raven (Australia) / Aug '88.

Scream

BANGING THE DRUM.
Tracks: Not Advised.
- ■ LP . . . . DISCHORD 25
- MC. . . . . .DISCHORD 25C

Dischord / Nov '87 / SRD.

FUMBLE.
Tracks: Not Advised.
- LP . . . . DIS 83V
- MC. . . . . DIS 83C

Dischord / Jul '93 / SRD.

FUMBLE/BANGING THE DRUM.
Tracks: Not Advised.
- CD . . . . DIS 82D

Dischord / Jul '93 / SRD.

LIVE IN EUROPE (At Van Hall, Amsterdam).
Tracks: Not Advised.
- ■ LP . . . . K 001/113

Konkurrel / Sep '88.

NO MORE CENSORSHIP.
Tracks: Not Advised.
- CD . . . . RASCD 4001
- LP . . . . RAS 4001

Ras / Dec '88 / Greensleeves / Jetstar.

SCREAM: LIVE.
Tracks: Not Advised.
- CD . . . . YCLS 010CD
- LP . . . . YCLS 010

Your Choice / Jun '94 / Plastic Head.

STILL SCREAMING.
Tracks: Not Advised.
- ■ LP . . . . DISCHORD 9

Dischord.

STILL SCREAMING/THIS SIDE UP.
Tracks: Not Advised.
- CD . . . . DIS 81D

Dischord / Jul '93 / SRD.

THIS SIDE UP.
Tracks: Not Advised.
- ■ LP . . . . .DISCHORD 155

Dischord.

WALKING BY MYSELF.
Tracks: Walking by myself.
- ■ 7″ . . . . PIH 1

Jungle Hop / Mar '87.

Scream

LET IT SCREAM.
Tracks: Not Advised.
- CD . . . . HWDCD 16
- ■ LP . . . . HWDLP 16
- MC. . . . . HWDMC 16

Hollywood (2) / Oct '91 / Sony.

MAN IN THE MOON.
Tracks: Man in the moon.
- ■ 12″ . . . . .HWD 112TX
- ■ 7″ . . . . HWD 112
- ■ CD Single . . . . .HWD 112CD

Hollywood (2) / Oct '91.

Screaming Jets

ALL FOR ONE.
Tracks: C'mon / No point / Better / Needle / Shine on / Starting out / Stop the world (and let me off) / Blue sashes / Sister tease / F.R.C.
- ■ CD 8484412
- ■ MC 8484414
- ■ LP 8484411
Roo Art / Jul '91.

BETTER.
Tracks: Better / Rocket man (Only on 7" Single.) / Needle (live) (Only on 12" and CD Single.) / Blue sashes (live) (Only on 12" and CD Single.).
- ■ 12" . . . . RART 712
- ■ 7" . . . . RART 7
- ■ CD Single . . . . RARCD 7
Roo Art / Sep '91.

C'MON.
Tracks: C'mon / Sister Tease / Blue sashes (12" & CD only.).
- ■ 12" . . . . RART 612
- ■ 7" . . . . RART 6
- ■ CD Single . . . . RARTCD 6
Phonogram / Jul '91.

HERE I GO.
Tracks: Here I go / Rocket man / Think (On CDs only.).
- ■ 12" . . . . YZ 748T
- ■ CD Single . . . . YZ 748CD
East West / May '93.

TEAR OF THOUGHT.
Tracks: Dream on / Here I go / Meet anybody / Alright / Night child / Helping hand / Everytime / Living in England / Think / Best of you / Rich bitch / Tunnel / Hard drugs / Sick & tired / Shivers / Feeble.
CD 4509906782
MC 4509906784
WEA / Feb '93 / WEA.

Screaming Marionettes

LIKE CHRISTABEL.
Tracks: Like Christabel / Screaming master.
- ■ 12" . . . . SMM 001T
- ■ 7" . . . . SMM 001
Mandrake / Aug '89.

OBSESSION.
Tracks: Obsession / Play dead.
- ■ 12" . . . . LTST 25
- ■ 7" . . . . LTS 25
Lambs To The Slaughter / Mar '88.

Screaming Trees

ANTHOLOGY.
Tracks: Not Advised.
CD . . . . SST 260 CD
LP . . . . SST 260
MC . . . . SST 260 C
SST / May '93 / Pinnacle.

ASYLUM.
Tracks: Asylum / Take it to the tree native.
- ■ 12" . . . . 12 NTV 24
- ■ 7" . . . . NTV 24
Native (1) / Jan '88.

BEATEN BY THE UGLY STICK.
Tracks: Beaten by the ugly stick.
- ■ 12" . . . . NTV 12010
Native (1) / Feb '87.

BUZZ FACTORY.
Tracks: Black sun morning / Flower web / End of the universe.
CD . . . . SST 248 CD
- ■ LP . . . . SST 248
MC . . . . SST 248 C
SST / Mar '89 / Pinnacle.

CHANGE HAS COME.
Tracks: Not Advised.
CD . . . . GRCD 80
LP . . . . GR 80
Sub Pop / May '93 / RTM.

DOLLAR BILL.
Tracks: Dollar bill / (There'll be) Peace in the valley for me / Tomorrow's dream (Features on CDS only.).
- ■ 12" .659179 6
- ■ 7" 659179 7
- ■ CD Single 659179 2
Epic / Apr '93.

EVEN IF AND ESPECIALLY WHEN.
Tracks: Transfiguration / Straight out to any place / World painted / Don't look down / Girl behind the

mask / Flying / Cold rain / Other days and different planets / Pathway / You know where it's at / Back together / In the forest.
- ■ LP . . . . SST 132
SST / Sep '87.
CD . . . . SST 132 CD
MC . . . . SST 132 C
SST / May '93 / Pinnacle.

FRACTURE IN TIME, A.
Tracks: Asylum / Understand / Balance / Coliseum / Big hitter / M 1 l 3 s / Don't afraid / Fractured time.
CD . . . . NTVCD 29
LP . . . . NTVLP 29
MC . . . . NTVC 29
Native (1) / Aug '90 / Grapevine Distribution.

HIT THE FLOOR.
Tracks: Hit the floor / Hit the floor (version).
- ■ 7" . . . . NTV 38
Native (1) / Oct '88.

INVISIBLE LANTERN.
Tracks: Not Advised.
CD . . . . SST 188 CD
MC . . . . SST 188 C
SST / Sep '88 / Pinnacle.
- ■ . . . . SST 188
SST / Sep '88.

IRON-GURU.
Tracks: Iron-guru.
- ■ 12" .12 NTV 23
- ■ EP . . . . NTV 23
Native (1) / Aug '88.

NEARLY LOST YOU.
Tracks: Nearly lost you / E.S.K. / Song of a baker / Winter song (Acoustic version).
- ■ 7" 658237 6
- ■ CD Single 658237 2
Epic / Feb '93.

OTHER WORLDS.
Tracks: Not Advised.
CD . . . . SST 105 CD
MC . . . . SST 105 C
- ■ LP . . . . SST 105
SST / May '93.

RELEASE.
Tracks: Release.
- ■ 12" . . . . NTV 6
Native (1) / Mar '86.

SWEET OBLIVION.
Tracks: Shadow of the season / Nearly lost you / Dollar bill / More or less / Butterfly / Secret kind / Winter song / Troubled times / No one knows / Julie paradise.
CD 4717242
- ■ LP 4717241
MC 4717244
Sony Music / '91 / Sony.

TANGIERS.
Tracks: Tangiers / Big hitter.
- ■ 12" .12 NTV 34
- ■ 7" . . . . NTV 34
Native (1) / Jul '88.

UNCLE ANESTHESIA.
Tracks: Beyond this horizon / Bed of roses / Uncle Anethesia / Story of her fate / Caught between / Lay your head down / Before we arise / Something about today / Alice said / Time for light / Disappearing / Ocean of confusion / Closer.
CD 4673072
- ■ LP 4673071
- ■ MC 4673074
Epic / Jun '92.

WORLD CRASH.
Tracks: Not Advised.
LP . . . . NTVLP 065
Native (1) / Jul '91 / Grapevine Distribution.

Scum

BORN TOO SOON.
Tracks: Have away from home / Ain't no you / American mould / Double cross / Bunker life / Go to war / Junkhead / Beer can nightmare / Pyramid mail blues / Pool hunt / Exit death / No hope for religion / So m.u.c.h. hate.
- ■ LP . . . . GURT 18
Children Of The Revolution / Mar '87.

MOTHER NATURE.
Tracks: Not Advised.
CD . . . . BMCD 46
Black Mark / Aug '94 / Plastic Head.

Sea Hags

HALF THE WAY VALLEY.
Tracks: Half the valley.
- ■ 12" . . . . CHS 123396
- ■ 7" . . . . CHS 3396
Chrysalis / Jul '89.

SEA HAGS, THE.
Tracks: Not Advised.
- ■ LP . . . . CHR 1665
- ■ CD . . . . CCD 1665
- ■ MC . . . . ZCHR 1665
Chrysalis / May '89.

Seance

BLUE DOLPHIN BLUE.
Tracks: Not Advised.
- ■ LP . . . . 150 BPM
Various / '89.

FORNEVER LAID TO REST.
Tracks: Who will not be dead / Reincarnage / Blessing of death / Sin / Haunted / Fornever laid to rest / Necronomicon / Wind of Gehenna / Inferna cabbala.
CD . . . . BMCD 017
LP . . . . BMLP 017
MC . . . . BMCT 017
Black Mark / Jun '92 / Plastic Head.

SALTRUBBED EYES.
Tracks: Not Advised.
CD . . . . BMCD 44
Black Mark / Jan '94 / Plastic Head.

Secrecy

ART IN MOTION.
Tracks: Not Advised.
- ■ CD . . . . CDNUK 157
- ■ LP . . . . NUK 157
- ■ MC . . . . ZCNUK 157
Noise / Nov '90.

RAGING ROMANCE.
Tracks: Not Advised.
CD . . . . N 0182-2
LP . . . . N 0182-1
MC . . . . N 0182-4
Noise / '91 / Pinnacle.

Seducer

'EADS DOWN - SEE YOU AT THE END.
Tracks: Not Advised.
- ■ LP . . . . STUDLP 2
Stud / Apr '87.

CAUGHT IN THE ACT (SEDUCER).
Tracks: Don't fall in love (rock'n'roll) / Do you believe / Creeper / Wednesday / Remember (walkin' in the sand) / Call your name / Take you home / Halloween / Rollercoaster / Blizzard / On the run.
- ■ LP . . . . THBL 016
Thunderbolt / Oct '85.

INDECENT EXPOSURE.
Tracks: Indecent exposure / Down, down / No no / D.T.'s / Wild joker.
- ■ 12" . . . . THBE 1.007
Thunderbolt / Nov '84.

TOO MUCH AIN'T ENOUGH.
Tracks: Not Advised.
- ■ LP . . . . ILP 027
I.R.S. (Illegal) / Aug '88.

Sempiternal Death Reign

SPOOKY GLOOM, THE.
Tracks: Not Advised.
CD . . . . FDN 8099CD
LP . . . . FDN 8099
Plastic Head / Jan '92 / Plastic Head.

Sensefield

KILLED FOR LESS.
Tracks: Not Advised.
CD . . . . REVEL 32CD
LP . . . . REVEL 32LP
Revelation / May '94 / Plastic Head.

■ DELETED

Sentenced

TROOPER, THE.
Tracks: Trooper.
CD Single . . . . SPI 15CDS
Spinefarm / Feb '94 / Plastic Head.

Sentinel Beast

DEPTHS OF DEATH.
Tracks: Not Advised.
■ LP . . . . RR 9694
Road Runner / Aug '86.

Septic Death

GORE STORY.
Tracks: Not Advised.
LP . . . . LF 021
Lemon Flower / Jun '92.

KICHIGAI.
Tracks: Kichigai.
■ 7" . . . . PUS 007-03
Pusmort / Dec '88.

NOW THAT I HAVE THE ATTEN.
Tracks: Not Advised.
■ LP 0012-01D
Pusmort.

Septic Flesh

MYSTIC PLACES OF DAWN.
Tracks: Not Advised.
CD . . . . HOLY 5CD
Holy Records / May '94 / Plastic Head.

Sepultura

A superb, aggressive band fuelled by the poverty, injustice and hardships of their native land, Brazil. As youngsters they used to escape the struggles and violence of day-to-day living in Brazil's second city, Sao Paulo, by channelling their frustrations into some serious brutal Metal. They could never have dreamed - as they struggled to organise gigs then thrashed away on substandard equipment - that the rest of the world would one day recognise their potential to rival heroes like Motorhead, Metallica and Slayer. Stylistically closest to the latter, Sepultura made *Morbid visions* and *Beneath The Remains* for Brazillian label Cogumelo, then got the break they deserved: a deal with Roadrunner. Since then the band - Max Cavalera (guitar, vocal), Andreas Kisser (guitar), Paulo Jnr (bass) and Max's brother Igor (drums) - have gone from strength to strength; 1993 album *Chaos AD* entered U.K. chart at no. 11.

ARISE.
Tracks: Not Advised.
CD . . . . RO 93282
LP . . . . RO 93281
MC . . . . RO 93284
Roadracer / Apr '91 / Pinnacle.
LP P.Disc . . . . RO 93288
Road Runner / Jun '91 / Pinnacle.

BENEATH THE REMAINS.
Tracks: Not Advised.
CD . . . . RO 95112
■ LP . . . . RO 9511-1
MC . . . . RO 95114
Roadracer / May '89 / Pinnacle.

CHAOS A.D.
Tracks: Refuse/Resist / Territory / Slave new world / Amen / Kaiowas / Propoganda / Biotech is godzilla / Nomad / We are not as others / Manifest / Hunt / Clenched fist / Policia / Inhuman nature.
CD . . . . RR 90005
CD . . . . RR 90002
LP . . . . RR 90001
MC . . . . RR 90004
MiniDisc. . . . . RR 90007
Road Runner / Oct '93 / Pinnacle.
DCC . . . . RR 90009
Road Runner / Oct '93 / Pinnacle.
CD . . . . RR 90000
Road Runner / Mar '94 / Pinnacle.

MORBID VISIONS.
Tracks: Not Advised.
■ LP . . . . SHARK 4
Shark / Apr '89.
CD . . . . RO 92762
LP . . . . RO 92761

MC . . . . RO 92764
Road Runner / Sep '91 / Pinnacle.

MORBID VISIONS/CEASE TO EXIST.
Tracks: Not Advised.
CD . . . . SHARK 012 CD
Shark / Nov.'89 / Plastic Head.

REFUSE/RESIST.
Tracks: Refuse/Resist.
12" . . . . RR 23776
7" . . . . RR 23777
CD Single . . . . RR 23773
MC Single . . . . RR 23774
Road Runner / Jan '94 / Pinnacle.

SCHIZOPHRENIA.
Tracks: Not Advised.
CD . . . . SHARK 006 CD
■ LP . . . . SHARK 006
Shark / May '88.
CD . . . . RO 93602
LP . . . . RO 93601
MC . . . . RO 93604
Roadracer / Oct '90 / Pinnacle.

SCHIZOPHRENIA/ MORBID VISIONS.
Tracks: Not Advised.
MC . . . . SHARKMC 017
Shark / May '90 / Plastic Head.

SLAVE NEW WORLD.
Tracks: Slave new world.
10" . . . . RR 23748
CD Single . . . . RR 23743
CD Single . . . . RR 23745
MC Single . . . . RR 23744
Road Runner / May '94 / Pinnacle.

UNDER SEIGE (LIVE IN BARCELONA).
Tracks: Not Advised.
Laser Disc . . . . RR 91230
Road Runner / Jul '92 / Pinnacle.
VHS . . . . RRV 09963
Road Runner / Mar '94 / Pinnacle.

Sevenchurch

BLEAK INSIGHT.
Tracks: Perceptions / Low / Surreal wheel / Crawl line / Sanctum / Autobituary.
CD . . . . N 0222-2
Noise / Sep '93 / Pinnacle.

Seventh Angel

TORMENT, THE.
Tracks: Not Advised.
LP . . . . FLAG 51
Under One Flag / Dec '90 / Pinnacle.

Seventh Seance

ANOTHER EMPTY FACE.
Tracks: Another empty face.
■ 12" . . . . IC 003
Icon / May '84.

INTO THE OUTSIDE.
Tracks: Into the outside / Another empty face.
■ 7" . . . . ICS 001
Icon / Aug '84.

Severed Heads

20 DEADLY DISEASES.
Tracks: Twenty deadly kisses.
■ 12" . . . . NT 12 3003
Nettwerk / Sep '87.

ALL SAINTS DAY.
Tracks: All Saints Day.
■ 12" . . . . NET 012
Nettwerk / Oct '89.

ART OF NOISE VOL 2.
Tracks: Not Advised.
CD . . . . INKCD 005
Ink / Jan '89 / Pinnacle.

BAD MOOD GUY.
Tracks: Hot with fleas / Nation / Unleash your sword / Jet lag / Contempt / Bad mood guy / Dressed in air / Rabbi Nardoc Flagoon / Heaven in what heaven eats / Mad dad mangles a strad.
■ LP . . . . VOLT 10
Volition (Australia) / Nov '87.
■ LP . . . . NET 005
Nettwerk / '89.

BAD MOOD GUY.
Tracks: Not Advised.
■ 12" . . . . NET 001
Nettwerk / Dec '87.

BIG BIGOT, THE.
Tracks: Not Advised.
■ LP . . . . VOLT 7
Volition (Australia) / Nov '87.

BIG CAR.
Tracks: Not Advised.
CD W2-3043
Nettwerk / '89 / Vital Distribution.

BULKHEAD.
Tracks: Dead eyes opened / Greater reward / Hot with fleas / Goodbye tonsils / Twenty deadly diseases / Propellor / Petrol.
CD . . . . NTCD 041
■ LP . . . . NTL 30018
Nettwerk / Mar '89.

CITY SLAB HORROR.
Tracks: Not Advised.
■ LP . . . . INK 9
Ink / Mar '85.
CD . . . . W 230033
Nettwerk / May '91 / Vital Distribution.

CLIFFORD DARLING (Please don't live in the past).
Tracks: Not Advised.
■ Double LP . . . . INK 16 D
Ink / Dec '85.

COME VISIT THE BIG BIGOT.
Tracks: Not Advised.
■ LP . . . . NTL 30003
MC . . . . NTLC 30003
Nettwerk / Sep '87 / Vital Distribution.

COME VISIT THE BIG BIGOT/DEAD EYES OPENED.
Tracks: Not Advised.
CD . . . . NTCD 31
Nettwerk / '89 / Vital Distribution.

CUISINE (WITH PISCATORIAL).
Tracks: Pilot in hell / Seven of oceans / Finder / Estrogen / King of the sea / Host of quadrille / Life in the whale / Twister / Ugly twenties / Piggy smack / Golden height / I'm your antidote / Tingler (they shine within) / Goodbye / Her teeth the ally / Skippy roo kangaroo / Ottoman / Quest for oom pa pa / Wonder of all the world.
CD . . . . NET 028CD
LP . . . . NET 028
Nettwerk / Mar '92 / Vital Distribution.

DEAD EYES OPENED.
Tracks: Dead eyes opened / Bullet.
■ 12" . . . . INK 122
Rough Trade / Mar '84.
■ 12" . . . . NTM 6303
■ MC Single . . . . NTMC 6303
Nettwerk / '88.
■ 12" . . . . NET 011
Nettwerk / '89.

GOODBYE TONSILS.
Tracks: Goodbye tonsils.
■ 7" . . . . INK 129
Ink / Feb '85.

GREATER REWARD.
Tracks: Greater reward / Nation.
■ 12" . . . . NT 12 3019
Nettwerk / Aug '88.
■ CD Single . . . . NET 004
Nettwerk / Sep '88.

HEAT SEEKING SUSAN.
Tracks: Heat seeking Susan.
■ 12" . . . . INK 1214
Ink / Sep '85.

HEAVY METAL.
Tracks: Heavy metal / Killin' the Kidz.
■ 7" . . . . PC 002
Plastic Canvas / Apr '83.

HOT WITH FLEAS.
Tracks: Hot with fleas.
■ 12" . . . . NT 12 3011
Nettwerk / Oct '87.

IF I'VE TOLD YOU ONCE, I'VE TOLD YOU 1000 TIMES.
Tracks: Hot with fleas / Petrol / Halo / Harold and Cindy / Hospital / Million angels / Propellor / Bless the house / Canine / Mambo fist miasma / Umbrella.

■ VHS . . . . IKON 36
Ikon Video / Jun '89.

KATO GETS THE GIRL.
Tracks: Goodbye Tonsils / Petrol / Lower than the grave / Dead eyes opened / Kato gets the girl.
VHS . . . . VCSYZ 114
Chart Attack (Video) / Sep '87 / Pinnacle.
■ VHS . . . . IKON 20
Ikon Video / '88.

MEDIA JINGLES.
Tracks: Not Advised.
MC. MFM 42
Music For Midgets / May '84 / Backs Distribution.

PROPELLOR.
Tracks: Propellor / Harold and Cindy hospital.
■ 12" . . . . INK 1222
Ink / Jul '86.

RETREAD.
Tracks: Not Advised.
LP . . . . NET 032LP
MC. . . . . NET 032CD
Nettwerk / Dec '91 / Vital Distribution.

ROTUND FOR SUCCESS.
Tracks: Not Advised.
■ CD . . . . NET 014CD
■ LP . . . . NET 014
Nettwerk / Dec '89.

SIDE 2.
Tracks: Not Advised.
MC. MFM 41
Music For Midgets / May '84 / Backs Distribution.

SINCE THE ACCIDENT.
Tracks: Not Advised.
CD. . . . . INKCD 002
■ LP . . . . INK 002
Ink / Mar '84.
CD. W2-30039
Nettwerk / '89 / Vital Distribution.

SINGLES - SEVERED HEADS.
Tracks: Not Advised.
CD. . . . . NTCD 033
Nettwerk / '88 / Vital Distribution.

Sex Pistols

Musically outclassed by the Clash and historically trumped by the Damned (first punk band to release single), Pistols remain most influential band from class of '76. Despite bragging that they had no musical ability, band soundtracked controversy with highly potent singles: biggest of band's seven U.K. Top 10 hits was *God Save The Queen*. Replacement of talented bassist Glen Matlock by genuinely incompetent Sid Vicious began Pistols' downfall; band split in '78. An inspiration to host of U.K. acts, band acquired posthumous U.S. following; hence Pistols covers by Megadeth, Guns N' Roses and Motley Crue. Among post-Pistols projects, vocalist John Lydon recruited Steve Vai and Ginger Baker for P.I.L.'s 1986 *Album*, while guitarist Steve Jones worked with Iggy Pop and ex-Silverhead vocalist Michael Des Barres.

10TH ANNIVERSARY.
Tracks: Not Advised.
■ LP . . . . JOCK LP 3
McDonald Brothers / Aug '86.

ANARCHY IN THE UK.
Tracks: Anarchy in the U.K. / No fun / EMI (On CD & 12" only).
■ 12" . . . . VS 609-12
■ 7" . . . . VS 609
Virgin / '83.
■ CD Single . . . . CDT 3
Virgin / Jun '88.
■ CD Single . . . . VSCDX 1431
■ 7" . . . . VS 1431
■ CD Single . . . . VSCDT 1431
■ MC Single. . . . . VSC 1431
Virgin / Sep '92.

ANARCHY IN THE UK.
Tracks: Anarchy in the U.K. / I wanna be me.
■ 7" . . . . EMI 2566
EMI / Dec '76.

ANARCHY IN THE UK (LIVE VERSION).
Tracks: Anarchy in the U.K. (Live) / Flogging a dead horse.
■ 12" . . . . JOCK 1201
McDonald Brothers / Apr '86.

ANARCHY WORLDWIDE.
Tracks: Seventeen / Anarchy in the U.K. / Pretty vacant (live) / Holidays in the sun (live) / EMI (live).
CD. . . . . SPAW 101
Specific / Oct '88 / Pinnacle.

BEST OF AND THE REST OF, THE.
Tracks: Anarchy in the U.K. / I wanna be me / I'm a lazy sod / Dolls (new york) / Don't give me no lip child / Substitute / Liar / No feelings / No fun / Pretty vacant / Problems.
■ CD . . . . CDAR 1008
Action Replay / '89.
■ MC . . . . ARLC 1008
Action Replay / Mar '94.

BEST OF..AND WE DON'T CARE.
Tracks: Not Advised.
■ LP . . . . YX 7247
Flyover / Jan '80.

BETTER LIVE THAN DEAD.
Tracks: Substitute / No fun / Pretty vacant / Anarchy in the U.K.
CD. 722 552
■ LP 722 551
Restless (USA) / May '88.
CD. . . . . DOJOCD 73
Dojo / Feb '94 / Castle Communications / BMG.

C'MON EVERYBODY.
Tracks: C'mon everybody / God save the Queen (symphony) / Watcha gonna do about it.
■ 7" . . . . VS 272
Virgin / '79.

CASH FOR CHAOS.
Tracks: Submission (live) / God save the Queen / Liar.
CD. . . . . SPCFC 102
Specific / Oct '88 / Pinnacle.

EARLY   DAZE - THE   STUDIO COLLECTION.
Tracks: I wanna be me / No feelings / Anarchy in the U.K. / Satellite / Seventeen / Submission / Pretty vacant / God save the queen / Liar / EMI / New York / Problems.
■ CD . . . . STR CD 019
Street Link / Oct '92.
CD. . . . . DOJOCD 119
Dojo / May '93 / Castle Communications / BMG.

FILTH AND THE FURY, THE (Six-album box set).
Tracks: Not Advised.
■ LP Set . . . . JOCK BOX 1
McDonald Brothers / Jan '87.

FLOGGING A DEAD HORSE.
Tracks: Anarchy in the U.K. / I wanna be me / God save the Queen / Do you no wrong / Pretty vacant / Holidays in the sun / No fun / My way / Something else / Silly thing / C'mon everybody / I'm not your stepping stone / Great rock'n'roll swindle / No one is innocent.
■ LP . . . . V 2142
■ MC . . . . TCV 2142
Virgin / Feb '80.
■ LP . . . . OVED 165
■ MC . . . . OVEDC 165
Virgin / Apr '86.
CD. . . . . CDV 2142
Virgin / Oct '86 / EMI.

GOD SAVE THE QUEEN.
Tracks: God save the Queen / Did you no wrong / Don't give me no lip child (CD only).
■ 7" . . . . VS 181
Virgin / May '77.
■ CD Single . . . . CDT 37
Virgin / '88.

GREAT ROCK'N'ROLL SWINDLE.
Tracks: Not Advised.
VHS . . . . VIRV 0101 A
Virgin Vision / Gold & Sons / TBD.
VHS . . . . VVB 010
Virgin Vision / '88 / Gold & Sons / TBD.

GREAT ROCK'N'ROLL SWINDLE, THE.
Tracks: Great rock'n'roll swindle / Rock around the clock.
■ 7" . . . . VS 290
Virgin / '80.

HOLIDAYS IN THE SUN.
Tracks: Holidays in the sun / Satellite.
■ 7" . . . . VS 191
Virgin / Oct '77.

I'M NOT YOUR STEPPING STONE.
Tracks: I'm not your stepping stone / Pistols propaganda.
■ 7" . . . . VS 339
Virgin / Jun '80.

INTROSPECTIVE: SEX PISTOLS.
Tracks: Not Advised.
CD. . . . . CINT 5008
LP . . . . LINT 5008
MC. . . . . MINT 5008
Baktabak / Apr '92 / Arabesque Ltd.

IT SEEMED TO BE THE END UNTIL THE NEXT BEGINNING.
Tracks: Not Advised.
CD. . . . . JOCK 12
■ LP . . . . JOCKLP 12
MBC / Jun '88.

KISS THIS.
Tracks: Anarchy in the U.K. / God Save The Queen / Pretty vacant / Holidays in the sun / I wanna be me / Did you no wrong / No Fun / Satellite / Don't Give Me No Lip, Child / (I'm Not On Your Stepping Stone) / Bodies / No Feelings / Liar / Problems / Seventeen / Submission / New York / My Way / Silly thing / Anarchy in the U.K. (Live) / I Wanna Be Me (Live) / Seventeen (Live) / New York (Live) / NO Fun (Live) / Problems (Live) / God Save The Queen (Live).
CD. . . . . CDVX 2702
CD. . . . . CDV 2702
■ LP . . . . V 2702
MC. . . . . TCV 2702
Virgin / Oct '92 / EMI.
MiniDisc. . . . . MDV 2702
Virgin / Feb '93 / EMI.
DCC 463 167
Virgin / Jan '93 / EMI.

LAST SHOW ON EARTH.
Tracks: Not Advised.
■ LP . . . . JOCK LP 1
McDonald Brothers / May '86.

LIVE AND LOUD.
Tracks: Seventeen / New York / E.M.I. / Belson was a gas / Bodies / Holidays in the sun / No feelings / Problems / Pretty vacant / Anarchy in the U.K. / I wanna be me / God save the queen / No fun.
■ LP . . . . LINKLP 063
MC. . . . . LINKMC 063
Link / Jun '89 / ACD Trading Ltd.
CD. . . . . LINK CD 063
Street Link / Oct '92 / BMG.

LIVE AT CHELMSFORD PRISON.
Tracks: Lazy sod / New York / No lip / Stepping stone / Suburban kids / Submission / Liar / Ararchy in the UK / Did you no wrong / Substitute / No fun / Pretty vacant / Problems / I wanna be me.
CD. . . . . DOJOCD 66
Dojo / Mar '93 / Castle Communications / BMG.

LIVE WORLDWIDE.
Tracks: Not Advised.
■ LP . . . . KOMA 788017
Konnexion / Aug '85.

MINI LP, THE.
Tracks: Not Advised.
Mini LP . . . . MINI 1
Chaos / Jan '85.
Mini LP . . . . APOCA 3
Chaos / Jan '89.
CD. . . . . APOCA 3 CD
Chaos / Mar '89.

MUSIC AND MEDIA INTERVIEW PICTURE DISCS.
Tracks: Not Advised.
■ LP P.Disc . . . . SP 1001
Music & Media / Feb '88.

NEVER MIND THE BOLLOCKS-HERE'S THE SEX PISTOLS.
Tracks: Holidays in the sun / Bodies / No feelings / Liar / God save the queen / Problems / Seventeen / Anarchy in the U.K. / Submission / Pretty vacant / New York / EMI.
■ LP . . . . V 2086
■ MC. . . . . TCV 2086
■ CD . . . . CDVX 2086
Virgin / Oct '86.
■ MC . . . . OVEDC 136
Virgin / '87.
■ LP . . . . OVED 136
Virgin / Aug '88.

NO FUTURE U.K.?.
Tracks: Not Advised.
CD. . . . . RRCD 117

■ MC.	RRLP 117
■ MC.	RRLC 117

Receiver / Jul '93.

NO ONE IS INNOCENT (A punk prayer by Ronald Biggs).
Tracks: My way / No one is innocent (7" only) / Biggest blow (12" only).

■ 12".	VS 220-12
■ 7"	VS 220

Virgin / Jun '78.

ORIGINAL PISTOLS.
Tracks: Not Advised.

■ MC.	RRLC 101

Receiver / Jul '85.

■ LP	APKPD 13

Demon / Jul '86.

■ LP	FA 4131491

Fame / Jul '86.

■ CD	RRCD 101
■ LP	RRLP 101

Receiver / Jul '93 / Total / BMG / Grapevine Distribution.

ORIGINAL PISTOLS (CD).
Tracks: Original Pistols (CD).

■ CD Single	CDEP 13 C

Counterpoint / Nov '88.

ORIGINAL PISTOLS LIVE.
Tracks: No feelings / Anarchy in the U.K. / I'm a lazy sod / Liar / Dolls (New York) / Don't give me no lip child / Substitute / Pretty vacant / I wanna be me / Problems / Submission / No fun.

■ CD	DOJOCD 45

Dojo / '86.

■ LP	FA 3149

Fame / May '86 / EMI.

MC.	TCFA 3149

Fame / May '86 / EMI.

MC.	DOJOTC 45

Dojo / '87 / Castle Communications / BMG.

CD	CDFA 3149

Fame / Jul '89 / EMI.

■ LP	DOJOLP 45

Dojo / Sep '89.

PRETTY VACANT.
Tracks: Pretty vacant / No fun / No feelings / No feelings (Demo version) / Satellite (Demo version) / Submission (Demo version No 1) / EMI (Unlimited edition)(Demo version) / Seventeen (Demo version) / Submission (Demo version) / Watcha gonna do about it.

■ 7"	VS 184

Virgin / Jul '77.

■ 12".	VST 1448
■ 7"	VS 1448
■ CD Single	VSCDT 1448
■ CD Single	VSCDG 1448

Virgin / Nov '92.

PRETTY VACANT.
Tracks: Not Advised.

CD Set	RRDCD 004
LP Set	RRLD 004

Receiver / Jul '93 / Total / BMG / Grapevine Distribution.

SEX PISTOLS LIVE.
Tracks: Anarchy in the U.K. / I'm a lazy sod / Pretty vacant / Substitute.

■ 12"	TOF 104

Archive 4 / Aug '86.

SILLY THING.
Tracks: Silly thing / Who killed Bambi.

■ 7"	VS 256

Virgin / Mar '79.

SOME PRODUCT.
Tracks: Very name "Sex Pistols" / From beyond the grave / Big tits across America / Complex world of John Rotten / Sex Pistols will play / Is the Queen a moron / F**king rotter.

■ LP	VR 2

Virgin / Jul '79.

SOMETHING ELSE.
Tracks: Something else / Friggin' in the riggin'.

■ 7"	VS 240

Virgin / Feb '79.

SUBMISSION.
Tracks: Submission / No feelings.

■ 7"	DICK 1

Chaos / Mar '87.

WHO KILLED BAMBI (Sex Pistols & Tenpole Tudor).
Tracks: Who killed Bambi.

■ 7"	VS 443

Virgin / Sep '81.

Shadow King

SHADOW KING.
Tracks: What would it take / Anytime anywhere / Once upon a time / Don't even know I'm alive / Boy / I want you / This heart of stone / Danger in the dance of love / No man's land / Russia.

CD.	7567823242
■ LP	7567823241
MC.	7567823244

East West / Sep '91 / WEA.

Shah

BEWARE.
Tracks: Total devastation / Coward / Save the human race / Threshold of pain / Beware / Bloodbrothers / Age of dismay / Say hi to Anthrax.

CD.	RO 9470-2

Roadracer / Jul '89 / Pinnacle.

■ LP	ATOMH 009

Atom / Jul '89.

CD.	ATOMH 009CD

Atom / '90 / Cadillac.

Shakin' Street

SHAKIN' STREET.
Tracks: No compromise / Solid as a rock / No time to lose / Soul dealer / Susie Wong / Every man, every woman is a star / Generation X / So fine / I want to box you.

■ LP	84115

CBS / May '80.

SUSIE WONG.
Tracks: Susie Wong / Every man, every woman is a star.

■ 7"	CBS 8512

CBS / Apr '80.

Shark Island

LAW OF THE ORDER.
Tracks: Paris calling / Shake for me / Somebody's falling / Bad for each other / Passion to ashes / Spellbound / Get some strange / Why should I believe / Ready or not / Chain.

MC.	4659564
■ CD	4659562
■ LP	4659561

Epic / Apr '90.

Sharman, Dave

1990.
Tracks: Not Advised.

■ CD	CDNUK 152
■ LP	NUK 152
■ MC.	ZCNUK 152

Noise / Aug '90.

EXIT WITHIN.
Tracks: Not Advised.

CD	NO 1852
LP	NO 1851
MC.	NO 1854

Noise / Feb '92 / Pinnacle.

Shaw, Tommy

AMBITION.
Tracks: No such thing / Dangerous games / Weight of the world / Ambition / Ever since the world began / Are you ready for me / Somewhere in the night / Love you too much / Outsider / Lay them down.

■ LP	K 781 798 1
MC.	K 781 798 4

Atlantic / Sep '87 / WEA.

■ CD	781798 2

WEA / Sep '87.

EVER SINCE THE WORLD BEGAN.
Tracks: Ever since the world began / Outsider / No such thing (on 12" version only).

■ 12".	A 9138 T
■ 7"	A 9138

Atlantic / May '88.

GIRLS WITH GUNS.
Tracks: Girls with guns / Come in and explain / Lonely school / Heads up / Kiss me hello / Fading

---

away / Little girl world / Outside in the rain / Free to love you / Race is on.

■ LP	AMA 5020
■ MC.	AMC 5020

A&M / Oct '84.

Shihad

CHURN.
Tracks: Factory / Screwtop / Scacture / Stations / Clapper-loader / I only said / Derail / Bone orchard / Happy meal.

CD.	N 0249-2

Noise / Jul '94 / Pinnacle.

Shiva

ANGEL OF MONZ.
Tracks: Angel of Monz.

■ 7"	HEAVY 16

Heavy Metal / Nov '82.

FIREDANCE.
Tracks: How can I / En cachent / Wild machine / Borderline / Stranger lands / Angel of monz / Rendezvous with death / User / Call me in the morning / Shiva.

■ LP	HMRLP 6

Heavy Metal / Nov '82.

ROCK LIVES.
Tracks: Rock lives / Sympathy for the devil.

■ 7"	HEAVY 13

Heavy Metal / Feb '82.

Shok Paris

STEEL AND STARLIGHT.
Tracks: Not Advised.

■ LP	ILP 020
■ MC.	ILPC 020

I.R.S. (Illegal) / Mar '88 / EMI.

Shortino, Paul

BACK ON TRACK.
Tracks: Kid is back in town / Body & soul / Girls like you / Pieces / Bye-bye to love / Everybody can fly / Give me love / Remember me / Rough life / Forgotten child / When there's a life.

CD.	CDVEST 3

Bulletproof / Mar '94 / Pinnacle.

Shotgun Messiah

I WANT MORE.
Tracks: I want more / Search and destroy / 53rd and 3rd / Babylon / Nobody's home.

■ CD	RR 91032

Road Runner / Nov '92.

SECOND COMING, THE.
Tracks: Not Advised.

CD.	RR 92392
■ LP	RR 92391
■ MC.	RR 92394

Road Runner / Nov '91.

SHOTGUN MESSIAH.
Tracks: Bop city / Shout it out / Explorer / Dirt talk / Nervous / Don't care 'bout nothin' / Squeezin' teazin' / Nowhere fast / I'm your love.

LP	MFN 105
MC.	TMFN 105

Music For Nations / Jul '90 / Pinnacle.

VIOLENT NEW BREED.
Tracks: I'm a gun / Come down / Violent breed / Enemy in me / Revolution / Monkey needs / Rain / Jihad / Side F/X / Sex / Overkill / I come in peace.

CD.	RR 90362
MC.	RR 90364

Road Runner / Sep '93 / Pinnacle.

Shout

IN YOUR FACE.
Tracks: Borderline / Give me an answer / Getting ready / Getting on with life / Ain't givin' up / When the love is gone / Faith hope and love / In your face / Moonlight sonata / Waiting on you.

CD.	CDMFN 92
■ LP	MFN 92
MC.	TMFN 92

Music For Nations / May '89 / Pinnacle.

IT WON'T BE LONG.
Tracks: Not Advised.

CD.	CDMFN 88
■ LP	MFN 88

■ DELETED

MC. . . . . TMFN 88
Music For Nations / Aug '89 / Pinnacle.

STARTING LINE.
Tracks: Starting line.
■ 7" . . . . SHOUT 1
Mercury / Apr '82.

SUSPICION.
Tracks: Suspicion.
■ 12" . . . . PASH 39(12)
Passion (1) / Jan '85.

THEY'VE GOT YOU WHERE THEY WANT YOU.
Tracks: Not Advised.
■ 12" . . . . LM 12 033
Lost Moment.

TRIBAL.
Tracks: Tribal.
■ 7" . . . . LM 015
Lost Moment / Feb '85.

Shudder To Think

HIT LIQUOR.
Tracks: Hit Liquor.
■ 7" . . . . DIS 76V
Dischord / Nov '92.

LIVE.
Tracks: Not Advised.
CD. . . . . YCLS 020
Your Choice / Aug '94 / Plastic Head.

Shy

BE BY MY SIDE.
Tracks: Be by my side / Turnaround.
■ 7" . . . . GA 3
Gallery / Aug '80.

BRAVE THE STORM.
Tracks: Hold on / My apollo / Reflections / Keep the fires burning / Hunter / Shy / Brave the storm / Wild wild woman / Caught in the act / Was I wrong.
■ LP . . . . PL 70605
■ MC . . . . PK 70605
RCA / May '85.

BROKEN HEART.
Tracks: Broken heart.
■ 12" . . . . MCATB 1399
■ 12" . . . . MCAT 1399
■ 7" . . . . MCA 1399
MCA / Apr '90.

EXCESS ALL AREAS.
Tracks: Emergency / Can't fight the nights / Young heart / Just love me / Break down the walls / Under fire / Devil woman / Talk to me / When the love is over / Telephone.
CD. . . . . PD 71221
■ MC . . . . PK 71221
■ LP . . . . PL 71221
RCA / '87.

GIRL.
Tracks: Girl / Hey you.
■ 7" . . . . GA 1
Gallery / Mar '80.

GIVE IT ALL YOU'VE GOT.
Tracks: Give it all you've got / She's got what it takes.
■ 12" . . . . MCAT 1369
■ 12" Remix. MCATT 1369
■ 7" . . . . MCA 1369
■ CD Single . . . . DMCAT 1369
MCA / Oct '89.

HOLD ON (TO YOUR LOVE).
Tracks: Hold on (to your love) / Strangers in town.
■ 12" . . . . PT 40054
■ 7" . . . . PB 40053
RCA / Mar '85.

JUST LOVE ME.
Tracks: Just love me / Deep water / Hold on to your love / Break down the walls.
■ 12" . . . . 12 VHF 43
FM Records / Feb '88.

MISSPENT YOUTH.
Tracks: Not Advised.
■ CD . . . . DMCG 6069
■ LP . . . . MCG 6069
■ MC . . . . MCGC 6069
MCA / Oct '89.

MONEY.
Tracks: Money.
■ 12" . . . . MCATB 1391
■ 12" . . . . MCAT 1391
■ 7" . . . . MCA 1391
MCA / Jan '90.

ONCE BITTEN TWICE SHY.
Tracks: Not Advised.
■ LP . . . . EBON 15
Ebony (Pinnacle) / Nov '83.

REFLECTIONS.
Tracks: Reflections / Hunter / Deep water (on 12" only).
■ 12" . . . . PT 40230
■ 7" . . . . PB 40229
RCA / May '85.

UNDER FIRE.
Tracks: Under fire / Young heart / Break down the walls.
■ 7" . . . . SHY 100
RCA / '87.

YOUNG HEART.
Tracks: Young heart / Run for cover / Don't want to lose your love (Available on 12" only.).
■ 12" . . . . PT 41296
■ 7" . . . . PB 41295
RCA / Apr '87.

Sick Of It All

JUST LOOK AROUND.
Tracks: Not Advised.
CD. . . . . RR 91912
■ LP . . . . RR 91911
Road Runner / Sep '92.

LIVE IN A WORLD FULL OF HATE.
Tracks: Not Advised.
CD. . . . . LF 073CD
Lost & Found / Dec '93 / Plastic Head.

REVELATION RECORDINGS 1987-89, THE.
Tracks: Not Advised.
CD. . . . . LF 083CD
Lost & Found / May '94 / Plastic Head.

SPREADING THE HARDCORE REALITY.
Tracks: Not Advised.
CD. . . . . LF 084MCD
Lost & Found / May '94 / Plastic Head.

Silent Rage

OH BABY.
Tracks: Oh baby.
■ 7" . . . . LM 025
Lost Moment / May '85.

REBEL WITH A CAUSE.
Tracks: Rebel with a cause.
■ 12" . . . . CH 12006
Chameleon (USA) / Sep '88.

Silverfish

DOLLY PARTON E.P.
Tracks: Dolly Parton / On the motorway / Weird shit / Don't fuck.
■ 12" . . . . WIIIJIT 004
Wiiija / Feb '93.

F**KIN' DRIVIN' OR WHAT.
Tracks: Not Advised.
■ 12" . . . . CRE 113T
■ CD Single . . . . CRESCD 113
Creation / Jul '91 / Pinnacle.

FAT AXL.
Tracks: Not Advised.
CD. . . . . WIJ 6CD
LP . . . . WIJ 6
MC. . . . . WIJ 6C
Wiiija / Jan '91 / Vital Distribution.

ORGAN FAN.
Tracks: Not Advised.
CD. . . . . CRECD 118
LP . . . . CRELP 118
MC. . . . . CCRE 118
Creation / May '92 / Pinnacle.

SILVERFISH.
Tracks: Silverfish.
■ 12" . . . . WIIIJI T4
Wiiija / Jul '89.

SILVERFISH WITH SCRAMBLED EGGS.
Tracks: Silverfish with scrambled eggs.
■ 12" . . . . CRE 118T
Creation / Feb '92.

Silverhead

16 AND SAVAGED.
Tracks: Not Advised.
■ LP . . . . PURL 701
Purple / Jun '85.
CD. . . . . LICD 900325
Line / '89 / C.M. Distribution / Grapevine Distribution / A.D.A. Distribution / Conifer Records.

FIRST/16 AND SAVAGE.
Tracks: Long legged Lisa / Underneath the light / Ace supreme / Johnny / In your eyes / Rolling with my baby / Wounded heart / Sold me down the river / Rock 'n' roll band / Silver boogie / Hello New York / More than your mouth can hold / Only you / Bright light / Heavy hammer / Cartoon princess / Rock out Claudette rock out / This ain't a parody / 16 and savage.
CD Set . . . . LICD 921174
Line / Mar '92 / C.M. Distribution / Grapevine Distribution / A.D.A. Distribution / Conifer Records.

SILVERHEAD.
Tracks: Long legged Lisa / Underneath the light / Ace supreme / Johnny / In your eyes / Rolling with my baby / Wounded heart / Sold me down the river / Rock'n'roll band / Silver boogie.
■ LP . . . . PURL 700
Purple / Jun '85.

Silverwing

ALIVE AND KICKING.
Tracks: Teenage love affair / That's entertainment / Flashbomb fever / Adolescent sex / Everything happens at night / Rock and roll are four-letter words / Soldier girl.
■ LP . . . . BULP 1
Bullet / Jul '83.

ROCK AND ROLL ARE FOUR LETTER WORDS.
Tracks: Rock and roll are four letter words / High class woman.
■ 7" . . . . SILVER 1
Mayhem / Aug '80.

SITTING PRETTY.
Tracks: Sitting pretty / Teenage love / Flashbomb fever (Only on 12" single.) / Rock'n'roll mayhem (Only on 12" single.).
■ 12" . . . . SILV 00212
■ 7" . . . . SILV 002
Neon Music / Apr '82.

THAT'S ENTERTAINMENT.
Tracks: That's entertainment / Flashborne fever.
■ 7" . . . . SILV 3
Mayhem / Nov '82.

■ DELETED

Simple Agression

FORMULATIONS IN BLACK.
Tracks: Quiddity / Formulation in black / Lost / Phychoradius / Sea of eternity / Of winter / Simple aggression / Frenzy / Madd / Spiritual voices / Jedi mind trick / Share your pain.
CD . . . . .CDVEST 1
Bulletproof / Mar '94 / Pinnacle.

Sinister

DIABOLICAL SUMMONING.
Tracks: Not Advised.
CD . . . . NB 081
LP . . . . NB 081 1
MC . . . . NB 081 4
Nuclear Blast / Aug '93 / Plastic Head.

Sinner

DANGEROUS CHARM.
Tracks: Not Advised.
CD . . . . .N 0101 3
■ LP . . . . .N 0101 1
MC . . . . .N 0101 2
Noise / Nov '87 / Pinnacle.

NO MORE ALIBIS.
Tracks: Not Advised.
CD 9040082
Posh / Oct '92 / TBD.

TOUCH OF SIN.
Tracks: Not Advised.
■ LP . . . . .N 0026
Noise / '88.

Sister Double Happiness

DO WHAT YOU GOTTA DO.
Tracks: Do what you gotta do.
■ 7" . . . . SP 104/276
■ CD Single . . . . SPCD 104/276
Sub Pop / Jun '93.

HEART AND MIND.
Tracks: Bobby Shannon / Ain't it a shame / Exposed to you / Sweet talker / You don't know me / Sailor song / Dark heart / Heart and mind / Hey kids / I'm drowning / Don't worry / You for you.
CD 7599266572
MC 7599266574
Reprise / May '92 / WEA.

SISTER DOUBLE HAPPINESS.
Tracks: Not Advised.
■ LP . . . . .SST 162
SST / '88.
CD . . . . .SST 162 CD
MC . . . . .SST 162 C
SST / May '93 / Pinnacle.

UNCUT.
Tracks: Not Advised.
CD . . . . SPCD 105277
LP . . . . .SP 105277
Sub Pop / Jul '93 / RTM.

Skagarak

SKAGARACK.
Tracks: Move it in the night / I'm alone / Saying / Damned woman / Don't turn me upside down / Lies / Victim of the system / City child / Double crossed.
■ LP 8294 461
IMS / Nov '86.
CD 829 446 2
■ MC 8294 464
IMS / Nov '86.

Skatenigs

LOUDSPEAKER.
Tracks: Loudspeaker.
■ 12" . . . . VIRUS 104
■ CD Single . . . . .VIRUS 104CD
Alternative Tentacles / Feb '92.

OH WHAT A MANGLED WEB WE HAVE.
Tracks: Not Advised.
CD . . . . CDVEST 14
Bulletproof / Jun '94 / Pinnacle.

STUPID PEOPLE SHOULDN'T BREED.
Tracks: Not Advised.
CD . . . . VIRUS 105CD
LP . . . . VIRUS 105
Alternative Tentacles / Mar '92 / RTM / Pinnacle.

Skeletal Earth

EULOGY FOR A DYING FOETUS.
Tracks: Not Advised.
CD . . . . FDNCD 8215
LP . . . . FDN 8215
Plastic Head / Jan '92 / Plastic Head.

Skid Row

Formed by guitarist Dave 'Snake' Sabo in late 1986, Skid Row's rapid ascent was aided by endorsement of Jon Bon Jovi. Self-titled, hook-filled '89 debut was massive US success, spawning hits *18 And Life* and *I Remember You*. Support slots with Bon Jovi, Motley Crue and Guns N' Roses established UK fanbase, which sent much heavier follow-up, *Slave To The Grind*, straight into Top 10. Last release was fan-orientated *B Side Ourselves* collection in 1992.

18 AND LIFE.
Tracks: 18 and life / Midnight tornado.
■ 12" . . . . A 8883T
■ 7" . . . . .A 8883
■ CD Single . . . . A 8883CD
Atlantic / Jan '90.

34 HOURS.
Tracks: Not Advised.
CD . . . . REP 4073-WZ
LP . . . . REP 2073
MC .REP 2073-TI
Repertoire (Germany) / Aug '91 / Pinnacle.

B SIDE OURSELVES.
Tracks: Not Advised.
CD 7567824312
■ LP 7567824311
MC 7567824314
Atlantic / Oct '92 / WEA.

I REMEMBER YOU.
Tracks: I remember you / Makin' a mess / Big guns (live).
■ 12" . . . . A 8886TW
■ 12" . . . . A 8886T
■ 7" . . . . .A 8886
■ 7" . . . . A 8886X
■ CD Single . . . . A 8886CD
■ MC Single . . . . A 8886C
Atlantic / Mar '90.

MONKEY BUSINESS.
Tracks: Monkey business.
■ 7" . . . . .A7673 C
■ 7" P.Disc A7673
■ CD Single . . . . A7673 CD
■ 12" . . . . A7673 TW
Atlantic / Jun '91.

NO FRILLS VIDEO.
Tracks: Not Advised.
VHS 8536505343
WEA / Jan '94 / WEA.

OH SAY CAN YOU SCREAM.
Tracks: Not Advised.
VHS 7567501793
Warner Music Video / Feb '91 / WEA.

ROAD KILL.
Tracks: Not Advised.
VHS 8536504363
WEA / Jan '94 / WEA.

SKID ROW.
Tracks: Big guns / Sweet little sister / Can't stand the heartache / Piece of me / 18 and life / Rattlesnake shake / Youth gone wild / Here I am / Makin' a mess / I remember you / Midnight tornado.
CD . . . . K 781 936 2
■ LP . . . . K 781 936 1
MC . . . . K 781 936 4
Atlantic / Jan '89 / WEA.

SLAVE TO THE GRIND.
Tracks: Monkey business / Slave to the grind / Threat / Quicksand Jesus / Psycho love / Get the fuck out / Livin' on a chain gang / Creepshow / In a darkened room / Riot act / Mudkicker / Wasted time.
CD 7567822422
■ LP . . . . WX 423
MC . . . . WX 423C
Atlantic / Jun '91 / WEA.

SLAVE TO THE GRIND.
Tracks: Slave to the grind / C'mon and love me.
■ 12" . . . . A 7963 TX
■ CD Single . . . . A 7963 CD
■ MC Single . . . . A 7903 C
■ 7" . . . . A 7603
East West / Sep '91.

WASTED TIME.
Tracks: Wasted time.
■ CD Single . . . . A 7570CD
■ 7" . . . . .A 7570
Atlantic / Nov '91.

YOUTH GONE WILD.
Tracks: Youth gone wild / Sweet little sister.
■ 12" . . . . A 8935T
■ 7" . . . . .A 8935
Atlantic / Nov '89.

YOUTH GONE WILD.
Tracks: Youth gone wild.
■ 12" . . . . A 7444T
■ 7" . . . . .A 7444
■ CD Single . . . . A 7444CD
■ MC Single . . . . A 7444C
East West / Aug '92.

Skid Row

GARY MOORE, BRUSH SHIELS AND NOEL BRIDGEMAN.
Tracks: Not Advised.
■ LP . . . . ESSLP 025
■ CD . . . . ESSCD 025
■ MC . . . . ESSMC 025
Essential / Aug '90.

SKID.
Tracks: Sandie's gone / Man who never was heading home again / Felicity / Un co-op showband blues / Morning star avenue / Oi'll tell you later / Virgo's daughter / New faces old places.
CD 477360-2
Columbia / Aug '94 / Sony.

SKID ROW.
Tracks: Not Advised.
■ LP 450 263 1
MC 4502634
CBS / Apr '87 / Sony.
CD . . . . CLACD 343
Castle / Jun '94 / BMG.

Skin

1000 YEARS.
Tracks: 1000 years / My own hands.
■ 7" . . . . .7 PROD 3
■ 12" .12PROD 3
Product Inc. / Mar '87.

BLOOD, WOMAN, ROSES.
Tracks: Not Advised.
CD . . . . CDPROD 4
Product Inc. / '89 / Vital Distribution.

BLOOD/SHAME.
Tracks: Not Advised.
■ Double LP . . . . PROD 33025
Product Inc. / Jun '89.

GIRL COME OUT.
Tracks: Girl come out / Girl come out (dub).
■ 7" . . . . PROD 6
■ 12" .12PROD 6
Product Inc. / Jul '87.

HOUSE OF LOVE.
Tracks: House of love.
■ 12" 12RG 6374
■ CD Single . . . . CDR 6374
■ MC Single . . . . TCR 6374
EMI / Feb '94.

■ DELETED

MONEY.
Tracks: Money / Unbelievable / Express yourself (Does not feature on CDRS 6381.) / Down down down (Features on 12" & CDR 6381.) / Funktied (Features on MCS & CDRS 6381.) / All I want (Features on CDR 6381.).
- 12" 12RP 6381
- CD Single . . . . CDRS 6381
- CD Single . . . . CDR 6381
- MC Single . . . . TCR 6381
EMI / Apr '94.

SHAME, HUMILITY, REVENGE.
Tracks: Not Advised.
- LP 33PROD 11
Product Inc. / Jul '88.
CD . . . . .CDPROD 11
Product Inc. / Mar '88 / Vital Distribution.

SKIN.
Tracks: Money / Shine your light / House of love / Colourblind / Which are the tears / Look but don't touch / Nightsong / Tower of angel / Revolution / Raised on radio / Wings of an angel.
CD . . . . CDPCSD 151
LP . . . . PCSD 151
MC . . . . TCPCSD 151
Parlophone / May '94 / EMI.

SKIN UP E.P., THE.
Tracks: Look but don't touch / Shine your light / Monkey.
- 12" .12RP 6363
- CD Single . . . . CDR 6363
EMI / Oct '93.

TOWER OF STRENGTH.
Tracks: Tower of strength / Money (Live) (Does not feature on TCR 6387 & CDR 6387.) / Shine your light (Live) (Features on 12R 6387.) / Colourblind (Features on 12R 6387 & CDRS 6387.) / Look but don't touch (Features on CDR 6387.) / Unbelievable (Features on TCR 6387 & CDR 6387.).
12" 12R 6387
CD Single . . . . CDRS 6387
CD Single . . . . CDR 6387
MC Single . . . . TCR 6387
EMI / Jul '94 / EMI.

WORLD OF SKIN.
Tracks: Not Advised.
CD . . . . YGCD 002
LP . . . . YGLP 002
Young God / Sep '90 / Vital Distribution.

Skin Chamber

TRAIL.
Tracks: Not Advised.
- CD . . . . RR 90752
Road Runner / Jan '94.

TRIAL.
Tracks: On a drunk / Throb / Ripping fist / Torturous world / Sloven / Glisten / Slowcrime / Trial / Swallowing scrap metal Pt 5.
CD . . . . CDRR 9075 2
Road Runner / Apr '93 / Pinnacle.

WOUND.
Tracks: Not Advised.
CD 92742
LP 92741
MC 92744
Road Runner / Oct '91 / Pinnacle.

WOUNDED.
Tracks: Not Advised.
- CD . . . . RO 972742
Road Runner / Feb '93.

Skinny Puppy

ADDICTION.
Tracks: Addiction.
- 12" . . . . NT 12 3010
Nettwerk / Oct '87.

BACK AND FORTH SERIES TWO.
Tracks: Intro (Live in Winnipeg) / Sleeping beast / K-9 / Monster radio man / Quiet solitude / Pit / Sore in a masterpiece/Dead of winter / Unovis on a stick / To a baser nature / A.M./Meat flavour / My voice sounds like shit / Smothered hop (demo) / Explode the P.A. / Assimilate (original inst. demo) / Edge of insanity.
CD W2-30078
Nettwerk / Jan '93 / Vital Distribution.

BITE.
Tracks: Not Advised.
- LP . . . . .FACE 15
Scarface / Feb '86.

CENSOR.
Tracks: Censor (ext. mix) / Punk in park zoo's / Yes he ran / Censor.
- 12" 12CL 517
Capitol / Nov '88.

CHAINSAW.
Tracks: Chainsaw.
- 12" . . . . NTM 6305
MC . . . . NTMC 6305
Nettwerk / May '87 / Vital Distribution.

CLEANSE, FOLD AND MANIPULATE.
Tracks: First aid / Addiction / Shadow cast / Draining faces / Mourn / Second touch / Tear or beat / Trauma hounds / Anger / Epilogue.
- LP . . . . NTL 30011
MC . . . . NTLC 30011
Nettwerk / Sep '87 / Vital Distribution.

DIG IT.
Tracks: Digit.
- 12" . . . . BIAS 037
Play It Again Sam / Nov '86.

LAST RIGHTS.
Tracks: Hinder / Killing game / Cancelled / Xception / Catbowl / Hurtful 2 / Rivers end / Fester / Premonition / Wrek / Epilogue 2.
CD . . . . NET 038CD
Nettwerk / Apr '92 / Vital Distribution.

MIND: THE PERPETUAL INTERCOURSE.
Tracks: One time one place / Gods gift / Three blind mice / Love / Stairs and flowers / Antagonism / 200 years / Dig it / Burnt with water.
- LP . . . . EST 2028
- MC . . . . .TCEST 2028
Capitol / Feb '87.
CD . . . . NTCD 037
Nettwerk / '88 / Vital Distribution.
- LP . . . . BIAS 43
Play It Again Sam / Aug '89.

RABIES.
Tracks: Not Advised.
CD . . . . NETCD 023
LP . . . . NET 023
Nettwerk / Jul '90 / Vital Distribution.

REMISSION AND BITES.
Tracks: Not Advised.
- LP . . . . MFACE 010
Scarface / Jun '85.
CD . . . . BIAS 048
Play It Again Sam / Jan '87 / Vital Distribution.

SKINNY PUPPY.
Tracks: Not Advised.
- LP . . . . .FACE 10
Scarface / Jun '85.

TESTURE.
Tracks: Not Advised.
- CD CD3-15439
Nettwerk / '89 / Vital Distribution.

TOO DARK PARK.
Tracks: Not Advised.
CD . . . . NET 026CD
Nettwerk Europe / Sep '93 / Vital Distribution.

VIVISECT VI.
Tracks: Dogsh*t / VS gas attack / Harsh stone white / Human disease (S.K.U.M.M.) / Who's laughing now / Testure / State aid / Hospital waste / Fritter (Stella's home).
- CD . . . . CDP 791 040 2
- LP . . . . EST 2079
Capitol / Nov '88.
- MC . . . . .TCEST 2079
Capitol / Nov '88.
CD . . . . NETCD 021
Nettwerk / Nov '90 / Vital Distribution.

WORLOCK (Twelve Inch Anthology).
Tracks: Not Advised.
CD W2-30041
Nettwerk / '89 / Vital Distribution.

Skrapp Metal

SENSITIVE.
Tracks: Not Advised.
CD . . . . PAR 2008CD
Par / Nov '92 / New Note.

Skrew

BURNING IN WATER, DROWNING IN FLAME.
Tracks: Not Advised.
CD . . . . .CDDVN 15
LP . . . . DVN 15
MC . . . . .TDVN 15
Devotion / May '92 / Pinnacle.

DUSTED.
Tracks: Not Advised.
CD . . . . .CDDVN 28
Devotion / May '94 / Pinnacle.

Skull

NO BONES ABOUT IT.
Tracks: No bones about it.
CD . . . . .CDMFN 117
LP . . . . MFN 117
MC . . . . .TMFN 117
Music For Nations / Jun '91 / Pinnacle.

YOUR LOVE IS ALRIGHT.
Tracks: Your love is alright / Spinn on warning.
- 12" . . . . .RCAT 423
- 7" .RCA 423
RCA / Jun '84.

Skyclad

BURNT OFFERING FOR THE BONE IDOL, A.
Tracks: War and disorder (intro) / Broken promised land / Spinning Jenny / Salt on earth (another man's poison) / Karmageddon (the suffering silence) / Ring stone round / Men of straw / R'vannith / Declaration of indifference / Alone in death's shadow.
CD . . . . .NO 1862
LP .NO 1861
- MC . . . . .NO 1864
Noise / Mar '92.

JONAH'S ARK.
Tracks: Not Advised.
CD . . . . .NO 2092
LP .NO 2091
MC . . . . .NO 2094
Modern Music / May '93 / Plastic Head.

PRINCE OF THE POVERTY LINE.
Tracks: Not Advised.
CD . . . . .N 0239-2
LP .N 0239-1
MC . . . . .N 0239-4
Noise / Mar '94 / Pinnacle.

THINKING ALOUD.
Tracks: Thinking aloud.
- CD Single . . . . .NO 2093
Noise / Apr '93.

WAYWARD SONS OF MOTHER EARTH.
Tracks: Not Advised.
LP .NO 1631
- CD . . . . .NO 1632
- MC . . . . .NO 1634
Noise / May '91.

Skyscraper

CHOKE.
Tracks: Choke / Red raw / Drag.
- 12" . . . . .INCO 003
- CD Single . . . . INCO 003CD
Incoherent / Jul '93.

LOVESICK.
Tracks: Lovesick / Safer ground / Silicosis (Not on 7").
- 12" . . . . .INCO 004
- 7" . . . . .INCO 004S
- CD Single . . . . INCO 004CD
Incoherent / Oct '93.

MAN MADE HELL.
Tracks: Man made hell / Dead 1970 / TV Sky.
- 12" . . . . .12 FOOD 48
- CD Single . . . . .CDFOOD 48
EMI / May '94.

Slade

Managed by ex-Animal Chas Chandler, Slade's brand of power-rock earned them an incredible series of 12 top 5 hits between 1971 and 1974. Very much a 'people's band' and live attraction, songs such as *Mama Weer All Crazee Now*, *Gudbye T'Jane* and *Cum On Feel The Noise* (Polydor), were ear

■ DELETED

shattering chant-a-long anthems that reverberated around many football grounds in the early 1970's. Slade's popularity waned with the emergence of punk, but their *Merry Christmas Everybody*, is a perennial favourite.

ALL JOIN HANDS.
Tracks: All join hands / Here's to..
■ 12" . . . . RCAT 455
■ 7" . . . . RCA 455
RCA / Nov '84.

AMAZING KAMIKAZE SYNDROME, THE.
Tracks: My oh my / Run runaway / C'est la vie / Slam the hammer down / Cocky rock boys / In the doghouse / Ready to explode / Razzle dazzle man / Cheap 'n' nasty love / High and dry.
■ LP . . . . PL 70116
■ MC . . . . PK 70116
RCA / Dec '83.

AND NOW THE WALTZ, C'EST LA VIE.
Tracks: (And now the waltz) C'est la vie / Merry Christmas everybody.
■ 7" . . . . RCA 291
RCA / Nov '82.

BANGIN' MAN.
Tracks: Bangin' man / She did it to me.
■ 7" 2058 492
Polydor / Jul '74.

BEGINNINGS (Ambrose Slade).
Tracks: Not Advised.
CD 849 185-2
■ MC 849 185-4
Polydor / May '91.

COLLECTION.
Tracks: Not Advised.
CD . . . . CCSCD 372
Castle / Mar '93 / BMG.
■ MC . . . . CCSMC 372
Castle / May '93.

COZ I LUV YOU.
Tracks: Coz I luv you.
■ 7" 2058 155
Polydor / Oct '71.

CRACKERS.
Tracks: Not Advised.
CD . . . . CCSCD 401
MC . . . . CCSMC 401
Castle / Nov '93 / BMG.

CRACKERS' -THE CHRISTMAS PARTY ALBUM.
Tracks: Let's dance / Santa Claus is coming to town / Hi ho silver lining / We'll bring the house down / Cum on feel the noize / All join hands / Okey cokey / Merry Christmas everybody / Do you believe in miracles / Let's have a party / Get down and get with it / My oh my / Run runaway / Here's to .(the New Year) / Do they know it's Christmas / Auld lang syne / You'll never walk alone.
■ LP . . . . STAR 2271
MC . . . . STAC 2271
Telstar/Ronco / Dec '85 / BMG.

CUM ON FEEL THE NOIZE.
Tracks: Cum on feel the noize / Coz I luv you / Take me back 'ome / Goodbye to Jane.
■ 7" 2058 339
Polydor / Mar '73.
■ 12" . . . . POSPX 399
Polydor / Dec '81.

DANCE YOUR LIFE AWAY.
Tracks: Not Advised.
CD . . . . CLACD 383
Castle / Apr '93 / BMG.

DO YOU BELIEVE IN MIRACLES.
Tracks: Do you believe in miracles / Time to rock.
■ 12" . . . . PT 40450
■ 7" . . . . PB 40449
RCA / Nov '85.

EVERYDAY.
Tracks: Everyday.
■ 7" 2058 453
Polydor / Apr '74.

FAR FAR AWAY.
Tracks: Far far away.
■ 7" 2058 522
Polydor / Oct '74.

GET DOWN AND GET WITH IT.
Tracks: Get down and get with it.
■ 7" 2058 112
Polydor / Jun '71.

GINNY GINNY.
Tracks: Ginny ginny / Dizzy mama.
■ 7" . . . . BARN 002
Barn / '79.

GIVE US A GOAL.
Tracks: Give us a goal / Daddio.
■ 7" 2014121
Barn / Mar '78.

GUDBUY T'JANE.
Tracks: Gudbuy t'Jane.
■ 7" 2058 312
Polydor / Nov '72.

GYPSY ROAD HOG.
Tracks: Gypsy road hog / Forest full of needles.
■ 7" 2014 105
Barn / Jan '77.

HOKEY COKEY.
Tracks: Hokey cokey / Get down and get with it.
■ 7" . . . . SPEED 201
Speed / Dec '82.

HOW DOES IT FEEL.
Tracks: How does it feel.
■ 7" 2058 547
Polydor / Feb '75.

IN FOR A PENNY.
Tracks: In for a penny.
■ 7" 2058 663
Polydor / Nov '75.

KAMIKAZE.
Tracks: Not Advised.
CD . . . . CLACD 381
Castle / Apr '93 / BMG.

KEEP YOUR HANDS OFF.
Tracks: Not Advised.
CD . . . . ZK 3936
CBS / '88 / Sony.

KNUCKLE SANDWICH NANCY.
Tracks: Knuckle sandwich Nancy / I'm mad.
■ 7" . . . . CHEAP 24
Cheapskate / May '81.

LET'S CALL IT QUITS.
Tracks: Let's call it quits / When the chips are down.
■ 7" 2058 690
Polydor / Feb '76.

LET'S DANCE (REMIX 1988).
Tracks: Let's dance (remix 1988) / Standing in the corner.
■ 7" . . . . BOYZ 3
Cheapskate / Dec '88.
■ CD Single . . . . BOYZCD 3
Cheapskate / Feb '89.

LOCK UP YOUR DAUGHTERS.
Tracks: Lock up your daughters.
■ 7" . . . . RCA 124
RCA / Sep '81.

LOOK WOT YOU DUN.
Tracks: Look wot you dun.
■ 7" 2058 195
Polydor / Feb '72.

MAMA WEER ALL CRAZEE NOW.
Tracks: Mama weer all crazee now.
■ 7" 2058 274
Polydor / Sep '72.

MERRY XMAS EVERYBODY.
Tracks: Merry Xmas everybody / Hokey cokey.
■ 7" 2058422
Polydor / Dec '73.

MERRY XMAS EVERYBODY (REISSUES).
Tracks: Don't blame me / Merry Xmas everybody.
■ 7" . . . . CHEAP 11
Cheapskate / Nov '80.
■ 12" . . . . POSPX 780
■ 7" . . . . POSP 780
Polydor / Nov '86.
■ 7" . . . . BOYZ 4
■ CD Single . . . . BOYZCD 4
Cheapskate / Dec '89.
■ 12" . . . . PZ 112
■ 7" . . . . PO 112
Polydor / Nov '90.

MY BABY LEFT ME-THAT'S ALL RIGHT (MEDLEY).
Tracks: My baby left me - that's all right.
■ 7" 2014 114
Barn / Oct '77.

MY FRIEND STAN.
Tracks: My friend Stan.
■ 7" 2058 407
Polydor / Oct '73.

MY OH MY.
Tracks: My oh my.
■ 12" . . . . RCAT 373
■ 7" . . . . RCA 373
RCA / Nov '83.

MYZSTERIOUS MIZSTER JONES.
Tracks: Myzsterious Mizster Jones / Mama nature is a rocker / My oh my.
■ 12" . . . . PT 40028
■ 7" . . . . PB 40027
RCA / Mar '85.

NIGHT STARVATION.
Tracks: Night starvation / When I'm dancin', I'm not fightin' / I'm a rocker / Don't waste your time / Wheels ain't coming down / Nine to five.
■ EP 45-3
RCA (USA) / Jun '80.

NOBODY'S FOOL.
Tracks: Not Advised.
■ LP 2383 377
Polydor / Mar '76.

OKEY COKEY.
Tracks: Okey Cokey / My baby's got it.
■ 7" . . . . BARN 011
Barn / Dec '79.
■ 7" P.Disc . . . . SPEEDP 201
Speed / Dec '82.
■ 7" . . . . SPEED 201
Receiver / Dec '86.

OLD, NEW, BORROWED AND BLUE.
Tracks: Not Advised.
■ LP 2383 261
Polydor / Feb '74.

ON STAGE.
Tracks: Rock 'n' roll preacher / When I'm dancin' I ain't fighting / Take me bak 'ome / Everyday / Lock up your daughters / We'll bring the house down / Night to remember / Gudbuy t'Jane / Mama weer all crazee now / You'll never walk alone.
■ LP . . . . RCALP 3107
RCA / Feb '83.
■ LP . . . . PL 70080
MC . . . . PK 70080
RCA / '84 / BMG.

PLAY IT LOUD.
Tracks: Raven / See us here / Dapple rose / Could I / One way hotel / Shape of things to come / Know who you are / I remember / Pouk hill / Angelina / Dirty joker / Sweet box.
CD 849 178-2
■ MC 849 178-4
Polydor / May '91.

RADIO WALL OF SOUND.
Tracks: Radio wall of sound.
■ 7" . . . . PO 180
■ CD Single . . . . PZCD 180
■ MC Single . . . . POCS 180
Polydor / Oct '91.

ROCK 'N' BOLERO.
Tracks: Rock 'n' bolero / It's alright by me.
■ 7" 2014127
Barn / Oct '78.

ROGUES GALLERY.
Tracks: Not Advised.
■ LP . . . . PL 70604
■ MC . . . . PK 70604
RCA / Feb '85.

CD. . . . . CLACD 378
Castle / Apr '93 / BMG.

RUBY RED.
Tracks: Ruby red.
■ 7". . . . . .RCA 191
RCA / Mar '82.

RUN RUNAWAY.
Tracks: Run runaway / Two track stereo, one track mind.
■ 12". . . . . .RCAT 385
■ 7". . . . . .RCA 385
RCA / Feb '84.

SEVEN YEAR (B)ITCH, THE.
Tracks: Seven year (B)itch / Leave little girls alone.
■ 12". . . . . .RCAT 475
■ 7". . . . . .RCA 475
RCA / Jan '85.

SIGN OF THE TIMES.
Tracks: Sign of the times / Not tonight Josephine.
■ 7". . . . . .BARN 010
Barn / Oct '79.

SKWEEZE ME PLEEZE ME.
Tracks: Skweeze me pleeze me.
■ 7". 2058 377
Polydor / Jun '73.

SLADE ALIVE.
Tracks: Hear me calling / In like a shot from my gun / Darling be home soon / Know who you are / Keep on rocking / Get down with it / Born to be wild.
■ LP. 2383 101
Polydor / Apr '72.
■ LP. . . . . SPELP 84
Polydor / Nov '84 / PolyGram.
MC. . . . . SPEMC 84
CD. 841 114-2
■ MC. 841 114-4
Polydor / Apr '91.

SLADE ALIVE AT READING '80.
Tracks: When I'm dancin' I ain't fighting / Born to be wild / Something else / Pistol packin' mama / Keep a rollin'.
■ EP. . . . . CHEAP 5
Cheapskate / Oct '80.

SLADE COLLECTION 81-87, THE.
Tracks: Run runaway / Everyday (live) / We'll bring the house down / Ruby red / (And now the waltz) C'est la vie / Do you believe in miracles / Still the same / My oh my / All join hands / Wheels ain't coming down / 7 year bitch / Myzterious Mizter Jones / Lock up your daughters / Me and the boys / Gudbuy t'Jane (live) / Mama weer all crazee now (Live) / Love is like a rock (Bonus track on CD only.).
CD. . . . . ND 74926
MC. . . . . NK 74926
■ LP. . . . . NL 74926
RCA / Apr '91.

SLADE ON STAGE.
Tracks: Not Advised.
CD. . . . . CLACD 388
Castle / Jun '93 / BMG.

SLADE SMASHES.
Tracks: Cum on feel the noize / My friend Stan / Far far away / Coz I luv you / Gypsy roadhog / Thanks for the memory (wham bam thank you mam) / Bangin' man / In for a penny / Skweeze me, pleeze me / Mama weer all crazee now / Look wot you dun / Take me bak 'ome / Lets call it quits / Give us a goal / Merry Xmas everybody / How does it feel / My baby left me / That's alright mama / Get down get with it / Gudby t'Jane.
■ LP. . . . . .POLTV 13
Polydor / Nov '80.

SLADES GREATS.
Tracks: Cum on feel the noize / My friend Stan / Far far away / Coz I luv you / Everyday / Thanks for the memory / Far far away / Skweeze me, pleeze me / Mama weer all crazee now / Look wot you dun / Take me bak 'ome / Let's call it quits / Merry Xmas everybody / How does it feel / Get down with it / Gudbuy T'Jane.
■ LP. . . . . SLAD 1
MC. . . . . SLADC 1
Polydor / May '84 / PolyGram.

SLADEST.
Tracks: Not Advised.
■ LP. 2442 119
Polydor / Oct '73.

SLAYED ?.
Tracks: How d'you ride / Whole world's goin crazee / Look at last nite / I won't let it appen agen / Move over / Gudbuy t' Jane / Gudbuy gudbuy / Mama weer

all crazee now / I don't mind / Let the good times roll.
■ LP. 2383 163
Polydor / Dec '72.

STILL THE SAME.
Tracks: Gotta go home / Still the same.
■ 12". . . . . PT 41137
RCA / Feb '87.
■ 7". . . . . PB 41137
RCA / Jan '87.

STORY OF SLADE VOL.1.
Tracks: Coz I luv you / Gudbuy t' Jane / Keep on rocking / Good time gals / Nobody's fools / Look wot you dun / Mama weer all crazee now / When the lights are out / Miles out to see / Bangin' man / My town / Lay it down.
■ CD. . . . . BTCD 979411
Beartracks / Oct '90.

STORY OF SLADE VOL.2.
Tracks: Cum on feel the noize / Far far away / Everyday / Skweeze me, pleeze me / Don't blame me / Summer song / Get down and get with it / In for a penny / Just want a little bit / I'm mee, I'm now, an that's orl / Get on up / How does it feel.
CD. . . . . BTCD 979412
Beartracks / Oct '90 / Rollercoaster Records.

STORY OF: SLADE.
Tracks: Not Advised.
■ Double LP. 2689 001
Polydor / '81.
MC Set. 3539 101
Polydor / Apr '81 / PolyGram.

TAKE ME BAK 'OME.
Tracks: Take me bak 'ome.
■ 7". 2058 231
Polydor / Jun '72.

THANKS FOR THE MEMORY (WHAM BAM THANK YOU MAM).
Tracks: Thanks for the memory.
■ 7". 2058 585
Polydor / May '75.

THAT'S WHAT FRIENDS ARE FOR.
Tracks: That's what friends are for / Wild party.
■ 12". . . . . PT 41272
■ 7". . . . . PB 41271
RCA / Apr '87.

TILL DEAF DO US PART.
Tracks: Rock 'n' roll preacher / Lock up your daughters / Til deaf do us part / Ruby red / She brings out the devil in me / Night to remember / M'hat m'coat / It's your body not your mind / Let the rock roll out of control / That was no lady that was my wife / Knuckle sandwich Nancy / Til deaf resurrected.
■ LP. . . . . RCALP 6021
MC. . . . . RCAK 6021
RCA / Dec '81 / BMG.
■ CD. 291110
Ariola Express / Nov '92.
CD. . . . . CLACD 377
Castle / Apr '93 / BMG.

WALL OF HITS.
Tracks: Radio wall of sound / Coz I luv you / Take me bak 'ome / Mama weer all crazee now / Cum on feel the noize / Skweeze me pleeze me / Universe / Merry Xmas everybody / Get down and get with it / Look wot you dun / Gudbuy t'Jane / My friend Stan / Everyday / Bangin' man / Far far away / How does it feel (Only on CD and MC) / Thanks for the memory (wham bam thank you mam) (Only on CD and MC) / Let's call it quits / My oh my / Run run away.
CD. 5116122
■ LP. 5116121
■ MC. 5116124
Polydor / Nov '91.

WALL OF HITS.
Tracks: Coz I luv you / Gudbuy t Jane / My frien stan / How does it feel / Them kind of monkeys can't swing / Far far away / Thanks for the memory / Let's call it quits / Nobody's fool / My baby left me / Give us a goal / Merry xmas everybody / My oh my / Run run away / Radio wall of sound.
VHS. 0839683
Polygram Music Video / '91 / PolyGram.

WE WON'T GIVE IN.
Tracks: We won't give in.
■ 7". . . . . BOYZ 2
Cheapskate / '88.

WE'LL BRING THE HOUSE DOWN.
Tracks: We'll bring the house down / Night starvation / Wheel's ain't coming down / Hold on to your hats / My baby's got it / When I'm dancin' I ain't fighting /

Dizzy mama / Nuts, bolts and screw / Lemme lov into ya / I'm a rocker.
■ LP. . . . . SKATE
■ MC. . . . . KAT
Cheapskate / Mar '81.
■ LP. . . . . NL 7114
■ MC. . . . . NK 7114
RCA / Oct '86.
CD. . . . . CLACD 38
Castle / Apr '93 / BMG.

WE'LL BRING THE HOUSE DOWN.
Tracks: We'll bring the house down / Hold on to you hats.
■ 7". . . . . .CHEAP 1
Cheapskate / Jan '81.

WE'RE REALLY GONNA RAISE THE ROOF.
Tracks: We're really gonna raise the roof / Goo time gals.
■ 7". . . . . .WB 777
WEA / '74.

WHEELS AIN'T COMING DOWN.
Tracks: Wheels ain't coming down.
■ 7". . . . . .CHEAP 2
Cheapskate / Apr '81.

WIZZARD/SLADE (Slade/Wizzard).
Tracks: Wizzard/Slade.
■ CD Single. . . . . CDEP 12 (
Counterpoint / Nov '88.

YOU BOYZ MAKE BIG NOIZE.
Tracks: Love is like a rock / That's what friends are for / Still the same / Fools go grazy / She's heavy We won't give in / Won't you rock with me / Ooh la la in L.A. / Me and the boys / Sing shout (knock yoursel out) / Roaring silence / It's hard having fun nowa days / You boyz make big noize / Boyz (inst).
■ CD. . . . . PD 71260
■ LP. . . . . PL 71260
■ MC. . . . . PK 71260
RCA / Jan '87.
CD. . . . . CLACD 379
Castle / Apr '93 / BMG.

YOU BOYZ MAKE BIG NOIZE.
Tracks: You boyz make big noize.
■ 12". . . . . TBOYZ 1
■ 7". . . . . BOYZ 1
Cheapskate / Jul '87.

Slammer

BRING THE HAMMER DOWN.
Tracks: Bring the hammer down / IOU / Maniac.
■ CD Single. . . . . HEAVYXD 66
Heavy Metal / Oct '90.
■ 12". 12HM 66
Heavy Metal / Oct '90.

NIGHTMARE SCENARIO.
Tracks: Not Advised.
■ CD. . . . . .HMRXD 170
■ LP. . . . . HMRLP 170
■ MC. . . . . HMRMC 170
Heavy Metal / Apr '91.

WORK OF IDLE HANDS.
Tracks: Fenement zone / If thine eye / Johnny's home / Razor's edge / Hellbound / Hunt you down / God's prey / Fight or fall / No excuses / Born for war (Only on CD).
CD. 246000 2
■ LP. . . . . WX 273
■ MC. . . . . WX 273C
WEA / Jun '89.

Slaughter

EAST SIDE OF TOWN.
Tracks: East side of town / One by one.
■ 7". . . . . .DJS 10936
DJM / Mar '81.

FLY TO THE ANGELS.
Tracks: Fly to the angels (edit) / Up all night (live) / Loaded gun (live) (12" & CD single only.) / Fly to the angels (acoustic version) (CD single only.
■ 7" P.Disc. . . . . CHSP 3634
■ 12" P.Disc. . . . . CHSP 123634
■ 7". . . . . CHS 3634
■ CD Single. . . . . CHSCD 3634
Chrysalis / Jan '91.

FROM THE BEGINNING.
Tracks: Not Advised.
VHS. 0832363
Chrysalis Music Video / May '91 / EMI.

STICK IT TO YA.
Tracks: Eye to eye / Burnin' bridges / Up all night / Spend my life / Thinking of June / She wants more / Fly to the angels / Mad about you / That's not enough / You are the one / Gave me your heart / Desperately / Loaded gun.
- ■ LP . . . . CHR 1702
- ■ CD . . . . CCD 1702
- ■ MC . . . . ZCHR 1702
Chrysalis / Apr '90.
DCC 3217025
Chrysalis / Jan '93 / EMI.

UP ALL NIGHT.
Tracks: Up all night / Eye to eye / Stick it to ya medley (On 12" format only.).
- ■ 7" P.Disc . . . . CHSP 3556
- ■ 12" P.Disc . . . . CHSP 123556
- ■ 7" . . . . CHS 3556
- ■ CD Single . . . . CHSCD 3556
Chrysalis / Sep '90.

WILD LIFE, THE.
Tracks: Reach for the sky / Out of love / Wild life / Days gone by / Dance for me baby / Times they change / Move to the music / Real love / Shake this place / Street of broken hearts / Hold on / Do ya know.
- ■ CD . . . . CCD 1911
- ■ LP . . . . CHR 1911
- ■ MC . . . . ZCHR 1911
Chrysalis / May '92.
DCC 3219115
Chrysalis / Jan '93 / EMI.

Slaughter House

SLAUGHTER HOUSE.
Tracks: Not Advised.
LP . . . . ZORRO 11
- ■ CD . . . . CDZORRO 11
Music For Nations / Sep '90.

Slave Raider

TAKE THE WORLD BY STORM.
Tracks: Take the world by storm / Back stabbing / Make some noise / Burning too hot / Long way from home / Survival of the fittest / Devil comes out in me / Black hole.
- ■ LP . . . . HIP 60
- ■ MC . . . . HIPC 60
Jive / Mar '88.

WHAT DO YOU KNOW ABOUT ROCK 'N' ROLL?.
Tracks: Is there rock'n'roll in Heaven / Bye bye baby / Sin city social / High priest of good times / What do you know about rock'n'roll / Iron bar motel / Jailbreak / Youngblood / Keep on pushing / Rollercoaster / Magistrate / Guilty / Wreckin' machine.
- ■ LP . . . . HIP 68
- ■ MC . . . . HIPC 68
- ■ CD . . . . CHIP 68
Jive / Apr '89.

YOUNG BLOOD.
Tracks: Young blood.
- ■ 12" . . . . JIVET 198
- ■ 7" . . . . JIVE 198
Jive / Apr '89.

Slayer

Unquestionably the ultimate Thrash band on the planet - the fastest, nastiest, most evil and sinister. It all began with 1984's *Show No Mercy* and got even more hellish with every step. The original line-up of Tom Araya (bass,vocals), Jeff Hanneman (guitar), Kerry King (guitar) and Dave Lombardo (drums, now replaced by ex-Forbidden man Paul Bostaph) started out in LA clubs in 1982. Their Venom-esque fury and breakneck speed made for an almost indescribable live experience which came closest to being captured in the studio come their third album, *Reign In Blood*. Purists argue that their debut from Rick Rubin's Def American, *South Of Heaven* (1988), had them wimping out by slowing down but Slayer just grinned and got on with it. The double live CD *Decade Of Aggression* was an awesome reminder of their brutal back catalogue and 1994's *Divine Intervention* pointed towards an ever-more gruesome future.

CRIMINALLY INSANE.
Tracks: Criminally insane (remix) / Aggressive perfector / Post mortem.
- ■ 12" . . . . LONX 133

- ■ 7" . . . . LON 133
London / May '87.

DECADE OF AGGRESSION.
Tracks: Hell awaits / Anti-christ / War ensemble / South of Heaven / Raining blood / Alter of sacrifice / Jesus saves / Captor of sin / Born of fire / Postmortem / Spirit in black / Dead skins mask / Seasons in the abyss / Mandatory suicide / Angel of death / Hallowed point / Blood red / Die by the sword / Expendable youth / Chemical warfare / Black magic.
CD Set 5106052
MC Set 5106054
- ■ Double LP. 5106051
American Recordings / Oct '91.

HAUNTING THE CHAPEL.
Tracks: Haunting the chapel / Chemical warfare / Captor of sin.
- ■ 12" . . . . RR 1255087
Road Runner / Oct '84.
- ■ CD Single . . . . RR 24442
Road Runner / Dec '89.

HELL AWAITS.
Tracks: Hell awaits / At dawn they sleep / Praise of death / Captor of sin / Hardening of the arteries / Kill again / Haunting the chapel / Necrophiliac / Crypts of eternity.
- ■ LP . . . . RR 979 51
Road Runner / May '85.
CD . . . . RR 349795
MC . . . . RR 979 54
Road Runner / Feb '89 / Pinnacle.
CD . . . . CDZORRO 8
LP . . . . ZORRO 8
MC . . . . TZORRO 8
Zorro / Aug '90 / Pinnacle.

LIVE UNDEAD.
Tracks: Not Advised.
- ■ LP P.Disc 720151
Enigma (EMI) / Oct '87.
CD . . . . RR 349574
- ■ LP . . . . RR 9574
Road Runner / Dec '88.
MC . . . . RR 957 44
Road Runner / Dec '88 / Pinnacle.
CD . . . . CDZORRO 29
LP . . . . ZORRO 29
MC . . . . TZORRO 29
Music For Nations / Sep '91 / Pinnacle.

REIGN IN BLOOD.
Tracks: Angel of death / Piece by piece / Necrophobic / Altar of sacrifice / Jesus saves / Criminally insane / Reborn / Epidemic / Postmortem / Raining blood.
- ■ LP P.Disc . . . . LONPP 34
- ■ LP . . . . LONLP 34
- ■ MC . . . . LONC 34
London / Apr '87.

SEASONS IN THE ABYSS.
Tracks: Seasons in the abyss / Aggressive perfector / Chemical warfare (live) (Only on 12" single).
- ■ 12" P.Disc. . . . . DEFAP 912
- ■ CD Single . . . . DEFAC 9
- ■ 12" . . . . DEFA 912
- ■ 7" . . . . DEFA 9
American Recordings / Oct '91.

SEASONS IN THE ABYSS.
Tracks: Not Advised.
CD 84968712
- ■ LP 84968711
MC 84968714
American Recordings / Sep '90 / PolyGram.

SHOW NO MERCY.
Tracks: Evil has no boundaries / Die by the sword / Metal storm / Black magic / Final command / Show no mercy / Antichrist / Fight till death / Aggressive perfector / Tormentor / Crionics / Face the Slayer.
- ■ LP . . . . RR 9868
Road Runner / Jun '84.
- ■ LP P.Disc 722141
Metal Blade / Dec '88.
CD . . . . RR 349868
MC . . . . RR 986 84
Road Runner / Feb '89 / Pinnacle.
CD . . . . CDZORRO 7
LP . . . . ZORRO 7
MC . . . . TZORRO 7
Zorro / Aug '90 / Pinnacle.

SLAYER: INTERVIEW PICTURE DISC.
Tracks: Not Advised.
LP P.Disc . . . . BAK 2046
Baktabak / Jun '87 / Arabesque Ltd.

SOUTH OF HEAVEN.
Tracks: South of heaven / Silent scream / Live undead / Behind the crooked cross / Mandatory suicide

/ Ghosts of war / Read between the lies / Cleanse the soul / Dissident aggressor / Spill the blood.
- ■ LP . . . . LONLP 63
MC . . . . LONC 63
- ■ CD 828 820-2
London / Jun '88.
CD 828 080 2
London / Jul '90 / PolyGram.

SOUTH OF HEAVEN.
Tracks: South of heaven.
- ■ 12" . . . . LONX 201
London / Sep '88.

Sledgehammer

BLOOD ON THEIR HANDS.
Tracks: Not Advised.
- ■ LP . . . . JAMS 32
Illuminated / Feb '85.

IN THE QUEUE.
Tracks: In the queue / Oxford City.
- ■ 7" P.Disc . . . . ILL 333
Illuminated / Mar '85.

LIVING IN DREAMS.
Tracks: Living in dreams / Fantasia.
- ■ 7" . . . . CELL 2
Slammer / Jan '81.

Sleep

SLEEPS HOLY MOUNTAIN.
Tracks: Dragonaut / Druid / Evil gypsy / Some grass / Aquarian / Holy mountain / Inside the sun / From beyond / Nain's baptism.
CD . . . . MOSH 079CD
LP . . . . MOSH 079
MC . . . . MOSH 079MC
Earache / Mar '93 / Vital Distribution.

SUFFOCATE E.P.
Tracks: Not Advised.
- ■ 7" . . . . COX 030
Meantime / Apr '92.

VOLUME ONE.
Tracks: Not Advised.
CD . . . . TUPCD 034
LP . . . . TUPLP 034
MC . . . . TUPMC 034
Tupelo / Feb '92 / Vital Distribution.

WHO'S THE SAVAGE.
Tracks: Who's the savage.
- ■ 7" . . . . COXEP 005
Meantime / Nov '90.

Slick, Earl

IN YOUR FACE.
Tracks: Not Advised.
CD . . . . CDZORRO 34
LP . . . . ZORRO 34
MC . . . . TZORRO 34
Music For Nations / Sep '91 / Pinnacle.

Slide

DOWN SO LONG.
Tracks: Not Advised.
- ■ CD 838 964 2
- ■ LP 838 964 1
- ■ MC 838 964 4
Mercury / Oct '89.

DOWN SO LONG.
Tracks: Down so long / Don't turn your back / Listen (Available on CD and cassette single only.)
- ■ 12" . . . . MERX 312
- ■ 7" . . . . MER 312
- ■ CD Single . . . . MERCD 312
- ■ MC Single . . . . MERMX 312
Mercury / Jan '90.

SUPERMAN'S SHOES.
Tracks: Superman's shoes / Meet your new neighbour.
- ■ 7" . . . . POW 4
Crash / Oct '80.

WHY IS IT A CRIME?.
Tracks: Why is it a crime / Never ever / Leave your love (Only on 12" and CD single.)
- ■ 12" . . . . MERX 292
- ■ 7" . . . . MER 292
- ■ CD Single . . . . MERCD 292
Mercury / Aug '89.

WHY IS IT A CRIME? (REMIX).
Tracks: Why is it a crime / I want to be satisfied.
- 12" .... MERX 324
- 7" .... MER 324
- CD Single .... MERCD 324

Mercury / Jul '90.

Sloppy Seconds

DESTROYED.
Tracks: I don't wanna be a homosexual / Come back Traci / Take you home / Black roses / Runnin from the C.I.A. / Horror of party beach / Black mail / So fucked up / Germany / Janie is a nazi / I want 'em dead / If I had a woman / Veronica / Candy man / Steal your beer / Time bomb.
- CD .... CDZORR 071

Metal Blade / Mar '94 / Pinnacle.

KNOCK YOUR BLOCK OFF.
Tracks: Not Advised.
- CD .... TAANG 71CD
- LP .... TAANG 71
- MC .... TAANG 71MC

Taang / Jun '93 / Plastic Head.

LONELY CHRISTMAS.
Tracks: Not Advised.
- 7" .... TAANGS 68
- CD Single .... TAANG 68

Taang / Dec '93.

SLOPPY SECONDS.
Tracks: Not Advised.
- CD .... TAANG 059CD
- LP .... TAANG 059

Taang / Jun '92 / Plastic Head.

WHERE THE EAGLES DARE.
Tracks: Not Advised.
- CD .... MA 113231CD

Musical Tragedy / Nov '92 / SRD.

Slug The Night Watchman

IT'S ALRIGHT.
Tracks: It's alright.
- 7" .... LGY 107

Legacy / Dec '90.

SLUG THE NIGHT WATCHMAN.
Tracks: Slap my face / Jesus and Mary / British steel / Don't build me up / Drinking my whisky / Holy man / Consuela / Happening thing / Sweet Louise / Texas information / Can't stop it (Only on CD.) / Sell my soul (Only on CD.) / L.U.R.V.E. (Only on CD.).
- CD .... LLCD 131
- LP .... LLP 131
- MC .... LLK 131

Legacy / Mar '90.

Smashed Gladys

17 GOIN' ON CRAZY.
Tracks: 17 goin' on crazy / Hard to swallow.
- 7" .... VHF 22

FM Records / Oct '85.

SMASHED GLADYS.
Tracks: Not Advised.
- LP .... USA 49
- MC .... HMAMC 49

Heavy Metal America / Nov '85 / FM Revolver / Sony.
- CD .... HMUSA 49

Heavy Metal America / Nov '85 / FM Revolver / Sony.

SOCIAL INTERCOURSE.
Tracks: Lick it into shape / 17 goin' on crazy / Play dirty / Dive in the dark / Eye of the storm / Hard to swallow / Legs up / Eye for an eye / Cast of nasties / Sermonette.
- CD .... K 9607762
- LP .... K 9607761
- MC .... K 9607764

Elektra / Apr '88.

Smashing Pumpkins

Undeservedly eclipsed by *Nevermind*, Smashing Pumpkins' debut *Gish*, released at the same time as Nirvana's mega-seller, nontheless sold respectably. Excellent *I Am One*, one of '92's best singles, paved way for *Siamese Dream* album, which entered U.K. Top Five and Billboard Top Ten in July '93. Six years after formation, and having overcome internal strife, Pumpkins headlined Lollapalooza '94.

CHERUB ROCK.
Tracks: Cherub rock.
- 12" .... HUTT 31

- CD Single .... HUTTCD 31
- 7" .... HUT 31

Hut / Jun '93.

DISARM.
Tracks: Disarm / Siamese dream (Available on 7 only) / Soothe (demo) (Not available on 7) / Blew away (Not available on 7) / Landslide (Available on CDS only) / Dancing in the moonlight (Available on CDS only).
- 12" .... HUTT 43
- 7" .... HUT 43
- CD Single .... HUTDX 43
- CD Single .... HUTCD 43

Hut / Feb '94.

GISH.
Tracks: I am one / Siva / Rhinoceros / Bury me / Crush / Snail / Fristessa / Window paine / Daydream / Suffer.
- CD .... HUTCD 002
- LP .... HUTLP 002
- MC .... HUTMC 002

Hut / Feb '92 / EMI.
- CD .... HUTCDX 2
- LP .... HUTLPX 2
- MC .... HUTMCX 2

Hut / May '94 / EMI.

I AM ONE.
Tracks: I am one.
- 10" .... HUTEN 018
- 12" .... HUT 018T
- 7" .... HUT 018
- CD Single .... HUT 018CD

Hut / Aug '92.

LULL.
Tracks: Lull.
- 12" .... HUT 010T
- CD Single .... HUT 010CD

Hut / Jan '92.

PEEL SESSIONS.
Tracks: Not Advised.
- 12" .... HUT 017T
- CD Single .... HYT 017CD
- MC Single .... HUT 017C

Hut / Jun '92.

SIAMESE DREAM.
Tracks: Cherub rock / Quiet / Today / Hummer / Rocket / Disarm / Soma / Geek USA / Mayonaise / Spaceboy / Silverfuck / Sweet sweet / Luna.
- CD .... CDHUT 11
- LP .... HUTLP 11
- MC .... HUTMC 11

Hut / Jun '93 / EMI.

TODAY.
Tracks: Today.
- 12" .... HUTT 37
- CD Single .... HUTCD 37
- MC Single .... HUTC 37
- 7" .... HUT 37

Hut / Sep '93.

TRISTESSA.
Tracks: Not Advised.
- 12" .... SP 137

Sub Pop / May '93.

So Much Hate

BLIND ALLEY.
Tracks: Not Advised.
- LP .... XM 012

X-Mist Records / Apr '92 / Plastic Head.

DAY AT THE STAT, A.
Tracks: Day at the stat.
- 7" .... XM 030

X-Mist Records / Apr '92.

LIES.
Tracks: Not Advised.
- CD .... XM 040
- LP .... XM 040LP

X-Mist Records / Dec '93 / Plastic Head.

SEEING RED.
Tracks: Not Advised.
- LP .... XM 026

X-Mist Records / Apr '92 / Plastic Head.

SO MUCH HATE: LIVE.
Tracks: Not Advised.
- LP .... YCR 001

Your Choice / '92 / Plastic Head.

Sodom

AGENT ORANGE.
Tracks: Agent orange / Tired and red / Incest / Remember the fallen / Magic dragon / Exhibition bout / Ausgebombt / Baptism of fire.
- LP 08-7598

Steamhammer (Germany) / Jun '89.

AUSGEBOMBT.
Tracks: Not Advised.
- LP 507604

Steamhammer (Germany) / '90 / Pinnacle.

BETTER OFF DEAD.
Tracks: Eye for an eye / Saw is the law / Capture the flag / Never healing wound / Resurrection / Shellfire defense / Turn your head around / Bloodtrials / Better off dead / Stalinorgel.
- CD 8476261
- LP 0876261
- MC 0876264

Steamhammer (Germany) / Nov '90 / Pinnacle.

BUTT WITH WHIPPED CREAM.
Tracks: Butt with whipped cream.
- 12" .... SPV 055-76723
- CD Single .... SPV 055-76723 2

SPV / May '94 / Plastic Head.

EXPOSURE OF SODOM.
Tracks: Exposure of sodom.
- 12" 502123

S.P.V. / Aug '89.

GET WHAT YOU DESERVE.
Tracks: Not Advised.
- CD .... SPV 0847676-2
- LP .... SPV 0087676-1
- MC .... SPV 0087676-4

SPV / May '94 / Plastic Head.

IN THE SIGN OF EVIL.
Tracks: Outbreak of evil / Blasphemer / Burst command 'til war / Sepulchral voice / Witching metal.
- CD 607 598

S.P.V. / Jul '89.
- LP 602 120

Steamhammer (Germany) / Jul '89.

OBSESSED BY CRUELTY.
Tracks: Not Advised.
- LP .... SH 0040

Steamhammer (Germany) / Jun '86.
- CD 857 533
- LP 082 121

Steamhammer (Germany) / '88.

PERSECUTION MANIA.
Tracks: Not Advised.
- CD 857 509
- LP 087 507
- MC 085 708

Steamhammer (Germany) / Jun '88 / Pinnacle.

THIS MORTAL WAY OF LIFE.
Tracks: Not Advised.
- LP 807 575

Steamhammer (Germany) / '89.

THIS WAY OF LIFE.
Tracks: Not Advised.
- CD 847576

Steamhammer (Germany) / '90 / Pinnacle.

Soho Roses

SO ALONE.
Tracks: So alone / Yesterday's girl.
- 12" .... TWAT 00212
- 7" .... TWAT 002

Trashcan / Sep '88.

Solitude Aeturnus

BEYOND THE CRIMSON HORIZONS.
Tracks: Not Advised.
- LP .... RO 91681

Road Runner / May '92.
- CD .... RO 91682

Road Runner / Jan '94 / Pinnacle.

INTO THE DEPTHS OF SORROW.
Tracks: Not Advised.
- CD .... RO 92652
- LP .... RO 92651
- MC .... RO 92654

Roadracer / Sep '91 / Pinnacle.

Sonic Violence

CASKET CASE.
Tracks: Not Advised.
■ LP . . . . VILE 023
Peaceville / Dec '90.

JAGD.
Tracks: Not Advised.
■ CD . . . . VILE 020 CD
■ LP . . . . VILE 020
■ MC . . . . VILE 020 MC
Peaceville / Sep '90.

SACRIFICE TO STRENGTH.
Tracks: Sacrifice to strength.
■ 12" . . . . SV 1844
Sound Violation / May '90.

TRANSFIXION.
Tracks: Not Advised.
CD . . . . KTB 004CD
LP . . . . KTB 004
■ MC . . . . KTB 004MC
Dreamtime / May '92.

Sonic Youth

Hugely influential alternative act who seem destined to remain eclipsed by bands who cite them as influence; notably Nirvana, signed to Geffen at behest of Youth mainman Thurston Moore. Formed in '83, band released series of highly-acclaimed and modestly-successful albums, before Geffen deal brought them slightly closer to mainstream: '92's *Dirty* and '94's *Experimental Jet Set, Trash* and *No Star* both entered U.K. Top 10. Uncompromising sound suggests that selective appeal is deliberate rather than unfortunate.

100%.
Tracks: 100%.
■ 10" . . . . DGCV 11
■ 12" . . . . DGCT 11
■ CD Single . . . . .DGCTD 11
■ MC Single . . . . DGCS 11
Geffen / Jun '92.

1991: THE YEAR THAT PUNK BROKE.
Tracks: Schizophrenia / Negative creep / Brother James / School / Teenage riot / Freak scene / Dustcake boy / Dirty boots / Endless, nameless / I love her all the time / Gumball / Wagon / Mote / Smells like teen spirit / Cammando / Kool thing / Polly / Expressway to yr skull.
VHS . . . . .GEFV 39518
Geffen / Feb '93 / BMG.

BAD MOON RISING.
Tracks: Not Advised.
■ LP . . . . BFFP 1
Blast First / Mar '85.
CD . . . . BFFP 1 CD
Blast First / Nov '86 / RTM / Pinnacle.

BULL IN THE HEATHER.
Tracks: Bull in the heather.
■ 12" . . . . .GFSV 72
■ CD Single . . . . .GFSTD 72
■ MC Single . . . . GFSC 72
Geffen / Apr '94.

CONFUSION IS SEX.
Tracks: Inhuman / World looks red / Confusion is sex / Making the nature scene / Lee is free / She's in a bad mood / Protect me you / Freezer burn / Shaking hell / I wanna be your dog.
■ LP . . . . ND 02
Neutral / Feb '84.
■ LP . . . . SST 096
SST / Oct '87.
■ CD . . . . .SST 096 CD
SST / Sep '87.

DAYDREAM NATION.
Tracks: Not Advised.
CD .BFFP 34 CD
■ LP . . . . BFFP 34
MC . . . . BFFP 34C
Blast First / Oct '88 / RTM / Pinnacle.

DEATH VALLEY 69 (Sonic Youth & Lydia Lunch).
Tracks: Death valley 69.
■ 12" . . . . BFFP 2
Blast First / Jun '85.

DIRTY.
Tracks: 100% / Swimsuit issue / Theresa's sound world / Drunken butterfly / Shoot / Wish fulfillment / Sugar kane / Orange rolls, angel's spit / Youth

against facism / Nic fit / On the strip / Chapel hill / Stalker / JC / Purr creme brulee.
CD . . . . DGCD 24425
■ LP . . . . DGC 24485
MC . . . . DGCC 24485
Geffen / Aug '92 / BMG.

DIRTY BOOTS EP.
Tracks: Dirty boots (edit) / White kross (live) / Eric's trip (live) / Cinderella's big score (live) / Dirty boots (live) / Bedroom, The (live).
■ CD . . . . DGCD 21634
■ MC . . . . DGCC 21634
■ Mini LP . . . . DGC 21634
Geffen / Apr '91.
■ MC . . . . DGLC 19060
■ CD . . . . DGLD 19060
Geffen / Apr '92.

E.V.O.L.
Tracks: Not Advised.
■ LP . . . . BFFP 4
MC . . . . BFFP 4C
Blast First / May '86 / RTM / Pinnacle.
CD .BFFP 4CD
Blast First / Nov '86 / RTM / Pinnacle.

EXPERIMENTAL JET SET.
Tracks: Not Advised.
CD . . . . GED 24632
MC . . . . GEC 24632
Geffen / May '94 / BMG.

FLOWER.
Tracks: Flower.
■ 12" . . . . BFFP 3
Blast First / Jan '86.

GOO.
Tracks: Dirty boots / Tunic (song for Karen) / MaryChrist / Kool thing / Mote / My friend Goo / Disappearer / Mildred Pierce / Cinderella's big score / Scooter and Jinx / Titanium expose.
CD 7599242972
■ LP 7599242971
MC 7599242974
Geffen / Jun '90 / BMG.
■ CD . . . . DGCD 24297
■ LP . . . . DGC 24297
MC . . . . DGCC 24297
Geffen / May '91 / BMG.

GOO.
Tracks: Not Advised.
VHS . . . . DGCV 39508
Geffen Video / '91 / BMG.

HALLOWEEN 2/SAVAGE PENCIL.
Tracks: Halloween 2.
■ 12" . . . . .BFFP 3P
Blast First / Jul '86.

I'M GONNA FUCK YOUR MOTHER.
Tracks: Not Advised.
■ Double LP . . . . .KAR 006
No. 6 (USA) / '88.

KILL YOUR IDOLS.
Tracks: Not Advised.
■ LP . . . . ZS 010
Zensor (Germany) / Feb '84.
■ LP . . . . ZENSOR 10
Zensor (Germany) / Sep '87.

KOOL THING.
Tracks: Kool thing.
■ 12" . . . . .GEF 81T
■ 7" . . . . GEF 81
■ CD Single . . . . .GEF 81CD
■ MC Single . . . . GEF 81C
Geffen / Sep '90.

MASTER DIK.
Tracks: Beat on the brat / Master Dik.
■ 12" . . . . BFFP 12T
Blast First.

SISTER.
Tracks: Not Advised.
CD . . . . BFFP 20CD
Blast First / RTM / Pinnacle.
■ LP . . . . .BFFP 20
MC . . . . BFFP 20C
Blast First / Jun '87 / RTM / Pinnacle.

SONIC DEATH (Early Sonic Youth - live 1981-83).
Tracks: Not Advised.
CD . . . . BFFP 32CD
Blast First / '89 / RTM / Pinnacle.

SONIC LIFE.
Tracks: Sonic life.
■ 7" P.Disc . . . . .SY 001
Nuovi Equilibri / Mar '92.

SONIC YOUTH.
Tracks: Not Advised.
■ LP . . . . ND 01
Neutral / Feb '84.
■ LP . . . . ND 001
Zensor (Germany) / Mar '86.
CD . . . . .SST 097 CD
■ LP . . . . SST 097
SST / Oct '87.

SONIC YOUTH.
Tracks: Not Advised.
VHS . . . . DGCV 39508
MCA / Jul '91 / BMG.

STARPOWER.
Tracks: Starpower / Bubblegum / To your soul (Available on 12" version only).
■ 12" . . . . .BFFP 7T
■ 7" . . . . BFFP 7
Blast First / Oct '86.

SUGAR KANE.
Tracks: Sugar kane.
■ 12" . . . . .GFSV 37
■ CD Single . . . . .GFSTD 37
■ MC Single . . . . GFSC 37
Geffen / Mar '93.

TOUCH ME I'M SICK (Sonic Youth & Mudhoney).
Tracks: Touch me I'm sick / Halloween.
■ 12" . . . . .BFFP 46
Blast First / Jan '89.

YESTERDAY ONCE MORE/SUPERSTAR
(see under Redd Kross).

Sons Of Angels

SONS OF ANGELS.
Tracks: Not Advised.
■ CD 7567821012
■ LP 7567821011
MC 7567821014
WEA / Aug '90 / WEA.

Sore Throat

DIGGIN' A DREAM.
Tracks: Diggin' a dream / Stocker stomp.
■ 7" . . . . FIRE 13
Hurricane (1) / Apr '80.

DISGRACE TO THE CORPSE OF SID.
Tracks: Not Advised.
■ LP . . . . MOSH 10
Earache / May '89.

KAMIKAZI KID.
Tracks: Kamikazi kid / Crack down.
■ 7" . . . . .FIRE 2
Hurricane (1) / May '79.

NEVER MIND THE NAPALM HERE'S SORE THROAT.
Tracks: Intro (rapists die) / D.T.C.H.C. / Vac head / Process of elimination / S.S.A. (part 2) / R.O.T. / Only the dead / War system / Sacrilege / Pesticide death / Trenchfoot / Satans radish / Funicidal tendencies / Bomb The Whitehouse.
■ LP . . . . EARLP 001
Manic Ears / Nov '89.

SOONER THAN YOU THINK.
Tracks: Wonder drug / 7th heaven / Flak jacket / Routine patrol / British subject / Mr. Right / Off the hook / Crackdrown / Sooner than you think.
■ LP . . . . FLAK 101
Hurricane (1) / Nov '79.

UNHINDERED BY TALENT.
Tracks: Not Advised.
■ LP . . . . .COX 012
Meantime / Mar '89.

ZOMBIE ROCK.
Tracks: Zombie rock / I don't wanna go home.
■ 7" . . . . ION 3
Albion / Sep '78.

Sorrow

FORGOTTEN SUNRISE.
Tracks: Not Advised.
CD. . . . . R 09262
LP . . . . R 09261
Road Runner / Sep '91 / Pinnacle.

HATRED & DISGUST.
Tracks: Insatiable / Forced repression / Illusion of freedom / Human error / Separative adjectives / Unjustified reluctance.
■ CD. . . . . RR 91262
■ LP . . . . RR 91261
Road Runner / Oct '92.

TAKE A HEART.
Tracks: Not Advised.
CD. . . . . REP 4093-WZ
Repertoire (Germany) / Aug '91 / Pinnacle.

Soul Asylum

Minneapolis based four-piece were initially overshadowed by The Replacements and Husker Du before the single *Cartoon* from the album *Hang Time* provided them with a college radio hit. With the rise of 'grunge' and the sudden appeal of U.S. indie rock Soul Asylum landed a deal with Columbia and the single *Runaway Train* from their second Columbia album *Grave Dancer's Union* propelled them into the charts on both sides of the Atlantic.

AND THE HORSE THEY RODE IN ON.
Tracks: Spinnin / Bitter pill / Veil of tears / Nice guys (Don't get paid) / Something out of nothing / Gullible's travels / Brand new shine / Easy street / Grounded / Be on your way / We 3 / All the king's friend.
■ CD. 3953182
■ LP 3953181
■ MC. 3953184
A&M / Sep '90.
CD. . . . . CDMID 190
MC. . . . . CMID 190
A&M / Nov '93 / PolyGram.

BLACK GOLD.
Tracks: Black gold / Black gold (Live) / Break / 99% / Somebody to shove (unplugged) (On '94 re-issue only) / Closer to the stairs (On '94 CD single re-issue only) / Square root (On '94 CD single re-issue only).
■ 10". 659088 0
■ CD Single. 659088 2
Columbia / Mar '93.
■ 7". 659844 7
■ CD Single. 659844 2
■ CD Single. 659844 5
■ MC Single. 659844 4
Columbia / Jan '94.

CARTOON.
Tracks: Cartoon / Twiddly dee / Standing in the doorway (Only on the 12" version).
■ 12". . . . . AMY 463
■ 7". AM 463
A&M / Aug '88.

CLAM DIP & OTHER DELIGHTS.
Tracks: Just plain evil / Chains / Secret no more / Artificial heart / P-9 / Take it to the root.
■ LP . . . . GOES ON 22
What Goes On / '87.
CD. . . . . CDRR 9097 2
Twin Tone / Mar '93 / Pinnacle.

GRAVE DANCERS UNION.
Tracks: Somebody to shove / Black gold / Runaway train / Keep it up / Homesick / Get on out / New world / April fool / Without a trace / Growing into you / 99% / Sun maid.
CD. .472253-2
■ LP .472253-1
MC. .472253-4
Columbia / Oct '92 / Sony.
MiniDisc. 472253 8
Columbia / Jul '94 / Sony.

HANG TIME.
Tracks: Down on up to me / Little too clean / Sometime to return / Cartoon / Beggars and choosers / Endless farewell / Standing in the doorway / Marionette / Ode / Jack of all trades / Twiddly dee / Heavy rotation.
■ CD. . . . . CDA 5197
■ LP . . . . AMA 5197
■ MC. . . . . AMC 5197
A&M / Jun '88.
CD. . . . . CDMID 189
MC. . . . . CMID 189
A&M / Nov '93 / PolyGram.

MADE TO BE BROKEN.
Tracks: Tied to the tracks / Ship of fools / Can't go back / Another world, Another Day / Made to be broken / Never really been / Whoa / New feelings / Growing pain / Long way home / Lone rider / Ain't that tough / Don't it..
■ LP . . . . .ROUGH 102
Rough Trade / Sep '86.
CD. .RR 9094 2
Twin Tone / Mar '93 / Pinnacle.

RUNAWAY TRAIN.
Tracks: Runaway train / By the way (live) / Never really been (live) / Black gold (live) (On 12' only) / Everybody loves a winner (On CD single only).
■ 12". 6593908
■ 12". 6593906
■ 7". 6593907
■ CD Single. 6593902
■ MC Single. 6593904
Columbia / Jun '93.

SAY WHAT YOU WILL, CLARENCE, KARL SOLD THE TRUCK.
Tracks: Draggin me down / Long day / Money talks / Voodoo doll / Stranger / Do you know / Sick of that song / Religiavision / Spacehead / Walking / Broken glass / Masquerade / Happy / Black and blue.
CD. . . . . RR 9093 2
Twin Tone / Mar '93 / Pinnacle.

SOMEBODY TO SHOVE.
Tracks: Somebody to shove / By the way (Available on 7 & MCS only) / Somebody to shove (unplugged) (Not available on 7 or MCS) / Without a trace (live) (Not available on 7 or MCS) / Stranger (unplugged) (Available on CDS 2 only).
■ 7". 660224 7
■ CD Single. 660224 2
■ CD Single. 660224 5
■ MC Single. 660224 4
Columbia / Mar '94.

SOMETIME TO RETURN.
Tracks: Sometime to return / Put the bone in.
■ 12". . . . . AMY 447
■ 7". AM 447
A&M / Jun '88.

WHILE YOU WERE OUT.
Tracks: Freaks / Carry on / No man's land / Crashing down / Judge / Sun don't shine / Closer to the stars / Never too soon / Miracle mile / Lap of luxury / Passing sad daydream.
■ LP . . . . GOES ON 16
What Goes On / Mar '88.
CD. .RR 9096 2
Twin Tone / Mar '93 / Pinnacle.

Sound Barrier

FASTEN YOUR SEAT BELT.
Tracks: Fasten your seat belts / Fasten your seat belt.
■ 12". . . . . .ACTX 17
Compact Organisation / Jul '85.

MORNINGTON CRESCENT.
Tracks: Mornington crescent / Bank holiday.
■ 7". ACT 11
Compact Organisation / Jun '84.

SUBURBIA SUITE, THE.
Tracks: Not Advised.
■ LP . . . . .PACT 10
Compact Organisation / Jun '85.

Soundgarden

One of the first Seattle bands to be signed by a major label, therefore neatly avoiding getting lumped in with the worst of the Grunge hysteria. Consequently, they also managed to miss out on some of the glory but will surely benefit in the long-run as they have been given the space to develop at their own pace. Fronted by the excellent Chris Cornell, Soundgarden were originally compared to Led Zeppelin and Black Sabbath but have carved a niche all their own - whilst retaining a firm grip on their early 70's routes. Great guitar work by Kim Thayil helped the albums *Louder Than Love*, *Superunknown* and *Badmotorfinger* touch a nerve with rock fans too young to remember the band's mentors as well as those older who could.

BADMOTORFINGER.
Tracks: Rusty cage / Outshined / Slaves & bulldozers / Jesus christ pose / Face pollution / Somewhere /

Searching with my good eye closed / Room a thousand years wide / Mind riot / Drawing flies / Holy water / New damage.
CD. 395374 2
LP .395374 1
MC. 395374 4
A&M / Oct '91 / PolyGram.

BLACK HOLE SUN.
Tracks: Black hole Sun / My wave / Beyond the wheel / Fell on black days (On 1st CD only) / Birth ritual (On 1st CD only) / Jesus Christ pose (On 2nd CD only) / Spoonman (On 2nd CD only).
CD Single. 580737-2
A&M / Aug '94 / PolyGram.
7". 580736-7
CD Single. 580753-2
MC Single. 580736-4
A&M / Jul '94 / PolyGram.

DAY I TRIED TO LIVE, THE.
Tracks: Day I tried to live / Like suicide / Kickstand (On 12"/CDs only).
■ 12". 580595-1
■ 7". 580594-7
■ MC Single. 580594-4
A&M / Apr '94.
CD Single. 580595-2
A&M / Aug '94 / PolyGram.

FLOWER.
Tracks: Flower.
■ 12". . . . . .SST 231
■ CD Single. . . . . .SST 231 CD
■ MC Single. . . . . .SST 231 C
SST / May '89.
■ 10". . . . . .SST 911
SST / May '93.

HANDS ALL OVER.
Tracks: Hands all over / Come together / Heretic / Big dumb sex.
■ 10". . . . . .AMX 560
■ CD Single. . . . . .AMCD 560
A&M / Apr '90.

JESUS CHRIST POSE.
Tracks: Jesus Christ pose.
■ 7". . . . . .AM 862
■ CD Single. . . . . .AMCD 862
A&M / Apr '92.

LOUD LOVE.
Tracks: Loud love.
■ 12". . . . . .AMY 574
■ 7". . . . . .AM 574
A&M / Jul '90.

LOUDER THAN LOVE.
Tracks: Ugly truth / Hands all over / Gun / Power trip / Get on the snake / Full on Kevin's Mom / Loud love / I wake / Now wrong no right / Uncovered / Big dumb sex.
CD. . . . . .CDA 5252
■ LP . . . . .AMA 5252
MC. . . . . .AMC 5252
A&M / Sep '89 / PolyGram.

LOUDER THAN LOVE.
Tracks: Not Advised.
VHS . . . . .AMV 070
A&M Sound Pictures / Aug '90 / Gold & Sons / PolyGram Music Video / TBD.

LOUDER THAN LOVE/BADMOTORFINGER.
Tracks: Not Advised.
CD. . . . . CDA 24118
A&M / Oct '93 / PolyGram.

RUSTY CAGE.
Tracks: Rusty cage.
■ 12". . . . . .AMY 723
■ 7". . . . . .AM 874
■ CD Single. . . . . .AMCD 724
A&M / Jun '92.

SCREAMING LIFE.
Tracks: Not Advised.
CD. . . . . .SPCD 12B
MC. SP 12A
Sub Pop / Oct '93 / RTM.

SCREAMING LIFE/FOPP.
Tracks: Not Advised.
CD. . . . . .SPCD 12A/B
MC. . . . . .SP 12A/B
Sub Pop / Feb '94 / RTM.

SPOONMAN.
Tracks: Spoonman / Fresh tendrils / Cold bitch (On 12"/CDs only) / Exit Stonehenge (On 12"/CDs only).
CD Single. 580539-2
A&M / Aug '94 / PolyGram.

■ DELETED

■ 12″. .580539-1
■ 7″. 580538-7
■ MC Single. 580538-4
A&M / Feb '94.

SUPERUNKNOWN.
Tracks: Let me drown / My wave / Fell on black days / Mailman / Superunknown / Head down / Black hole sun / Spoonman / Limo wreck / Day I tried to live / Kickstand / Fresh tendrils / 4th of July / Half / Like suicide / She likes surprises.
CD. 540215-2
LP Set. .540215-1
MC. 540215-4
A&M / Mar '94 / PolyGram.

ULTRAMEGA OK.
Tracks: Not Advised.
CD . . . . .SST 201 CD
■ LP . . . . .SST 201
MC. . . . . .SST 201 C
SST / Nov '88 / Pinnacle.

Spartan Warrior

STEEL N CHAINS.
Tracks: Not Advised.
■ LP . . . . .GRC 2164
Guardian / Aug '84.

Spellbound

ABCDEFGHIJKL.O.V.E I LOVE YOU.
Tracks: ABCDEFGHIJKL.O.V.E I love you / Don't ya do me that way.
■ 12″. . . . . .SPELX 1
■ 7″. . . . . .SPELL 1
Chrysalis / Jun '83.

BEST IS YET TO COME.
Tracks: Best is yet to come / TGast of the devil.
■ 7″. . . . . .AMI 502
EMI-America / Jun '78.

BREAKING THE SPELL.
Tracks: Not Advised.
■ LP . . . . .SNTF 934
Sonet / Jul '88.

DARK DAYS EP.
Tracks: Not Advised.
CD. . . . . .NBX 005
Backs / Jun '94 / RTM / Pinnacle.

MY KINDA GIRL.
Tracks: My kinda girl / Gone rockin'.
■ 7″. .SON 2294
Sonet / May '86.

ROCKIN' RECKLESS.
Tracks: Rockin' reckless.
■ LP . . . . .SNTF 952
Sonet / Jul '88.

ROCKIN' RECKLESS.
Tracks: Rockin' reckless.
■ 7″. .SON 2306
Sonet / Sep '86.

Sphinx

BURNING LIGHTS.
Tracks: Not Advised.
■ LP . . . . .SKULL 8389
Mausoleum / May '85.

Spider

ALL THE TIME.
Tracks: All the time.
■ 7″. . . . . .NIK 7
City / '81.

BREAKAWAY.
Tracks: Breakaway / Morning after.
■ 12″. .AMX 204
■ 7″. . . . . .AM 204
A&M / Jul '84.

COLLEGE LUV.
Tracks: College luv / Born to be wild.
■ 7″. .ALIEN 16
Alien / Oct '80.

GIMME GIMME IT ALL.
Tracks: Gimme gimme it all / Rock tonight / Live recording from the Kerrang concert (This track on double pack single) / Gimme gimme it all (extended version:see notes) (12″ Version only) / Did ya like it baby (12″ Version only).
■ 12″. .12P 344
■ 7″. 7P 344

■ 7″ Set 7PX 344
PRT / Mar '86.

HERE WE GO ROCK 'N' ROLL.
Tracks: Here we go 'n' roll / Death row / I just wanna make love to you (on 12″ only).
■ 12″. .AMX 180
■ 7″. . . . . .AM 180
■ 7″ P.Disc . . . . .AMP 180
A&M / Mar '84.

ROCK 'N' ROLL FOREVER WILL LAST.
Tracks: Rock 'n' roll forever will last / Did ya like it baby.
■ 7″. . . . . .RCA 268
RCA / Aug '82.

ROCK 'N' ROLL GYPSIES.
Tracks: A.W.O.L. / Talkin' bout rock 'n' roll / Part of the legend / Did ya like it baby / Them that start the fightin' (don't fight) / What you're doing to me / Lady (I'm dyin' for you) / Till I'm certain / Rock 'n' roll forever will last / All the time.
■ LP .RCALP 3101
■ MC .RCAK 3101
RCA / Oct '82.

ROUGH JUSTICE.
Tracks: Here we go rock 'n' roll / Moring after the night before / Rock 'n' roll gypsies / Martyred / Time to go now / Death row / Minstrel / You make me offers / Midsummer morning.
■ LP .AMLX 68563
A&M / Apr '84.

TALKIN' 'BOUT ROCK 'N' ROLL.
Tracks: Talkin' 'bout rock 'n' roll / Down 'n' out.
■ 7″. . . . . .RCA 294
RCA / Nov '82.

TALKIN' 'BOUT ROCK 'N' ROLL (2).
Tracks: Talkin' 'bout rock'n'roll / 'Til I'm certain.
■ 7″. . . . . .CR 30
Creole / Mar '82.

WHY D'YA LIE TO ME.
Tracks: Why d'ya lie to me / Footloose / 9 to 5.
■ 12″. .RCAT 313
■ 7″. . . . . .RCA 313
RCA / Feb '83.

Spider

BETTER BE GOOD TO ME.
Tracks: Better be good to me / Our love.
■ 7″. . . . . .DLSP 11
Dreamland / May '81.

EVERYTHING IS ALRIGHT.
Tracks: Everything is alright / Shady lady.
■ 7″. . . . . .DLSP 4
Dreamland / Aug '80.

NEW ROMANCE.
Tracks: New romance / Cross fire.
■ 7″. .209044-1
RSO / May '80.

SPIDER.
Tracks: New romance / Burning love / Shady lady / Everything is alright / Crossfire / Little darlin' / Brotherly love / What's going on / Don't waste your time / Zero.
■ LP 2394 260
RSO / Aug '80.

Spinal Tap

Spoof metal band spawned by mock documentary film *This Is Spinal Tap* in 1984. Movie became obligatory tour-bus viewing, especially among bands who recognised own excesses in Tap's antics. Of those lampooned, only Kiss' Gene Simmons declined to see joke. Act was revived in 1992, yielding acclaimed appearance at Freddie Mercury tribute concert and appropriately minor chart success with *Bitch School* single and *Break Like The Wind* album.

BITCH SCHOOL.
Tracks: Bitch school / Springtime.
■ 12″ P.Disc. . . . . .MCSTP 1624
■ 7″. .MCS 1624
■ CD Single. . . . . .MCSD 1624
■ MC Single. . . . . .MCSC 1624
MCA / Mar '92.

BREAK LIKE THE WIND.
Tracks: Not Advised.
■ CD . . . . .MCAD 10514
■ LP .MCA 10514

■ MC . . . . .MCAC 10514
MCA / Mar '92.

MAJESTY OF ROCK.
Tracks: Majesty of rock.
■ 7″. .MCS 1629
■ CD Single . . . . .MCSTD 1629
■ MC Single. . . . . .MCSC 1629
MCA / Apr '92.

THIS IS SPINAL TAP (Tour Soundtrack).
Tracks: Hell hole / Tonight I'm gonna rock you / Heavy duty / Rock'n'roll creation / America / Cups and cakes / Big bottom / Sex farm / Stonehenge / Gimme some money / Flower people.
■ LP . . . . .LUSLP 2
■ MC .LUSMC 2
Priority / Mar '89.
CD 817 846-2
■ LP 817 846-1
MC. 817 846-4
Polydor / Aug '90 / PolyGram.

Split Beaver

SAVAGE.
Tracks: Savage / Hound of hell.
■ 7″. .HEAVY 7
Heavy Metal / Sep '81.

WHEN HELL WON'T HAVE YOU.
Tracks: Savage / Going straight / Gimme head / Cruisin / Levington gardens / Hounds of hell / Likewise / Living in and out / Get out, stay out / Bailiff.
■ LP . . . . .HMRLP 3
Heavy Metal / Jun '82.

Spooky Tooth

Progressive group, formed in U.K. in 1967, but more successful in U.S. Split and reformed in early '70s, permanently disbanding in 1975. Personnel included future members of Mott the Hoople, Only Ones and Humble Pie, although guitarist Mick Jones led pack with Foreigner. Keyboardist/ singer Gary Wright hit with 1976's *Dream Weaver*.

BEST OF SPOOKY TOOTH.
Tracks: Tobacco Road / Better by you better than me / It's all about a roundabout / Waitin for the wind / Last puff / Evil woman / That was only yesterday / I am the walrus / Self seeking man / All sewn up / Times have changed / As long as the world keeps turning / Weight.
CD. 842 688 2
Island / Mar '94 / PolyGram.

MIRROR, THE.
Tracks: Not Advised.
CD . . . . .CDCD 1032
Charly / Mar '93 / Charly.

Spread Eagle

SPREAD EAGLE.
Tracks: Broken city / Back on the bitch / Switchblade serenade / Hot sex / Suzy suicide / Dead of winter / Scratch like a cat / Thru these eyes / Spread eagle / 42nd street / Shotgun kiss.
■ CD . . . . .DMCG 6092
■ LP .MCG 6092
■ MC. . . . . .MCGC 6092
MCA / May '90.

Spy

WHOLE LOTTA WAYS (TO CATCH A FISH).
Tracks: Whole lotta ways (to catch a fish) / Gone fishing.
■ 7″. . . . . .BD 95
Mission Discs / Jun '84.

Squier, Billy

Bostonite Squier formed Sidewinders at school; then, after two, late '70s albums with Piper, went solo. Second album *Don't Say No* yielded three U.S. hits in 1981; Squier has made no impression in U.K., despite Anglophile leanings. Still going strong in '90s, evinced by 1993 *Tell the truth* album.

DON'T SAY NO.
Tracks: In the dark / Stroke / My kinda lover / You know what I like / Too daze gone / Lonely is the night / Whadda you want from me / Nobody knows / I need you / Don't say no.

■ LP . . . . .EST 12146
Capitol / May '81.
■ CD . . . . CDP 746 479 2
EMI / Mar '87.

EMOTIONS IN MOTION.
Tracks: Everybody wants you / Emotions in motion / Learn how to live / In your eyes / Keep me satisfied / It keeps you rocking / One good woman / She's a runner / Catch 22 / Listen to the heartbeat.
■ CD . . . . .CZ 72
Capitol / Mar '87.

EMOTIONS IN MOTION.
Tracks: Emotions in motion / Catch 22.
■ 7" . . . . .CL 261
Capitol / Sep '82.

ENOUGH IS ENOUGH.
Tracks: Shot of love / Love is the hero / Lady with a tenor sax / All we have to give / Come home / Break the silence / Powerhouse / Lonely one / Till its over / Wink of an eye.
■ LP . . . . EST 2024
■ MC . . . . .TCEST 2024
Capitol / Nov '86.
■ CD . . . . .BU 1
EMI / Mar '88.

EVERYBODY WANTS YOU.
Tracks: Everybody wants you / Keep me satisfied.
■ 7" . . . . .CL 273
Capitol / Jan '83.

HOTTEST NIGHT OF THE YEAR, THE.
Tracks: Everybody wants you / Emotions in motion / Learn how to live / In your eyes / Keep me satisfied / It keeps you rocking / One good woman / She's a runner / Catch 22 / Listen to the heartbeat.
■ LP . . . . .EST 12217
■ LP . . . . .EST 12225
■ MC . . . . TC EST 12217
Capitol / Sep '82.

IN THE DARK.
Tracks: In the dark / Rich kid.
■ 7" . . . . .CL 206
Capitol / Jun '81.

LIVE IN THE DARK.
Tracks: Not Advised.
■ VHS . . . . MVP 99 1023 2
PMI / Jun '86.
■ VHS . . . . HEN 2169
Hendring Video / Mar '89.

LOVE IS THE HERO.
Tracks: Learn how to live (live).
■ 12" 12CL 433
■ 7" .CL 433
Capitol / Jan '87.

ROCK ME TONITE.
Tracks: Rock me tonite / Can't get next to you.
■ 7" . . . . .SQD 1
Capitol / Aug '84.

SIGNS OF LIFE.
Tracks: All night long / Rock me tonite / Eye on you / Take a look behind ya / Reach for the sky / 1984, (Another) / Fall for love / Can't get next to you / Hand me downs / Sweet release.
■ LP . . . . EJ 2401921
Capitol / Oct '84.
■ CD . . . . .CZ 71
Capitol / Mar '87.

STROKE, THE.
Tracks: Stroke / My kinda lover.
■ 7" . . . . .CL 214
Capitol / Oct '81.

TALE OF THE TAPE.
Tracks: Big beat / Calley oh / Rich kid / Like I'm lovin' you / Who knows what a love can do / You should be high love / Who's your boyfriend / Music's all right / Young girls.
■ LP . . . . .EST 12062
Capitol / Jul '80.

TELL THE TRUTH.
Tracks: Angry / Tryin' to walk a straight line / Rhythm//(A bridge so far) / Hercules / Lovin' you ain't so hard / Timebomb / Stranger to myself / Girl's all right / Break down / Not a colour / Mind-machine / Shocked straight.
■ CD . . . . CDEST 2194
■ MC . . . . .TCEST 2194
Capitol / Apr '93.

TOO DAZE GONE.
Tracks: Too daze gone / Whadda you want from me.
■ 7" . . . . .CL 231
Capitol / Feb '82.

YOU SHOULD BE HIGH LOVE.
Tracks: You should be high love / Music's all right.
■ 7" . . . . CL 16160
Capitol / Aug '80.

St. Paradise

St. PARADISE.
Tracks: Straight to you / Gamblin' man / Jackie / Miami slide / Hades / Live it up / Jesse James / Tighten the knot / Beside the sea.
■ LP . . . . K 56689
WEA / '77.

St. Vitus

BORN TOO LATE.
Tracks: Not Advised.
CD . . . . .SST 082 CD
SST / Oct '87 / Pinnacle.
LP . . . . .SST 082
MC .SST 082 C
SST / May '93 / Pinnacle.

C.O.D.
Tracks: Intro / Children of doom / Planet of judgement / Shadow of a skeleton / (I am) the screaming banshee / Plague of man / Imagination man / Fear.
■ CD . . . . .HELLCD 017
■ LP . . . . .HELLLP 017
Hellhound / May '92.

HALLOW'S VICTIM.
Tracks: Not Advised.
■ LP .SST 052
SST / Apr '86.
MC. . . . . SST 052 C
SST / May '93 / Pinnacle.

HEAVIER THAN THOU.
Tracks: Not Advised.
CD . . . . .SST 266 CD
LP . . . . .SST 266
MC. . . . . SST 266 C
SST / May '93 / Pinnacle.

LIVE.
Tracks: Not Advised.
■ CD 8468732
■ LP 8468731
Hellhound / Jan '91.

MOURNFUL CRIES.
Tracks: Not Advised.
CD . . . . .SST 161 CD
■ LP .SST 161
MC . . . . SST 161 C
SST / Sep '88 / Pinnacle.

St. VITUS.
Tracks: Not Advised.
■ LP .SST 022
SST / Jun '85.
MC . . . . SST 022 C
SST / May '93 / Pinnacle.

THIRSTY AND MISERABLE.
Tracks: Thirsty and miserable.
■ EP .SST 119
SST / Jul '87.
■ MC Single. . . . . .SST 119 C
SST / May '93.

V.
Tracks: Living backwards / When emotion dies / Ice monkey / Angry man / I bleed black / Patra / Jack Frost / Mind food.
CD .H 0005-2
Hellhound / Apr '90 / Plastic Head.
LP 086 806
S.P.V. / Apr '90.

WALKING DEAD, THE.
Tracks: Walking dead / White stallions / Darkness.
■ LP .SST 042
SST / Nov '85.
MC. . . . . SST 042 C
SST / May '93 / Pinnacle.

Stabbing Westward

UNGOD.
Tracks: Lost / Control / Nothing / ACF / Lies / UnGod / Throw / Violent moodswings / Red on white / Can't happen here.
CD .475735 2
LP 475735 1
MC. 475735 4
Columbia / May '94 / Sony.

Stage Dolls

LOVE CRIES.
Tracks: Love cries / Hanoi waters / Don't stop believin'
■ 12" .PZ 68
■ 7" .PO 68
■ CD Single . . . . .PZCD 68
Polydor / Feb '90.

STAGE DOLLS.
Tracks: Still in love / Wings of steel / Lorraine / Waitin' for you / Love cries / Mystery / Don't stop believin' / Hanoi waters / Ammunition.
■ CD 841 259-2
■ LP 841 259-1
■ MC 841 259-4
Polydor / Feb '90.

STILL IN LOVE.
Tracks: Still in love.
■ 12" .PZ 78
■ 7" . . . . .POG 78
■ 7" .PO 78
■ MC Single . . . . .POCS 78
Polydor / Apr '90.

Stampede

DAYS OF WINE AND ROSES.
Tracks: Days of wine and roses / Photographs.
■ 12" . . . . .POSPX 507
■ 7" . . . . POSP 507
Polydor / Sep '82.

HURRICANE TOWN.
Tracks: I've been told / Love letters / Casino junkie / Other side / Turning in circles / Hurricane town / Girl / Runner / Mexico.
■ LP . . . . POLS 1083
Polydor / Jul '83.

OFFICIAL BOOTLEG.
Tracks: Missing you / Moving on / Days of wine and roses / Hurrican town / Shadows of the night / Baby driver / Runner / There and back.
■ LP .ROCK 1
Polydor / '83.

OTHER SIDE.
Tracks: Other side / Runner.
■ 7" . . . . .POSP 592
Polydor / May '83.

Stanley, Paul

HOLD ME, TOUCH ME.
Tracks: Hold me, touch me / Goodbye.
■ 7" . . . . .CAN 140
Casablanca / Feb '79.

PAUL STANLEY SOLO ALBUM.
Tracks: Not Advised.
■ LP 6399085
Casablanca / Oct '87.

Star Star

HOLD BACK THE NIGHT.
Tracks: Hold back the night.
■ 12" .PZ 7
■ 7" .PO 7
Polydor / Jun '88.

LOVE DRAG YEARS, THE.
Tracks: Not Advised.
LP . . . . RR 91931
MC. . . . . RR 91934
■ CD . . . . RR 91932
Road Runner / Sep '92.

Starcastle

REAL TO REEL.
Tracks: Half a mind to leave ya / Whatcha gonna do / We did it / Nobody's fool / Song for Alaya / So here we are / She / Stars are out tonight / When the sun shines at midnight.
■ LP . . . . CBS 82916
CBS / Feb '79.

Starfighters

ALLEY CAT BLUES.
Tracks: Alley cat blues / Don't touch me / Rock 'em dead (Only on 12" single.).
■ 12" . . . . .JIVET 3
■ 7" .JIVE 3
Jive / Aug '81.

POWER CRAZY.
Tracks: Not Advised.
■ LP . . . . .HOP 200
MC. . . . . .HOPC 200
Jive / Oct '81 / BMG.

POWER CRAZY.
Tracks: Power crazy / I want you / Get out while you can (12" only).
■ 12" . . . . JIVET 6
■ 7" . . . . JIVE 6
Jive / Oct '81.

STARFIGHTER I TO STARFIGHTER II.
Tracks: Starfighter I to Starfighter II / Starfighter's theme.
■ 7" . . . . MAG 107
Magnet / Nov '77.

Starr, Jack

BLAZE OF GLORY.
Tracks: Not Advised.
■ LP . . . . US 8
U.S. Metal / Nov '87.

BURNING STARR.
Tracks: Not Advised.
CD. . . . . US 16CD
LP . . . . US 16
U.S. Metal / Jan '90 / Vital Distribution.

OUT OF THE DARKNESS.
Tracks: Not Advised.
■ LP . . . . MFN 34
Music For Nations / Aug '84.

ROCK THE AMERICAN WAY.
Tracks: Not Advised.
■ LP . . . . PBL 101
Passport (USA) / Nov '85.

Starz

BRIGHTEST STARZ.
Tracks: Rock six times / Cherry baby / Pull the plug / So young, so bad / Violation / Subway terror / Sing it shout it / She / Coliseum rock / Boy's in action.
■ LP . . . . HMUSA 8
MC. . . . . HMAMC 8
Heavy Metal America / Jan '85 / FM Revolver / Sony.

COLLOSEUM ROCK.
Tracks: So young, so bad / Take me / No regrets / My sweet child / Don't stop now / Outfit / Last night I wrote a letter / Coliseum rock / It's a riot / Where will it end.
■ LP . . . . .EST 11861
Capitol / Feb '79.

LIVE IN ACTION.
Tracks: (She's just a) fallen angel / Tear it down / Live wire / Monkey business / Detroit girls / She / Rock six times / Subway terror / Cool one / X ray specs / Cherry baby / Waiting on you / Greatest riffs of all time / Coliseum rock / Pull the plug / Boys in action / Johnny all alone.
CD . . . . RO 94272
■ Double LP . . . . RO 94271
Roadracer / Dec '89.

LIVE IN CANADA.
Tracks: Not Advised.
■ LP . . . . HMUSA 46
MC. . . . . HMAMC 46
Heavy Metal America / Oct '85 / FM Revolver / Sony.

PISS PARTY.
Tracks: Not Advised.
■ LP . . . . HMASP 50
Heavy Metal America / Nov '85.

SING IT, SHOUT IT.
Tracks: Sing it, shout it / Subway terror.
■ 7" . . . . CL 15932
Capitol / Jul '77.

SO YOUNG, SO BAD.
Tracks: So young, so bad.
■ 7" . . . . VHF 6
FM Records / May '85.

Statetrooper

SHE GOT THE LOOK.
Tracks: Veni, vidi, vici / Set fire to the night / She got the look.
■ 12" . . . . NEAT 52 12
■ 7" . . . . .NEAT 52
Neat / '88.

STATETROOPER.
Tracks: Shape of things to come / Set fire to the night / Dreams of the faithful / Stand me up / Veni vidi vici / Last stop to heaven / She got the look / Too late / Armed and ready.
CD . . . . WKFMXD 91
■ LP . . . . WKFMLP 91
MC. . . . . WKFMMC 91
FM Records / May '87 / FM Revolver / Sony.

Status Quo

With origins in early '60s, Quo are among U.K.'s 'rock institutions'. First hit was 1967's *Pictures Of Matchstick Men*, although characteristic sound emerged with 1973's *Paper Plane* single and *Piledriver* album. Critical derision for 'boogie' style did nothing to halt success: band have had over 30 hit singles, over 25 hit albums, and appeared on 'Top of the Pops' more than any other act. Mid-'80s split was predictably short-lived; mainstays Francis Rossi and Rick Parfitt assembled new line-up and resumed successful career in 1986. Band never 'cracked' U.S., but can take comfort from record-breaking domestic career.

100 MINUTES OF STATUS QUO.
Tracks: Not Advised.
MC. . . . . ZCTON 101
PRT (100 Minute Series) / Jun '82.

1982.
Tracks: She don't fool me / Young pretender / Get out and walk / Jealousy / I love rock 'n' roll / Resurrection / Dear John / Doesn't matter / I want the world to know / I should have known / Big man.
■ LP .6302 169
Vertigo / Apr '82.
CD 800 035-2
Vertigo / '83 / PolyGram.

ACCIDENT PRONE.
Tracks: Accident prone.
■ 7" . . . . .QUO 2
Vertigo / Nov '78.

AGAIN AND AGAIN.
Tracks: Again and again / Too far gone.
■ 7" . . . . .QUO 1
Vertigo / Sep '78.

AIN'T COMPLAINING.
Tracks: Not Advised.
■ CD 834 604-2
■ LP . . . . VERH 58
■ MC. VERHC 58
Vertigo / May '88.

AIN'T COMPLAINING.
Tracks: Ain't complaining / That's alright / Ain't complaining (extended) / Lean machine (on 12" only.) / In the army now (on CD version.)
■ 12" . . . . QUO 2212
■ 7" . . . . QUOH 22
■ 7" . . . . QUO 22
■ CD Single . . . . QUOCD 22
Vertigo / Mar '88.

AIN'T COMPLAINING (CD VIDEO).
Tracks: Not Advised.
CD Video 080 322 2
Polygram Music Video / Oct '88 / PolyGram.

ANNIVERSARY WALTZ.
Tracks: Anniversary waltz / Power of rock / Perfect remedy.
■ 12" . . . . QUO 2812
■ 12" Remix . . . . QUOX 28
■ 7" . . . . QUO 28
■ 7" . . . . QUOG 28
■ CD Single . . . . QUOCD 28
■ MC Single . . . . QUOMC 28
Vertigo / Sep '90.

ANNIVERSARY WALTZ (PART 2).
Tracks: Anniversary waltz (Part 2) / Dirty water (Live at The Nec).
■ 7" . . . . QUO 29
■ CD Single . . . . QUOCD 29
■ MC Single . . . . QUOMC 29
Vertigo / Nov '90.

ANNIVERSARY WALTZ, THE.
Tracks: Caroline / Roll over, lay down / Again and again / Down down / Dirty water / Whatever you want / In the army now / Rocking all over the world / Don't waste your time / Wanderer / Marguerita time.
■ VHS . . . . CMP 6029
Castle Music Pictures / Feb '91.

ARE YOU GROWING TIRED OF MY LOVE.
Tracks: Are you growing tired of my love.
■ 7" 7N 17728
Pye / May '69.

B SIDES AND RARITIES.
Tracks: I (who have nothing) / Neighbour neighbour / Hurdy gurdy man / Laticia / (We ain't got) nothin' yet / I want it / Almost but not quite there / Wait just a minute / Gentleman Joe's sidewalk cafe / To be free / When my mind is not alive / Make me stay a little bit longer / Auntie Nellie / Price of love / Little Miss Nothing / Down the dustpipe / Face without a soul / In my chair / Gerdundula / Tune to the music / Good thinking Batman / Time to fly / Do you live in fire / Josie.
CD. . . . . CCSCD 271
■ Double LP . . . . CCSLP 271
■ MC. .CCSMC 271
Castle Collector Series / Sep '90.

BACK TO BACK.
Tracks: Mess of the blues / Ol' rag blues / Can't be done / Too close to the ground / No contract / Win or lose / Margerita time / Your kind of love / Stay the night / Gin down town tonight.
■ LP . . . . VERH 10
MC. . . . . .VERHC 10
■ CD 814 662 2
Vertigo / Nov '83.

BACK TO THE BEGINNING.
Tracks: Not Advised.
CD Set . . . . CDLIK 81
Decal / Sep '91 / Charly / Swift.

BEST OF 1968-71.
Tracks: Mean girl / Down the dustpipe / Spinning wheel blues / Need your love / Lazy poker blues / Daughter / In my chair / Railroad / Gerdundula / Hey little woman / Good thinking batman / Josie / To be free / Shy fly / (April) spring, summer and wednesdays / Everything.
CD. . . . . PWKS 4080
MC. . . . . PWKMC 4080
Pickwick / Aug '91 / Pickwick.

BEST OF STATUS QUO.
Tracks: Caroline / Night ride / Don't waste my time / Like a good girl / Again and again / Fine, fine, fine / Accident prone / Roll over lay down / Down down / She don't fool me / Keep me guessing / Oh what a night / Just take me / Let's ride / Late last night / Mess of blues.
CD. . . . . PWKS 4087P
MC. . . . . PWKMC 4087P
Pickwick / Nov '91 / Pickwick.

BEST OF STATUS QUO (THE EARLY YEARS).
Tracks: Down the dustpipe / Gerdundula / In my chair/ Umleitung / Lakky lady / Daughter / Railroad / Tune to the music / April, Spring, Summer and Wednesdays / Mean girl / Spinning wheel blues.
■ LP .NSPL 18402
■ MC. ZCP 18402
PRT / '73.
■ CD . . . . CDNSP 7773
PRT / '86.

BEST OF STATUS QUO, PRESERVED.
Tracks: Not Advised.
VHS . . . . CFV 02442
Channel 5 / Nov '86 / Channel 5 Video / P.R.O. Video / Gold & Sons.
VHS . . . . SPC 00012
Spectrum (1) / Oct '89 / PolyGram.

BLUE FOR YOU.
Tracks: Is there a better way / Mad about the boy / Ring of a change / Blue for you / Rain / Rollin' home / That's a fact / Ease your mind.
■ LP 9102 006
Vertigo / Mar '76.
■ LP . . . . PRICE 55
Vertigo / Jan '84.

BREAK THE RULES.
Tracks: Break the rules.
■ 7" 6059 101
Vertigo / May '74.

BURNING BRIDGES (ON AND OFF AND ON AGAIN).
Tracks: Burning bridges (on and off and on again) / What ever you want / Marguerite time (Only on 12" version and CD single.) / Burning bridges (on and off and on again)(extended) (Only on 12" version and CD single.).
■ CD Single . . . . QUOCD 25
■ 12" . . . . QUO 2512

■ 7" . . . . QUO 25
Vertigo / Nov '88.

BURNING BRIDGES (ON AND OFF AND ON AGAIN) (CD VIDEO).
Tracks: Burning bridges (on and off and on again).
CD Video 080 620 2
Polygram Music Video / Sep '89 / PolyGram.

C.90 COLLECTOR.
Tracks: Down the dustpipe / Mean girl / Lakky lady / Spinning wheel blues / Railroad / Race without a soul / Ice in the sun / Sheila / Antique Angelique / Mr. Mind detector / Price of love / Technicolour dreams / Spicks and specks / In my chair / Gerdundula / Na na na / Need your love / Umleitung / Pictures of matchstick men / Are you growing tired of my love / Green tambourine / Black veils of melancholy / Poor old man / So ends another life / Clown.
CD. GHCD 3
MC. C 903
Legacy / Apr '89 / Sony.

CAN'T GIVE YOU MORE.
Tracks: Can't give you more / Dead in the water / Mysteries from the ball (Only on 12" and CD single).
■ 12" . . . . QUO 3012
■ 7" . . . . QUO 30
■ CD Single . . . . QUOCD 30
■ MC Single . . . . QUOMC 30
Vertigo / Aug '91.

CAN'T STAND THE HEAT.
Tracks: Not Advised.
■ LP 9102 027
Vertigo / Nov '78.

CAN'T STAND THE HEAT/ 1982.
Tracks: Again and again / I'm giving up my worrying / Gonna teach you to love me / Someone show me home / Long legged Linda / Oh what a night / Accident prone / Stones / Let me fly / Like a good girl / She don't fool me / Young pretender / Get out and walk / Jealousy / I love rock and roll / Resurrection / Dear John / Doesn't matter / I want the world to know / I should have known / Big man.
■ MC 8480904
■ CD 8480902
Vertigo / Feb '91.

CAROLINE.
Tracks: Caroline.
■ 7" 6059 085
Vertigo / Sep '73.

CAROLINE (LIVE AT THE NEC).
Tracks: Caroline.
■ 7" . . . . QUO 10
Vertigo / Oct '82.

CAROLINE (OLD GOLD).
Tracks: Caroline / Down down.
■ 7" . . . . OG 9565
Old Gold / Sep '85.

COLLECTION: STATUS QUO.
Tracks: Pictures of matchstick men / Green tambourine / Technicolour dreams / Sunny cellophane skies / Paradise flat / Clown / Antique Angelique / Ice in the sun / Lakky lady / Is it really me / Gerdundula / Neighbour neighbour / Paradise flat (2).
■ Double LP . . . . CCSLP 114
■ MC . . . . CCSMC 114
Castle Collector Series / Nov '85.
CD. . . . . CCSCD 114
Castle Collector Series / '88 / BMG / Pinnacle / Castle Communications.

DEAR JOHN.
Tracks: Dear John.
■ 7" . . . . QUO 7
Vertigo / Mar '82.

DOG OF TWO HEAD.
Tracks: Umleitung / Na na na / Something's going on in my head / Railroad / Gerdundula / Mean girl / Someone's learning.
■ LP . . . . .NSPL 18371
PRT / Nov '71.
■ CD . . . . CDMP 8837
PRT / '86.
■ CD . . . . PYC 6023
■ LP . . . . PYL 6023
■ MC . . . . PYM 6023
PRT / Sep '87.
CD. . . . . CLACD 206
■ LP . . . . CLALP 206
■ MC . . . . CLAMC 206
Castle Classics / Sep '90.

DOUBLE GOLD DISC.
Tracks: Not Advised.
■ LP . . . . VG 416006
Vogue / '88.

DOWN DOWN.
Tracks: Down down.
■ 7" 6059 114
Vertigo / Dec '74.

DOWN THE DUSTPIPE.
Tracks: Down the dustpipe.
■ 7" 7N 17907
PRT / '74.
■ 12" . . . . BD 103
Big Deal / Jun '77.

DREAMIN'.
Tracks: Dreamin' / Long legged girl with the short dress on / Quo Christmas cake mix (On 12" only).
■ 7" . . . . QUO 21
Vertigo / Nov '86.
■ 12" . . . . QUO 2112
Vertigo / Nov '86.

EARLY WORKS, THE.
Tracks: I (who have nothing) / Neighbour, neighbour / Hurdy gurdy man / Laticia / (We ain't got) nothin' yet / I want it / Almost but not quite there / Wait just a minute / Pictures of matchstick men / Gentleman Joe's sidewalk cafe / Black veils of melancholy / To be free / Ice in the sun / When my mind is not live / Elizabeth dreams / Paradise flat / Technicolour dreams / Spicks and specks / Sheila / Sunny cellophane skies / Green tambourine / Make me stay a little bit longer / Auntie Nellie / Are you growing tired of my love / So ends another life / Price of love / Face without a soul / You're just what I was looking for today / Antique Angelique / Poor old man / Mr. Mind Detector / Clown / Velvet curtains / Little Miss Nothing / When I awake / Nothing at all / Josie / Down the dustpipe / Time to fly / Do you live in fire / (April), Spring, Summer and Wednesdays / Daughter / Everything / Lazy poker blues / Is it really me / Gotta go home / Junior's waiting / Shy fly / Lakky lady / Need your love / Spinning wheel blue / In my chair / Gerdundula (original version) / Tune to the music / Good thinking batman / Umleitung / Nanana / Something going on in my head / Mean girl / Railroad / Someone's learning / Nanana (2) / Nanana (3) / Gerdundula.
■ CD Set . . . . ESBCD 136
■ LP Set . . . . ESBLP 136
Essential / Dec '90.

EARLY YEARS, THE.
Tracks: Pictures of matchstick men / Ice in the sun / Poor old man / Antique angelique / Nothing at all / Price of love / Down the dustpipe / Good thinking / Time to fly / Need your love / Spinning wheel blues / Shy fly / In my chair / Gerdundula / Juniors wailing / Tune to the music / Nanana / Mean girl.
CD. . . . . EARLD 8
Dojo / Feb '94 / Castle Communications / BMG.

END OF THE ROAD 84.
Tracks: Not Advised.
VHS . . . . CFV 02362
Channel 5 / Jul '86 / Channel 5 Video / P.R.O. Video / Gold & Sons.

FEW BARS MORE, A.
Tracks: Whatever you want / What you are proposing / Softer ride / Price of love / Drifting away / She don't fool me / Who gets the love / Let's work together / Bring it on home / Backwater / I saw the light / Don't stop me now / Come rock with me / Rockin' all over the world.
CD. 550002-2
MC. 550002-4
Spectrum (1) / May '93 / PolyGram.

FRESH QUOTA.
Tracks: Do you live in fire / Time to fly / Josie / Good thinking Batman / Neighbour neighbour / Hey little woman.
■ LP . . . . .DOW 2
■ MC . . . . ZCDOW 2
PRT / Sep '81.

FROM THE BEGINNING.
Tracks: Not Advised.
■ CD . . . . PYC 4007
■ LP . . . . PYZ 4007
■ MC . . . . PYM 4007
PRT / Sep '88.
■ LP P.Disc . . . . PYX 4007
PRT / Sep '88.

FROM THE MAKERS OF...
Tracks: Pictures of matchstick men / Ice in the sun / Down the dustpipe / In my chair / Junior's wailing / Mean girl / Gerdundula / Paper plane / Big fat mama / Roadhouse blues / Break the rules / Down down / Bye bye Johnny / Rain / Mystery song / Blue for you / Is there a better way / Again and again / Accident prone / Wild side of life / Living on an island / What you're proposing / Lies / Rock 'n' roll / Something 'bout you baby / Dear John / Caroline / Roll over lay

down / Backwater / Little lady / Don't drive my car / Whatever you want / Hold you back / Rockin' all over the world / Don't waste my time.
■ LP Set . . . . PRO LP 1
■ LP Set . . . . PRO BX 1
MC Set . . . . PRO MC 1
Vertigo / Nov '82 / PolyGram.

GERDUNDULA.
Tracks: Gerdundula.
■ 7" 7N 45253
PRT / Jun '73.

GOING DOWN TOWN TONIGHT.
Tracks: Going down town tonight / To close to the ground.
■ 7" . . . . QUO 15
Vertigo / Apr '84.

GOLDEN HOUR OF STATUS QUO VOL. 1.
Tracks: Pictures of matchstick men / Mr. Mind Detector / You're just what I was looking for today / Clown / When I awake / Ice in the sun / Spicks and specks / Poor old man / Gentleman Joe's sidewalk cafe / Sheila / Black veils of Melancholy / Price of love / Paradise flat / When my mind is not live / Elizabeth dreams / Are you growing tired of my love / So ends another life / Velvet curtains / Sunny cellophane skies / Face without a soul / Green tambourine.
■ MC . . . . ZCGH 556
■ LP . . . . GH 556
Golden Hour / '73.
■ CD . . . . .KGHCD 110
■ MC . . . . .KGHMC 110
Knight / Apr '90.

GOLDEN HOUR OF STATUS QUO VOL. 2.
Tracks: Not Advised.
■ MC . . . . ZCGH 604
■ LP . . . . GH 604
Golden Hour / '75.

HELLO.
Tracks: And it's better now / Blue eyed lady / Caroline / Claudie / Forty five hundred times / Reason for living / Roll over lay down / Softer ride.
■ LP 6360 098
Vertigo / Oct '73.
■ LP . . . . PRICE 16
MC. . . . . PRIMC 16
Vertigo / May '83 / PolyGram.
CD. 8481722
■ MC 8481724
Vertigo / Feb '91.

I DIDN'T MEAN IT.
Tracks: I didn't mean it / Survival (On 2nd CD only) / She knew too much (On 2nd CD only) / Whatever you want / Down down (On 1st CD only) / Rockin' all over the world (On 1st CD only).
7" . . . . QUO 34
CD Single. . . . . QUODD 34
CD Single. . . . . QUOCD 34
MC Single . . . . QUOMC 34
Polydor / Aug '94 / PolyGram.

ICE IN THE SUN.
Tracks: Ice in the sun.
■ 7" 7N 17581
Pye / Aug '68.

IN MY CHAIR.
Tracks: In my chair / Gerdundula.
■ 7" 7N 17998
Pye / Nov '70.
■ 7" 7P 103
PRT / Jun '79.

IN THE ARMY NOW.
Tracks: Rollin home / Calling / In your eyes / Save me / In the army now / Dreamin / End of the line / Invitation / Red sky / Speechless / Overdose.
CD. 830 049-2
■ LP . . . . VERH 36
MC. . . . . .VERHC 36
Vertigo / Aug '86 / PolyGram.

IN THE ARMY NOW.
Tracks: In the army now / Heartburn / Late last night.
■ 12" . . . . QUO 2012
■ 7" . . . . QUO 20
Vertigo / Sep '86.

INTROSPECTIVE: STATUS QUO.
Tracks: Mean girl / Ice in the sun / Pictures of matchstick men / Interview part one / Down the dustpipe / Little Miss Nothing / Is it really me / Interview part two.
CD. . . . . CINT 5003
LP. . . . . LINT 5003
MC. . . . . MINT 5003
Baktabak / Nov '90 / Arabesque Ltd.

■ DELETED

IT'S ONLY ROCK & ROLL.
Tracks: Not Advised.
CD 550 1902
MC 550 1904
Spectrum (1) / Sep '94 / PolyGram.

JUST FOR THE RECORD.
Tracks: In my chair / Something's going on in my head / Umleitung / Railroad / Lakky lady / Nanana / Mean girl / Someone's learning / Gotta go home / Spinning wheel blues / Down the dustpipe / Gerdundula.
■ MC . . . . ZCP 18607
■ LP . . . . NSPL 18607
PRT / Jun '79.

JUST SUPPOSIN'.
Tracks: What you're proposing / Run to mummy / Don't drive my car / Lies / Over the edge / Wild ones / Name of the game / Coming and going / Rock 'n' roll.
■ LP 6302 057
Vertigo / Oct '80.

LIES.
Tracks: Lies / Don't drive my car.
■ 7" . . . . .QUO 4
Vertigo / Dec '80.

LITTLE DREAMER.
Tracks: Little dreamer / Rotten to the bone / Doing it for all for you.
■ 12" . . . . QUO 2712
■ 12" Remix . . . . QUOX 2712
■ 7" . . . . QUO 27
■ 7" P.Disc . . . . QUOP 27
■ CD Single . . . . QUOCD 27
■ MC Single . . . . QUOMC 27
Vertigo / Dec '89.

LIVE ALIVE QUO.
Tracks: Whatever you want / In the army now / Burning bridges / Rockin' all over the world / Roadhouse blues / Caroline / Don't drive my car / Hold you back / Little lady.
CD 5173 672
MC 5173 674
Vertigo / Nov '92 / PolyGram.

LIVE AT THE N.E.C.
Tracks: Caroline / Roll over lay down / Backwater / Little lady / Over the edge / Whatever you want / Hold you back / Rockin all over the world / Over the edge / Big fat mama / Road house blues / Rain / Down down / Johnny B (be) good.
VHS 790688 2
Polygram T.V. / Sep '84 / PolyGram.
VHS . . . . CFV 00052
Channel 5 / Mar '86 / Channel 5 Video / P.R.O. Video / Gold & Sons.

LIVE: STATUS QUO.
Tracks: Backwater / Big fat mama / Bye bye Johnny / Caroline / Don't waste my time / Forty five hundred times / In the chair / Is there a better way / Junior's wailing / Just take me / Little Lady / Most of the time / Rain / Roudhose blues / Roll over lay down.
■ LP 6641 580
Vertigo / Mar '77.
■ Double LP . . . . .PRID 5
■ MC Set . . . . .PRIDC 5
Vertigo / Sep '84.

LIVING ON AN ISLAND.
Tracks: Living on an island / Runaway.
■ 7" 6059 248
Vertigo / Nov '79.

MA KELLY'S GREASY SPOON.
Tracks: Spinning wheel blues / Daughter / Everything / Shy fly / Junior's wailing / Lakky lady / Need your love / Lazy poker blues / Is it really me / Gotta go home / April, Spring, Summer and Wednesdays.
■ LP . . . . NSPL 18344
PRT / '74.
■ CD . . . . CDMP 8834
PRT / '86.
■ CD . . . . PYC 6022
■ MC . . . . PYM 6022
PRT / Sep '87.
■ LP . . . . PYL 6022
PRT / Sep '87.
CD . . . . CLACD 169
Castle Classics / Dec '89 / BMG / Castle Communications.

MARGUERITA TIME.
Tracks: Marguerita time / Resurrection.
■ 7" . . . . QUO 14
■ 7" P.Disc . . . . QUOP 4
Vertigo / Dec '83.

MEAN GIRL.
Tracks: Mean girl.
■ 7" 7N 45229
Pye / Apr '73.
■ 7" 7N 46095
Pye / Jul '78.
■ 7" . . . . .OG 9142
Old Gold / Jul '82.

MESS OF THE BLUES, A.
Tracks: Mess of the blues / Big man.
■ 7" . . . . QUO 12
Vertigo / Nov '83.

MUSIC AND MEDIA INTERVIEW PICTURE DISC.
Tracks: Not Advised.
■ LP P.Disc . . . . MM 1221
Music & Media / Feb '88.

MUSIC OF STATUS QUO, THE (1972-1974).
Tracks: All the reasons / Backwater / Big fat mama / Blue eyed lady / Break the rules / Caroline / Drifting away / Just take me / Paper plane / Reason for living / Roll over lay down / Softer ride.
■ MC 7215 038
Vertigo / Dec '76.

MYSTERY SONG.
Tracks: Mystery song.
■ 7" 6059 146
Vertigo / Jul '76.

NA NA NA.
Tracks: Pictures of matchstick men / Ice in the sun / In my chair / Railroad / Umleitung / Daughter / Down the dustpipe / Shy fly / Mean girl / Na na na / Gerdundula / Lakky lady.
■ LP . . . . FBLP 8082
MC . . . . .ZCFBL 8082
Flashback / Oct '85.

NAUGHTY GIRL.
Tracks: Naughty girl.
■ 12" . . . . QUO 1712
Vertigo.

NEVER TOO LATE.
Tracks: Something 'bout you baby I like / Take me away / Never too late / Falling in, falling out / Carol / Long ago / Mountain lady / Don't stop me now / Enough is enough / Riverside.
■ LP 6302 104
Vertigo / Mar '81.
CD 800 053-2
Vertigo / '83 / PolyGram.

NEVER TOO LATE/ BACK TO BACK.
Tracks: Never too late / Something bout you baby I like / Take me away / Falling in falling out / Carol / Long ago / Mountain lady / Don't stop me now / Enough is enough / Riverside / Mess of blues / Ol rag blues / Can't be done / Too close to the ground / No contract / Win or lose / Marguerita time / Your kind of love / Stay the night / Going down town tonight.
CD 8480882
■ MC 8480884
Vertigo / Feb '91.

NIGHTRIDING: STATUS QUO.
Tracks: Pictures of matchstick men / Gerdundula / Are you growing tired of my love / Black veils of melancholy / Green tambourine / Mean girl / Ice in the sun / Down the dustpipe / Poor old man / Spicks and specks / In my chair / Technicolour dreams / Gotta go home / Sunny cellophane skies.
■ MC . . . . KNMC 10018
■ CD . . . . KNCD 10018
Nightriding / Dec '90.

NOT AT ALL.
Tracks: Not at all / Gone thru the slips / Everytime I think of you.
■ 12" . . . . QUO 2612
■ 7" . . . . QUO 26
■ CD Single . . . . QUOCD 26
■ MC Single . . . . QUOMC 26
Vertigo / Oct '89.

OL' RAG BLUES.
Tracks: Ol' rag blues / Stay the night.
■ 12" . . . . QUOB 11
■ 7" . . . . QUO 11
Vertigo / Sep '83.

ON THE LEVEL.
Tracks: Broken man / Bye bye Johnny / Down, down / I saw the light / Most of the time / Night ride / Over and one / What to do / Where am I.
■ LP 9102 002
Vertigo / Mar '75.
MC . . . . PRIMC 39
■ LP . . . . PRICE 39
Vertigo / Aug '83.
CD 8481742
■ MC 8481744
Vertigo / Feb '91.

PAPER PLANE.
Tracks: Paper plane.
■ 7" 6059 071
Vertigo / Jan '73.

PERFECT REMEDY.
Tracks: Not Advised.
■ LP 842 098 1
■ MC 842 098 4
■ CD 842 098 2
Vertigo / Nov '89.

PICTURES OF MATCHSTICK MEN.
Tracks: Pictures of matchstick men.
■ 7" 7N 17449
Pye / Jan '68.
■ 7" . . . . FBS 2
Flashback / Apr '79.

PICTURES OF MATCHSTICK MEN (OLD GOLD).
Tracks: Pictures of matchstick men / Down the dustpipe.
■ 7" . . . . .OG 9298
Old Gold / Apr '83.

PICTURESQUE MATCHSTICKABLE MESSAGES FROM THE STATUS QUO.
Tracks: Black veils of melancholy / When my mind is not alive / Ice in the sun / Elizabeth dreams / Gentleman Joe's sidewalk cafe / Paradise flat / Technicolour dreams / Spicks and specks / Sheila / Sunny cellophane skies / Green tambourine / Pictures of matchstick men.
■ CD . . . . PYC 6020
■ LP . . . . PYL 6020
■ MC . . . . PYM 6020
PRT / Oct '87.
CD . . . . CLACD 168
Castle Classics / Dec '89 / BMG / Castle Communications.

PILEDRIVER.
Tracks: All the reasons / Big fat mama / Don't waste my time / O baby / Paper plane / Roadhouse blues / Unspoken words / Year.
■ LP 6360 082
Vertigo / Jan '73.
MC . . . . PRIMC 17
■ LP . . . . PRICE 17
Vertigo / May '83.
CD . . . . REP 4119-WP
Repertoire (Germany) / Aug '91 / Pinnacle.
CD 8841712
■ MC 8481714
Vertigo / Feb '91.

PORTRAIT: STATUS QUO.
Tracks: Not Advised.
■ LP . . . . .BRLP 54
MC . . . . BRMC 54
BR Music/BR Music (Holland) / Oct '88 / BMG.

QUO.
Tracks: Backwater / Break the rules / Don't think it matters / Drifting away / Fine, fine, fine / Just take me / Lonely man / Slow train.
■ LP 9102 001
Vertigo / Mar '74.
■ LP . . . . PRICE 38
■ MC . . . . PRIMC 38
Vertigo / Aug '83.

QUO/ BLUE FOR YOU.
Tracks: Backwater / Just take me / Break the rules / Drifting away / Don't think it matters / Fine fine fine / Lonely man / Slow train / Is there a better way / Mad about the boy / Ring of a change / Blue for you / Rain / Rolling home / That's a fact / Ease you mind / Mystery song.
CD 8480892
■ MC 8480894
Vertigo / Feb '91.

QUOTATIONS VOL 2 (Alternatives).
Tracks: To be free / Make me stay a little bit longer / Auntie Nellie / Price of love / Down the dustpipe / In my chair / Gerdundula / Tune to the music / Good thinking Batman / Time to fly / Do you live in fire / Jose.

■ CD . . . . **PYC 6025**
■ LP . . . . **PYL 6025**
■ MC. **PYM 6025**
PRT / Oct '87.

QUOTATIONS VOL. 1 (The Early Years).
Tracks: I (who have nothing) / Neighbour neighbour / Hurdy gurdy man / Laticia / (We ain't got) nothin' yet / I want it / Almost but not quite there / Wait just a minute.
■ CD . . . . **PYC 6024**
■ LP . . . . **PYL 6024**
■ MC. **PYM 6024**
PRT / Oct '87.

RAIN.
Tracks: Rain / Is there a better way.
■ 7" **6059 133**
Vertigo / Feb '76.

RED SKY.
Tracks: Red sky / Don't give it up / Milton Keynes medley (Extra track on 12" version only).
■ 12" . . . . **QUO 1912**
■ 7" . . . . **QUO 19**
Vertigo / Jul '86.

REST OF STATUS QUO, THE.
Tracks: Not Advised.
■ LP . . . . **PKL 5546**
■ MC. . . . . **ZCPKB 5546**
PRT / Sep '76.

ROCK 'N' ROLL.
Tracks: Rock 'n' roll / Hold you back.
■ 7" . . . .**QUO 6**
Vertigo / Nov '81.

ROCK 'TIL YOU DROP.
Tracks: Rock 'til you drop / Forty five hundred times (Only on 12" and CD Single.).
■ 12" . . . . **QUO 3212**
■ 7" . . . . **QUO 32**
■ CD Single. . . . . **QUOCD 32**
■ MC Single. . . . . **QUOMC 32**
Vertigo / Nov '91.

ROCK TIL YOU DROP.
Tracks: Like a zombie / All we really wanna do (Polly) / Fakin' the blues / One man band / Rock 'til you drop / Can't give you more / Warning whot / Let's work together / Bring it on home / No problems / Good sign / Tommy / Nothing comes easy / Fame or money / Price of love / Forty five hundred times.
■ LP **5103411**
Vertigo / Sep '91.
CD. **5103412**
MC. **5103414**
Vertigo / Jan '93 / PolyGram.

ROCK TIL YOU DROP.
Tracks: Mystery song / Railroad / Most of the time / Wild side of life / Rollin' home / Again and again / Slow train / Down down / Roll over lay down / Little lady / What ever you want / Rockin' all over the world / Burnin' bridges / Bye bye Johnny.
VHS **0838363**
Polygram Music Video / Oct '91 / PolyGram.

ROCKIN' ALL OVER THE WORLD.
Tracks: Baby boy / Can't give you more / Dirty water / For you / Hard time / Hold you back / Let's ride / Rockin' all over the world / Too far gone / Who am I / You don't own me / Rockers rollin'.
■ LP . . . . **PRICE 87**
■ MC. **PRIMC 87**
Vertigo / Aug '85.
CD. **8481732**
Vertigo / Feb '91 / PolyGram.

ROCKIN' ALL OVER THE WORLD.
Tracks: Rockin' all over the world / Ring of a change.
■ 7" **6059 184**
Vertigo / Oct '77.

ROCKIN' ALL OVER THE WORLD (OLD GOLD).
Tracks: Rockin' all over the world / Paper plane.
■ 7" . . . . **OG 9567**
Old Gold / Nov '85.

ROCKING ALL OVER THE YEARS.
Tracks: Pictures of matchstick men / Ice in the sun / Paper plane / Caroline / Break the rules / Down down / Roll over lay down / Rain / Wild side of life / Rockin' all over the world / Whatever you want / What you're proposing / Something 'bout you baby I like / Rock 'n' roll / Dear John / Ol' rag blues / Marguerita time / Wanderer / Rollin' home / In the army now / Burning bridges (on and off and on again) / Anniversary waltz (part 1).
CD. **846 797 2**
MC. **846 797 4**
■ Double LP. **846 797 1**

Vertigo / Oct '90.
DCC **846 797-5**
Vertigo / Jan '93 / PolyGram.

ROCKING ALL OVER THE YEARS.
Tracks: Only you / Pictures of matchstick men / Caroline / Roll over lay down / Little lady / In my chair / Little dreamer / Perfect remedy / Mystery song / Railroad / Most of the time / Wild side of life / Again and again / Slow train / Hold ya back / Power of rock'n'roll / Dirty water / Whatever you want / In the army now / Rockin' all over the world / Don't waste my time / Wanderer / Marguerita time / Living on an island / Break the rules / Somethin' 'bout you baby I like / Burning bridges.
VHS . . . . **CFV 05972**
Channel 5 / Nov '87 / Channel 5 Video / P.R.O. Video / Gold & Sons.
CD Video **080 170 1**
Polygram Music Video / Oct '88 / PolyGram.
VHS . . . . **CFM 02644**
Channel 5 / Oct '90 / Channel 5 Video / P.R.O. Video / Gold & Sons.
VHS . . . . **LED 80152**
4 Front / May '91 / PolyGram Video.

ROLL OVER LAY DOWN.
Tracks: Roll over lay down.
■ 7" . . . . **QUO 13**
Vertigo / May '75.

ROLLIN' HOME.
Tracks: Rollin' home / Lonely / Keep me guessing (12" vesion only).
■ 12" . . . . **QUO 1812**
■ 7" . . . . **QUO 18**
Vertigo / Apr '86.

RUNNING ALL OVER THE WORLD.
Tracks: Running all over the world / Magic / Whatever you want.
■ CD Single . . . . **QUACD 1**
■ 12" . . . . **QUAID 112**
■ 7" . . . .**QUAID 1**
Vertigo / Aug '88.

SHE DON'T FOOL ME.
Tracks: She don't fool me / Never too late.
■ 7" . . . . **QUO 8**
Vertigo / Jun '82.

SOMETHING 'BOUT YOU BABY I LIKE.
Tracks: Something 'bout you baby I like / Enough is enough.
■ 7" . . . . **QUO 5**
Vertigo / Feb '81.

SPARE PARTS.
Tracks: Face without a soul / You're just what I was looking for today / Are you growing tired of my love / Antique Angelique / So ends another life / Poor old man / Mr. Mind detector / Clown / Velvet curtains / Little Miss Nothing / When I awake / Nothing at all.
■ CD . . . . **PYC 6021**
■ MC. **PYM 6021**
PRT / Sep '87.
■ LP . . . . **PYL 6021**
PRT / Sep '87.
CD. . . . . **CLACD 205**
■ LP . . . . **CLALP 205**
■ MC. . . . . **CLAMC 205**
Castle Classics / Sep '90.

SPOTLIGHT ON STATUS QUO.
Tracks: Pictures of matchstick men / Ice in the sun / Spicks and specks / Antique Angelique / Are you growing tired of my love / Black veils of melancholy / Down the dustpipe / Spinning wheel blues / Umleitung / Someone's learning / Daughter / Lakky lady / Is it really me / Gotta go home / Tune to the music / Everything / Something's going on in my head / Shy fly / Lazy poker blues / Na na na / Gerdundula.
■ Double LP. . . . . **SPOT 1010**
■ MC Set . . . . **ZCSPT 1010**
PRT / '80.

SPOTLIGHT ON STATUS QUO VOLUME 2.
Tracks: Need your love / Face without a soul / To be free / Sheila / Green tambourine / Price of love / Spring, summer and Wednesdays / Gentleman Joe's sidewalk cafe / When my mind is not live / So ends another life / Mr. Mind Detector / Poor old man / Little Miss Nothing / When I awake / Sunny cellophane skies / Paradise flat / Velvet curtains / Clown / Nothing at all / Jose / Make me stay a little bit longer / Technicolour dreams / You're just what I was looking for today / Elizabeth dreams.
■ LP . . . . **SPOT 1028**
■ MC. . . . . **ZCSPT 1028**
PRT Spotlight / Oct '82.

STATUS QUO.
Tracks: Not Advised.
MC. **MATMC 291**
Castle / Aug '94 / BMG.
CD. . . . .**MATCD 291**
Castle / Mar '94 / BMG.

STATUS QUO (1).
Tracks: Sunny cellophane skies / Paradise / Mr Mind detector / Clown / When my mind is not alive / Antique Angelique.
■ LP . . . . **HMA 260**
■ MC. . . . .**HSC 322**
Marble Arch / May '78.

STATUS QUO (2).
Tracks: Down the dustpipe / Lakky lady / Spinning wheel blues / Shy fly / Gerdundula / Daughter / Railroad / Umleitung / Mean girl / Everything / Little Miss Nothing / Junior's wailing / Tune to the music / In my chair / When I awake / So ends another life / Nothing at all / Something on my head / Someone's learning / Sheila / Price of love / Ice in the sun / Got to go home / Na na na.
■ Double LP. . . . . **SSD 8035**
■ MC Set . . . . **SSDC 8035**
Pickwick / Sep '80.

STATUS QUO COLLECTION.
Tracks: Not Advised.
■ Double LP. . . . . **PDA 046**
■ MC Set . . . . **PDC 046**
Pickwick / Aug '78.

STATUS QUO: INTERVIEW PICTURE DISC.
Tracks: Not Advised.
LP P.Disc . . . . **BAK 2110**
Baktabak / Aug '88 / Arabesque Ltd.

STATUS QUO: THE FILE.
Tracks: Pictures of matchstick men / Gentleman Joe's sidewalk cafe / Black veils of melancholy / To be free / Spicks & specks / Technicolour dreams / Paradise flat / Ice in the sun / Face without a soul / Price of love / Poor old man / Down the dustpipe / Daughter / Railroad / Spinning wheel blues / Is it really me / Gotta go home / Umleitung / Gerundula / Nanana / Something's going on in my head / In my chair / Mean girl.
■ LP . . . . **FILD 005**
Pye / Nov '77.

THIRSTY WORK.
Tracks: Not Advised.
CD. **5236072**
MC. **5236074**
Vertigo / Aug '94 / PolyGram.

TO BE OR NOT TO BE.
Tracks: Drifting away / Let me fly / Night ride / Softer ride / Lonely nights / Too far gone / Runaway / Don't drive my car / Hard ride / Backwater / Ring of a change / All through the night.
■ LP . . . . **CN 2062**
MC. **CN4 2062**
Contour / Apr '83 / Pickwick.
CD. . . . . **PWKS 4051P**
Pickwick / Apr '91 / Pickwick.

TUNE TO THE MUSIC.
Tracks: Not Advised.
■ CD **291008**
Ariola Express / Nov '92.

TWELVE GOLD BARS VOL.1.
Tracks: Rockin' all over the world / Down down / Caroline / Paper plane / Break the rules / Again and again / Mystery song / Roll over lay down / Rain / Wild side of life / Whatever you want / Living on an island.
■ LP . . . . **QUOTV 1**
Vertigo / Jun '80.
CD. **800 062-2**
Vertigo / Nov '84 / PolyGram.

TWELVE GOLD BARS VOL.2.
Tracks: Not Advised.
■ CD **822 985-2**
Vertigo / Nov '84.

TWELVE GOLD BARS VOLS. 1 & 2.
Tracks: Rockin' all over the world / Down down / Caroline / Paper plane / Break the rules / Again and again / Mystery song / Roll over lay down / Rain / Wild side of life / Whatever you want / Living in an island / What you're proposing / Lies / Something 'bout you baby I like / Don't drive my car / Dear John / Rock 'n' roll / Ol' rag blues / Mess of the blues / Marguerita time / Going down town tonight / Wanderer.
■ Double LP. . . . . **QUOTV 2**

■ DELETED

■ MC . . . . .QUOMC 2
Vertigo / Nov '84.

WANDERER, THE.
Tracks: Wanderer / Can't be done.
■ 7" P.Disc . . . . QUOP 16
Vertigo / Dec '84.
■ 7" . . . . QUO 16
Vertigo / Oct '84.

WHAT YOU'RE PROPOSING.
Tracks: What you're proposing / AB blues.
■ 7" . . . . .QUO 3
Vertigo / Oct '80.

WHATEVER YOU WANT.
Tracks: Breaking away / Come rock with me / High flyer / Living on an island / Rockin' on / Runaway / Shady lady / Whatever you want / Who asked you / Your smiling face.
■ LP 9102 037
Vertigo / Oct '79.

WHATEVER YOU WANT.
Tracks: Whatever you want.
■ 7" 6059 242
Vertigo / Sep '79.

WHATEVER YOU WANT/ JUST SUPPOSIN'.
Tracks: Whatever you want / Shady lady / Who asked you / Your smiling face / Living on an island / Come rock with me / ROckin on / Runaway / Breaking away.
CD 8480872
■ MC 8480874
Vertigo / Feb '91.

WHO GETS THE LOVE.
Tracks: Who gets the love / Wanderer.
■ 12" . . . . .QUO 2312
■ 7" . . . . QUO 23
■ 7" . . . . .QUOH 23
■ CD Single . . . . .QUOCD 23
Vertigo / May '88.

WILD SIDE OF LIFE.
Tracks: Wild side of life / All through the night.
■ 7" 6059 153
Vertigo / Dec '76.

WORKS: STATUS QUO.
Tracks: Pictures of matchstick men / Ice in the sun / Black veils of melancholy / Are you growing tired of my love / Down the dustpipe / In my chair / Mean girl / Lakky lady.
■ LP . . . . .DOW 10
■ MC . . . . ZCDOW 10
PRT / Jul '83.

Steel Fury

LESSER OF TWO EVILS.
Tracks: Not Advised.
CD 859 803
Steamhammer (Germany) / '89 / Pinnacle.

Steel Pole Bath Tub

BOZEMAN.
Tracks: Bozeman.
■ 7" . . . . BR 031
■ CD Single . . . . TUPO 372
Tupelo / May '92.

I DREAMED A DREAM.
Tracks: I dreamed a dream / Sweet young thing ain't sweet anymore.
■ 12" . . . . TPEP 010
Tupelo / Aug '90.

LIVE.
Tracks: Not Advised.
CD . . . . YCLS 019
Your Choice / Jun '94 / Plastic Head.

LURCH.
Tracks: Christina / Hey you / Paranoid / I am Sam I am / Bee sting / Swerve / Heaven on dirt / Lime away / River / Time to die / Welcome aboard it's love / Hey Bo Diddley / Thru the windshield of love / Tear it apart.
CD . . . . .TUPCD 16
LP . . . . .TUPLP 16
Tupelo / Jul '90 / Vital Distribution.

MIRACLE OF SOUND IN MOTION, THE.
Tracks: Pseudoephedrine hydrochloride / Train to Miami / Exhale / Thumbnail / Down all the days / Carbon / Bozeman / Borstal / 594 / Waxl.
CD . . . . .TUP 472
LP . . . . .TUP 471

MC . . . . .TUP 474
Tupelo / Apr '93 / Vital Distribution.

SOME COCKTAIL SUGGESTIONS.
Tracks: Ray / Living end / Slip / Hit it / Speaker phone / Wasp jar.
CD . . . . .TUP 051-2
LP . . . . .TUP 051-1
MC . . . . .TUP 051-4
Tupelo / Jan '94 / Vital Distribution.

STEEL POLE BATH TUB: LIVE.
Tracks: Not Advised.
LP . . . . .YCR 015
Your Choice / '92 / Plastic Head.

Steele, Chrissy

MAGNET TO STEELE.
Tracks: Love you till it hurts / Armed and dangerous / Move over / Love don't last forever / Try me / Two bodies / Murder in the first degree / King of hearts / Magnet to Steele / Two lips (don't make a kiss) / Cry myself to sleep.
■ LP . . . . CHR 1843
■ MC . . . . ZCHR 1843
■ CD . . . . CCD 1843
Chrysalis / Sep '91.

Steeler

RULIN' THE EARTH.
Tracks: Not Advised.
■ LP . . . . ES 4009
Earthshaker (Germany) / Jun '85.

STEELER.
Tracks: Not Advised.
■ LP . . . . ES 4001
Earthshaker (Germany) / Aug '84.
■ LP . . . . SH 1007
Shrapnel (USA) / Aug '87.

STRIKE BACK.
Tracks: Not Advised.
LP 081 890
Steamhammer (Germany) / Nov '87.
CD 851 861
Steamhammer (Germany) / '88 / Pinnacle.
MC 087 511
Steamhammer (Germany) / '90 / Pinnacle.

UNDERCOVER.
Tracks: Not Advised.
CD 857 510
LP 087 510
Steamhammer (Germany) / '89.

Steelheart

STEELHEART.
Tracks: Love ain't easy / Can't stop me lovin' you / Like never before / I'll never let you go / Everybody loves Eileen / Shelia / Gimme gimme gimme / Rock 'n' roll (I just wanna) / She's gone / Down 'n' dirty.
CD . . . . .DMCC 6118
■ LP . . . . .MCG 6118
■ MC .MCGC 6118
MCA / Nov '90.

TANGLED IN REINS.
Tracks: Loaded mutha / Sticky side up / Electric love child / Late for the party / All your love / Love 'em and I'm gone / Take me back home / Steelheart / Mama don't you cry / Dancin' in the fire.
■ LP . . . . MCA 10426
■ CD . . . . MCAD 10426
■ MC . . . . MCAC 10426
MCA / May '92.

Steinman, Jim

Having first collaborated in obscure early '70s productions, Meatloaf and Jim Steinman won fortune and fame with *Bat Out of Hell*. Intended follow-up, *Bad For Good*, appeared as Steinman solo album, but pair reunited for *Dead Ringer* in '81. Subsequently, Sisters of Mercy and Bonnie Tyler fronted Steinman's Wagnerian productions; Def Leppard, however, fired him from *Hysteria* sessions. Reunion with Meatloaf spawned multi-million selling *Bat Out of Hell II*, which reworked some songs from Steinman's micro-selling 1989 *Original Sin* folly (credited to Pandora's Box).

BAD FOR GOOD.
Tracks: Bad for good / Lost boys and golden girls / Love and death and an American guitar / Stark

raving love / Out of the frying pan (and into the fire) / Surf's up / Dance in my pants / Left in the dark.
■ LP . . . . EPC 84361
Epic / May '81.
■ LP . . . . EPC 32791
■ MC .40 32791
Epic / Aug '86.
CD 4720422
MC 4720424
Epic / Oct '92 / Sony.

DANCE IN MY PANTS.
Tracks: Dance in my pants / Left in the dark.
■ 7" . . . . EPCA 1707
Epic / Oct '81.

LOST BOYS AND THE GOLDEN GIRLS.
Tracks: Lost boys and the golden girls / Left in the dark.
■ 7" . . . . EPAA 1561
Epic / Sep '81.

NOWHERE FAST (Steinman, Jim Fire Inc.).
Tracks: Nowhere fast / Sorcerer.
■ 7" . . . . MCA 920
MCA / Oct '84.

ROCK 'N' ROLL DREAMS COME THROUGH.
Tracks: Rock 'n' roll dreams come through / Life and death of an American guitar.
■ 7" . . . . .A 1236
Epic / Jul '81.

TONIGHT IS WHAT IT MEANS TO BE YOUNG (Steinman, Jim Fire Inc.).
Tracks: Tonight is what it means to be young / Hold that snake.
■ 12" . . . . .MCAT 889
■ 7" . . . . MCA 889
MCA / May '84.

Steppenwolf

Hard rockers Steppenwolf formed in California in 1967 by John Kay, Goldy McJohn and Jerry Edmunton. Essentially famous for one song; *Born To Be Wild* which supposedly contained the first reference to the phrase 'Heavy Metal'. This song and *The Pusher* featured in cult biker movie *Easy Rider*. Steppenwolf split in 1972, although Kay continues to record/tour under the name.

16 GREATEST HITS: STEPPENWOLF.
Tracks: Not Advised.
■ CD . . . . MCAD 37049
MCA / Feb '91.

BORN TO BE WILD.
Tracks: Born to be wild.
■ 7" . . . . SS 8017
Stateside / Jun '69.

BORN TO BE WILD.
Tracks: Not Advised.
CD . . . . MPG 74016
Movieplay Gold / May '93 / Target / BMG.

BORN TO BE WILD (OLD GOLD).
Tracks: Born to be wild / Pusher.
■ 7" . . . . .OG 9323
Old Gold / Apr '83.

GOLD.
Tracks: Magic carpet ride / Pusher / Born to be wild / Sookie sookie / It's never too late / Rock me / Hey lawdy mama / Move over / Who needs you / Jupiter child / Screaming night hog.
■ LP . . . . MCL 1502
MCA / Oct '80.
■ LP . . . . MCL 1619
■ MC . . . . MCLC 1619
MCA / Aug '81.
■ LP . . . . FA 3052
MC . . . . TCFA 3052
Fame / Jan '83 / EMI.

GOLDEN GREATS: STEPPENWOLF.
Tracks: Born to be wild / Magic carpet ride / Rock me / Move over / Hey lawdy mama / It's never too late / Who needs you / Monster / Snow blind friend / Pusher / Sookie sookie / Jupiter's child / Screaming dog night / Ride with me / For ladies only / Tenderness.
■ LP . . . . MCM 5002
■ MC . . . . .MCMC 5002
MCA / Jul '85.

MONSTER.
Tracks: Not Advised.
■ LP . . . . SSL 5021
Stateside / Feb '70.
CD. . . . . .BGOCD 126
Beat Goes On / Sep '91 / Pinnacle.

NIGHTRIDING: STEPPENWOLF.
Tracks: Not Advised.
■ CD. . . . . KNCD 10022
■ MC. . . . . KNMC 10022
Nightriding / Aug '91.

REST IN PEACE.
Tracks: Don't step on the grass Sam / Foggy mental breakdown / Everybody's next one / Desperation / Ostrich / Regenade / Hippo stomp / Your walls too high / Take what you need / None of your doing.
■ LP . . . . SPB 1059
Probe / Sep '72.

RISE AND SHINE.
Tracks: Let's do it all / Do or die / Wall / Keep rockin' / Sign on the line / Time out / Rise and shine / Daily blues / Rock'n'roll war / We like it, we love it.
■ LP . . . . EIRSA 1037
I.R.S. (Illegal) / Aug '90.

STEPPENWOLF.
Tracks: Sookie Sookie / Everybody's next one / Berry rides again / Hoochie coochie man / Born to be wild / Your wall's too high / Desperation / Pusher / Girl I knew / Take what you need / Ostrich.
■ LP . . . . SSL 5020
Stateside / Apr '70.
■ CD . . . . CMCAD 31020
MCA / Jul '87.
■ LP . . . . MCL 1857
■ MC. . . . . MCLC 1857
MCA / Jun '87.
■ MC. . . . . MCLC 19019
MCA / Apr '92.
■ CD . . . . MCLD 19019
MCA / Feb '94.

STEPPENWOLF LIVE.
Tracks: Not Advised.
■ LP . . . . SSL 5029
Stateside / Jul '70.

STEPPENWOLF THE SECOND.
Tracks: Faster than the speed of life / Tighten up your wig / None of your doing / Spiritual fantasy / Don't step on the grass, Sam / 28 / Magic carpet ride / Disappointment number / Lost and found by trial and error / Hodge, podge strained through a leslie / Reflections / Resurrection.
■ CD . . . . CMCAD 31021
MCA / Aug '87.

Sterling Cooke Force

FULL FORCE.
Tracks: Not Advised.
■ LP . . . . EBON 20
Ebony (Pinnacle) / Aug '84.

Stevens, Stevie

ATOMIC PLAYBOYS.
Tracks: Atomic playboys / Power of suggestion / Action / Desperate heart / Soul on ice / Crackdown / Pet the hot kitty / Evening eye / Woman of 1000 years / Run across desert hearts / Slipping into fiction.
■ CD 9259202
WEA / '89.

Stone

EMOTIONAL PLAYGROUND.
Tracks: Small tales / Home base / Last chance / Above the grey sky / Mad Hatter's den / Dead end / Adrift / Haven / Years after / Time dive / Missionary of charity / Emotional playground.
CD 8410562
LP 0810561
Black Mark / Feb '92 / Plastic Head.

Stone Fury

BURNS LIKE A STAR.
Tracks: Not Advised.
■ LP . . . . MCF 3249
■ MC. . . . . MCFC 3249
MCA / Mar '85.

Stone Temple Pilots

Second division 'grunge' band have enjoyed success on both sides of the pond despite a luke warm response from many critics. They are accused of being Pearl Jam and Alice in Chains copyists and have yet to shake off the impression that they are chancers with an eye for the Seattle bandwagon. However debut album *Core* hit the Top 30 and the follow up *Purple* has consolidated their position as 'the next Pearl Jam'.

CORE.
Tracks: Dead and bloated / Sex type thing / Wicked garden / No memory / Sin / Naked Sunday / Creep / Piece of pie / Plush / Wet my bed / Crackerman / Where the river goes.
CD 7567824182
MC. 7567824184
WEA / Nov '92 / WEA.
LP 7567824181
WEA / Sep '93 / WEA.

PLUSH.
Tracks: Plush / Swing / Sex type thing (On 12" & CDs only).
■ 12" . . . . A 7349T
■ 7" . . . . .A 7349
■ CD Single . . . . A 7349CD
■ MC Single . . . . A 7349C
Atlantic / Aug '93.

PURPLE.
Tracks: Not Advised.
CD 756782607-2
LP 756782607-1
MC. 756782607-4
Warner Bros. / Jun '94 / WEA.

SEX TYPE THING.
Tracks: Sex type thing / Wicked garden.
■ 12" . . . . A 5769T
■ CD Single . . . . A 5769CD
Atlantic / Mar '93.
■ 12" . . . . A 7293T
■ CD Single . . . . A 7293CD
■ MC Single. . . . . A 7293C
Atlantic / Nov '93.

VASOLINE.
Tracks: Vasoline / Meatplow.
12" . . . . A 5650T
CD Single. . . . . A 5650CD
CD Single. . . . . A 5650CDX
MC Single . . . . A 5650C
Atlantic / Jul '94 / WEA.

Storm

IT'S HARD NOT TO LIKE YOU.
Tracks: It's hard not to like you / Just like you.
■ 7" . . . . .SOFD 006
Sound Off / Aug '79.

IT'S MY HOUSE.
Tracks: It's my house.
■ 7" . . . . SC 10
Scope / Nov '79.

MALICE IN WONDERLAND.
Tracks: Malice in Wonderland / Dr. Storm.
■ 12" . . . . SILENT 1
Silent Record Company / Mar '86.

STORM, THE.
Tracks: You keep me waiting / I've got a lot to learn about love / In the raw / You're gonna miss me / Call me / Show me the way / I want you back / Still loving you / Touch & go / Gimme love / Take me away / Can't live without love.
CD 91741-2
■ LP 91741-1
MC. 91741-4
East West / Sep '91 / WEA.

TODAY IS MY BIRTHDAY.
Tracks: Today is my birthday / Celebration.
■ 7" . . . . .SOFD 005
Sound Off / Aug '80.

Stormbringer

STORMBRINGER.
Tracks: Not Advised.
■ LP . . . . .SKULL 8391
Mausoleum / Jun '85.

Stormtrooper

ARMIES OF THE NIGHT.
Tracks: Armies of the night.
■ EP . . . . IW 1005
Iron Works (USA) / Jan '87.

Stormwitch

BEAUTY AND THE BEAST.
Tracks: Call of the wicked / Beauty and the beast / Just for one night / Emerald eyes / Tears by the firelight / Tigers of the sea / Russia's on fire / Cheyenne / Welcome to Bedlam.
■ LP . . . . GAMA 880763
Gama / Jan '88.
CD. 15 348
MC. 79 348
Laserlight / Aug '91 / TBD / BMG / Target.

STRONGER THAN HEAVEN.
Tracks: Not Advised.
■ LP 941 312
Powerstation / Sep '86.

WALPURGIS NIGHT.
Tracks: Not Advised.
CD. 15 391
MC. 79 391
Laserlight / Aug '91 / TBD / BMG / Target.

Stradlin, Izzy

IZZY STRADLIN AND THE JU JU HOUNDS.
Tracks: Somebody knockin' / Pressure drop / Time gone by / Shuffle it all / Bucket o' trouble / Train tracks / How will it go / Cuttin the rug / Take a look at the guy / Come on now inside.
CD. . . . . GED 24490
■ LP . . . . GEF 24490
MC. . . . . GEC 24490
Geffen / Oct '92 / BMG.

PRESSURE DROP.
Tracks: Pressure drop.
12" . . . . .GFST 25
7" . . . . GFS 25
CD Single . . . . .GFSTD 25
MC Single . . . . .GFSC 25
Geffen / Sep '92 / BMG.

SHUFFLE IT ALL.
Tracks: Shuffle it all.
■ 12" . . . . .GFSTR 33
■ CD Single . . . . .GFSTD 33
■ MC Single. . . . . GFSC 33
Geffen / Dec '92.

Strangeways

ALL THE SOUNDS OF FEAR.
Tracks: All the sounds of fear / Wasting time.
■ 7" . . . . .ARE 7
Real / Feb '79.

CLOSE TO THE EDGE.
Tracks: Close to the edge / Hold back your love / Heartbeat zone (Extra track on 12" version only).
■ 12" 608 104
■ 7" 108 104
Bonaire / Mar '86.

NATIVE SONGS.
Tracks: Dance with somebody / Only a fool / So far away / Where do we go from here / Goodnight LA / Empty street / Stand up and shout / Shake the seven / Never gonna lose it / Face to face.
■ LP 208579
Arista / Jan '88.
■ CD 258579
■ MC 408579
Arista / Jan '88.

ONLY A FOOL.
Tracks: Only a fool / Empty street / Stand up & shout (live) (Extra track on 12" only) / Breaking down the barriers(live) (Extra track on 12" only).
■ 12" . . . . BON 126
■ 7" . . . . .BON 6
Bonaire / Nov '87.

SHOW HER YOU CARE.
Tracks: Show her you care / You're on your own.
■ 7" . . . . .ARE 2
Real / Aug '78.

STRANGE WAYS.
Tracks: Not Advised.
■ LP 207648
■ MC 407648
Arista / Mar '86.

Strapps

BRIXTON.
Tracks: Brixton / No liquor.
■ 7" .... DONUT 3
Donut / Jul '82.

CHILD OF THE CITY.
Tracks: Child of the city / Soft touch.
■ 7" .... HAR 5119
Harvest / Feb '77.

STRAPS.
Tracks: House of the rising sun / Brixton / Ex directory / Police news / Lies / New age / Pox kid / What's on the box.
■ LP .... CYC 2
Cyclops / Jan '83.

TURN OUT ALRIGHT.
Tracks: Turn out alright / Take it, break it.
■ 7" .... HAR 5163
Harvest / Jun '78.

Stratus

THROWING SHAPES.
Tracks: Not Advised.
■ LP .... STEEL 31001
MC .... STEELC 31001
Steeltrax / Sep '85.

Streets

CRIMES IN MIND.
Tracks: Don't look back / Nightmare begins / Broken glass / Hit n run / Crimes in mind / I can't wait / Gun runner / Desiree / Hate race / Turn my head.
■ LP 781 246-1
Atlantic / Jul '85.

Stressball

STRESSBALL.
Tracks: Not Advised.
CD .... IRSCD 981201
Intercord / Jan '94 / Pinnacle / C.M. Distribution.

Strife

RUSH.
Tracks: Backstreets of heaven / Man of the wilderness / Magic of the dawn / Indian dream / Life is easy / Better than I / Rush.
■ LP .... CHR 1063
■ MC .... ZCHR 1063
Chrysalis / '83.

Strike

STRIKE.
Tracks: Not Advised.
■ LP .... SWORDLP 002
Music For Nations / Jan '85.

Stryper

AGAINST THE LAW.
Tracks: Against the law / Two time woman / Rock the people / Two bodies (one mind, one soul) / Not that kind of guy / Shining star / Ordinary man / Lady / Caught in the middle / All for one / Rock the hell out of you.
■ LP .... ENVLP 1010
■ CD .... CDENV 1010
■ MC .... TCENV 1010
Enigma (EMI) / Aug '90.

ALWAYS THERE FOR YOU.
Tracks: Always there for you (on all versions) / In God we trust (NOT on CD) / Soldiers under command (On 12" only) / Reign (On CD only) / Soldiers under command (live) / Robert Sweet interview-part one (On CD only).
■ 12" .... ENVT 1
■ 7" .... ENV 1
■ 7" .... ENVS 1
■ CD Single .... ENVCD 1
■ 7" P.Disc .... ENCS 1
Enigma (EMI) / Aug '88.

CALLING ON YOU.
Tracks: Calling on you.
■ 12" .... 12 KUT 126
■ 7" .... KUT 126
Music For Nations / Apr '87.

CAN'T STOP THE ROCK.
Tracks: Not Advised.
CD .... HWDCD 8
■ LP .... HWDLP 8
MC .... HWDMC 8
Hollywood (2) / Oct '91 / Sony.

IN GOD WE TRUST.
Tracks: In God we trust / Always there for you / Keep the fire burning / I believe in you / Writing on the wall / It's up 2 U / World of you and I / Come to the everlife / Lonely / Reign.
CD .... CDENV 501
■ LP .... ENVLP 501
Enigma (EMI) / Aug '88.
■ LP P.Disc .... PENVLP 501
Enigma (EMI) / Aug '88.
MC .... TCENV 501
Enigma (EMI) / Aug '88 / EMI.
■ LP .... MYRR 1252
MC .... MYRC 1252
Myrrh / Jun '88 / Word Records (UK) / Sony.
■ CD .... CDENV 1008
■ LP .... ENVLP 1008
■ MC .... TCENV 1008
Enigma (EMI) / Aug '90.

LIVE IN JAPAN.
Tracks: Not Advised.
■ VHS .... HEN 2045
Hendring Video / Aug '90.

SOLDIERS UNDER COMMAND.
Tracks: Not Advised.
■ LP .... MFN 72
■ LP .... MYR R 1228
MC .... MYR C 1228
Myrrh / Feb '87 / Word Records (UK) / Sony.
CD .... CDMFN 72
Music For Nations / Aug '89 / Pinnacle.

STRYPER: INTERVIEW PICTURE DISC.
Tracks: Not Advised.
LP P.Disc .... BAK 2052
Baktabak / Jul '87 / Arabesque Ltd.

TO HELL WITH THE DEVIL.
Tracks: Abyss (to hell with the devil) / To hell with the devil / Calling on you / Free / Honestly / Way / Sing along song / Rockin' the world / All of me / More than a man.
■ LP .... MFN 70
Music For Nations / Oct '86.
CD .... CDMFN 70
Music For Nations / Aug '87 / Pinnacle.
■ LP .... MYR R 1129
MC .... MYR C 1229
Myrrh / Feb '87 / Word Records (UK) / Sony.
MC .... TMFN 70
Music For Nations / Sep '87 / Pinnacle.
■ LP .... ENVLP 1009
Enigma (EMI) / Jul '90.

WINTER WONDERLAND.
Tracks: Winter wonderland.
■ 7" .... STRY 1
Enigma (EMI) / Nov '85.

YELLOW AND BLACK ATTACK, THE.
Tracks: Loud 'n' clear / My love I'll always show / You know what to do / Common rock / You won't be lonely / Loving you / Reasons for the season.
■ LP .... MFN 74
Music For Nations / Apr '87.
CD .... CDMFN 74
Music For Nations / Aug '89 / Pinnacle.

Stupids

FRANKFURTER.
Tracks: Frankfurter.
■ 12" .... FART 1
Vinyl Solution / Aug '87.

JESUS MEETS THE STUPIDS.
Tracks: Not Advised.
■ LP .... SOL 7
Vinyl Solution / Dec '87

PEEL SESSIONS: STUPIDS (12.5.87).
Tracks: Life's a drag / Heard it all before / Shaded eyes / Dog log / Stupid Monday.
■ 12" .... SFPS 054
Strange Fruit / Sep '88.

PERUVIAN VACATION.
Tracks: Not Advised.
■ LP .... GURT 9
Children Of The Revolution / May '86.

PERUVIAN VACATION & VIOLENT NUN.
Tracks: Not Advised.
CD .... EWM 4038
Uplands / Sep '93 / Total.
CD .... CLAYCD 116
Clay / Apr '94 / Plastic Head.

RETARD PICNIC.
Tracks: Not Advised.
■ LP .... GURT 15
Children Of The Revolution / Oct '86.
CD .... CLAYCD 117
Clay / Apr '94 / Plastic Head.

VAN STUPID.
Tracks: Not Advised.
Mini LP .... SOL 2
Vinyl Solution / May '87 / RTM / Pinnacle.

VIOLENT NUN.
Tracks: Violent nun.
■ 7" .... COR 3
Children Of The Revolution / Mar '85.

Styx

AOR giants, formed in 1970, who enjoyed U.S. success from 1975 until split in 1984. Critically-reviled, band enjoyed transatlantic success with 1980 single *Babe* and 1981 album *Paradise theater*. Guitarist Tommy Shaw, instrumental in turning Styx into hitmakers, has continued success with solo career and the Damn Yankees.

BABE.
Tracks: Not Advised.
■ 7" .... AMS 7489
A&M / Jan '80.

BABE (OLD GOLD).
Tracks: Best of times / Prime time / White punks on dope / Babe.
■ 7" .... OG 9545
Old Gold / Sep '85.
■ 12" .... OG 4013
Old Gold / Jan '87.

BEST OF STYX.
Tracks: You need love / Lady / I'm gonna make you feel it / What has come between us / Southern woman / Rock and roll feeling / Winner takes all / Best thing / Witch wolf / Grove of Eglantine / Man of miracles.
■ LP .... PL 13116
■ MC .... PK 13116
■ CD .... PD 83597
RCA / Oct '79

BEST OF TIMES, THE.
Tracks: Best of times / Lights.
■ 7" .... AMS 8102
A&M / Jan '81.

CAUGHT IN THE ACT.
Tracks: Music time / Too much time on my hands / Babe / Snow blind / Best of times / Suite madame blue / Rockin' the paradise / Blue collar man / Miss America / Don't let it end / Fooling yourself / Crystal ball / Come sail away / Mr. Roboto.
■ Double LP .... AMLM 66704
A&M / Apr '84.

CAUGHT IN THE ACT (Live).
Tracks: Mr. Roboto / Rockin' the paradise / Blue collar man / Snowblind / Too much time on my hands / Don't let it end / Heavy metal poisoning / Cold war / Best of times / Come sail away / Renegade / Haven't we been here before / Don't let it end (reprise).
■ VHS .... AMV 824
A&M Sound Pictures / Sep '84.

COME SAIL AWAY.
Tracks: Come sail away / Put me on.
■ 7" .... AMS 7321
A&M / Nov '77.

COMPACT HITS: STYX.
Tracks: Babe / Come sail away / Rockin' the paradise / Best of times.
■ CD Single .... AMCD 904
A&M / Apr '88.

CORNERSTONE.
Tracks: Lights / Why me / Babe / Never say never / Boat on the river / Borrowed time / First time / Eddie / Love in the moonlight.
■ LP .... AMLK 63711
■ MC .... CKM 63711
A&M / Feb '80.

CRYSTAL BALL.
Tracks: Put me on / Mademoiselle / Jennifer / Crystal ball / Shooz / This old man / Clair de lune / Ballerina.
■ LP . . . . AMLH 64604
A&M / '76.

DON'T LET IT END.
Tracks: Don't let it end / Rockin' the paradise.
■ 7" . . . . AM 120
A&M / Jun '83.

EDGE OF THE CENTURY.
Tracks: Love is the ritual / Show me the way / Edge of the century / Love at first sight / All in a days work / Not dead yet / World tonite / Carrie Ann / Homewrecker / Back to Chicago.
■ LP 395327 1
■ CD 395327 2
■ MC 395327 4
A&M / Nov '90.

EQUINOX.
Tracks: Light up / Lorelei / Mother dear / Lonely child / Midnight ride / Born for adventure / Prelude 12 / Suite Madame blue.
■ LP . . . . AMLH 64559
A&M / Jan '76.

FOOLING YOURSELF.
Tracks: Fooling yourself / Grand finale.
■ 7" . . . . AMS 7343
A&M / Apr '78.

GRAND ILLUSION, THE.
Tracks: Grand illusion / Fooling yourself / Superstars / Come sail away / Miss America / Man in the wilderness / Castle walls / Grand finale.
■ LP . . . . AMLH 64637
■ MC . . . . CAM 64637
A&M / Aug '77.
CD . . . . CDA 3223
A&M / Jul '87 / PolyGram.

KILROY WAS HERE.
Tracks: Mr. Roboto / Cold war / Don't let it end / High time / Heavy metal poisoning / Just get through this night / Double life / Haven't we been here before.
■ LP . . . . AMLX 63734
A&M / Mar '83.
CD . . . . CDA 63734
A&M / Apr '84 / PolyGram.

LADY (Styx II).
Tracks: You need love / Lady / Day / You better ask / Little fugue in 'G' / Father O.S.A. / Earl of Roseland / I'm gonna make you feel it.
■ LP . . . . PL 13594
RCA / Oct '80.

LADY.
Tracks: Lady / Children of the land.
■ 7" . . . . RCA 2518
RCA / Feb '75.

LIGHTS.
Tracks: Lights / Renegade / Light up (on 12" only).
■ 12" . . . . AMSP 7528
■ 7" . . . . AMS 7528
A&M / Jun '80.

LOVE IS THE RITUAL.
Tracks: Love is the ritual / Homewrecker.
■ 12" . . . . AMY 709
■ 7" . . . . AM 709
■ 7" P.Disc . . . . AMX 709
A&M / Dec '90.

MADEMOISELLE.
Tracks: Mademoiselle / Light up.
■ 7" . . . . AMS 7273
A&M / Jan '77.

MADEMOISELLE.
Tracks: Mademoiselle / Come sail away / Crystal ball / Lorelei.
■ 7" . . . . AMS 7355
A&M / May '78.

MR ROBOTO.
Tracks: Mr. Roboto / Snowblind.
■ 7" . . . . AMS 8308
A&M / Mar '83.

PARADISE THEATRE.
Tracks: A.D. 1928 / Rockin' in paradise / Too much time on my hands / Nothing ever goes as planned / Best of times / Lonely people / She cares / Snowblind / Halfpenny, two penny / A.D. 1958 / State street Sadie.
■ LP . . . . AMLK 63719
A&M / Feb '81.
■ LP . . . . AMLH 63719

■ MC . . . . CKM 63719
A&M / Jan '81.
■ CD . . . . CDA 63719
A&M / Jun '84.
CD . . . . CDMID 154
MC . . . . CMID 154
A&M / Oct '92 / PolyGram.

PIECES OF EIGHT.
Tracks: I'm OK / Great white hope / Sing for the day / Message / Lords of the ring / Blue collar man / Queen of spades / Renegade / Pieces of eight / Aku-aku.
■ LP . . . . AMLH 64724
■ MC . . . . CAM 64724
A&M / Sep '78.

RENEGADE.
Tracks: Renegade / Sing for the day.
■ 7" . . . . AMS 7446
A&M / Nov '79.

ROCK GALAXY.
Tracks: Movement for the common man / Children of the land / Street college / Fanfare for the common man / Mother nature's matinee / Right away / What has come between us / Best thing / Quick is the beat of my heart / After you leave me / You need love / Lady / Day / You better ask / Little fugue in G / Father O S A / Earl of Roseland / I'm gonna make you feel it.
MC . . . . PK 43215
RCA / Jul '83 / BMG.

ROCKIN' THE PARADISE.
Tracks: Rockin' the paradise / Snow blind.
■ 7" . . . . AMS 8175
A&M / Nov '81.

SERPENT IS RISING, THE.
Tracks: Witch wolf / Grove of Eglantine / Young man / As bad as this / Winner take all / 22 Years / Jonas Psalter / Serpent is rising / Krakatoa / Hallelujah chorus.
■ LP . . . . BXL 10287
Wooden Nickel / '73.

STYX.
Tracks: Movement for the common man / Right away / What has come between us / Best thing / Quick is the beat of my heart / After you leave me.
■ LP . . . . PL 13593
RCA / Oct '80.

TOO MUCH TIME ON MY HANDS.
Tracks: Too much time on my hands / Queen of spades.
■ 7" . . . . AMS 8118
A&M / Mar '81.

DAY OF LIGHT, THE.
Tracks: Not Advised.
CD . . . . .FH 022
■ LP . . . . FH 12017
Funhouse / Oct '89.

STORMBRINGER.
Tracks: Stormbringer.
■ 12" 506 117
Parade / Apr '90.

UNKNOWN GENDER.
Tracks: Not Advised.
CD . . . . WB 1099-2
We Bite / Aug '93 / Plastic Head.

GLOBAL WARMING.
Tracks: Not Advised.
CD . . . . NPR 002CD
Napalm / Mar '94 / Plastic Head.

BREEDING THE SPAWN.
Tracks: Beginning of sorrow / Breeding the spawn / Epitaph of the credulous / Marital decimation / Prelude to repulsion / Anomalistic offerings / Ornaments of decrepancy / Ignorant deprivation.
CD . . . . CD RR 9113 2
■ LP . . . . .RR 9113 1
Road Runner / Mar '93.

EFFIGY OF THE FORGOTTEN.
Tracks: Not Advised.
CD . . . . RC 92752
■ LP . . . . RC 92751
■ MC . . . . RC 92754
Road Runner / Sep '91.

HUMAN WASTE.
Tracks: Not Advised.
CD . . . . .NB 051CD
■ LP . . . . NB 051
Revolver / Jul '91.

After Husker Du split, guitarist Bob Mould maintained tradition of critical acclaim and minute sales with *Workbook* album. Profile dipped further with gloomy *Black Sheets of Rain* before formation of new trio, Sugar. Posthumous honouring of Huskers as founding fathers of Grunge reawoke interest and *Copper Blue* blasted into U.K. Top 10; success repeated with resolutely uncommercial follow-up *Beaster* in '93. '94's *File Under Easy Listening* consolidated Sugar's position in upper ranks of alternative rock.

BEASTER.
Tracks: Come around / Tilted / Judas cradle / J C Auto / Feeling better / Walking away.
CD . . . . CRECD 153
LP . . . . CRELP 153
MC . . . . C-CRE 153
Creation / Apr '93 / Pinnacle.

CHANGES.
Tracks: Changes.
■ 12" . . . . CRE 126T
■ 7" . . . . CRE 126
■ CD Single . . . . CRESCD 126
Creation / Jul '92.

COPPER BLUE.
Tracks: Not Advised.
CD . . . . CRECD 129
LP . . . . CRELP 129
MC . . . . CCRE 129
Creation / Jul '92 / Pinnacle.
DCC . . . . CREDCC 129
MiniDisc. . . . . CREMD 129
Creation / Feb '93 / Pinnacle.

FILE UNDER EASY LISTENING.
Tracks: Gift / Company book / Your favorite thing / What do you want it to be / Gee Angel / Panama city motel / Can't help you anymore / Granny cool / Believe what you're saying / Explode & make up.
CD . . . . CRECD 172
LP . . . . CRELP 172
MC . . . . CCRE 172
Creation / Sep '94 / Pinnacle.

GOOD IDEA, A.
Tracks: Good idea / Where diamonds are halos / Slick / Armenia In The Sky (Not on 7").
■ 12" . . . . CRE 143T
■ 7" . . . . CRE 143
■ CD Single . . . . CRESCD 143
■ MC Single. . . . . CRECS 143
Creation / Oct '92.

IF I CAN'T CHANGE YOUR MIND.
Tracks: If I can't change your mind.
■ 12" . . . . CRE 149T
■ 7" . . . . CRE 149
■ CD Single . . . . CRESCD 149
■ MC Single. . . . . CRESC 149
Creation / Jan '93.

TILTED.
Tracks: J.C.Auto (Live) / Tilted (Live) / Tilted (Edit).
■ 7" . . . . CRE 156
Creation / Jul '93.

YOUR FAVORITE THING.
Tracks: Your favorite thing / Mind is an island / Frustration / And you tell me.
12" . . . . CRE 186T
7" . . . . CRE 186
CD Single . . . . CRESCD 186
MC Single . . . . CRECS 186
Creation / Aug '94 / Pinnacle.

Having emerged into public eye amidst skatecore movement, Suicidal Tendencies released nine albums and starred in *Miami Vice* without overly troubling chart compilers. By release of *Suicidal For Life* in '94,

■ DELETED

band had yet to graduate above cult/support band status. Best album considered to be 1991's *Lights, Camera, Revolution*, featuring fans' favourite *Give Me Your Money*.

ART OF REBELLION, THE.
Tracks: Can't stop / Accept my sacrifice / Nobody hears / Tap into the power / Monopoly on sorrow / We call this mutha revenge / I wasn't meant to feel this / Asleep at the wheel / Gotta kll Captain Stupid / I'll hate you better / Which way to free / It's going down / Where's the truth.
CD. **4718852**
■ LP **4718851**
MC. **4718854**
Epic / Jul '92 / Sony.

CONTROLLED BY HATRED/FEEL LIKE SHIT..DEJA-VU.
Tracks: Master of no mercy / How will I laugh tomorrow / Just another love song / Waking the dead / Controlled by hatred / Choosing my own way of life / Feel like shit..deja vu / It's not easy / How will I laugh tomorrow (heavy emotion ver.).
MC. **4653994**
■ CD **4653992**
■ LP **4653991**
Epic / Jun '89.

F.N.G.
Tracks: Not Advised.
CD. . . . . **CDVM 9003**
MC. . . . . **TCVM 9003**
Virgin / Jun '92 / EMI.

FIRST ALBUM.
Tracks: Suicide's an alternative/You'll be sorry / I shot the devil / Won't fall in love today / Memories of tomorrow / I saw your mommy.. / I want more / Two sided politics / Subliminal / Institutionalised / Possessed / Fascist pig / Suicidal failure / Possessed to skate (CD only) / Human guinea pig (CD only) / Two wrongs don't make a right (but they make me feel better) (CD only).
■ LP **FLP1011**
Frontier (USA) / Aug '87.
■ LP . . . . **V 2495**
■ MC. . . . . **TCV 2495**
Virgin / Jan '88.
CD. . . . . **CDV 2495**
Virgin / Jan '88 / EMI.

HOW WILL I LAUGH TOMORROW WHEN I CAN'T EVEN SMILE TODAY.
Tracks: Trip at the brain / Hearing voices / Pledge your allegiance / How will I laugh tomorrow / Miracle / Surf and slam / If I don't wake up / Sorry / One too many times / Feeling's back / Suicyco mania (CD only).
CD. . . . . **CDV 2551**
■ LP . . . . **V 2551**
MC. . . . . **TCV 2551**
Virgin / Sep '88 / EMI.

INSTITUTIONALISED.
Tracks: Institutionalised / War inside my head / Cyco.
■ 12" . . . . **VST 1039**
Virgin / Feb '88.

JOIN THE ARMY.
Tracks: Suicidal maniac / Join the army / You got, I want / Little each day / Prisoner / War inside my head / I feel your pain and I survive / Human guinea pig (CD only) / Possessed to skate / No name, no words / Cyco / Two wrongs don't make a right (but they make me feel better) / Looking in your eyes.
■ LP . . . . **V 2424**
■ MC. . . . . **TCV 2424**
Virgin / Apr '87.
CD. . . . . **CDV 2424**
Virgin / Jun '87 / EMI.
MC. . . . . **OVEDC 307**
■ LP . . . . **OVED 307**
Virgin / Apr '90.

LIGHTS..CAMERA..REVOLUTION!.
Tracks: You can't bring me down / Lost again / Alone / Lovely / Give it revolution / Get whacked / Send me your money / Emotion No. 13 / Disco's out / Murder's in / Go'n breakdown.
CD. **4665692**
■ LP **4665691**
■ MC. **4665694**
Epic / Jun '90.

POSSESSED TO SKATE.
Tracks: Possessed to skate / Human guinea pig / Two wrongs don't make a right (but they make me feel better) (12" only).
■ 7" . . . . **VS 967**
■ 12" . . . . **VS 967-12**
Virgin / May '87.

SEND ME YOUR MONEY.
Tracks: Send me your money / You can't bring me down / Waking the dead (Available on 12" format.) / Don't give me your nothing (Available on 12" format.).
■ 12" **6563326**
■ 7" **6563317**
■ 7" P.Disc **6563310**
Epic / Oct '90.

STILL CYCO AFTER ALL THESE YEARS.
Tracks: Suicide's an alternative / Two sided politics / Subliminal / I shot the devil / Won't fall in love / Institionalized / War inside my head / Don't give me your nothin' / Memories of tomorrow / Possessed / I saw your mummy / Fascist pig / Little each day / I want more / Suicidal failure.
CD. . . . . **.473749 2**
LP. . . . . **.473798 1**
MC. . . . . **.473749 4**
Epic / Jun '93 / Sony.

SUICIDAL FOR LIFE.
Tracks: Invocation / Don't give a fuck / No fuck'n problem / Suicyco Muthafucka / Fucked up just right / No bullshit / What else could I do / What you need's a friend / I wouldn't mind / Depression & anguish / Evil / Love v. lonliness / Benediction.
CD. . . . . **.476885-2**
LP. . . . . **.476885-1**
MC. . . . . **.476885-4**
Epic / Jun '94 / Sony.

SUICIDAL TENDENCIES.
Tracks: Suicides an alternative / You'll be sorry / Two sides politics / I shot the devil / Subliminal / Won't fall in love today / Institutionalised / Memories of tomorrow / Possessed / I saw your mommy / Fascist pig / I want more / Suicidal failure / Possessed to skate / Human guinea pig / Two wrongs don't make a right.
■ LP . . . . **OVED 384**
Virgin / Nov '91.

TRIP AT THE BRAIN.
Tracks: Trip at the brain / Suicyco mania.
■ 12" . . . . **VST 1127**
Virgin / Aug '88.

Suicide Squad

LIVE IT WHILE YOU CAN.
Tracks: Live it while you can / Can't use ya / No solution / Bad boy blues.
■ LP . . . . **.MFN 85 M**
Music For Nations / Nov '88.

Surgin

WHEN MIDNIGHT COMES.
Tracks: Not Advised.
■ LP . . . . **MFN 58**
Music For Nations / Dec '85.

Survivor

U.S. AOR quintet formed in '78 and chiefly remembered for transatlantic hits with *Rocky* movie themes *Eye of the Tiger* and *Burning Heart* ('82 and '86, respectively). Other releases were less successful and band split in mid-'80s. However, like Rocky, they returned for yet another go in 1993.

AMERICAN HEARTBEAT.
Tracks: American heartbeat / Silver girl.
■ 7" . . . . **SCTA 2813**
Scotti Bros (USA) / Oct '82.

BURNING HEART.
Tracks: Feels like love / Burning heart / Rocky 4 theme / Eye of the tiger.
■ 7" P.Disc . . . . **.WA 6708**
■ 7" Set . . . . **.DA 6708**
■ 12" . . . . **.TX 6708**
■ 7" . . . . **.A 6708**
Scotti Bros (USA) / Feb '86.

CAUGHT IN THE GAME.
Tracks: Caught in the game / Jackie don't go / I never stopped loving you / It doesn't have to be this way / Ready for the real thing / Half life / What do you really think / Slander / Santa Ana winds.
■ LP . . . . **SCT 25575**
Scotti Bros (USA) / Oct '83.
MC. . . . . **.40 25575**
Epic / Oct '83 / Sony.

CAUGHT IN THE RAIN.
Tracks: Caught in the rain / Slander.
■ 7" . . . . **.A 3789**
Scotti Bros (USA) / Sep '83.

EYE OF THE TIGER.
Tracks: Hesitation dance / One that really matters / I'm not that man anymore / Children of the night / Ever since the world began / American heartbeat / Silver girl / Feels like love / Eye of the tiger / Take you on a Sunday.
■ LP . . . . **SCT 85845**
Scotti Bros (USA) / Aug '82.
CD. . . . . **.CDSCT 85845**
Scotti Bros (USA) / '86 / PolyGram.
■ LP . . . . **SCT 32537**
MC. . . . . **.40 32537**
Scotti Bros (USA) / Feb '86 / PolyGram.
■ LP . . . . **EPC 32537**
Epic / Mar '86.

EYE OF THE TIGER.
Tracks: Eye of the tiger / Take you on a Saturday.
■ 12" . . . . **.TA 2411**
■ 7" . . . . **.A 2411**
■ 7" P.Disc . . . . **SCTA 112411**
Scotti Bros (USA) / Jan '84.

HIGH ON YOU.
Tracks: High on you / It's the singer, not the song.
■ 7" . . . . **.A 4946**
Scotti Bros (USA) / Jan '85.

I CAN'T HOLD BACK.
Tracks: I can't hold back / I see you in everyone.
■ 7" . . . . **.A 4737**
Scotti Bros (USA) / Sep '84.

I CAN'T HOLD BACK.
Tracks: I can't hold back.
■ 12" . . . . **.TA 6989**
■ 7" . . . . **.A 6989**
Scotti Bros (USA) / Mar '86.

IS THIS LOVE.
Tracks: Can't let you go / Is this love.
■ 12" . . . . **.650195-6**
■ 7" . . . . **.650195-7**
Scotti Bros (USA) / Nov '86.

MOMENT OF TRUTH.
Tracks: Moment of truth.
■ 7" . . . . **CAN 1021**
Casablanca / Aug '84.

ONE THAT REALLY MATTERS.
Tracks: One that really matters / Hesitation dance.
■ 7" . . . . **.SCT A 3038**
Scotti Bros (USA) / Jan '83.

POOR MAN'S SON.
Tracks: Poor man's son / Love is on my side.
■ 7" . . . . **SCTA 1903**
CBS / Feb '82.

PREMONITION.
Tracks: Chevy nights / Summer nights / Poor man's son / Runaway lights / Take you on a Saturday / Light of a thousand smiles / Love is on my side / Heart's a lonely hunter.
■ LP . . . . **SCT 85289**
Scotti Bros (USA) / Dec '82.

SEARCH IS OVER, THE.
Tracks: Search is over / It's the singer not the song.
■ 12" . . . . **.TA 6344**
■ 7" . . . . **.A 6344**
Scotti Bros (USA) / May '86.

SOMEWHERE IN AMERICA.
Tracks: Somewhere in America / Freelance.
■ 7" . . . . **K 11453**
Scotti Bros (USA) / Mar '80.

SURVIVOR.
Tracks: Somewhere in America / Can't getcha offa my mind / Let it be now / As soon as love finds me / Youngblood / Love has got me / Whole town's talking / 20/20 / Freeland / Nothing can shake me (from your love) / Whatever it takes.
■ LP . . . . **K 50698**
Scotti Bros (USA) / Nov '80.

SURVIVOR - GREATEST HITS.
Tracks: Eye of the tiger / You know who you are / Burning heart / Search is over / High on you / Is this love / I can't hold back / Hungry years / American heartbeat / Poor man's son / Momemt of truth / Somewhere in America.
CD. . . . . **.518139-2**
MC. . . . . **.518139-4**
Scotti Bros (USA) / Aug '93 / PolyGram.

TOO HOT TO SLEEP.
Tracks: She's a star / Too hot to sleep / Rhythm of the city / Across the miles / Can't give it up / Desperate dreams / Didn't know it was love / Here comes desire / Tell me I'm the one / Burning bridges.

■ LP 836 589-1
■ CD 836 589-2
■ MC 836 589-4
Polydor / Apr '89.

VERY BEST OF SURVIVOR.
Tracks: Not Advised.
CD 288 14 001
Bellaphon / '86 / New Note.

VITAL SIGNS.
Tracks: I can't hold back / High on you / First night / Search is over / Broken promises / Popular girl / Everlasting / It's the singer not the song / I see you in everyone / Moment of truth (Extra track available on cassette only.).
CD 290 14 030
Bellaphon / '86 / New Note.
■ LP . . . . SCT 26126
MC 4026126
Scotti Bros (USA) / Apr '86 / PolyGram.

WHEN SECONDS COUNT.
Tracks: How much love / Keep it right here / This love / Man against the world / Rebel son / Oceans / When seconds count / Backstreet love affair / In good faith / Can't let you go.
■ LP 4501361
■ MC 450136 4
Scotti Bros (USA) / Jan '86.

Sven Gali

SVEN GALI.
Tracks: Under the influence / Tie dyed skies / Sweet little gypsy in my garden / Freaxz / Love don't live here anymore / Stiff competition / Real thing / Whisper in the rain / 25 Hours a day / Here today, gone tomorrow / Disgusteen.
CD 74321 11442-23
MC 74321 11442-47
RCA / Mar '93 / BMG.

Swampwalk

STRANGLED AT BIRTH.
Tracks: Not Advised.
CD . . . . CDBLEED 6
Bleeding Hearts / Oct '93 / Pinnacle.

Sweet

Influential glam-rockers who scored series of U.K. hits between 1971 and '78, many written by '70s hitmaking duo Chinn and Chapman. Successes included U.S. million-sellers *Little Willy* and *Fox On The Run* and U.K. chart-topper *Blockbuster*; hits compensated for virtually non-existent album sales. Singer Brian Connolly and bassist Steve Priest reformed group in 1988.

ACTION.
Tracks: Action / Sweet F.A.
■ 7" . . . . RCA 2578
RCA / Jul '75.

ALEXANDER GRAHAM BELL.
Tracks: Alexander Graham Bell.
■ 7" . . . . RCA 2121
RCA / Oct '71.

BALLROOM BLITZ.
Tracks: Ballroom blitz.
■ 7" . . . . RCA 2403
RCA / Sep '73.

BALLROOM BLITZ.
Tracks: Not Advised.
VHS . . . . CASH 5092
Castle Hendring Video / Mar '90 / BMG / Gold & Sons / TBD.

BALLROOM BLITZ (GOLDEN GROOVE).
Tracks: Wigwam bam.
■ 7" . . . . GOLD 551
RCA Golden Grooves / May '82.

BALLROOM BLITZ VOL. 2.
Tracks: Not Advised.
■ VHS . . . . HEN 2310
Hendring Video / Oct '90.

BIG APPLE WALTZ.
Tracks: Big apple waltz / Why don't you.
■ 7" . . . . POSP 73
Polydor / Aug '79.

BLOCKBUSTER.
Tracks: Blockbuster / Hellraiser.
■ 7" . . . . RCA 2305
RCA / Jan '73.

■ 7" . . . . GOLD 524
RCA Golden Grooves / Aug '81.

BLOCKBUSTER (OLD GOLD).
Tracks: Blockbuster / Little Willy.
■ 7" . . . . OG 9707
Old Gold / Apr '87.

BLOCKBUSTERS.
Tracks: Ballroom blitz / Hellraiser / New York connection / Little Willy / Burning / Need a lot of lovin' / Wig wam bam / Blockbuster / Rock and roll disgrace / Chop chop / Alexander Graham Bell / Poppa Joe / Co Co / Funny funny.
CD . . . . ND 74313
MC . . . . NK 74313
■ LP . . . . NL 74313
RCA / Dec '89.

BREAKDOWN (LIVE).
Tracks: Not Advised.
CD . . . . RRCD 189
Reciever / Jul '94 / Total / BMG.

CALIFORNIA NIGHTS.
Tracks: California nights / Show me the way.
■ 7" . . . . POSP 5
Polydor / May '78.

CALL ME.
Tracks: Call me / Why don't you.
■ 7" . . . . POSP 36
Polydor / '79.

CO CO.
Tracks: Co co.
■ 7" . . . . RCA 2087
RCA / Jun '71.

COLLECTION: SWEET.
Tracks: Teenage rampage / Rebel rouser / Solid gold brass / Stairway to the stars / Turn it down / Sixteens / Into the night / No you don't / Fever of love / Lies in your eyes / Fox on the run / Restless / Set me free / AC DC / Sweet f.a. / Action / Peppermint twist / Heartbreak today / Lost angels / Lady Starlight.
CD . . . . CCSCD 230
■ Double LP . . . . CCSLP 230
■ MC . . . . CCSMC 230
Castle Collector Series / Oct '89.

CUT ABOVE THE REST.
Tracks: Call me / Play all night / Big apple waltz / Dorian Gray / Discophony / Eye games / Mother Earth / Hold me / Stay with me.
■ LP . . . . POLD 5022
Polydor / '79.

DESOLATION BOULEVARD.
Tracks: Ballroom blitz / Six-teens / No you don't / A.C.D.C. / I wanna be committed / Sweet F.A. / Fox on the run / Set me free / Into the night / Solid gold brass.
CD . . . . CLACD 170
Castle Classics / Dec '89 / BMG / Castle Communications.
■ LP . . . . CLALP 170
■ MC . . . . CLAMC 170
Castle Classics / Feb '90.

FEVER OF LOVE.
Tracks: Fever of love / Distinct lack of ancient.
■ 7" . . . . PB 5011
RCA / Feb '77.

FIRST RECORDINGS 1968-171.
Tracks: Not Advised.
CD . . . . REP 4140-WZ
LP . . . . REP 2140
MC . . . . REP 2140-TS
Repertoire (Germany) / Aug '91 / Pinnacle.

FOX ON THE RUN.
Tracks: Fox on the run.
■ 7" . . . . RCA 2524
RCA / Mar '75.

FOX ON THE RUN (EP).
Tracks: Fox on the run / Hellraiser / Ballroom blitz / Blockbuster.
■ EP . . . . PE 5226
RCA / Jul '80.

FOX ON THE RUN (OLD GOLD).
Tracks: Fox on the run / Ballroom blitz.
■ 7" . . . . OG 9709
Old Gold / Apr '87.

FUNNY FUNNY.
Tracks: Funny funny.
■ 7" . . . . RCA 2051
RCA / Mar '71.

GIVE THE LADY SOME RESPECT.
Tracks: Give the lady some respect / Tall girls.
■ 7" 2001946
Polydor / Apr '80.

GIVE US A WINK.
Tracks: Not Advised.
CD . . . . REP 4084-WZ
LP . . . . REP 2084
MC . . . . REP 2084-TI
Repertoire (Germany) / Aug '91 / Pinnacle.

GREATEST HITS: SWEET (1971 historic original re-releases).
Tracks: Not Advised.
CD 290586
MC 490586
Ariola Express / Dec '92 / BMG.

HARD CENTRES (The rock years).
Tracks: Set me free / Sweet F A / Restless / Yesterday's rain / White mice / Cockroach / Keep it in / Live for today / Windy City / Midnight to daylight.
■ LP . . . . ZEB 11
MC . . . . CZEB 11
Zebra (1) / Jul '87 / Pinnacle.
CD . . . . CDMZE 811
Zebra (1) / Jan '88 / Pinnacle.

HELLRAISER.
Tracks: Hellraiser.
■ 7" . . . . RCA 2357
RCA / May '73.

IDENTITY CRISIS.
Tracks: Not Advised.
■ LP 2311 179
Polydor / Nov '82.

IT'S IT'S THE SWEET MIX.
Tracks: It's it's the sweet mix / Fox on the run.
■ 12" . . . . 12 ANA 28
■ 7" . . . . ANA 28
Anagram / Dec '84.

LAND OF HOPE AND GLORY.
Tracks: Not Advised.
CD . . . . RRCD 171
Receiver / Jul '93 / Total / BMG / Grapevine Distribution.

LEVEL HEADED.
Tracks: Not Advised.
CD . . . . REP 4234-WP
Repertoire (Germany) / Aug '91 / Pinnacle.

LIES IN YOUR EYES.
Tracks: Lies in your eyes / Cockroach.
■ 7" . . . . RCA 2641
RCA / Jan '76.

LITTLE WILLY.
Tracks: Little Willy.
■ 7" . . . . RCA 2225
RCA / Jun '72.

LIVE FOR TODAY.
Tracks: Not Advised.
CD . . . . RRCD 181
Reciever / Nov '93 / Total / BMG.

LOST ANGELS.
Tracks: Lost angels / Funk it up.
■ 7" . . . . RCA 2748
RCA / Oct '76.

LOVE IS LIKE OXYGEN.
Tracks: Love is like oxygen / Cover girl.
■ 7" . . . . POSP 1
Polydor / Jan '78.

OFF THE RECORD.
Tracks: Fever of love / Lost angels / Midnight to daylight / Windy city / Live for today / She gimme lovin' / Laura Lee / Hard times / Funk it up.
■ LP . . . . PL 25072
RCA / '79.
CD . . . . REP 4085-WZ
LP . . . . REP 2085
MC . . . . REP 2085-TI
Repertoire (Germany) / Aug '91 / Pinnacle.

POPPA JOE.
Tracks: Poppa Joe.
■ 7" . . . . RCA 2164
RCA / Feb '72.

ROCKIN' THE RAINBOW.
Tracks: Not Advised.
CD . . . . RRCD 169
Receiver / Jul '93 / Total / BMG / Grapevine Distribution.

SIX TEENS, THE.
Tracks: Six teens.
■ 7" . . . . LPBO 5037
RCA / Jul '74.
■ 7" . . . . ANA 27
■ 12" . . . . 12 ANA 27
Anagram / Sep '84.

SIXTIES MAN.
Tracks: Sixties man / Oh yeah.
■ 7" . . . . POSP 160
Polydor / Sep '80.

STRUNG UP.
Tracks: Hellraiser / Burning / Someone else will / Rock 'n' roll disgrace / Need a lot of lovin' / Done me wrong alright / You're not wrong for loving me / Man with the golden arm / Action / Fox on the run / Set me free / Miss Demeanour / Ballroom blitz / Burn on the flame / Solid gold brass / Sixteen / I wanna be committed / Blockbuster.
■ Double LP . . . . SPC 001
■ MC . . . . SPK 0001
RCA / '79.

SWEET FANNY ADAMS.
Tracks: Not Advised.
■ LP . . . . LPK 15038
RCA / May '74.

SWEET LIVE 1973, THE.
Tracks: Ballroom blitz / Little Willie / Rock 'n' roll disgrace / Done me wrong alright / Hellraiser / You're not wrong for loving me / Burning/Someone else will / Man with the golden arm / Need a lot of loving / Wig wam bam / Teenage rampage / Blockbuster / Keep on knockin / Shakin' all over / Lucille / Great balls of fire / Reeling and rocking / Peppermint twist / Shout.
CD . . . . DOJOCD 89
Dojo / Mar '93 / Castle Communications / BMG.

SWEET SIXTEEN.
Tracks: Alexander Graham Bell / Poppa Joe / Little Willy / Wigwam bam / Blockbuster / Hellraiser / Ballroom blitz / Teenage rampage / Rebel rouser / Sixteens / Fox on the run / Action / Lies in your eyes / Stairway to the stars / Lost angels / Love is like oxygen / Sweet sixteen.
■ LP . . . . GRAM 16
■ MC . . . . CGRAM 16
Anagram / Aug '84.

SWEET SIXTEEN.
Tracks: Sweet sixteen.
■ 7" P.Disc . . . . PGRAM 16
Anagram / Aug '84.

SWEET'S BIGGEST HITS.
Tracks: Wig wam bam / Little Willy / Done me wrong alright / Poppa Joe / Funny funny / Co co / Alexander Graham Bell / Chop chop / You're not wrong for loving me / Jeannie / Spotlight.
■ LP . . . . SF 8316
RCA / '79.

SWEETS GOLDEN GREATS.
Tracks: Blockbuster / Hellraiser / Ballroom blitz / Teenage rampage / Sixteens / Turn it down / Fox on the run / Action / Lost angels / Lies in your eyes / Fever of love / Stairway to the stars.
■ LP . . . . PL 25111
RCA / '83.

TEENAGE RAMPAGE.
Tracks: Teenage rampage.
■ 7" . . . . LPBO 5004
RCA / Jan '74.

TEENAGE RAMPAGE (OLD GOLD).
Tracks: Teenage rampage / Hellraiser.
7" . . . . OG 9762
Old Gold / Mar '90 / Pickwick.

TURN IT DOWN.
Tracks: Turn it down.
■ 7" . . . . RCA 2480
RCA / Nov '74.

WATER'S EDGE.
Tracks: Sixties man / Getting in the mood for love / Tell the truth / Own up / Too much talking / Thank you for loving me / At midnight / Water's edge / Hot shot gambler / Give the lady some respect.
■ LP . . . . POLS 1021
Polydor / Aug '80.

WIG WAM BAM.
Tracks: Wig wam bam.
■ 7" . . . . RCA 2260
RCA / Sep '72.
■ 7" . . . . PB 43337
RCA / Nov '89.

WIG WAM BAM (OLD GOLD).
Tracks: Wig wam bam / Co co / Little Willy (Only on CD single).
■ 7" . . . . OG 9760
Old Gold / Jan '88.
CD Single . . . . OG 6174
Old Gold / Jun '92 / Pickwick.

WIG WAM WILLY MIX.
Tracks: Wig Wam Willy mix / Teen action mix.
■ 12" . . . . 12 ANA 29
■ 7" . . . . ANA 29
Anagram / Apr '85.

Sweet Addiction

ALL I WANTED TO DO.
Tracks: All I wanted to do / Broken bottles / Off the cuff (Only on 12" single.) / Before it shows (Only 12" single.).
■ 12" . . . . SURT 050
■ 7" . . . . SUR 050
Survival (1) / Apr '90.

CAUGHT ON A LINE.
Tracks: Caught on a line.
■ 12" . . . . SURT 51
■ 12" P.Disc . . . . SURP 51
■ 7" . . . . SUR 51
■ CD Single . . . . SURCD 51
Survival (1) / Oct '90.

ENOUGH IS ENOUGH.
Tracks: Enough is Enough / The Seeker (Only on 7" and CD Single) / Enough is Enough (Full length version) (Only on 12" and CD Single) / Sympathy (Only on 12" and CD Single) / Enough is Enough (7" mix).
■ 12" . . . . ZT 44580
■ 7" . . . . ZB 44579
■ CD Single . . . . ZD 44580
Survival (1) / May '91.

Sweet Savage

TAKE NO PRISONERS.
Tracks: Take no prisoners / Killing time.
■ 7" . . . . PKR 1001
Park / Dec '81.

Sword

METALIZED.
Tracks: Not Advised.
■ LP . . . . GWLP 10
GWR / Aug '89.

SWEET DREAMS.
Tracks: Not Advised.
■ LP . . . . RO 9476 1
MC . . . . RO 9476 4
Roadracer / '89 / Pinnacle.
MC . . . . GWTC 45
■ LP . . . . GWLP 45
GWR / Apr '89.
■ CD . . . . GWCD 45
GWR / Dec '89.

Syar

DEATH BEFORE DISHONOUR.
Tracks: Not Advised.
■ LP . . . . SKULL 8308
Mausoleum / Apr '84.
MC . . . . TAPE 78308
Mausoleum / Jul '84 / Pinnacle.

Sye

TURN ON THE FIRE.
Tracks: Not Advised.
■ LP . . . . RR 9781
Road Runner / Jun '85.

Syrinx

KALEIDOSCOPE OF SYMPHONIC ROCK.
Tracks: Not Advised.
CD . . . . CYBERCD 9
Cyber / Aug '94 / Plastic Head.

T

T.K.O.

BELOW THE BELT.
Tracks: Not Advised.
CD . . . . RR 349730
Road Runner / '89 / Pinnacle.

IN YOUR FACE.
Tracks: Not Advised.
■ LP . . . . MFN 33
Music For Nations / Dec '84.

T.S.O.L.

BENEATH THE SHADOWS.
Tracks: Not Advised.
■ LP . . . . GWLP 52
GWR / '89.

CHANGE TODAY.
Tracks: Not Advised.
■ LP 1076 1
Enigma (EMI) / Nov '86.

DANCE WITH ME.
Tracks: Sounds of laughter / Core blue / Triangle / 80 times / I'm tired of life / Love storm / Silent scream / Funeral march / Die for me / Peace thru power / Dance with me.
■ LP . . . . WS 033
Weird Systems / Apr '88.

HIT AND RUN.
Tracks: Not Advised.
■ LP . . . . ENIG 32621
Enigma (EMI) / Jun '76.
■ LP . . . . ENIG 32631
Enigma (EMI) / Jun '87.

REVENGE.
Tracks: Not Advised.
■ LP 3211 1
Enigma (EMI) / Nov '86.

STRANGE LOVE.
Tracks: Not Advised.
CD . . . . LS 9392
LP . . . . LS 9391
Road Runner / May '90 / Pinnacle.

Tad

GOD'S BALLS.
Tracks: Not Advised.
■ LP . . . . GR 0051
Glitterhouse / Jul '89.

INHALER.
Tracks: Grease box / Throat locust / Leafy incline / Luminol / Ulcer / Lycanthrope / Just bought the farm / Rotor / Paregoric / Pansy / Gouge.
CD 74321 16570-20
MC 74321 16570-44
■ LP 74321 16570-13
Mechanic / Oct '93.

SALEM.
Tracks: Salem.
■ 12" . . . . .SP 229
■ CD Single . . . . SPCD 229
Sub Pop / Jan '93.

SALT LICK.
Tracks: Not Advised.
LP . . . . GR 0076
Glitterhouse / Apr '90 / SRD.

Tafolla, Joey

INFRA RED.
Tracks: Not Advised.
CD . . . . RR 93422
LP . . . . RR 93421
MC . . . . RR 93424
Road Runner / Apr '91 / Pinnacle.

OUT OF THE SUN.
Tracks: Not Advised.
CD . . . . .RR 9573 2
LP . . . . RR 9573
Road Runner / '89.

Tailgators

HIDE YOUR EYES.
Tracks: Not Advised.
CD . . . . LS 93962
LP . . . . LS 93961
Road Runner / Mar '90 / Pinnacle.

MUMBO JUMBO.
Tracks: Mumbo jumbo / Little girl blue / I need love / Thank you baby / Allon's rock 'n' roll / Chase the devil / Maria Elena / Yard dog / Behind the wheel / Tail shaker / Colinda.
■ LP . . . . .ZONG 010
Zippo / Sep '86.
■ LP . . . . WR 986
MC . . . . WRC 986
Wrestler (USA) / '88 / Pinnacle / A.D.A. Distribution / C.M. Distribution.

OK, LET'S GO.
Tracks: Not Advised.
■ LP . . . . LS 94461
GWR / Aug '89.

SWAMP ROCK.
Tracks: Not Advised.
■ LP . . . . GRUB 6
Food For Thought / Aug '85.

TORE UP.
Tracks: Not Advised.
■ LP . . . . .WR 1987
Wrestler (USA) / Oct '87.
MC . . . . .WRC 1987
Wrestler (USA) / Oct '87 / Pinnacle / A.D.A. Distribution / C.M. Distribution.

Talas

SINK YOUR TEETH INTO THAT.
Tracks: Sink your teeth into that / Hit and run / NV 443345 / High speed on ice / Shy boy / King of the world / Outside lookin' in / Never see my cry / Smart lady / Hick town.
■ LP . . . . GRUB 1
Food For Thought / Aug '86.
CD . . . . CDGRUB 1
Food For Thought / Sep '91 / Pinnacle.

TALAS.
Tracks: Not Advised.
CD .CDZORRO 32
LP . . . . ZORRO 32
Music For Nations / Sep '91 / Pinnacle.

Talion

KILLING THE WORLD.
Tracks: Not Advised.
CD . . . . WADES 001CD
■ LP . . . . WADES 001
Major / Nov '89.

Talisman

TALISMAN.
Tracks: Snowbird / Sailing / Leaving on a jet plane / Morning town ride / Our last song together / Help me make it through the night / That'll be the day / To love somebody / All around my hat / Jolene / Streets of London / I'm a song.
■ LP .SRTZ 76371
SRT / Jan '77.

Talon

NEVER LOOK BACK.
Tracks: Not Advised.
■ LP . . . . SH 009
Steamhammer (Germany) / Nov '85.

Tangier

FOUR WINDS.
Tracks: Not Advised.
CD 979125 2
■ LP 979125 1
■ MC 979125 4
WEA / Jul '89.

STRANDED.

Tracks: Down the line / Caution to the wind / You're not the lovin' kind / Since you been gone / Takes just a little time / Excited / Back in the limelight / Stranded / It's hard if ya can't find love.
CD 7567916032
■ LP 7567916031
MC 7567916034
Atco / Feb '91 / WEA.

Tank

(HE FELL IN LOVE WITH A) STORM TROOPER.
Tracks: (He fell in love with a) storm trooper / Blood, guts and beer.
■ 7" . . . . .KAP 1
Kamaflage / Nov '82.

ARMOURED PLATED.
Tracks: Don't walk away / Power of the hunter / Run Like Hell / Filth hounds of Hades / (He fell in love with a) storm trooper / Red Skull Rock / Snake / Who needs love songs / Stepping on a Land mine / Turn your head around / Crazy horses / Some came running / Hammer on / Shellshock / T.W.D.A.M.O. / Biting and scratching / Used leather (hanging loose) / Blood, guts and beer / Filth bitch boogie / T.A.N.K.
■ LP . . . . .RAWLP 009
MC .RAWTC 009
Raw Power / Apr '86 / Pinnacle.

CRAZY HORSES.
Tracks: Crazy horses / Filth bitch boogie.
■ 7" . . . . .KAM 7
Kamaflage / Sep '82.

DONT WALK AWAY.
Tracks: Don't walk away.
■ 7" . . . . .KAM 1
Kamaflage / Sep '81.

ECHOES OF A DISTANT BATTLE.
Tracks: Echoes of a distant battle / Man that never was.
■ 12" . . . . 12 KUT 101
■ 7" . . . . .KUT 101
Music For Nations / Jul '83.

FILTH HOUNDS OF HADES.
Tracks: Shellshock / Struck by lightning / Run like hell / Blood, guts and beer / That's what dreams are made of / Turn your head around / Heavy artillery / Who needs love songs / Filth hounds of Hades / Stormtrooper.
■ LP . . . . KAM L1
Kamaflage / Apr '82.
CD .REP 4149-WP
Repertoire (Germany) / Aug '91 / Pinnacle.

FILTH HOUNDS OF HADES.
Tracks: Filth hounds of hades.
■ 7" . . . . KAMLP 1
Kamaflage / Mar '82.

HONOUR AND BLOOD.
Tracks: Not Advised.
■ LP . . . . MFN 26
Music For Nations / Dec '84.

POWER OF THE HUNTER.
Tracks: Not Advised.
CD .REP 4150-WP
Repertoire (Germany) / Aug '91 / Pinnacle.

TANK.
Tracks: Reign of thunder / With your life / Enemy below / Suffer / March on, sons of nippon / None but the brave / Lost / It fell from the sky.
CD . . . . GWCD 23
■ LP . . . . GWLP 23
■ MC . . . . GWTC 23
GWR / Mar '88.

THIS MEANS WAR.
Tracks: Not Advised.
■ LP P.Disc . . . . MFN 3P
Music For Nations / Jun '83.
■ LP . . . . .MFN 3
MC . . . . TMFN 3
Music For Nations / May '83 / Pinnacle.

TURN YOUR HEAD AROUND.
Tracks: Turn your head around / Steppin' on a landmine.
■ 7" . . . . KAM 3
Kamaflage / Feb '82.

Tankard

ALIEN.
Tracks: Not Advised.
■ CD . . . . N 0131-3
■ Mini LP . . . . NUK 131
Noise / Apr '89.

CHEMICAL INVASION.
Tracks: Not Advised.
■ CD . . . . CDNUK 096
■ LP . . . . NUK 096
■ MC . . . . ZCNUK 096
Noise / Oct '89.

FAT, UGLY AND LIVE.
Tracks: Not Advised.
■ CD . . . . NO 1662
■ LP . . . . NO 1661
■ MC . . . . NO 1664
Noise / Jul '91.

HAIR OF THE DOG.
Tracks: Not Advised.
■ CD . . . . CDNUK 150
■ LP . . . . NUK 150
■ MC . . . . ZCNUK 150
Noise / Apr '90.

MEANING OF LIFE, THE.
Tracks: Open all night / We are us / Dancing on our grave / Mechanical man / Beermuda / Meaning of life / Space beer / Always them / Wheel of rebirth / Barfly.
■ CD . . . . CDNUK 156
■ LP . . . . NUK 156
■ MC . . . . ZCNUK 156
Noise / Sep '90.

MORNING AFTER, THE.
Tracks: Not Advised.
■ CD . . . . CDNUK 123
■ LP . . . . NUK 123
■ MC . . . . ZCNUK 123
Noise / Oct '89.

OPEN ALL NIGHT.
Tracks: Not Advised.
VHS . . . . NFV 112
Fotodisk Video / Jul '90.

STONE COLD SOBER.
Tracks: Jurisdiction / Broken image / Mindwild / Ugly beauty / Centrefold / Behind the back / Stone cold sober / Blood, guts and rock 'n' roll / Lost and found (tantrum part 2) / Sleeping with the past / Freibier / Of strange people talking under Arabian skies.
CD . . . . NO 190-2
LP . . . . NO 190-1
MC . . . . NO 190-4
Noise / Jun '92 / Pinnacle.

TWO-FACED.
Tracks: Not Advised.
CD . . . . N 0233-2
LP . . . . N 0233-1
MC . . . . N 0233-4
Noise / Feb '94 / Pinnacle.

ZOMBIE ATTACK.
Tracks: Not Advised.
■ CD . . . . CDNUK 046
■ LP . . . . NUK 046
Noise / Oct '89.

Tantrum

RATHER BE ROCKIN'.
Tracks: Rather be rockin' / Don't turn me off / You are my world / Sammy and Susie / Runnin' / How long / You need me / Take a look / Applaud the winner / Search for a reason.
■ LP . . . . OV 1247
Ovation / Jul '80.

Taramis

QUEEN OF THIEVES.
Tracks: Not Advised.
■ LP . . . . RR 9526 1
Road Runner / '89.

Target Of Demand

TARGET OF DEMAND: LIVE.
Tracks: Not Advised.
LP . . . . YCR 006
Your Choice / '92 / Plastic Head.

Task Force

FORBIDDEN FRUIT.
Tracks: Forbidden fruit / Remember these eyes / Cry baby cry / You'll never leave me / I got something for you / Tobacco Road.
■ LP . . . . THBM 001
Thunderbolt / May '83.

Tattooed Love Boys

BLEEDING HEARTS.
Tracks: Not Advised.
■ CD . . . . LUSCD 1
■ LP . . . . LUSLP 1
■ MC . . . . LUSMC 1
Episode / May '89.

BREAKDOWN DEAD AHEAD.
Tracks: Breakdown dead ahead.
■ 12" 12LUS 1
Episode / Aug '89.

NO TIME FOR NURSERY RHYMES.
Tracks: Not Advised.
CD . . . . LUSCD 7
LP . . . . LUSLP 7
MC . . . . LUSMC 7
Episode / Aug '90 / Grapevine Distribution.
CD . . . . CDMFN 120
LP . . . . MFN 120
MC . . . . TMFN 120
Music For Nations / Nov '91 / Pinnacle.

WHY WALTZ WHEN YOU CAN ROCK 'N' ROLL.
Tracks: Why waltz when you can rock 'n' roll.
■ 12" . . . . TLB 001
Razor / Jul '88.

Tea Party

RIVER, THE.
Tracks: River.
12" 12CHS 5011
CD Single . . . . CDCHS 5011
Chrysalis / Jun '94 / EMI.

SPLENDOR SOLIS.
Tracks: River / Midsummer day / Certain slant of light / Winter solstice / Save me / Sun going down / In this time / Dreams of reason / Raven skies / Haze on the hills / Majestic song.
CD . . . . CDCHR 6072
LP . . . . CHR 6072
MC . . . . TCCHR 6072
Chrysalis / May '94 / EMI.

Teaze

ONE NIGHT STANDS.
Tracks: Back in action / Young and reckless / Heartless world / Red hot ready / Through the years / Reach out / Loose change / Touch the wind.
■ LP . . . . HMUSA 30
Heavy Metal America / Feb '85.

TASTE OF TEAZE.
Tracks: Not Advised.
■ LP . . . . HMUSA 4
Heavy Metal America / Aug '84.

Teeze

TEEZE.
Tracks: Not Advised.
■ LP . . . . RR 9741
Road Runner / Nov '85.

Temple Of The Dog

A shortlived studio-only project that began as a vehicle for the grief, anger and frustration Chris Cornell felt after the death of his friend Andrew Wood (singer with Mother Love Bone) in 1990 from a heroin overdose. Other Seattle musicians like Stone Gossard and Jeff Ament (ex-Mother Love Bone), Soundgarden drummer Matt Cameron, guitarist Mike McCready plus San Diego surf-bum-cum singer Eddie Vedder joined in and two songs became an album of unique beauty and tenderness. When it was done, all returned to their own bands and one of those grew into Pearl Jam.

TEMPLE OF THE DOG.
Tracks: Say hello to heaven / Reach down / Hunger strike / Pushin forward back / Call me a dog / Times of trouble / Wooden Jesus / Your savior / Four, walled world / All night thing.
CD 395 350-2
LP 395 350-1
MC 395 350-4
A&M / Jun '92 / PolyGram.

Templebeat

BLACK SUBURBIA.
Tracks: We / Metal 2 (money or sex) / Interzone / Softly September / Heidi S. / Message 4 / Trans / She's lost control / God sent / Einstein on the bitch / Intolerance / Message 2 / Fight / Message 1.
CD . . . . DY 7-2
Dynamica / Jun '94 / Pinnacle.

HEIDI S.
Tracks: Heidi S.
CD Single . . . . DY 43
Dynamica / Jun '94 / Pinnacle.

INTERZONE.
Tracks: Interzone (mixes) / Human (foolish rape mix) / Interspeed (rave mix).
CD Single . . . . DY 12-3
Dynamica / Sep '94 / Pinnacle.

Ten Foot Pole

REV.
Tracks: Not Advised.
CD . . . . E 86436-2
LP . . . . E 86436
MC . . . . E 86436-4
Epitaph / Aug '94 / Plastic Head.

Tender Fury

IF ANGER WERE SOUL I'D BE JAMES BROWN.
Tracks: Not Advised.
CD . . . . TX 92582
LP . . . . TX 92581
Road Runner / Nov '91 / Pinnacle.

Tension

BREAKING POINT.
Tracks: One nation / Wreckin' crew / Reach for your sword / Angels from the past / W O C / Shock treatment.
■ LP . . . . RR 9599
Road Runner / Aug '87.

Terminal Cheesecake

ANGELS IN PIG-TAILS.
Tracks: Not Advised.
CD . . . . PATH 003 CD
LP . . . . PATH 003
MC . . . . PATH 003 MC
Pathological / Sep '90 / Cadillac.

BLADDERSACK.
Tracks: Bladdersack.
■ 12" . . . . WIIJIT 1
Wiiija / Aug '88.

GATEAU D'ESPACE.
Tracks: Gateau D'espace.
■ 12" . . . . JAK 3
■ CD Single . . . . JAK 3CD
Jackass / Nov '93.

JOHNNY TOWN MOUSE.
Tracks: Not Advised.
■ LP . . . . WIIJLP 1
Wiiija / Feb '89.

KING OF ALL SPACEHEADS.
Tracks: Not Advised.
CD . . . . JAKCD 8
CD . . . . JAKCDX 8
LP . . . . JAKX 8
LP . . . . JAK 8
Jackass / Jul '94 / Pinnacle.

OILY HOT KNIFE.
Tracks: Oily hot knife.
7" . . . . JAK 5
Jackass / Jun '94 / Pinnacle.

■ DELETED

VCL.
Tracks: Not Advised.
■ LP . . . . UNKNOWN
Wiiija / Dec '89.

Terraplane

GOOD THING GOING.
Tracks: Good thing going / Night of madness / Good life (extra track on 12").
■ MC Single. . . . . MCTERRAC 2
■ 12". . . . . .TERRAT 2
■ 7" . . . . TERRA 2
Epic / Jun '87.

I CAN'T LIVE WITHOUT YOUR LOVE.
Tracks: I can't live without your love / Beginning of the end / Let the wheels go round (on 12" only).
■ 12". . . . . TX 4936
■ 7". . . . . .A 4936
Epic / Dec '84.

I SURVIVE.
Tracks: I survive / All night and day / Money.
■ 12". 12NIK 8
■ 7". . . . . NIK 8
City / Mar '83.
■ 12". . . . . TX 6110
■ 7". . . . . .A 6110
■ EP . . . . QTX 6110
Epic / Mar '85.

IF THAT'S WHAT IT TAKES.
Tracks: Living after dark / Drugs* / If that's what it takes.
■ 12". . . . . .TERRAT 1
■ 7". . . . . TERRA 1
Epic / Jan '87.

IF THAT'S WHAT IT TAKES.
Tracks: If that's what it takes / Living after dark / If that's what it takes (19th nervous breakdance mix) (*Track on 12" version only.) / Drugs* (*Extra track on 12" version only.).
■ 12". . . . . .TERRA T4
■ 12" Remix. . . . . TERRA Q4
■ 7". . . . . TERRA 4
Epic / Feb '88.

MOVING TARGET.
Tracks: Moving target / When I sleep alone / I survive (live) / I can't live without your love (live) / If that's what it takes / Good things going / Promised land / Hostage to fortune / Heartburn / Hearts on fire / I will come out fighting / Nothing on but the radio.
■ CD. 4601572
■ LP. 4601571
■ MC. 4601574
Epic / Sep '87.

MOVING TARGET.
Tracks: Moving target.
■ 12". . . . . .TERRAT 3
■ 7". . . . . TERRA 3
■ 7". . . . . TERRA G3
Epic / Aug '87.

TALKING TO MYSELF.
Tracks: Talking to myself / Get your face out of my dreams / Gimme the money.
■ 12". . . . . TX 6584
■ 7". . . . . .A 6584
Epic / Oct '85.

WHEN YOU'RE HOT.
Tracks: When you're hot / Tough kind of life.
■ 12". . . . . TX 6352
■ 7". . . . . .A 6352
Epic / Jul '85.

Terrorizer

WORLD DOWNFALL.
Tracks: After world obliteration / Tear of napalm / Corporation pull in / Resurrection / Need to live / Dead shall rise / Injustice / Storm of stress / Human prey / Condemned system / Enslaved by propaganda / Whirlwind struggle / World downfall / Ripped to shreds.
CD. . . . . .MOSH 16 CD
■ LP. . . . . MOSH 16
MC. . . . . .MOSH 16 MC
Earache / Nov '89 / Vital Distribution.

Terrorvision

UK quartet from Batley in Yorkshire that shrugged off years as a dodgy Glam Rock band called Spoilt Brats by reinventing themselves on stage as a kind of alternative Faith No More. However, 1993's debut album, Formaldehyde (released twice as an

indie and a major!) showed they had an identity all of their own. Since then they have cast their musical net even wider, touching bases as far apart as Kiss, The Beatles and doo-wop with a host of singles from their stunning second album, How To Make Friends And Influence People. Very definitely a band on the up.

AMERICAN T.V.
Tracks: American T.V. / Don't shoot my dog again (Available on 12" only) / Killing time (Available on 12" only) / Psyco killer (Available on CDS only) / Hole for a soul (Available on CDS only).
■ 12". 12VEGAS 3
■ CD Single. . . . . .CDVEGAS 3
EMI / Jun '93.

FORMALDEHYDE.
Tracks: Problem solved / Ships that sink / American T.V. / New policy one / Jason / Killing time / Urban space crime / Hole for a soul / Don't shoot my dog / Desolation town / My house / Human being.
CD. . . . . .ATVR CD 001
LP . . . . ATVRLP 001
Total Vegas / Jan '93 / Vital Distribution.
CD. . . . . .VEGASCD 1
LP. . . . . .VEGASLP 1
MC. . . . . .VEGASTC 1
EMI / May '93 / EMI.

HOW TO MAKE FRIENDS AND IN-FLUENCE PEOPLE.
Tracks: Alice, what's the matter / Oblivion / Stop the bus / Discotheque wreck / Middle man / Still the rhythm / Ten shades of grey / Stab in the back / Pretend best friend / Time o' the signs / What the doctor ordered / Some people say / What makes you tick.
CD. . . . . .VEGASCD 2
LP. . . . . .VEGASLP 2
MC. . . . . .VEGASTC 2
EMI / Apr '94 / EMI.

MIDDLEMAN.
Tracks: Middleman / Surrender / Passenger / I'll be your sister / Wishing well / Oblivion.
12". 12VEGAS 7
CD Single. . . . . .CDVEGAS 7
MC Single . . . . TCVEGAS 7
EMI / Jun '94 / EMI.

MY HOUSE.
Tracks: My House / Coming up / Tea Dance.
■ 12". . . . . .12 VEGAS 2
■ 7". . . . . VEGAS 2
■ CD Single. . . . . .CDVEGAS 2
EMI / Sep '92.

MY HOUSE.
Tracks: My house / My house (mixes) / Psycho killer (Available on 12" only) / Tea dance (Available on 7 only) / Discotheque wreck (Available on CDS only) / Down under (Available on CDS only).
■ 12". . . . . .12 VEGAS 5
■ 7". . . . . .VEGAS 5
■ CD Single. . . . . .CDVEGAS 5
■ CD Single. . . . . .CDVEGAS 5
EMI / Dec '93.

NEW POLICY ONE.
Tracks: New policy one.
■ 12". 12VEGASP 4
■ 7". . . . . .VEGASS 4
■ CD Single. . . . . .CDVEGASS 4
EMI / Nov '93.

OBLIVION.
Tracks: Oblivion / What do you do that for / Model / Remember Zelda / Problem solved / Oblivion (demo) (Available on CDS 1 only).
■ 12". 12VEGAS 6
■ 7". . . . . .VEGAS 6
■ CD Single . . . . .CDVEGAS 6
■ CD Single . . . . .CDVEGASS 6
EMI / Mar '94.

PRETEND BEST FRIEND.
Tracks: Pretend best friend (Mixes) / What makes you tick (On CDVEGASS 8 only.) / Still the rhythm (Live) (On 12VEGASS 8.) / Bus stop (Live) (On 12VEGAS 8.) / Discotheque wreck (Live) (On 12VEGAS 8.) / Time o' the signs (On CDVEGAS 8.) / Oblivion (Live) (On CDVEGASS 8.) / Middleman (Live) (On TCVEGAS 8.).
12". . . . . .12 VEGAS 8
CD Single. . . . . .CDVEGAS 8
CD Single. . . . . .CDVEGAS 8
MC Single . . . . TCVEGAS 8
EMI / Aug '94 / EMI.

PROBLEM SOLVED E.P.
Tracks: Problem solved / Corpse fly / We are the roadcrew / Sailing home.

■ 12". 12ATVR001
■ CD Single. CDATVR001
Total Vegas / Jan '93.

THRIVE E.P.
Tracks: Urban space crime / Jason / Blackbird / Pain reliever.
■ 12". 12VEGAS 1
■ CD Single . . . . .CDVEGAS 1
EMI / Jan '92.

Tesla

Named after an eccentric scientist Tesla released their debut album Mechanical Resonance in 1987 to universal acclaim. Their simple roots-rock struck a chord at a time when hairspray bands were prevalent. Their third album Five Man Acoustical Jam proved that they were willing to take a risk and gave them yet more positive publicity. They have yet to capitalise fully on the impact that their first three albums have had, but continue to garner critical acclaim for both studio and live work. Their latest album is Bust A Nut released in 1994.

BUST A NUT.
Tracks: Not Advised.
CD. . . . . GED 24713
MC. . . . . GEC 24713
Geffen / Aug '94 / BMG.

CALL IT WHAT YOU WANT.
Tracks: Call it what you want.
■ 12". . . . . .GFST 15
■ 7". . . . . .GFS 15
■ CD Single . . . . .GFSTD 15
Geffen / Dec '91.

EDISON'S MEDICINE.
Tracks: Edison's medicine.
■ 12". . . . . .GFST 13
■ 12" Remix. . . . . .GFSX 13
■ 7". . . . . .GFS 13
■ CD Single . . . . .GFSTD 13
Geffen / Oct '91.

FIVE MAN ACOUSTICAL JAM.
Tracks: Not Advised.
CD. . . . . .GEFD 24311
MC. . . . . .GEFC 24311
■ LP . . . . GEF 24311
Geffen / Feb '91.

FIVE MAN VIDEO BAND.
Tracks: Not Advised.
■ VHS . . . . .GEFV 39507
Geffen Video / Apr '91.

GREAT RADIO CONTROVERSY.
Tracks: Hang tough / Lady luck / Heaven's trail / Be a man / Lazy days, crazy nights / Did it for the money / Yesterdaze gone / Making magic / Way it is / Flight to nowhere / Love song / Paradise / Party's over.
■ CD 924224 2
■ LP . . . . WX 244
■ MC. . . . . WX 244C
Geffen / Jan '89.
■ CD . . . . .GEFD 24224
■ LP . . . . GEF 24224
■ MC. . . . . .GEFC 24224
Geffen / Jan '91.

LITTLE SUZIE'S ON THE UP.
Tracks: Little suzie's on the up / Before my eyes / Comin' atcha live (remix).
■ 12". . . . . .GEF 19T
■ 7". . . . . GEF 19
Geffen / Mar '87.

LOVE SONG.
Tracks: Love song / I ain't superstitious.
■ 12". . . . . .GEF 74T
■ 7". . . . . GEF 74
■ CD Single . . . . .GEF 74CD
Geffen / Apr '90.

MECHANICAL RESONANCE.
Tracks: Ez come ez go / Cumin' atcha live / Gettin' better / 2 late 4 love / Rock me to the top / We're no good together / Modern day cowboy / Changes / Little Suzie's on the up / Love me / Cover queen / Before my eyes.
■ CD 924120 2
■ LP 924120 1
■ MC. 924120 4
WEA / Jan '87.
■ CD . . . . .GEFD 24120
■ LP . . . . GEF 24120
■ MC. . . . . .GEFC 24120
Geffen / Jan '91.

MODERN DAY COWBOY.
Tracks: Love me (live) (Available on 12" only.) / Cover queen (live) (Available on 12" only.) / Modern day cowboy / Love me / Cover queen.
■ 12"........................GEF 28T
■ 7".........................GEF 28
Geffen / Aug '87.

PSYCHOTIC SUPPER.
Tracks: Not Advised.
CD.......................GEFD 24424
■ LP......................GEF 24424
■ MC......................GEFC 24424
Geffen / Aug '91.

SIGNS.
Tracks: Signs.
■ CD Single..................GFSTD 3
■ 12"........................GSFX 3
■ 12"........................GFST 3
■ 7".........................GFS 3
Geffen / Apr '91.

Testament

LEGACY,THE.
Tracks: Over the wall / Haunting / Burnt offerings / Raging waters / Curse of the legions of death / First strike is deadly / Do or die / Alone in the dark / Apocalyptic city.
■ LP......................781 741-1
MC........................781 741-4
Atlantic / Jun '87 / WEA.

LIVE IN EINDHOVEN.
Tracks: Over the wall / Burnt offerings / Do or die / Apocalyptic city / Reign of terror.
■ LP......................780 226-1
MC........................780 226-4
Atlantic / Dec '87 / WEA.

NEW ORDER, THE.
Tracks: Eerie inhabitants / New order / Trial by fire / Into the pit / Hypnosis / Disciples of the watch / Preacher / Day of reckoning / Musical death (a dirge).
■ CD......................781 849-2
■ LP....................K 781 849 1
MC......................K 781 849 4
Atlantic / May '88 / WEA.

PRACTICE WHAT YOU PREACH.
Tracks: Practice what you preach / Perilous nation / Envy time / Time is coming / Blessed in contempt / Greenhouse effect / Sins of omission / Ballad, The (A song of hope) / Nightmare (coming back to you) / Confusion fusion.
CD........................WX 297CD
CD.....................K 782 009 2
■ LP.......................WX 297
■ MC.......................WX 297C
Atlantic / Aug '89.

RETURN TO THE APOCALYPSE CITY.
Tracks: Over the wall / So many lies / Disciples of the watch / Reign of terror / Return to serenity.
CD.....................756782487-2
LP.....................756782487-1
MC.....................756782487-4
WEA / Apr '93 / WEA.

RITUAL, THE.
Tracks: Sermon / As the seasons grey / Electric crown return to serenity / Ritual / Deadline / So many lies / Let go of my world / Agony / Troubled dreams / Signs of chaos / Electric crown / Return to serenity.
CD.....................756782392-2
■ LP...................756782392-1
MC.....................756782392-4
East West / May '92 / WEA.

SEEN BETWEEN THE LINES.
Tracks: Not Advised.
VHS......................8536501923
Warner Music Video / Oct '92 / WEA.

SOULS OF BLACK.
Tracks: Beginning of the end / Face in the sky / Falling fast / Souls of black / Absence of light / Love to hate / Malpractice / One man's fate / Legacy / Seven days in May.
CD.....................7567821432
■ LP...................7567821431
MC.....................7567821434
Megaforce / Sep '90 / Pinnacle.

TRIAL BY FIRE.
Tracks: Trial by fire / Nobody's fault / Reign of terror.
■ 12".......................A 9092 T
■ 7"........................A 9092
Atlantic / Apr '88.

Testimony

SATISFACTION WARRANTED.
Tracks: Not Advised.
CD.......................MABCD 006
M.A.B. / Jan '94 / Plastic Head.

Thanatos

EMERGING FROM THE NETHERWORLDS.
Tracks: Not Advised.
CD.......................SHARK 015 CD
LP.......................SHARK 015
Shark / Apr '90 / Plastic Head.

REALM OF ECSTASY.
Tracks: Not Advised.
CD.......................SHARKCD 025
LP.......................SHARK 025
Shark / Jan '92 / Plastic Head.

Thee Hypnotics

COAST TO COAST.
Tracks: Coast to coast.
■ 12".......................SIT 94T
Situation 2 / Feb '92.

COME DOWN HEAVY.
Tracks: Half man half boy / All messed up / Unearthed / Release the feeling / Resurrection Joe / (Let it) come down heavy / Bleeding heart / What to do / Sonic lament / Revolution stone.
CD.......................SITU 028 CD
LP.......................SITU 028
MC.......................SITU 028 C
Situation 2 / Jun '90 / RTM / Pinnacle.

FLOATING IN MY HOODOO DREAM.
Tracks: Floating in my hoodoo dream / Hoodoo reprise (samedis cookbook).
■ 12".......................SIT 73T
Situation 2 / Oct '90.

HALF MAN HALF BOY.
Tracks: Half man half boy.
■ 12".......................SIT 067 T
■ 7".......................SIT 067
■ CD Single................SIT 067 TCD
Situation 2 / Apr '90.

JUSTICE IN FREEDOM.
Tracks: Justice in freedom.
■ 12".......................SIT 056 T
Situation 2 / Feb '89.

LIVER THAN GOD.
Tracks: Not Advised.
CD.........................SP 54B
MC.........................SP 54A
Sub Pop / Jan '94 / RTM.

LIVER'N'GOD.
Tracks: All night long / Let's get naked / Revolution stone / Rock me baby / Justice in freedom.
CD.......................SITL 026CD
■ LP.......................SITL 026
Situation 2 / Oct '89.

LOCO.
Tracks: Loco.
■ 12".......................SIT 082T
■ CD Single...............SIT 082CD
Situation 2 / Aug '91.

LOVE IN A DIFFERENT VEIN.
Tracks: Love in a different vein.
■ 7".........................HIP 1
Hipsville / Jul '88.

SOUL TRADER.
Tracks: Soul trader / Earth blues.
■ 12".......................SIT 62T
■ 7".........................SIT 62
Situation 2 / Sep '89.

SOUL, GLITTER AND SIN.
Tracks: Not Advised.
CD.......................SITU 34CD
LP.......................SITU 34
MC.......................SITUC 34
Situation 2 / Oct '91 / RTM / Pinnacle.

THIS HOUSE IS MINE.
Tracks: This house is mine.
■ CD Single................RSN 4CD
■ 12".......................RSN 4
Rising High / Sep '91.

Therapy

Irish power trio from Larne, who mixed Hardcore fury with pop sensibilities and a healthy tongue-in-cheek appreciation of the absurd side of Metal. Began life in 1989 as a duo comprising Andy Cairns (guitar, bass, vocals) and Fyfe Ewing (drums). The pair demoed but didn't really get going until Michael KcKeegan came in five months later to take over on bass. Initially, their music was more Hardcore than Metal as the pair of mini albums - *Babyteeth* (1991) and *Pleasure Death* (1992) - illustrated. But after signing to A&M, Therapy moved closer to the alternative Metal scene. A series of value-for-money EP's raised their profile and one, *Screamager*, gave them a hit. Then in 1994 they were swamped with praise upon the release of the sublime *Troublgum*.

BABY TEETH.
Tracks: Not Advised.
CD.........................185072
LP.........................185071
MC.........................185074
Southern / Mar '93 / SRD.

DIE LAUGHING.
Tracks: Die laughing / Stop it you're killing me / Trigger inside / Evil Elvis.
■ 12".......................580588-1
■ 7".......................580588-7
■ CD Single................580589-2
■ MC Single................580588-4
A&M / May '94.

FACE THE STRANGE EP.
Tracks: Turn / Speedball / Bloody Blue / Neck freak.
■ 7".......................580304-7
■ CD Single................580304-2
A&M / May '93.

HATS OFF TO THE INSANE.
Tracks: Not Advised.
CD.........................540139-2
MC.........................540139-4
A&M / Sep '93 / PolyGram.

NOWHERE.
Tracks: Nowhere / Pantapon rose / Breaking the law / C C rider / Nowhere (mixes).
■ 7".......................580504-7
■ CD Single................580519-2
■ CD Single................580505-2
■ MC Single................580504-4
A&M / Jan '94.

OPAL MANTRA.
Tracks: Opal mantra.
■ 7".......................580361-7
■ CD Single................580361-2
■ MC Single................580361-4
A&M / Aug '93.

PLEASURE DEATH.
Tracks: Not Advised.
CD.........................WIJ 11CD
LP..........................WIJ 11
MC.........................WIJ 11C
Wiiija / Feb '92 / Vital Distribution.
LP.........................185081
MC.........................185084
Southern / Apr '93 / SRD.

SHORT SHARP SHOCK E.P.
Tracks: Screamager / Auto surgery / Totally random man / Accelerator.
■ 12".......................AMY208
■ 7".......................AM208
■ CD Single...............AMCD 208
■ MC Single...............AMMC 208
A&M / Mar '93.

TRIGGER INSIDE.
Tracks: Trigger inside / Nice 'n' sleazy (Not on 12") / Reuters (Not on 12") / Tatty seaside town (Not on 12") / Trigger inside (Mixes) (On 12" only) / Nowhere (Mixes) (On 12" only).
■ 12".......................580535-1
■ 7".......................580534-7
■ CD Single................580535-2
■ MC Single................580540-4
A&M / Feb '94.

TROUBLEGUM.
Tracks: Knives / Screamager / Hellbelly / Stop it you're killing me / Nowhere / Die laughing / Unbeliever / Trigger inside / Lunacy booth / Isolation / Turn / Femtex / Unrequited / Brainsaw / You are my sunshine.
CD.........................540196-2
LP.........................540196-1

■ DELETED

MC. 540196-4
A&M / Nov '93 / PolyGram.

Thergothon

STEAM FROM THE HEAVENS.
Tracks: Not Advised.
CD. . . . . .CDAV 001
Avant Garde / May '94 / Plastic Head.

Therion

BEYOND SANCTORIUM.
Tracks: Not Advised.
CD. . . . . .CDATV 23
LP . . . . .ATV 23
Active / Jul '92 / Pinnacle.

OF DARKNESS.
Tracks: Not Advised.
CD . . . . DEAF 006CD
LP . . . . DEAF 006
Deaf / Mar '91 / Vital Distribution.

Thin Lizzy

One of U.K.'s best-loved rock bands, Lizzy formed in 1970 in Ireland. Despite early hit with *Whiskey In The Jar*, it took five years and five albums before band broke big: 1976's *Jailbreak* album and *Boys Are Back In Town* single were U.K. and U.S. smashes. Subsequently, alcoholism and drug abuse wore band down; tragedy of 1983 farewell tour eclipsed only by death of leader Phil Lynott in January '86. An accomplished songwriter and charismatic front-man, Lynott never recovered standing after split, although he did enjoy U.K. hit with former bandmate Gary Moore: 1985's *Out In The Fields*.

ADVENTURES OF THIN LIZZY, THE.
Tracks: Not Advised.
■ LP . . . . LIZTV 1
Vertigo / Apr '81.

ARE YOU READY.
Tracks: Are you ready / Dear Miss lonely hearts.
■ 7" . . . . .LIZZY 812
Vertigo / Apr '81.

BAD REPUTATION.
Tracks: Bad reputation / Dancing in the moonlight / Dear Lord / Downtown sundown / Killer without cause / Opium train / Soldier of fortune / Southbound / That woman's gonna break your heart.
■ LP 9102 016
Vertigo / Oct '77.
■ LP . . . . PRICE 12
■ MC. PRIMC 12
Vertigo / May '83.
CD. 8424342
Vertigo / Apr '90 / PolyGram.

BBC RADIO ONE LIVE IN CONCERT.
Tracks: Not Advised.
CD . . . . WINCD 024
LP . . . . WINLP 024
MC. . . . . WINMC 024
Windsong / Sep '92 / Pinnacle / A.D.A. Distribution.

BEST OF PHIL LYNOTT & THIN LIZZY.
Tracks: Whisky in the jar / Waiting for an alibi / Sarah / Parisienne walkways / Do anything you want to / Yellow pearl / Chinatown / King's call / Boys are back in town / Rosalie (cowgirl's song) / Dancing in the moonlight / Don't believe a word / Jailbreak / Out in the fields / Killer on the loose / Still in love with you.
■ CD . . . . TCD 2300
■ LP . . . . STAR 2300
■ MC. . . . . STAC 2300
Telstar/Ronco / Nov '87.

BLACK ROSE.
Tracks: Do anything you want to / Toughest street in town / S & M / Waiting for an alibi / Sarah / Got to give it up / Get out of here / With love / Roisin dubh.
■ LP . . . . PRICE 90
■ MC. . . . . PRIMC 90
Vertigo / Oct '86.
CD. 8303922
Vertigo / Jun '89 / PolyGram.

BLACK ROSE: A ROCK LEGEND.
Tracks: Black rose / Shenandoah / Danny boy / Mason's apron / Waiting for an alibi / Get out of here / Got to give it up / S & M / Sarah / Toughest street in town / Waiting for an alibi / With love.
■ LP .9102 032
■ MC. 7231 032
Vertigo / Apr '79.

BOYS ARE BACK IN TOWN.
Tracks: Boys are back in town / Don't play around with love / Emerald / Half caste / Bad reputation / Me and the boys / Memory pain / Sha-la-la / Got to give it up / For those who love to live / Pressure will blow.
■ LP . . . . CN 2066
MC. CN4 2066
Contour / Nov '83 / Pickwick.

BOYS ARE BACK IN TOWN.
Tracks: Boys are back in town / Sarah / Johnny the fox (12" single and CD single only.) / Black boys on the corner (12" single and CD single only.) / Me and the boys (12" single and CD single only.).
■ 12". . . . . .LIZZY 115
■ 7" . . . . LIZZY 15
■ CD Single. . . . . LIZCD 15
■ MC Single. . . . . LIZMC 15
Vertigo / Mar '91.

BOYS ARE BACK IN TOWN.
Tracks: Boys are back in town
■ 7" 6059 139
Vertigo / May '76.

BOYS ARE BACK IN TOWN (OLD GOLD).
Tracks: Boys are back in town / You ain't seen nothin' yet.
. . . . .OG 9764
Old Gold / Feb '88.

CHINATOWN.
Tracks: We will be strong / Chinatown / Sweetheart / Sugar blues / Killer on the loose / Havin' a good time / Genocide / Didn't I / Hey you.
■ LP .6359 030
Vertigo / Oct '80.
■ LP . . . . PRICE 95
■ MC. PRIMC 95
Vertigo / Oct '86.
CD 83033932
Vertigo / Jun '89 / PolyGram.

CHINATOWN.
Tracks: Chinatown / Sugar blues.
■ 7" . . . . .LIZZY 6
Vertigo / May '80.

COLD SWEAT.
Tracks: Cold sweat / Bad habits.
■ 12". . . . . LIZZY 1112
■ 7" . . . . LIZZY 11
■ 7" Set . . . . .LIZZY 11-22
Vertigo / Feb '83.

COLLECTION: THIN LIZZY.
Tracks: Black boys on the corner / Little girl in bloom / Randolph's tango / Return of the farmer's son / Remembering / Whisky in the jar / Rocker / Buffalo gal / Sitamoia / Song for while I'm away / Baby face / Ray gun and Sarah / Eire / Vagabond of the western world / Friendly ranger at Clontarf Castle / Mama Nature said / Here I go again / Hero and the madman / Little darlin'.
■ Double LP. . . . . CCSLP 117
■ MC. . . . . .CCSMC 117
Castle Collector Series / Nov '85.
CD . . . . CCSCD 117
Castle Collector Series / Jul '87 / BMG / Pinnacle / Castle Communications.

CONTINUING SAGA OF THE AGEING ORPHANS.
Tracks: Things ain't working out down at the farm / Buffalo gal / Sarah / Honesty is no excuse / Look what the wind blew in / Mama Nature said / Hero and the madman / Slow blues / Dublin / Brought down / Vagabond of the western world.
■ LP . . . . SKL 5298
Decca / '79.

DANCIN' IN THE MOONLIGHT.
Tracks: Dancin' in the moonlight / Bad reputation.
■ 7" 6059 177
Vertigo / Aug '77.

DANCIN' IN THE MOONLIGHT (OLD GOLD).
Tracks: Dancin' in the moonlight / Don't believe a word.
■ 7" . . . . .OG 9484
Old Gold / Jan '85.

DEDICATION.
Tracks: Dedication / Cold sweat / Emerald (live) (12" & CD only.) / Still in love with you (live) (12" & CD only.) / China town (12" pic disc only.) / Bad reputation (12" pic disc only.).
■ 12". . . . . .LIZZY 114
■ 12" P.Disc. . . . . LIZP 114
■ 7" . . . . LIZZY 14
■ CD Single. . . . . LIZCD 14

■ MC Single. . . . . LIZMC 14
Vertigo / Jan '91.

DEDICATION.
Tracks: Not Advised.
VHS .CFM 2568
PMV / Jan '91 / PolyGram.

DEDICATION - THE BEST OF THIN LIZZY.
Tracks: Whiskey in the jar / Boys are back in town / Dancin' in the moonlight / Parisienne walkways / Out in the fields / Sarah / Jailbreak / Rosalie / Cowgirl song (live) / Waiting for an alibi / Do anything you want to do / Killer on the loose / Rocker / Don't believe a word / Dedication / Bad reputation (Only on MC and CD.) / Still in love with you (live) (Only on MC and CD.) / Emerald (live) (Only on MC and CD.) / China Town (Only on MC and CD.).
CD 848 192 2
MC 848 192 4
■ LP 848 192 1
Vertigo / Feb '91.

DO ANYTHING YOU WANT.
Tracks: Do anything you want to / Just the two of us.
■ 7" . . . . LIZZY 4
Vertigo / Jun '79.

DON'T BELIEVE A WORD.
Tracks: Don't believe a word.
■ 7" . . . . LIZZY 1
Vertigo / Jan '77.

FIGHTING.
Tracks: Ballad of a hard man / Fighting my way back / For those who love to live / Freedom song / King's vengeance / Rosalie / Silver dollar / Spirit slips away / Suicide / Wild one.
■ LP .6360 121
Vertigo / Sep '75.
CD 842 433-2
■ LP . . . . PRICE 32
■ MC. . . . . PRIMC 32
Vertigo / Aug '83.

HOLLYWOOD.
Tracks: Hollywood / Pressure will blow.
■ 7" . . . . LIZZY 10
■ 7" P.Disc . . . . LIZPD 10
Vertigo / Feb '82.

JAILBREAK.
Tracks: Angel from the coast / Boys are back in town / Cowboy song / Emerald / Fight or fall / Jailbreak / Romeo and the lonely girl / Running back / Warriors.
■ LP .9102 008
Vertigo / Apr '76.
■ LP . . . . PRICE 50
■ MC. . . . . PRIMC 50
Vertigo / Oct '83.
CD 8227852
Vertigo / Jun '89 / PolyGram.

JAILBREAK.
Tracks: Jailbreak.
■ 7" 6059 150
Vertigo / Aug '76.

JOHNNY THE FOX.
Tracks: Boogie woogie dance / Borderline / Don't believe a word / Fools' gold / Johnny / Johnny the fox meets Jimmy the weed / Massacre / Old flame / Rocky / Sweet Marie.
■ LP .9102 012
Vertigo / Nov '76.
■ LP . . . . PRICE 11
■ MC. . . . . PRIMC 11
Vertigo / May '83.
CD 822 687 2
Vertigo / May '90 / PolyGram.

KILLER ON THE LOOSE.
Tracks: Killer on the loose.
■ 7" . . . . LIZZY 7
Vertigo / Sep '80.

KILLERS LIVE.
Tracks: Bad reputation / Are you ready / Dear Miss Lonely hearts / Opium trail (12" only).
■ EP . . . . LIZZY 8
Vertigo / May '81.

LIFE.
Tracks: Not Advised.
CD 812 882 2
Vertigo / Aug '90 / PolyGram.

LITTLE DARLING.
Tracks: Little darlin'.
■ 7" . . . . F 13507
Decca / Apr '74.

LIVE.
Tracks: Thunder and lightning / Waiting for an alibi / Jailbreak / Baby please don't go / Holy war / Renegade / Hollywood / Got to give it up / Angel of death / Are you ready / Boys are back in town / Cold sweat / Don't believe a word / Killer on the loose / Sun goes down / Emerald / Black rose / Still in love with you / Rocker.
■ **Double LP**. . . . . **VERD 6**
MC Set. . . . . **VERDC 6**
Vertigo / Nov '83.

LIVE AND DANGEROUS.
Tracks: Introduction / Boys are back in town / Emerald / Dancing in the moonlight / Massacre / Call on me / Don't believe a word / Are you ready / Sha la la / Baby drives me crazy / Finale.
■ **VHS** . . . . **V 064 B**
VCL / Sep '86.
■ **VHS** . . . . **HEN 2021**
Hendring Video / Aug '88.
■ **VHS** . . . . **COL 1031**
Castle Collector Series / Jun '92.

LIVE AND DANGEROUS - IN CONCERT.
Tracks: Boys are back in town / Dancing in the moonlight / Massacre / I'm still in love with you / Me and the boys (Full title: Me and the boys were wondering what you and the girls were) / Don't believe a word / Warriors / Are you ready / Sha-la-la-la / Baby drives me crazy.
■ **Double LP**. **6641 807**
Vertigo / Jun '78.
■ **Double LP**. . . . .**PRID 6**
■ **MC Set** . . . .**PRIDC 6**
Vertigo / Nov '84.
CD. **8380302**
Vertigo / Jun '89 / PolyGram.

LIZZY KILLERS.
Tracks: Do anything you want to / Sarah / Whisky in the jar / Jailbreak / Baby face / Killer on the loose / Don't believe a word / Dancing in the moonlight / Waiting for an alibi.
CD. **800 060-2**
Vertigo / '83 / PolyGram.

LIZZY LIVES 1976-84.
Tracks: Not Advised.
■ **LP** . . . . **SLAM 4**
Grand Slam (USA) / '88.

NIGHT LIFE.
Tracks: Banshee / Dear heart / Frankie Carroll / It's only money / Night life / Philomena / Sha-la-la / She knows / Showdown / Still in love with you.
■ **LP**. . . . . **PRICE 31**
■ **MC**. . . . . **PRIMC 31**
Vertigo / Aug '83.
■ **CD** **8380292**
Vertigo / Jun '89.

REMEMBERING.
Tracks: Not Advised.
■ **LP** **DT6 28377**
Teldec (1) / Jun '81.

REMEMBERING, PART 1.
Tracks: Black boys on the corner / Song for while I'm away / Randolph tango / Little girl in bloom / Sitamoia / Little darlin' / Remembering / Gonna creep up on you / Whisky in the jar / Rocker.
■ **LP** . . . . **SKL 5249**
■ **MC** . . . . **KSKC 5249**
Decca / Aug '76.

RENEGADE.
Tracks: Angel of death / Renegade / Pressure will blow / Leave this town / Hollywood (down on your luck) / No one told him / Fats / Mexican blood / It's getting dangerous.
■ **LP** **6359 083**
MC. **7150 083**
Vertigo / Nov '81 / PolyGram.
CD. **842 435-2**
Vertigo / Jun '90 / PolyGram.

ROCKERS.
Tracks: Whisky in the jar / Baby face / Mama Nature said / Song for while I'm away / Call the police / Rocker / Sarah / Slow blues / Little darlin' / Sitamoia / Gonna creep up on you.
■ **MC**. . . . . **KTBC 28**
■ **LP** . . . . **TAB 28**
Decca / Dec '81.
CD. **820 526-2**
MC. **820 526-4**
Deram / Oct '93 / PolyGram.

ROSALIE.
Tracks: Rosalie / Half caste.
■ **7"** **6059124**
Vertigo / Jul '75.

ROSALIE - COWGIRLS' SONG.
Tracks: Rosalie - Cowgirls' song.
■ **7"** . . . . **LIZZY 2**
Vertigo / May '78.

SARAH.
Tracks: Sarah / Got to give it up.
■ **7"** . . . . **LIZZY 5**
Vertigo / Oct '79.

SHADES OF A BLUE ORPHANAGE.
Tracks: Rise and dear demise of the funky nomadic tribes / Buffalo gal / I don't want to forget how to live / Sarah / Brought down / Baby face / Chatting today / Call the police / Shades of a blue orphanage.
■ **LP** . . . . **TXS 108**
Decca / '72.
CD. **8205272**
Decca / Nov '88 / PolyGram.

SUN GOES DOWN, THE.
Tracks: Sun goes down / Baby please don't go.
■ **7"** . . . . **LIZZY 13**
Vertigo / Aug '83.

THIN LIZZY.
Tracks: Friendly ranger at Clontarf Castle / Honesty is no excuse / Diddy levine / Ray gun / Look what the wind blew in / Eire / Return of the farmer's son / Clifton Grange Hotel / Saga of the ageing orphan / Remembering part 1 / Dublin / Remembering part 2 / Old moon madness / Thing's ain't working out down at the farm.
■ **LP** . . . . **SKL 5082**
Decca / '71.
CD **8205282**
Deram / Jan '89 / PolyGram.
MC. **8205284**
Deram / Aug '93 / PolyGram.

THINGS AIN'T WORKING OUT DOWN ON THE FARM.
Tracks: Things ain't working out down on the farm / Rocker / Little darlin'.
■ **7"** . . . .**THIN 1**
Decca / Aug '79.

THUNDER AND LIGHTNING.
Tracks: Thunder and lightning / This is the one / Sun goes down / Holy war / Cold sweat / Someday / She is going to hit back / Baby please don't go / Bad habits / Heart attack.
■ **LP** . . . .**VERL 3**
MC. . . . . **VERLC 3**
Vertigo / Mar '83 / PolyGram.
CD. **8104902**
Vertigo / Jun '89 / PolyGram.

THUNDER AND LIGHTNING.
Tracks: Thunder and lightning / Still in love with you.
■ **12"** . . . . **LIZZY 1212**
■ **7"** . . . . **LIZZY 12**
Vertigo / Apr '83.

TROUBLE BOYS.
Tracks: Trouble boys / Memory pain.
■ **7"** . . . . **LIZZY 9**
Vertigo / Aug '81.

VAGABONDS OF THE WESTERN WORLD.
Tracks: Mama nature said / Hero & the madman / Slow blues / Rocker / Vagabond of the western world / Little girl in bloom / Gonna creep up on you / Song for while I'm away / Whisky in the jar / Black boys on the corner / Randolph's tango / Broken dreams.
■ **LP** . . . . **SKL 5170**
Decca / '73.
CD **820 969 2**
Deram / May '91 / PolyGram.

WAITING FOR AN ALIBI.
Tracks: Waiting for an alibi / With love.
■ **7"** . . . . **LIZZY 3**
Vertigo / Feb '79.

WHISKEY IN THE JAR.
Tracks: Whisky in the jar / Rocker / Vagabond of the western world / Sitamoia.
■ **7"** . . . . **F 13748**
Decca / Oct '79.
■ **7" Set** . . . . **POSPD 777**
Polydor / Nov '85.

WHISKEY IN THE JAR.
Tracks: Whiskey in the jar.
■ **7"** . . . . **F 13355**
Decca / Jan '73.

WHISKEY IN THE JAR (CONTOUR).
Tracks: Whiskey in the jar / Rocker / Black boys on the corner / Little darlin' / Buffalo gal / Sitamoia / Honesty is no excuse / Things ain't working down on the farm / Song for while I'm away / Remembering / Sarah / Vagabond of the Western world.
■ **LP** . . . . **CN 2080**
MC. **CN4 2080**
Contour / Apr '86 / Pickwick.

WHISKEY IN THE JAR (KARUSSELL).
Tracks: Boys are back in town / Jailbreak / Don't believe a word / Sarah / Renegade / Thunder and lightning / Whiskey in the jar / Dancing in the moonlight / Waiting for an alibi / Chinatown / Do anything you want to / Killer on the loose.
■ **LP** **822 694 1**
MC. **822 694 4**
Karussell Gold / Nov '85.

WHISKEY IN THE JAR (OLD GOLD).
Tracks: Whiskey in the jar / Rocker.
■ **7"** . . . .**OG 9330**
Old Gold / Oct '83.

WILD ONE.
Tracks: Wild one.
■ **7"** **6059129**
Vertigo / Oct '75.

Thor

KEEP THE DOGS AWAY.
Tracks: Not Advised.
■ **LP** . . . . **GULP 1042**
Gull / Jun '85.

KNOCK 'M' DOWN.
Tracks: Knock 'm' down.
■ **12"** . . . . **RR 125513**
■ **7"** . . . . **RR 5513**
Road Runner / Jul '85.

LET THE BLOOD RUN RED.
Tracks: Let the blood run red / When Gods collide.
■ **12"** **12ION 165**
■ **7"** . . . . **ION 165**
■ **7" P.Disc** . . . . **PION 165**
Albion / Apr '84.

LIVE IN DETROIT.
Tracks: Thunder on the tundra / Let the blood run red / Knock 'm' down / Rock the city / Lightning strikes / Anger / Keep the dogs away / Hot flames / Now comes the storm / When gods collide.
■ **LP** . . . . **RAWLP 008**
MC. . . . . **RAWTC 008**
Raw Power / Apr '86 / Pinnacle.

ONLY THE STRONG.
Tracks: Not Advised.
■ **LP** . . . . **RR 9790**
Road Runner / Apr '85.

OVER TO YOU.
Tracks: Over to you / Anita.
■ **7"** . . . . **KA 11**
KA / Nov '82.

THUNDER ON THE TUNDRA.
Tracks: Thunder on the tundra.
■ **12"** **12ION 168**
■ **7"** . . . . **ION 168**
■ **7" P.Disc** . . . . **PION 168**
Albion / Jun '84.

UNCHAINED.
Tracks: Not Advised.
■ **LP** . . . . **NOISE 102**
Ultranoise / Feb '84.

Thrasher

BURNING AT THE SPEED OF LIGHT.
Tracks: Not Advised.
■ **LP** . . . . **MFN 45**
Music For Nations / Jun '85.

Threnody

AS THE HEAVENS FALL.
Tracks: Not Advised.
CD . . . . **MASSCD 024**
Massacre / Feb '94 / Plastic Head.

■ **DELETED**

Thrilled Skinny

PIECE OF PLASTIC.
Tracks: Blast / Quicker than the blinking eye / Media music / I'm on a groovy strait / Pregnant pause / Pinless.
■ EP . . . . HUNCH 001
Hunchback / Dec '87.

POPSTAR PRAT.
Tracks: Popstar prat.
■ 7" . . . . DAM 24
Damaged Goods / Sep '93.

SMELLS A BIT FISHY.
Tracks: Not Advised.
CD . . . . LOS 3CD
Artios / Nov '93 / RTM / Pinnacle.

SO GLAD TO BE ALIVE.
Tracks: So glad to be alive / Clinging to the shelf.
■ 7" . . . . HUNCH 003
Hunchback / Jun '88.

Thunder

Rising out of the ashes of Terraplane, Thunder proved an instant hit with their cheeky, one-of-the-lads stage-craft and a debut album, Back Street Symphony (1990) that proved a heady mix of Bad Company and Led Zeppelin, thanks to the writing talents of Luke Morley, the twin guitar attack of Morley and Ben Matthews, and the glorious vocals of Danny Bowes. Constant touring made Thunder one of the UK's top acts, although they struggled to make an impact in the States, even after an impressive second album, Laughing On Judgement Day (1992), and crop of mid-table singles secured their status at home. Rumours of a split in 1993 proved unfounded and as long as Bowes and Morley stick together, success shouldn't be far away.

BACKSTREET SYMPHONY.
Tracks: She's so fine / Dirty love / Don't wait for me / Higher ground / Until my dying day / Backstreet symphony / Love walked in / Englishman on holiday, An / Girl's going out of her head / Gimme some lovin' / Distant thunder (Not on album.)
CD . . . . CDEMC 3570
MC . . . . TCEMC 3570
■ LP . . . . EMC 3570
EMI / Feb '90.
■ LP P.Disc . . . . EMCPD 3570
EMI / Nov '90.

BACKSTREET SYMPHONY.
Tracks: Backstreet symphony / No way out of the wilderness / Englishman on holiday, An (live) (12" Picture disc & CD single only.) / Girl's going out of her head (live) (CD single only.).
■ 12" P.Disc. 12EMPD 137
■ 7" . . . . EM 137
■ 7" . . . . EMS 137
■ CD Single . . . . CDEM 137
■ MC Single. . . . . TCEM 137
EMI / Apr '90.

BACKSTREET SYMPHONY (& Donnington 1990 Special).
Tracks: She's so fine / Dirty love / Backstreet symphony / Gimme some lovin' / She's so fine (Live) / Backstreet symphony (Live) / Higher ground / Don't wait for me.
VHS . . . . MVP 991 252 3
PMI / Nov '90 / EMI / Gold & Sons / TBD.

BACKSTREET SYMPHONY/BACKSTREET SYMPHONY (LIVE).
Tracks: She's so fine / Dirty love / Don't wait for me / Higher ground / Until my dying day / Backstreet symphony / Love walked in / Englishman on holiday, An / Girl's going out of her head / Gimme some lovin' / Distant thunder / Another shot of love (live) / Girl's going out of her head (live) / Englishman on holiday (live) / Until my dying day (live) / Fired up (live) / Dirty love (live) / She's so fine (live) / Backstreet symphony (live) / Higher ground (live) / Don't wait for me (live).
CD Set . . . . TOCP 6729
EMI / Oct '91 / EMI.

BETTER MAN, A.
Tracks: Better man / Bigger than both of us / Low life in high places (Live) / New York, New York (Harry's theme)(Live) / Higher ground (Live) / Lazy Sunday (Live).
■ 12". 12BETTER 1
■ 7" . . . . BETTER 1
■ CD Single . . . . CDBETTER 1

■ MC Single. . . . . TCBETTER 1
EMI / Feb '93.

DIRTY LOVE.
Tracks: Dirty love (Not on 12".) / Fired up / She's so fine (live) (12" only.) / Brown sugar (live) (CD single only.)
■ 12". 12EM 126
■ 7" . . . . EMG 126
■ 7" . . . . EM 126
■ 7" P.Disc . . . . .EMPD 126
■ CD Single . . . . CDEM 126
■ MC Single. . . . . TCEM 126
■ 12" P.Disc. 12EMP 126
EMI / Jan '90.

EVERYBODY WANTS HER.
Tracks: Everybody wants her.
■ 12". . . . . 12 EMPD 249
■ 7" . . . . EM 249
■ CD Single . . . . CDEM 249
■ MC Single. . . . . TCEM 249
EMI / Sep '92.

GIMME SHELTER.
Tracks: Gimme shelter / Gimme Shelter (2) / Gimme Shelter (3)
■ CD Single . . . . CDORDERR 1
EMI / Apr '93.

GIMME SOME LOVIN'.
Tracks: Gimme some lovin' / I wanna be her slave / Dirty love (live) (Not on 7".) / Until the night is through (Not on 7".).
■ 10". 10EM 148
■ 12". 12EM 148
■ 7" . . . . EM 148
■ CD Single . . . . CD EM 148
■ MC Single. . . . . TC EM 148
EMI / Jul '90.

LAUGHING ON JUDGEMENT DAY.
Tracks: Does it feel like love / Everybody wants her / Low life in high places / Laughing on judgement day / Empty city / Today the world stopped turning / Long way from home / Fire to ice / Feeding the flame / Better man / Moment of truth / Flawed to perfection / Like a satellite / Baby I'll be gone.
■ Double LP . . . . EMD 1035
EMI / Aug '92.
CD . . . . CDEMD 1035
MC . . . . TCEMD 1035
EMI / Feb '94 / EMI.

LIKE A SATELLITE.
Tracks: Like a satellite / Like a satellite (live) / Gimme shelter / Damage is done.
■ 12". 12EMS 272
■ CD Single . . . . CDEM 272
EMI / Jun '93.

LOVE WALKED IN.
Tracks: Love walked in (7" & cassingle only.) / Flawed to perfection (demo) / Until my dying day (live) (12" Picture disc & CD single only.) / World problems: A solution (10" only.).
■ 10". 10EMPD 175
■ 12" P.Disc. 12EMPD 175
■ 7" . . . . EM 175
■ CD Single . . . . CDEM 175
■ MC Single. . . . . TCEM 175
EMI / Feb '91.

LOW LIFE IN HIGH PLACES.
Tracks: Low life in high places / Low life in high places (demo) (12" & CD single set only.) / With a little help from my friends (12" & CD single set only.) / Baby I'll be gone (7" only.) / Backstreet symphony (CD single only.) / She's so fine (CD single only.) / Love walked in (CD single only.) / She's my inspiration (CD single set only.).
■ 12". 12EMS 242
■ 7" . . . . EM 242
■ CD Single . . . . CDEMS 242
■ CD Single . . . . CDEM 242
EMI / Jul '92.

SHE'S SO FINE.
Tracks: She's so fine (7" & CD single only.) / Girl's going out of her head / She's so fine (full length version) (Not on 7".) / Another shot of love (live) (Not on 7".).
■ CD Single . . . . CDEM 111
EMI / Nov '89.
■ 12". 12EMP 111
■ 12". 12EM 111
■ 7" . . . . EMS 111
■ 7" . . . . EM 111
EMI / Oct '89.

SHE'S SO FINE.
Tracks: She's so fine (Not on 10" or CD single.) / I can still hear the music (Not on CD single.) / Don't wait for me (live at Donington) (12" & CD single

only.) / Backstreet symphony (live at Donington) (10" & CD single only.)
■ 10". 10EM 158
■ 12". 12EMP 158
■ 7" . . . . EM 158
■ CD Single . . . . CDEM 158
■ MC Single. . . . . TCEM 158
EMI / Sep '90.

Thunderhead

BEHIND THE EIGHT BALL.
Tracks: Behind the eight ball / Ready to roll / Take it to the highway / You don't keep me satisfied / Fire's burning / Let go / Open all night / Life in the city / Just another lover / Straight shooter / Take me to the limit.
■ CD . . . . LLCD 127
■ LP . . . . LLP 127
■ MC. . . . . LLK 127
Legacy / Oct '89.

BUSTED AT THE BORDER.
Tracks: Not Advised.
LP . . . . MFN 110
MC. . . . . TMFN 110
■ CD . . . . CDMFN 110
Music For Nations / Sep '90.

CRIME PAYS.
Tracks: Not Advised.
LP . . . . MFN 116
MC. . . . . TMFN 116
■ CD . . . . CDMFN 116
Music For Nations / Sep '91.

Thunders, Johnny

Ex-New York Doll Thunders stumbled through ill-fated career with own band Heartbreakers in late '70s and variety of collaborations in '80s, before years of drug abuse took their fatal toll in April 1991. Notable disciples include Guns N' Roses bassist Duff McKagan, who dedicated So Fine on Use Your Illusion 2 to Thunders, and covered his You Can't Put Your Arms Around A Memory on "The Spaghetti Incident?".

ALBUM COLLECTION.
Tracks: Not Advised.
■ LP Set . . . . JT BOX 1
Jungle / May '88.

BOOTLEGGING THE BOOTLEGGERS.
Tracks: You can't put your arms around a memory / Personality crisis / Sad vacation / I can tell / Little queenie / Stepping stone / As tears go by.
CD . . . . FREUDCD 30
LP . . . . FREUD 30
MC. . . . . FREUDC 30
Jungle / Jan '90 / RTM / Pinnacle.

BORN TO CRY.
Tracks: Born to cry / Treat her right / Can't seem to make her mine (Only on 12" version.).
■ 12" . . . . JUNG 43T
■ 7" . . . . JUNG 43
Jungle / Nov '88.

BORN TO LOSE (Thunders, Johnny & The Heartbreakers).
Tracks: Born to lose.
■ 7" . . . . T 1702
Twins / Feb '85.

CAN'T PUT YOUR ARMS AROUND A MEMORY.
Tracks: Can't put your arms around a memory / Hurtin'.
■ 7" . . . . ARE 3
Real / Sep '78.

CHINESE ROCKS (Thunders, Johnny & The Heartbreakers).
Tracks: Chinese rocks.
■ 7" 2094135
Track / May '77.

CHINESE ROCKS (Thunders, Johnny & The Heartbreakers).
Tracks: Chinese rocks / Born to lose.
■ 12". . . . . JUNG 20T
■ 7" . . . . JUNG 1
■ EP . . . . JUNG 20
Jungle / May '85.

COPY CATS (Thunders, Johnny & Patti Palladin).
Tracks: Not Advised.
CD . . . . FREUDCD 20

■ LP .FREUD 20
MC . . . . FREUDC 20
Jungle / Jun '88 / RTM / Pinnacle.

CRAWFISH (Thunders, Johnny & Patti Palladin).
Tracks: Crawfish / Tie me up.
■ 12" .JUNG 23T
■ 7" . . . . JUNG 23
■ 7" P.Disc . . . . .JUNG 23P
Jungle / Apr '87.

D.T.K. (Thunders, Johnny & The Heartbreakers).
Tracks: Not Advised.
CD . . . . .RRCD 191
Receiver / Aug '94 / Total / BMG / Grapevine Distribution.

DEAD OR ALIVE.
Tracks: Dead or alive / Downtown.
■ 7" . . . . ARE 1
Real / Jun '78.

DEAD OR ALIVE (Thunders, Johnny & The Heartbreakers).
Tracks: Not Advised.
VHS . . . . JVD 1
Jungle Video Displays / May '88 / RTM / Pinnacle.

DTK - LIVE '77 (Thunders, Johnny & The Heartbreakers).
Tracks: Not Advised.
■ LP . . . . .FREUD 01
Jungle / May '81.
■ LP P.Disc . . . . .FREUD P01
Jungle / May '88.

GANG WAR.
Tracks: Not Advised.
LP . . . . DM 003
De Milo / May '90.

GET OFF THE PHONE (Thunders, Johnny & The Heartbreakers).
Tracks: Get off the phone / All by myself.
■ 7" . . . . JUNG 14
Jungle / Mar '84.
■ 12" . . . . .JUNG 14X
■ 7" P.Disc . . . . .JUNG 14P
Jungle / Sep '84.

HAVE FAITH.
Tracks: Not Advised.
CD 422365
New Rose / May '94 / Pinnacle / Topic Records / Direct Distribution.

HURT ME.
Tracks: Not Advised.
■ LP . . . . ROSE 26
New Rose / Aug '83.
■ CD .ROSE 26CD
New Rose / Aug '86.
CD 422366
New Rose / May '94 / Pinnacle / Topic Records / Direct Distribution.

HURT ME.
Tracks: Hurt me / It's not enough / Like a rolling stone.
■ 7" . . . . NEW 27
New Rose / Feb '84.

IN COLD BLOOD.
Tracks: Not Advised.
■ LP . . . . ROSE 18
New Rose / Jan '83.
CD 422367
New Rose / May '94 / Pinnacle / Topic Records / Direct Distribution.

IN COLD BLOOD.
Tracks: In cold blood.
■ CD Single . . . . NEAT 5CD
New Rose / Apr '89.

L.A.M.F. (Thunders, Johnny & The Heartbreakers).
Tracks: Born to lose / Baby talk / All by myself / I wanna be loved / It's not enough / Get off the phone / Chinese rocks / Pirate love / One tracked wind / I love you / Goin' steady / Let go.
■ LP 2409 218
Track / Nov '77.
■ LP P.Disc . . . . .FREUD P04
■ LP . . . . .FREUD 04
■ CD .FREUDCD 04
■ MC .FREUDC 04
Jungle / May '84.

L.A.M.F. - THE LOST '77 MIXES (Thunders, Johnny & The Heartbreakers).
Tracks: Not Advised.
CD .FREUDCD 044
LP . . . . FREUD 044
MC .FREUDC 044
Jungle / Jul '94 / RTM / Pinnacle.

L.A.M.F. REVISITED (Thunders, Johnny & The Heartbreakers).
Tracks: Not Advised.
CD . . . . .RRCD 190
Receiver / Aug '94 / Total / BMG / Grapevine Distribution.

LIVE ALBUM.
Tracks: Pipeline / Countdown live / Personality crisis / Little bit of whore / M.I.A. / Stepping stone (live) / So alone (live) / Endless party / Copy cats (live) / Don't mess with cupid / Born to lose / Too much junkie business (live) / Chinese rocks / Pills.
CD .CDGRAM 70
Cherry Red / Oct '93 / Pinnacle.

LIVE AT MAX'S, KANSAS CITY (Thunders, Johnny & The Heartbreakers).
Tracks: Intro / Milk me / Chinese rocks / Get off the phone / London / Take a chance / One track mind / All by myself / Let's go / I love you / Can't keep my eyes on you / I wanna be loved / Do you love me.
■ LP . . . . BEGA 9
Beggars Banquet / Sep '79.

LIVE AT THE LYCEUM BALLROOM, LONDON 1984 (Thunders, Johnny & The Heartbreakers).
Tracks: Not Advised.
■ LP . . . . .ABCLP 2
ABC (Indie) / Jun '84.
CD . . . . ABCD 2
ABC (Indie) / Jan '89.
CD . . . . .RRCD 134
MC . . . . .RRLC 134
■ LP .RRLP 134
Receiver / Jul '93.

QUE SERA SERA.
Tracks: Not Advised.
■ LP . . . . .FREUD 09
MC . . . . .FREUDC 09
Jungle / Nov '85 / RTM / Pinnacle.
CD .FREUDCD 9
Jungle / Dec '86 / RTM / Pinnacle.
■ LP P.Disc . . . . FREUD P09
Jungle / Jun '87.

QUE SERA SERA.
Tracks: Que sera sera.
■ 12" .JUNG 33T
■ 7" . . . . .JUNG 33
Jungle / Jun '87.

SHE WANTS TO MAMBO (Thunders, Johnny & Patti Palladin).
Tracks: Uptown / She wants to mambo.
■ 12" .JUNG 38T
■ 7" . . . . .JUNG 38
Jungle / May '88.

SO ALONE.
Tracks: Pipe line / You can't put your arm around a memory / Great big kiss / Ask me no questions / Leave me alone / Daddy rollin' stone / London boys / Untouchable / Subway train / Downtown.
■ LP . . . . RAL 1
Real / '77.

SO ALONE.
Tracks: Pipeline / You can't put your arms around a memory / Great big kiss / Ask me no questions / Leave me alone / Daddy rollin' stone / London boys / (She's so) untouchable / Subway train / Dowtown / Dead or alive / Hurtin' / So alone / Wizard.
CD .7599269822
WEA / Aug '92 / WEA.

STATIONS OF THE CROSS.
Tracks: Wipeout / In cold blood / Just another girl / Too much junkie business / Sad vacation / Who needs girls / Do you love me / So alone / Seven day weekend / Chinese rocks / Re-entry interlude / Voodoo dub / Surfer jam / Just because I'm white / One track mind (dub) / Little London boys / Stepping stone / I don't mind Mr. Kowalski / Creature from E.T. rap / Rather be with the boys / Wipe out.
MC . . . . A 146
Reach Out International / Feb '87 / Reach Out Int. Records / Windsong International Ltd.
MC .DANMC 043
Danceteria / Sep '90.

■ CD .DANCD 043
■ Double LP . . . . .DANLP 043
Danceteria / Jun '92.

STATIONS OF THE CROSS (REVISITED) (Thunders, Johnny & The Heartbreakers).
Tracks: Not Advised.
CD . . . . .RRCD 188
Receiver / Jun '94 / Total / BMG / Grapevine Distribution.

TOO MUCH JUNKIE BUSINESS.
Tracks: Not Advised.
MC . . . . A 118
Reach Out International / '83 / Reach Out Int. Records / Windsong International Ltd.
MC .DANMC 044
■ CD .DANCD 044
■ LP .DANLP 044
Danceteria / Sep '90.

VINTAGE '77 (Thunders, Johnny & The Heartbreakers).
Tracks: Vintage '77.
■ 12" . . . . .JUNG 5
Jungle / May '83.

Thunderstick

ALECIA.
Tracks: Alecia / Buried alive / runaround.
■ 7" . . . . .THBE 1001
Thunderbolt / Nov '83.

BEAUTY AND THE BEASTS.
Tracks: Contact angel / Afraid of the dark / Another turnaround / Heartbeat (in the night) / Rich girls (don't cry) / In the name of the father / Long way to go.
■ LP . . . . .THBL 008
MC . . . . .THBC 008
Thunderbolt / Apr '84 / TBD / Jazz Music.

FEEL LIKE ROCK 'N' ROLL.
Tracks: Feel like rock 'n' roll / Alecia / Runaround / Buried alive.
■ 12" .THBE 1.002
Thunderbolt / Nov '83.

Tiamat

ASTRAL SLEEP, THE.
Tracks: Not Advised.
CD .CM 9722CD
LP . . . . .CM 9722
Century Media / '92 / Plastic Head.

SLEEPING BEAUTY (LIVE IN ISRAEL), THE.
Tracks: Not Advised.
CD .CM 77065-2
Century Media / May '94 / Plastic Head.

SUMERIAN CRY.
Tracks: Not Advised.
CD .CMFTCD 6
■ LP . . . . .CMFT 6
Total / Jul '90.
CD .CORE 009CD
LP . . . . .CORE 009
Metalcore / Jan '92 / Pinnacle.

Tigertailz

BEZERK.
Tracks: Sick sex / Love bomb baby / I can fight dirty too / Noise level critical / Heaven / Love overload / Action city / Twist and shake / Squeeze it dry / Call of the wild.
CD .CDMFN 96
LP . . . . .MFN 96
MC . . . . .TMFN 96
Music For Nations / Jan '90 / Pinnacle.

BEZERK - LIVE.
Tracks: Not Advised.
VHS . . . . .LFV 114
Fotodisk Video / Aug '90.

HEAVEN.
Tracks: Heaven.
■ 12" .12KUT 137
■ 7" . . . . .KUT 137
■ CD Single . . . . .CDKUT 137
Music For Nations / Jan '91.

LIVIN' WITHOUT YOU.
Tracks: Living without you / Nine livez.
■ 12" .12 KUT 129
■ 7" . . . . .KUT 129
Music For Nations / Jun '88.

OVE BOMB BABY.
Tracks: Love bomb baby / Love bomb baby (version) / She's too hot (live) / Few dollars more (live) (12" nly).
■ 12" 12KUT 132
■ 7" . . . . .KUT 132
Music For Nations / Jun '89.

NOISE LEVEL.
Tracks: Noise level.
■ 12" . . . . 12 KUT 134
■ 7" .KUT 134
■ CD Single . . . . CD KUT 134
■ MC Single. . . . . T KUT 134
Music For Nations / Jun '90.

SHOOT TO KILL.
Tracks: Shoot to kill (Shoot to kill (3 track).
■ 12" . . . . .TAILZ 001
European Rock Promotions / Mar '87.

VIDEO FRENZY.
Tracks: Not Advised.
VHS . . . . VFN 6
Video For Nations / Jul '92 / Pinnacle.

YOUNG AND CRAZY.
Tracks: Star attraction / Hollywood killer / Living without you / Shameless / City kids / Shoot to kill / Turn me on / She's too hot / Young & crazy / Fall in ove again.
■ LP . . . . MFN 78
■ LP P.Disc . . . . MFN 78P
Music For Nations / Nov '87.
Music For Nations / Jan '88.
CD. . . . . CDMFN 78
MC. TMFN 78
Music For Nations / Aug '89 / Pinnacle.

Tilt

RIDE THE TIGER.
Tracks: Ride the tiger / Jumping the gun / Blood and sand / Six string T's / Bedlam rock / One night / Wanda / Wayward child / Dark heart / Red handed / May day.
■ LP . . . . .UEZLP 2001
Meteor / Apr '87.

Tin Machine

BABY UNIVERSAL.
Tracks: Baby universal / You belong in rock'n'roll (Only on 7" and MC single) / Big hurt, A (live) (Only on 12" single) / Baby universal (live) (Only on 12" single) / Stateside (live) (Only on CD single) / If there is something (live) (Only on CD single) / Heaven's in here (live) (Only on CD single).
■ 12" . . . . LONX 310
■ 7" .LON 310
■ CD Single . . . . LOCDT 310
■ MC Single. . . . . LONCS 310
London / Oct '91.

PRISONER OF LOVE.
Tracks: Baby can dance (live) / Prisoner of love (LP version) (12" & CD single only.) / Crack City (live) (12" & CD single only.) / Prisoner of love.
■ 12" 12MT 76
■ 7" . . . . MTS 76
■ 7" . . . . MT 76
■ 7" P.Disc . . . . MTPD 76
■ MC Single. . . . . TCMT 76
■ CD Single . . . . CDMT 76
EMI-Manhattan / Nov '89.

TIN MACHINE.
Tracks: Heaven's in here / Tin machine / Prisoner of love / Crack city / I can't read / Under the God / Amazing / Working class hero / Bus stop / Pretty thing / Video crimes / Run (Not on album.) / Sacrifice yourself (Not on album.) / Baby can dance.
MC. 791 990 4
■ CD . . . . CDMTLS 1064
■ LP . . . . MTLS 1044
■ MC . . . . .TCMTLS 1044
EMI-Manhattan / May '89.

TIN MACHINE.
Tracks: Tin Machine / Maggie's farm (live) / I can't read (live) (12", Poster bag & CD single only.) / Maggie's farm (Cassingle only.) / Bus stop (live country version) (CD single only.).
■ 12" 12MTP 73
■ 12" 12MT 73
■ 7" . . . . MT 73
■ 7" . . . . MTG 73
■ 7" P.Disc . . . . MTPD 73
■ CD Single . . . . CDMT 73
■ MC Single. . . . . TCMT 73
EMI-Manhattan / Aug '89.

TIN MACHINE II.
Tracks: Baby universal / One shot / You belong in rock 'n' roll / If there is something / Amlapura / Betty wrong / You can't talk / Stateside / Shopping for girls / Big hurt / Sorry / Goodbye Mr. Ed.
■ LP 8282721
■ CD 8282722
■ MC 8282724
London / Sep '91.

UNDER THE GOD.
Tracks: Under the God / Sacrifice yourself / Interview (Not on 7"or Cassingle.).
■ 10" 10MT 68
■ 12" 12MT 68
■ 7" . . . . MT 68
■ 7" . . . . MTLH 68
■ CD Single . . . . CDMT 68
■ MC Single. . . . . TCMT 68
EMI-Manhattan / Jun '89.

YOU BELONG IN ROCK 'N' ROLL.
Tracks: You belong in rock 'n' roll / Amlapura / Stateside (Only on CD Single.) / Hammerhead (Only on CD Single.).
■ 12" . . . . LONX 305
■ 7" .LON 305
■ CD Single . . . . LONCD 305
London / Aug '91.

Titan Force

TITAN FORCE.
Tracks: Not Advised.
CD . . . . US 017 CD
■ LP . . . . US 017
U.S. Metal / Jun '89.

WINNER/LOSER.
Tracks: Not Advised.
CD . . . . SHARK 021CD
LP . . . . SHARK 021
Shark / '92 / Plastic Head.

TNT

BACK ON THE ROAD.
Tracks: Rockin' the night / Back on the road.
■ 7" .NEAT 39
Neat / Apr '84.

HEART TO HEART.
Tracks: Heart to heart / Where are you.
■ 7" . . . . CHOP 1
Chopper / Nov '79.

INTUITION.
Tracks: Nation free / Tonight I'm falling / Learn to love / Take me down / Caught between the tigers / Forever shine on / Ordinary lover / Wisdom.
■ LP 836 777-1
■ CD 836 777-2
■ MC 836 777-4
Vertigo / Feb '89.

TELL NO TALES.
Tracks: Everyone's a star / 10,000 lovers (in one) / Sapphire / Northern lights / As far as the eye can see / Child's play / Smooth syncopation / Listen to your heart / Desperate night / Incipits / Tell no tales.
■ MC . . . . .VERHC 39
Vertigo / Dec '87.
■ LP 830 979-1
■ CD 830 979-2
■ LP . . . . VERH 39
Vertigo / May '87.

WHIP YOUR LOVING ON ME.
Tracks: Whip your loving on me / Night train.
■ 7" . . . . BD 3
Bulldog Records / Feb '75.

Tobruk

FALLING.
Tracks: Falling / Like lightning / Under the gun.
■ 12" 12R 6093
■ 7" . . . . .R 6093
Parlophone / Mar '85.

ON THE REBOUND.
Tracks: On the rebound / Poor girl.
■ 12" 12R 6101
■ 7" . . . . .R 6101
Parlophone / Aug '85.

PLEASURE AND PAIN.
Tracks: Rock 'n' roll casualty / Love is in motion / Alleyboy / No paradise in Heaven / Burning up / Two hearts on the run / Let me out of here / Cry out in the night / Set me on fire.
■ CD . . . . WKFMXD 105

■ LP . . . . WKFMLP 105
■ MC. . . . . WKFMMC 105
FM Records / May '88.

WILD ON THE RUN.
Tracks: Wild on the run / Falling / Running from the night / Hotline / Rebound / Poor girl / She's nobody's angel / Breakdown / Going down for the third time / Show must go on.
■ LP .TK 1
MC. TCTK 1
Parlophone / Mar '85 / EMI.

WILD ON THE RUN.
Tracks: Wild on the run / Must go on.
■ 7" . . . . .NEAT 32
Neat / Sep '83.

Together

PLAYING GAMES.
Tracks: Not Advised.
■ LP . . . . NE 1053
■ MC. . . . . CE 2053
K-Tel / Oct '79.

PLAYING GAMES.
Tracks: Playing games.
■ 12" . . . . TEST 128368
Mausoleum / May '85.

Token Entry

JAYBIRD.
Tracks: Not Advised.
CD . . . . .HR 9539 2
■ LP . . . . .HR 9539 1
Hawker / '89.

WEIGHT OF THE WORLD.
Tracks: Not Advised.
CD . . . . EM 93942
LP . . . . EM 93941
Road Runner / Sep '90 / Pinnacle.

Tokyo Blade

BLACK HEARTS AND JADED SPADES.
Tracks: Not Advised.
■ LP . . . . TBR 1
European Rock Promotions / Feb '86.

CAVE SESSION,THE.
Tracks: Cave session.
■ 12" . . . . .LEG 1 T
Powerstation / Jun '85.

LIGHTNING STRIKES.
Tracks: Lightning strikes / Fever / Attack attack.
■ 12" . . . . OHM 7 T
Powerstation / Sep '84.

MADAM GUILLOTINE.
Tracks: Not Advised.
■ 12" . . . . .OHM 9T
Powerstation / Jan '85.

MIDNIGHT RENDEZVOUS.
Tracks: Midnight rendezvous.
■ 12" . . . . OHM 4 T
Powerstation / Feb '84.

MOVIE STAR.
Tracks: Movie star.
■ 12" . . . . .ERA 001
Areba / Apr '88.

NIGHT OF THE BLADE.
Tracks: Not Advised.
■ LP . . . . .AMP 4
Powerstation / Sep '84.

POWER GAME.
Tracks: Power game / Death on Main Street.
■ 7" . . . . .OHM 2
Powerstation / Oct '83.

TOKYO BLADE.
Tracks: Not Advised.
■ LP . . . . .AMP 1
Powerstation / Oct '83.
CD. . . . . RR 349883
Road Runner / '89 / Pinnacle.

UNDERCOVER HONEYMOON.
Tracks: Undercover honeymoon.
■ 12" . . . . BLADE 001
European Rock Promotions / Apr '86.

WARRIOR OF THE RISING SUN.
Tracks: Madam Guillotine / Fever / Night of the blade / Breakout / Unleash the beat / Attack attack /

Lightning strikes (Extended version) / Warrior of the rising sun / Someone to love / Mean Streak / If heaven is hell (Extended Version) / Break the chains / Dead of the night / Power game / Highway passion / Midnight rendezvous / Sunrise in Tokyo / Killer City / Liar / Death on mainstreet (Previously unreleased.).
■ **Double LP** . . . . **RAWLP 005**
■ **MC Set** . . . . **RAWTC 005**
Raw Power / Apr '86 / Pinnacle.

Tool

OPIATE.
Tracks: Sweat / Hush / Part of me / Cold and ugly (live) / Jerk-off (live) / Opiate.
CD 724451102723
MC 724451102747
Zoo Entertainment / Jul '92 / BMG.

PRISON SEX.
Tracks: Prison sex / Undertow / Opiate (live) / Prison sex (version).
■ **12"** 7432119432-1
■ **CD Single** 7432119432-2
RCA / Mar '94.

UNDERTOW.
Tracks: Intolerance / Prison sex / Sober / Bottom / Crawl away / Swamp song / Undertow / 4 Degrees / Flood / Disgustipated.
CD 72445 11052-2
MC 72445 11052-4
RCA / Apr '93 / BMG.
LP 7244511052-1
RCA / May '94 / BMG.

Tora Tora

RED SUN SETTING.
Tracks: Red sun setting / Highway.
■ **7"** . . . . TT 5000
Mancunian Metal / Aug '80.

SURPRISE ATTACK.
Tracks: Love's a bitch / 28 days / Hard times / Guilty / Phantom rider / Walkin' shoes / Riverside drive / She's good she's bad / One for the road / Being there.
MC . . . . .AMC 5261
■ **CD** . . . . CDA 5261
■ **LP** . . . . AMA 5261
A&M / Apr '90.

WALKING SHOES.
Tracks: Walking shoes.
■ **12"** . . . . AMY 557
■ **7"** . . . . AM 557
A&M / May '90.

WILD AMERICA.
Tracks: Wild America / Amnesia / Dead man's band / As time goes by / Lay your money down / Shattered / Dirty secrets / Faith healer / Cold fever / Nowhere to go but down / City of kings.
■ **CD** 3953712
A&M / May '92.

Toranaga

BASTARD BALLADS.
Tracks: Sentenced / Dealers in death / Bastard ballads / Soldiers be brave / Time to burn / Retribution.
■ **CD** . . . . VILE 005 CD
■ **LP** . . . . VILE 005
Peaceville / Mar '89.

GOD'S GIFT.
Tracks: Not Advised.
■ **CD** . . . . CCD 1771
■ **LP** . . . . CHR 1771
■ **MC** . . . . ZCHR 1771
Chrysalis / Apr '90.

Torch

ELECTIKISS.
Tracks: Not Advised.
■ **LP** . . . . SWORDLP 004
Music For Nations / Nov '84.

TORCH.
Tracks: Not Advised.
■ **LP** . . . . SWORDLP 001
Music For Nations / Jan '85.

Torchure

BEYOND THE VEIL.
Tracks: Not Advised.
CD .1MF3770026
LP . . . . IMF 3770026LP
1 MF / Nov '92 / Plastic Head.

Torino

CUSTOMIZED.
Tracks: Not Advised.
■ **LP** . . . . WKFMLP 104
■ **MC** . . . . WKFMMC 104
FM Records / Nov '87.

ROCK IT.
Tracks: Rock it / Nights on fire / Seven mountains / Baby blue / It takes a man to cry / Showdown / Dance all night / One in a million / Shine / Turn it up.
■ **CD** . . . . WKFMXD 123
■ **LP** . . . . WKFMLP 123
■ **MC** . . . . WKFMMC 123
FM Records / Mar '89.

Torme

DEMOLITION BALL.
Tracks: Fallen angel / Black sheep / Action / Ball and chain / Slip away / Long time coming / Spinnin' your wheels / Don't understand / Industry / Draw the line / U.S. made / Let it go / Walk it / Man o' means.
CD . . . . .CDBLEED 2
Bleeding Hearts / Apr '93 / Pinnacle.

DIE PRETTY, DIE YOUNG.
Tracks: Let it rock / Real thing / Ready / Sex action / Ways of the East / Killer / Memphis / Louise / Crimes of passion / Ghost train.
■ **LP** . . . . HMRLP 94
Heavy Metal / Jun '87.
■ **CD** . . . . HMRXD 94
■ **MC** . . . . HMRMC 94
Heavy Metal / Nov '89.

OFFICIAL LIVE BOOTLEG.
Tracks: Not Advised.
■ **LP** . . . . ONS 3
Onsala International / Jul '87.

START.
Tracks: Start / T.V.O.D. / Kerrap / Love, guns & money.
■ **12"** . . . . 12 RA 6
■ **7"** . . . . RA 6
Zebra (1) / Apr '86.

Tormentors

GODDESS OF LOVE.
Tracks: Not Advised.
■ **LP** . . . . .SKULL 8344
Mausoleum / Sep '84.

HANGING AROUND.
Tracks: Not Advised.
■ **LP** . . . . EVA 12055
EVA / Apr '86.

Toronto

GIRLS NIGHT OUT.
Tracks: Not Advised.
■ **LP** . . . . MCF 3195
■ **MC** . . . . MCFC 3195
MCA / Mar '84.

HEAD ON.
Tracks: Head on / Silver screen / Still talkin' 'bout love / Someone will play the blues / It comes from you / Enough is enough / Master of disguise / Blackmail / Gone in a flash.
■ **LP** . . . . AMLH 64872
A&M / Oct '81.

LOOKIN' FOR TROUBLE.
Tracks: Even the score / 5035 / Get your hands off me / You better run / Don't stop me / Lookin' for trouble / Do watcha: be watcha / Delicious / Shot down / Tie me down.
■ **LP** . . . . AMLH 64821
A&M / Oct '80.

Torture

STORM ALERT.
Tracks: Igominous slaughter / Slay ride / Storm alert / Whips / Blood portraits / Terror kingdom / Enter the chamber / Deceiver.
LP . . . . CORE 2
Metalcore / Jul '90 / Pinnacle.

Total

BEYOND THE RIM.
Tracks: Not Advised.
LP . . . . .VPAGLP 5755
Majora / Nov '93 / Plastic Head.

Touch

BACK ALLEY VICES.
Tracks: Not Advised.
■ **LP** . . . . EBON 28
Ebony (Pinnacle) / Jan '85.

TOUCH.
Tracks: Not Advised.
CD . . . . .CDMFN 107
LP . . . . MFN 107
MC . . . . .TMFN 107
Music For Nations / Aug '90 / Pinnacle.

Tour De Force

TOUR DE FORCE.
Tracks: Flesh / Perfect lover / Love and money / Watercolour / Dirty white boy / Shattered dreams / Believer / Butthead / Bad penny / Say goodbye.
CD . . . . .CDATV 27
Active / May '93 / Pinnacle.

Toxic Reasons

ANYTHING FOR MONEY.
Tracks: Just another day / Screamin' / Bad Georgia / Committed / Swingin' the hammer / Shoot to kill / Shut you down / Take this city / Anything for money / Wildin'.
LP 086 808 1
S.P.V. / Mar '90.

BULLETS FOR YOU.
Tracks: Not Advised.
■ **LP** . . . . VIRUS 55
Alternative Tentacles / Oct '86.

DEDICATION.
Tracks: Payback mix / Killing game / Your perfect world / Us and them / Critical condition / I'm ready / Whole world's on fire.
■ **LP** . . . . .FH 12-005
Funhouse / May '88.

GOD BLESS AMERICA.
Tracks: God bless America.
■ **7"** . . . . HANG 1
Skysaw / Sep '84.

IN THE HOUSE OF GOD.
Tracks: Not Advised.
CD . . . . BC 1685CD
Bitzcore / Nov '93 / Plastic Head.

INDEPENDENCE.
Tracks: Not Advised.
■ **LP** . . . . BC 1655
Bitzcore / May '89.

KILL BY REMOTE CONTROL.
Tracks: Not Advised.
■ **LP** . . . . VIRUS 41
Alternative Tentacles / Nov '84.

ZERO BOYS.
Tracks: Zero boys.
■ **7"** . . . . SFLS 006
SFL / Nov '92.

Toxic Shock

CHANGE FROM REALITY.
Tracks: Breakout / Burning down your life / Forbidden lust / Mad sounds / State of madness / Overloaded / Raging speed / United forces.
LP . . . . NB 1001 R
Nuclear Blast / Nov '88 / Plastic Head.
■ **LP** . . . . .MB 1001
Metal Blast / Feb '89.

DUBIOUS DEAL.
Tracks: Dubious deal.
■ **7"** . . . . YUS 2
Vindaloo / Sep '84.

JUST ANOTHER DAY.
Tracks: Just another day.
■ **12"** . . . . YUS 5
Vindaloo / Nov '85.

WELCOME HOME.
Tracks: Not Advised.
LP 082 927

■ DELETED

.P.V. / Apr '90.
P .... NB 027
uclear Blast / Dec '90 / Plastic Head.

Toxic Waste

WE WILL BE FREE (see under Asylum).

Toxik

THINK THIS.
Tracks: Think this / Creed / Spontaneous / There stood the fence / Black and white / WIR NJN 8 (In God) / Machine dream / Shotgun logic / Time after time / Technical arrogance (Only on CD.) / Out on he tiles (Only on CD.).
CD .... RO 94602
■ LP .... RO 94601
Roadracer / Oct '89.

WORLD CIRCUS.
Tracks: Heart attack / Social overload / Pain & misery / Voices / Door to hell / World circus / 47 seconds of sanity / False prophets / Haunted earth / Victims.
CD .... RR 349572
■ LP .... RR 9572
Road Runner / Mar '88.

Toxodeth

MYSTERIES ABOUT LIFE AND DEATH.
Tracks: Not Advised.
CD .... WRE 903CD
LP .... WRE 903
Wild Rags / Dec '90 / Plastic Head.

Tractor

AVERAGE MAN'S HERO.
Tracks: Average man's hero / Big big boy.
■ 7" .... RR 2
Roach / Oct '81.

TRACTOR.
Tracks: All ends up / Little girl in yellow / Watcher / Ravenscroft's 13 bar boogie / Shubunkin / Hope in favour / Every time it happens / Make the journey.
■ LP .... THBL 002
Thunderbolt / Jul '83.
CD .... REP 4081-WP
LP .... REP 2081
MC .... REP 2081-SX
Repertoire (Germany) / Aug '91 / Pinnacle.

WAY WE LIVE/TRACTOR, THE.
Tracks: Kick Dick II / Squares / Siderial / Angle / Storm / Willow / Madrigal / Way ahead / All ends up / Little girl in yellow / Watcher / Reavenscroft / Bar boogie / Shubunkin / Hope in favour / Everytime it happens / Make the journey.
CD Set .... SEECD 409
See For Miles / Sep '94 / Pinnacle.

Traitors Gate

DEVIL TAKES THE HIGH ROAD.
Tracks: Devil takes the high road / Love after midnight / Shoot to kill.
■ 12" .... BOLT 12
Bullet / Apr '85.

Trance

ROCKERS.
Tracks: Not Advised.
CD 367 0002.2
LP 367 0002.1
Mausoleum / Oct '91 / Pinnacle.

WHEN A MAN LOVES A WOMAN (Trance featuring Percy Sledge).
Tracks: When a man loves a woman.
■ 12" 367 0002.0
■ CD Single 367 0002.3
Mausoleum / Oct '91.

Transgression

COLD WORLD.
Tracks: Think for yourself / Prejudice kills / Pressures of society / It's here to stay / Go to hell / Won't bend my knees / Cold world / Regroup / Killing you / Senseless game / We've got to fight / Head in the smoke / Death to all / Final conflict.
■ LP .... ACHE 16
Manic Ears / Oct '88.

Transmetal

BURIAL AT SEA.
Tracks: Not Advised.
CD .... GCI 89804
Plastic Head / Jun '92 / Plastic Head.

Transmisia

DUMBSHOW.
Tracks: Not Advised.
CD .... INV 027CD
Invisible / Jun '94 / Plastic Head.

MINCING MACHINE.
Tracks: Not Advised.
LP .... WD 010
Wide / Apr '92 / Plastic Head.

Trapeze

DON'T ASK ME HOW I KNOW.
Tracks: Don't ask me how I know / Take good care.
■ 7" .... AUS 114
Aura / Jan '80.

HOLD ON.
Tracks: Don't ask me how I know / Take good care / When you get to heaven / Livin' on love / Hold on / Don't break my heart / Running / You are / Time will heal.
■ LP .... AUL 708
■ MC .... AUC 708
Aura / Oct '79.

HOT WIRE.
Tracks: Back street love / Take it on down the road / Midnight flyer / Wake up, shake up / Turn it on / Steal a mile / Goin' home / Feel it inside.
■ LP .... K 56064
WEA / '74.

LIVE IN TEXAS - DEAD ARMADILLOS.
Tracks: Black cloud / You are the music, we're just the band / Way back to the bone.
■ LP .... AUL 717
Aura / Nov '81.

MEDUSA.
Tracks: Black cloud / Jury / Your love is alright / Touch my life / Seafull / Mates you wanna cry / Medusa.
■ LP .... THS 4
Threshold / '70.

RUNNING AWAY.
Tracks: Running away / Don't break my heart.
■ 7" .... AUS 116
Aura / Mar '81.

TRAPEZE.
Tracks: Star breaker / It's alright / Chances / Raid / On the sunny side of the street / Gimmie good love / I need you / Soul stealer / Nothing for nothing.
■ LP .... K 56165
WEA / '75.

TRAPEZE.
Tracks: It's only a dream / Giants dead, hoorah / Over / Nancy Gray / Fairytale / Verily verily / It's my life / Am I / Suicide / Wings / Another day / Send me no more letters.
■ LP .... THS 2
Threshold / '70.

WAY BACK TO THE BONE.
Tracks: Coast to coast / Loser / Your love is alright / Touch my life / Way back to the bone / Seafull / Black cloud / You are the music / Medusa.
■ LP .... BRF 2001
Bandit / Oct '86.

YOU ARE THE MUSIC, WE'RE THE BAND.
Tracks: Keepin' time / Coast to coast / What is a woman's role / Way back to the bone / Feelin' so much better now / Will your love end / Loser / We are the music.
■ LP .... THS 8
Threshold / '72.

Travers, Pat

Canadian guitarist of whom ex-employee Nicko McBrain (now Iron Maiden drummer) declared, "I wouldn't piss on him if he was on fire." Achieved minor success after he came to London in mid-'70s but has since slumped into obscurity shared by numerous would-be guitar heroes.

ANTHOLOGY VOL.1, AN.
Tracks: Not Advised.
■ CD 841 208-2
Polydor / Mar '90.

ANTHOLOGY VOL.2, AN.
Tracks: Not Advised.
■ CD 841 209-2
Polydor / Mar '90.

BLACK PEARL.
Tracks: I la la la love you / I'd rather see you dead / Stand up / Who'll take the fall / Fifth / Misty morning / Can't stop the heartaches / Amgwanna kick booty / Rockin'.
■ LP 2391553
Polydor / Nov '82.

BLUES TRACKS.
Tracks: Not Advised.
CD .... RR 91472
Road Runner / Sep '92 / Pinnacle.

BOOM BOOM.
Tracks: Snorting whiskey, drinking cocaine / Life in London / I la la la love you / Getting better / Watcha gonna do without me / Daddy long legs / Heat in the street / School of hard knocks / Help me / Stevie / Ready or not / Boom boom / Born under a bad sign / Guitars from hell.
CD .... ESSCD 140
MC .... ESDMC 140
■ LP .... ESDLP 140
Essential / Apr '91.

BOOM BOOM.
Tracks: Boom boom / Statesboro blue.
■ 7" .... POSP 77
Polydor / Oct '79.

BOOM BOOM.
Tracks: Snorting whiskey, drinking cocaine / Life in London / I la la la love you / Getting better / Watcha gonna do without me / Daddy long legs / Heat in the street / School of hard knocks / Help me / Stevie / Ready or not / Boom boom / Born under a bad sign / Guitars from hell.
■ VHS .... HEN 2328
Hendring Video / Apr '91.

CRASH AND BURN.
Tracks: Crash and burn / Can't be right / Snortin' whiskey / Born under a bad sign / Is this love / Big event / Love will make you strong / Material eyes.
■ LP .... POLS 1017
Polydor / '80.

GO FOR WHAT YOU KNOW (Travers, Pat Band).
Tracks: Hooked on music / Gettin' better / Go all night / Boom boom / Stevie / Making magic / Heat in the street / Makes no difference.
■ LP .... POLS 1011
Polydor / Aug '79.

HEAT IN THE STREET.
Tracks: Heat in the street / Killer's instinct / I tried to believe / Hammerhead / Go all night / Evie / One for me and one for you.
■ LP .... POLD 5005
Polydor / Apr '79.

IS THIS LOVE.
Tracks: Is this love / Snorting.
■ 7" .... POSP 144
Polydor / Apr '80.

JUST A TOUCH.
Tracks: Not Advised.
CD .... RR 90452
Road Runner / Oct '93 / Pinnacle.

MAKIN' MAGIC.
Tracks: Making magic / Rock 'n' roll Susie / You don't love me / Stevie / Statesboro blues / Need love / Hooked on music / What you mean to me.
■ LP 2383 436
Polydor / Apr '77.
■ LP 2384 122
Polydor / Sep '81.
■ LP 2485 238
Polydor (Germany) / Aug '85.

PAT TRAVERS.
Tracks: Stop and smile / Feelin' right / Magnolia / Makes no difference / Boom boom (out go the lights) / Mabelline / Hot rod Lincoln / As my life flies.
■ LP 2383395
Polydor / '76.

PUTTING IT STRAIGHT.
Tracks: Life in London / Gettin' betta / Runnin' from the future / It ain't what it seems / Off beat ride / Loving you / Dedication / Speakeasy.

■ LP 2383471
Polydor / '77.

RADIO ACTIVE.
Tracks: New age music / My life is on the line / (I just wanna) live it my way / I don't wanna be awake / I can love you / Untitled / Feelin' in love / Play it like you see it / Electric detective.
■ LP 2391 499
Polydor / May '81.

SCHOOL OF HARD KNOCKS.
Tracks: Not Advised.
■ CD . . . . LUSCD 4
■ LP . . . . LUSLP 4
■ MC . . . . LUSMC 4
Episode / Jul '90.

SNORTIN' WHISKEY (Travers, Pat Band).
Tracks: Snortin' whiskey / Your love can't be right / Life in London / Evie / Rock'n'roll Susie.
■ 7" . . . . POSP 164
Polydor / Aug '80.
■ 12" . . . . POSPX 164
Polydor / Sep '80.

TURNING POINT (Travers, Pat Band).
Tracks: Not Advised.

Treat

ORGANISED CRIME.
Tracks: Ready for the taking / Party all over / Keep your hands to yourself / Stay away / Conspiracy / Mr. Heartache / Gimme one more night / Get you on the run / Home is where your heart is / Fatal smile.
■ CD 838 929 2
■ LP 838 929 1
■ MC 838 929 4
Vertigo / Feb '90.

SCRATCH AND BITE.
Tracks: Changes / Scratch and bite / Get you on the run / Hiding / Too wild / We are one / No room for strangers / You got me / Run with the fire.
■ LP 824 353 1
MC 824 353 4
Mercury / Sep '85 / PolyGram.

TREAT.
Tracks: Winner / Rev it up / Sole survivor / Strike without a warning / Outlaw / Fallen angel / Ride me high / World of promises / Save yourself / Best of me.
■ LP 836 727-1
■ MC 836 727-4
Vertigo / Feb '89.

Treponem Pal

AGGRAVATION.
Tracks: Not Advised.
CD . . . . RO 93322
LP . . . . RO 93321
MC . . . . RO 93324
Roadracer / Feb '91 / Pinnacle.

EXCESS & OVERDRIVE.
Tracks: Not Advised.
CD . . . . CD RR 9076 2
LP . . . . .RR LP 9076 1
MC . . . . RR MC 9076 4
Road Runner / Jun '93 / Pinnacle.

PUSHING YOU TOO FAR.
Tracks: Pushing you too far.
12" . . . . RR 23816
CD Single . . . . RR 23813
Road Runner / Apr '94 / Pinnacle.

TREPONEM PAL.
Tracks: Silico / Embodiment of frustration / Prettiest star / In out / Low man / Soft mouth vagina.
CD . . . . .RO 9456 2
■ LP . . . . .RO 9456 1
MC . . . . .RO 9456 4
Roadracer / Sep '89 / Pinnacle.

Trespass

BRIGHT LIGHTS.
Tracks: Bright lights / Duel/Man and machine.
■ 7" . . . . CASE 3
Trial / Jan '82.

JEALOUSY.
Tracks: Jealousy.
■ 7" . . . . CASE 2
Trial / Sep '82.

ONE OF THESE DAYS.
Tracks: One of these days.
■ 7" . . . . CASE 1
Trial / Jan '80.

Tribe After Tribe

LOVE UNDER WILL.
Tracks: Hold on / Ice below / Spell / Dance of the wu li masters / I spit / Nikita / Congo Sky / World of promises / Proud & beautiful / Let's go outside / Delight / Lovers (a)In the face of the sun (b) In the dark (c) Babalon.
CD . . . . CDZAZ 4
LP . . . . ZAZ 4
MC . . . . TZAZ 4
Megaforce / Jun '93 / Pinnacle.

TRIBE AFTER TRIBE.
Tracks: Remember / Build a subway / Sally / Just for a while / Come to see you fall / Mode / White boys in the jungle / Rolling stoney / What are we now / Everything and more / Out of control / Poor Afrika.
CD 7567822352
■ LP 7567822351
MC 7567822354
East West / Sep '91 / WEA.

Tribulation

CLOWN OF THORNS.
Tracks: Borka intro / Born bizarre / My world is different / Rise of prejudice / Everything's floating / Safe murder of emotions / Angst / Decide (take a stand) / angel in a winterpile / Beautiful views / Landslide of losers / Down my lungs / Pick an image (make sure it sells) / Herr Ober / Tiny little skeleton / Disgraceland / Dogmother (LP only).
CD 8410602
LP 0810601
Black Mark / Feb '92 / Plastic Head.

Triligy

NEXT IN LINE.
Tracks: Not Advised.
■ LP . . . . AXE 7026
Axe Killer / Jan '87.

Triumph

ALLIED FORCES.
Tracks: Fool for your love / Magic power / Air raid / Allied forces / Hot time (In this city tonight) / Fight the good fight / Ordinary man / Petite etude / Say goodbye.
■ LP . . . . RCALP 6002
MC . . . . RCAK 6002
RCA / Sep '81 / BMG.
■ CD . . . . MCAD 5542
MCA / '87.

ALLIED FORCES.
Tracks: Allied forces / Hot time.
■ 12" . . . . RCAT 135
■ 7" . . . . RCA 135
RCA / Oct '81.

AMERICAN GIRLS.
Tracks: American girls / Movin' on.
■ 7" . . . . PB 9451
RCA / Jan '80.

HOLD ON.
Tracks: Hold on / Just a game.
■ 7" . . . . PB 1569
RCA / '79.

I CAN SURVIVE.
Tracks: I can survive / Nature's child.
■ 7" . . . . PB 1945
RCA / May '80.

I LIVE FOR THE WEEKEND.
Tracks: I live for the weekend / Lay it on the line.
■ 12" . . . . RCAT 13
■ 7" . . . . RCA 13
RCA / Nov '80.

JUST A GAME.
Tracks: Movin'on / Lay it on the line / Young enough to try / American girls / Just a game / Fantasy serenade / Hold on / Suitcase blues.
■ LP . . . . PL 13224
RCA / '79.
■ LP . . . . INTS 5154
■ MC . . . . INTK 5154
RCA / Sep '81.

MAGIC POWER.
Tracks: Magic power / Fight the good fight.
■ 7" . . . . .RCA 19
RCA / Mar '82.

NEVER SURRENDER.
Tracks: Too much thinking / World of fantasy / Min prelude / All the way / Battle cry / Overture (proces sional) / Never surrender / When the lights go down Writing on the wall / Epilogue (resolution).
■ LP . . . . RCALP 606
■ MC . . . . RCAK 606
RCA / Feb '83 / BMG.

NIGHT OF TRIUMPH (LIVE).
Tracks: Not Advised.
■ VHS . . . . HEN 209
Hendring Video / '88.

PROGRESSIONS OF POWER.
Tracks: I live for the weekend / I can survive / In th night / Nature's child / Woman in love / Take m heart / Tear the roof off / Fingertalkin' / Hard road
■ LP . . . . PL 1352
RCA / May '80.
■ LP . . . . RCALP 303
■ MC . . . . RCAK 303
RCA / Sep '81 / BMG.
■ LP . . . . MCL 185
■ MC . . . . MCLC 185
MCA / Jun '87.

ROCK 'N' ROLL MACHINE.
Tracks: Takes time / Bringing it on home / Rocky mountain way / Street fighter / Street fighter (re prise) / 24 hours a day / Blinding light show/Moon child / Rock 'n' roll machine.
■ LP . . . . MCL 1856
■ MC . . . . MCLC 1856
MCA / Jun '87.

SOMEBODY'S OUT THERE.
Tracks: Somebody's out there.
■ 12" . . . . MCAT 118
■ 7" . . . . MCA 118
MCA / Feb '87.

SPORT OF KINGS, THE.
Tracks: Not Advised.
■ CD . . . . MCAD 5786
MCA / Apr '86.
■ LP . . . . MCF 3331
■ MC . . . . MCFC 3331
MCA / Sep '86.

STAGES.
Tracks: When the lights go down / Never surrender / Hold on / Magic power / Rock and roll machine / Lay it on the line / World of fantasy / Midsummer's daydream / Spellbound / Follow your heart / Fight the good fight / Mind games / Empty inside / Allied forces / Druh mer selbo.
■ Double LP . . . . .MCMD 7002
■ MC Set . . . . MCMDC 7002
MCA / Nov '85.
■ CD . . . . MCAD 8020
MCA / '87.
■ CD . . . . MCAD 7002
MCA / Jul '87.

THUNDER SEVEN.
Tracks: Spellbound / Midsummer's daydream / Kill ing time / Little boy blues / Follow your heart / Rock out, roll on / Time goes by / Time canon / Stranger in a strange land / Cool down.
■ MC . . . . MCFC 3246
■ LP . . . . MCF 3246
MCA / Mar '85.
■ CD . . . . MCAD 5537
MCA / '86.
■ CD . . . . DIDX 199
MCA / '88.

TRIUMPH.
Tracks: Takes time / Bringing it on home / Rocky Mountain way / Street fighter / 24 hours a day / Blinding light show / Moonchild / Rock'n'roll machine.
■ LP . . . . PL 12982
RCA / Feb '79.
■ LP . . . . INTS 5153
■ MC . . . . INTK 5153
RCA / Sep '81.
■ LP . . . . LAT 1012
Noir / Mar '82.

TRIUMPH: AT THE US FESTIVAL.
Tracks: Not Advised.
■ VHS . . . . HEN 2042
Hendring Video / '88.

■ DELETED

WORLD OF FANTASY.
Tracks: World of fantasy / Too much thinking.
■ 7" . . . . .RCA 319
RCA / Mar '83.

Trixter

GIVE IT TO ME GOOD.
Tracks: Give it to me good.
■ 12" . . . . MCST 1554
■ 7" . . . . MCS 1554
■ CD Single . . . . MCSTD 1554
MCA / Jul '91.
■ 12" Remix . . . . MCSX 1554
MCA / Jul '91.

TRIXTER.
Tracks: Line of fire / Heart of steel / One in a million / Surrender / Give it to me good / Only young once / Bad / Always a victim / Play rough / You'll never see me cryin' / Ride the whip / On and on.
■ CD . . . . MCAD 6389
■ MC . . . . MCAC 6389
■ LP . . . . MCA 6389
MCA / Oct '90.
■ CD . . . . DMCG 6114
■ LP . . . . MCG 6114
■ MC . . . . MCGC 6114
MCA / Jul '91.

Trojan

CHASING THE STORM.
Tracks: Not Advised.
■ LP . . . . RR 9756
Road Runner / Sep '85.

MARCH IS ON, THE.
Tracks: Not Advised.
CD . . . . GICD 444
■ LP . . . . GILP 444
MC . . . . GIMC 444
G.I. / Mar '89 / Backs Distribution.

Trouble

Chicago Doom Metal quintet who formed in 1979 and quickly developed a reputation for sounding as much like Black Sabbath as Black Sabbath did. Happily, it was an affectionate tribute rather than pure plagiarism. Their career picked up after three albums for Metal Blade when Rick Rubin signed them to his label Def American and produced the awesome *Manic Frustration* (1992). Sadly, however, it failed to bring the band's long-brewing sales potential to the boil. Could happen any day, though.

MANIC FRUSTRATION.
Tracks: Touch the sky / Scuse me / Sleeper / Fear / Rain / Tragedy man / Memory's garden / Plastic green card / Hello strawberry skies / Mr White / Breathe.
CD 512 556-2
MC 512 556-4
American Recordings / Sep '92 / PolyGram.

PSALM 9/THE SKULL.
Tracks: Not Advised.
CD Set . . . . ZORRO 19 CD
Double LP . . . . ZORRO 19
MC Set . . . . ZORRO 19 M
Music For Nations / Apr '91 / Pinnacle.

RUN TO THE LIGHT.
Tracks: Misery show / Thinking of the past / Peace of mind / Born in a prison / Tuesdays child / Beginning.
■ LP . . . . RR 9606
Road Runner / Jul '87.
CD . . . . .CDMZORRO 74
Metal Blade / May '94 / Pinnacle.

SKULL.
Tracks: Not Advised.
■ LP . . . . RR 9791
Road Runner / Jul '85.

TROUBLE.
Tracks: At the end of my daze / Wolf / Psychotic reaction / Sinner's fame / Misery shows (act II) / Rip / Black shapes of doom / Heaven on my mind / END / All is forgiven.
CD 8424211
■ LP 8424211
■ MC 8424214
American Recordings / Feb '90.

TROUBLE IN MY LIFE.
Tracks: Trouble in my life / Last time.
■ 12" . . . . MDM 19-12

■ 7" . . . . MDM 19
MDM / Jul '87.

Trower, Robin

Trower's career began in early '60s with The Paramounts. In 1967 he joined Procul Harum for five years before abortive collaboration with Frankie Miller in Jude. First solo album *Twice Removed From Yesterday* was melting pot of previous musical experiences. 1974's follow-up *Bridge Of Sighs* established Trower as major act in U.S. In 1981, *BLT*, a collaboration with Cream bassist Jack Bruce and Sly Stone drummer Bill London, went Top 40 in that country and Trower still commands large U.S. following. Minor UK success peaked with 1976's *Live* album, which reached no. 15. Most recent album is 1994's *20th Century Blues*.

20TH CENTURY BLUES.
Tracks: Not Advised.
CD . . . . FIENDCD 753
Demon / Aug '94 / Pinnacle / A.D.A. Distribution.

ANTHOLOGY.
Tracks: Not Advised.
CD . . . . VSOPCD 197
Connoisseur Collection / Apr '94 / Pinnacle.

B.L.T.
Tracks: Into money / What it is / Won't let you down / No island lost / It's too late / Life on earth / Once the bird has flown / Carmen / Feel the heat / End game.
■ LP . . . . CHR 1324
Chrysalis / Feb '81.
■ MC . . . . ZCHR 1324
Chrysalis / '83.

BACK IT UP.
Tracks: Back it up / River / Black to red / Benny dancer / Time is short / Islands / None but the brave / Captain Midnight / Settling the score.
■ LP . . . . CHR 1420
■ MC . . . . ZCHR 1420
Chrysalis / '83.

BBC LIVE IN CONCERT.
Tracks: Not Advised.
CD . . . . WINCD 013
Windsong / Feb '92 / Pinnacle / A.D.A. Distribution.

BEYOND THE MIST.
Tracks: Not Advised.
■ LP . . . . MFN 51
■ MC . . . . TMFN 51
Music For Nations / Jun '85.

BRIDGE OF SIGHS.
Tracks: Day of the eagle / Bridge of sighs / In this place / Fool and me / Too rolling stoned / About to begin / Lady love / Little bit of sympathy.
■ LP . . . . CHR 1057
■ MC . . . . ZCHR 1057
■ CD . . . . ACCD 1057
Chrysalis / Jan '82.
CD CD25CR 15
Chrysalis / Mar '94 / EMI.

CALEDONIA.
Tracks: Caledonia / Messin' the blues.
■ 7" . . . . CHS 2124
Chrysalis / Dec '76.

CARAVAN TO MIDNIGHT.
Tracks: My love (burning love) / I'm out to get you / Lost in love / Fool / It's for you / Birthday boy / King of the dance / Sail on.
■ LP . . . . CHR 1189
■ MC . . . . ZCHR 1189
Chrysalis / Dec '78.

COLLECTION: ROBIN TROWER.
Tracks: Not Advised.
CD . . . . CCSCD 291
■ MC . . . . CCSMC 291
Castle Collector Series / Aug '91.

FOR EARTH BELOW.
Tracks: Shame the Devil / It's only money / Confessin' / Midnight / Fine day / Althea / Take untold / Gonna be more suspicious / For earth below.
■ LP . . . . CHR 1073
■ MC . . . . ZCHR 1073
Chrysalis / Jan '75.

IN CITY DREAMS.
Tracks: Somebody calling / Sweet wine of love / Bluebird / Falling star / Farther on up the road / Pride / Sailing / S.M.O. / I can't live without you / Messin' the blues.
■ LP . . . . CHR 1148

MC . . . . ZCHR 1148
Chrysalis / '86 / EMI.

IT'S FOR YOU.
Tracks: It's for you / My love (burning love) / In city dreams.
■ EP . . . . CHS 2247
Chrysalis / '78.

LIVE: ROBIN TROWER.
Tracks: Too rolling stoned / Daydream / Rock me baby / Lady love / I can't wait much longer / Alethea / Little bit of sympathy.
■ LP . . . . CHR 1089
■ MC . . . . ZCHR 1089
Chrysalis / Mar '76.

LONG MISTY DAYS.
Tracks: Same rain falls / Long misty days / Hold me / Caledonia / Pride / Sailing / S.M.O. / I can't live without you / Messin' the blues.
■ LP . . . . CHR 1107
■ MC . . . . ZCHR 1107
Chrysalis / Oct '76.

PASSION.
Tracks: Caroline / Secret doors / If forever / Won't even think about you / Passion / No time / Night / Bad time / One more word.
■ LP . . . . PRT N6563
■ MC . . . . ZCN 6563
PRT / Feb '87.
CD . . . . GNPD 2187
GNP Crescendo / Jun '92 / Swift / Silva Screen / Flexitron Ltd. / C.M. Distribution.

PORTFOLIO (The Classic Collection).
Tracks: Bridge of sighs / Too rolling stoned / For earth below / Caravan to midnight / Day of the eagle / Shame the devil / Fine day / Daydream (live) / Lady love (live) / Alethea (live) / Caledonia live / Messin' the blues / Bluebird / Victims of fury / Mad house / Into money / Gonna shut you down / Thin ice / Benny dance.
CD . . . . MPCD 1600
■ LP .CNW 3
Chrysalis / Jul '87.
■ MC . . . . ZCNW 3
Chrysalis / Aug '92.

TAKE WHAT YOU NEED.
Tracks: Tear it up / Take what you need / Love attack / I want you home / Shattered / Over you / Careless / Second time / Love won't wait forever.
CD 781 838-2
■ MC . . . . K 781 838 4
■ LP . . . . K 781 838 1
Atlantic / May '88.

TRUCE (see under Bruce, Jack).

TWICE REMOVED FROM YESTERDAY.
Tracks: I can't wait much longer / Daydream / Hannah / Man of the world / I can't stand it / Rock me baby / Twice removed from yesterday / Sinner's song / Ballerina.
■ LP . . . . CHR 1039
■ MC . . . . ZCHR 1039
Chrysalis / '74.

VICTIMS OF THE FURY.
Tracks: Jack & Jill / Roads to freedom / Victims of the fury / Ring / Only time / Into the flame / Shout / Mad house / Ready for the taking / Fly low.
■ MC . . . . ZCHR 1215
Chrysalis / Feb '80.
■ LP . . . . CHR 1215
Chrysalis / '86.

VICTIMS OF THE FURY.
Tracks: Victims of the fury / One in a million.
■ 7" . . . . CHS 2402
Chrysalis / Jan '80.

WHAT IT IS.
Tracks: What it is / Into money.
■ 7" . . . . CHS 2497
Chrysalis / Feb '81.

Trust

ANTISOCIAL.
Tracks: Antisocial / Sects.
■ 7" . . . . .A 1006
CBS / Mar '81.

BEST OF TRUST.
Tracks: Antisocial / L'elite / Busser huit heures / M comedie / Le mitard / Serre les poings / Police milice / Saumur / Ideal / Ton dernier acte.
■ LP 4505941
MC 4505944
Premier (Sony) / Feb '88 / Sony / Pinnacle.

REPRESSION.
Tracks: Antisocial / Mr. Comedy / In the name of the race / Death instinct / Walk alone / Paris is still burning / Pick me up, put me down / Get out your claws / Sects / Le mitard.
■ LP . . . . CBS 84958
MC. 40 84958
CBS / Feb '81 / Sony.

SAVAGE.
Tracks: Big illusion / Savage / Repression / Junta / Mindless / Loneliness / Work or die / Crusades / Your final gig.
■ LP . . . . CBS 85546
CBS / May '82.

Tuff

WHAT COMES AROUND GOES AROUND.
Tracks: Not Advised.
CD. 7567 82244-2
LP 7567 82244-1
MC. 7567 82244-4
East West / Jul '91 / WEA.

Tuff Luck

TUFF LUCK.
Tracks: Not Advised.
■ LP . . . . NRR 18
MC. . . . . NRC 18
New Renaissance(USA) / Nov '87 / Pinnacle.

Tumor Circus

MEATHOOK UP MY RECTUM.
Tracks: Meathook up my rectum.
■ 7" . . . . VIRUS 102
Alternative Tentacles / Feb '92.

SWINE FLU.
Tracks: Swine flu.
■ 12" . . . . DG 003
Alternative Tentacles / Feb '91.

TUMOR CIRCUS.
Tracks: Not Advised.
CD. . . . . VIRUS 087CD
LP . . . . VIRUS 087
MC. . . . . VIRUS 087C
Alternative Tentacles / Oct '91 / RTM / Pinnacle.

Tungsten

183.85.
Tracks: Not Advised.
CD. IRSCD 981202
Intercord / Jan '94 / Pinnacle / C.M. Distribution.

Turbo

CHARGED FOR GLORY.
Tracks: Charged for glory.
■ 7" . . . . CUS 1261
Turbo Music / Sep '82.

DEAD END.
Tracks: Not Advised.
CD. . . . . CDFLAG 47
LP . . . . .FLAG 47
MC. . . . . TFLAG 47
Under One Flag / Sep '90 / Pinnacle.

LAST WARRIOR, THE.
Tracks: Last warrior / Berud's sword / Trojan horse / Seance with vampire / Tempest's son / Goddess of confusion / Angel from hell.
■ LP . . . . N 0113
Noise / May '88.
■ LP . . . . NUK 113
■ MC . . . . ZCNUK 113
Noise / Oct '89.

Turner, Joe Lynn

Poached from late '70s U.S. act Fandango by Ritchie Blackmore, Turner sang on Rainbow's biggest hit I Surrender (U.K. no. 3 in 1981). Following band's split, released solo album Rescue You, then joined Yngwie Malmsteen's Rising Force in 1988. Later reunited with Blackmore when he briefly replaced Ian Gillan in Deep Purple.

ENDLESSLY.
Tracks: Endlessly / Race is on.
■ 7" . . . . EKR 25
Elektra / Oct '85.

RESCUE YOU.
Tracks: Losing you / Young hearts / Prelude - endlessly / Rescue you / Feel the fire / Get tough / Eyes of love / On the run / Soul searcher / Race is on.
■ LP . . . . EKT 20
■ MC. . . . . .EKT 20C
Elektra / Nov '85.

Twelfth Night

ART AND ILLUSION.
Tracks: Counterpoint / Art and illusion / C.R.A.B. / Kings and queens / First new day.
■ LP . . . . MFN 36
Music For Nations / Oct '84.

COLLECTOR'S ITEM.
Tracks: Not Advised.
CD. . . . . CDGRUB 18
Double LP . . . . GRUB 18
MC Set . . . . .TGRUB 18
Food For Thought / Feb '91 / Pinnacle.

FACT AND FICTION.
Tracks: We are sane / World without end / Creep show / Poet sniffs a flower / Human being / Love song / Fact and fiction.
■ LP . . . . .TN 006
Twelfth Night / Jan '83.

IT'S JUST NOT CRITIC.
Tracks: It's just not critic.
■ 12" 12EMI 5518
■ MC Single. . . . . .TCEMI 5518
EMI / Aug '85.

LIVE AND LET LIVE (LIVE AT THE MARQUEE).
Tracks: Ceiling speaks / Fact and fiction / End of the endless majority / Poet sniffs a flower / Sequences / We are sane.
■ LP . . . . MFN 18
Music For Nations / Feb '84.

LIVE AT THE TARGET.
Tracks: Fur helene (pt 1) / After the eclipse / East to West / Sequences.
■ LP . . . . .TN 002
Twelfth Night / Feb '81.

SHAME.
Tracks: Shame / Blue powder monkey.
■ 12" . . . . CB 42412
■ 7" . . . . CB 424
Charisma / May '86.

SMILING AT GRIEF.
Tracks: East of Eden / This city / Honeymoon is over / Creepshow / Puppets (intro) / Puppets / Make no sense / Three dancers / Fur helene (pt 2).
MC. . . . . .TN 003
Twelfth Night / Jan '82 / Pinnacle.

TAKE A LOOK.
Tracks: Take a look / Blonden fair.
■ 12" . . . . CB 42512
■ 7" . . . . CB 425
Charisma / Aug '86.

TWELFTH NIGHT.
Tracks: Last song / Pressure / Jungle / Craft / Blue powder monkey / Theatre / Shame / This is war / Take a look.
■ LP . . . . CHC 72
■ MC . . . . CHCMC 72
Charisma / Jul '86.
■ LP . . . . CASG 1174
Charisma / Nov '86.

Twisted Ace

FIREBIRD.
Tracks: Firebird / I won't surrender.
■ 7" . . . . HEAVY 9
Heavy Metal / Nov '81.

Twisted Sister

Formed in New york in 1976, Sister took off in early '80s. Scene-stealing U.K. appearances led to hit single I am, I'm me in 1983. Highly visual act (guitarist JJ French was in early incarnation of Kiss), band became MTV favourites. However, popularity slumped and band split in '87.

COME OUT.
Tracks: Not Advised.
■ VHS . . . . HEN 2060
Hendring Video / '88.

COME OUT AND PLAY.
Tracks: Come out and play / Leader of the pack / You want what we got / I believe in rock'n'roll / Fire still burns / Be chrool to your scuel / I believe in you / Out in the street / Looking after no. 1 / Kill or be killed.
CD 781 275-
■ LP P.Disc 781275 1
■ LP 781 275-
Atlantic / Dec '85.

I AM.
Tracks: I am.
■ 7" . . . . .A 985
Atlantic / Mar '83.

I WANNA ROCK.
Tracks: I wanna rock / Burn in hell / SMF (on 12 only).
■ 12" . . . . A 9634
■ 7" . . . . .A 963
Atlantic / Oct '84.

KIDS ARE BACK, THE.
Tracks: Kids are back / Shoot 'em down.
■ 12" . . . . A 9827
■ 7" . . . . .A 982
Atlantic / May '83.

KIDS ARE BACK, THE (OLD GOLD).
Tracks: Kids are back / I am (I'm me).
7" . . . . OG 994
Old Gold / Jun '90 / Pickwick.

LEADER OF THE PACK.
Tracks: Leader of the pack / I wanna rock.
■ 12" . . . . A 9478
■ 7" . . . . .A 9478
Atlantic / Jan '86.

LIVE AT HAMMERSMITH.
Tracks: What you don't know / Kids are back / Stay hungry / Destroyer / We're not gonna take it / You can't stop rock 'n' roll / Knife in the back / Shoot 'em down / Under the blade / Burn in hell / I am I'm me / wanna rock / S.M.F. / We're gonna make it / Jail house rock / Train kept a rollin'.
CD . . . . .CDMFN 170
Music For Nations / Oct '94 / Pinnacle.

LOVE IS FOR SUCKERS.
Tracks: Wake up (the sleeping guitar) / Hot love / Love is for suckers (like me and you) / I'm so hot for you / Tonight / Me and the boys / One bad habit / want this night (to last forever) / You are all that I need / Yeah right.
CD 781 772-
■ LP . . . . WX 120
■ MC . . . . WX 120C
Atlantic / Aug '87.

PRICE.
Tracks: Price / S.M.F.
■ 12" . . . . A 9591 T
■ 7" . . . . A 9591
Atlantic / Mar '85.

RUFF CUTTS (EP).
Tracks: Not Advised.
■ 12" . . . . SHH 137 12
Secret / Jul '82.

STAY HUNGRY.
Tracks: Stay hungry / We're not gonna take it / Burn in hell / Horrorteria / I wanna rock / Price / Don't let me down / Beast / S.M.F.
■ LP 780 156-1
MC. 780 156-4
Atlantic / Jun '84 / WEA.

STAY HUNGRY.
Tracks: Not Advised.
VHS .VVD 050
Virgin Vision / Oct '84 / Gold & Sons / TBD.

TWISTED SISTER: INTERVIEW PICTURE DISC.
Tracks: Not Advised.
LP P.Disc . . . . BAK 2088
Baktabak / Apr '88 / Arabesque Ltd.

UNDER THE BLADE.
Tracks: What you don't know / Bad boys (of rock'n'-roll) / Run for your life / Sin after sin / Shoot 'em down / Destroyer / Under the blade / Tear it loose / Day of the rocker.
■ LP . . . . SECX 9
■ MC . . . . TSECX 9
Secret / Sep '82.
CD . . . . RR 349946
■ LP . . . . RR 9946
Road Runner / '88.
CD . . . . SECXCD 9
Secret / Jun '88.

WE'RE NOT GONNA TAKE IT.
Tracks: We're not gonna take it / Kids are back / You can't stop rock'n'roll (Only on 12" single.) / We're gonna make it.
- ◄ 12" . . . . A 9657 T
- ◄ 7" . . . . .A 9657
Atlantic / Jun '84.

YOU CAN'T STOP ROCK 'N' ROLL.
Tracks: Kids are back / Like a knife in the back / Ride to live, live to ride / I am (I'm me) / Power and the glory / We're gonna make it / I've had enough / I'll take you alive / You're not alone (Suzette's song) / You can't stop rock 'n' roll.
- ■ LP . . . . .A 0074
- ■ MC. . . . . .A 0074 4
Atlantic / Jun '83.

YOU CAN'T STOP ROCK 'N' ROLL.
Tracks: You can't stop rock 'n' roll / Let the good times roll.
- ■ 7" . . . . .A 9792
Atlantic / Aug '83.

YOU WANT WHAT WE GOT.
Tracks: You want what we got / Stay hungry / We're not gonna take it (12" only) / King of fools (12" only).
- ■ 7" . . . . .A 9435
- ■ 12" . . . . A 9435 T
WEA / Apr '86.

Tygers Of Pan Tang

NWOBHM graduates who peaked with 1982's *The Cage* album (U.K. no 13) and split in '87. Guitarist John Sykes joined Thin Lizzy in 1983 and Whitesnake in '86, before forming explosive Blue Murder in '88.

BEST OF TYGERS OF PAN TANG.
Tracks: Not Advised.
- ■ LP . . . . MCF 3191
MCA / Dec '83.

BURNING IN THE SHADE.
Tracks: Not Advised.
- ■ LP . . . . ZEB 10
Zebra (1) / May '87.

CAGE, THE.
Tracks: Rendezvous / Lonely at the top / Letter from L.A. / Paris by air / Tides / Making tracks / Actor / Cage / Love potion no. 9 / You always see what you want to see / Danger in paradise.
- ■ LP . . . . MCF 3150
MCA / Aug '82.
- ■ LP . . . . MCL 1797
- ■ MC . . . . MCLC 1797
MCA / Jun '84.

CRAZY NIGHTS.
Tracks: Not Advised.
- ■ LP . . . . MCF 3123
MCA / Nov '81.
- ■ LP . . . . MCL 1780
MCA / '84.

DO IT GOOD.
Tracks: Do it good / Slip away.
- ■ 7" . . . . MCA 759
MCA / Jan '82.

DON'T STOP BY.
Tracks: Don't stop by / Slave to freedom / Raised on rock (Available on 12" only).
- ■ 12" . . . . .MCAT 723
- ■ 7" . . . . MCA 723
MCA / Jun '81.

DON'T TOUCH ME THERE.
Tracks: Don't touch me there / Burning up bad times.
- ■ 7" . . . . MCA 582
MCA / Mar '80.

EUTHANASIA.
Tracks: Euthanasia / Straight as a die.
- ■ 7" . . . . MCA 644
MCA / Oct '80.

FIRST KILL.
Tracks: Not Advised.
- ■ LP . . . . NEAT 1037
Neat / Aug '86.

HELLBOUND.
Tracks: Hellbound / Don't give a damn.
- ■ 7" . . . . MCA 672
MCA / Feb '81.

LONELY AT THE TOP.
Tracks: Lonely at the top.
- ■ 7" . . . . MCA 841
MCA / Oct '83.

LOVE DON'T STAY.
Tracks: Love don't stay / Paradise drive.
- ■ 7" . . . . MCA 755
MCA / Nov '81.

LOVE POTION NO. 9.
Tracks: Love potion no. 9.
- ■ 7" . . . . MCA 769
MCA / Mar '82.

MAKING TRACKS.
Tracks: Making tracks / What you saying.
- ■ 12" . . . . .MCAT 798
- ■ 7" . . . . MCA 798
MCA / Oct '82.

PARIS BY AIR.
Tracks: Paris by air / Love's a lie.
- ■ 7" . . . . MCA 790
MCA / Sep '82.

RENDEZVOUS.
Tracks: Rendezvous.
- ■ 7" . . . . MCA 777
MCA / Jul '82.

ROCK 'N' ROLL MAN.
Tracks: Rock'n'roll man / Alright on the night / Wildcats.
- ■ 7" . . . . MCA 612
MCA / Jun '80.

SPELLBOUND.
Tracks: Gangland / Take it / Minotaur / Hellbound / Mirror / Silver & gold / Tyger Bay / Story so far / Black Jack / Don't stop by.
- ■ LP . . . . MCF 3104
MCA / Apr '81.
- ■ LP . . . . MCL 1747
- ■ MC . . . . MCLC 1747
MCA / Jun '87.
- CD . . . . REP 4015-WZ
Repertoire (Germany) / Aug '91 / Pinnacle.

STORY SO FAR.
Tracks: Story so far / Silver & gold / All or nothing.
- ■ EP . . . . MCA 692
MCA / Mar '81.

SUZIE SMILED.
Tracks: Suzie smiled / Tush.
- ■ 7" . . . . MCA 634
MCA / Aug '80.

WILD CAT.
Tracks: Euthanasia / Slave to freedom / Don't touch me there / Money / Killers / Fireclown / Wild cat / Badger badger / Insanity.
- ■ LP . . . . MCF 3075
MCA / Aug '80.
- ■ LP . . . . FA 3063
- MC. . . . . TCFA 3063
Fame / May '83 / EMI.
- ■ LP . . . . MCL 1610
- ■ MC . . . . MCLC 1610
MCA / Sep '86.
- CD . . . . REP 4014-WZ
Repertoire (Germany) / Aug '91 / Pinnacle.

WRECK-AGE, THE.
Tracks: Not Advised.
- MC. . . . . TMFN 50
- ■ LP . . . . MFN 50
Music For Nations / Jun '85.

Tynator

LIVING IN PAIN.
Tracks: Not Advised.
- LP . . . . CCG 003
C.C.G. Underground / Jan '90 / Backs Distribution.
- CD. . . . . .CCGCD 003
C.C.G. Underground / Mar '90 / Backs Distribution.

Tyran' Pace

LONG LIVE METAL.
Tracks: Not Advised.
- ■ LP . . . . .N 0027
Noise / '88.

WATCHING YOU.
Tracks: Not Advised.
- ■ LP . . . . .N 0055
Noise / '89.

Tyrant

BLIND REVOLUTION.
Tracks: Not Advised.
- CD. 15 199
- MC. 79 073
Laserlight / Aug '91 / TBD / BMG / Target.

FIGHT FOR YOUR LIFE.
Tracks: Not Advised.
- ■ LP 934308
Powerstation / Jul '86.

LEGIONS OF THE DEAD.
Tracks: Not Advised.
- ■ LP . . . . RR 9765
Road Runner / Aug '85.

MEAN MACHINE.
Tracks: Not Advised.
- ■ LP . . . . .SKULL 8366
Mausoleum / Mar '85.

METAL RULES.
Tracks: Not Advised.
- CD. 15 393
- MC. 79 393
Laserlight / Aug '91 / TBD / BMG / Target.

RUNNING HOT.
Tracks: Rock your bottom / Breakout / Taste of paradise / When the raven flies again / Running hot / Fire at sea / Take the most dangerous way / Get ready / She's a killer / Starlight.
- ■ LP 805 072
Powerstation / Mar '87.

TOO LATE TO PRAY.
Tracks: Tyrants revelation II / Too late to pray / Beyond the grave / Valley of death / Nazarene / Bells of Hades / Into the flames / Babylon / Verdalack / Beginning of the end / Eve of destruction.
- ■ LP . . . . RR 9658
Road Runner / Feb '88.

Tytan

BLIND MEN AND FOOLS.
Tracks: Blind men and fools / Ballad of Edward Case.
- ■ 12" . . . . .KAMA 6
- ■ 7" . . . . .KAM 6
Kamaflage / Sep '82.

ROUGH JUSTICE.
Tracks: Blind men and fools / Money for love / Women on thr frontline / Cold bitch / Ballad of Edward Case / Rude awakening / Watcher / Far cry / Sadman / Forever gone / Don't play their way / Far side of destiny.
- ■ LP . . . . METALP 105
Razor / Aug '85.

U

UDO

ANIMAL HOUSE.
Tracks: Animal house / Go back to Hell / They want war / Black widow / In the darkness / Lay down the law / We want it loud / Warrior / Coming home / Run or cover.
- MC . . . . PK 71552
- LP . . . . PL 71552

RCA / Mar '88.

FACELESS WORLD.
Tracks: Heart of gold / Blitz of lightning / System of life / Faceless world / Stranger / Restricted area / Living on a frontline / Trip to nowhere / Born to run / Can't get enough / Unspoken words / Future land.
- CD . . . . PD 74510
- LP . . . . PL 74510
- MC . . . . PK 74510

RCA / Apr '90.

MEAN MACHINE.
Tracks: Don't look back / Break the rules / We're history / Painted love / Mean machine / Dirty boys / Streets on fire / Lost passion / Sweet little child / Catch my fall / Still in love with you.
- LP . . . . PL 71994
- CD . . . . PD 71994
- MC . . . . PK 71994

RCA / Apr '89.

TIMEBOMB.
Tracks: Gutter, The (instrumental) / Metal eater / Thunderforce / Overloaded (instrumental) / Burning heat / Back in pain / Timebomb / Powersquad / Kick in the face / Soldiers of darkness / Metal maniac master mind.
- CD . . . . PD 74953
- LP . . . . PL 74953
- MC . . . . PK 74953

RCA / May '91.

UFO

UK band formed in 1969. Early, progressive style won fans in Europe and Japan; domestic and American success followed switch to melodic hard rock. Most popular incarnation featured vocalist Phil Mogg, bassist Pete Way, drummer Andy Parker and guitarists Paul Chapman and Michael Schenker; the line-up behind classic live album *Strangers In The Night*. Departure of Schenker, first for Scorpions, then Michael Schenker Group, began round of personnel changes; band disintegrated in 1983. Mogg revived name in 1985, and subsequent re-formations reunited him with Way. A major act in '70s, UFO are now virtually forgotten outside hardcore of fans (and writers who gleefully detailed band's excesses).

AIN'T MISBEHAVIN'.
Tracks: (Between a) rock and a hard place / Another Saturday night / At war with the world / Hunger in the night / Easy money / Rock boyz, rock / Lonely cities (of the heart) (Extra track on CD.).
- CD . . . . WKFMXD 107
- LP . . . . WKFMLP 107
- MC . . . . WKFMMC 107

FM Records / Mar '88.
- LP P.Disc . . . . WKFMHP 107

FM Records / Jan '89.

ALONE AGAIN.
Tracks: Alone again or.
- 7" . . . . CHS 2146

Chrysalis / May '77.

ANTHOLOGY.
Tracks: Rock bottom / Built for comfort / Highway lady / Can you roll her / Fool for love / Shoot shoot / Too hot to handle / Gettin' ready / Only you can rock me / Lookin' for No.1 / Hot 'n ready / Mystery train / No place to run / Profession of violence / Chains chains / Something else / Doing it for all of you / When it's time to rock / Diesel in the dust.
- CD . . . . CCSCD 316

Castle / Jan '94.

ANTHOLOGY - UFO.
Tracks: Rock bottom / Built for comfort / Highway lady / Can you roll her / Fool for love / Shoot shoot /

Too hot to handle / Gettin' ready / Only you can rock me / Looking for number one / Hot 'n' ready / Mystery train / No place to run / Profession and violence / Chains chains / Something else / Doing it for all of you / When it's time to rock / Diesel in the dust.
- LP . . . . RAWLP 029
- MC . . . . RAWTC 029
- CD . . . . RAWCD 029

Raw Power / Mar '87.

BACK INTO MY LIFE.
Tracks: Back into my life / Writer.
- 7" . . . . CHS 2607
- 7" P.Disc . . . . CHSP 2607

Chrysalis / Apr '82.

BBC LIVE IN CONCERT - UFO.
Tracks: Not Advised.
- CD . . . . WINCD 016

Windsong / Apr '92 / Pinnacle / A.D.A. Distribution.

C'MON EVERYBODY.
Tracks: Not Advised.
- LP 6.24836

Teldec (1) / Dec '81.

COLLECTION: UFO.
Tracks: Flying / Silver bird / Starstorm / Unidentified flying object / Shake it about / Timothy / Evil / (Come away) Melinda / Follow you home / Treacle people / C'mon everybody (live) / Who do you love (live) / Prince Kajuku (coming of Prince Kajuku).
- Double LP . . . . CCSLP 101
- MC . . . . CCSMC 101

Castle Collector Series / Nov '85.

COULDN'T GET IT RIGHT.
Tracks: Couldn't get it right / Hot 'n' ready.
- 7" . . . . CHS 2454

Chrysalis / Oct '80.

DOCTOR DOCTOR.
Tracks: Doctor doctor / On with the action / Try me.
- 7" . . . . CHS 2287

Chrysalis / Jan '79.

EARLY YEARS.
Tracks: Unidentified flying object / C'mon everybody / Shake it about / Timothy / Who do you love / Evil silver bird / Coming of Prince Kajuku / Loving cup (Live) / Boogie for George (Live).
- CD . . . . EARLD 9

BMG / Nov '92 / BMG.

ESSENTIAL UFO.
Tracks: Doctor doctor / Rock bottom / Out in the street / Mother Mary / Natural thing / I'm a loser / Only you can rock me / Lookin' out for No 1 / Cherry / Born to lose / Too hot to handle / Lights out / Love to love / This kids / Let it roll / Shoot shoot.
- CD . . . . CDCHR 1888
- MC . . . . TCCHR 1888

Chrysalis / Oct '92.

FORCE IT.
Tracks: Let it roll / Shoot shoot / High flyer / Love lost love / Out in the street / Mother Mary / Too much of nothing / Dance your life away / This kid's.
- LP . . . . CHR 1074
- MC . . . . ZCHR 1074

Chrysalis / '83.

HEADSTONE - THE BEST OF UFO.
Tracks: Doctor doctor / Rock bottom / Fool for your loving / Shoot shoot / Too hot to handle / Only you can rock me / Love drive / She said she said / Lights out / Armed and ready / Young blood / Criminal tendencies / Lonely heart / We belong to the night / Let it rain / Couldn't get it right / Electric phase / Doing it all for you.
- Double LP . . . . CTY 1437
- MC . . . . ZCTY 1437

Chrysalis / Aug '83.

LET IT RAIN.
Tracks: Let it rain / Heel of a stranger / You get love.
- 12" . . . . CHS 122576

Chrysalis / Feb '82.
- 7" . . . . CHS 2576

Chrysalis / Feb '82.

LIGHTS OUT.
Tracks: Too hot to handle / Just another suicide / Try me / Lights out / Gettin' ready / Alone again or / Electric phase / Love to love.
- LP . . . . CHR 1127
- MC . . . . ZCHR 1127

Chrysalis / Aug '77.
- CD . . . . ACCD 1127

Chrysalis / '87 / EMI.
- CD . . . . LUSCD 9

Razor / Jul '91.

LIGHTS OUT IN TOKYO-LIVE.
Tracks: Not Advised.
- CD . . . . VICP 5204

Trident / Nov '92 / Pinnacle.
- CD . . . . ESSCD 191

Castle / Apr '93 / BMG.

LONELY HEARTS.
Tracks: Lonely heart / Long gone.
- 7" . . . . CHS 2482

Chrysalis / Jan '81.

MAKING CONTACT.
Tracks: Blinded by a lie / Diesel in the dust / Fool for love / You and me / When it's time to rock / Way the wild wind blows / Call my name / All over you / No getaway / Push / It's love.
- MC . . . . ZCHR 1402
- LP . . . . CHR 1402

Chrysalis / Jan '83.

MECHANIX.
Tracks: Writer / Something else / Back into my life / You'll get love / Doing it all for you / We belong to the night / Let it rain / Terri / Feel it / Dreaming.
- LP . . . . CHR 1360
- MC . . . . ZCHR 1360

Chrysalis / Feb '82 / EMI.

MECHANIX / LIGHTS OUT.
Tracks: Not Advised.
- MC Set . . . . ZCDP 107

Chrysalis / Dec '82 / EMI.

MISDEMEANOR.
Tracks: This time / One heart / Meanstreets / Name of love / Blue / Dream the dream / Heaven's gate / Wreckless.
- LP . . . . CHR 1518
- MC . . . . ZCHR 1518

Chrysalis / Nov '85 / EMI.

MISDEMEANOR.
Tracks: Heaven's gate / Chase / This time / Meanstreets / Name of love / Only ones / Wreckless / Night run / Only you can rock me / Doctor doctor.
- VHS . . . . HEN 2332

Hendring Video / Apr '91.

NO HEAVY PETTING.
Tracks: Natural thing / I'm a loser / Can you roll her / Belladonna / Reasons love / Highway / On with the action / Fool in love / Martian landscape.
- LP . . . . CHR 1103
- MC . . . . ZCHR 1103

Chrysalis / May '76.

NO HEAVY PETTING/LIGHTS OUT.
Tracks: Natural thing / I'm a loser / Can you roll her / Belladonna / Reasons love / Highway lady / On with the action / Fool in love / Martian landscape / Too hot to handle / Just another suicide / Try me / Lights out / Gettin' ready / Alone again or / Electric phase / Love to love.
- CD . . . . BGOCD 228

Beat Goes On / Aug '94 / Pinnacle.

NO PLACE TO RUN.
Tracks: Alp-ha Centauri / Letting go / Mystery train / This fire burns tonight / Gone in the night / Young blood / No place to run / Take it or leave it / Money money / Anyday.
- LP . . . . CHR 1239
- MC . . . . ZCHR 1239

Chrysalis / Jan '80 / EMI.

OBSESSION/NO PLACE TO RUN.
Tracks: Only you can rock me / Pack it up (and go) / Arbory hill / Ain't no baby / Lookin' out for No.1 / Hot 'n' ready / Cherry / You don't fool me / Lookin' out for No.1 (Reprise) / One more for the rodeo / Born to

lose / Alpha centauri / Lettin' go / Mystery train / This fire burns tonight / Gone in the night / Young blood / No place to run / Take it or leave it / Money, money / Any day.
CD.....................BGOCD 229
Beat Goes On / May '94 / Pinnacle.

OBSESSIONS.
Tracks: Only you can rock me / Pack it up (and go) / Arbory Hill / Ain't no baby / Looking after no. 1 / Hot 'n' ready / Cherry / You don't fool me / One more for the rodeo / Born to lose.
■ MC.....................ZCDL 1182
■ LP.....................CDL 1182
Chrysalis / Jun '78.
CD.....................LUSCD 11
Razor / Sep '91 / Grapevine Distribution.

PHENOMENON.
Tracks: Oh my / Crystal light / Doctor doctor / Space child / Rock bottom / Too young to know / Time on my hands / Built for comfort / Lipstick traces / Queen of the deep.
■ LP.....................CHR 1059
■ MC.....................ZCHR 1059
Chrysalis / '74.
CD.....................LUSCD 10
Episode / Aug '91 / Grapevine Distribution.

SHOOT SHOOT.
Tracks: Shoot shoot / Only you can rock me / I'm a loser.
■ 7".....................CHS 2318
Chrysalis / Mar '79.

SPACE METAL.
Tracks: Not Advised.
■ LP.....................6 28363
Teldec (1) / Jan '85.
CD.....................GACD 900704
Line / Sep '89 / C.M. Distribution / Grapevine Distribution / A.D.A. Distribution / Conifer Records.

STRANGERS IN THE NIGHT.
Tracks: Natural thing / Out in the street / Only you can rock me / Doctor doctor / Mother Mary / This kid's / Love to love / Lights out / Rock bottom / Too hot to handle / I'm a loser / Let it roll / Shoot shoot.
■ Double LP.....................CJT 5
■ MC Set.....................ZCJT 5
Chrysalis / '79.
CD.....................CCD 1209
Chrysalis / Sep '91 / EMI.
CD.....................CD25CR 22
Chrysalis / Mar '94 / EMI.

THIS TIME.
Tracks: This time / Chase.
■ 12".....................UFOX 1
■ 7".....................UFO 1
Chrysalis / Oct '85.

TOO HOT TO HANDLE - THE BEST OF UFO.
Tracks: Only uou can rock me (Live) / Too hot to handle / Long gone / Profession of violence / We belong to the night (live) / Let it rain (Live) / Lonely heart / This time / Lettin' go / Light's out (live) / Natural thing / Blinded by a lie / Wreckless / When it's time to rock / Shoot shoot / Young blood / Let it roll / Doctor doctor (Live).
CD.....................MCCD 153
MC.....................MCTC 153
Music Club / Feb '94 / Gold & Sons / TBD / Video Collection / C.M. Distribution.

UFO 1.
Tracks: Not Advised.
CD.....................GACD 900691
Line / Apr '91 / C.M. Distribution / Grapevine Distribution / A.D.A. Distribution / Conifer Records.

UFO 2 FLYING.
Tracks: Not Advised.
CD.....................GACD 900694
Line / Jun '91 / C.M. Distribution / Grapevine Distribution / A.D.A. Distribution / Conifer Records.

UFO TOO HOT TO HANDLE: THE STORY OF UFO.
Tracks: This kids / Out in the street / Shoot shoot / Come on everybody / Love to love / Doctor doctor / Lettin' go / Mystery train / Lights out / Too hot to handle / Rock bottom / Let it roll / Coming of Prince Kujuku / Borderline / Running up the highway / Backdoor man.
■ VHS.....................CMP 6085
Castle / Nov '92.

WHEN IT'S TIME TO ROCK.
Tracks: When it's time to rock / Everybody knows / Push, it's love (Only on 12" version).
■ 12".....................CHS 122672

■ 7".....................CHS 2672
Chrysalis / Mar '83.

WILD, THE WILLING AND THE INNOCENT, THE.
Tracks: Chains chains / Long gone / Wild, the willing and the innocent / It's killing me / Makin' moves / Lonely heart / Couldn't get it right / Profession of violence.
MC.....................ZCHR 1307
■ LP.....................CHR 1307
Chrysalis / Jan '81.

WILD, THE WILLING AND THE INNOCENT/MECHANIX.
Tracks: Chains chains / Long gone / Wild, the willing and the innocent / It's killing me / Makin' moves / Lonely heart / Couldn't get it right / Profession of violence / Writer / Somethin' else / Back into my life / You'll get love / Doing it all for you / We belong to the night / Let it rain / Terri / Feel it / Dreaming.
CD.....................BGOCD 230
Beat Goes On / Sep '94 / Pinnacle.

YOU CAN ROCK ME.
Tracks: You can rock me.
■ 7".....................CHS 2241
Chrysalis / Jul '76.

YOUNG BLOOD.
Tracks: Young blood / Lights out.
■ 7".....................CHS 2399
Chrysalis / Jan '80.

Ugly Kid Joe

Tongue-in-cheek U.S. quartet best known for 1992 Top Three hit *Everything About You*. Group's two 1992 albums made unexpectedly good showing in U.K. charts, to which they returned in 1993 with cover of Harry Chapin's *Cats In The Cradle*.

AMERICA'S LEAST WANTED.
Tracks: Neighbor / Goddamn devil / Come tomorrow / Panhandlin prince / Busy bee / Don't go / So damn cool / Same side / Cat's in the cradle / I'll keep tryin' / Everything about you' / Madman ('92 Re-mix) / Mr. Record man.
CD.....................512 571-2
MC.....................512 571-4
■ LP.....................512 571-1
Mercury / '92.
DCC.....................512 571-5
Mercury / Jan '93 / PolyGram.

AS UGLY AS THEY WANNA BE.
Tracks: Madman / Whiplash / Too bad / Everything about you / Sweet leaf / Funky fresh country club / Heavy metal.
CD.....................8688232
MC.....................8688234
■ LP.....................8688231
Mercury / May '92.

BUSY BEE.
Tracks: Busy bee.
■ 7".....................MER 389
■ CD Single.....................MERCD 389
■ MC Single.....................MERMC 389
Mercury / Jun '93.

CATS IN THE CRADLE.
Tracks: Cats in the cradle.
■ 12".....................MERX 385
■ 7".....................MER 385
■ CD Single.....................MERCD 385
■ MC Single.....................MERMC 385
Mercury / Mar '93.

EVERYTHING ABOUT YOU.
Tracks: Everything about you / Whiplash liquor / Sin city (live) (Only available on 12" and CD Single.).
■ 12".....................MERX 367
■ 7".....................MER 367
■ CD Single.....................MERCD 367
■ MC Single.....................MERMC 367
Mercury / May '92.

NEIGHBOUR.
Tracks: Neighbour.
■ CD Single.....................MERMD 374
■ MC Single.....................MERMC 374
■ 12".....................MERX 374
■ 7".....................MER 374
Mercury / Sep '92.

Ultraviolence

I, DESTRUCTOR E.P.
Tracks: I, destructor / Zeus / Treason.
■ 12".....................MOSH 102V
■ CD Single.....................MOSH 102CD
Earache / Oct '93.

I, DESTRUCTOR E.P. - THE MIXES.
Tracks: I, destructor (mixes).
■ 12".....................MOSH 102TF
Earache / Mar '94 / Vital Distribution.

LIFE OF DESTRUCTOR.
Tracks: I am destructor / Electric chair / Joan / Hardcore motherfucker / Digital killing / Only love / We will break / Hiroshima / Destructor's fall / Death of a child.
■ CD.....................MOSH 103CD
LP.....................MOSH 103
Earache / Jun '94 / Vital Distribution.

Uncle Sam

FOURTEEN WOMEN.
Tracks: Not Advised.
CD.....................CMGCD 010
Communique / Nov '93 / Plastic Head.

HEAVEN OR HOLLYWOOD.
Tracks: Live for the day / Don't be shy / Alice D / No reason why / Candy man / Don't you ever / All alone / Peace of mind, piece of body / Under sedation / Heaven or Hollywood / Steppin stone / Train kept a rollin'.
CD.....................RAZCD 38
■ LP.....................RAZ 40
Razor / Oct '88.
CD.....................3MC3
Skeller / Nov '90 / Pinnacle.

PRETTY WOMAN.
Tracks: Pretty woman / Do it for love.
■ 7".....................ARO 116
Ariola / Feb '78.

WHISKEY SLICK.
Tracks: Whiskey slick.
■ 12".....................3MT 12
Skeller / Dec '90.

WILL WORK FOR FOOD.
Tracks: Not Advised.
■ CD.....................RR 90802
Road Runner / Mar '93.

Underdog

RABIES IN TOWN.
Tracks: Not Advised.
■ LP.....................SKULL 8331
Mausoleum / Oct '84.

UNDERDOG.
Tracks: Lightnin' fever / Night shock / Shut up you dudes / No way to lose / Burnin' eyes / Damned man alive / Red alert / Speed attack / Hammer my nail into you / Underdog / Shout it out together.
■ LP.....................THBL 005
Thunderbolt / Nov '83.

Unholy

SECOND RING OF POWER, THE.
Tracks: Not Advised.
CD.....................CDAV 005
Avant / Aug '94 / Harmonia Mundi (UK) / A.D.A. Distribution.

Union Carbide

IN THE AIR TONIGHT.
Tracks: Not Advised.
■ LP.....................CALCLP 056
Ediesta / Sep '88.

SWING (Union Carbide Productions).
Tracks: Not Advised.
■ CD.....................RA 91362
Road Runner / Nov '92.

United Mutations

FREAKS OUT.
Tracks: Not Advised.
■ LP.....................BC 1659
Bitzcore / '88.

GOTTERDAMMERUNG.
Tracks: Gotterdammerung.
■ 7".....................LF 028
Lost & Found / Apr '92.

■ DELETED

Unjust

HAMMERHEAD.
Tracks: Not Advised.
■ LP . . . . BCR 11
Big City / Oct '87.

Unleashed

ACROSS THE OPEN SEA.
Tracks: Not Advised.
CD . . . . CM 77055-2
LP . . . . CM 77055-1
MC . . . . CM 77055-4
Century Media / Nov '93 / Plastic Head.

LIVE IN VIENNA.
Tracks: Not Advised.
CD . . . . CM 77056
Century Media / Jan '94 / Plastic Head.

SHADOWS IN THE DEEP.
Tracks: Not Advised.
LP . . . . CM 7732
Century Media / Aug '92 / Plastic Head.

WHERE NO LIFE DWELLS.
Tracks: Not Advised.
CD . . . . CM 9718CD
LP . . . . CM 9718
MC . . . . CM 9718MC
Century Media / '92 / Plastic Head.

Unleashed Power

QUINTET OF SPHERES.
Tracks: Not Advised.
CD . . . . RS 101
S.O.R.T. / Nov '93 / Plastic Head.

Unorthodox

ASYLUM.
Tracks: Not Advised.
CD . . . . .HELL 0021CD
Hellhound / '90 / Plastic Head.

BALANCE OF POWER.
Tracks: Not Advised.
CD . . . . .HELL 0030CD
Hellhound / Apr '94 / Plastic Head.

Unseen Terror

HUMAN ERROR.
Tracks: Not Advised.
■ LP . . . . .MOSH 4
Earache / Dec '87.

PEEL SESSIONS: UNSEEN TERROR (22.3.88).
Tracks: Incompatible / Burned beyond recognition / Oblivion descends / Divivions / Voice your opinion / Strong enough to change / Odie's revenge / It's my life.
■ 12" . . . . SFPS 069
Strange Fruit / Feb '89.

Urge Overkill

Chicago trio best known for Cheap Trick fixation and endorsement of Pretenders' Chrissie Hynde; latter collaborated with them, as Superfan, on Wayne's World 2 soundtrack. Garage sound developed over three independent albums; Geffen debut Saturation in '93 offered more polished version of noisy formula.

AMERICRUISER.
Tracks: Not Advised.
LP . . . . .TGLP 52
Touch & Go / Jun '90 / SRD.

JESUS URGE SUPERSTAR.
Tracks: Not Advised.
LP . . . . .TGLP 37
Touch & Go / May '89 / SRD.

POSITIVE BLEEDING.
Tracks: Not Advised.
■ 12" . . . . .GFST 57
■ 7" . . . . GFS 57
■ CD Single . . . . .GFSTD 57
■ MC Single. . . . . .GFSC 57
Geffen / Oct '93.

SATURATION.
Tracks: Sister Havana / Tequila sundae / Positive bleeding / Back on me / Woman 2 woman / Bottle of

fur / Crackbabies / Stalker / Dropout / Erica Kane / Nite and grey / Heaven 90210.
CD . . . . GED 24529
MC . . . . GEC 24529
■ LP . . . . GEF 24529
Geffen / Jun '93.

SISTER HAVANA.
Tracks: Sister Havana.
■ 12" . . . . .GFST 51
■ 7" . . . . GFS 51
■ CD Single . . . . .GFSTD 51
■ MC Single. . . . . .GFSC 51
Geffen / Aug '93.

STULL (EP).
Tracks: Not Advised.
CD . . . . NECKMCD 009
LP . . . . NECKMLP 009
Roughneck / Jun '92 / Pinnacle / RTM.

Uriah Heep

UK group formed in 1969 by guitarist Mick Box. Overcame critical derision to win U.K. and U.S. success; peaking with 1975 Top 10 album Return To Fantasy. Band underwent crippling personnel changes in late '70s: among those to pass through ranks were John Wetton (later of Asia) and ex-Spider From Mars Trevor Bolder. Most serious loss was songwriter Ken Hensley, who left in early '80s, later joining Blackfoot. Rejuvenated by early '80s metal boom, Heep scored handful of hit albums after years in chart wilderness, to which they have since returned. Box is sole remnant of original line-up.

ABOMINOG.
Tracks: Too scared to run / Chasing shadows / On the rebound / Hot night in a cold town / That's the way it is / Prisoner sell your soul / Hot persuasion / Think it over / Running all night (with the lion).
■ LP . . . . .BRON 538
Bronze / Mar '82.
■ LP . . . . .CLALP 110
■ MC . . . . .CLAMC 110
Castle Classics / Apr '86.
CD . . . . .CLACD 110
Castle Classics / Nov '86 / BMG / Castle Communications.

ABOMINOG JUNIOR.
Tracks: Not Advised.
■ EP . . . . BRO 143
Bronze / Mar '82.

ANTHOLOGY - URIAH HEEP.
Tracks: Gypsy / Bird of prey / Lady in black / Look at yourself / Salisbury / Love machine / Easy livin' / Wizard / Sweet Lorraine / Magician's birthday / Come back to me / Free me / Fools / Too scared to run / Think it over.
■ Double LP . . . . .RAWLP 012
MC . . . . .RAWTC 012
■ CD . . . . .RAWCD 012
Raw Power / Apr '86.

BEST OF URIAH HEEP.
Tracks: Gypsy / Bird of prey / July morning / Look at yourself / Easy livin / Wizard / Sweet Lorraine / Stealin' / Suicidal man / Return to fantasy.
■ LP . . . . .BRON 375
Bronze / Apr '77.
CD 610 358
Starr / '88 / PolyGram.

BLOOD RED ROSES.
Tracks: Blood red roses / Rough justice / Look at yourself (12" only).
■ 12" . . . . .LGYT 101
■ 7" . . . . .LGY 101
Legacy / Jul '89.

CARRY ON.
Tracks: Carry on / Been hurt.
■ 7" . . . . BRO 88
Bronze / Jan '80.

COLLECTION: URIAH HEEP.
Tracks: Love machine / Look at yourself / Firefly / Return to fantasy / Rainbow demon / That's the way it is / Love is blind / On the rebound / Easy livin' / July morning / Running all night (with the lion) / Been away too long / Gypsy / Wake up (set your sights) / Can't keep a good band down / All of my life.
■ Double LP . . . . .CCSLP 177
■ MC . . . . .CCSMC 177
Castle Collector Series / '88.
■ LP . . . . LLM 3019
Legacy / Feb '89.
CD . . . . .CCSCD 226

■ Double LP. . . . . CCSLP 226
■ MC . . . . .CCSMC 226
Castle Collector Series / Jul '89.

COME BACK TO ME.
Tracks: Come back to me / Cheater.
■ 7" . . . . BRO 62
Bronze / Oct '78.

CONQUEST.
Tracks: Carry on / Feelings / Fools / Imagination / It ain't easy / No return / Out on the street / Won't have to wait too long.
■ LP . . . . .BRON 524
Bronze / Feb '80.

DEMONS AND WIZARDS.
Tracks: Wizard / Traveller in time / Easy loving / Poet's justice / Circle of hands / Rainbow demon / All my life / Paradise / Spell.
■ LP . . . . ILPS 9193
Bronze / Jun '72.
■ LP . . . . .BRNA 193
Bronze / Apr '77.
■ LP . . . . .CLALP 108
Castle Classics / Apr '86.
CD . . . . .CLACD 108
■ MC . . . . .CLAMC 108
Castle Classics / Apr '86.

DIFFERENT WORLD.
Tracks: Not Advised.
CD . . . . .LCD 137
■ LP . . . . .LLP 137
MC. . . . . .LK 137
Legacy / Feb '91 / Sony.
CD . . . . .CLACD 279
Castle / Feb '93 / BMG.

EASY LIVIN'.
Tracks: Easy livin' / Corina, Corina / Gypsy (Only on 12").
■ 12" . . . . .LGYT 65
■ 7" . . . . LGY 65
Legacy / Sep '88.

EASY LIVIN'.
Tracks: Not Advised.
VHS . . . . .VVD 081
Virgin Vision / '88 / Gold & Sons / TBD.

EASY LIVIN'.
Tracks: Not Advised.
■ CD 291004
Ariola Express / Nov '92.

ECHOES IN THE DARK.
Tracks: Echoes in the dark / Wizard / Come away Melinda / Devil's daughter / Hot persuasion / Showdown / I'm alive / Look at yourself / Spider woman / Woman of the night / I want to be free / Gypsy / Sunrise / Bird of prey / Love machine / Lady in black.
MC . . . . ELITE 020 MC
Pickwick / Oct '91 / Pickwick.
CD . . . . .ELITE 020 CD
Pickwick / Aug '93 / Pickwick.

EQUATOR.
Tracks: Rockarama / Bad blood / Lost one love / Angel / Holding on / Party time / Poor little rich girl / Skool's burning / Heartache city / Night of the wolf.
■ LP . . . . PRT 26414
Portrait / Mar '85.

FALLEN ANGEL.
Tracks: Woman of the night / Falling in love / One more night / Last farewell / Put your lovin' on me / Come back to me / Whad'ya say / Save it / Love or nothing / I'm alive / Fallen angel.
■ LP . . . . .BRNA 512
Bronze / Sep '78.
CD . . . . .CLACD 176
■ LP . . . . .CLALP 176
■ MC . . . . .CLAMC 176
Castle Classics / Feb '90.

FIREFLY.
Tracks: Hanging tree / Been away too long / Who needs me / Wise man / Do you know / Rollin on / Sympathy.
■ LP . . . . .BRNA 483
Bronze / Apr '77.
CD . . . . .CLACD 190
■ LP . . . . .CLALP 190
Castle Classics / Mar '91.

GYPSY.
Tracks: Not Advised.
■ VHS . . . . .COL 1051
Castle Collector Series / Jun '92.

GYPSY.
Tracks: Not Advised.
■ VHS . . . . HEN 2265
Hendring Video / Aug '90.

HEAD FIRST.
Tracks: Other side of midnight / Stay on top / Lonely nights / Sweet talk / Love is blind / Roof-overture / Red light / Rollin' the rock / String through the heart / Weekend warriors.
■ LP . . . . BRON 545
MC . . . . BRONC 545
Bronze / May '83 / WEA.
CD . . . . CLACD 208
■ LP . . . . CLALP 208
Castle Classics / Dec '90.

HIGH AND MIGHTY.
Tracks: One way or another / Weep in silence / Misty eyes / Midnight / Can't keep a good band down / Woman of the world / Footprints in the snow / Can't stop singing / Make a little love / Confession.
■ LP . . . . ILPS 9384
Island / Jun '76.
■ LP . . . . BRNA 384
Bronze / Apr '77.
CD . . . . CLACD 191
■ LP . . . . CLALP 191
Castle Classics / Mar '91.

HOLD YOUR HEAD UP.
Tracks: Hold your head up.
■ 12" . . . . LGYT 67
■ 7" . . . . LGY 67
Legacy / Apr '89.

INNOCENT VICTIM.
Tracks: Keep on ridind / Flyin' high / Roller / Free 'n' easy / Illusion / Free me / Cheat and lie / Dance / Choice.
■ LP . . . . BRON 504
Bronze / '77.
CD . . . . CLACD 210
■ LP . . . . CLALP 210
Castle Classics / Jan '90.

LANSDOWNE TAPES.
Tracks: Born in a trunk / Simon the bullet freak / Here I am / Magic lantern / Why / Astranaz / What's within my heart / What should be done / Lucy blues / I want you babe / Celebrate / Schoolgirl / Born in a trunk (instrumental version) / Look at yourself.
CD . . . . RPM 115
RPM / Jul '93 / Pinnacle.

LIVE 1973.
Tracks: Sunrise / Sweete Lorraine / Traveller in time / Easy livin' / July morning / Tears in my eyes / Gypsy / Circle of hands / Look at yourself / Magician's birthday / Love machine / Rock 'n' roll medley.
CD . . . . CCSCD 317
Castle / Oct '91 / BMG.

LIVE AT SHEPPERTON '74.
Tracks: Easy loving / So tired / I won't mind / Something or nothing / Stealin' / Love machine / Easy road / Rock'n'roll medley.
CD . . . . HEEPCD 1
■ LP . . . . HEEPLP 1
MC . . . . HEEPTC 1
Castle / Dec '88 / BMG.

LIVE IN EUROPE,1979.
Tracks: Easy livin' / Look at yourself / Lady in black / Free me / Stealin' / Wizard / July morning / Falling in love / Woman of the night / I'm alive / Who needs me / Sweet Lorraine / Free'n'easy / Gypsy.
CD . . . . RAWCD 030
Raw Power / '87 / Pinnacle.
■ LP . . . . RAWLP 030
MC . . . . RAWTC 030
Raw Power / Mar '87 / Pinnacle.

LIVE IN MOSCOW (Cam B Mockbe).
Tracks: Not Advised.
■ CD . . . . LLCD 118
■ LP . . . . LLP 118
■ MC . . . . LLK 118
Legacy / Jul '88.

LIVE LEGENDS.
Tracks: Not Advised.
■ VHS . . . . CMP 6002
Castle Music Pictures / Aug '90.

LIVE: URIAH HEEP.
Tracks: Sunrise / Sweet Lorraine / Traveller in time / Easy livin' / July morning / Tears in my eyes / Gypsy / Circle of hands / Look at yourself / Magician's birthday / Love machine / Rock and roll medley / Roll over Beethoven / Blue suede shoes / Mean woman blues / Hound dog / At the hop / Whole lotta shakin' goin' on.

■ Double LP . . . . BRSP 1
Bronze / Apr '77.

LONELY NIGHTS.
Tracks: Lonely nights / Weekend warriors.
■ 12" P.Disc . . . . BROP 166
■ 7" . . . . BRO 166
Bronze / Jun '83.

LOOK AT YOURSELF.
Tracks: Look at yourself / I wanna be free / July morning / Tears in my eyes / Shadows of grief / What should be done / Love machine.
■ LP . . . . ILPS 9169
Island / Nov '71.
■ LP . . . . CLALP 107
■ MC . . . . CLAMC 107
Castle Classics / Apr '86.
CD . . . . CLACD 107
Castle Classics / Apr '89 / BMG / Castle Communications.

LOOK AT YOURSELF/VERY 'EAVY, VERY 'UMBLE.
Tracks: Look at yourself / I wanna be free / July morning / Tears in my eyes / Shadows of grief / What should be done / Love machine / Gypsy / Walking in your shadow / Come away Melinda / Lucy blues / Dreammare / Real turned on / I'll keep on trying / Wake up (set your sights).
■ CD Set . . . . TFOCD 7
■ MC . . . . TFOMC 7
That's Original / Mar '88.
■ Double LP . . . . TFOLP 7
That's Original / Feb '89.

LOVE STEALER.
Tracks: Love stealer / No return.
■ 7" . . . . BRO 96
Bronze / Jun '80.

MAGICIAN'S BIRTHDAY, THE.
Tracks: Sunrise / Spider woman / Blind woman / Echoes in the dark / Rain / Sweet Lorraine / Tales / Magician's birthday.
■ LP . . . . ILPS 9213
Bronze / Dec '72.
■ LP . . . . BRNA 213
Bronze / Jul '77.
■ LP . . . . CLALP 109
Castle Classics / Apr '86.
CD . . . . CLACD 109
■ MC . . . . CLAMC 109
Castle Classics / '88.

ON THE REBOUND.
Tracks: On the rebound.
■ 7" . . . . BRO 142
Bronze / Feb '82.

POOR LITTLE RICH GIRL.
Tracks: Poor little rich girl / Bad blood.
■ 7" . . . . A 6309
CBS / May '85.

PRIMA DONNA.
Tracks: Prima donna / Shout it out.
■ 7" . . . . BRO 17
Bronze / Jun '75.

RAGING SILENCE.
Tracks: Not Advised.
■ LP P.Disc . . . . LLPPD 120
Legacy / Aug '89.
■ CD . . . . LLCD 120
■ LP . . . . LLP 120
■ MC . . . . LLK 120
Legacy / May '89.
CD . . . . CLACD 277
Castle / Feb '93 / BMG.

RAGING THROUGH THE SILENCE (Live At The Astoria).
Tracks: Not Advised.
VHS . . . . FLV 2
Virgin Vision / '88 / Gold & Sons / TBD.
VHS . . . . LFV 102
Fotodisk Video / May '90.

RARITIES FROM THE BRONZE AGE.
Tracks: Not Advised.
CD . . . . NEXCD 184
Sequel / Feb '92 / Castle Communications / BMG / Hot Shot.

RETURN TO FANTASY.
Tracks: Return to fantasy / Shady lady / Devil's daughter / Beautiful dream / Prima donna / Your turn to remember / Showdown / Why did you go / Year or a day.
■ LP . . . . ILPS 9335
Bronze / Jul '75.
■ LP . . . . BRNA 335
Bronze / Jul '77.

CD . . . . CLACD 175
■ LP . . . . CLALP 175
■ MC . . . . CLAMC 175
Castle Classics / Feb '90.

ROCKERAMA.
Tracks: Rockerama / Backstage girl.
■ 7" . . . . A 6103
■ 7" P.Disc . . . . WA 6103
Epic / Mar '85.

SALISBURY.
Tracks: Bird of prey / Park / Time to live / Lady in black / High priestess / Salisbury.
■ LP . . . . BRNA 152
Bronze / Jul '77.
■ LP . . . . CLALP 106
Castle Classics / Apr '86.
■ MC . . . . CLAMC 106
Castle Classics / Apr '86.
CD . . . . CLACD 106
Castle Classics / '88 / BMG / Castle Communications.

STAY ON TOP.
Tracks: Stay on top / Playing for time / Gypsy (Only on 7" set.) / Easy livin' (Only on 7" set.) / Sweet Lorraine (Only on 7" set.) / Stealin' (Only on 7" set.).
■ 7" . . . . BRO 168
Bronze / Aug '83.

STILL 'EAVY, STILL PROUD.
Tracks: Not Advised.
■ CD . . . . LLCD 133
■ LP . . . . LLP 133
■ MC . . . . LLK 133
Legacy / Apr '90.

SWEET FREEDOM.
Tracks: Dreamin / Stealin' / One day / Sweet freedom / If I had the time / Seven stars / Circus / Pilgrim.
■ LP . . . . ILPS 9245
Bronze / Sep '73.
■ LP . . . . BRNA 245
Bronze / '79.
CD . . . . CLACD 183
■ LP . . . . CLALP 183
Castle Classics / Aug '90.

THAT'S THE WAY THAT IT IS.
Tracks: That's the way that it is / Hot persuasion.
■ 7" . . . . BRO 148
Bronze / Jun '82.

THINK IT OVER.
Tracks: Think it over / My Joanna needs tuning.
■ 7" . . . . BRO 112
Bronze / Jan '81.

TWO DECADES IN ROCK.
Tracks: July morning / Sweet Lorraine / Gypsy / Look at yourself / Easy livin'.
CD Set . . . . ESBCD 022
■ LP Set . . . . ESBLP 022
Essential / Jun '90.

URIAH HEEP - CD BOX SET.
Tracks: Not Advised.
■ CD Set . . . . CLA BX 903
Castle Classics / Feb '92.

URIAH HEEP LIVE.
Tracks: Not Advised.
■ Double LP . . . . ISLD 1
Island / May '73.

URIAH HEEP LIVE JAN '73.
Tracks: Not Advised.
CD . . . . RAWCD 041
LP . . . . RAWLP 041
Raw Power / Aug '90 / Pinnacle.

URIAH HEEP STORY, THE.
Tracks: Not Advised.
CD . . . . ROHACD 2
■ LP P.Disc . . . . ROHALP 2
MC . . . . ROHAMC 2
EMI / Feb '90 / EMI.

VERY 'EAVY ..VERY 'UMBLE.
Tracks: Gypsy / Walking in your shadow / Come away Melinda / Lucy blues / Dreammare / Real turned on / I'll keep on trying / Wake up (set your sights).
■ LP . . . . CLALP 105
■ MC . . . . CLAMC 105
Castle Classics / Apr '86.
CD . . . . CLACD 105
Castle Classics / Dec '90 / BMG / Castle Communications.

■ DELETED

WONDERWORLD.
Tracks: Not Advised.
■ LP . . . . ILPS 9280
Bronze / Jun '74.
CD . . . . CLACD 184
■ LP . . . . CLALP 184
Castle Classics / Aug '90.

USA: UK

CALIFORNIA BOUND.
Tracks: California bound / Perfect feeling.
■ 7" . . . . MAM 173
M.A.M / Mar '78.

WILL YOU STILL LOVE ME.
Tracks: You've got nothing that I need Wendy / Will
you still love me.
■ 7" . . . . TACK 5
Flat Records / Dec '90.

Utopia

ADVENTURES IN UTOPIA.
Tracks: Road to Utopia / You make me crazy /
Second nature / Set me free / Caravan / Last of the
new wave riders / Shot in the dark / Very last time /
Love alone / Rock love.
■ LP . . . . ILPS 9602
Island / Feb '80.
CD .812270872-2
WEA / Mar '93 / WEA.

ANOTHER LIVE.
Tracks: Not Advised.
CD 8122708672
WEA / Jul '93 / WEA.

ANTHOLOGY.
Tracks: Not Advised.
CD 8122708922
WEA / Jul '93 / WEA.

COLLECTION: UTOPIA.
Tracks: Where does the world go to hide / Freedom
fighters / All smiles / Lysistrata / Always late / Love
in action / Rock love / Set me free / Seven rays /
Trapped / Swing to the right / One world / Heavy
metal kids / Very last time / Crazy lady blue / Feel
too good / Love alone / Love is the answer.
■ MC . . . . CCSMC 181
■ Double LP . . . . CCSLP 181
■ CD . . . . CCSCD 181
Castle Collector Series / Jun '88.

CRYBABY.
Tracks: Cry baby / Winston Smith takes it on the jaw.
■ 7" . . . . YZ 5
WEA / May '84.

DEFACE THE MUSIC.
Tracks: I just want to touch you / Crystal ball / Where
does the world to go hide / Silly boy / Alone / That's
not right / Take it home / Hoi poloi / Life goes on /
Feel too good / Always late / All smiles / Everybody
else is wrong.
■ LP . . . . ILPS 9642
Island / Nov '80.
CD 812270873-2
WEA / Mar '93 / WEA.

FEET DON'T FAIL ME NOW.
Tracks: Feet don't fail me now / Forgotten but not
gone.
■ 7" . . . . EPCA 2972
Epic / Nov '82.

I JUST WANT TO TOUCH YOU.
Tracks: I just want to touch you / Silly boy / Life goes
on / All smiles.
■ EP . . . . IEP 12
Island / Oct '80.

LOVE WITH A THINKER.
Tracks: Love with a thinker / Welcome to my
revolution.
■ 7" . . . . YZ 11
WEA / Jul '84.

OBLIVION.
Tracks: Maybe I could change / Cry baby / Welcome
to my revolution / Winston Smith takes it on the jaw /
I will wait / Itch in my brain / Love with a thinker /
Bring me my longbow / If I didn't try / Too much
water.
■ LP . . . . .WX 4
■ MC . . . . .WX 4C
WEA / Apr '84.

ONE WORLD.
Tracks: One world.
■ 7" . . . . .AAA 126
Bearsville (USA) / Apr '82.

OOPS SORRY WRONG PLANET.
Tracks: Trapped / Windows / Love in action / Martyr /
Abandon city / Gangreen / Crazy lady blue / Back on
the street / Marriage of heaven and hell / Mt. angel /
Rape of the young / Love is the answer.
■ LP . . . . K 55517
Bearsville (USA) / Oct '77.
CD 812270870-2
WEA / Mar '93 / WEA.

OOPS WRONG PLANET / ADVENTURES IN UTOPIA.
Tracks: Trapped / Windows / Love in action / Crazy
lady blue / Back on the street / Marriage of heaven
and hell / Martyr / Abandon city / Gangrene / My
angel / Rape of the young / Love is the answer /
Road to Utopia / You make me crazy / Second nature
/ Set me free / Caravan / Last of the new wave riders
/ Shot in the dark / Very last time / Love alone / Rock
love.
■ CD Set. . . . . TFOCD 9
■ Double LP. . . . . .TFOLP 9
■ MC. TFOMC 9
That's Original / Mar '88.

RA.
Tracks: Not Advised.
CD .812270869-2
WEA / Mar '93 / WEA.

REDUX 92: LIVE IN JAPAN.
Tracks: Fix your gaze / Zen machine / Trapped /
Princess of the universe / Abandon city / Hammer in
my heart / Swing to the right / Ikon / Hiroshima /
Back on the street / Only human / Love in action /
Caravan / Last of the new wave riders / One world /
Love is the answer.
CD .812271185-2
WEA / Jun '93 / WEA.

SET ME FREE.
Tracks: Set me free / Umbrella.
■ 7" . . . . WIP 6581
Island / Mar '80.

SWING TO THE RIGHT (see under Rundgren, Todd).

TRIVIA (12 Track Compilation).
Tracks: Not Advised.
CD . . . . PBCD 6053
■ LP . . . . PB 6053
■ MC . . . . PBC 6053
Passport (USA) / '87.

UTOPIA.
Tracks: Libertine / Bad little actress / Feet don't fail
me now / Neck on up / Say yeah / Call it what you
will / I'm looking at you but I'm talking to myself /
Hammer in my heart / Burn three times / There goes
my inspiration.
■ LP . . . . EPC 25207
Epic / '83.
CD 8122707132
WEA / Jul '93 / WEA.

V

V.V.S.I.

NO ACE AT HAND.
Tracks: Not Advised.
■ LP . . . . NRR 21
MC. . . . . NRC 21
New Renaissance(USA) / Nov '87 / Pinnacle.

V2

V2.
Tracks: Not Advised.
■ CD . . . . .CDNUK 114
■ LP .NUK 114
■ MC . . . . ZCNUK 114
Noise / Oct '89.

Vader

ULTIMATE INCANTATION.
Tracks: Not Advised.
CD . . . . .MOSH 059CD
LP . . . . MOSH 059
MC. . . . . .MOSH 059MC
Earache / Nov '92 / Vital Distribution.

Vai, Steve

Long Island guitarist who served apprenticeship with Frank Zappa. Guitar hero role established by stints with Alcatrazz and PIL, plus scene-stealing performance in *Crossroads* film. Spectacular talent finally met match in Dave Lee Roth, with whom Vai recorded two albums before jumping ship to Whitesnake. After latter's temporary demise, Vai resumed solo career (first product of which was highly-acclaimed *Flex-Able* in early '80s); two subsequent albums made U.K. Top 20. Collaboration with fellow Zappa graduate Terry Bozzio in 1993 looked as stable as Vai's previous endeavours.

DOWN DEEP INTO THE PAIN.
Tracks: Down deep into the pain / Just cartilage (album version) / Down deep into the pain (edit).
■ 12" P.Disc. 659491 6
■ CD Single 659491 2
Relativity / Aug '93.

FLEX-ABLE.
Tracks: Little green men / Viv women / Lovers are crazy / Salamanders in the sun / Boy / Girl song / Attitude song / Call it sleep / Junkie / Bill's private parts / Next stop earth / There's something dead in here.
■ LP . . . . GRUB 3
Food For Thought / Aug '86.
MC. . . . . TGRUB 3
Food For Thought / Aug '86 / Pinnacle.
CD . . . . CDGRUB 3
Food For Thought / '89 / Pinnacle.

IN MY DREAMS WITH YOU.
Tracks: In my dreams with you (mixes) / I would love to / Erotic nightmares.
■ 12" P.Disc. 659614 6
■ CD Single 659614 2
Relativity / Nov '93.

PASSION AND WARFARE.
Tracks: Liberty / Erotic nightmares / Animal / Answers / Riddle / Ballerina 12/24 / For the love of God / Audience is listening / I would love to / Blue powder / Greasy kids stuff / Alien water kiss / Sisters / Love secrets.
■ CD . . . . .CDGRUB 17
■ LP . . . . GRUB 17
■ MC . . . . .TGRUB 17
Food For Thought / May '90.
CD .467109 2
MC. .467109 4
Relativity / Oct '93 / Sony.

SEX AND RELIGION.
Tracks: Earth dweller's return / Here and now / In my dreams with you / Still my bleeding heart / Sex & religion / Dirty black hole / Touching tongues / State of grace / Survive / Pig / Road to Mt. Calvary / Deep down into the pain / Rescue me or bury me.
MiniDisc. 473947-8

Relativity / Aug '93 / Sony.
CD. .473947-2
LP 473947-1
MC. .473947-4
Relativity / Jul '93 / Sony.

Vain

BEAT THE BULLET.
Tracks: Beat the bullet / Secrets / Smoke and shadows (On 12" and CD only).
■ CD Single . . . . CID 432
■ CD Single . . . . .CIDX 432
■ 12" . . . . 12 IS 432
■ 7" . . . . IS 432
Island / Jul '89.
■ 12" Remix. . . . . ISX 432
Island / Oct '89.

MOVE ON IT.
Tracks: Breakdown / Whisper / Long time ago / Ivy's dream / Hit & run / Family / Planets turning / Get up / Crumpled glory / Resurrection / Ticket outta here.
CD . . . . .HMRXD 194
Heavy Metal / Sep '94 / Sony / FM Revolver.

NO RESPECT.
Tracks: Secrets / Beat the bullet / Who's watching you / 1000 degrees / Aces / Smoke and shadows / No respect / Laws against love / Down for the 3rd time / Icy / Without you.
■ LP . . . . ILPS 9938
■ MC. . . . . .ICT 9938
■ CD . . . . CID 9938
Island / Aug '89.

Valentine

TINA ARE YOU READY.
Tracks: Tina are you ready.
■ 12" . . . . FRUIT 6T
■ 7" . . . . FRUIT 6
Banana / '88.

Valhalla

COMIN' HOME.
Tracks: Comin' home / Through with you.
■ 7" .NEAT 22
Neat / '88.

STILL IN LOVE WITH YOU.
Tracks: Still in love with you / Jack.
■ 7" .NEAT 36
Neat / Jan '84.

Van Halen

Van Halen convened in California, 1974. Signed to Warner Bros in 1977, band released superb, eponymous debut. Frontman David Lee Roth's engaging brand of bullshit (he once proclaimed Lewisham "the rock 'n' roll capital of the world") and Eddie Van Halen's guitar pyrotechnics captivated fans; including Michael Jackson, on whose *Beat It* Eddie Van Halen guested. Band's reputation secured by classic *1984* album and *Jump* hit. Replacement of Roth with Sammy Hagar (ex-Montrose) did not interrupt run of success; UK highlight of which has been hit single *Why Can't This Be Love*. Roth's solo career has been less successful but more fun.

1984.
Tracks: 1984 / Jump / Panama / Top Jimmy / Drop dead legs / Hot for teacher / I'll wait / Girl gone bad / House of pain.
CD .923985 2
■ LP .923985 1
MC. .923985 4
WEA / Jan '84 / WEA.

5150.
Tracks: Good enough / Why can't this be love / Get up / Dreams / Summer nights / Best of both worlds / Love walks in / "5150" / Inside.
CD .925394 2
■ LP . . . . W 5150
MC. . . . . .W 5150C
WEA / Apr '86 / WEA.

BLACK AND BLUE.
Tracks: Black and blue.
■ 12" . . . . W 7891T
■ 7" . . . . W 7891
WEA / May '88.

DANCE THE NIGHT AWAY.
Tracks: Dance the night away / Outta love again.
■ 7" . . . . .K 17371
WEA / May '79.

DANCING IN THE STREET.
Tracks: Dancing in the street / Big bad Willie.
■ 7" . . . . .K 17957
WEA / May '82.

DIVER DOWN.
Tracks: Where have all the good times gone / Hang 'em high / Cathedral / Secrets / Intruder / Oh pretty woman / Dancing in the street / Little guitar (intro) / Little guitars / Big bad Bill is sweet William now / Bull bug / Happy trails.
■ LP .K 57003
MC. K4 57003
WEA / Apr '82 / WEA.
CD K257 003
WEA / Jan '84 / WEA.

DREAMS.
Tracks: Dreams / Inside.
■ 12" . . . . W 8642 T
■ 7" . . . . W 8642
■ 7" P.Disc . . . . W 8642 P
WEA / Jun '86.

FAIR WARNING.
Tracks: Mean street / Dirty movies / Sinners swing / Hear about it later / Unchained / Push comes to shove / So this is love / Sunday afternoon in the park / One foot out of the door.
■ LP . . . . .K 56899
MC. K4 56899
WEA / May '81 / WEA.
CD . . . . .K 9235402
WEA / Jun '89 / WEA.

FEELS SO GOOD.
Tracks: Feels so good.
■ 12" . . . . W 7565 T
■ 7" . . . . W 7565
■ CD Single . . . . W 7565 CD
WEA / Mar '89.

FOR UNLAWFUL CARNAL KNOWLEDGE.
Tracks: Poundcake / Judgement day / Spanked / Runaround / Pleasure dome / In 'n' out / Man on a mission / Dream is over / Right now / 316 / Top of the world.
CD. 7599265942
■ LP . . . . WX 420
MC. WX 420C
WEA / Jun '91 / WEA.

HOT FOR TEACHER.
Tracks: Hot for teacher / Little dreamer / Hear about it later.
■ 12" . . . . W 9199 T
■ 7" . . . . W 9199
WEA / Jun '85.

I'LL WAIT.
Tracks: I'll wait / Drop dead legs.
■ 12" . . . . W 9213T
■ 7" . . . . W 9213
WEA / Jul '84.

JUMP.
Tracks: Jump / House of pain.
■ 12" . . . . .W 9384T
■ 7" . . . . W 9384
WEA / Jan '84.

JUMP (LIVE).
Tracks: Jump / Love walks in
■ 7" . . . . W 0155
■ CD Single. . . . . .W 0155CDX
■ CD Single. . . . . .W 0155CD
■ MC Single. . . . . .W 0155C
WEA / Mar '93.

LIVE - RIGHT HERE, RIGHT NOW.
Tracks: Right now / One way to rock / Why can't this be love / Give to live / Finish what ya started / Best of both worlds / 316 / You really got me / Won't get fooled again / Jump / Top of the world / Poundcake / Judgement day / When it's love / Spanked / Ain't talkin' bout love / I'n 'n' out / Dreams / Man on a mission / Ultra bass / Pleasure dome (Drum solo) / Panama / Love walks in / Runaround.
CD 9362451982
MC 9362451984
WEA / Feb '93 / WEA.

LIVE : RIGHT HERE, RIGHT NOW.
Tracks: Not Advised.
VHS 759938290-3
Warner Music Video / Mar '93 / WEA.

LIVE WITHOUT A NET.
Tracks: Not Advised.
■ VHS . . . . K 938129 3
WEA / May '87.

OU812.
Tracks: Mine all mine / When it's love / A.F.U. (naturally wired) / Cabo wabo / Source of infection / Feels so good / Come back and finish what you started / Black and blue / Sucker in a 3 piece.
CD . . . . K 925732 2
■ LP . . . . WX 177
■ MC . . . . WX 177C
WEA / Jun '88.

PANAMA.
Tracks: Panama / Girl gone bad.
■ 12" . . . . W 9273 T
■ 7" . . . . W 9273
WEA / May '84.

POUNDCAKE.
Tracks: Poundcake.
■ 12" . . . . W 0045 T
■ 7" . . . . W 0045
■ CD Single . . . . W 0045 CD
■ MC Single . . . . W 0045 C
WEA / Jun '91.

PRETTY WOMAN.
Tracks: Pretty woman / Happy trails.
■ 7" . . . . K 17909
WEA / Feb '85.

RUNNIN' WITH THE DEVIL.
Tracks: Runnin' with the devil / Eruption.
■ 7" . . . . K 17162
WEA / '79.
■ 7" . . . . HM 10
Atlantic / Jul '80.

TOP OF THE WORLD.
Tracks: Top of the world.
■ CD Single . . . . W 0066 CD
■ 7" . . . . W 0066
■ MC Single . . . . W 0066 C
WEA / Oct '91.

VAN HALEN.
Tracks: You really got me / Jamie's cryin' / On fire / Runnin' with the Devil / I'm the one / Ain't talkin' bout love / Little dreamer / Feel your love tonight / Atomic punk / Eruption / Ice cream man.
MC K4 58470
■ LP . . . . K 58470
WEA / May '78.
CD K2 56470
WEA / Jul '86 / WEA.

VAN HALEN I & II (Double play cassette).
Tracks: Runnin' with the devil / Eruption / You really got me / Ain't talkin' 'bout love / I'm the one / Jamie's cryin' / Atomic punk / Feel your love tonight / Little dreamer / Ice cream man / On fire / You're no good / Dance the night away / Somebody get me a doctor / Bottom's up / Outta love again / Light up the sky / Spanish fly / D.O.A. / Women in love / Beautiful girls.
■ MC K4 66104
WEA / Oct '82.

VAN HALEN II.
Tracks: You're no good / Dance the night away / Somebody get me a doctor / Bottoms up / Outta love again / Light up the sky / D.O.A. / Women in love / Spanish fly / Beautiful girls.
CD 256 616
WEA / Mar '87 / WEA.
■ LP . . . . K 56616
MC K4 56616
WEA / '89 / WEA.

WHEN IT'S LOVE.
Tracks: When it's love / Apolitical blues / Why can't this be love.
■ 12" . . . . W 7816 T
■ 12" P.Disc. . . . . W 7816 TP
■ 7" . . . . W 7816
■ CD Single . . . . W 7816 CD
WEA / Jul '88.

WHY CAN'T THIS BE LOVE.
Tracks: Why can't this be love / Get up.
■ 7" P.Disc . . . . W 8740 P
■ 12" . . . . W 8740 T
■ 7" . . . . W 8740
WEA / Mar '86.

WOMEN AND CHILDREN FIRST.
Tracks: Tora tora / Cradle will rock / Romeo delight / Fools / In a simply rhyme / Could this be magic / Loss of control / Take your whiskey home / Every body wants some.
MC K4 56793
WEA / Apr '80 / WEA.
■ LP . . . . K 56793
WEA / Feb '80.
CD .K 9234152
WEA / Jun '89 / WEA.

YOU REALLY GOT ME.
Tracks: You really got me / Atomic punk.
■ 7" . . . . K 17107
WEA / Mar '78.

Vandenburg

ALIBI.
Tracks: All the way / Pedal to the metal / Once in a lifetime / Voodoo / Dressed to kill / Fighting against the world / How long / Prelude mortale / Alibi / Kamikaze.
■ LP 790 295-1
■ MC 790 295-4
Atco / Oct '85.

BEST OF VANDENBURG.
Tracks: Your love is in vain / Nothing to lose / Rock on / Burning heart / Wait / Welcome to the club / Prelude mortale / Alibi / Different worlds / Pedal to the metal / Fighting against the world.
CD . . . . .K 790 928 2
■ LP . . . . .K 790 928 1
■ MC . . . . .K 790 928 4
Atlantic / Jun '88.

HEADING FOR A STORM.
Tracks: Friday night / Welcome to the club / Time will tell / Different worlds / This is war / I'm on fire / Heading for a storm / Rock on / Waiting for the night.
■ LP .790121 1
WEA / '84.

LIVE IN JAPAN.
Tracks: Not Advised.
■ VHS . . . . HEN 2033
Hendring Video / '88.

ONCE IN A LIFETIME.
Tracks: Once in a lifetime / Voodoo.
■ 7" . . . . .B 9610
Atco / Oct '85.

VANDENBURG.
Tracks: Your love is in vain / Back on my feet / Wait / Burning heart / Ready for you / Too late / Nothing to lose / Lost in a city / Out in the streets.
■ LP . . . . K 50904
Atco / Nov '82.

Varathron

HIS MAJESTY AT THE SWAMP.
Tracks: Not Advised.
CD . . . . .CYBERCD 8
Cyber / Mar '94 / Plastic Head.

Vardis

100 M.P.H.
Tracks: Out of the way / Move along / Lion's share / Situation negative / Destiny / Loser / Living out of touch / Let's go / 100 m.p.h. / If I were king / Dirty money.
■ LP . . . . .MOGO 4012
Logo / Nov '80.
■ LP . . . . .METALPS 115
Razor / Dec '86.

ALL YOU'LL EVER NEED.
Tracks: All you'll ever need / If I were King / Jumpin' Jack flash.
■ EP . . . . VAR 4
Logo / May '81.

IF I WERE KING.
Tracks: If I were king.
■ 7" . . . . .QUEL 2/100
O / Apr '80.

LET'S GO.
Tracks: Let's go.
■ 7" . . . . VAR 1
Logo / Sep '80.

LIONS SHARE, THE.
Tracks: Not Advised.
■ LP . . . . RAZ 3
Razor / Jul '83.

QUO VARDIS.
Tracks: Do I stand accused / Where there's mods there's rockers / Please do / Dream with me / Gary Glitter (Part 1) / Walkin' / To be with you / Together tonight / Boogie blitz / Plot to rock the world.
■ LP . . . . UNKNOWN
MC. UNKNOWN
Logo / Mar '82 / C.M. Distribution.

SILVER MACHINE.
Tracks: Silver machine / Come on.
■ 7" . . . . VAR 3
Logo / Mar '81.

STANDING IN THE ROAD.
Tracks: Standing in the road / Freezing history.
■ 12" . . . . NST 103
■ 7" . . . . NS 103
Big Beat / Jan '85.

TO BE WITH YOU.
Tracks: To be with you / Gary Glitter (Part 1).
■ 7" . . . . GO 406
Logo / Feb '82.

TOO MANY PEOPLE.
Tracks: Too many people / Lion's share.
■ 7" . . . . VAR 2
Logo / Sep '80.

VIGILANTE.
Tracks: Don't mess with the best / Radio rockers / Learn how to shoot straight / All the world's eyes / I wanna be a guitar hero (just for you) / Bad company (the contract) / I must be mad / Wild sound / Radio-active / Running.
■ LP . . . . .RAWLP 022
MC. . . . . .RAWTC 022
Raw Power / Sep '86 / Pinnacle.

WORLD'S INSANE, THE.
Tracks: Powder under foot / Money grabber / World's insane / Blue rock (I miss you) / Silver machine / Police patrol / All you'll ever need / Curse the gods / Love is dead / Steamin' along.
■ LP . . . . LOGO 1026
MC. . . . . KLOGO 1026
Logo / Apr '81 / C.M. Distribution.

Varga

PROTOTYPE.
Tracks: Unconscience / Greed / Wawnan mere / Freeze don't move / Self proclaimed / Thief / Bring the hammer down / Cast into the shade / Strong / Film at eleven / Goodbye boogaloo (Instrumental) / Freeze don't move (Krash's psycho mix).
CD 74321 19080-2
MC. 74321 19080-4
RCA / Aug '94 / BMG.

Vectom

RULES OF MYSTERY.
Tracks: Der Anfang / Prisoner's back / Dipsomania / Metallic war / Why am I alive / Outlaw / Feelings of freedom / Caught by insanity / Evil run / This/is/the/end.
■ LP 805 034
Scratch (Germany) / Mar '87.

SPEED REVOLUTION.
Tracks: Not Advised.
■ LP .934317
Powerstation / Jun '86.

Veil

BEST DAYS OF OUR LIVES, THE.
Tracks: Best days of our lives / Double up / Pistol boys / Last voice / Only the lonely / Run with the wild / Zinc alloy / December skies / View inside / Kiss your body blue / Hearts on fire / Free from the gun.
■ LP .EAR 006
Earache / Apr '88.

■ DELETED

HEAVY HEART.
Tracks: Is this sin (watching the nite world work).
■ 12" . . . . AIR 001
Andusias International / Apr '86.

MANIKIN.
Tracks: Manikin.
■ 12" . . . . .12 CLAY 39
Clay / Oct '84.

SURRENDER.
Tracks: Not Advised.
■ LP . . . . CLAYLP 14
Clay / Mar '85.

TWIST.
Tracks: Twist / Sway.
■ 7" . . . . .CLAY 45
Clay / Aug '85.

Vendetta

BRAIN DAMAGE.
Tracks: Not Advised.
■ CD . . . . .CDNUK 121
■ LP . . . . .NUK 121
■ MC . . . . ZCNUK 121
Noise / Oct '89.

COULD HAVE DONE WITHOUT IT.
Tracks: Row / Living one day at a time (Extra track on 12" version only).
■ 12" . . . . .PZA 021 T
■ 7" . . . . .PZA 021
Plaza / Aug '86.

DON'T LET THE WORLD DRAG YOU UNDER.
Tracks: Don't let the world drag you under / Don't let the world drag you under (instrumental).
■ 7" . . . . .PZA 042
Plaza / Nov '88.

GO AND LIVE, STAY AND DIE.
Tracks: Not Advised.
■ LP . . . . .N 0102
Noise / Nov '87.
■ CD . . . . .CDNUK 102
■ LP . . . . .NUK 102
■ MC . . . . ZCNUK 102
Noise / Oct '89.

I'VE GOT YOU IN MY HEART.
Tracks: I've got you in my heart.
■ 12" . . . . .PZA 037T
■ 7" . . . . .PZA 037
Plaza / Aug '88.

I'VE GOT YOU IN MY SIGHTS.
Tracks: I've got you in my sights / One step at a time.
■ 12" . . . . PZA 8 T
■ 7" . . . . .PZA 8
Plaza / Jan '84.

I'VE GOTTA SEE JANE.
Tracks: I've gotta see Jane / One step at a time.
■ 7" . . . . .PZA 004
Plaza / Apr '83.

IF YOU WANT MY LOVE.
Tracks: If you want my love.
■ 12" . . . . .PZA 009 T
■ 7" . . . . .PZA 009
Plaza / Jun '84.
■ 7" . . . . .PZA 015
Plaza / Jun '85.
■ 7" . . . . .PZA 058
Plaza / Sep '90.

LARSEN EFFECT, THE.
Tracks: Larsen effect.
■ 7" . . . . .PZA 016
Plaza / Oct '85.

ONLY YOU CAN SAVE MY LIFE.
Tracks: Only you can save my life.
CD Single . . . . .PZA 075CD
Roberto Danova / Feb '94 / Pinnacle.

SO DO I.
Tracks: So do I / One step at a time.
■ 7" . . . . .PZA 006
Plaza / Oct '83.

SO DO I (1986).
Tracks: So do I (remix 86) / One step at a time.
■ 12" . . . . .PZA 018T
■ 7" . . . . .PZA 018
Plaza / Feb '86.

SO DO I (1989).
Tracks: So do I.
■ 12" . . . . .PZA 051 T

■ 7" . . . . .PZA 051
Plaza / Aug '89.

SOMEWHERE IN THE NIGHT.
Tracks: Somewhere in the night / Don't let the world drag you under / I've got you in my heart.
■ 12" . . . . .PZA 013T
■ 7" . . . . .PZA 013
Plaza / Mar '85.

SOMEWHERE IN THE NIGHT.
Tracks: Somewhere in the night / So do I / 1-2-3 / I've got you in my heart / Could have done without it / Don't let the world drag you under / I've got you in my sight tonight / Living day at a time / Gotta see Jane / Somewhere in the night (AOR) / So do I (AOR) / In and out of love / Stay tonight / Only you can save my life / If you want my love / One step at a time / Larsen effect / Somewhere in the night (Reprise).
CD . . . . .PZA 006CD
MC . . . . .PZA 006MC
Plaza / Mar '04 / Pinnacle.

Vengeance

ARABIA.
Tracks: Arabia / Broadway-Hollywood-Beverly hills / Cry of the sirens / Castles in the air / If lovin' you is wrong / Children of the streets / Just what the doctor ordered / That's the way the story goes / Bad boy for love / How about tonight.
■ LP 4634371
Epic / Jun '89.

ROCK 'N' ROLL SHOWER.
Tracks: Rock 'n' roll shower / Code of honour / Only the wind (special remix) (Extra track on 12" version only.) / Deathride to glory (live) (Extra track on 12" version only.).
■ 12" 6511496
■ 7" 6511497
Epic / Feb '88.

TAKE IT OR LEAVE IT.
Tracks: Take it or leave it / Code of honour / Rock 'n' roll shower / Take me to the limit / Engines / Hear me out / Women in the world / Looks of a winner / Ain't gonna take you home.
■ LP 4600701
■ MC 4600704
Epic / Feb '88.

Venom

Newcastle Upon Tyne trio, formed in 1980, who invented Black Metal even before their second album of the same name. At the time, they claimed to be serious as hell about loving the Devil; although, following murders and arson attacks in Norway in 1993 by bands who claimed to have descended from them, Venom recanted and admitted it had all been a bit of a laugh. Back in the 80's those listening to the band - Cronos (bass, vocals), Mantas (guitar) and Abaddon (drums) - for the first time certainly needed a sense of humour: it was poorly produced thrash with satanic and sexist overtones. Hindsight has made the records seem far stronger, and they have proved very influential; tribute album appeared in 1994. But beware of albums recorded by inferior line-ups since 1985.

AT WAR WITH SATAN.
Tracks: At war with Satan / Rip pride / Genocide / Cry wolf / Stand up (and be counted) / Women, leather and hell / Aaaaarrghh.
CD . . . . NEATCD 1015
■ LP . . . . NEAT 1015
MC . . . . NEATC 1015
Neat / '85 / Grapevine Distribution.
CD . . . . RR 349869
Road Runner / '89 / Pinnacle.

BLACK METAL.
Tracks: Side black / Black metal / To hell and back / Buried alive / Raise the dead / Teacher's pet / Leave me in hell / Sacrifice / Heaven's on fire / Countess Bathory / Don't burn the witch / At war with Satan (intro).
CD . . . . NEATCD 1005
■ LP . . . . NEAT 1005
Neat / '85.
■ LP . . . . RR 9708
Road Runner / '89.

BLOOD LUST.
Tracks: Blood lust / In nomine satanus.
■ 7" . . . . .NEAT 13
Neat / Aug '82.

BLOODLUST (Witching Hour EP).
Tracks: Not Advised.
VHS . . . . NEATVID 001V
Neat / '88 / Grapevine Distribution.
■ VHS . . . . HEN 2331
Hendring Video / Apr '91.

CALM BEFORE THE STORM.
Tracks: Black Xmas / Chanting of the priest / Metal punk / Under a spell / Calm before the storm / Fire / Beauty and the Beast / Deadline / Gypsy / Muscle.
■ CD . . . . MOMCD 115
■ LP . . . . MOMENT 115
■ MC . . . . MOMENTC 115
Filmtrax / Nov '87.

COLLECTION.
Tracks: Welcome to hell / Dead on arrival / Snots shit / Black metal / Hounds of hell / At war with Satan (TV Adverts) / At war with Satan (Full re-edited version) / Bitch witch / Intro tapes / Possessed / Sadist (Mistress of the whip) / Manitou / Angel dust / Raise the dead / Red light fever / Venom station ids for America & Spain.
CD . . . . CCSCD 367
Castle / Mar '93 / BMG.

DIE HARD.
Tracks: Die hard / Acid queen / Bursting out.
■ 12" . . . . NEAT 27 12
■ 7" . . . . .NEAT 27
Neat / May '83.

EINE KLEINE NACHTMUSIK.
Tracks: Too loud (for the crowd) / Seven gates of hell / Leave me in hell / Nightmare / Countess Bathory / Die hard / Schizo / Guitar solo by Mantas / Inomine Satanas / Witching hour / Black metal / Chanting of the priest / Satanchrist / Fly trap / Warhead / Buried alive / Love amongst / Bass solo Cronos / Welcome to hell / Bloodlust.
■ Double LP . . . . NEAT 1032
MC Set . . . . NEATC 1032
Neat / Dec '86 / Grapevine Distribution.
CD . . . . NEATXSO 132
Neat / Nov '87 / Grapevine Distribution.
■ LP . . . . RR 9639
Road Runner / '89.

FROM HELL TO THE UNKNOWN...
Tracks: Sons of Satan / Welcome to hell / Schizo / Mayhem with mercy / Poison / Live like an angel / Witching hour / 1000 days in sodom / Angel dust / In league with Satan / Red light fever / Bursting out / At war with satan (intro) / Die hard (live version) / Manitou / Senile decay / Black metal / Possessed / Seven gates of hell (live version) / Buried alive / Too loud for the crowd / Radio interview (metro radio with Alan Robson).
■ Double LP . . . . RAWLP 001
MC . . . . RAWTC 001
Raw Power / Apr '86 / Pinnacle.

GERMAN ASSAULT.
Tracks: Not Advised.
■ LP . . . . RR 9659
Road Runner / '89.

IN LEAGUE WITH SATAN.
Tracks: In league with Satan / Live like an angel.
■ 7" . . . . .NEAT 08
Neat / Jan '82.

IN MEMORIUM - BEST OF VENOM.
Tracks: Angel dust / Raise the dead / Red light fever / Buried alive / Witching hour / At war with satan / Warhead / Manitou / Under a spell / Nothing sacred / Dead love / Welcome to hell / Black metal / Countess bathory / 1000 Days in sodom / Prime evil / If you wanna war / Surgery.
CD . . . . MCCD 097
MC . . . . MCTC 097
Music Club / Mar '93 / Gold & Sons / TBD / Video Collection / C.M. Distribution.

LIVE '90.
Tracks: Not Advised.
VHS . . . . .LFV 113
Fotodisk Video / Aug '90.

LIVE 84/85.
Tracks: Not Advised.
■ LP . . . . .APK 12
Metalworks / Feb '86.

LIVE IN '85.
Tracks: Teachers pet / Witching hour / Poison.
■ 12" . . . . NEAT 53 12
Neat / Dec '85.

LIVE OFFICIAL BOOTLEG.
Tracks: Leave me in hell / Countess bathory / Die hard / Seven gates of hell / Buried alive / Don't burn

the witch / In nomine satanus / Welcome to hell /
Warhead / Stand up and be counted / Bloodlust.
CD . . . . CDTL 004
The CD Label / Jul '87 / Jazz Music / TBD.
CD . . . . CDTB 110
Thunderbolt / '91 / TBD / Jazz Music.

MANITOU.
Tracks: Manitou / Woman.
■ 12" . . . . NEAT 43 12
■ 7" . . . . NEAT 43
■ MC Single . . . . NEATC 43
Neat / Oct '84.

NIGHTMARE.
Tracks: Nightmare / Satanchrist / F.O.A.D.
■ 12" . . . . NEAT 47 12
■ 7" . . . . NEAT 47
■ MC Single . . . . NEATC 47
Neat / Aug '85.
■ 7" P.Disc . . . . NEATP 47
Neat / Aug '85.
■ 12" RR125487
Road Runner / '89.

OBSCENE MIRACLE.
Tracks: Not Advised.
■ LP P.Disc . . . . APKPD 12
Demon / Jul '86.

OLD, NEW, BORROWED AND BLUE.
Tracks: Rose garden.
CD . . . . CDBLEED 7
Bleeding Hearts / Oct '93 / Pinnacle.

POSSESSED.
Tracks: Powerdrive / Flytrap / Satanchrist / Burn this
place (to the ground) / Harmony dies / Possessed /
Hellchild / Moonshine / Wing and a prayer / Suffer
not the children / Voyeur / Mystique / Too loud (for
the crowd).
■ LP . . . . NEAT 1024
■ LP P.Disc . . . . NEATP 1024
MC . . . . NEATC 1024
Neat / '85 / Grapevine Distribution.
■ LP . . . . RR 9794
Road Runner / '89.
CD . . . . CLACD 402
Castle / Jun '94 / BMG.

PRIME EVIL.
Tracks: Not Advised.
CD . . . . CDFLAG 36
■ LP . . . . FLAG 36
MC . . . . TFLAG 36
Under One Flag / Oct '89 / Pinnacle.

SEVENTH DATE OF HELL.
Tracks: Bloodlust / Don't burn the witch / Warhead /
In league with Satan / Live like an angel / Blood lust
/ In nomine satanus / Die hard / Acid Queen /
Busting out / Lady lust / Seven gates of hell /
Manitou / Dead of the nite.
VHS 041 051 2
Polygram Music Video / Oct '84 / PolyGram.
VHS . . . . CFV 074232
Channel 5 / '88 / Channel 5 Video / P.R.O. Video /
Gold & Sons.

SINGLES '80-'86.
Tracks: In league with Satan / Live like an angel /
Blood lust / In nomine satanus / Die hard / Acid
queen / Busting out / Warhead / Lady lust / Seven
gates of hell / Manitou / Dead of the nite.
■ LP . . . . RAWLP 024
MC . . . . RAWTC 024
Raw Power / Sep '86 / Pinnacle.
CD . . . . RAWCD 024
Raw Power / Aug '87 / Pinnacle.

SPEED REVOLATION.
Tracks: Not Advised.
■ LP 941317
Powerstation / Jul '86.

TEAR YOUR SOUL APART.
Tracks: Not Advised.
CD . . . . CDFLAG 50
LP . . . . FLAG 50
Under One Flag / Sep '90 / Pinnacle.

TEMPLES OF ICE.
Tracks: Temples of ice.
CD . . . . CDFLAG 56
LP . . . . FLAG 56
MC . . . . TFLAG 56
Music For Nations / Jun '91 / Pinnacle.

WARHEAD.
Tracks: Warhead / Lady lust.
■ 12" . . . . NEAT 38 12
■ 7" . . . . NEAT 38
Neat / Jan '84.

WASTELAND, THE.
Tracks: Cursed / I'm paralysed / Back legions /
Riddle of steel / Need to kill / Kissing the beast /
Crucified / Shadow king / Wolverine / Clarisse.
CD . . . . CDFLAG 72
LP . . . . FLAG 72
MC . . . . TFLAG 72
Under One Flag / Nov '92 / Pinnacle.

WELCOME TO HELL.
Tracks: Sons of Satan / Welcome to hell / Schizo /
Mayhem with mercy / Poison / Live like an angel /
Witching hour / One thousand days in Sodom / Angel
dust / In league with Satan / Red light fever.
■ LP . . . . NEAT 1002
■ LP P.Disc . . . . NEATP 1002
Neat / '85.
■ LP . . . . RR 9707
Road Runner / '89.

WELCOME TO HELL/BLACK METAL.
Tracks: Not Advised.
MC Set . . . . RR 49653
Road Runner / '89 / Pinnacle.

Verbal Assault

EXIT.
Tracks: Not Advised.
■ 10" . . . . K 137
Konkurrel / Sep '92.

LIVE.
Tracks: Not Advised.
CD . . . . YCLS 004
Your Choice / May '94 / Plastic Head.

TINY GIANTS.
Tracks: Tiny giants.
■ LP . . . . K 001/115
Konkurrel / Nov '88.
■ 7" . . . . K 100/115
Konkurrel / Oct '88.

TRIAL.
Tracks: Not Advised.
■ LP . . . . K 001/114
Konkurrel / Jan '89.

VERBAL ASSAULT: LIVE.
Tracks: Not Advised.
LP . . . . YCR 004
Your Choice / '92 / Plastic Head.

Verity

INTERRUPTED JOURNEY.
Tracks: Rescue me / Just another day (in the life of a
fool) / Stay with me baby / Love is blind / Are you
ready for this / You're the loser / It's comin' right /
Chippin' away at the stone / In the arms of someone
else / Falling.
■ LP . . . . LBP 100
■ MC . . . . ZCLB 100
PRT / Oct '83.

RESCUE ME.
Tracks: Rescue me / Stop pretending.
■ 12" 12LB 2
■ 7" . . . . LB 2
PRT / Feb '84.

STAY WITH ME BABY.
Tracks: Stay with me baby.
■ 12" 12LB 1
■ 7" . . . . LB 1
PRT / Oct '83.

Vex

SANCTUARY.
Tracks: Sanctuary.
■ 12" . . . . FIGHT 1
Fight Back / May '88.

VEX.
Tracks: Not Advised.
CD 841152
LP 081152
Ruff & Roll / Aug '90.

Vicious Circle

BARBED WIRE SLIDE.
Tracks: Not Advised.
CD . . . . SBZCD 0022
■ MC . . . . SBZLP 002
Some Bizzare / Feb '91.

BARBED WIRE SLIDES.
Tracks: Not Advised.
CD . . . . CDSA 54027
Semantic / Feb '94 / Plastic Head.

PRICE OF PROGRESS.
Tracks: Not Advised.
■ LP . . . . GURT 5
Children Of The Revolution / Nov '85.

RHYME WITH REASON.
Tracks: Rule 17 / Pseudo genocide / Broadcast of
terror / Turn to stone / Hope and wait / Inside
operation / Personality crisis / Doubtful season /
Nightmare so quick / Under the surface / Police
brutality / One more step.
■ LP . . . . ACHE 12
Manic Ears / Feb '88.

Vicious Rumors

ANYTIME DAY OR NIGHT.
Tracks: Not Advised.
■ LP . . . . OIR 005
Oi! / May '86.

DIGITAL DICTATOR.
Tracks: Replicant / Digital dictator / Minute to kill /
Lady took a chance / Towns on fire / Out of sounds /
Worlds and machines / Crest / Condemned / R L H /
Out of the shadows.
CD . . . . RR 9571 2
■ LP . . . . RR 9571
Road Runner / Feb '88.

LOOK DON'T TOUCH.
Tracks: Look don't touch / Nighthawk Rita.
■ 7" . . . . UR BOB 8
Dork / Oct '85.

RITA.
Tracks: Rita.
■ 7" . . . . UR BOB 5
Dork / Nov '84.

SICKEST MAN IN TOWN.
Tracks: Not Advised.
■ LP . . . . LINK LP 022
Link / Dec '87.

SOLDIER OF THE NIGHT.
Tracks: Not Advised.
■ LP . . . . RR 9734
Road Runner / Nov '85.
CD . . . . RO 97342
Road Runner / Feb '93 / Pinnacle.

VICIOUS RUMOURS.
Tracks: Don't wait for me / World church / On the
edge / Ship of fools / Can you hear it / Down to the
temple / Hellraiser / Electric twilight / Thrill of the
hunt / Axe and smash.
CD 7567820752
■ LP 7567820751
MC 7567820754
Geffen / Feb '90 / BMG.

WELCOME TO THE BALL.
Tracks: Abandoned / You only live twice / Saviour
from anger / Children / Dust to dust / Raise your
hands / Strange behaviour / Six stepsisters / Master-
mind / When love comes down / Ends of the earth.
CD 7568227612
■ LP 7568227611
MC 7568227614
Atlantic / Nov '91 / WEA.

WORD OF MOUTH.
Tracks: Not Advised.
CD . . . . SPV 084-62232
Rising Sun / Jun '94 / Plastic Head.

Victory

CULTURE KILLED THE NATIVE.
Tracks: More and more / Never satisfied / Don't tell
no lies / Always the same / Power strikes the earth /
Lost in the night / On the loose / Let it rock on / So
they run / Standing on the edge / Warning / Into the
darkness (Only on CD).
■ CD 837 781-2
■ LP 837 781-1
■ MC 837 781-4
London / Mar '89.

DON'T GET MAD GET EVEN.
Tracks: Not Advised.
CD . . . . **MERD 2105**
Mercenary / Dec '93 / C.M. Distribution.

HUNGRY HEARTS.
Tracks: One track mind / Bigger they are / I'm a survivor / Never leave you again / Tough on love / You run away / Look in a mirror / Look in the mirror / Feel the fire / Hi honey.
CD . . . . **METALCD 120**
■ LP . . . . **METALLP 120**
Razor / Oct '87.

Vigilants

RUN FOR COVER.
Tracks: Not Advised.
■ LP . . . . **HMASP 45**
Heavy Metal / Nov '85.

Viking

DO OR DIE.
Tracks: Warlord / Hellbound / Militia of death / Prelude - scavenger / Valhalla / Burning from within / Berserker / Killer unleashed / Do or die.
■ LP . . . . **RR 9569**
Road Runner / Feb '88.

Vincent, Vinnie

ALL SYSTEMS GO.
Tracks: Let freedom rock / Naughty naughty / Ecstasy / That time of year / Breakout / Burn / Love kills / Dirty rhythm / Deeper and deeper / Heavy pettin' / Ashes to ashes.
■ CD . . . . **CCD 1626**
■ LP . . . . **CHR 1626**
■ MC . . . . **ZCHR 1626**
Chrysalis / Apr '88.

LOVE KILLS.
Tracks: Love kills / Animal / Shoot you full of love.
■ 12" . . . . **INVSX 1**
■ 7" . . . . **INVS 1**
Arista / Apr '89.

VINNIE VINCENT INVASION.
Tracks: Boys are gonna rock / Shoot you full of love / No substitute / Animal / Twisted / Do you wanna make love / Back on the streets / I wanna be your victim / Baby o / Invasion.
■ LP . . . . **CHR 1529**
MC . . . . **ZCHR 1529**
Chrysalis / Aug '86 / EMI.

Vio-Lence

ETERNAL NIGHTMARE.
Tracks: Eternal nightmare / Serial killer / Phobophobia / Calling in the coroner / T.D.S. take it as you will / Bodies on bodies / Kill on command.
■ CD . . . . **DMCF 3423**
■ LP . . . . **MCF 3423**
■ MC . . . . **MCFC 3423**
MCA / Aug '88.

ETERNAL NIGHTMARE.
Tracks: Eternal nightmare.
■ 7" . . . .**VOMIT 1**
MCA / Oct '88.

NOTHING TO GAIN.
Tracks: Atrocity / 12-Gauge justice / Ageless eyes / Pain of pleasure / Virtues of vice / Killing my words / Psychotic memories / No chains / Welcoming party / This is system / Color of life.
CD . . . . **CD BLEED 4**
■ LP . . . . **BLEED 4**
Bleeding Hearts / Mar '93.

Violent Force

MALEVOLENT ASSAULT.
Tracks: Not Advised.
■ LP . . . . **RR 9612**
Road Runner / Oct '87.

Virus

(I'M NOT YOUR) STEPPING STONE.
Tracks: Stepping stone / Salute to the Afghan Rebels.
■ 7" . . . . **FC 1**
5th Column / Dec '82.

FORCE RECON.
Tracks: Not Advised.
■ LP . . . . **VOV 669**

MC . . . . **VOVC 669**
Metalworks / Apr '88.

LUNACY.
Tracks: Not Advised.
■ CD . . . . **VOVCD 677**
■ LP . . . . **VOV 677**
■ MC . . . . **VOVMC 677**
Metalworks / May '89.

PRAY FOR WAR.
Tracks: Not Advised.
■ LP . . . . **VOV 665**
Metalworks / May '87.

SYSTEMATIC DEATH, MAD CONFLUX ETC.
Tracks: Not Advised.
■ LP . . . . **JHL 108**
Jungle Hop / Jun '88.

WIPE OUT.
Tracks: Wipe out.
■ 7" . . . . **BEP 1**
Big Sleep / Jun '85.

Vixen

CRYIN'.
Tracks: Crying / Desperate / Crying (ext. remix) (12" remix only.) / Give it away (CD single only.) / Edge of a broken heart (CD single only.).
■ 12" **12MTP 60**
■ 7" . . . . **MTG 60**
■ 7" P.Disc . . . . **MTPD 60**
■ CD Single . . . . **CDMT 60**
EMI-Manhattan / Feb '89.
■ 12" **12MT 60**
■ 7" . . . . **MT 60**
EMI-Manhattan / Feb '89.

EDGE OF A BROKEN HEART.
Tracks: Edge of a broken heart / Charmed life / Edge of a broken heart (ext. mix) (Not on 7".) / Love made me (Live) (CD single only.) / Cryin' (Live) (CD single only.).
■ 12" **12MT 48**
■ 7" . . . . **MT 48**
■ 7" P.Disc . . . . **MTP 48**
■ 7" P.Disc . . . . **MTPD 48**
■ CD Single . . . . **CDMT 48**
■ MC Single . . . . **TCMT 48**
EMI-Manhattan / Aug '88.

HOW MUCH LOVE.
Tracks: How much love (single version) (7", cassingle & CD single only.) / Wrecking ball / How much love (LP version) (12" 's only.) / Bad reputation (Not on 7" or CD single.).
■ 12" P.Disc **12MTPD 87**
■ MC Single . . . . **TCMT 87**
■ 12" **12MT 87**
■ 7" . . . . **MT 87**
■ CD Single . . . . **CDMT 87**
EMI-Manhattan / Jul '90.

LOVE IS A KILLER.
Tracks: Love is a killer (edit) (Not on picture disc or 10".) / Streets in paradise (Not on 12" or CD single.) / Love is a killer (LP) (Not on 7" or 10".) / Jam, The (live) (12" only.) / I want you to rock me (live) (12" & CD single only.) / Edge of a broken heart (live acoustic) (10" & CD single only.).
■ 10" **10MT 91**
■ 7" . . . . **MT 91**
■ CD Single . . . . **CDMT 91**
■ MC Single . . . . **TCMT 91**
■ 12" P.Disc **12MTPD 91**
EMI-Manhattan / Sep '90.

LOVE MADE ME (REMIX).
Tracks: Love made me (remix) / Give it away / Cruisin' (live) (Not on 7".) / Edge of a broken heart (live) (Not on 7".) / Hellraisers (live) (Not on 7".).
■ 7" . . . . **MTS 66**
■ 12" **12MT 66**
■ 7" . . . . **MT 66**
■ 7" P.Disc . . . . **MTPD 66**
■ CD Single . . . . **CDMT 66**
EMI-Manhattan / Apr '89.

NOT A MINUTE TOO SOON.
Tracks: Not a minute too soon (radio edit) (7" & cassingle only.) / Fallen hero / Desperate (Demo) (CD single & 12" Picture disc only.) / Give it away (Demo) (CD single & 10" single only.) / Not a minute too soon (LP version) (Not on 7" or cassingle.).
■ 12" P.Disc **12MTPD 93**
■ 7" . . . . **MTS 93**
■ 7" . . . . **MT 93**
■ CD Single . . . . **CDMT 93**
■ MC Single . . . . **TCMT 93**
EMI-Manhattan / Mar '91.

REV IT UP.
Tracks: Rev it up / How much love / Love is a killer / Not a minute too soon / Streets in paradise / Hard 16 / Bad reputation / Fallen hero / Only a heartbeat away / It wouldn't be love / Wrecking ball.
CD . . . . **CDMTL 1054**
■ LP . . . . **MTL 1054**
■ MC . . . . **TCMTL 1054**
EMI-Manhattan / Aug '90.

REVVED UP.
Tracks: Edge of a broken heart / Crying / Love made me / How much love / Love is a killer / Not a minute too soon.
VHS . . . . **MVP 9912503**
PMI / Mar '91 / EMI / Gold & Sons / TBD.

VIXEN.
Tracks: Edge of a broken heart / I want you to rock me / Crying / American dream / Desperate / One night alone / Hellraisers / Love made me / Waiting / Cruisin' / Charmed life (CD only).
■ CD . . . . **CDMTL 1028**
■ LP . . . . **MTL 1028**
■ MC . . . . **TCMTL 1028**
EMI-Manhattan / Sep '88.
CD . . . . **CDFA 3256**
LP . . . . **FA 3256**
MC . . . . **TCFA 3256**
Fame / Aug '91 / EMI.

VIXEN: INTERVIEW PICTURE DISC.
Tracks: Not Advised.
LP P.Disc . . . . **BAK 2159**
Baktabak / Nov '89 / Arabesque Ltd.

VoiVod

ANGEL RAT.
Tracks: Not Advised.
■ CD . . . . **MCAD 10293**
■ LP . . . . **MCA 10293**
■ MC . . . . **MCAC 10293**
MCA / Oct '91.

BEST OF.
Tracks: Not Advised.
MC . . . . **NO 1964**
Noise / Oct '92 / Pinnacle.

COCKROACHES.
Tracks: Cockroaches.
■ 12" . . . . **N 0085**
Noise / Nov '87.

DIMENSION HATROSS.
Tracks: Not Advised.
■ CD . . . . **CDNUK 106**
■ LP . . . . **NUK 106**
■ MC . . . . **ZCNUK 106**
Noise / Oct '89.

KILLING TECHNOLOGY.
Tracks: Not Advised.
■ LP . . . . **NUK 058**
■ MC . . . . **ZCNUK 058**
Noise / May '87.
■ CD . . . . **CDNUK 058**
Noise / Oct '89.

OUTER LIMITS.
Tracks: Fix my heart / Moonbeam rider / Le pont noir / Nile song / Lost machine / Time warp / Jack luminous / Wrong way street / We are not alone.
CD . . . . **MCD 10701**
■ LP . . . . **MCA 10701**
■ MC . . . . **MCC 10701**
MCA / Jun '93.

RRROOOAAARRR.
Tracks: Not Advised.
■ CD . . . . **CDNUK 040**
■ LP . . . . **NUK 040**
Noise / Oct '89.

TOO SCARED TO SCREAM.
Tracks: Too scared to scream.
■ 12" P.Disc . . . . **NPD 085**
Noise / Sep '89.

WAR AND PAIN.
Tracks: Voi void / Suck your bone / War and pain / Live for violence / Nuclear war / Warriors of ice / Iron gang / Blower / Black city.
■ LP . . . . **RR 9825**
Road Runner / Sep '84.
■ CD . . . . **RO 98252**
Roadracer / May '89.
CD . . . . **CDMZORRO 75**
Metal Blade / May '94 / Pinnacle.

■ DELETED

Vomito Negro

DARE.
Tracks: Not Advised.
CD . . . . KK 009 CD
■ LP . . . . KK 009
K K / '89.

HUMAN.
Tracks: Not Advised.
CD . . . . KK 050 CD
LP . . . . KK 050
K K / Sep '90 / Plastic Head.

SAVE THE WORLD.
Tracks: Not Advised.
CD . . . . KKUK 002CD
LP . . . . KKUK 002
K K / '90 / Plastic Head.

SHOCK.
Tracks: Not Advised.
CD . . . . KK 023 CD
LP . . . . KK 023
K K / '89 / Plastic Head.

STAY ALIVE.
Tracks: Stay alive.
■ 12" . . . . KK 004
K K / Apr '88.

WAKE UP.
Tracks: Leathal weapon / Wake up and smell the 90's / Unclose your fears / Touch the sky / Saturday night / Innercity / Hate / Sex, Violence, Drugs.
CD . . . . AS 5078
Antler / Sep '92 / Backs Distribution.

Vortex Of Insanity

VORTEX OF INSANITY.
Tracks: End is nigh / Social decay / What you get / Immoral standing / C.I.A. / Zone / Shut up / Thorzine / Assimilation / Misfit of society.
CD . . . . H 028
Noise / Feb '94 / Pinnacle.

Vow Wow

CRY NO MORE.
Tracks: Cry no more / Sign of the times / Shockwaves (Extra track available on 12" version only.).
■ 12" . . . . RIST 46
■ 7" . . . . RIS 46
Arista / Nov '87.

CYCLONE.
Tracks: Not Advised.
■ LP . . . . ERLP 50
■ MC . . . . ERMC 50
East Rock / Jul '86.

DON'T LEAVE ME NOW.
Tracks: Don't leave me now / Nightless city / Shot in the dark.
■ 12" . . . . RIST 38
■ 7" . . . . RIS 38
Arista / Sep '87.

DON'T TELL ME LIES.
Tracks: Don't tell me lies / Siren song (Recorded live at Town And Country Club.).
■ 12" P.Disc. 609805
Arista / Feb '88.

HELTER SKELTER.
Tracks: Helter skelter / Keep on moving / Sign of the times (Available on 12" only) / Fade away (on CD single only.).
■ 12" 612013
■ 7" 112013
■ CD Single 162013
■ CD Single 662013
■ 12" . . . . 12 VWW 2
■ 7" . . . . VWWPD 2
■ 7" . . . . VWW 2
■ 7" . . . . VWWG 2
Arista / Feb '89.

HELTER SKELTER.
Tracks: I feel the power / Talking 'bout you / Spellbound / Helter skelter / Boy / Rock me now / Turn on the light / Never let you go / Night by night / You're the one for me / Sign of the times.
■ CD 259691
■ LP 209691
■ MC 409691
Arista / Feb '89.

I FEEL THE POWER.
Tracks: I feel the power / Shot in the dark / Hurricane (On 12" and 10" single.) / Nightless city (Only on 12".) / You know what I mean (Only on 10".).
■ 12" . . . . 122 VWW 3
■ 12" . . . . VWWPP 3
■ 12" . . . . 12 VWW 3
■ 7" . . . . VWW 3
■ CD Single . . . . VWWCD 3
Arista / Apr '89.

LIVE IN THE U.K.
Tracks: Doncha wanna cum / Helter skelter / Night by night / Don't leave me now / Don't tell me lies / I feel the power / You're the one for me / Keep on moving / Hurricane / Rock me now / Shot in the dark.
■ VHS . . . . MVP 99 1204 3
PMI / Feb '90.

LIVE: VOW WOW.
Tracks: Introduction - beat of metal motion / Doncha wanna come (hangar 15) / Too late to turn back / Mask of flesh (Masquerade) / Pains of love / Love walks / Premonition / Hurricane / Shot in the dark / Nightless city.
■ LP . . . . PBL 102

Pacific / Feb '87.
MC . . . . PBLT 102
Pacific / Feb '87.

ROCK ME NOW.
Tracks: Rock me now / Girl in red / Somewhere in the night / Don't leave me now / Don't wanna come (On VWW PK 1 only).
■ 12" . . . . 12 VWW 1
■ 7" . . . . VWW 1
■ CD Single . . . . VWWCD 1
■ 7" . . . . VWW PK 1
Arista / Jul '88.

VOW WOW.
Tracks: Don't tell me lies / Somewhere in the night / Girl in red / Breakout / Cry no more / Same town / Born to die / Waited for a lifetime / Don't leave me now / War man / Don't leave me now (extended version) (Extra track on cassette and CD only.).
■ Double LP . . . . HMILP 109
MC Set . . . . HMIMC 109
Heavy Metal / Mar '88 / Sony / FM Revolver.

VOW WOW V.
Tracks: You're mine / Jets / Clean machine / Can't get back to you / Heels of the wind / Poor man's Eden / 20th century child / Abnormal weather / Welcome to the monster city / Breakout the trick / Warning from stardust / Getting back on the road / Don't cry baby / Devil woman / Vow wow, Theme from.
■ CD 258678
■ LP 208678
■ MC 408678
Arista / Oct '87.

VOW WOW: INTERVIEW PICTURE DISC.
Tracks: Not Advised.
■ LP P.Disc . . . . CT 1022
Music & Media / Feb '88.

WARNING FROM STARDUST.
Tracks: You're mine / Jets / Clean machine / Can't get back to you / Heels of the wind / Poor man's Eden / 20th century child / Abnormal weather / Welcome to the monster city / Breakout the trick / Warning from stardust.
■ LP . . . . HMILP 5
Heavy Metal / Apr '83.

Vulcano

BLOODY VENGEANCE.
Tracks: Dominions of death / Spirits of evil / Ready to explode / Holocaust / Incubus / Death metal / Voices from hell / Bloody vengeance.
■ LP . . . . VOV 676
AVM / Nov '89.

W.A.S.P.

Formed by Blackie Lawless in 1982, W.A.S.P. were self styled glam-rock revivalists taking elements of Kiss and the more risque shock tactics of their peers, they achieved the notoriety Lawless craved with the release of *Animal (Fuck Like A Beast)* in 1988 and commercial success with *The Headless Children* which reached no. 8 in 1989, but sales have dwindled and the band are currently without a deal in the US following a disastrous concept album, *The Crimson Idol*, which sold reasonably but was savaged by the critics.

9.5 NASTY.
Tracks: 9.5 nasty / Easy living / Flesh and fire (available on 12" single only).
- ■ 12" 12CL 432
- ■ 7" . . . . .CL 432

Capitol / Sep '86.

ANIMAL (FUCK LIKE A BEAST).
Tracks: Animal (f**k like a beast) (live) / Animal (f**k like a beast).
- ■ 7" . . . . .CL 331
- ■ 12" 12CL 331

Capitol / Apr '84.

BLIND IN TEXAS.
Tracks: Blind in Texas / Savage / I wanna be somebody.
- ■ 7" P.Disc . . . . .CLP 374
- ■ 12" 12CL 374
- ■ 7" . . . . .CL 374

Capitol / Sep '85.

CHAINSAW CHARLIE (MURDERS IN THE NEW MORGUE).
Tracks: Chainsaw Charlie (murders in the new morgue) / Phantoms in the mirror (Not on 7" pic. disc.) / Story of Jonathan (prologue to The Crimson Idol) part 1 (Not on 7").
- ■ 12" 12RG 6308
- ■ 7" . . . . RS 6308
- ■ 7" P.Disc . . . . RPD 6308
- ■ CD Single . . . . CDR 6308

Parlophone / Apr '92.

CRIMSON IDOL, THE.
Tracks: Titanic overture / Invisible boy / Arena of pleasure / Chainsaw Charlie (murders in the new morgue) / Gypsy meets the boy / Dr. Rockter / I am one / Idol / Hold on to my heart / Great misconception of me.
- ■ LP . . . . PCSD 118

Parlophone / May '92.
- CD . . . . CDPCSD 118
- ■ MC . . . . TCPCSD 118

Parlophone / Feb '94.

FIRST BLOOD..LAST CUTS.
Tracks: Animal (fuck like a beast) / L.O.V.E. machine (remix) / I wanna be somebody (remix) / On your knees / Blind in Texas / Wild child (remix) / I don't need no doctor (remix) / Real me / Headless children / Mean man / Forever free / Chainsaw Charlie / Idol / Sunset and Babylon / Hold on to my heart / Rock and roll to death.
- CD . . . . CDESTG 2217
- LP . . . . ESTG 2217
- MC . . . . TCESTG 2217

Capitol / Nov '93 / EMI.

FIRST BLOOD..LAST VISIONS.
Tracks: Animal (fuck like a beast) / L.O.V.E. machine / I wanna be somebody / On your knees / Blind in Texas / Wild child / I don't need no doctor / Real me / Forever free / Idol / Hold on to my heart.
- VHS . . . . MVP 4911473

PMI / Nov '93 / EMI / Gold & Sons / TBD.

FOREVER FREE.
Tracks: Forever free (Eagle edit) / L.O.V.E. machine (live '89) / Blind in Texas (live '89) (12", Special product & CD single only).
- ■ 7" P.Disc . . . . CLPD 546
- ■ 12" 12CL 546
- ■ 7" . . . . CLS 546
- ■ 7" . . . . .CL 546
- ■ CD Single . . . . CDCL 546

- ■ MC Single . . . . TCCL 546

Capitol / Aug '89.

HEADLESS CHILDREN, THE.
Tracks: Heretic (the lost child) / Real me / Headless children / Thunderhead / Mean man / Neutron bomber / Mephisto waltz / Forever free / Maneater / Rebel in the F.D.G.
- ■ LP . . . . EST 2087

Capitol / Mar '89.
- ■ LP P.Disc . . . . .ESTPD 2087

Capitol / Oct '89.
- ■ LP . . . . FA 3261
- ■ CD . . . . CDFA 3261
- ■ MC . . . . TCFA 3261

Fame / Oct '91.
- CD . . . . CDEST 2087
- MC . . . . TCEST 2087

Capitol / Jul '94 / EMI.

I AM ONE.
Tracks: I am one / Wild child (On 10" only) / Chainsaw Charlie (On 10" only) / I wanna be somebody (On 10" only) / Invisible boy (On CDs only) / Real me (On CDs only) / Great misconception of me (On Cds only).
- ■ 10" 10RG 6324
- ■ CD Single . . . . CDRS 6324

Parlophone / Oct '92.

I DON'T NEED NO DOCTOR.
Tracks: Widow maker / I don't need no Doctor / Sex drive.
- ■ 12" 12CL 469
- ■ 12" P.Disc 12CLP 469
- ■ 7" . . . . CLS 469
- ■ 7" . . . . .CL 469

Capitol / Oct '87.

I WANNA BE SOMEBODY.
Tracks: I wanna be somebody / Tormentor.
- ■ 12" P.Disc 12CLP 336
- ■ 7" . . . . .CL 336

Capitol / Aug '84.

IDOL, THE.
Tracks: Idol / Story of Jonathan / Eulogy (Only available on 7"PD, 12" and CD Single.).
- ■ 12" 12RS 6314
- ■ 7" P.Disc . . . . RPD 6314
- ■ CD Single . . . . CDR 6314
- ■ 7" . . . . RS 6314

Parlophone / Jun '92.

INSIDE THE ELECTRIC CIRCUS.
Tracks: Big welcome / I don't need no doctor / Nasty restless gypsy / Shoot from the hip / I'm alive / Easy living / Sweet cheetah / Mantronic / King of Sodom and Gomorrah / Rock rolls on.
- ■ LP . . . . EST 2025

Capitol / Oct '86.
- ■ CD . . . . CDP 746 346 2

Capitol / Apr '87.
- CD . . . . CZ 212
- ■ LP . . . . ATAK 133
- MC . . . . TCATAK 133

Capitol / '89 / EMI.
- ■ LP . . . . FA 3238
- ■ CD . . . . CDFA 3238
- ■ MC . . . . TCFA 3238

Fame / Jul '90.
- CD . . . . CDEST 2025
- MC . . . . TCEST 2025

Capitol / Jul '94 / EMI.

LAST COMMAND, THE.
Tracks: Wild child / Ballcrusher / Fistful of diamonds / Cries in the night / Blind in Texas / Widowmaker / Running wild in the streets / Sex drive / Last command / Jack action.
- ■ LP . . . . WASP 2
- MC . . . . TCWASP 2

Capitol / Oct '85 / EMI.
- ■ LP . . . . FA 3218
- ■ CD . . . . CDFA 3218
- ■ MC . . . . TCFA 3218

Fame / May '89.
- CD . . . . CDCMP 1004
- MC . . . . TCCMP 1004

Capitol / Jul '94 / EMI.

LIVE AT THE LYCEUM.
Tracks: On your knees / Flame / Hellion / Sleeping / Animal / I wanna be somebody.

LIVE IN THE RAW.
Tracks: Inside the electric circus / I don't need no doctor / L.O.V.E. machine / Wild child / 9.5 nasty / Sleeping (in the fire) / Manimal / I wanna be somebody / Harder faster / Blind in Texas / Scream until you like it.
- ■ LP . . . . EST 2040

Capitol / Sep '87.
- ■ LP . . . . FA 3249
- ■ CD . . . . CDFA 3249
- ■ MC . . . . TCFA 3249

Fame / Oct '90.
- CD . . . . CDEST 2040
- MC . . . . TCEST 2040

Capitol / Jul '94 / EMI.

MEAN MAN.
Tracks: Mean man / Locomotive breath / For whom the bell tolls.
- ■ 7" . . . . CLM 521
- ■ CD Single . . . . CDCL 521
- ■ 12" 12CLG 521
- ■ 12" 12CL 521
- ■ 7" . . . . .CL 521
- ■ 7" P.Disc . . . . CLP 521

Capitol / Feb '89.

MUSIC AND MEDIA INTERVIEW PICTURE DISC.
Tracks: Not Advised.
- ■ LP P.Disc . . . . MM 1240

Music & Media / Feb '88.

REAL ME, THE.
Tracks: Real me / Lake of fools / War cry (Not on 7".).
- ■ 12" 12CL 534
- ■ 12" 12CLS 534
- ■ 7" .CLG 534
- ■ 7" . . . . .CL 534
- ■ 7" P.Disc . . . . CLPD 534
- ■ CD Single . . . . CDCL 534

Capitol / May '89.

SCHOOL DAZE.
Tracks: School daze / Paint it black.
- ■ 12" 12CL 344
- ■ 7" . . . . .CL 344

Capitol / Nov '84.

SCREAM UNTIL YOU LIKE IT.
Tracks: Scream until you like it / Shoot from the hip / Sleeping in the fire (Extra track available on 12" version only.).
- ■ 12" 12CL 458
- ■ 12" P.Disc 12CLP 458
- ■ 7" . . . . .CL 458

Capitol / Aug '87.

SUNSET & BABYLON.
Tracks: Sunset & Babylon.
- ■ 12" 12CLG 698
- ■ 12" 12CLPD 698
- ■ 7" . . . . CLP 698
- ■ CD Single . . . . CDCL 698

EMI / Nov '93.

W.A.S.P.
Tracks: I wanna be somebody / L.O.V.E. machine / Flame / B.A.D. / School daze / Hellion / Sleeping (in the fire) / On your knees / Tormentor / Torture never stops.
- ■ LP . . . . EJ 2401951

Capitol / Aug '84.
- ■ LP . . . . FA 3201
- ■ MC . . . . TCFA 3201

Fame / Jul '88.
- ■ CD . . . . CDFA 3201

Fame / May '89.
- CD . . . . CDP 7466612
- MC . . . . EJ 2401954

Capitol / Jul '94 / EMI.

W.A.S.P. INTERVIEW PICTURE DISC.
Tracks: Not Advised.
LP P.Disc . . . . BAK 2025

Baktabak / Apr '87 / Arabesque Ltd.

W.A.S.P. VIDEOS .. IN THE RAW.
Tracks: I wanna be somebody / L.O.V.E. machine / Hellion / Blind in Texas / Wild child / I don't need no doctor / Scream until you like it / Mamimal.
- ■ VHS . . . . MVR 99 0040 2

PMI / Jun '85.

■ VHS . . . . MVP 99 1161 3
PMI / May '88.

WILD CHILD.
Tracks: Wild child / Mississippi queen / On your knees / Hellion.
■ 7" Set . . . . .CLD 388
■ 12" 12CL 388
■ 7" . . . . .CL 388
Capitol / May '86.

Waite, John

Lancashire-born Waite came to fame in late '70s as leader of the Babys, who enjoyed substantial U.S. success before folding in 1981. Subsequent solo career peaked with 1984's U.S. chart-topping single *Missing You* (U.K. no. 9). In 1989, Waite reunited with ex-Baby Jonathon Cain in Bad English, before resuming solo career.

CHOICE, THE.
Tracks: Choice / No breaks.
■ 7" . . . . EA 211
EMI-America / Jan '86.

DEAL FOR LIFE.
Tracks: Deal for life.
■ 12" 6565166
■ 7" 6565167
■ 7" P.Disc 6565160
■ CD Single. 6565162
■ MC Single. 6565164
Epic / Nov '90.

ESSENTIAL JOHN WAITE.
Tracks: Head above the waves / Piece of action / Broken heart / Love don't prove I'm right / Love is a rose to me / White lightning / Run to Mexico / World in a bottle / Union Jack / Jesus are you there / Darker side of town / Rock 'n' roll is alive and well / Gonna be somebody / White heat / Make it happen / Change / Mr. Wonderful / If anybody had a heart / Missing you.
CD. CDCHR 1864
■ MC . . . . TCCHR 1864
Chrysalis / Oct '92.

EVERY STEP OF THE WAY.
Tracks: Every step of the way / No brakes.
■ 7" . . . . EA 206
EMI-America / Sep '85.

IF ANYBODY HAD A HEART.
Tracks: If anybody had a heart / Just like lovers.
■ 7" . . . . EA 220
EMI-America / Aug '86.

IGNITION.
Tracks: White heat / Change / Mr. Wonderful / Going to the top / Desperate love / Temptation / By my baby tonight / Make it happen / Still in love with you / Wild life.
■ LP . . . . CHR 1376
MC . . . . ZCHR 1376
Chrysalis / Jun '82 / EMI.

MASK OF SMILES.
Tracks: Every step of the way / Lay down / Welcome to paradise / Lust for life / Ain't that peculiar / Just like lovers / Choice / You're the one / No brakes.
■ LP . . . . .WAITE 1
MC . . . . .TC WAITE 1
EMI / Oct '85 / EMI.

MISSING YOU.
Tracks: Missing you / For your love.
■ 12" 12EA 182
■ 7" . . . . EA 182
EMI-America / Aug '84.

MISSING YOU.
Tracks: Missing you / Head above the waves / Love is a rose to me (Available on CD Single only.) / Broken heart (Available on CD Single only.)
■ 7" . . . . CHS 3938
■ CD Single . . . . CDCHS 3938
■ MC Single. . . . . TCCHS 3938
Chrysalis / Feb '93.

NO BRAKES.
Tracks: Saturday night / Missing you / Dark side of the sun / Restless heart / Tears / Euroshima / Dreamtime - shake it up / For your love / Love collision.
■ LP . . . . WAIT 1
MC . . . . TC WAIT 1
EMI-America / Nov '84 / EMI.
■ CD . . . . CDP 7460742
EMI-America / '87.

NO BRAKES LIVE.
Tracks: Not Advised.
■ VHS . . . . HEN 2225
Hendring Video / Feb '90.

RESTLESS HEART.
Tracks: Restless heart / Missing you / Euroshima.
■ 12" 12EA 193
■ 7" . . . . EA 193
EMI-America / Mar '85.

ROVER'S RETURN.
Tracks: These times are hard / Act of love / Encircled / Woman's touch / Wild one / Don't lose any sleep / Sometimes / She's the one / Big time for love.
■ CD . . . . CDP 746 332 2
■ LP . . . . AML 3121
■ MC . . . . TCAML 3121
EMI-America / Aug '87.

TEARS.
Tracks: Tears.
■ 7" . . . . EA 186
EMI-America / Nov '84.

THESE TIMES ARE HARD.
Tracks: These times are hard / For lovers / Missing you* (*Extra track on 12").
■ 12" 12EA 236
■ 7" . . . . EA 236
EMI-America / Jul '87.

Waltari

SO FINE.
Tracks: Not Advised.
CD. . . . . RR 90082
LP . . . . RR 90081
MC. . . . . RR 90084
Road Runner / Apr '94 / Pinnacle.

TORCHA.
Tracks: Not Advised.
CD. . . . . EM 91292
Road Runner / Aug '92 / Pinnacle.

Warfare

ADDICTED TO LOVE (MAYHEM MIX).
Tracks: Addicted to love / Hungry dogs (live).
■ 7" .NEAT 58
Neat / Jul '87.

CONCEPT OF HATRED, A (Anthems from the Altar).
Tracks: Dance of the dead / This machine kills / Generator / Military shadow / Atomic slut / Projectile vomit / Burn the Kings Road / Hate to create / Fatal vision.
VHS .JE 168
Jettisoundz / '88 / TBD / Visionary Communications.

CONFLICT OF HATRED.
Tracks: Waxworks / Revolution / Dancing in the flames of insanity / Evolution / Fatal vision / Death-charge / Order of the dragons / Elite forces / Rejoice the feast of quarantine / Noise filth and fury.
CD. . . . . NEATCD 1044
■ LP . . . . NEAT 1044
MC. . . . . NEATC 1044
Neat / Mar '88 / Grapevine Distribution.

DECADE OF DECIBELS.
Tracks: Not Advised.
CD. . . . . .CDBLEED 8
Bleeding Hearts / Oct '93 / Pinnacle.

HAMMER HORROR.
Tracks: Hammer horror / Plague of the zombies / Ballad of the dead / Phantom of the opera / Baron Frankenstein / Velvet rhapsody / Sold of shadows / Prince of Darkness / Tales of the gothic genre / Scream of the vampire.
■ LP . . . . REVLP 147
■ CD . . . . REVXD 147
■ MC . . . . REVMC 147
FM Records / Jun '90.
CD . . . . .FILMCD 130
Silva Screen / Apr '93 / Silva Screen / Conifer Records / Total / BMG.

MAYHEM FUCKIN' MAYHEM.
Tracks: Mayhem fucking mayhem.
■ 10" . . . . UNKNOWN
Neat / Dec '86.

MAYHEM FUCKIN' MAYHEM - HARD-CORE '88.
Tracks: Abortion sequence / Hungry dogs / Generator / You've really got me / Ebony dreams / Extremely finance / Projectile vomit / M.F.M. / Atomic slut / Machine gun breath / Murder in Melrose.

■ LP . . . . NEAT 1040
MC. . . . . NEATC 1040
Neat / '88 / Grapevine Distribution.

METAL ANARCHY.
Tracks: Electric mayhem / Death vigilance / Wrecked society / Living for the last days / Disgrace / Military shadow / Metal anarchy / Psycho / Rape / Burning up / Destroy.
■ LP . . . . NEAT 1029
Neat / Jan '86.

NOISE, FILTH AND FURY EP, THE.
Tracks: Burn the Kings road / New the age of total warfare / Noise, filth and fury.
■ EP . . . . .NEAT 41
Neat / Jul '84.

PURE FILTH.
Tracks: Warning / Total Armageddon (full scale attack) / This machine kills / Let the show go on / Breakout / Burn the Kings Road / New age of total warfare / Collision / Dance of the dead / Limit Crescendo / Rose petals fall from her face / Warfare and venom.
■ LP . . . . NEAT 1021
Neat / '85.

TOTAL DEATH.
Tracks: Total death.
■ 12" . . . . .NEAT 49 12
Neat / Jun '85.

TWO TRIBES.
Tracks: Two tribes / Hell / Blown to bits.
■ 12" . . . . .NEAT 45 12
Neat / Nov '84.

Wargasm

FIREBALL.
Tracks: Not Advised.
CD . . . . MASSCD 036
Massacre / Jul '94 / Plastic Head.

UGLY.
Tracks: Not Advised.
CD . . . . MASSCD 020
Massacre / Nov '93 / Plastic Head.

Warhead

CRY OF TRUTH.
Tracks: Cry of truth.
■ 7" . . . . AMOK 009
Amok / Jun '93.

SPEEDWAY.
Tracks: Not Advised.
■ LP . . . . FIST 8357
Mausoleum / Apr '85.

Warhorse

BEST OF WARHORSE.
Tracks: St. Louis / Ritual / Woman of the devil / Red sea / Back in time / Sybilla / I who have nothing.
■ LP . . . . THBL 030
Thunderbolt / '88.

OUTBREAK OF HOSTILITIES.
Tracks: Vulture blood / No chance / Burning / St. Louis / Ritual / Solitude / Woman of the devil / Red Sea / Back in time / Confident but wrong / Feeling better / Sybilla / Mouthpiece / I who have nothing.
CD. . . . . .CDTB 104
Magnum Music / May '91 / Magnum Music Group / TBD.

RED SEA.
Tracks: Red sea / Back in time / Confident but wrong / Feeling better / Sybilla / Mouth piece / I who have nothing.
■ LP . . . . THBL 010
MC. . . . . THBC 010
Thunderbolt / May '84 / TBD / Jazz Music.
CD. . . . . REP 4056-WP
LP . . . . REP 2056
MC. . . . . REP 2056-TT
Repertoire (Germany) / Aug '91 / Pinnacle.

VULTURE BLOOD.
Tracks: Vulture blood / No chance / Burning / St. Louis / Ritual / Solitude / Woman of the devil.
■ LP . . . . THBL 004
Thunderbolt / Sep '83.

WARHORSE.
Tracks: Not Advised.
CD. . . . . REP 4055-WP
LP . . . . REP 2055
MC. . . . . REP 2055-TS
Repertoire (Germany) / Aug '91 / Pinnacle.

■ DELETED

Warlock

BURNING THE WITCHES.
Tracks: Signs of satan / After the bomb / Dark fade / Homicide rocker / Without you / Metal racer / Burning the witches / Hateful guy / Holding me.
- ■ LP . . . . .SKULL 8325
Mausoleum / Mar '84.
MC. . . . . SKULL 78323
Mausoleum / May '84 / Pinnacle.
- ■ CD 830 902-2
- ■ LP . . . . VERH 42
- ■ MC . . . . .VERHC 42
Vertigo / Mar '87.

HELLBOUND.
Tracks: Hellbound / All night / Earth shaker rock / Wrathchild / Down and out / Out of control / Time to die / Shout it out / Catch my heart.
CD 824 660-2
- ■ LP 824 660-1
MC. 024 660-4
Vertigo / Jul '85 / PolyGram.

METAL RACER.
Tracks: Not Advised.
- ■ VHS . . . . HEN 2298
Hendring Video / Nov '90.

MUSIC AND MEDIA INTERVIEW PICTURE DISCS.
Tracks: Not Advised.
- ■ LP P.Disc . . . . MM 1246
Music & Media / Feb '88.

TRIUMPH AND AGONY.
Tracks: All we are / 3 minute warning / I rule the ruins / Kiss of death / Make time for love / East meets west / Touch of evil / Metal tango / Cold cold world / Fur immer.
- ■ CD 832 804 2
- ■ LP . . . . VERH 50
Vertigo / Nov '87.

TRUE AS STEEL.
Tracks: Mr. Gold / Fight for rock / Love in the danger zone / Speed of sound / Midnight in China / Vorwarts.all right / True as steel / Lady in a rock'n'roll hell / Love song / Igloo on the moon (reckless) / T.O.L.
- ■ CD 830 237-2
- ■ LP . . . . VERH 41
- ■ MC . . . . .VERHC 41
Vertigo / Aug '86.

WITHOUT YOU.
Tracks: Without you / Burning the witches.
- ■ 7" . . . . GUTS 8402
Mausoleum / Nov '84.

Warlord

ALPHA AND OMEGA.
Tracks: Alpha and omega.
- ■ 7" . . . . CR 18
Creole / Aug '81.

THY KINGDOM COME.
Tracks: Mrs. Victoria / Aliens / Child of the damned / Beginning/Lucifer's hammer / Black mass / Lost and lonely days / Soliloquy / Deliver us from evil / Hands and feet.
- ■ LP . . . . RR 9637
Road Runner / Apr '87.

ULTIMATE WARLORD.
Tracks: Ultimate warlord / I shall return.
- ■ 7" . . . . BN 106
Birds Nest / May '78.

Warp Drive

GIMME GIMME.
Tracks: Bang the drum / I 4 U / Words / Take take me now / Stay on stay on / Moments away / Crying girl / Eyes on you / Rock 'n' the boat / Making time stand still.
CD . . . . CDMFN 99
LP . . . . MFN 99
MC. . . . . TMFN 99
Music For Nations / May '90 / Pinnacle.

Warrant

CHERRY PIE.
Tracks: Cherry pie / Uncle Tom's cabin / I saw red / Bed of roses / Sure feels good to me / Love in stereo / Blind faith / Song and dance man / Only hell your mama ever raised / Mr. Rainmaker / Train, train.
CD 4671902
- ■ LP 4671901
- ■ MC 4671904
Columbia / Sep '90.

CHERRY PIE.
Tracks: Cherry pie (Not on 12" single) / Cherry pie (LP version) (Only on 12" single) / Thin disguise / D.R.F.S.R. (Only on 12" and CD single).
- ■ 12" 6562588
- ■ 7" 6562587
- ■ 7" P.Disc 6562580
- ■ CD Single 6562585
- ■ MC Single. 6562584
CBS / Oct '90.
- ■ 12" 6566866
- ■ 7" 6566867
- ■ 7" Set 6566860
- ■ CD Single 6566865
- ■ MC Single. 6566864
CBS / Feb '91.

DIRTY ROTTEN FILTHY STINKING RICH.
Tracks: 32 pennies in a ragu jar / Down boys / Big talk / Sometimes she cries / So damn pretty (against the law) / D R F S R / In the sticks / Heaven / Riding high / Cold sweat.
CD 4650522
- ■ LP 4650521
- ■ MC 4650524
CBS / Jun '89.

DOG EAT DOG.
Tracks: Machine gun / Hole in my wall / April 2031 / Andy Warhol was right / Defenders of creation (So far,so good) / All my bridges are burning / Quicksand / Let it rain / Inside out / Sad Theresa.
CD 4720332
- ■ LP 4720331
- ■ MC. 4720334
Columbia / Sep '92.
MiniDisc. 472033-3
Columbia / Feb '93 / Sony.

ENFORCER, THE.
Tracks: Not Advised.
- ■ LP . . . . .N 0023
Noise / '88.

HEAVEN.
Tracks: Heaven / Cold sweat / In the sticks.
- ■ 12" . . . . .HEAVN T1
- ■ 12" P.Disc. . . . . HEAVN P1
- ■ 7" . . . . HEAVN 1
- ■ 7" . . . . HEAVN Q1
- ■ CD Single . . . . HEAVN C1
CBS / Sep '89.

Warrior

BREAKOUT.
Tracks: Breakout / Dragon slayer / Take your chance.
- ■ 7" . . . . W 002
Warrior / Mar '84.

DEAD WHEN IT COME TO LOVE.
Tracks: Dead when it come to love / Kansas City / Stab in the back.
- ■ 7" . . . . .NEAT 20
Neat / Aug '82.

FIGHTING FOR THE EARTH.
Tracks: Fighting for the earth / Only the strong survive / Ruler / Mind over matter / Defenders of creation / Day of evil (beware) / Cold fire / PTM 1 / Welcome aboard.
- ■ LP . . . . XID 6
- ■ MC. . . . . .CDIX 6
10 / Jun '88.
- ■ CD . . . . .DIXCD 9
10 / Sep '90.

FIGHTING FOR THE EARTH.
Tracks: Fighting for the earth / Only the strong survive.
- ■ 12" P.Disc. . . . . .TENY 38
- ■ 7" . . . . TEN 38
10 / Feb '85.

FOR EUROPE ONLY.
Tracks: For Europe only.
- ■ 12" . . . . WT 001
- ■ 7" . . . . W 001
Warrior / Jul '83.

Warrior Soul

U.S. "acid punk" act whose reputation far outstrips their sales. Formed by Kory Clarke in 1988, band have released three albums since debut *Last Decade, Dead Century* but strained relationship with Geffen label may sink band for good.

CHILL PILL.
Tracks: Mars / Cargos of doom / Song in your mind / Shock um down / Let me go / Ha ha ha / Concrete frontier / I want some / Soft / High road.
CD . . . . GED 24608
MC. . . . . GEC 24608
Geffen / Nov '93 / BMG.

DRUGS, GOD AND THE NEW REPUBLIC.
Tracks: Not Advised.
CD . . . . DGCD 24389
- ■ LP . . . . DGC 24389
- ■ MC . . . . DGCC 24389
Geffen / May '91.

HERO.
Tracks: Hero.
- ■ 12" . . . . DGCT 10
- ■ CD Single . . . . .DGCTD 10
Geffen / Jul '92.

LAST DECADE, DEAD CENTURY.
Tracks: I see the ruins / We cry out / Losers / Down town / Trippin' on ecstasy / One minute years / Super power dreamland / Charlie's out of prison / Blown away / Lullaby / In conclusion / Four more years.
CD 7599242852
- ■ LP . . . . WX 344
MC. . . . . WX 344C
Geffen / Apr '90 / BMG.
CD. . . . . DGCD 24285
- ■ MC . . . . DGCC 24285
Geffen / Aug '91.

SALUTATIONS FROM THE GHETTO NATION.
Tracks: Love destruction / Blown / Shine like it / Dimension / Punk and belligerent / Ass-kickin' / Party / Golden shore / Trip rider / I love you / Fallen / Ghetto nation.
- ■ CD . . . . GED 24488
- ■ LP . . . . GEF 24488
- ■ MC . . . . GEC 24488
Geffen / Sep '92.

Wasted Youth

BEGINNING OF THE END.
Tracks: Paris France / Don't get me wrong / Naked emotions / Wildlife / Man found dead in graveyard / Something going wrong / Jealousy (Funk version) / Little Jack / Come midnight / (Do the caveman) / Real good time together / Caveman (Live).
- ■ LP . . . . BHLP 007
MC. . . . . BHLP 007C
Bridgehouse / May '88 / Pinnacle / Jungle Records / Kingdom Records.
CD. . . . . .BHCD 002
Bridgehouse / Oct '93 / Pinnacle / Jungle Records / Kingdom Records.

BLACK DAZE.
Tracks: Not Advised.
CD. . . . . GWCD 44
- ■ LP . . . . GWLP 44
GWR / '89.

FROM THE INNER DEPT.
Tracks: Jealousy (remixed) / She said to me / This world / If tomorrow / Comments / Caveman (re-mixed) / Rebecca's room / I wish I was a girl / Housewife / Games (a true story).
CD . . . . .BHCD 003
Bridgehouse / Oct '93 / Pinnacle / Jungle Records / Kingdom Records.

FROM THE INNER DEPTHS.
Tracks: Not Advised.
- ■ LP . . . . VCLP 5
V.C. / Dec '85.

I'LL REMEMBER YOU.
Tracks: I'll remember you / My friends are dead.
- ■ 7" . . . . BHS 10
Bridgehouse / Sep '80.

JEALOUSY.
Tracks: Jealousy / Baby.
- ■ 12" . . . . BHS 5
Bridgehouse / Mar '82.

REACH OUT.
Tracks: Reach out / Gone midnight.
- ■ 7" . . . . BHS 14
Bridgehouse / Aug '82.

REBECCA'S ROOM.
Tracks: Rebecca's room.
- ■ 7" . . . . .FRESH 30
Fresh (1) / Jun '81.

■ DELETED

WILD AND WANDERING.
Tracks: Maybe we'll die / Housewife / Games / Pinned and grinning / Wasted / I wish I was a girl / If tomorrow / Survivors Pt 1 / Survivors Pt 2.
CD . . . . BHCD 001
Bridgehouse / Oct '93 / Pinnacle / Jungle Records / Kingdom Records.

WILD AND WONDERFUL CRIES.
Tracks: Not Advised.
■ LP . . . . BHLP 006
Bridgehouse / Oct '81.

WILD LIFE.
Tracks: Wild life / Games.
■ 7" . . . . BHS 13
Bridgehouse / Apr '82.

Watchtower

CONTROL AND RESISTANCE.
Tracks: Instruments of random murder / Eldritch / Mayday in Kiev / Fall of reason / Control and resistance / Hidden instincts / Life cycles / Dangerous toy.
CD . . . . .N 0140 2
LP . . . . .N 0140 1
MC . . . . .N 0140 4
Noise / Feb '90 / Pinnacle.

NOTHINGFACE.
Tracks: Not Advised.
CD . . . . .N 0142-2
LP . . . . .N 0142-1
MC . . . . .N 0142-4
Noise / '91 / Pinnacle.

Waxface

GRAVES OF GOD, THE.
Tracks: Graves of God.
■ 12" . . . . TEST 128399
Mausoleum / Jun '86.

Waysted

Quitting UFO in 1982, bassist Pete Way sped through bands with Eddie Clark (ex-Motorhead) and Ozzy Osbourne (latter more impressed by Way's rock n' roll excesses than his bass-playing). Own project Waysted, formed 1983, lasted four albums before splitting in '88. Way returned to reformed UFO in 1990.

BLACK AND BLUE.
Tracks: Black and blue / Out of control / Wild night (Extra track on 12" version only).
■ 12" 12R 6142
■ 7" . . . . .R 6142
Parlophone / Nov '86.

CAN'T TAKE THAT LOVE AWAY.
Tracks: Can't take that love away.
■ 7" . . . . CHS 2736
Chrysalis / Oct '83.

COMPLETELY WAYSTED.
Tracks: Women in chains / Hang 'em high / Won't get out alive / Sleazy / Hot love / Dead on your legs / Hurt so good / Somebody to love / Around and around / Rock steady / Love loaded / Hi ho my baby / Toy with passion.
■ LP . . . . RAWLP 019
MC . . . . RAWTC 019
Raw Power / Sep '86 / Pinnacle.

GOOD THE BAD AND THE WAYSTED, THE.
Tracks: Not Advised.
■ LP . . . . MFN 43
MC . . . . TMFN 43
Music For Nations / May '85 / Pinnacle.

GOOD,THE BAD,THE WAYSTED, THE.
Tracks: Hang 'em high / Hi ho my baby / Heaven tonight / Manuel / Dead on your legs / Rolling out the pie / That's lost the love / Crazy 'bout the stuff / Around and around / Won't get out alive / Price you pay / Rock steady / Hurt so good / Cinderella boys / Ball and chain.
CD . . . . CDMFN 43
Music For Nations / Dec '92 / Pinnacle.

HEAVEN TONIGHT.
Tracks: Heaven tonight.
■ 12" . . . . 12 KUT 117
■ 7" . . . . .KUT 117
Music For Nations / May '85.

HEAVEN TONIGHT.
Tracks: Fire under the wheels / Hell comes home.
■ 12" 12R 6150

■ 7" . . . . .R 6150
Parlophone / Feb '87.

SAVE YOUR PRAYERS.
Tracks: Walls fall down / Black and blue / Singing to the night / Hell comes home / Heroes die young / Heaven tonight / How the west was won / Wild night / Out of control / So long.
■ LP . . . . PCS 7307
■ MC . . . . TCPCS 7307
Parlophone / Nov '86.

VICES.
Tracks: Love loaded / Sleazy / Night of the wolf / Toy with the passion / Can't take that love away / Hot love / All belongs to you / Somebody to love.
■ LP . . . . CHR 1438
■ MC . . . . ZCHR 1438
Chrysalis / Sep '83.

WAYSTED.
Tracks: Not Advised.
■ LP . . . . MFN 31
MC . . . . TMFN 31
Music For Nations / Sep '84 / Pinnacle.

Webster, Max

BATTLE SCAR.
Tracks: Battle scar / April in Toledo.
■ 7" . . . . MER 59
Mercury / Jan '81.

MAGNETIC AIR (Webster, Max Band).
Tracks: Paradise skies / Night fights / Lip service / Charmonium / Waterline / High class in borrowed shoes / Diamonds, diamonds / Gravity / Coming off the moon / Hangover.
■ LP .EST 25392
■ MC . . . . TC EST 25392
Capitol / '80.

MILLION VACATIONS.
Tracks: Paradise skies / Night flights / Charmonium / Sun voices / Moon voices / Million vacations / Lookout / Let go the line / Rascal Houdi / Research.
■ LP .EST 11937
Capitol / '79.

MUTINY UP MY SLEEVE.
Tracks: Not Advised.
■ LP .EST 11776
Capitol / Aug '78.

NIGHT FLIGHTS.
Tracks: Night flights / Hangover / High class in borrowed shoes.
■ 7" . . . . CL 16104
Capitol / Feb '80.

PARADISE SKIES.
Tracks: Paradise skies / Party / Let your man fly (Available on 12" only).
■ 12" 12CL 16079
■ 7" . . . . CL 16079
Capitol / May '79.

UNIVERSAL JUVENILES.
Tracks: In the world of giants / Check / Battle scar / April in Toledo / Juveniles don't stop / Chalkers / Drive and desire / What do you do with the urge / Blue river liquor shine / Cry out for your life.
■ LP 633 714 4
Mercury / Dec '80.

Wehrmacht

BIERMACHT.
Tracks: You broke my heart / Gore fix / Beer is here / Drink beer be free / Everb / Micro E / Balance of opinion / Suck / Drink Jack / Radical dissection / Beermacht / Outro.
■ LP . . . . SHARK 009
CD . . . . SHARK 009CD
Shark / Jun '88.
Shark / Apr '92 / Plastic Head.

BIERMACHT/SHARK ATTACK.
Tracks: Not Advised.
CD . . . . SHARK 9CD
Shark / May '89 / Plastic Head.

SHARK ATTACK.
Tracks: Not Advised.
■ LP . . . . NRR 23
New Renaissance(USA) / Oct '88.
■ LP . . . . SHARK 2
Shark / Apr '89.

Whiplash

INSULT TO INJURY.
Tracks: Voice of sanity / Hiroshima / Insult to injury / Dementia B / Essence of evil / Witness to the terror / Battle scars / Rape to the mind / Ticket to mayhem / 4.E.S. / Pistolwhipped.
CD . . . . .RO 9482-2
■ LP . . . . .RO 9482-1
Roadracer / Oct '89.

POWER AND PAIN.
Tracks: Not Advised.
■ LP . . . . RR 9718
Road Runner / '89.
CD . . . . RO 97182
Roadracer / Mar '90 / Pinnacle.

TICKET TO MAYHEM.
Tracks: Not Advised.
CD . . . . RO 95962
■ LP . . . . RR 9596
Road Runner / Apr '89.

White Lion

BEST OF WHITE LION.
Tracks: Wait / Radar love / Broken heart / Hungry / Little fighter / Lights and thunder / All you need is rock'n'roll (live version) / When the children cry / Love don't come easy / Cry for freedom / Lady of the valley (live version) / Tell me / Farewell to you.
CD 7567824252
■ LP 7567824251
MC 7567824254
Atlantic / Oct '92 / WEA.

BIG GAME.
Tracks: Goin' home tonight / Dirty woman / Little fighter / Broken home / Baby be mine / Living on the edge / Let's get crazy / Don't say it's over / If my mind is evil / Radar love / Cry for freedom.
CD 781 969-2
■ LP . . . . WX 277
■ MC . . . . WX 277C
Atlantic / Jun '89.

ESCAPE FROM BROOKLYN.
Tracks: Not Advised.
VHS 8536502763
Warner Music Video / Oct '92 / WEA.

FIGHT TO SURVIVE.
Tracks: Not Advised.
CD . . . . SLAMCD 1
■ LP . . . . SLAM 1
Grand Slam (USA) / Aug '87.
CD . . . . CDMFN 130
LP . . . . MFN 130
MC . . . . TMFN 130
Music For Nations / Jul '92 / Pinnacle.

LIGHTS AND THUNDER.
Tracks: Lights and thunder / Fight to survive / She's got everything.
■ 7" . . . . A 7727
■ MC Single . . . . A 7727C
■ CD Single . . . . A 7727CD
Atlantic / Apr '91.

MANE ATTRACTION.
Tracks: Lights and thunder / Leave me alone / Love don't come easy / You're all I need / Broken heart / Warsong / It's over / Till death do us part / Out with the boys / Farewell to you / She's got everything (Not available on LP).
CD .756782193-2
MC . . . . WX 415C
■ LP . . . . WX 415
Atlantic / Apr '91.

PRIDE.
Tracks: Hungry / Lonely nights / Don't give up / Sweet little loving / Lady of the valley / Wait / All you need is rock 'n' roll / Tell me / All join our hands / When the children cry.
CD 781 768-2
■ LP 781 768-1
MC 781 768-4
Atlantic / Jul '87 / WEA.

RADAR LOVE.
Tracks: Radar love.
■ 7" . . . . A 8836
Atlantic / Oct '89.

WAIT.
Tracks: Wait / All join our hands / Lady of the valley (Track on 12" version).
■ 7" . . . . A 9178
■ 12" . . . . A 9178 T
Atlantic / Jan '88.

WAIT.
Tracks: Wait / All you need is rock 'n' roll / Lonely nights (12" only).
- **7"** .... A 9063
- **12"** .... A 9063 T
WEA / Jul '88.

WHEN THE CHILDREN CRY.
Tracks: Then the children cry / Lady of the valley / Tell me (live) (Only on 12" single).
- **12" Remix.** .... A 9015TW
- **12"** .... A 9015T
- **7"** .... A 9015
Atlantic / Mar '89.

WHITE LION: ESCAPE FROM BROOKLYN.
Tracks: Not Advised.
VHS 85365022763
Warner Music Video / Feb '92 / WEA.

White Sister

FASHION BY PASSION.
Tracks: Place in the heart / Fashion by passion / Dancin' on midnight / Save me tonight / Ticket to ride / April / Until it hurts / Troubleshooters / Lonely teardrops / Place in my heart.
- **MC.** .... WKFMMC 76
- **LP** .... WKFMLP 76
- **CD** .... WKFMXD 76
FM Records / Mar '87.
- **LP P.Disc** .... WKFMPD 76
FM Records / May '88.

TICKET TO RIDE.
Tracks: Fashion by passion / Ticket to ride.
- **12"** .... 12 VHF 32
- **7"** .... VHF 32
FM Records / Oct '86.

WHITE SISTER.
Tracks: Don't say that you're mine / Straight from the heart / Love don't make it right / Breakin' all the rules / Whips / Can't say no / Promises / Walk away / One more night / Just for you.
- **LP** .... HMUSA 7
Heavy Metal America / Jan '85.

White Spirit

BACK TO THE GRIND.
Tracks: Back to the grind / Cheetah.
- **7"** .... NEAT 03
Neat / May '80.

HIGH UPON HIGH.
Tracks: High upon high / No reprieve.
- **7"** .... MCA 652
MCA / Nov. '80.

MIDNIGHT CHAFER.
Tracks: Midnight chafer / Suffragettes.
- **7"** .... MCA 638
MCA / Aug '80.

WHITE SPIRIT.
Tracks: Midnight chaser / Red skies / High upon high / Way of the kings / No reprieve / Don't be fooled / Fool for the gods.
- **LP** .... MCF 3079
MCA / '80.

White Trash

ON THE JOB.
Tracks: On the job.
- **12"** .... BRUTE 1
Brute International / Oct '93.

WHITE TRASH.
Tracks: Apple pie / Don't U judge me do / Take my soul / Po' white trash / Backstage pass / Lil' Nancy / Buzz / Crawl / Baby / E.D.A.S.E. / Party line / Good God / Prayer b4 pizza.
- **CD** 7559610532
- **LP** .... EKT 93
- **MC.** .... EKT 93C
WEA / Jul '91 / WEA.

White Zombie

GOD OF THUNDER.
Tracks: God of thunder / Love razor / Disaster blaster 2.
- **12"** .... CLNT 1
Virgin / '89.

LA SEXORCISTO: DEVIL MUSIC VOL. 1.
Tracks: Welcome to planet motherfucker/Psychoholic slag / Knuckle duster (Radio 1-A) / Thunder kiss / Black sunshine / Soul-crusher / Cosmic monsters inc. / Spiderbaby (yeah-yeah-yeah) / I am legend / Knuckle duster (Radio 2-B) / Thrust / One big crunch / Grindhouse (A go-go) / Starface / Warp asylum.
- **CD** .... GEFD 24460
- **MC.** .... GEFC 24460
- **LP** .... GEF 24460
Geffen / Mar '92.

MAKE THEM DIE SLOWLY.
Tracks: Demonspeed / Disaster blaster / Murderworld / Revenge / Acid flesh / Power hungry / Godslayer.
- **CD** .... CARCD 3
- **LP** .... CARLP 3
- **MC.** .... CARC 3
Caroline / Feb '89.

SOUL CRUSHER.
Tracks: Not Advised.
- **LP** .... SILENT 002
Silent Explosion / Jan '88.

Whitesnake

Whitesnake were formed in 1978 by singer David Coverdale, and named after one of two solo albums he made after leaving Deep Purple. Whitesnake's following was maintained by heavy touring, but the band made little impact in America until multimillion selling *1987* set, which included *Is This Love* hit. Next album, *Slip Of The Tongue* saw arrival of guitar virtuoso Steve Vai, but Whitesnake ground to halt in early '90s. Following collaboration with Jimmy Page (yielding one album and brief Japanese tour), Coverdale revived Whitesnake in 1994; opening new era with successful *Greatest Hits* album.

AIN'T NO LOVE IN THE HEART OF THE CITY.
Tracks: Ain't no love in the heart of the city / Take me with you.
- **7"** .... BP 381
- **12"** 12BP 381
United Artists / Nov '80.

CHRIS TETLEY INTERVIEWS WHITESNAKE.
Tracks: Not Advised.
- **LP P.Disc** .... CT 1006
Music & Media / Oct '87.

COME AN' GET IT.
Tracks: Come an' get it / Hot stuff / Don't break my heart again / Lonely days, lonely nights / Wine, women and song / Child of Babylon / Would I lie to you / Girl / Hit and run / Til the day I die.
- **LP** .... LBG 30327
- **MC.** .... TC LBG 30327
Liberty / Apr '81.
- **LP** .... FA 3219
- **CD** .... CDFA 3219
- **MC.** .... TCFA 3219
Fame / May '89.
- **CD** .... CDEMS 1528
- **MC.** .... TCEMS 1528
EMI / Jul '94 / EMI.

DEEPER THE LOVE, THE.
Tracks: Deeper the love / Judgement day / Sweet lady luck (12" & CD single only.) / Fool for your loving (Vai voltage mix) (CD single only.).
- **CD Single** .... CDEM 128
- **12"** 12EM 128
- **12"** 12EMS 128
- **7"** .... EM 128
- **7" P.Disc** .... EMPD 128
- **MC Single** .... TCEM 128
EMI / Feb '90.

DON'T BREAK MY HEART AGAIN.
Tracks: Don't break my heart again / Child of Babylon.
- **7"** .... BP 395
Liberty / Apr '81.

FOOL FOR YOUR LOVING.
Tracks: Fool for your loving / Mean business / Don't mess with me.
- **7"** .... BP 352
Liberty / Apr '80.

FOOL FOR YOUR LOVING.
Tracks: Fool for your loving (7" 's only.) / Slow poke music / Fool for your loving (album version) (Not on

---

7" 's) / Walking in the shadow of the blues (live) (12" 's only.).
- **12"** 12EM 123
- **12"** 12EMS 123
- **7"** .... EM 123
- **7" P.Disc** .... EMP 123
EMI / Nov '89.

FORKED TONGUE THE INTERVIEW.
Tracks: Not Advised.
CD P.Disc .... CBAK 4064
Baktabak / Feb '94 / Arabesque Ltd.

FOURPLAY.
Tracks: Fool for your loving / Here I go again / Don't break my heart again / Guilty of love.
VHS .... MVS 99 0006 2
PMI / Jan '84.
VHS .... PM 0008
Video Collection / May '87 / Gold & Sons / Video Collection / TBD.
VHS .... MC 2006
Music Club Video / May '87 / Video Collection / Gold & Sons / TBD.

GIVE ME ALL YOUR LOVE.
Tracks: Give me all your love (Edit version on 7" single.) / Fool for your loving / Don't break my heart again / Here I go again (Only on CD single.) / Straight for the heart (Only on 3"CD single.).
- **12"** 12EM 23
- **7"** .... EM 23
- **7"** .... EMW 23
- **CD Single** .... CDEM 23
- **12" P.Disc** 12EMP 23
EMI / Jan '88.

GIVE ME MORE TIME.
Tracks: Give me more time / Need your love so bad.
- **7"** .... BP 422
- **12"** 12BP 422
Liberty / Jan '84.

GREATEST HITS.
Tracks: Still of the night / Here I go again / Is this love / Love ain't no stranger / Now you're gone / Slide it in / Slow an' easy / Judgement day / You're gonna break my heart again / Deeper the love / Crying in the rain / Fool for your loving / Sweet lady luck.
CD .... CDEMD 1065
LP .... EMD 1065
MC. .... TCEMD 1065
EMI / Jun '94 / EMI.

GUILTY OF LOVE.
Tracks: Guilty of love / Gambler.
- **7"** .... BP 420
- **7" P.Disc** .... BPP 420
Liberty / Aug '83.

HERE I GO AGAIN.
Tracks: Here I go again (USA remix) / Guilty of love / Guilty of love (USA remix)
- **7"** .... BP 416
Liberty / Oct '82.
- **12" Remix.** 12EMI 35
- **10"** 10EM 35
- **12"** 12EM 35
- **7"** .... EM 35
- **7" P.Disc** .... EMP 35
EMI / Oct '87.

IS THIS LOVE.
Tracks: Is this love / Standing in the shadow / Need your love so bad (Extra track on 12" & CD only) / Still of the night (Extra track on CD only).
- **EP** .... EMX 3
- **12" P.Disc** 12EMP 3
- **CD Single** .... CDEM 3
- **12"** 12EM 3
- **7"** .... EM 3
EMI / May '87.

IS THIS LOVE.
Tracks: Is this love / Sweet lady luck / Now you're gone (Features on CDEM 329 only.).
7" .... EMS 329
7" .... EM 329
CD Single .... CDEM 329
MC Single .... TCEM 329
EMI / Jul '94 / EMI.

LIE DOWN.
Tracks: Lie down / Don't mess with me.
- **7"** .... INT 568
EMI International / Sep '78.

LIVE IN THE HEART OF THE CITY.
Tracks: Come on / Sweet talker / Walking in the shadow of the blues / Love hunter / Fool for your loving / Ain't gonna cry no more / Ready an' willing / Take me with you / Might just take your life / Lie

---

down / Ain't no love in the heart of the city / Trouble /
Mistreated.
■ **Double LP**. . . . . SNAKE 1
United Artists / Oct '80.
■ **MC Set** TC2SNAKE 1
United Artists / Oct '80.
■ **CD Set**. . . . . CDS 7908602
United Artists / Jul '88.
■ **CD** . . . . CDFA 3265
■ **MC** . . . . TCFA 3265
Fame / Nov '91.
CD. . . . . CDEMS 1525
MC. . . . . TCEMS 1525
EMI / Jul '94 / EMI.

LONG WAY FROM HOME.
Tracks: Long way from home / Trouble / Ain't no love
in the heart of the city.
■ **7″** . . . . BP 324
United Artists / Nov '79.

LOVE AIN'T NO STRANGER.
Tracks: Love ain't no stranger / Slow an' easy / Slide
it in.
■ **12″** 12BP 424
■ **7″** . . . . BP 424
Liberty / Jan '85.

LOVEHUNTER.
Tracks: Long way from home / Walking in the sha-
dow of the blues / Help me thro' the day / Medicine
man / You'n'me / Mean business / Love hunter /
Outlaw / Rock'n'roll women / We wish you well.
■ **LP** . . . . UAG 30264
United Artists / Oct '79.
■ **LP** . . . . FA 3095
MC. . . . . TCFA 3095
Fame / Apr '84 / EMI.
■ **CD** . . . . CDFA 3095
Fame / Apr '88.
CD . . . . CDEMS 1529
EMI / Jul '94 / EMI.

NORTHWINDS (see under Coverdale, David).

NOW YOU'RE GONE.
Tracks: Now you're gone (remix) / Wings of the
storm (LP version) (Not on 12″.) / Kittens got claws
(LP version) (Not on 7″.) / Cheap an' nasty (LP
version).
■ **12″** 12EMG 150
■ **7″** . . . . EM 150
■ **CD Single**. . . . . CDEM 150
■ **MC Single**. . . . . TCEM 150
EMI / Sep '90.

READY AN' WILLING.
Tracks: Fool for your loving / Sweet talker / Ready
an' willing / Carry your load / Blindman / Ain't gonna
cry no more / Love man / Black and blue / She's a
woman.
■ **LP** . . . . UAG 30302
United Artists / Jun '80.
■ **LP** . . . . FA 3134
MC. . . . . TCFA 3134
Fame / Sep '85 / EMI.
■ **CD** . . . . CDFA 3134
Fame / Apr '88.
CD . . . . CDEMS 1526
EMI / Jul '94 / EMI.

READY AN' WILLING.
Tracks: Ready an' willing / Nighthawk / We wish you
well.
■ **7″** . . . . BP 363
United Artists / Jul '80.

SAINTS 'N' SINNERS.
Tracks: Young blood / Rough and ready / Bloody
luxury / Victim of love / Crying in the rain / Here I go
again / Love and affection / Rock and roll angels /
Dancing girls / Saints and sinners.
■ **LP** . . . . LBG 30354
Liberty / Nov '82.
■ **LP** . . . . ATAK 10
MC. . . . . TCATAK 10
Liberty / '85 / EMI.
■ **LP** . . . . FA 3177
MC. . . . . TCFA 3177
Fame / May '87 / EMI.
■ **CD** . . . . CDFA 3177
Fame / Apr '88.
CD. . . . . CDEMS 1521
EMI / Jul '94 / EMI.

SLIDE IT IN.
Tracks: Gambler / Slide it in / Standing in the sha-
dow / Give me more time / Love ain't no stranger /
Slow an' easy / Spit it out / All or nothing / Hungry for
love / Guilty of love / Need your love so bad (Slide
only.).
MC. . . . . TCATAK 120
■ **LP** . . . . WHITE 1

■ **MC**. TCWHITE 1
EMI / Jan '84.
CD. . . . . CZ 88
EMI / Apr '88 / EMI.

SLIP OF THE TONGUE.
Tracks: Slip of the tongue / Cheap an' nasty / Fool for
your loving / Now you're gone / Kittens got claws /
Wings of the storm / Deeper the love / Judgment day
/ Slow poke music / Sailing ships.
■ **LP** . . . . EMD 1013
■ **CD** . . . . CDEMD 1013
■ **MC** . . . . TCEMD 1013
EMI / Nov '89.
CD . . . . CDEMS 1527
MC. . . . . TCEMS 1527
EMI / Jul '94 / EMI.

SNAKEBITE.
Tracks: Keep on giving me love / Queen of hearts /
Breakdown.
CD. . . . . CGHS 24174
MC. . . . . XGHS 24174
Geffen / Jan '89 / BMG.

SNAKEBITE (EP).
Tracks: Bloody Mary / Steal away / Ain't no love in
the heart of the city / Come on.
■ **EP** . . . . INEP 751
EMI International / Jun '78.

STANDING IN THE SHADOW.
Tracks: Standing in the shadow / All or nothing.
■ **7″** . . . . BP 423
■ **7″ P.Disc** . . . . BPP 423
Liberty / Apr '84.

STILL OF THE NIGHT.
Tracks: Still of the night / Here I go again (1987) /
You're gonna break my heart again (Extra track on
12″ only).
■ **12″** 12EMI 5606
■ **12″ P.Disc**. 12EMIP 5606
■ **7″** . . . . EMI 5606
EMI / Mar '87.

TIME IS RIGHT FOR LOVE.
Tracks: Time is right for love / Come on.
■ **7″** . . . . INT 578
EMI International / '79.

TRILOGY.
Tracks: Still of the night / Here I go again / Is this
love / Give me all your love.
VHS . . . . MVS 99 0073 3
PMI / Mar '88 / EMI / Gold & Sons / TBD.

TROUBLE.
Tracks: Take me with you / Love to keep you warm /
Lie down / Day tripper / Nighthawk (vampire blues) /
Time is right for love / Trouble / Belgian Tom's hat
trick / Free flight / Don't mess with me.
■ **LP** . . . . INS 3022
EMI International / Nov '78.
■ **LP** . . . . UAG 30305
United Artists / May '80.
■ **LP** . . . . FA 3002
■ **MC** . . . . TCFA 3002
Fame / May '82.
■ **LP** . . . . EMS 1257
MC. . . . . TCEMS 1257
Liberty / Aug '87 / EMI.
CD . . . . CZ 9
EMI / Apr '88 / EMI.
CD . . . . CDFA 3234
■ **LP** . . . . FA 3234
MC. . . . . TCFA 3234
Fame / May '90 / EMI.

WHITESNAKE (see under Coverdale, David).

WHITESNAKE 1987.
Tracks: Still of the night / Bad boys / Give me all your
love / Looking for love / Crying in the rain / Is this
love / Straight for the heart / Don't turn away /
Children of the night / Here I go again (1987) / You're
gonna break my heart again (CD only.)
CD . . . . CDEMC 3528
■ **LP** . . . . EMC 3528
■ **MC** . . . . TCEMC 3528
■ **LP P.Disc** . . . . EMCP 3528
EMI / Apr '87.
■ **LP** . . . . EMCX 3528
■ **CD** . . . . CDEMCX 3528
■ **MC** . . . . TCEMCX 3528
EMI / Nov '87.
MiniDisc. 746702-3
EMI / Apr '93 / EMI.
DCC . . . . DCCEMC 3528
EMI / Jan '93 / EMI.
CD . . . . CDEMS 1531
MC. . . . . TCEMS 1531
EMI / Jul '94 / EMI.

WHITESNAKE LIVE.
Tracks: Not Advised.
VHS . . . . MVP 99 1044 2
PMI / Oct '84 / EMI / Gold & Sons / TBD.

WHITESNAKE/NORTHWINDS (see under Coverdale, David).

WHITESNAKE: INTERVIEW PICTURE DISC.
Tracks: Not Advised.
LP P.Disc. . . . . BAK 2049
Baktabak / Jul '87 / Arabesque Ltd.

WOULD I LIE TO YOU.
Tracks: Would I lie to you / Girl.
■ **7″** . . . . BP 399
Liberty / Jun '81.

Who

One of the most significant rock bands to
emerge from the 1960's. The Who - Roger
Daltry, Pete Townsend, John Entwistle, and
Keith Moon (d. 7/9/78) - progressed from
pop and R&B covers as the Detours and
High Numbers to the 'ace faces' of the burgeoning London mod scene. Their exhilarating live show climaxed in a frenzy of
instrument trashing. First hit single - *I Can't
Explain* (1965), third single *My Generation*
released later the same year became the
anthem for the young. The Who enjoyed
many more hit singles - *Substitute, Happy
Jack, I'm a Boy* etc - but by the close of the
decade they began to concentrate on albums and touring. Rock opera *Tommy* was
a resounding success, as was *Live At Leeds*
which confirmed their status as one of the
world's top live acts. 1971's *Who's Next*,
yielded classic *Won't Get Fooled Again* single. *Quadrophenia* (1973) was spiritual successor to *Tommy*, albums since have been
less memorable. Kenny Jones (ex-Small
Faces/Faces) joined as drummer following
Moon's tragic death. The Who split in 1982,
but reformed to play at Live-Aid in 1985.

30 YEARS OF MAXIMUM R'N'B.
Tracks: I'm the face / Here 'tis / Zoot suit / Leaving
here / I can't explain / Anyway, anyhow, anywhere /
Daddy rolling stone / My generation / Kids are
alright / Ox / Legal matter / Substitute / I'm a boy /
Disguises / Happy Jack / Boris the spider / So sad
about us / Quick one / Pictures of Lily / Early
morning cold taxi / (This could be) The last time / I
can't reach you / Girl's eyes / Bag o' nails / Call me
lightning / I can see for miles / Mary Anne with the
shaky hand / Armenia city in the sky / Tattoo / Our
love was / Rael 1 / Rael 2 / Sunrise / Jaguar /
Melancholia / Fortune teller / Magic bus / Little Billy
/ Dogs / Overture / Acid queen / Underture (Live) /
Pinball wizard / I'm free / See me feel me (Live) /
Heaven and hell / Young man blues (Live) / Summertime blues (Live) / Shakin' all over / Baba O' Riley /
Bargain / Pure and easy / Song is over / Behind blue
eyes / Won't get fooled again / Seeker / Bony Moronie (Live) / Let's see action / Join together / Replay /
Real me / 5.15 / Bell boy / Love reign o'er me / Long
live rock / Naked eye (Live) / Slip kid / Dreaming
from the waist (Live) / Blue, red and grey / Squeeze
box / My wife (Live) / Who are you / Music must
change / Sister disco / Guitar and pen / You better
you bet / Eminence front / Twist and shout (Live) /
I'm a man (Live) / Saturday night's alright for
fighting.
CD Set 521751-2
Polydor / Feb '94 / PolyGram.

5:15.
Tracks: 5:15.
■ **7″** 2094 115
Track / Oct '73.
■ **7″** . . . . WHO 3
Polydor / Oct '79.

ANYWAY, ANYHOW, ANYWHERE.
Tracks: Anyway, anyhow, anywhere.
■ **7″** 05935
Brunswick / May '65.

ATHENA.
Tracks: Athena.
■ **12″**. . . . . WHOX 6
■ **12″ P.Disc**. . . . . WHOPX 6
■ **7″** . . . . WHO 6
■ **7″ P.Disc** . . . . WHOP 6
Polydor / Sep '82.

BEST OF THE SIXTIES.
Tracks: Substitute / I'm a boy / Pictures of Lily /
Won't get fooled again / Long live rock / Happy Jack

/ Kids are alright / I can see for miles / Seeker / 5:15 / Magic bus.
- ■ LP 825 746-1
- MC. 825 746-4

Karussell Gold / Aug '85.

COLLECTION: WHO.
Tracks: Not Advised.
- CD Set . . . . SMD 570
- ■ Double LP . . . . SMR 570
- MC Set . . . . SMC 570

Stylus / Oct '88.

DOGS.
Tracks: Dogs.
- ■ 7" 604 023

Track / Jun '68.

DON'T LET GO THE COAT.
Tracks: Don't let go the coat / You.
- ■ 7" . . . . .WHO 5

Polydor / Apr '81.

FACE DANCES.
Tracks: You better you bet / Don't let go the coat / Cache cache / Quiet one / Did you steal my money / How can you do it alone / Daily records / You / Another tricky day.
- ■ LP . . . . WHOD 5037
- MC . . . . WHODC 5037

Polydor / Mar '81 / PolyGram.
- MC. SPEMC 112
- ■ LP . . . . SPELP 112

Polydor / May '88.

GREATEST HITS: WHO.
Tracks: Not Advised.
- MC . . . . ADAHC 427
- ■ LP . . . . ADAH 427

Arcade Music Gala / Apr '86.

HAPPY JACK.
Tracks: Happy Jack.
- ■ 7" 591 010

Reaction / Dec '66.

HOOLIGANS.
Tracks: Not Advised.
- ■ LP . . . . MCA 212001
- ■ MC . . . . MCAC 212001

MCA / Dec '88.

I CAN SEE FOR MILES.
Tracks: I can see for miles.
- ■ 7" 604 011

Track / Oct '67.

I CAN'T EXPLAIN.
Tracks: I can't explain.
- ■ 7" 05926

Brunswick / Feb '65.

I'M A BOY.
Tracks: I'm a boy.
- ■ 7" 591 004

Reaction / Sep '66.

IT'S HARD.
Tracks: Athena / It's your turn / Cooks county / Dangerous / Eminence front / I've known no war / One life's enough / It's hard / One at a time / Why did I fall for that / Man is a man / Cry if you want.
- ■ LP . . . . WHOD 5066
- ■ CD 800 106-2

Polydor / '83.

JOIN TOGETHER.
Tracks: Overture / 1921 / Amazing journey / Sparks / Hawker, The (eyesight to the blind) / Christmas / Cousin Kevin / Acid queen / Pinball wizard / Do you think it's alright / Fiddle about / There's a doctor / Go to the mirror / Smash the mirror / Tommy can you hear me / I'm free / Miracle cure / Sally Simpson / Sensation / Tommy's holiday camp / We're not gonna take it / Eminence front / Face the face / Dig / I can see for miles / Little is enough / 5.15 / Love, reign o'er me / Trick of the light / Rough boys / Join together / You better you bet / Behind blue eyes / Won't get fooled again.
- CD . . . . CDVDT 102
- ■ LP Set . . . . VDT 102
- ■ MC Set . . . . TCVDT 102

Virgin / Mar '90.

JOIN TOGETHER.
Tracks: Join together / I can see for miles / Behind blue eyes / Christmas (Only on CD single).
- ■ 12" . . . . VST 1259
- ■ 7" . . . . VS 1259
- ■ CD Single . . . . VSCDT 1259

Virgin / Mar '90.

JOIN TOGETHER.
Tracks: Join together.
- ■ 7" .2094 102

Track / Jun '72.

KIDS ARE ALRIGHT, THE (Film Soundtrack).
Tracks: My generation / I can't explain / Happy Jack / I can see for miles / Magic bus / Long live rock / Anyway anyhow anywhere / Young man blue / Baba O'Riley / My wife / Quick one / Tommy can you hear me / Sparks / Pinball wizard / See me, feel me / Join together / Road runner / My generation blues / Won't get fooled again.
- ■ Double LP 2675 179
- ■ MC 3577 343

Polydor / Jun '79.

KIDS ARE ALRIGHT, THE.
Tracks: Kids are alright.
- ■ 7" 05965

Brunswick / Sep '66.

KIDS ARE ALRIGHT, THE.
Tracks: Not Advised.
- VHS 791 5142

Polygram T.V. / Sep '84 / PolyGram.
- ■ VHS 74321 10087-30

BMG / Oct '92.

KIDS ARE ALRIGHT, THE.
Tracks: Not Advised.
- Laser Disc 7432110087-6

BMG / Feb '94 / BMG.

LAST TIME, THE.
Tracks: Last time.
- ■ 7" 604 006

Track / Jul '67.

LEGAL MATTER, A.
Tracks: Legal matter / Instant party.
- ■ 7" 05956

Brunswick / Mar '66.

LET'S SEE ACTION.
Tracks: Let's see action.
- ■ 7" .2094 012

Track / Oct '71.

LIVE AT LEEDS.
Tracks: Magic bus / My generation / Shakin' all over / Substitute / Summer time blues / Young man blues.
- ■ LP . . . . SPELP 50
- ■ MC . . . . SPEMC 50

Track / Nov '83.
- CD 825 339-2

Polydor / May '88 / PolyGram.

LONG LIVE ROCK.
Tracks: Long live rock / I'm the face / My wife.
- ■ 7" . . . . .WHO 2

Polydor / Apr '79.

MAGIC BUS.
Tracks: Magic bus.
- ■ 7" 604 024

Track / Oct '68.

MEATY, BEATY BIG AND BOUNCY.
Tracks: I can't explain / Kids are alright / Happy Jack / I can see for miles / Pictures of Lily / My generation / Seeker / Anyway, anyhow, anywhere / Pinball wizard / Legal matter / Boris the spider / Magic bus / Substitute / I'm a boy.
- ■ MC .3191 006
- ■ LP .2406 006

Track / '74.

MY GENERATION.
Tracks: My generation / Shout and shimmy.
- ■ 7" 05944

Brunswick / Nov '65.

MY GENERATION.
Tracks: My generation / Substitute / Baba O'Riley (Only on 12", CD, and MC single.) / Behind blue eyes (Only on 12", CD, and MC single.).
- ■ 12" . . . . POSPX 907
- ■ 7" . . . . POSP 907
- ■ CD Single . . . . POCD 907
- ■ MC Single. . . . . POSPC 907

Polydor / Feb '88.

MY GENERATION (BRUNSWICK).
Tracks: Not Advised.
- ■ LP . . . . LAT 8616

Brunswick / Dec '65.

MY GENERATION (POLYDOR).
Tracks: My generation / Substitute / Seeker / Magic bus / Happy jack / I'm free / Pictures of Lily / Let's see action / I'm a boy / Kids are alright / Pinball wizard / I can see for miles.
- ■ LP .2486 140
- MC .3195 235

Polydor / May '81 / PolyGram.

MY GENERATION (VIRGIN).
Tracks: Out in the street / I don't mind / Good's gone / La la la lies / Much too much / My generation / Kid's are alright / Please please please / It's not true / I'm a man / Legal matter / Ox.
- ■ LP . . . . V 2179
- ■ MC . . . . TCV 2179

Virgin / Oct '80.

ODDS AND SODS.
Tracks: Not Advised.
- ■ MC .3191 116
- ■ LP .2406 116

Track / Nov '74.

PICTURES OF LILY.
Tracks: Pictures of Lily.
- ■ 7" 604 002

Track / Apr '67.

PINBALL WIZARD.
Tracks: Pinball wizard.
- ■ 7" 604 027

Track / Mar '69.

QUADROPHENIA.
Tracks: I am the sea / Real me / Cut my hair / Punk and the godfather / I've had enough / 5:15 / Helpless dancer / Is it in my head / I've had enough / 5:15 / Sea and sand / Drowned / Bell boy / Dr. Jimmy / Rock / Love reign o'er me.
- ■ Double LP 265 701 3
- ■ MC Set 352 600 1

Polydor / Sep '79.
- CD Set 831 074-2

Polydor / '88 / PolyGram.

QUADROPHENIA.
Tracks: Not Advised.
- CD 519 999-2

Polydor / Sep '93 / PolyGram.

QUICK ONE, A.
Tracks: Run, run, run / Boris the spider / I need you / Whiskey man / Heatwave / Cobwebs and strange / Don't look away / See my way / So sad / About us / Quick one / While he's away.
- ■ LP 593 002

Reaction / Dec '66.
- ■ LP .2683 038
- ■ MC .3533 022

Track / '74.
- CD 835 728-2
- ■ LP . . . . SPELP 114
- MC. . . . . SPEMC 114

Polydor / Aug '88 / PolyGram.

RARITIES VOLUME 1 (1966-68).
Tracks: Not Advised.
■ LP .SPELP 9
■ MC . . . . SPEMC 9
Track / Aug '83.

RARITIES VOLUME 2 (1970-1973).
Tracks: Not Advised.
■ LP . . . . SPELP 10
■ MC . . . . SPEMC 10
Polydor / Aug '83.

RARITIES VOLUMES 1 AND 2.
Tracks: Not Advised.
CD. 847 670-2
MC. 847 670-4
Polydor / Jan '91 / PolyGram.

READY STEADY WHO.
Tracks: Disguises / Circles / Batman / Bucket "T" / Barbara Ann.
■ EP .WHO 7
Polydor / Nov '83.

RELAY.
Tracks: Relay.
■ 7" 2094 106
Track / Jan '73.

SEEKER, THE.
Tracks: Seeker.
■ 7" 604 036
Track / Apr '70.

SINGLES, THE.
Tracks: Substitute / I'm a boy / Happy Jack / Pictures of lily / I can see for miles / Magic bus / Pinball wizard / My generation / Summertime blues / Won't get fooled again / Let's see action / Join together / Squeeze box / Who are you / You better you bet.
CD. 815 965-2
MC . . . . WHOHC 17
■ LP . . . . WHOH 17
Polydor / Nov '84.

SQUEEZE BOX.
Tracks: Squeeze box / Success story.
■ 7" 2121 275
Polydor / Jan '76.

STORY OF THE WHO, THE.
Tracks: Magic bus / Substitute / Boris the spider / Run, run, run / I'm a boy / Heatwave / My generation / Pictures of Lily / Happy Jack / Seeker / I can see for miles / Bargain / Squeeze box / Amazing journey / Acid queen / Do you think it's alright / Fiddle about / Pinball wizard / I'm free / Tommy's holiday camp / We're not gonna take it / See me feel me / Summertime blues / Baba O'Riley / Behind blue eyes / Slip kid / Won't get fooled again.
■ MC. 3519 020
■ Double LP. 2683 069
Polydor / Oct '76.

SUBSTITUTE.
Tracks: Substitute.
■ 7" 591 001
Reaction / Mar '66.

SUBSTITUTE.
Tracks: Substitute / I'm a boy / Pictures of Lily.
■ 7" 2058803
Polydor / Oct '76.

SUMMERTIME BLUES.
Tracks: Summertime blues.
■ 7" 2094 002
Track / Aug '70.

TALKIN' BOUT THEIR GENERATION.
Tracks: Not Advised.
CD P.Disc. . . . . CBAK 4067
Baktabak / Feb '94 / Arabesque Ltd.

TOMMY (Who & London Symphony Orchestra).
Tracks: Not Advised.
■ Double LP. . . . . ESSLP 029
■ MC . . . . ESSMC 029
Essential / Aug '90.
■ CD . . . . ESSCD 029
Essential / Dec '92.

TOMMY - PART 2.
Tracks: Do you think it's alright / Fiddle about / Pinball wizard / There's a doctor / Go to the mirror / Tommy, can you hear me / Smash the mirror / Sensation / Miracle cure / Sally Simpson / I'm free / Welcome / Tommy's holiday camp / We're not gonna take it.
■ LP 2406 008
■ MC 914 625
Track / '74.

TWIST AND SHOUT.
Tracks: Twist and shout / I can't explain.
■ 7" . . . . MCA 927
MCA / Nov '84.

TWO'S MISSING.
Tracks: Not Advised.
CD . . . . SPECD 117
■ LP . . . . SPELP 117
MC. . . . . SPEMC 117
Polydor / Oct '88 / PolyGram.

WHO ARE YOU.
Tracks: New song / Had enough / 905 / Music must change / Trick of the light / Guitar and pen / Love is coming down / Who are you.
■ LP . . . . WHOD 5004
Polydor / Sep '78.
■ LP . . . . SPELP 77
■ MC. . . . . SPEMC 77
Polydor / Aug '84.
CD 831 557-2
Polydor / Jul '89 / PolyGram.
■ MC 831 557-4
Polydor / Oct '90.

WHO ARE YOU.
Tracks: Who are you.
■ 7" . . . . .WHO 1
Polydor / Jul '78.

WHO BY NUMBERS, THE.
Tracks: Slip kid / However much I booze / Squeeze box / Dreaming from the waist / Imagine a man / Success story / They are all in love / Blue, red and grey / How many friends / In a hand or a face.
■ LP 2490 129
■ MC 3194 129
Polydor / '75.
■ MC . . . . SPEMC 68
■ LP . . . . SPELP 68
Polydor / Mar '84.
CD 831 552-2
■ MC 831 552-4
Polydor / Jul '89.

WHO COLLECTION VOLUME 1, THE.
Tracks: I can't explain / Anyway, anyhow, anywhere / My generation / Substitute / Legal matter / Kids are alright / I'm a boy / Happy Jack / Boris the spider / Pictures of Lily / I can see for miles / Won't get fooled again / Seeker / Let's see action / Join to-gether / Relay / Love reign o'er me / Squeeze box / Who are you / Long live rock / 5:15 / You better, you bet / Magic bus / Summertime blues / Shakin' all over / Pinball wizard / Acid queen / I'm free / We're not gonna take it / Baba O'Riley / Behind blue eyes / Bargain.
■ Double LP. . . . . IMDP 4
MC Set . . . . IMDK 4
Impression / Oct '85 / Pinnacle.

WHO COLLECTION VOLUME 2, THE.
Tracks: Not Advised.

WHO LIVE, THE (Featuring the Rock Opera, Tommy).
Tracks: Not Advised.
VHS 490282
CMV Enterprises (Video) / Nov '89 / Sony.

WHO ROCKS AMERICA, THE.
Tracks: Not Advised.
VHS 623450
CBS-Fox / '88 / Sony / TBD.

WHO SELL OUT, THE.
Tracks: Armenia City in the sky / Heinz baked beans / Mary Anne with the shaky hand / Odorono / Tattoo / Our love was / I can see for miles / Can't reach you / Medac / Silas Stingy / Sunrise / Rael (1 and 2).
■ LP 613 002
Track / Jan '68.
MC. . . . . TWOMC 8
Polydor / Oct '84 / PolyGram.
CD 835 782-2
■ LP . . . . SPELP 115
MC. . . . . SPEMC 115
Polydor / Aug '88 / PolyGram.

WHO'S BETTER WHO'S BEST (Very best of The Who).
Tracks: My generation / Anyway, anyhow, anywhere / Kids are alright / Substitute / I'm a boy / Happy Jack / Pictures of Lily / I can see for miles / Who are you / Won't get fooled again / Magic bus / I can't explain / Pinball wizard / I'm free / See me feel me / Squeeze box / Join together / You better you bet / Baba O'Riley (Extra track on CD.).
CD 835 389-2
■ LP . . . . WTV 1
MC. . . . . WTVC 1
Polydor / Mar '88 / PolyGram.

DCC 835 389-5
Polydor / Jan '93 / PolyGram.

WHO'S BETTER WHO'S BEST.
Tracks: Not Advised.
VHS . . . . CFV 05562
Channel 5 / Mar '88 / Channel 5 Video / P.R.O. Video / Gold & Sons.
CD Video 080 344 1
Polygram Music Video / Oct '88 / PolyGram.

WHO'S LAST.
Tracks: My generation / I can't explain / Substitute / Boris the spider / Magic bus / Twist and shout.
■ LP . . . . .WHO 1
■ MC. . . . . .WHOC 1
MCA / Dec '84.
■ CD . . . . .DWHO 1
MCA / Dec '88.
CD . . . . MCLD 19005
■ MC . . . . MCLC 19005
MCA / Apr '92.

WHO'S MISSING.
Tracks: Not Advised.
CD . . . . SPECD 116
■ LP . . . . SPELP 116
MC. . . . . SPEMC 116
Polydor / Oct '88 / PolyGram.

WHO'S NEXT.
Tracks: Baba O'Riley / Getting in tune / Love ain't for keeping / My wife / Song is over / Bargain / Going mobile / Behind blue eyes / Won't get fooled again.
■ LP 2408 102
Track / Sep '71.
■ LP . . . . SPELP 49
■ MC . . . . SPEMC 49
Track / Feb '83.

WHO: INTERVIEW PICTURE DISC.
Tracks: Not Advised.
LP P.Disc. . . . . BAK 2040
Baktabak / May '87 / Arabesque Ltd.

WON'T GET FOOLED AGAIN.
Tracks: Won't get fooled again / Bony Moronie (live).
■ 7" 2094 009
Polydor / Aug '79.

WON'T GET FOOLED AGAIN.
Tracks: Won't get fooled again / Bony Moronie (live) / Dancing in the street (live) (on 12" and CD single only) / Marie Anne with the shaky hand (on 12" and CD single only) / Won't get fooled again (extended version) (on 12" and CD single only).
■ 12" . . . . .POSP 917
■ 12" Remix . . . . .POSPX 917
■ CD Single . . . . .POCD 917
Polydor / Jun '88.

YOU BETTER YOU BET.
Tracks: You better you bet / Quiet one.
■ 7" . . . . .WHO 4
Polydor / Feb '81.

Whores Of Babylon

METROPOLIS.
Tracks: Not Advised.
CD. . . . . CANDLE 006CD
Candlelight (1) / Aug '94 / Plastic Head.

WHORES OF BABYLON.
Tracks: Whores of Babylon (mixes).
■ 12" . . . . LGEP 001
Love Gun / Dec '93.

Widowmaker

BLOOD & BULLETS.
Tracks: Not Advised.
CD. . . . . .CDMFN 161
Music For Nations / Apr '94 / Pinnacle.

Widowmaker

ON THE ROAD.
Tracks: On the road / Pin a rose on me.
■ 7" . . . . .JET 766
Jet / Feb '76.

WHAT A WAY TO FALL.
Tracks: What a way to fall / Here comes the queen.
■ 7" . . . . UP 36263
United Artists / Jun '77.

Wild Dogs

REIGN OF TERROR.
Tracks: Metal fuel (in the blood) / Man against machine / Call of the dark / Siberian vacation / Psychoradio / Streets of Berlin / Spellshock / Reign of terror / We rule the night.
■ LP . . . . MFN 80
Music For Nations / Nov '87.

Wild Horses

Short-lived creation of Thin Lizzy guitarist Brian Robertson and Rainbow bassist Jimmy Bain. Eponymous 1980 debut made deservedly minor impact; second album failed even to chart and band was defunct by end of 1981. Robertson made cameo in Motorhead and Bain joined former Rainbow cohort Ronnie Dio's band.

EVER LASTING LOVE.
Tracks: Ever lasting love / Axe.
■ 7" . . . . EMI 5199
EMI / Jun '81.

FACE DOWN.
Tracks: Face down / Dealer.
■ 7" . . . . EMI 5047
EMI / Mar '80.

FLYAWAY.
Tracks: Flyaway / Blackmail.
■ 7" . . . . EMI 5078
EMI / May '80.

I'LL GIVE YOU LOVE.
Tracks: I'll give you love / Kid / Rocky mountain way / Saturday night.
■ 7" . . . . EMI 5149
EMI / Apr '81.

STAND YOUR GROUND.
Tracks: I'll give you love / In the city / Another lover / Back in the U.S.A. / Stand your ground / Axe / Miami justice / Precious / New York City / Stake out.
■ LP . . . . EMC 3368
EMI / May '81.

WILD HORSES.
Tracks: Reservation / Face down / Blackmail / Fly away / Dealer / Street girl / No strings attached / Criminal tendencies / Nights on the town / Woman.
■ LP . . . . EMC 3324
EMI / Apr '80.
■ LP . . . . EMC 3326
■ MC . . . . TCEMC 3326
EMI / May '80.

Wild Strawberries

WILD STRAWBERRIES.
Tracks: Not Advised.
■ LP . . . . METALP 116
Metal Masters / Apr '87.

Wildfire

BRUTE FORCE AND IGNORANCE.
Tracks: Not Advised.
MC . . . . TAPE 78307
Mausoleum / Jul '84 / Pinnacle.

JERUSALEM.
Tracks: Jerusalem.
■ 7" . . . . GUTS 8405
Mausoleum / Mar '85.

NOTHING LASTS FOREVER.
Tracks: Nothing lasts forever / Blood money.
■ 7" . . . . GUTS 8403
Mausoleum / Nov '84.

SUMMER LIGHTNING.
Tracks: Not Advised.
■ LP . . . . SKULL 8338
Mausoleum / Sep '84.

Wildhearts

Volatile band formed by the unpredictable Ginger after he left the Quireboys in 1990. The first surprise he sprung on an unsuspecting world was that Wildhearts sounded nothing like either his erstwhile employers or those of his guitar-slinging partner CJ, who had been in glam/sleaze rockers Tattooed Love Boys. Instead, the first two EP's *Mondo Akimbo A-Go-Go* and *Don't Be Happy..Just Worry* were a blindingly unusual mixture of sounds, prompting comparisons

with everyone from the Beatles and Soul Asylum, to Metallica and Husker Du. The immaculate debut album, *Earth Versus The Wildhearts*, heralded tidal waves of media appreciation but Ginger was still not satisfied. The line-up now seems in constant flux with only he and bassist Danny left from the original band.

DON'T BE HAPPY..JUST WORRY.
Tracks: Not Advised.
CD 4509912022
■ LP 4509912021
East West / Nov '92.
CD 450996067-2
MC 450996067-4
WEA / Apr '94 / WEA.

EARTH VS THE WILDHEARTS.
Tracks: Greetings from Shitsville / TV tan / Everlone / Shame on me / Loveshit / Miles away baby / My baby is a headfuck / Suckerpunch / News of the world / Drinking about life (Not available on LP.) / Love you til I don't.
CD 4509932012
LP 4509932011
MC 4509932014
Bronze / Feb '94 / WEA.

GIRLFRIEND'S CLOTHES.
Tracks: Caffeine bomb / Girlfriend clothes.
■ 12" . . . . YZ 794T
■ 7" . . . . YZ 794
■ CD Single . . . . YZ 794CD
■ MC Single . . . . YZ 794C
East West / Jan '94.

GREETINGS FROM SHITSVILLE.
Tracks: Greetings from Shitsville / Bullshit goes on.
■ 7" . . . . YZ 773
East West / Oct '93.

TV TAN.
Tracks: TV Tan / Show a little emotion.
■ 12" . . . . YZ 784T
■ 7" . . . . YZ 784
■ CD Single . . . . YZ 784CD
■ MC Single . . . . YZ 784C
WEA / Oct '93.

Wildlife

AFRICAN BABY.
Tracks: African baby / Barcelona.
■ 12" . . . . POLO 12-20
■ 7" . . . . POLO 20
Polo / Mar '82.

BURNING.
Tracks: Burning / Playing it too close to the heart / Alena / Misplaced love / If the night / Incredible shrinking love / I'm winning / That diamond / Too late / Only a fool.
■ LP . . . . CHR 1288
Chrysalis / Jun '80.

BURNING.
Tracks: Burning / Too late.
■ 7" . . . . CHS 2430
Chrysalis / May '80.

DANCED MY LIFE AWAY.
Tracks: Danced my life away / Need your love so bad / Original sin.
■ 12" 6565776
■ 7" 6565777
■ CD Single 6565772
■ MC Single 6565774
Epic / Jan '91.

POWER TO WIN, THE.
Tracks: Power to win / Warrior.
■ 12" 12BRUNO 1
■ 7" . . . . BRUNO 1
PRT / Feb '89.

RAT RACE.
Tracks: Rat race / Buck-she / Original sin.
■ MC Single 6560354
■ 12" 6560356
■ 7" 6560357
■ CD Single 6560352
Epic / Aug '90.

SOMEWHERE IN THE NIGHT.
Tracks: Somewhere in the night / Sun don't shine.
■ 7" . . . . B 9842
WEA / Oct '83.

WILDLIFE.
Tracks: Rat race / Mr. Wonderful / Who do you love / Hey, don't let me down / Let's go / Lament for the lost / Land of the lost / Million to one shot blues / Life's end / So long / Danced my life away / Wildlife.

■ CD 4673612
■ LP 4673611
■ MC 4673614
Epic / Sep '90.

WILDLIFE (SWANSONG).
Tracks: Somewhere in the night / Just a friend / Surrender / Charity / One last chance / Haven't you heard the news / Midnight stranger / Rock and roll dreams / Downtown heartbreak.
■ LP . . . . B 0078
Swansong / Jul '83.

Wildside

UNDER THE INFLUENCE.
Tracks: Hang on Lucy / So far away / Monkey see monkey do / Just another night / Looks like love / Lad in sin / Drunkin' man's blues / How many lies / Hair of the dog / Heart-n-soul / Kiss this love goodbye / Clock strikes 12.
■ CD . . . . CDP 798 654 2
■ LP . . . . EST 2176
■ MC . . . . TCEST 2176
Capitol / Aug '92.

Willard

STEEL MILL.
Tracks: Not Advised.
■ CD . . . . RO 91622
■ MC . . . . RO 91621
Road Runner / Jul '92.

Winger

CAN'T GET ENUFF.
Tracks: Can't get enuff / Loosen up / Time to surrender.
■ 12" . . . . A 6112T
East West / Nov '90.

IN THE HEART OF THE YOUNG.
Tracks: Can't get enuff / Miles away / Rainbow in the rose / Under one condition / Baptized by fire / In the heart of the young / Loosen up / Easy come, easy go / In the day we'll never see / Little dirty blonde / You are the Saint, I am the sinner.
CD 7567821032
■ LP 7567821031
MC 7567821034
Atlantic / Jul '90 / WEA.

IN THE HEART OF THE YOUNG.
Tracks: Not Advised.
VHS 8536502223
Warner Music Video / Oct '92 / WEA.

MILES AWAY.
Tracks: Miles away / In the day we'll never see / All I ever wanted / Seventeen.
■ 12" . . . . A 7802W
■ 12" . . . . A 7802T
■ 7" . . . . A 7802
■ CD Single . . . . A 7802CD
■ MC Single . . . . A 7802C
East West / Jan '91.

PULL.
Tracks: Blind revolution mad / Down incognito / Spell I'm under / In my veins / Junkyard dog (tears on stone) / Lucky one / In for the kill / No man's land / Like a ritual / Who's the one.
CD 756782485-2
MC 756782485-4
East West / May '93 / WEA.

WINGER.
Tracks: Madalaine / Hungry / Seventeen / Without the night / Purple haze / State of emergency / Time to surrender / Poison angel / Hangin' on / Headed for a heartbreak.
CD . . . . K 781 867 2
■ LP . . . . K 781 867 1
MC . . . . K 781 867 4
Atlantic / Aug '88 / WEA.

Winters Reign

IN THE BEGINNING.
Tracks: Not Advised.
CD . . . . LOPCD 501
■ LP . . . . LOPL 501
MC . . . . LOPC 501
Loop / Feb '88 / EMI.

WINTERS REIGN.
Tracks: Not Advised.
CD . . . . GWCD 100
LP . . . . GWLP 100
MC . . . . GWTC 100
GWR / Apr '90 / Pinnacle.

■ DELETED

Wishbone Ash

Formed in 1969, Ash enjoyed heyday between '71 and '73; celebrated '72 album *Argus* made U.K. Top Three. Between 1974's *There's The Rub* and '82's *Twin Barrels Burning*, Ash managed UK chart placing for virtually every album but these tended to be of minor nature. They were kept afloat by live following in U.S., Europe and Britain, but their music remained ensconced in early '70s. Having split in 1983, band reformed in '87 to record one-off instrumental for Miles Copeland's *No Speak* album series. Reunion became permanent although Ash have yet to return to even minor chart status.

ARGUS.
Tracks: Time was / Sometime world / Blowin' free / King will come / Leaf and stream / Warrior / Throw down the sword.
■ LP . . . . MDKS 8006
MCA / May '72.
■ MC. . . . . MCLC 1787
■ LP . . . . MCL 1787
MCA / Feb '84.
■ LP . . . . CLALP 140
■ MC . . . . CLAMC 140
Castle Classics / '88.
■ LP . . . . DMCL 1787
MCA / Jul '91.
MC. . . . . MCLC 19085
MCA / Nov '91 / BMG.
CD. . . . . MCLD 19085
MCA / Nov '92 / BMG.

BEST OF WISHBONE ASH.
Tracks: Blind eye / Blowin' free / King will come / Persephone.
■ LP . . . . MCF 3134
MCA / Jun '82.

BLOWIN' FREE.
Tracks: Blind eye / Phoenix / Persephone / Outward bound / Pilgrim / (In all my dream) You rescue me / Time was / King will come / Blowin' free / Throw down the sword / Lady whiskey / Rock 'n' roll widow / Ballad of the beacon / Jailbait / Everybody needs a friend / Mother of pearl.
CD. . . . . NTRCD 014
MC. . . . . NTRC 014
Quality / Feb '94 / Pinnacle.

CLASSIC ASH.
Tracks: Blind eye / Phoenix / Pilgrim / Blowin' free / King will come / Rock 'n' roll widow / Persephone / Outward bound / Throw down the sword (live).
■ LP . . . . MCL 1621
■ MC. . . . . MCLC 1621
MCA / Aug '81.
■ LP . . . . FA 3053
MC. . . . . TCFA 3053
Fame / Jan '83 / EMI.

COSMIC JAZZ.
Tracks: Cosmic jazz / T-Bone shuffle / Bolan's monument (12" only.).
■ 12" . . . . EIRST 104
■ 7" . . . . EIRS 104
I.R.S. (Illegal) / May '88.

ENGINE OVERHEAT.
Tracks: Engine overheat.
■ 7" . . . . WISH 1
AVM / Oct '82.

FRONT PAGE NEWS.
Tracks: Surface to air / Front page news / Midnight dancer / Goodbye baby, hello friend / Come in from the rain / Right or wrong / Heart beat / Day I found your love / Diamond Jack / 714.
■ LP . . . . MCG 3524
MCA / Oct '77.
■ LP . . . . MCL 1655
■ MC. . . . . MCLC 1655
MCA / Jan '82.

GET READY.
Tracks: Get ready / Kicks on the street.
■ 7" . . . . MCA 726
MCA / Jun '81.

HELPLESS.
Tracks: Helpless / Blowing free.
■ 12" . . . . MCAT 577
■ 7" . . . . MCA 577
MCA / May '80.

HERE TO HEAR.
Tracks: Cosmic jazz / Keeper of the light / Mental radio / Walk on water / Witness on wonder / Lost cause in paradise / Why don't we / In the case / Hole in my heart (part one) / Hole in my heart (part two).

CD. . . . . EIRSACD 1006
■ LP . . . . EIRSA 1006
MC. . . . . EIRSAC 1006
I.R.S. (Illegal) / May '89 / EMI.

IN THE SKIN.
Tracks: In the skin.
■ 7" . . . . IRM 164
I.R.S. (Illegal) / May '88.

JUST TESTING.
Tracks: Living proof / Haunting me / Insomnia / Helpless / Pay the price / New rising star / Master of disguise / Lifeline.
■ LP . . . . MCF 3052
MCA / Feb '80.

LIVE DATES.
Tracks: King will come / Warrior / Throw down the sword / Lady whiskey / Phoenix / Rock 'n' roll widow / Ballad of the beacon / Baby what you want me to do / Pilgrim / Blowin' free / Jailbait.
■ Double LP. . . . . MCSP 254
■ MC Set . . . . MCSPC 254
MCA / '74.

LIVE DATES II.
Tracks: Not Advised.
■ LP . . . . MCG 4012
MCA / Nov '80.
■ LP . . . . MCL 1799
MCA / Jul '84.

LIVING PROOF.
Tracks: Living proof.
■ 7" . . . . MCA 549
MCA / Jan '80.

LOCKED IN.
Tracks: Rest in peace / No water in the well / Moonshine / She was my best friend / It started in heaven / Half past lovin' / Trust in you / Say goodbye.
■ LP . . . . MCF 2750
MCA / Apr '76.

NEW ENGLAND.
Tracks: Mother of pearl / You rescue me / Runaway / Lorelei / Outward bound / Prelude / When you know love / Lonely island / Candlelight.
■ LP . . . . MCG 3523
MCA / Nov '76.
■ LP . . . . MCL 1699
■ MC. . . . . MCLC 1699
MCA / Jul '82.

NO MORE LONELY NIGHTS.
Tracks: No more lonely nights.
■ 7" . . . . AVM 1002
AVM / Dec '82.

NO SMOKE WITHOUT FIRE.
Tracks: You see red / Baby the angels are here / Ships in the sky / Stand and deliver / Anger in harmony / Like a child / Way of the world.
■ LP . . . . MCG 3528
MCA / Oct '78.

NOUVEAU CALLS.
Tracks: Tangible evidence / Clousseau / Flags of concenience / From Soho to Sunset / Arabesque / In the skin / Something's happening in room 602 / Johnny left home without it / Spirit flies free / Rose is a rose / Real guitars have wings.
■ LP . . . . MCF 1028
■ CD . . . . DMCF 1028
■ MC. . . . . MCFC 1028
MCA / Feb '88.
CD. . . . . ILPCD 39
■ LP . . . . MIRF 1028
I.R.S. (Illegal) / Jan '89.

NUMBER THE BRAVE.
Tracks: Loaded / Where is the love / Underground / Kicks on the street / Open road / Get ready / Rainstorm / That's that / Rollercoaster / Number the brave.
■ LP . . . . MCF 3103
MCA / Apr '81.

PHOENIX.
Tracks: Not Advised.
■ VHS . . . . HEN 2244
Hendring Video / Apr '90.

PILGRIMAGE.
Tracks: Vas dis / Pilgrim / Jailbait / Alone / Lullaby / Valediction / Where were you tomorrow.
■ LP . . . . MDKS 8004
MCA / Oct '71.
■ LP . . . . MCL 1762
■ MC. . . . . MCLC 1762
MCA / '83.
■ CD . . . . DMCL 1762

MCA / '91.
CD. . . . . MCLD 19084
■ MC. . . . . MCLC 19084
MCA / Nov '92.

PILGRIMAGE/ARGUS.
Tracks: Pilgrim / Time was / Vas dis / Throw down the sword / Warrior / Leaf and stream / King will come / Blowin' free / Sometime world / Jailbait / Alone / Valediction / Where were you tomorrow / Lullaby.
■ MC Set . . . . MCA 2 103
MCA (Twinpax Cassettes) / Apr '82.

RAW TO THE BONE.
Tracks: Cell of fame / People in motion / Don't cry / Love is blue / Long live the night / Rocket in my pocket / It's only love / Don't you mess / Dreams / Perfect timing.
■ LP . . . . NEAT 1027
■ LP P.Disc. . . . . NEATP 1027
MC. . . . . NEATC 1027
Neat / '85 / Grapevine Distribution.
CD. . . . . CLACD 390
Castle / Aug '93 / BMG.

SILVER SHOES.
Tracks: Silver shoes / Persephone.
■ 7" . . . . MCA 176
MCA / Feb '75.

STRANGE AFFAIR.
Tracks: Strange affair / Wings of desire / Dream train / You / Hard times / Standing in the rain / Renegade / Say you will / Rollin' / Some conversation.
CD. . . . . EIRSACD 1045
■ LP . . . . EIRSA 1045
MC. . . . . EIRSAC 1045
I.R.S. (Illegal) / Apr '91 / EMI.

THERE'S THE RUB.
Tracks: Silver shoes / Don't come back / Persephone / Hometown / Lady Jay / F.U.B.B.
■ LP . . . . MCF 2585
MCA / Nov '74.

TWIN BARRELS BURNING.
Tracks: Engine overheat / Can't fight love / Genevieve / My guitar / Hold on / Streets of shame / No more lonely nights / Angels have mercy / Wind up.
■ LP . . . . ASH 1
AVM / Oct '82.
CD. . . . . CLACD 389
Castle / Aug '93 / BMG.

UNDERGROUND.
Tracks: Underground / My mind is made up.
■ 7" . . . . MCA 695
MCA / Apr '81.

WISHBONE ASH.
Tracks: Blind eye / Lady whisky / Errors of my ways / Queen of torture / Handy / Phoenix.
■ LP . . . . MKPS 2014
MCA / Jan '71.

WISHBONE ASH - LIVE IN CHICAGO.
Tracks: Not Advised.
CD. . . . . PERMCD 6
MC. . . . . PERMMC 6
■ LP . . . . PERMLP 6
Permanent / Oct '92.

WISHBONE ASH IN CONCERT.
Tracks: Not Advised.
CD. . . . . WINCCD 4
MC. . . . . WINCMC 4
Windsong / Sep '91 / Pinnacle / A.D.A. Distribution.

WISHBONE ASH LIVE.
Tracks: Real guitars have wings / King will come / Cosmic jazz / Keeper of the light / Why don't we / Blowing free / Blind eye / Lady Whiskey / Sometime world / Phoenix / Jailbait.
■ VHS . . . . MVP 991 210 3
PMI / Jun '90.

WISHBONE FOUR.
Tracks: So many things to say / Ballad of the beacon / No easy road / Everybody needs a friend / Doctor / Sorrel / Sing out the song / Rock 'n' roll widow.
■ LP . . . . MDKS 8011
MCA / May '73.
■ CD . . . . MCAD 10350
MCA / Oct '91.
■ MC. . . . . MCLC 19149
MCA / Mar '93.
CD. . . . . MCLD 19149
MCA / Aug '94 / BMG.

YOU SEE RED.
Tracks: You see red / Bad weather blues.
■ 7" . . . . MCA 392
MCA / Sep '78.

Witchfinder General

BURNING A SINNER.
Tracks: Burning a sinner / Satans children.
■ 7" . . . . HEAVY 6
Heavy Metal / Sep '81.

DEATH PENALTY.
Tracks: Invisible hate / Free country / Death penalty / No stayer / Witchfinder general / Burning a sinner / R.I.P.
■ LP . . . . HMRLP 8
Heavy Metal / Nov '82.

FRIENDS OF HELL.
Tracks: Not Advised.
■ LP . . . . HMRLP 13
Heavy Metal / Nov '83.

MUSIC.
Tracks: Music / Last chance.
■ 7" . . . . HEAVY 21
■ 7" P.Disc . . . . HMPD 21
Heavy Metal / Dec '83.

SOVIET INVASION.
Tracks: Soviet invasion / Rabies / R.I.P.
■ 7" .12HM 17
Heavy Metal / Jan '83.

Witchfynde

CONSPIRACY.
Tracks: Conspiracy / Scarlet lady.
■ 7" . . . . GUTS 8404
Mausoleum / Mar '85.

GIVE 'EM HELL.
Tracks: Ready to roll / Divine victim / Leaving Nadir / Getting heavy / Give 'em hell / Unto the ages of the ages / Pay now love later.
■ LP . . . . ABOUT 1
MC. . . . . CARB 1
Rondelet Music / May '80 / Pinnacle.

GIVE 'EM HELL.
Tracks: Give 'em hell.
■ 7" . . . . ROUND 1
Rondelet Music / Feb '80.

I'D RATHER GO WILD.
Tracks: I'd rather go wild / Cry wolf.
■ 7" . . . . OUT 3
Expulsion / Jul '83.

IN THE STARS.
Tracks: In the stars.
■ 7" . . . . ROUND 4
Rondelet Music / Sep '80.

LORDS OF SIN.
Tracks: Not Advised.
■ LP . . . . .SKULL 8352
MC. . . . . TAPE 78352
Mausoleum / Dec '84 / Pinnacle.

STAGE FRIGHT.
Tracks: Stage fright / Doing the right thing / Would not be seen dead in heaven / Wake up screaming / Big deal / Moon magic / In the stars / Trick or treat / Madeleine.
■ LP . . . . ABOUT 2
MC. . . . . CARB 2
Rondelet Music / Oct '80 / Pinnacle.

Witchkiller

DAY OF THE SAXONS.
Tracks: Not Advised.
CD. 047554
■ LP .601826
Steamhammer (Germany) / '89.

Wolf

EDGE OF THE WORLD.
Tracks: Not Advised.
■ LP . . . . .SKULL 8323
MC. . . . . TAPE 78323
Mausoleum / Jun '84 / Pinnacle.

Wolf Spider

DRIFTEN IN THE SULLEN SEA.
Tracks: Not Advised.
CD. . . . . .CDFLAG 63
LP .FLAG 63
Under One Flag / Sep '91 / Pinnacle.

KINGDOM OF PARANOIA.
Tracks: Manifestants / Pain / Black'n'white / Foxes / Waiting for sense / Desert / Sickened nation / Nasty-ment / Survive / Weakness.
CD. . . . . .CDFLAG 49
LP .FLAG 49
MC. . . . . .TFLAG 49
Under One Flag / Nov '90 / Pinnacle.

Wolfsbane

Cheerful headbangers who made three albums for Rick Rubin's Def American label from '89-'91, but are likely to be best remembered for losing frontman Blaze Bayley to Iron Maiden. 1993 album *Massive Live Injection* provided handy epitaph.

AFTER MIDNIGHT.
Tracks: After midnight / Idol / Win or lose (Only on 12" and CD Single.) / Hey babe (acoustic) (Only on 12" and CD Single.).
■ 12". . . . . DEFA 1412
■ 7" . . . . .DEFA 14
■ CD Single . . . . .DEFAC 14
■ MC Single. . . . . DEFAM 14
American Recordings / Jan '92.

ALL HELL'S BREAKING LOOSE (Down at Little Kathy Wilson's Place).
Tracks: Steel / Paint the town red / Loco / Hey babe / Totally nude / Kathy Wilson.
■ Mini LP 8469671
■ MC. 8469674
■ CD 8469672
American Recordings / Oct '90.

DOWN FALL ALL THE GOOD GUYS.
Tracks: Love, smashed and blind / You load me down / Ezy / Black lagoon / Broken doll / Twice as mean / Cathode Ray clinic / Loveless / Midnight / Temple of rock / Dead at last / Moonlight.
■ LP 5104131
■ MC. 5104134
■ CD. 5104132
American Recordings / Oct '91.

EZY.
Tracks: Ezy / Black lagoon / Fucked off (Only on 12" and CD single).
■ 12". . . . . DEFA 1112
■ 7" . . . . .DEFA 11
■ CD Single . . . . .DEFAC 11
American Recordings / Sep '91.

I LIKE IT HOT.
Tracks: I like it hot / Limo (live) / Loco (live) (12" and CD only) / Manhunt (live) (CD only).
■ 12". . . . . DEFA 312
■ 7" . . . . DEFA 3
■ CD Single . . . . DEFAC 3
American Recordings / Dec '90.
■ 12" Remix. . . . . DEFAR 312
■ 7" . . . . DEFAT 3
American Recordings / Mar '90.

LIVE FAST DIE FAST.
Tracks: Man hunt / Shakin' killing machine / Fell out of heaven / Money to burn / Greasy / I like it hot / All or nothing / Tears from a fool / Pretty baby.
CD. 8384862
■ LP 8384861
MC. 8384864
American Recordings / Jul '89 / PolyGram.

MASSIVE NOISE INJECTION.
Tracks: Not Advised.
CD. . . . . ESSCD 193
■ MC. . . . . ESSMC 193
■ LP . . . . ESDLP 193
Essential / May '93.

SHAKIN'.
Tracks: Shakin' / Brando / Angel (On 12" and CD single only.) / Money to burn (On CD only.).
■ 7" . . . . DEFA 2
■ MC Single. . . . . DEFAM 2
■ 12". . . . . DEFA 212
■ 7" . . . . .DEFAS 2
■ CD Single . . . . .DEFAC 2
American Recordings / Nov '89.

WASTED BUT DANGEROUS.
Tracks: Loco (Nitro-methane injected turbo super fireball from hell mix.) / Dance dirty (Wickedly sensual grinding pelvis mix.) / Limousine (Stains on the back seat mix.) / Killer (Slow tortuous death - vomit under a full moon mix.) / Wasted but dangerous.
■ 12". . . . . .WSB 2
London / Oct '88.

WOLFSBANE.
Tracks: Not Advised.
CD. . . . . ESSCD 211
MC. . . . . ESSMC 211
Essential / Feb '94 / Total / BMG.

Wool

BUDSPAWN.
Tracks: Not Advised.
CD. ALLCD 1
■ LP . . . . ALLP 1
MC. . . . . ALLC 1
Parallel / May '93 / RTM / Pinnacle.

LITTLE DARLIN'.
Tracks: Little darlin'.
■ 7" . . . . .FU 001X
Scooby Doo / Jun '92.

MEDICATION.
Tracks: Medication.
■ 12". LLX 7
Parallel / Jun '93.

World War III

WORLD WAR III.
Tracks: Not Advised.
■ LP . . . . HWDLP 3
Hollywood (2) / Jul '91.

Wraith

DANGER CALLING.
Tracks: Not Advised.
CD. WARCD 7
LP . . . . WARLP 7
MC. . . . . .WARMC 7
Warhammer / Sep '92 / Grapevine Distribution.

NAKED AGGRESION.
Tracks: Not Advised.
■ LP . . . . AZTY 001
Aztec Communications / Oct '89.

RIOT.
Tracks: Not Advised.
CD. WARCD 9
LP . . . . WARLP 9
MC. . . . . .WARMC 9
Warhammer / May '93 / Grapevine Distribution.

Wrath

FIT OF ANGER.
Tracks: Not Advised.
■ LP . . . . MEGATON 0015
Megaton / Jul '86.

WRATH.
Tracks: Not Advised.
LP . . . . .MID 94011
Medusa (USA) / May '90.

Wrathchild

Kiss-style act from glam-capital Evesham, boasting equally-plausible members Rocky Shades, Lance Rokkit, Marc Angel and Eddie Starr. After 1984 debut *Stakk Attakk*, contractual disputes delayed next album for four years. Band toned down image, but were back to square one by 1989 release of *Delirium*.

BIZ SUXX (BUT WE DON'T CARE), THE.
Tracks: Biz suxx / Millionaire / Hooked / (Na na) nukklear rokket / Wild wild honey / Ring my bell / Hooligunz / She'z no angel / O.K. U.K. / Noo sensation / Stikky fingerz.
■ CD . . . . HMR XD 116
■ LP . . . . HMR LP 116
■ LP P.Disc . . . . HMR PD 116
■ MC. . . . . HMR MC 116
Heavy Metal / Nov '88.

CLIMBING THE WALLS.
Tracks: Not Advised.
■ LP . . . . PR 2572-4
Atlantic / Feb '89.

DELIRIUM.
Tracks: Delirium / Watch me shake it / That's what U get / My girlz / Long way 2 go / Good girlz / Do what you wanna / Kid pusher / She's high on luv / Rock me over / Only 4 the fun / Drive me krazy.
■ CD . . . . WKFMXD 137
■ LP . . . . WKFMLP 137

■ MC. . . . . WKFMMC 137
FM Records / Dec '89.

DO YOU WANT MY LOVE.
Tracks: Do you want my love / Twist of the knife.
■ 7" P.Disc . . . . PBOL 5
■ 12" . . . . BOLT 5
■ 7" . . . . BOL 5
Bullet / Sep '83.

NUKKLEAR ROKKET.
Tracks: (Na na) nukklear rokket / Pretty vacant (live)
(Only on 12" single.) / Trash queen (live).
■ 12" . . . . 12 VHF 50
■ 7" . . . . VHF 50
FM Records / Mar '89.

ROCK THE CITY DOWN.
Tracks: Rock the city down.
■ 12" . . . . BOLT 2
Bullet / Mar '83.

STACKHEELED STRUT.
Tracks: Stackheeled strut.

STAKK ATTAKK.
Tracks: Stakk attakk / Too wild to tame / Trash queen
/ Sweet surrender / Kick down the walls / Tonight /
Law abuzer / Shokker / Alrite with the boyz /
Wreckless.
■ LP . . . . HMR LP 18
■ LP P.Disc . . . . HMRPD 18
■ MC. . . . . HMRMC 18
Heavy Metal / Jun '84.
■ CD. . . . . HMRXD 18
Heavy Metal / Apr '89.

TRASH QUEENS.
Tracks: Do you want my love / Rock the city down /
Lipstik killers / Trash queen / Teenage revolution /
Twist of the knife / Cock rock shock / It's a party.
■ LP . . . . DOJOLP 6
Dojo / Apr '86.

WAR MACHINE.
Tracks: Not Advised.
■ VHS . . . . HEN 2023
Hendring Video / '88.

Wretched

LA TUA MORTE NON ASPETTA.
Tracks: Not Advised.
■ LP . . . . CP 8.9/86
Chaos Produzioni / Mar '87.

LIFE OUT THERE.
Tracks: Not Advised.
■ CD. HELL 024
Hellhound / Sep '93 / Plastic Head.

PSYCHOSMATIC MEDICINE.
Tracks: Not Advised.
■ CD. H 0031-2
Hellhound / May '94 / Plastic Head.

Wurzel

BESS.
Tracks: Bess / People say I'm crazy / Midnight in
London (Extra track on 12" only) / ESP (Extra track
on 12" only).
■ 12" . . . . GWT 4
■ 7" . . . . GWR 4
GWR / Mar '87.

Y

Y & T

Taking name from debut album title, *Yester-day And Today* (released in 1976), San Francisco's Y&T looked on verge of big things after release of cult classic *Earth-shaker* in 1981. Subsequent three albums made modest impact on U.K. chart, as did 1983 *Mean Streak* single, and band played well-received sets at Donington and Reading. However, they never lived up to *Earth-shaker*'s promise and eventually split in '91.

ANTHOLOGY: Y & T.
Tracks: Rescue me / I believe in you / Squeeze / Hungry for rock / Don't wanna lose / Hell or high water / Winds of change / Bar room boogie / Black tiger / In the name of rock / Summertime girls / All american boy / Hands of time / Mean streak / Take you to the limit / Down and dirty / Hang 'em high / Open fire (live) / Go for the throat (live) / Forever (live).
- ■ LP . . . . RAWLP 040
- MC . . . . RAWTC 040
- ■ CD . . . . RAWCD 040
Raw Power / Sep '89.

BLACK TIGER.
Tracks: From the moon / Open fire / Don't wanna lose / Hell or high water / Forever / Black tiger / Bar room boogie / My way or the highway / Winds of change.
- ■ LP . . . . AMLH 64910
- ■ MC . . . . CAM 64910
A&M / Sep '82.

COLLECTION: Y & T.
Tracks: Not Advised.
- ■ CD . . . . CCSCD 286
Castle Collector Series / May '91.

CONTAGIOUS.
Tracks: Contagious / L.A. rocks / Temptation / Kid goes crazy / Fight for your life / Armed and danger-ous / Rhythm or not / Bodily harm / Eyes of a stranger / I'll cry for you.
- MC 9241424
- ■ LP 9241421
Geffen / Jul '87.

DIRTY GIRL.
Tracks: Dirty girl.
- ■ 12" . . . . AMSX 8172
A&M / Oct '81.

DON'T WANNA LOSE.
Tracks: Don't wanna lose / Squeeze.
- ■ 12" . . . . AMSX 8251
- ■ 7" . . . . AMS 8251
A&M / Sep '82.

DOWN FOR THE COUNT.
Tracks: In the name of rock / All American boy / Anytime at all / Anything for money / Face like an angel / Summertime girls / Looks like trouble / Your mama don't dance / Don't tell me what to wear / Hands of time.
- ■ CD . . . . CDA 5101
- ■ LP . . . . AMA 5101
- ■ MC . . . . AMC 5101
A&M / Nov '85.

EARTHSHAKER.
Tracks: Hungry for rock / Dirty girl / Shake it loose / Squeeze / Rescue me / Young and tough / Hurricane / Let me go / Knock you out / I believe in you.
- ■ LP . . . . AMLH 64867
- MC . . . . CAM 64867
A&M / Jul '82 / PolyGram.

I BELIEVE IN YOU.
Tracks: I believe in you / Rescue me.
- ■ 12" . . . . AMSP 8229
A&M / Jun '82.

IN ROCK WE TRUST.
Tracks: Rock and roll's gonna save the world / Life, life, life / Masters and slaves / I'll keep on believin' (do you know) / Breakout tonight / Lipstick and

leather / Don't stop runnin' / Your love is driving me crazy / She's a liar / This time.
- ■ LP . . . . AMLX 65007
- ■ MC . . . . CXM 65007
A&M / Aug '84.
- ■ CD 395 007-2
A&M / '88.

MEAN STREAK.
Tracks: Mean streak / Straight thru the heart / Lonely side of town / Midnight in Tokyo / Breaking away / Hang 'em high / Take you to the limit / Sentimental fool / Down and dirty.
- ■ LP . . . . AMLX 64960
- MC . . . . CXM 64960
A&M / Sep '83 / PolyGram.

MEAN STREAK.
Tracks: Mean streak / Straight through the heart / Dirty girl (Only on 12" single.).
- ■ 12" . . . . AMX 135
- ■ 7" . . . . AM 135
- ■ 7" P.Disc . . . . AMP 135
A&M / Aug '83.

MIDNIGHT IN TOKYO.
Tracks: Midnight in Tokyo / Barroom boogie.
- ■ 12" . . . . AMX 161
- ■ 7" . . . . AM 161
A&M / Nov '83.

OPEN FIRE (Live at Civic).
Tracks: Hang 'em high / Dirty girl / Lipstick and leather / Don't stop runnin' / Rescue me / Mean streak / Rock and roll's gonna save the world / Hell or high water / Forever.
- ■ VHS . . . . AMV 832
A&M Sound Pictures / '88.

OPEN FIRE (LIVE).
Tracks: Open fire / Go for the throat / 25 hours a day / Rescue me / Summer time girls / Forever / Bar room boogie / I believe in you.
- ■ LP . . . . AMA 5076
- ■ MC . . . . AMC 5076
A&M / Jul '85.
- CD 395 076-2
A&M / '88 / PolyGram.

SUMMERTIME GIRLS.
Tracks: Summertime girls / Lipstick and leather.
- ■ 12" . . . . AMY 264
- ■ 7" . . . . AM 264
A&M / Aug '85.

TEN.
Tracks: Not Advised.
- CD 7599242832
- ■ LP 7599242831
- MC 7599242834
Geffen / Jun '90 / BMG.

YESTERDAY AND TODAY LIVE.
Tracks: Not Advised.
- CD . . . . CDZORRO 21
- LP . . . . ZORRO 21
- MC . . . . TZORRO 21
Metal Blade / Mar '91 / Pinnacle.

Year Zero

NIHIL'S FLAME.
Tracks: Prefall (Intro) / Planetfall / Headache station / Harsh believing / Civilisation dreaming / Wishing horse / Year zero / Evergreen (Fool's throne) / Shining violet / Invention of God / Eternal dawn.
- CD . . . . H 0027-2
Hellhound / Aug '94 / Plastic Head.

Yes

Archetypal 'progressive' band, Yes were formed by Chris Squire and Jon Anderson in 1968. Addition of guitarist Steve Howe and keyboardist Hick Wakeman led to clas-sic *Fragile* and *Close To The Edge* albums. Wakeman quit in 1974, citing dissatisfaction with convoluted music; line-up changes throughout ensuing decades are incompre-hensible to all bar most loyal followers.

Seemingly climactic dispute over name, leaving Chris Squire in Yes and former co-horts in prosaically-monickered Anderson Bruford Wakeman Howe, was topped by creation of predictably short-lived eight-man band. Non-fans' interest has centered on occasional hit singles, like *Wonderous Stories* and *Owner Of A Lonely Heart*.

9012 LIVE.
Tracks: Not Advised.
- VHS 041 362 2
Polygram Music Video / '86 / PolyGram.
- VHS . . . . CFV 06072
Channel 5 / '87 / Channel 5 Video / P.R.O. Video / Gold & Sons.

9012 LIVE-THE SOLOS.
Tracks: Hold on / Si / Solly's beard / Soon / Changes / Amazing grace / Whitefish.
- MC 790 474-4
- ■ LP 790 474-1
Atco / '86.

90125.
Tracks: Owner of a lonely heart / Hold on / It can happen / Changes / Cinema / Leave it / Our song / City of love / Hearts.
- CD 790 125-2
- ■ LP 790 125-1
- MC 790 125-4
Atlantic / Nov '83 / WEA.

AFFIRMATIVE - THE YES FAMILY ALBUM.
Tracks: Not Advised.
- CD . . . . VSOPCD 190
Connoisseur Collection / Sep '93 / Pinnacle.

BIG GENERATOR.
Tracks: Rhythm of love / Big generator / Shoot high aim low / Almost like love / Love will find a way / Final eyes / I'm running / Holy lamb.
- CD 790 522-2
- ■ LP . . . . WX 70
- ■ MC . . . . WX 70 C
Atlantic / Aug '87.

CLASSIC YES.
Tracks: Heart of the sunrise / Wondrous stories / Yours is no disgrace / Starship trooper / Long dis-tance runaround / Fish / And you and I.
- MC K4 50842
- ■ LP . . . . K 50842
Atlantic / Nov '81.
- ■ CD 250842 2
CD 756782687-2
Atlantic / Sep '94 / WEA.

CLOSE TO THE EDGE.
Tracks: Solid time of change / Total mass retain / I get up, I get down / Seasons of man / And you and I / Cord of life / Eclipse / Preacher / Teacher / Siberian Khatru.
- ■ LP . . . . K 50012
- MC K4 50012
Atlantic / '72 / WEA.
- ■ CD 250 012
Atlantic / Dec '86.
- CD 756782666-2
Atlantic / Aug '94 / WEA.

DON'T KILL THE WHALE.
Tracks: Don't kill the whale / Abalene.
- ■ 7" . . . . K 11184
Atlantic / Aug '78.

DRAMA.
Tracks: Machine messiah / White car / Does it really happen / Into the lens / Run through the light / Tempus fugit.
- ■ LP . . . . K 50736
Atlantic / Aug '80.
- CD 756782685-2
Atlantic / Sep '94 / WEA.

FRAGILE.
Tracks: Roundabout / Cans and Brahms / We have heaven / South side of the sky / Five per cent for nothing / Long distance runaround / Fish / Mood for a day / Heart of the sunrise.
- ■ LP . . . . K 50009
- ■ MC K4 50009

■ DELETED

Y 1

Atlantic / '71.
■ **LP** 2409 019
Atlantic / Dec '71.
■ **CD** 250 009
Atlantic / Dec '86.
CD 756782667-2
Warner Bros. / Aug '94 / WEA.

FRAGILE / CLOSE TO THE EDGE.
Tracks: Not Advised.
MC K4 60166
Atlantic / Oct '82 / WEA.

GOING FOR THE ONE.
Tracks: Going for the one / Turn of the century /
Parallels / Wondrous stories / Awaken.
■ **LP** . . . . K 50379
■ **MC** K4 50379
Atlantic / Jul '77.
■ **CD** . . . . K 250 379
Atlantic / Jul '88.
CD 756782670-2
Atlantic / Aug '94 / WEA.

GOING FOR THE ONE.
Tracks: Going for the one / Awaken.
■ **7"** . . . . K 11047
Atlantic / Nov '77.

GREATES VIDEO HITS.
Tracks: Not Advised.
VHS 8536501813
Warner Music Video / Oct '92 / WEA.

INTO THE LENS.
Tracks: Into the lens / Does it really happen.
■ **7"** . . . . K 11622
Atlantic / '80.

IT CAN HAPPEN.
Tracks: It can happen.
■ **7"** . . . . B 9745
Atco / Jul '84.

LEAVE IT.
Tracks: Leave it / Leave it (re-mix) (Re-mix).
■ **12"** . . . . B 9787T
■ **7"** . . . . B 9787
Atco / Mar '84.
■ **7"** . . . . B 9787 C
Atco / May '84.

LOVE WILL FIND A WAY.
Tracks: Love will find a way / Holy lamb.
■ **12"** . . . . A 9449 T
■ **7"** . . . . .A 9449
Atlantic / Sep '87.

OWNER OF A LONELY HEART.
Tracks: Owner of a lonely heart / Our song.
■ **12"** . . . . B 9817 T
■ **7"** . . . . .B 9817
Atlantic / Nov '83.

RELAYER.
Tracks: Gates of delirium / Sound chaser / To be
over.
■ **LP** . . . . K 50096
■ **MC** K4 50096
Atlantic / Nov '74.
CD . . . . K 250 096
Atlantic / Jul '88 / WEA.

SAVING MY HEART.
Tracks: Saving my heart / Lift me up (edit) / America
(Only on 12" and CD single).
■ **12"** 614553
■ **7"** 114553
■ **CD Single** 664553
Arista / Jul '91.

TALES FROM TOPOGRAPHIC OCEANS.
Tracks: Revealing science of God / Remembering /
Ancient / Ritual.
■ **Double LP** . . . . K 80001
■ **MC Set** K4 80001
Atlantic / '73.
■ **CD** .781325
WEA / Sep '89.
CD 756782683-2
Atlantic / Sep '94 / WEA.

TALK.
Tracks: Calling / I am waiting / Real love / State of
play / Walls / Where will you be / Endless dream
(Silent spring/Talk/Endless dream).
CD 828465-2
LP 828489-1
MC 828489-4
London / Mar '94 / PolyGram.

TIME AND A WORD.
Tracks: No opportunity necessary / No experience
needed / Then / Everdays / Sweet dreams / Prophet /
Clear days / Astral traveller / Time and a word.
■ **MC** K4 40085
■ **LP** . . . . K 40085
Atlantic / '70.
■ **LP** .2400 006
Atlantic / Aug '70.
CD 756782681-2
Atlantic / Sep '94 / WEA.

TORMATO.
Tracks: Future times / Rejoice / Don't kill the whale /
Madrigal / Release release / Arriving UFO / Circus
of heaven / Onward / On the silent wings of freedom.
■ **LP** . . . . K 50518
Atlantic / Oct '78.
CD 756782671-2
Atlantic / Aug '94 / WEA.

UNION.
Tracks: I would have waited forever / Shock to the
system / Masquerade / Lift me up / Without hope you
cannot start the day / Saving my heart / Miracle of
life / Silent talking / More we live-let go / Angkor Wat
(Only on cassette and CD.) / Dangerous / Holding on
/ Evensong / Take the water to the mountain / Give
and take (Only on cassette and CD.).
■ **LP** .211558
■ **MC** 411558
Arista / Apr '91.
DCC 07822186435
Arista / Jan '93 / BMG.
CD .261558
Arista / Apr '94 / BMG.

VERY BEST OF YES.
Tracks: Survival / Time and a word / Starship trooper
/ Life seeker / Disillusion / Wurm / I've seen all good
people / Your move / All good people / Roundabout /
Long distance runaround / Soon / Wonderous stories
/ Going for the one / Owner of a lonely heart / Leave
it / Rhythm of love.
CD 7567825172
MC 7567825174
Atlantic / Sep '93 / WEA.

WONDEROUS STORIES.
Tracks: Wondrous stories / Parellels.
■ **7"** . . . . K 10999
Atlantic / Sep '77.

YES.
Tracks: Beyond and before / I see you / Yesterday
and today / Looking around / Harold land / Every
little thing / Sweetness / Survival.
■ **MC** K4 40034
■ **LP** . . . . K 40034
Atlantic / '70.
CD 756782680-2
Atlantic / Aug '94 / WEA.

YES ALBUM, THE.
Tracks: Yours is no disgrace / Clap / Starship
trooper / Life seeker / Disillusion / Wurm / I've seen
all the good people / Your move / All good people /
Venture / Perpetual change.
■ **LP** . . . . K 40106
■ **MC** K4 40106
■ **LP** .2400 101
Atlantic / Apr '71.
■ **CD** . . . . K 240106
Atlantic / Jul '87.

YES SONGS.
Tracks: Close to the edge / I've seen all the good
people / Clap / And you and I / Six wives of Henry
VIII / Roundabout / Yours is no disgrace / Starship
trooper.
VHS . . . . .WNR 2021
Wienerworld Video / Aug '91 / VCI Distribution / TBD.

YES YEARS, THE.
Tracks: Something's coming / Survival / Every little
thing / Then / Everdays / Sweet dreams / No
opportunity necessary, no experience needed / Time
and a word / Starship trooper / Yours is no disgrace
/ I've seen all good people / Long distance runaround / Fish (schindleria praematurus) / Roundabout / Heart of the sunrise / America / Close to the
edge (medley) / Ritual (nous sommes du soleil) /
Sound chaser / Soon / Amazing grace / Vevey (part
1) / Wonderous stories / Awaken / Montreux's theme
/ Vevey (part 2) / Going for the one / Money / Abilene
/ Don't kill the whale / On the silent wings of freedom
/ Does it really happen / Tempus fugit / Run with the
fox / I'm down / Make it easy / It can happen / Owner
of a lonely heart / Hold on / Shoot high aim low /
Rhythm of love / Love will find a way / Changes /
And you and I (medley) / Love conquers all.
CD 7567916442

MC 7567916444
East West / Aug '91 / WEA.

YES YEARS, THE.
Tracks: Not Advised.
VHS 8536502503
Warner Music Video / Oct '92 / WEA.

YESSHOWS.
Tracks: Parallels / Time and a word / Going for the
one / Gates of Delirium.
■ **Double LP** . . . . K 60142
Atlantic / Jan '81.
CD 756782686-2
Atlantic / Sep '94 / WEA.

YESSONGS.
Tracks: Opening: Excerpt from the firebird suite /
Siberian Khatru / Heart of the sunrise / Perpetual
change / And you and I / Cord of life / Eclipse /
Preacher and the teacher / Apocalypse / Mood for a
day / Excerpts from the six wives of Henry VIII / I
get up, I get down / Seasons of man / Yours is no
disgrace / Starship trooper / Life seeker / Disillusion
/ Wurm.
■ **LP** . . . . K 60045
Atlantic / May '73.
■ **CD** 260 045
Atlantic / Feb '87.
CD 756782682-2
Atlantic / Sep '94 / WEA.

YESSTORY.
Tracks: Survival / No opportunity necessary, no
experience needed / Time and a word / Starship
trooper / I've seen all good people / Roundabout /
Heart of the sunrise / Close to the edge / Ritual -
nous sommes du soleil / Soon / Wonderous stories /
Going for the one / Don't kill the whale / Does it
really happen / Make it easy / Owner of a lonely
heart / Rhythm of love / Changes.
CD 7567917472
■ **LP** 7567917471
MC 7567917474
East West / Sep '91 / WEA.

YESTERDAYS.
Tracks: America / Looking around / Time and a word
/ Sweet dreams / Then / Survival / Astral traveller /
Dear father.
■ **LP** . . . . K 50048
Atlantic / Mar '75.
CD 756782684-2
Atlantic / Sep '94 / WEA.

Young & Moody Band

CHICAGO BLUE.
Tracks: Chicago blue / Warm winds.
■ **7"** . . . . MAG 87
Magnet / Mar '77.

DON'T DO THAT.
Tracks: Don't do that / How can I help you tonight.
■ **7"** . . . . BRO 130
Bronze / Oct '81.

THESE EYES.
Tracks: These eyes / I won't let you go.
■ **7"** . . . . BRO 120
Bronze / May '81.

Young, Neil

Tornoto-born Young is the most influential
of the proliferation of singer- songwriters of
the early 1970's. Formerly a member of
country/folk rockers, Buffalo Springfield, the
band split in 1968. The following year he
recorded with backing band, Crazy Horse,
what is often regarded as his best work,
Everybody Knows This Is Nowhere - the
classic country-rock LP. Teamed up with
Crosby, Stills & Nash for the *Deja Vu* in
1970. Neil Young's *Harvest* and *After The
Gold Rush* are his best known and biggest
selling LPs - the former yielding the Transatlantic hit single *Heart Of Gold*. Throughout the remainder of the 1970's and for
much of the next decade, Young's output
was erratic and unimaginative with only the
occasional flash of genius. However, after
re-uniting with Crazy Horse, he began recording some more memorable work. Particularly noteworthy are *Freedom* (1989) and
live studio set *Ragged Glory*. In 1992, Neil
Young recorded *Harvest Moon* - the acclaimed sequel to 1971's classic *Harvest* LP.
Hugely influential figure on the early 1990's
'grunge' scene.

■ DELETED

AFTER THE GOLDRUSH.
Tracks: Tell me why / After the goldrush / Only love can break a heart / Southern man / Til the morning comes / Oh, lonesome me / Don't let it bring you down / Birds / When you dance I can really love / I believe in you / Cripple Creek ferry.
■ LP . . . . RSLP 6383
Reprise / Oct '70.
■ LP . . . . K 44088
Reprise / '77.
CD . . . . K 244 088
Reprise (USA) / Jul '87 / WEA / Pinnacle.
MC . . . . K 444088
WEA / '89 / WEA.

AFTER THE GOLDRUSH/ HARVEST.
Tracks: Not Advised.
■ MC K4 64044
Reprise (USA) / Oct '82.

AMERICAN STARS AND BARS.
Tracks: Old country waltz / Saddle up the palomino / Hey babe / Hold back the tears / Bite the bullitt / Star of Bethlehem / Will to live / Like a hurricane / Homegrown.
■ LP . . . . K 54088
MC K4 54088
Reprise (USA) / Jun '77 / WEA / Pinnacle.
CD .759927234-2
Reprise / Jun '94 / WEA.

ARC WELD (Young, Neil & Crazy Horse).
Tracks: Hey hey, my my (into the black) / Crime in the city / Blowin' in the wind / Welfare mothers / Love to burn / Cinnamon girl / Mansion on the hill / Fuckin' up / Cortez the killer / Powderfinger / Love and only love / Rockin' in the free world / Like a hurricane / Farmer John / Tonight's the night / Roll another number / Arc.
CD 7599267462
WEA / Oct '91 / WEA.

BERLIN.
Tracks: Not Advised.
VHS . . . . CFV 05832
Channel 5 / '88 / Channel 5 Video / P.R.O. Video / Gold & Sons.

COMES A TIME.
Tracks: Goin' back / Comes a time / Look out for my love / Peace of mind / Lotta love / Human highway / Already one / Field of opportunity / Motorcycle mama / Four strong winds.
■ LP . . . . K 54099
MC K4 54099
Reprise (USA) / Jul '78 / WEA / Pinnacle.
CD .759927235-2
Reprise / Jun '93 / WEA.

CRAZY HORSE (Young, Neil & Crazy Horse).
Tracks: Gone dead train / Dance, dance, dance / Look at all the things / Beggars day / I don't want to talk about it / Carolay / Dirty, dirty / Nobody / I'll get by / Crow Lady Jane.
■ LP . . . . K 44114
MC K4 44114
Reprise / Mar '86 / WEA.
LP . . . . ED 175
Demon / Dec '90 / Pinnacle / A.D.A. Distribution.
CD .759926808-2
Warner Bros. / Apr '94 / WEA.

CRAZY MOON (Young, Neil & Crazy Horse).
Tracks: Not Advised.
■ LP . . . . PL 13054
RCA / Jan '83.

DECADE.
Tracks: Down to the wire / Burned / Mr. Soul / Broken arrow / Expecting to fly / Sugar mountain / I am a child / Loner / Old laughing lady / Cinnamon girl / Down by the river / Cowgirl in the sand / I believe in you / After the goldrush / Southern man / Helpless / Ohio / Soldier / Old man / Man needs a maid / Heart of gold / Star of Bethlehem / Needles and the damage done / Tonight's the night (part 1) / Turnstiles / Winterlong / Deep forbidden lake / Like a hurricane / Love is a rose / Cortez the killer / Campaigner / Long may you run / Harvest.
■ MC Set K4 64037
■ LP Set . . . . K 64037
Reprise (USA) / Dec '77.
CD .759927233-2
Reprise / Jun '93 / WEA.

EVERYBODY KNOWS THIS IS NOWHERE.
Tracks: Cinnamon girl / Everybody knows this is nowhere / round and 'round / Down by the river / Losing end / Running dry (Requiem for the rockets) / Cowgirl in the sand.

■ LP . . . . K 44073
Reprise (USA) / '69.
CD 244059
Reprise / '88 / WEA.

EVERYBODY'S ROCKIN'.
Tracks: Betty Lou's got a new pair of shoes / raining in my heart / Payole blues / Wonderin' / Kinda fonda Wanda / Jolly roll men / Bright lights / Big city / Cry, cry, cry / Mystery train / Everybody's rockin'.
■ LP . . . . GEF 25590
Geffen / Sep '83.
CD 9040131
Geffen / Sep '86.
MC 9040134
CD 9040132
Geffen / '88 / BMG.

FOUR STRONG WINDS.
Tracks: Four strong winds / Motor cycle mama.
■ 7" . . . . K 14493
Reprise / Jan '70.

FREEDOM.
Tracks: Not Advised.
VHS 7599 83166 3
Warner Music Video / Oct '90 / WEA.

FREEDOM (Young, Neil & The Restless).
Tracks: Rockin' in the free world / Crime in the city (sixty to zero part 1) / Don't cry / Hangin' on a limb / Eldorado / Ways of love / Someday / On Broadway / Wrecking ball / No more / Too far gone.
CD . . . . K 92589 2
■ LP . . . . WX 257
MC . . . . WX 257C
WEA / Sep '89 / WEA.

HARVEST.
Tracks: Out on the weekend / Harvest / Man needs a maid / Heart of gold / Are you ready for the country / Old man / There's a world / Alabama / Needle and the damage done / Words between the lines of age.
■ LP . . . . K 54005
■ MC K4 54005
Reprise (USA) / '72.
CD . . . . K 244 131
Reprise (USA) / May '83 / WEA / Pinnacle.

HARVEST MOON.
Tracks: Unknown legend / From Hank to Hendrix / You and me / Harvest moon / War of man / One of these days / Such a woman / Old king / Dreamin' man / Natural beauty.
CD 9362450572
■ LP 9362450571
MC 9362450574
Reprise / Nov '92 / WEA.

HARVEST MOON.
Tracks: Harvest moon / Winterlong / Deep forbidden lake (On W 0139CDX only) / Old king (On W 0139CD only).
■ 7" . . . . W 0139
■ CD Single . . . . W 0139CDX
■ CD Single . . . . W 0139CD
■ MC Single . . . . .W 0139C
WEA / Feb '93.

HAWKS & DOVES.
Tracks: Not Advised.
■ LP . . . . K 54109
Reprise (USA) / Aug '87.
CD .759925868-2
Reprise / Jun '94 / WEA.

HAWKS & DOVES.
Tracks: Hawks and doves / Union man.
■ 7" . . . . K 14508
Reprise (USA) / Nov '80.

JOURNEY THROUGH THE PAST.
Tracks: Not Advised.
■ LP . . . . K 64015
Warner / Jan '73.
CD .759926123-2
Reprise / Jun '94 / WEA.

LANDING ON WATER.
Tracks: Weight of the world / Violent side / Hippie dream / Bad news beat / Touch the night / People on the street / Hard luck stories / I got a problem / Pressure / Drifter.
CD 9241092
■ LP 9241091
MC 9241094
Geffen / Aug '86 / BMG.
■ CD . . . . .GEFD 24109
■ MC . . . . .GEFC 24109
Geffen / Apr '91.
CD .GFLD 19130
MC .GFLC 19130
Geffen / Jun '92 / BMG.

LIFE (Young, Neil & Crazy Horse).
Tracks: Mideast vacation / Long walk home / Around the world / Inca Queen / Too lonely / Prisoners of rock'n' roll / Crying eyes / When your lonely heart breaks / We never danced.
CD 9241542
■ LP . . . . WX 109
■ MC . . . . WX 109C
Geffen / Jul '87.

LIKE A HURRICANE.
Tracks: Like a hurricane / Hold back the tears.
■ 7" . . . . K 14482
Reprise / Aug '77.

LITTLE THING CALLED LOVE.
Tracks: Little thing called love / We are in control.
■ 7" . . . . GEFA 2781
Geffen / Jan '83.

LIVE IN BERLIN.
Tracks: Not Advised.
■ VHS .CMP 6102
BMG Video / Mar '93.

LIVE RUST (Young, Neil & Crazy Horse).
Tracks: Sugar mountain / I am a child / Comes a time / After the goldrush / My, my, hey, hey (out of the blue) / When you dance I can really love / Loner / Needle and the damage done / Lotta love / Sedan delivery / Powder finger / Cortez the killer / Cinnamon girl / Like a hurricane / Hey hey, my my (into the black) / Tonight's the night.
■ Double LP . . . . K 64041
MC K4 64041
Reprise (USA) / Oct '81 / WEA / Pinnacle.
CD .759927250-2
Reprise / Jun '93 / WEA.

LONG MAY YOU RUN.
Tracks: Long may you run / Sugar mountain.
■ 7" . . . . W 0207
■ CD Single . . . . W 0207CD1
■ CD Single . . . . W 0207CD2
MC . . . . .W 0207C
Reprise / Oct '93 / WEA.

LONG WALK HOME.
Tracks: Long walk home.
■ 7" . . . . GEF 24
Geffen / May '87.

LUCKY THIRTEEN.
Tracks: Sample and hold / Transformer man / Depression blues / Get gone / Don't take your love away from me / Once an angel / Where is the highway tonight / Hippie dream / Pressure / Around the world / Mideast vacation / Ain't it the truth / This note's for you.
CD . . . . GED 24452
MC . . . . GEC 24452
Geffen / Jan '93 / BMG.

MY HEART.
Tracks: My heart / Roll another number (for the road) / Change your mind (On CDs only).
CD Single . . . . .W 0266CD
MC Single . . . . .W 0266C
Reprise / Oct '94 / WEA.

MY MY HEY HEY.
Tracks: My my hey hey / Hey hey, my my (into the black).
■ 7" . . . . K 14498
WEA / '79.

NEEDLE AND THE DAMAGE DONE, THE.
Tracks: Needle and the damage done (Live) / You and me (LP Version) / You and me (Live) / From Hank to Hendrix (Available on CDS only).
■ 7" . . . . W 0191
■ CD Single . . . . .W 0191CD
■ MC Single . . . . .W 0191C
Reprise / Jul '93.

NEIL YOUNG.
Tracks: Emperor of Wyoming / Loner / If I could have her tonight / I've been waiting for you / Old laughing lady / String quartet from whiskey boot hill / Here we are in the years / What did you do to my life / I've loved her so long / Last trip to Tulsa.
■ LP . . . . K 44059
Reprise (USA) / '69.
■ MC .923956 4
WEA / Nov '83.

OLD WAYS.
Tracks: Wayward wind / Get back to the country / Are there any more real cowboys / Once an angel / Misfits / California sunset / Old ways / My boy / Bound for glory / Where is the highway tonight.
■ LP . . . . GEF 26377
MC 4026377
Geffen / Sep '85 / BMG.

ON THE BEACH.
Tracks: Walk on / See the sky about to rain / Revolution blues / For the turnstiles / Vampire blues / On the beach / Motion pictures / Ambulance blues.
■ **LP** . . . . K 54014
Reprise (USA) / Jul '74.
CD 759927213-2
Reprise / Jun '94 / WEA.

PHILADELPHIA.
Tracks: Philadelphia / Such a woman / Stringman.
■ **CD Single** . . . . W 0242CD
Reprise / Mar '94.

PIECE OF CRAP.
Tracks: Piece of crap.
CD Single . . . . W 0261CD
MC Single . . . . .W 0261C
Reprise / Aug '94 / WEA.

RAGGED GLORY (Young, Neil & Crazy Horse).
Tracks: Country home / White line / Fuckin' up / Over and over / Love to burn / Farmer John / Mansion on the hill / Days that used to be / Love and only love / Mother Earth (natural anthem).
CD 759926315-2
MC . . . . WX 374C
■ **LP** . . . . WX 374
Reprise / Sep '90.

RE-AC-TOR.
Tracks: Opera star / Surfer Joe and Moe the sleaze / T-Bone / Get back on it / Southern Pacific / Motor city / Rapid transit / Shots.
■ **LP** . . . . K 54116
Reprise / Nov '81.
CD 759925869-2
Reprise / Jun '94 / WEA.

ROCKIN' IN THE FREE WORLD.
Tracks: Rockin' in the free world.
■ **12"** . . . . .W 2776T
■ **7"** . . . . W 2776
Reprise / Apr '90.
■ **7"** . . . . W 0231
■ **CD Single** . . . . .W 0231CD
■ **MC Single** . . . . .W 0231C
Reprise / Feb '94.

RUST NEVER SLEEPS.
Tracks: Not Advised.
VHS . . . . RVT 33006
RCA / '84 / BMG.
VHS 7599383583
Warner Music Video / Oct '93 / WEA.

RUST NEVER SLEEPS (Young, Neil & Crazy Horse).
Tracks: My my, hey hey (out of the blue) / Thrasher / Ride my llama / Pocohontas / Sail away / Powder finger / Welfare mothers / Sedan delivery / Hey hey, my my (into the black).
■ **LP** . . . . K 54105
MC K4 54105

Reprise (USA) / Oct '81 / WEA / Pinnacle.
CD 759927249-2
Reprise / Jun '93 / WEA.

SLEEPS WITH ANGELS (Young, Neil & Crazy Horse).
Tracks: Not Advised.
CD 936245749-2
LP 936245749-1
MC 936245749-4
Reprise / Aug '94 / WEA.

THIS NOTE IS FOR YOU (Young, Neil & The Blue Notes).
Tracks: Ten men workin' / This note's for you / Coupe de ville / Life in the city / Twilight / Married man / Sunny inside / Can't believe your lyin' / Hey hey / One thing.
CD 925719 2
■ **LP** . . . . WX 168
■ **MC** . . . . WX 168C
Reprise / Apr '88.

TIME FADES AWAY.
Tracks: Not Advised.
■ **LP** . . . . K 54010
■ **MC** K4 54010
Reprise (USA) / Jan '74.
CD 759925934-2
Reprise / Jun '94 / WEA.

TONIGHT'S THE NIGHT.
Tracks: Tonight's the night / Speakin' out / World on a string / Borrowed tune / Come on baby / Let's go down-town / Mellow my mind / Roll another number (for the road) / Albuquerque / New mama / Look out, Joe / Tired eyes / Tonight's the night (part 2).
■ **LP** . . . . K 54040
Reprise (USA) / May '75.
CD 759927221-2
Reprise / Jun '93 / WEA.

TRANS.
Tracks: Not Advised.
■ **LP** . . . . GEF 25019
Geffen / Feb '83.
■ **LP** 9020181
■ **MC** 9020184
Geffen / Sep '86.

UNPLUGGED.
Tracks: Old laughing lady / Mr. Soul / World on a string / Pocahontas / Stringman / Like a hurricane / Needle & the damage done / Helpless / Harvest moon / Transformer man / Unknown legend / Look out for my love / Long may you run / From Hank to Hendrix.
CD 936245310-2
LP 936245310-1
MC 936245310-4
Reprise / Jun '93 / WEA.

WANDERIN'.
Tracks: Wanderin'.
■ **7"** . . . . .A 3581
Geffen / Sep '83.

WEIGHT OF THE WORLD.
Tracks: Weight of the world / Pressure.
■ **12"** . . . . GEF 7T
■ **7"** . . . . GEF 7
Geffen / Sep '86.

WELD (Young, Neil & Crazy Horse).
Tracks: Hey hey, my my (into the black) / Crime in the city / Blowin' in the wind / Welfare mothers / Love to burn / Cinnamon girl / Mansion on the hill / Fuckin' up / Cortez the killer / Powder finger / Love and only love / Rockin' in the free world / Like a hurricane / Farmer John / Tonight's the night / Roll another number.
CD 7599266712
■ **LP** 7599266711
MC 7599266714
Reprise / Nov '91 / WEA.

ZUMA.
Tracks: Don't cry no tears / Danger bird / Pardon my heart / Lookin' for a love / Barstool blues / Stupid girl / Drive back / Cortez the killer / Through my salis.
■ **LP** . . . . K 54057
Reprise (USA) / '75.
CD 759927226-2
Reprise / Jun '93 / WEA.

Youth Of Today

BREAK DOWN THE WALLS.
Tracks: Not Advised.
■ **LP** . . . . PF 11
Wishing Well (USA) / Aug '87.

CAN'T CLOSE MY EYES.
Tracks: Expectations / Crucial times / I have faith / Youth of today / Take a stand / Positive out / Can't close my eyes / We just. / Youth crew.
■ **LP** 601299
We Bite / Oct '89.

SHAKE HANDS AND MAKE A FRIEND.
Tracks: Shake hands and make a friend.
■ **7"** . . . . LD 5009
Daylight / Aug '85.

WE'RE NOT IN THIS ALONE.
Tracks: Not Advised.
■ **LP** . . . . FH 12014
Funhouse / Oct '89.

YOUTH OF TODAY E.P.
Tracks: Not Advised.
■ **7"** . . . . REVEL 017
■ **CD Single** . . . . REVEL 017 CD
■ **MC Single** . . . . REVEL 017 MC
Revelation / Apr '92.

Z

Zebra

NO TELLIN' LIES.
Tracks: Wait until the summer's gone / I don't like it / Bears / I don't care / Lullaby / No tellin' lies / Takin' a stance / But no more / Little things / Drive me crazy.
■ LP 780 159-1
Atlantic / Dec '84.

ZEBRA.
Tracks: Tell me what you want / One more chance / Slow down / Blue suede shoes / As I said before / Who's behind the door / When you get there / Take your fingers from my hair / Don't walk away / La la song.
■ LP 780 054-1
Atlantic / Sep '83.

Zed Yago

BLACK BONE SONG.
Tracks: Black bone song / Zed Yago / Rocking for the nation (Only on 12" formats.).
■ 12" . . . . PT 49388
■ 12" . . . . PT 49390
■ 7" . . . . PB 49389
■ 7" . . . . PB 49387
RCA / May '89.

PILGRIMAGE.
Tracks: Pilgrim choir / Fear of death / Black bone song / Man who stole the holy fire / Pale man / Fallen angel / Pilgrimage / Pioneer of the storm / Rose of martyrdom / Achilles heel / Omega child.
■ CD . . . . PD 719 49
■ LP . . . . PL 719 49
■ MC . . . . PK 719 49
RCA / Jan '89.

Zeno

DELILAH.
Tracks: Delilah / Hands off (that's mine).
■ 12" . . . . KSR 1207
■ 7" . . . . KSR 707
Stephan / Aug '90.

LITTLE MORE LOVE, A.
Tracks: Little more love / Signs on the sky / Don't tell the wind (Extra track on 12" only).
■ 12" 12R 6123
■ 7" . . . . .R 6123
Parlophone / Feb '86.
■ 12" P.Disc. 12RP 6123
Parlophone / Mar '86.

LOVE WILL LIVE.
Tracks: Love will live / Far away.
■ 12" 12EMI 5566
■ 7" . . . . EMI 5566
EMI / Jul '86.

ZENO.
Tracks: Eastern sun / Little more love / Love will live / Signs on the sky / Far away / Don't tell the wind / Heart on the wing / Circles of dawn / Sent by heaven / Sunset.
■ CD . . . . CDP 746 270 2
Parlophone / Jul '86.
■ LP . . . . PCSD 102
■ MC . . . . TCPCSD 102
Parlophone / Mar '86.

Zero 9

WHITE LIES.
Tracks: Not Advised.
■ LP . . . . HMILP 57
Heavy Metal / Dec '85.

Zeros

4-3-2-1.
Tracks: Not Advised.
CD . . . . LS 92422
LP . . . . LS 92421
Road Runner / Nov '91 / Pinnacle.

BOTTOMS UP.
Tracks: Bottoms up.
■ 7" . . . . ROCK 6091-7
Rockville / Jan '93.

KNOCKIN' ME DEAD.
Tracks: Knockin' me dead.
7" . . . . ROCK 6128-7
Rockville / Feb '94 / SRD.

Znowhite

ACT OF GOD.
Tracks: Last breath / Baptised by fire / Pure blood / Thunderdome / War machine / Disease bigotry / Something wicked / Rest in peace / Soldiers greed.
CD . . . . RR 95872
■ LP . . . . RR 95871
Road Runner / May '88.

ALL HAIL TO THEE.
Tracks: Sledgehammer / Saturday night / Something for nothing / Bringing the hammer down / Do or die / Never felt like this / Rock city destruction.
■ LP . . . . THBM 002
Thunderbolt / Aug '85.

Zodiac Mindwarp

BACK SEAT EDUCATION (Zodiac Mindwarp & The Love Reaction).
Tracks: Backseat education.
■ 12" . . . . ZOD 212
■ 7" . . . . ZOD 2
■ MC Single. . . . . ZOD 222
Mercury / Oct '87.

ELVIS DIED FOR YOU (Zodiac Mindwarp & The Love Reaction).
Tracks: Elvis died for you.
CD Single 108732
Musidisc / Mar '94 / Vital Distribution / Discovery / A.D.A. Distribution / Harmonia Mundi (UK).

HIGH PRIEST OF LOVE (Zodiac Mindwarp & The Love Reaction).
Tracks: Not Advised.
■ LP . . . . WARP 1
Food / Jul '86.
CD . . . . WARP 001 CD
Food / Jan '89 / EMI.

HOODLUM THUNDER (Zodiac Mindwarp & The Love Reaction).
Tracks: Not Advised.
CD 108642
■ LP 108641
■ MC 108644
Musidisc / Jan '92.

LIVE AT READING '87.
Tracks: Not Advised.
CD . . . . FRSCD 011
Raw Fruit / Aug '93 / Pinnacle.

LOVE REACTION, THE.
Tracks: Love reaction.
■ 12" . . . . SNAK 4
Food / Aug '85.

MEANSTREAK (Zodiac Mindwarp & The Love Reaction).
Tracks: Meanstreak / Trash Madonna / Force of nature.
■ 12" 109226
■ CD Single. 109222
Musidisc / Apr '92.

MY LIFE STORY.
Tracks: Not Advised.
CD 109832
LP 109831
Musidisc / Nov '92 / Vital Distribution / Discovery / A.D.A. Distribution / Harmonia Mundi (UK).

PLANET GIRL (Zodiac Mindwarp & The Love Reaction).
Tracks: Planet girl / Planet girl (ext) (Extra track on 12".) / Prime mover (Track on CD.).
■ 12" . . . . ZOD 312
■ 7" . . . . ZOD 3

■ 7" . . . . ZODS 3
■ CD Single. . . . . ZODCD 3
Mercury / Mar '88.

PRIME MOVER.
Tracks: Prime mover / Laughing in the face of death / Hangover from hell (Extra track on 12" only).
■ 12" . . . . .ZOD 112
■ 7" . . . . .ZOD 1
Mercury / Apr '87.

SLEAZEGRINDER (Zodiac Mindwarp & The Love Reaction).
Tracks: Prime mover / Backseat education / High priest of love / Planet girl.
VHS . . . . CFV 02012
Channel 5 / Feb '89 / Channel 5 Video / P.R.O. Video / Gold & Sons.

TATOOED BEAT MESSIAH.
Tracks: Prime mover / Sull spark joker / Backseat education / Let's break the law / Kid's stuff / Planet girl / Bad city girl / Tatooed beat messiah / Driving on holy gasoline / Spasm gang / Messianic reprise.
■ CD 832729-2
■ LP . . . . .ZODLP 1
■ MC . . . . .ZODMC 1
Mercury / Feb '88.

TOO.
Tracks: Too.
12" . . . . .12 STR 32
Stress / Jun '94 / Pinnacle.

ZODIAC MINDWARP INTERVIEW.
Tracks: Not Advised.
■ LP P.Disc . . . . CT 1014
Music & Media / Dec '87.

ZODIAC MINDWARP: INTERVIEW PICTURE DISC.
Tracks: Not Advised.
LP P.Disc. . . . . BAK 2095
Baktabak / Apr '88 / Arabesque Ltd.

Zoetrope

LIFE OF CRIME, A.
Tracks: Not Advised.
■ LP . . . . MFN 76
Music For Nations / Nov '87.

ZZ Top

Top's line-up has remained unchanged since 1970 formation in Texas: drummer Frank Beard, bassist Dusty Hill and guitarist Billy Gibbons. Issued first LP in 1971 but '73's *Tres Hombres* cemented band's U.S. status; bluesy rock 'n' roll proved huge concert attraction. Had first U.S. hit with *Tush*, from best-selling *Fandango!*. After gruelling '76/'77 world tour, they took two-year break, returning successfully with now-trademark beards. 1983's eight million-selling *Eliminator* album became band's biggest, aided by distinctive videos and synth-orientated sound; was band's first U.K. hit. Subsequent albums have maintained momentum, spawning hits, imaginative videos and successful tours.

AFTERBURNER.
Tracks: Sleeping bag / Stages / Woke up with wood / Rough boy / Can't stop rockin' / Planet of women / I got the message / Velcro fly / Dipping low / Delirious.
■ LP . . . . WX 27
WEA / Nov '85.
CD 925342-2
MC . . . . WX 27C
WEA / Mar '94 / WEA.

ANTENNA.
Tracks: Pincushion / PCH / Breakaway / Lizard life / Cover your rig / Antenna head / Fuzzbox voodoo / World of swirl / T-shirt / Deal goin' down / Cherry red / Everything.
CD 74321 18260-2
LP 74321 18260-1
MC 74321 18260-4
RCA / Jan '94 / BMG.

DCC 74321 18260-3
RCA / Jul '94 / BMG.

ARRESTED FOR DRIVING WHILE BLIND.
Tracks: Arrested for driving while blind / Neighbour. neighbour.
■ 7" . . . . HLU 10547
London-American / Apr '77.

BEST OF ZZ TOP.
Tracks: Tush / Waitin' for the bus / Jesus just left Chicago / Francine / Just got paid / La grange / Blue jean blues / Backdoor love affair / Beer drinkers and hell raisers / Heard it on the X.
■ LP . . . . K 56598
■ MC K4 56598
WEA / Dec '83.
■ CD 256 598
WEA / Jan '86.

BREAKAWAY.
Tracks: Breakaway.
■ 12" 7432120677-1
■ CD Single 7432119228-2
■ MC Single 7432120677-4
RCA / Apr '94.

CHRIS TETLEY INTERVIEWS ZZ TOP.
Tracks: Not Advised.
■ LP . . . . CT 1005
Music & Media / Oct '87.

DEGUELLO.
Tracks: I thank you / She loves my automobile / I'm bad I'm nationwide / Fool for your stockings / Manic mechanic / Dust my broom / Lowdown in the street / Hi-fi mama / Cheap sunglasses / Esther be the one.
CD 256 701
■ LP . . . . K 56701
WEA / Jan '85.
CD . . . . K 256701
MC . . . . K 456701
WEA / Mar '94 / WEA.

DOUBLE BACK.
Tracks: Double back.
■ 12" . . . . W 9812T
■ 7" . . . . W 9812
■ CD Single . . . . W 9812CD
■ MC Single . . . . W 9812C
WEA / Jul '90.

EL LOCO.
Tracks: Tube snake boogie / I wanna drive you home / Ten foot pole / Leila / Don't tease me / It's so hard / Pearl necklace / Groove little hippie pad / Heaven, Hell or Houston / Party on the patio.
■ LP . . . . K 56929
■ MC K4 56929
WEA / Sep '81.
■ CD 256 929
WEA / Mar '87.
CD 759923593-2
WEA / Mar '94 / WEA.

ELIMINATOR.
Tracks: Gimme all your lovin' / Got me under pressure / Sharp-dressed man / I need you tonight / I got the six / Legs / Thug / T.V. dinners / Dirty dog / If I could only flag her down / Bad girl.
■ LP . . . . W 3774
WEA / Jun '83.
■ CD 9 3774-2
WEA / Jun '84.
■ LP P.Disc . . . . W 3774 P
WEA / Aug '85.
CD . . . . W 37742
MC . . . . W 37744
WEA / Mar '94 / WEA.

FANDANGO.
Tracks: Thunderbird / Jailhouse rock / Backdoor medley / Backdoor love affair / Mellow down easy / Backdoor love affair no.2 / Long distance boogie / Nasty dogs and funky kings / Blue jean blues / Balinese / Mexican blackbird / Heard it on the X / Tush.
■ LP . . . . K 56604
WEA / Nov '83.
■ CD 256 604
WEA / Jan '87.
CD . . . . K 256604
MC . . . . K 456604
WEA / Mar '94 / WEA.

GIMME ALL YOUR LOVIN'.
Tracks: Gimme all your lovin' / Jesus just left Chicago.
■ 12" . . . . W 9693 T
WEA / May '83.
■ 7" . . . . W 9693
WEA / Sep '83.

GIVE IT UP.
Tracks: Give it up / Sharp dressed man / Cheap sunglasses (live).
■ MC Single . . . . W 9509C
■ 12" . . . . W 9509T
■ 7" . . . . W 9509
■ CD Single . . . . W 9509CD
WEA / Nov '90.

GREATEST HITS.
Tracks: Not Advised.
VHS 7599382993
Warner Music Video / May '92 / WEA.

GREATEST HITS.
Tracks: Gimme all your lovin' / Sharp dressed man / Rough boy / Tush / My head's in Mississippi / Viva Las Vegas / Legs / Doubleback / Gun love / Got me under pressure / Give it up / Sleeping bag / La grange / Tube snake boogie.
CD 7599268462
■ LP . . . . WX 459
MC. . . . . WX 459C
WEA / Apr '92 / WEA.

LA GRANGE.
Tracks: La grange / Just got paid.
■ 7" . . . . HLU 10475
London / Jan '75.

LEGS.
Tracks: Legs / La Grange.
■ 12" . . . . W 9272T
■ 7" . . . . W 9272
WEA / Feb '85.

MUSIC AND MEDIA INTERVIEW PIC-TURE DISC.
Tracks: Not Advised.
■ LP P.Disc . . . . ZZ 1016
Music & Media / Feb '88.

MY HEAD'S IN MISSISSIPPI.
Tracks: My head's in Mississippi.
■ 12" . . . . W 0009T
■ 7" . . . . W 0009
■ CD Single . . . . W 0009CD
■ MC Single . . . . W 0009C
WEA / Apr '91.

PINCUSHION.
Tracks: Pincushion / Cherry red.
■ 7" 7432118261-7
■ CD Single 7432118473-2
■ CD Single 7432118261-2
■ MC Single 7432118261-4
RCA / Jan '94.

RECYCLER.
Tracks: Concrete and steel / Lovething / Penthouse eyes / Tell it / My head's in Mississippi / Decision or collision / Give it up / 2000 blues / Burger man / Doubleback.
■ LP . . . . WX 390
WEA / Oct '90.
CD 759926265-2
MC. . . . . WX 390C
WEA / Mar '94 / WEA.

RIO GRANDE MUD.
Tracks: Francine / Just got paid / Mushmouth shou-tin' / Ko ko blue / Chevrolet / Apologies to pearly / Bar-b-q / Sure got cold after the rain fell / Whisky 'n' mama / Down brownie.
■ LP . . . . SHU 8433
London / Aug '72.
■ LP . . . . K 56602
■ MC K4 56602
WEA / Sep '84.
■ CD 256 602
WEA / Jan '87.
CD 759927380-2
WEA / Mar '94 / WEA.

ROUGH BOY.
Tracks: Rough boy / Delirious.
■ 12" . . . . W 2003T
■ 12" P.Disc . . . . W 2003TP
■ 7" . . . . W 2003
WEA / Mar '86.
■ 12" . . . . W 0111 T
■ 7" . . . . W 0111
■ CD Single . . . . W 0111 CD
■ MC Single . . . . W 0111 C
WEA / Jun '92.

SHARP DRESSED MAN.
Tracks: Sharp dressed man / I got the fix.
■ 7" . . . . W 9576
■ 12" . . . . W 9576T
WEA / Dec '84.

SLEEPING BAG.
Tracks: Sleeping bag / Party on the patio.
■ 7" . . . . W 2001
■ 12" . . . . W 2001T
WEA / Oct '85.

STAGES.
Tracks: Stages / Hi-fi mama.
■ 12" . . . . W 2002 T
■ 7" . . . . W 2002
WEA / Jan '86.

TEJAS.
Tracks: It's only love / Arrested for driving while blind / El diablo / Snappy kakkie / Enjoy and get it on / Ten dollar man / Pan Am highway blues / Avalon hideaway / She's a heartbreaker / Asleep in the desert.
■ LP . . . . K 56605
■ MC K4 56605
WEA / Sep '84.
■ CD 256 605
WEA / Mar '87.

TEXAS.
Tracks: Not Advised.
CD 759927383-2
WEA / Mar '94 / WEA.

TRES HOMBRES.
Tracks: Waitin' for the bus / Jesus just left Chicago / Beer drinkers and hell raisers / Master of sparks / Hot blues and righteous / Move me on down the line / Precious and grace / La grange / Sheik / Have you heard.
■ LP . . . . K 56603
WEA / Nov '83.
■ CD 256 603
WEA / Jan '87.
CD . . . . K 256603
MC . . . . K 456603
WEA / Mar '94 / WEA.

TRES HOMBRES / FANDANGO.
Tracks: Not Advised.
■ MC K4 66121
WEA / Nov '83.

TV DINNERS.
Tracks: T.V. dinners / Cheap sunglasses.
■ 12" . . . . W 9334T
■ 7" . . . . W 9334
■ MC Single . . . . W 9334C
WEA / Mar '84.

VELCRO FLY.
Tracks: Velcro fly(remix edit.) / Can't stop rockin'.
■ 12" . . . . W 8515T
■ 7" . . . . W 8515
WEA / Nov '86.

VIVA LAS VEGAS.
Tracks: Viva Las Vegas.
■ 7" . . . . W 0098
■ CD Single . . . . W 0098CD
■ MC Single . . . . W 0098C
WEA / Apr '92.

ZZ TOP SIXPACK.
Tracks: (Somebody else been) shaking your tree / Brown sugar / Squank / Goin' down to Mexico / Old man / Neighbour, neighbour / Certified blues / Bed-room thang / Just got back from baby's / Backdoor love affair / Francine / Just got paid / Mushmouth shoutin' / Ko ko blue / Chevrolet / Apologies to Pearly / Bar B Q / Sure got cold after the rain fell / Whisky 'n mama / Down brownie / Waitin' for the bus / Jesus just left Chicago / Beer drinkers and hell raisers / Master of sparks / Hot, blue and righteous / Move me on down the line / Precious and grace / La grange / Sheik / Have you heard / Thunderbird / Jailhouse rock / Mellow down easy / Back door love affair No.2 / Long distance boogie / Nasty dogs and funky kings / Blue jean blues / Balinese / Mexican blackbird / Heard it on the X / Tush / It's only love / Arrested for driving while blind / El diablo / Snappy kakkie / Enjoy and get it on / Ten dollar man / Pan am highway blues / Avalon hideaway / She's a heartbreaker / Asleep in the desert / Tube snake boogie / I wanna drive you home / Ten foot pole / Leila / Don't tease me / It's so hard / Pearl necklace /

Groovy little hippy pad / Heaven, hell or Houston /
Party on the patio.
CD Set 925661 2
WEA / Dec '87 / WEA.

ZZ TOP SUMMER HOLIDAY EP, THE.
Tracks: Tush / Got me under pressure / Beer
drinkers and hell raisers / I'm bad, I'm nationwide.
■ **12"**. . . . . **W 8946 T**
■ **EP** . . . . **W 8946**

■ **MC Single.** . . . . **W 8946 C**
WEA / Jul '85.

ZZ TOP'S FIRST ALBUM.
Tracks: Somebody else been shaking your tree /
Brown sugar / Squank / Goin' down to Mexico / Old
man / Neighbour, neighbour / Certified blues / Bed-
room thang / Just got back from my baby's / Back-
door love affair.
■ **LP** . . . . .K 5660 1
■ **MC**. **K4 56601**

WEA / Sep '84.
■ **CD**. **256 601**
WEA / Jan '87.
CD. . . . . **K 256601**
WEA / Mar '94 / WEA.

ZZ TOP: INTERVIEW PICTURE DISC.
Tracks: Not Advised.
■ **12" P.Disc.**. . . . . **ZZTOP 1**
Talkies / '87.

COMPILATIONS

NUMERICAL

3 WAY THRASH.
Tracks: Not Advised.
VHS . . . . LFV 105
Fotodisk Video / Aug '90.
VHS . . . . FLV 5
Virgin Vision / Feb '90 / Gold & Sons / TBD.

5 YEARS OF NUCLEAR BLAST.
Tracks: Not Advised.
CD . . . . NB 083CD
LP . . . . NB 083
MC. . . . . .NB 083C
Nuclear Blast / Dec '93 / Plastic Head.

10 METAL STARS VOL.1.
Tracks: Not Advised.
CD . . . . STACD 075
Wisepack / Nov '93 / TBD / Conifer Records.

10 METAL STARS VOL.2.
Tracks: Not Advised.
CD . . . . STACD 076
Wisepack / Nov '93 / TBD / Conifer Records.

60 MINUTES PLUS.
Tracks: Live at the Inferno: Raven / All systems go:
Steel / Fox: Crucifixion / Give me your love: Gold-
smith / Maybe someday: Valhalla / Dirty tricks: Ja-
guar (1) / Flame burns on: Axis / 50.000 stallions:
Persian Risk / Lucy: Dedringer / Bursting out: Venom
/ Cry to the wind: Sabre / Watch out: White Spirit /
Kansas City: Warrior / Absolute zero: Alien / All the
way: Hellenbach / Lost and found: Fist.
MC. . . . . .C 2001
Neat / Jun '83 / Grapevine Distribution.

AGE OF ATLANTIC, THE.
Tracks: Comin' home: Delaney & Bonnie / Tonight:
M.C. 5 / Black hearted woman: Allman Brothers /
Survival: Yes / I'm a good woman: Cold Blood /
Whole lotta love: Led Zeppelin / Termination: Iron
Butterfly / Last time: Dada (1) / Communication
breakdown: Led Zeppelin / Wash mama wash: Dr.
John / Need love: Vanilla Fudge / Broken arrow:
Buffalo Springfield.
■ LP . . . . K 20011
Atlantic / '77.

ALL GUITARS.
Tracks: Not Advised.
■ Double LP. . . . . BFFP 21/22
Blast First / Mar '88.

AMERICA'S ROCK.
Tracks: Not Advised.
CD 550 6402
MC. 550 6404
Spectrum (1) / Aug '94 / PolyGram.

ANGER, FEAR, SEX AND DEATH.
Tracks: Not Advised.
CD . . . . E 86402CD
Epitaph / Nov '92 / Plastic Head.

APOCALYPSE 84.
Tracks: Gimme more: Kiss / Cold sweat: Thin Lizzy /
Out for blood: Ford, Lita / Don't talk to strangers: Dio
/ Analog kid: Rush (1) / Trashed: Black Sabbath /
Trop fou pour yoi: Satan Jokers / Devil made me do
it: Golden Earring / Don't say make me: Coney Hatch
/ Whipping boy: Nazareth.
■ LP 818 601 1

MC. 818 601 4
Phonogram (Import) / May '84 / PolyGram.

APPOINTMENT WITH FEAR.
Tracks: Not Advised.
CD .CYBERCD 11
Cyber / Aug '94 / Plastic Head.

AT DEATH'S DOOR (A Collection of Bru-
tal Death Metal).
Tracks: Mass hypnosis: Sepultura / Dead by dawn:
Deicide / Out of the body: Pestilence / Burnt identity:
Morgoth / Last abide: Sadus / Open casket: Death /
Decadence within: Malevolent Creation / Culte des
mortes: Cerebral Fix / Desecrator: Exhorder / Til
death: Obituary / No even one: Believer / Deep in
your subconscious: Atrocity.
LP . . . . RC 93621
■ CD . . . . RC 93622
Road Runner / Nov '90.

AT DEATH'S DOOR 2.
Tracks: Matyr: Fear Factory / Stench of paradise
burning: Disincarnate / Prelude to repulsion: Suffo-
cation / Uriboric forms: Cynic / Hideous infirmity:
Gorguts / Illusion of freedom: Sorrow / God of
thunder: Death / Piece by piece: Malevolent Creation
/ Unspoken names: Atrocity / Padre nuestro: Brujer-
ia / No forgiveness: Immolation / Sucked inside: Skin
Chamber.
■ MC. . . . . RR 91054
Road Runner / Feb '93.
CD . . . . RR 91052
Road Runner / Jan '94 / Pinnacle.

AXE ATTACK.
Tracks: Not Advised.
■ LP . . . . JCI 7102
MC. JCT 7102
Steeltrax / Nov '85.

AXE ATTACK II.
Tracks: Not Advised.
■ LP . . . . NE 1120
MC. CE 2120
K-Tel / Apr '81 / I & B Records / C.M. Distribution /
Arabesque Ltd. / Mono Distributors (Jersey) Ltd. /
Prism Leisure PLC / PolyGram / Ross Records /
Prism Leisure PLC.

BACK ON THE ROAD.
Tracks: All right now: Free (1) / All along the watch-
tower: Hendrix, Jimi / Living in the past: Jethro Tull /
Hocus pocus: Focus / Eight miles high: Byrds /
Rainbow chaser: Nirvana (1) / America (2nd Amend-
ment): Nice / Northern sky: Drake, Nick / On the road
again: Canned Heat / Paranoid: Black Sabbath /
White rabbit: Jefferson Airplane / Mona: Quicksilver
Messenger Service / My white bicycle: Tomorrow /
Love really changed me: Spooky Tooth / Race with
the devil: Gun (1) / 10.30 returns to the bedroom: Soft
Machine / Silver machine: Hawkwind / Meet on the
ledge: Fairport Convention / Fire: Crazy World of
Arthur Brown / Woodstock: Matthew's Southern
Comfort / Paper sun: Traffic / Do it: Pink Fairies /
Tom Tiddler's ground: Harper, Roy / Black night:
Deep Purple / Love like a man: Ten Years After / Venus in
furs: Velvet Underground / Fresh garbage: Spirit /
One and one is one: Medicine Head / Change song:
Blodwyn Pig / Something in the air: Thunderclap
Newman.
CD . . . . SMD 854
■ Double LP . . . . SMR 854
MC Set . . . . SMC 854
Stylus / Jun '88.

BEAVIS & BUTTHEAD EXPERIENCE.
Tracks: I hate myself and want to die: Nirvana (1) /
Looking down the barrel of a gun: Anthrax (1) / Come
to Butthead: Beavis & Butthead / 99 Ways to die:
Megadeth / Bounce: Run D.M.C. / Deuces are wild:
Aerosmith / I am hell: White Zombie / Poetry and
prose: Primus / Monsta Mack: Sir Mix-a-Lot / Search
and destroy: Red Hot Chili Peppers / Mental: Jackyl /
I got you babe: Cher, Beavis & Butthead / Come
to Butthead (Positive K Version): Beavis &
Butthead.
CD . . . . GED 24613
MC. GEC 24613
■ LP . . . . GEF 24613
Geffen / Nov '93.

BEST OF BRITISH STEEL.
Tracks: Tales of destruction: Dogs D'Amour / Cleri-
cal conspiracy: Sabbat / (Na na) nukklear rokket:
Wrathchild / Seventh church of the apocalyptic lawnmower: Lawnmower Deth / Low life: Trixx Federation
/ Read my lips: Tattooed Love Boys / Goddess: Acid
Reign / Rock 'n' roll lady: Dominique, Lisa / I'm on
fire: Mantas / Deny reality: Re-Animator / Surrender:
Midnight Blue / Queen of the night: Deathtrash / Prey
to the Lord: Deathwish / Living without you: Tiger-
tailz / Looking for a lady: Last Of The Teenage Idols /
Testify to me: Virus / Nights on fire: Torino / Spirit
cry: Sacrilege / Love attack: After Hours (1) / One
way ride: Lixx / Madman: Metal Messiah / So alone:
Soho Roses.
■ CD Set. . . . . .WKFMXD 128
■ Double LP. . . . . .WKFMLP 128
■ MC. . . . . WKFMMC 128
FM Records / Jul '89.

BEST OF HARD ROCK.
Tracks: Not Advised.
■ LP . . . . .BRLP 10
MC. BRMC 10
BR Music/BR Music (Holland) / Dec '88 / BMG.

BEST OF METAL MASSACRE.
Tracks: Not Advised.
■ LP . . . . RR 95511
Road Runner / Oct '88.

BEST OF SCANDINAVIAN ROCK.
Tracks: Not Advised.
■ LP . . . . SWORDLP 005
Music For Nations / '85.

BEST ROCK ALBUM IN THE WORLD
EVER.
Tracks: We willl rock you: Queen / Inside: Stiltskin /
Are you gonna go my way: Kravitz, Lenny / I'd do
anything for love (But I won't do that): Meat Loaf /
Smoke on the water: Deep Purple / Pride (In the
name of love): U2 / Born to be wild: Steppenwolf /
Free bird: Lynyrd Skynyrd / All right now: Free (1) /
(Don't fear) The reaper: Blue Oyster Cult / Can't get
enough: Bad Company / School's out: Cooper, Alice
/ More than a feeling: Boston / Boys are back in
town: Thin Lizzy / Rex / Silver machine: Hawkwind /
Mama: Genesis / Sledgehammer: Gabriel, Peter / In
the air tonight: Collins, Phil / Paranoid: Black Sab-
bath / Ace of spades: Motorhead / All day and all of
the night: Kinks / Gimme all your lovin': ZZ Top / She
sells sanctury: Cult / Owner of a lonely heart: Yes /
Do the strand: Roxy Music / Passenger: Iggy Pop /
Sunshine of your love: Cream / Mannish boy:
Waters, Muddy / Life's been good: Walsh, Joe /
Won't get fooled again (Full length version): Who /
Crazy crazy nights: Kiss / Eye of the tiger: Survivor /
Caroline: Status Quo / Money for nothing: Dire
Straits / In a broken dream: Python Lee Jackson.
CD .VTDCD 35
MC. VTDMC 35
Virgin / Aug '94 / EMI.

BEYOND THE METAL ZONE.
Tracks: Not Advised.
■ Double LP. . . . . MFN 63
MC. TMFN 63
Music For Nations / Aug '89 / Pinnacle.

BLASTING CONCEPT VOL 1.
Tracks: Not Advised.
■ LP . . . . SST 013
SST / Dec '83.

CD .SST 013 CD
MC. .SST 013 C
SST / May '93 / Pinnacle.

BLASTING CONCEPT VOL 2.
Tracks: Not Advised.
■ LP . . . . .SST 043
SST / Jul '86.
CD. .SST 043 CD
SST / Aug '87 / Pinnacle.
MC. .SST 043 C
SST / May '93 / Pinnacle.

BLUDGEONED.
Tracks: Not Advised.
■ LP . . . . BLUD 1
MC. . . . . BLUDGE 1
Bludgeon-Riffola / Sep '86 / PolyGram.

BREAKIN' METAL.
Tracks: Oriental beat: Hanoi Rocks / Knock 'm'
down: Thor / Satisfied the crucified: Rock Goddess /
Paranoid: Black Sabbath / Sweet surrender: Wrath-
child / Going down town: Lords Of The New Church /
Garabandal: Sledgehammer / Massacre: Thin Lizzy /
Deathmarch: Thor / Hot rok shock: Wrathchild / Black
girl white girl: Lords Of The New Church / Road rat:
Di'Anno / Don't believe a word: Thin Lizzy / Kick
down the walls: Wrathchild / Let the blood run red:
Thor / Back to mystery city: Hanoi Rocks.
■ VHS . . . . HEN 2016
Hendring Video / Feb '90.

BRITISH STEEL.
Tracks: Not Advised.
■ LP . . . . .JCI 1100
MC. . . . . .JCT 1100
Steeltrax / '85.

BRONZE ROCKS.
Tracks: Not Advised.
VHS . . . . .VVD 057
Virgin Vision / Apr '86 / Gold & Sons / TBD.

CALIFORNIA'S BEST METAL.
Tracks: Not Advised.
■ LP . . . . GWD 90526
MC. . . . . GWC 90526
New Renaissance(USA) / Nov '87 / Pinnacle.

CASE CLOSED.
Tracks: Not Advised.
CD. . . . . SRC 19
LP . . . . SR 19
SPV / May '94 / Plastic Head.

CHUNKS.
Tracks: Not Advised.
CD. .SST 069 CD
LP . . . . SST 069
MC. .SST 069 C
SST / May '93 / Pinnacle.

CLASSIC ROCK.
Tracks: Not Advised.
CD. 550 6452
MC. 550 6454
Spectrum (1) / Aug '94 / PolyGram.

COAST TO COAST.
Tracks: Voice of America: Dark Star (1) / American
fool: Green, Jack / Better late than never: XS / How
far Jerusalem: Magnum / Call of the wild: Sabu /
Hold back the night: Multi-Story / Stand me up:
Statetrooper / Dancin' on midnight: White Sister /
Shoot for the heart: Lawrence, Karen / Surrender:
Joshua.
■ CD. WKFMXD 96
■ LP . . . . WKFMLP 96
■ MC. WKFMMC 96
FM Records / Jul '87.

CORPORATE DEATH.
Tracks: Not Advised.
CD. . . . . NB 095
Nuclear Blast / Apr '94 / Plastic Head.

DANGERHOUSE.
Tracks: Not Advised.
CD. 346402
MC. 346404
Frontier / Aug '92 / Vital Distribution.

DARK EMPIRE STRIKES BACK.
Tracks: Not Advised.
CD. .DARK 005-2
Darkemp / Apr '94 / SRD.

DEAF METAL.
Tracks: War in paradise: Vital Remains / Cast out the
flesh: Banished / Cold winds: Dissection / In the
shadows: Morta Skuld / Headstone: Chorus of Ruin /
Enormous anthem of death: Nightfall / Repel your
faith: Impaler / Return: Therion / Engulfed in cysts:
Maimed / Architects: At The Gates / Method of
murder: Accidental Suicide / View: Eucharist / Land-
fill: Pitch Shifter / Witches: Doomed / Insanity reigns
supreme: Prophecy Of Doom.
CD. DEAF 012CD
MC. DEAF 012MC
Deaf / Aug '93 / Vital Distribution.

DEATH METAL.
Tracks: Not Advised.
LP . . . . .N 0006
LP . . . . .NUK 006
Noise / Apr '90 / Pinnacle.

DECLINE OF WESTERN CIVILISATION
(Part II - The metal years).
Tracks: Under my wheels: Cooper, Alice / Bathroom
wall: Faster Pussycat / Cradle to the grave: Motor-
head / You can run but you can't hide: Armored Saint
/ In my darkest hour: Megadeth / Prophecy: Queens-
ryche / Brave: Metal Church / Foaming at the mouth:
Rigor Mortis / Colleen: Seduce.
■ CD . . . . CDEST 2065
■ LP . . . . EST 2065
■ MC. . . . . .TCEST 2065
Capitol / Jul '88.

DECLINE OF WESTERN CIVILISATION
PART II (The metal years).
Tracks: Not Advised.
VHS . . . . PVC 3020 M
Palace Video / '88 / Palace Video.

DEEP PURPLE FAMILY ALBUM, THE.
Tracks: If you've gotta pick a baby: Collins, Glenda &
The Outlaws / You'll never stop me loving you: MI5 /
I take what I see: Artwoods / I can see through you:
Episode Six / Hush: Deep Purple / Sun's a risin':
Zephyr / Black night: Deep Purple / Into the fire
(Live): Deep Purple / Burn: Deep Purple / Love is all:
Glover, Roger & Guests / You keep on moving: Deep
Purple / Kill the king (Live): Rainbow (1) / Arabella
(Live): Paice, Ashton, Lord / Northwinds: Whitesnake
/ L.A. Cutoff: Hughes, Glenn / Stallion: Simper, Nick
Fandango / Nervous: Gillan / Clouds & rain: Gillan,
Ian & Roger Glover / Perfect strangers (Live): Deep
Purple.
CD. VSOPCD 187
Connoisseur Collection / May '93 / Pinnacle.

DEEPER INTO THE VAULT.
Tracks: Not Advised.
CD. .CDMFN 124
MC. . . . . TMFN 124
Music For Nations / Nov '91 / Pinnacle.

DEF AMERICAN SAMPLER - TIL DEF DO
US PART.
Tracks: Not Advised.
■ LP 8485741
■ MC. 8485744
■ CD. 8485742
American Recordings / Apr '91.

DIGGING THE WATER.
Tracks: Our production: Disorder / Kill your baby:
Chaos UK / Senil fools: Concrete Sox / Single ticket
to hell: Ripcord / Coconut song: Vicious Circle /
Ultracool: CCM / Bullshit propoganda: Extreme
Noise / Life: Electro Hippies / Oldest trick in the
book: Generic / Slumber party: Stupids / Firing line:
Dpraved / Truth: Bad Dress Sense / Mr. Poison

([8]X): Bad Dress Sense / Fairer sex: Civilised So-
ciety / Face the facts: Eyes On You / Miseravle
bastards: Potential Threat / Pigs for the slaughter: O
Polloi.
■ LP .ACHE 003
Children Of The Revolution / Apr '87.

DISCHARGED.
Tracks: Not Advised.
CD. . . . . PREACH 001CD
LP . . . . PREACH 001
Rhythm Vicar / Jun '92 / Plastic Head.

DOOMSDAY NEWS.
Tracks: Galactos: Scanner / Before the storm: Rage
(1) / Arrogance in uniform: Coroner / Total addiction:
Tankard / Hosanna in excelsis: Sabbat / I'm alive:
Helloween / And the brave man fails: Vendetta /
Mesmerized: Celtic Frost / After the attack: Kreator /
Cockroaches: VoiVod.
■ LP P.Disc . . . . NUKPD 105
Noise / Nov '89.
■ CD .CDNUK 105
■ LP .NUK 105
Noise / Oct '89.

DOOMSDAY NEWS (Video compilation
vol. 1).
Tracks: Rock the city: V2 / Conquistadores: Running
Wild / Gamblin' fool: S.A.D.O. / Morning after: Tan-
kard / Don't fear the winter: Rage (1) / Toxic trace:
Kreator / Masked jackal: Coroner / Ravenous medi-
cine: VoiVod / Tribal convictions: VoiVod / Circle of
the tyrants: Celtic Frost / Cherry orchards: Celtic
Frost / Halloween: Helloween / I want out:
Helloween.
VHS . . . . FLVC 1
Fotodisk Video / Feb '90.

DOOMSDAY NEWS II.
Tracks: Not Advised.
■ CD .CDNUK 130
■ LP .NUK 130
■ MC. . . . . .ZCNUK 130
Noise / Apr '89.

DOOMSDAY NEWS III.
Tracks: Flat of hate: Kreator / Riot of violence: Krea-
tor / Love us or hate us: Kreator / Alien: Tankard /
Chemical invasion: Tankard / Hosanna in excelsis:
Sabbat / I for an eye: Sabbat / For those who died:
Sabbat / DOA: Coroner / Absorbed: Coroner.
CD. .CDNUK 155
■ LP .NUK 155
■ MC. . . . . .ZCNUK 155
Noise / Sep '90.

DOPE, GUNS AND FUCKING UP YOUR
VIDEO DECK (Amphetamine Reptile Vi-
deo Compilation).
Tracks: Not Advised.
VHS . . . . .ATV 18P
Atavistic / May '91 / SRD.

DOPE, GUNS AND FUCKING UP YOUR
VIDEO DECK 2.
Tracks: Not Advised.
■ VHS .ATV 22P
ReVision / Aug '92.

DUCK AND COVER.
Tracks: Not Advised.
CD. .SST 263 CD
LP . . . . SST 263
MC. .SST 263 C
SST / Aug '90 / Pinnacle.

DUNGEON OF DELIGHT.
Tracks: Not Advised.
CD Set . . . . NZ 010CD
LP Set. . . . . NZ 010DLP
Nova Zembla / Jun '94 / Plastic Head.

EARPLUGGED.
Tracks: Not Advised.
CD. .MOSH 115CD
Earache / Sep '94 / Vital Distribution.

■ DELETED

EARTHQUAKE ALBUM, THE.

Tracks: Smoke on the water: *Rock Aid Armenia* / Spirit of radio: *Rush (1)* / Headless cross: *Black Sabbath* / Owner of a lonely heart: *Yes* / Fool for your loving: *Whitesnake* / We built this city: *Starship* / Run to the hills: *Iron Maiden* / Silent running: *Mike & The Mechanics* / Since you been gone: *Rainbow (1)* / Turn it on again: *Genesis* / Fanfare for the common man: *Emerson, Lake & Palmer* / Heat of the moment: *Asia* / Jukebox hero: *Foreigner* / Black night: *Deep Purple*.

```
CD . . . . . . . . . . . . . . . . . . . AIDCD 001
■ LP . . . . . . . . . . . . . . . . . . . AIDLP 001
MC . . . . . . . . . . . . . . . . . . . AIDMC 001
```
Big Wave / Apr '90 / BMG.

FAREWELL TO ARMS, A (A Japanese Hardcore Compilation).

Tracks: Kill ugly pop / Cops / June / I like cola / Eyes / Distortion faith / Pressing on / Jerusalem / Ghost candle.
```
■ LP . . . . . . . . . . . . . . . . . . . NB 009
```
Nuclear Blast / Nov '88.

FAST FORWARD TO HELL.

Tracks: Not Advised.
```
■ LP . . . . . . . . . . . . . . . . . . . VOVC 664
MC . . . . . . . . . . . . . . . . . . . VOVCC 664
```
Metalworks / Jun '87.

FOUNDATIONS FORUM SPECIAL VOL.1.

Tracks: Not Advised.
```
VHS . . . . . . . . . . . . . . . . . . . MXS 001
```
Channel 5 / Jan '91 / Channel 5 Video / P.R.O. Video / Gold & Sons.

FREE FOR ALL.

Tracks: Not Advised.
```
■ LP . . . . . . . . . . . . . . . . . . . HR 9458 1
```
Hawker / '89.

FRIDAY ROCK SHOW.

Tracks: What you're doing to me: *Spider (1)* / Don't you ever leave me: *Diamond Head* / Eye of the storm: *Sweet Savage* / Dance of the music: *Last Flight* / One helluva night: *Demon* / Edge of the world: *Black Axe* / Belfast: *Witchfynde* / Cuttin' loose: *Xero*.
```
■ LP . . . . . . . . . . . . . . . . . . . REH 426
■ MC . . . . . . . . . . . . . . . . . . . ZCR 426
```
BBC / Nov '81.

FUCK ME I'M RICH.

Tracks: Not Advised.
```
LP . . . . . . . . . . . . . . . . . . . DAMP 104
```
Waterfront / Jul '90 / SRD / Jazz Music / A.D.A. Distribution / C.M. Distribution.

GBG HARDCORE 81-85.

Tracks: Not Advised.
```
CD . . . . . . . . . . . . . . . . . . . DOLCD 9
```
Distortion / Sep '93 / Plastic Head.

GEFFEN RARITIES.

Tracks: Not Advised.
```
LP . . . . . . . . . . . . . . . . . . . GFL 19247
MC . . . . . . . . . . . . . . . . . . . GFLC 19247
```
Geffen / Aug '94 / BMG.
```
CD . . . . . . . . . . . . . . . . . . . GFLD 19247
```
Geffen / Aug '94 / BMG.

GODS OF GRIND.

Tracks: Stranger aeons: *Entombed* / Incarnated solvent abuse: *Carcass* / Soul sacrafice: *Cathedral* / Condemned: *Confessor* / Tools of the trade: *Carcass* / Dusk: *Entombed* / Golden blood (flooding): *Cathedral* / Pyosified (Still rotten to the core): *Carcass* / Shreds of flesh: *Entombed* / Autumn twilight: *Cathedral* / Last judgement: *Confessor* / Hepatic tissue fermentation: *II Carcass* / Frozen rapture: *Cathedral* / Endtime: *Confessor*.
```
CD . . . . . . . . . . . . . . . . . . . MOSH 063CD
■ MC . . . . . . . . . . . . . . . . . . . MOSH 063MC
```
Earache / Mar '92.

GREEN METAL.

Tracks: Not Advised.
```
■ LP . . . . . . . . . . . . . . . . . . . METALPS 107
```
Metal Masters / Sep '85.

GRINDCORE.

Tracks: Not Advised.
```
CD . . . . . . . . . . . . . . . . . . . NB 084CD
```
Nuclear Blast / Dec '93 / Plastic Head.

GRINDCRUSHER (The Earache sampler).

Tracks: Chapel of ghouls: *Morbid Angel* / Exhume to consume: *Carcass* / Missing link: *Napalm Death* / Through the eye of terror: *Bolt Thrower* / Party and fight: *Filthy Christians* / He nota home (Only on CD.): *Spazztic Blurr* / Horrendify and kill (Only on CD.): *Sore Throat* / Radiation sickness: *Repulsion* / Streetcleaner: *Godflesh* / Dead shall rise: *Terrorizer* / Straight jacket: *Intense Degree* / Colostomy grab bag (Only on CD.): *Old Lady Drivers* / Heresy (Only on CD.) / Divisions (Only on CD.): *Unseen Terror*.
```
CD . . . . . . . . . . . . . . . . . . . MOSH 12 CD
■ LP . . . . . . . . . . . . . . . . . . . MOSH 12
MC . . . . . . . . . . . . . . . . . . . MOSH 12 MC
```
Earache / Jul '89 / Vital Distribution.

GRINDCRUSHER 2.

Tracks: Not Advised.
```
CD . . . . . . . . . . . . . . . . . . . MOSH 035 CD
■ LP . . . . . . . . . . . . . . . . . . . MOSH 035
■ MC . . . . . . . . . . . . . . . . . . . MOSH 035 MC
```
Earache / Mar '91.

GUITAR MOODS 4 - HARD ROCKIN' GUITAR.

Tracks: All night long: *Rainbow (1)* / I am the storm: *Blue Oyster Cult* / Spirit of radio: *Rush (1)* / Crystal ball: *Malmsteen, Yngwie* / Funk No 48: *James Gang* / Where have you been all my life: *Nugent, Ted* / Heat of the moment: *Asia* / Jail bait: *Wishbone Ash* / Chinatown: *Thin Lizzy* / Ready for love: *Mott The Hoople* / Roll with the changes: *REO Speedwagon* / Flirtin' with disaster: *Molly Hatchet* / Back on the streets: *Moore, Gary* / Born to be wild: *Steppenwolf* / Something 'bout you baby I like: *Status Quo*.
```
CD . . . . . . . . . . . . . . . . . . . MCLD 19230
MC . . . . . . . . . . . . . . . . . . . MCLC 19230
```
MCA / Jan '94 / BMG.

HARD 'N' HEAVY.

Tracks: Can I play with madness: *Iron Maiden* / Antisocial: *Anthrax (1)* / Psychic vacuum: *VoiVod* / Living over the edge: *Hurricane* / Hot blooded: *Party Ninjas* / Unknown: *Party Ninjas* / Hot legs: *Party Ninjas* / Wild child: *W.A.S.P.* / Eat the rich: *Motorhead* / Miracle: *Osbourne, Ozzy* / Assume the position: *Forrester, Rhett* / Calling in the coroner: *VioLence* / Chalice of blood: *Forbidden* / Last in line: *Dio, Ronnie James* / Fat man: *Mammoth* / Down boys: *Warrant* / Here we go again: *Quireboys* / I love the dead: *Cooper, Alice* / Steven: *Cooper, Alice* / Elected: *Cooper, Alice* / Ballad of Dwight Fry: *Cooper, Alice* / I got a line on you: *Cooper, Alice*.
```
■ VHS . . . . . . . . . . . . . . . . . . . MVP 99 1183 3
```
PMI / May '89.

HARD 'N' HEAVY VOL.10 (Monsters of rock special).

Tracks: Not Advised.
```
VHS . . . . . . . . . . . . . . . . . . . VVD 813
```
Virgin Vision / Jan '91 / Gold & Sons / TBD.

HARD 'N' HEAVY VOL.11.

Tracks: Not Advised.
```
VHS . . . . . . . . . . . . . . . . . . . VVD 864
```
Virgin Vision / '91 / Gold & Sons / TBD.

HARD 'N' HEAVY VOL.12.

Tracks: Not Advised.
```
VHS . . . . . . . . . . . . . . . . . . . VVD 871
```
Virgin Vision / '91 / Gold & Sons / TBD.

HARD 'N' HEAVY VOL.2.

Tracks: Not Advised.
```
■ VHS . . . . . . . . . . . . . . . . . . . MVP 99 1188 3
```
PMI / Jul '89.

HARD 'N' HEAVY VOL.3.

Tracks: Not Advised.
```
■ VHS . . . . . . . . . . . . . . . . . . . MVP 99 1192 3
```
PMI / Sep '89.

HARD 'N' HEAVY VOL.4.

Tracks: Not Advised.
```
■ VHS . . . . . . . . . . . . . . . . . . . MVP 9911983
```
PMI / Nov '89.

HARD 'N' HEAVY VOL.5.

Tracks: Not Advised.
```
■ VHS . . . . . . . . . . . . . . . . . . . MVP 9911033
```
PMI / Feb '90.

HARD 'N' HEAVY VOL.6.

Tracks: Not Advised.
```
■ VHS . . . . . . . . . . . . . . . . . . . MVP 99 1211 3
```
PMI / Mar '90.

HARD 'N' HEAVY VOL.7.

Tracks: Not Advised.
```
VHS . . . . . . . . . . . . . . . . . . . VVD 700
```
Virgin Vision / Apr '90 / Gold & Sons / TBD.

HARD 'N' HEAVY VOL.8.

Tracks: Not Advised.
```
VHS . . . . . . . . . . . . . . . . . . . VVD 731
```
Virgin Vision / Aug '90 / Gold & Sons / TBD.

HARD 'N' HEAVY VOL.9.

Tracks: Not Advised.
```
VHS . . . . . . . . . . . . . . . . . . . VVD 784
```
Virgin Vision / Nov '90 / Gold & Sons / TBD.

HARD ROCK.

Tracks: Spirit of radio: *Rush (1)* / You ain't seen nothin' yet: *Bachman-Turner Overdrive* / Come on Eileen: *Dexy's Midnight Runners & Emerald Express* / Final countdown: *Europe* / Living after midnight: *Judas Priest* / Pretty in pink: *Psychedelic Furs* / Paranoid: *Black Sabbath* / Bat out of hell: *Meat Loaf* / Down down: *Status Quo* / Bark at the moon: *Osbourne, Ozzy* / Cum on feel the noize: *Quiet Riot* / Skin deep: *Stranglers* / Ace of spades: *Motorhead* / Gipsy: *Uriah Heep* / Start talking love: *Magnum* / St. Elmo's fire: *Parr, John* / Rock 'n' roll children: *Dio* / Silver machine (live): *Hawkwind*.
```
CD . . . . . . . . . . . . . . . . . . . STACD 003
```
Pickwick / Oct '91 / Pickwick.
```
MC . . . . . . . . . . . . . . . . . . . STAMC 003
```
Wisepack / Nov '92 / TBD / Conifer Records.

HARD ROCK.

Tracks: Not Advised.
```
■ LP . . . . . . . . . . . . . . . . . . . 6685 140
MC . . . . . . . . . . . . . . . . . . . 7653 140
```
Vertigo / Dec '81 / PolyGram.

HARD ROCK.

Tracks: Not Advised.
```
CD . . . . . . . . . . . . . . . . . . . 550 6492
MC . . . . . . . . . . . . . . . . . . . 550 6494
```
Spectrum (1) / Aug '94 / PolyGram.

HARD ROCK'83.

Tracks: Gimme more: *Kiss* / Cold sweat: *Thin Lizzy* / Out for blood: *Ford, Lita* / Don't talk to strangers: *Dio* / Analog kid: *Rush (1)* / Trashed: *Black Sabbath* / Don't say make me: *Coney Hatch* / Devil made me do it: *Golden Earring* / Nighthunter: *Picture* / Whipping boy: *Nazareth*.
```
■ LP . . . . . . . . . . . . . . . . . . . 814 462 1
MC . . . . . . . . . . . . . . . . . . . 814 462 4
```
Vertigo / Mar '84 / PolyGram.

HARDCORE HOLOCAUST 2.

Tracks: Not Advised.
```
CD . . . . . . . . . . . . . . . . . . . SFRCD 113
LP . . . . . . . . . . . . . . . . . . . SFRLP 113
MC . . . . . . . . . . . . . . . . . . . SFRMC 113
```
Strange Fruit / '90 / Pinnacle.

HARDROCK BOX SET.

Tracks: Not Advised.
```
CD Set . . . . . . . . . . . . . . . . . . . TPAK 13
```
Virgin / Oct '90 / EMI.

HEAR'N'AID (Various artists).
Tracks: Up to the limit (live): *Accept* / Hungry for heaven (Live): *Dio* / Can you see me: *Hendrix, Jimi* / Heaven's on fire (Live): *Kiss* / On the road (live): *Motorhead* / Distant early warning (Live): *Rush (1)* / Zoo (Live): *Scorpions* / Go for the throat: *Y & T.*
■ LP . . . . VERH 35
Vertigo / Jun '86.

HEAVY METAL AMERICA.
Tracks: Boy's night out / Sing it, shout it / All right now / Liberty rebellion / Don't tempt the devil / Back in action / Feel the fire / Winter freeze / Road warrior / Rockin.
■ LP . . . . HMUSA 33
MC. . . . . HMAMC 33
Heavy Metal America / Apr '85 / FM Revolver / Sony.

HEAVY METAL HEROES VOL.2.
Tracks: Lionheart: *Lionheart* / En cachent: *Shiva* / Arrive alive: *Pallas* / What the hell's going on: *Mendes Prey* / Ice cold swallow: *Mantle Swallow* / Palmer* / Out of my head: *Over Kill* / Devil's triangle: *Cox, Jess* / This fire inside: *Twisted Ace* / Free country: *Witchfinder General* / Oh well: *No Faith* / Calling for you: *Persian Risk* / Power and the key: *No Quarter.*
■ LP . . . . HMRLP 7
Heavy Metal / Dec '82.

HEAVY METAL HEROES VOL.3.
Tracks: Not Advised.
MC. . . . . HMRMC 153
■ CD . . . . HMRXD 153
■ LP . . . . HMRLP 153
Heavy Metal / Aug '90.

HEAVY METAL MONSTERS.
Tracks: Not Advised.
■ Double LP . . . . CR 5151
■ MC Set . . . . CRT 5151
Cambra / Mar '85.

HEAVY METAL RECORDS (A TASTY TASTER).
Tracks: Not Advised.
■ LP . . . . HMRLP 24
MC. . . . . HMRMC 24
Heavy Metal / Dec '84 / Sony / FM Revolver.

HEAVY METAL RECORDS COMPILATION.
Tracks: Not Advised.
CD. . . . . HMRXD 143
■ LP . . . . HMRLP 143
MC. . . . . HMRMC 143
Heavy Metal / Jul '90 / Sony / FM Revolver.

HEAVY METAL THUNDER.
Tracks: Heavy metal thunder: *Saxon (1)* / One of the boys: *Rose Tattoo* / Long way from home: *Rage (1)* / Nightridge: *Dokken* / Total possession: *Demon* / Motorcycle man: *Saxon (1)* / Denim and leather: *Saxon (1)* / Assault & battery: *Rose Tattoo* / Liar: *Demon* / We're illegal: *Dokken* / Thank that woman: *Rage (1).*
■ LP . . . . CAL 3002
MC. . . . . CAC 3002
Carrere / Aug '82 / WEA.

HEAVY ROCK.
Tracks: Not Advised.
■ LP 6498 093
Vertigo / '81.
MC. 7133 093
Vertigo / Jun '81 / PolyGram.

HEAVY WAY, THE.
Tracks: Last in line: *Dio* / Gotta let go: *Ford, Lita* / Seven seas: *New Thunder* / Between the wheels: *Rush (1)* / Digital bitch: *Black Sabbath* / Rockin' all over the world: *Status Quo* / Breakout: *Bon Jovi* / Eternal dark: *Picture* / Lonely is the master: *Kiss* / This month's messiah: *Nazareth* / Don't say make me / Rocker: *Thin Lizzy.*
CD. 822750 2
■ LP 822750 1
MC. 822750 4
Vertigo (Holland) / Nov '84 / Pinnacle.

HELL ON EARTH.
Tracks: Not Advised.
■ LP . . . . MFN 12
Music For Nations / Nov '83.

HELLFIRE VOL.1.
Tracks: Not Advised.
CD . . . . PS 1003CD
Double LP . . . . PS 1003
PSI / Jul '91.

HELLHOUND COMPILATION.
Tracks: Not Advised.
CD. . . . . .H 0032-2
Hellhound / Aug '94 / Plastic Head.

HIATUS - THE PEACEVILLE SAMPLER.
Tracks: Not Advised.
■ LP . . . . VILE 006
Peaceville / Oct '88.
CD. . . . . VILECD 006
Peaceville / Apr '89 / Vital Distribution / Pinnacle.

HIS MASTER'S METAL.
Tracks: Not Advised.
■ LP . . . . IW 1016
Iron Works (USA) / Dec '87.

HM.
Tracks: Black and white: *Deep Purple* / Time to burn: *Dio, Ronnie James* / Livin' on a prayer: *Bon Jovi* / You don't remember I'll never forget: *Malmsteen, Yngwie & Rising Force* / Angry heart: *Black Sabbath* / Love song: *Warlock* / Shake me (live): *Cinderella* / Any way you slice it: *Kiss* / Get ready: *Paganini* / Speed demon: *Keel* / Rev it up: *Treat* / Rock on tonight: *Picture* / Talk dirty to me: *Poison* / Way: *Stryper.*
■ LP 8164931
MC. 8164934
Mercury (Import) / Mar '88.

HOT 'N' HEAVY.
Tracks: Hot girls: *Cherry Bombz* / Mad house: *Anthrax (1)* / Bump and grind: *Williams, Wendy O.* / Waiting: *Tygers Of Pan Tang* / Vanity: *Ligotage* / Rip ride: *Venom* / Underwater world: *Hanoi Rocks* / Needle gun: *Hawkwind* / Atlantic radio: *Rio (1)* / Night run: *UFO* / Shake it up: *Aaron, Lee* / Rock rock: *Baby Tuckoo* / Star: *Torme* / House of ecstasy: *Cherry Bombz.*
VHS . . . . .JE 152
Jettisoundz / '86 / TBD / Visionary Communications.

HOT WIRED MONSTERTRUX.
Tracks: Intro / Wish: *Nine Inch Nails* / Finger on the trigger: *Excessive Force* / Tool and die: *Consolidated* / Godlike: *KMFDM* / Jesus built my hotrod: *Ministry* / Kooler than Jesus: *My Life With The Thrill Kill Kult* / Provision: *Frontline Assembly* / Looking forward: *CNN* / Murder Inc: *Murder Inc.* / Edge of no control: *Meat Beat Manifesto* / Skinflower: *Young Gods* / Motorbike: *Sheep On Drugs* / Headhunter V.10: *Front 242* / Family man: *Nitzer Ebb.*
CD. 9548 31811-2
East West / Feb '93 / WEA.

HOTTER THAN HELL.
Tracks: Not Advised.
CD . . . . BMCD 50
Black Mark / Mar '94 / Plastic Head.

HOW TO BREAK INTO HEAVY METAL WITHOUT BEING SCREWED.
Tracks: Not Advised.
VHS . . . . .WNR 1055
Wienerworld Video / Sep '89 / VCI Distribution / TBD.

IRON TYRANTS I.
Tracks: Not Advised.
■ LP . . . . WMR 001
World Metal / Jul '86.

IRON TYRANTS II.
Tracks: Not Advised.
■ LP . . . . WMR 002
World Metal / Jul '87.

IRON TYRANTS III.
Tracks: Not Advised.
■ LP . . . . WMR 003
World Metal / Jul '88.

JAMMY MUSIC LIBRARY VOL.5 - HEAVY METAL.
Tracks: Not Advised.
■ LP . . . . JRML 005
Jammy Music Library / '88.

JAPANESE HARDCORE 1.
Tracks: Not Advised.
■ 12". . . . . .DISC 2
Vinyl Japan / '92.

JAPANESE HARDCORE 2.
Tracks: Not Advised.
LP . . . . .DISC 4
Vinyl Japan / '92 / Vital Distribution.

JOHN PEEL SUB POP SESSIONS.
Tracks: By her own hand: *Mudhoney* / Here comes sickness: *Mudhoney* / You make me die: *Mudhoney* / Helot: *Tad* / Sit in glass: *Seaweed* / She cracked: *Seaweed* / You pretty thins: *Pond* / Cinders: *Pond* / Here comes: *Velocity Girl* / Always: *Velocity Girl* / Crazy town: *Velocity Girl* / Broken hearted wine: *Codeine.*
CD. . . . . SFRCD 126
Strange Fruit / Mar '94 / Pinnacle.

JOURNEY TO THE EDGE (Progressive Rock Classics).
Tracks: Living in the past: *Jethro Tull* / Joybringer: *Manfred Mann's Earthband* / America: *Nice* / Cirkus (Including entry of the chameleons): *King Crimson* / In-a-gadda-da-vida: *Iron Butterfly* / Forty thousand headmen: *Traffic* / You keep me hangin' on: *Vanilla Fudge* / Child of the universe: *Barclay James Harvest* / Wishing well: *Free (1)* / Tomorrow night: *Atomic Rooster* / Jerusalem: *Emerson, Lake & Palmer* / Freefall: *Camel* / Back street luv: *Curved Air* / Suprise, surprise: *Caravan* / Natural born bugie: *Humble Pie* / Love like a man: *Ten Years After* / Burlesque: *Family* / My room (Waiting for wonderland): *Van Der Graaf Generator.*
CD. . . . . MUSCD 18
MC. . . . . MUSMC 18
Music Club / May '94 / Gold & Sons / TBD / Video Collection / C.M. Distribution.

KERRANG - THE ALBUM.
Tracks: Jesus Christ pose: *Soundgarden* / Another wordly device: *Prong* / Punishment: *Biohazard* / Autosurgery: *Therapy (1)* / Territory: *Sepultura* / Sweating bullets: *Megadeth* / Shedding skin: *Pantera* / Caffeine bomb: *Wildhearts* / My house: *Terrorvision* / Give it away (Edit): *Red Hot Chili Peppers* / Warfair (Cybersank mix edit): *Clawfinger* / Believe in me: *McKagan, Duff* / Ten miles high: *Little Angels* / Over the edge: *Almighty* / Down in a hole: *Alice In Chains* / Ace of spades (Live): *Motorhead* / Paranoid: *Black Sabbath* / Smoke on the water: *Deep Purple* / State of change (Live): *Judas Priest* / Stargazer: *Rainbow (1)* / Bat out of hell: *Meat Loaf* / Cats in the cradle: *Ugly Kid Joe* / In my darkest hour: *Megadeth* / Doctor doctor (Live): *UFO* / Spirit of radio: *Rush (1)* / Epic: *Faith No More* / Angel of death: *Slayer* / Youth gone wild: *Skid Row (2)* / Born to be wild: *Steppenwolf* / Freebird: *Lynyrd Skynyrd.*
CD. . . . . AHLCD 21
MC. . . . . AHLMC 21
Hit Label / Jun '94 / PolyGram.

KERRANG KLASSICS.
Tracks: Neon knights: *Black Sabbath* / New Orleans: *Gillan* / And the bands played on: *Saxon (1)* / Incommunicado: *Marillion* / Here I go again: *Whitesnake* /

Over the hills and far away: *Moore, Gary* / Out in the fields: *Moore, Gary & Phil Lynott* / Livin' on a prayer: *Bon Jovi* / Killer on the loose: *Thin Lizzy* / I surrender: *Rainbow (1)*.
VHS . . . . **MVP 99 1191 3**
PMI / Oct '89 / EMI / Gold & Sons / TBD.

KERRANG KOMPILATION.

Tracks: Love machine: *W.A.S.P.* / Take hold of the flame: *Queensryche* / God bless video: *Alcatrazz* / Gimme gimme: *Helix* / Wild on the run: *Tobruk* / Aces high: *Iron Maiden* / Assassing: *Marillion* / All men play on 10: *Manowar* / Fighting for the earth: *Warrior* / Victims of the future: *Moore, Gary* / Don't tell mama: *Mama's Boys* / Sailor to a siren: *Meat Loaf* / Ballroom blitz: *Krokus* / Can you deliver: *Armored Saint* / Rebel yell: *Idol, Billy* / Rock you like a hurricane: *Scorpions* / Slow 'n' easy: *Whitesnake* / Right to rock: *Keel* / Heaven's on fire: *Kiss* / Runaway: *Bon Jovi* / High in high school: *Madam X* / Follow your heart: *Triumph* / Break down the walls: *Stone Fury* / Heartline: *George, Robin*.
■ **LP** . . . . **KER 1**
■ **MC**. . . . . **TC KER 1**
Virgin / Jun '85.

KERRANG KOMPILATION 1 (20 Rock Monsters).

Tracks: Love machine: *W.A.S.P.* / Aces high: *Iron Maiden* / Slow 'n' easy: *Whitesnake* / Killed by death: *Motorhead* / Mama weer all crazee now: *Mama's Boys* / We ain't gonna take it any more: *Twisted Sister* / Heart line: *George, Robin* / Heaven's on fire: *Kiss* / Shape of things to come: *Moore, Gary* / Queen of the reich: *Queensryche* / High in high school: *Madam X* / Runaway: *Bon Jovi* / Rock you like a hurricane: *Scorpions* / God bless video: *Alcatrazz* / Gimme gimme good lovin': *Helix* / Follow your heart: *Triumph* / Can U deliver: *Armored Saint*.
■ **VHS** . . . . **MVP 99 1077 2**
PMI / Jul '85.

KERRANG KOMPILATION 2.

Tracks: Not Advised.
VHS . . . . **VVD 171**
Virgin Vision / '87 / Gold & Sons / TBD.

KERRANG KOMPILATION 3.

Tracks: Evil that men do: *Iron Maiden* / Still of the night: *Whitesnake* / Nothin' but a good time: *Poison* / Edge of a broken heart: *Vixen* / Living without you: *Tiger Tailz* / Anarchy in the U.K.: *Megadeth* / Tribal convictions: *VoiVod* / I'm the man: *Anthrax (1)* / Get it on: *Kingdom Come* / Rock me now: *Vow Wow* / Days of no trust: *Magnum* / Prime mover: *Zodiac Mindwarp* / Manimal: *W.A.S.P.*.
■ **VHS** . . . . **MVP 99 1166 3**
■ **VHS** . . . . **MVPKER 3**
PMI / Oct '88.

KERRANG KOMPILATION 4.

Tracks: Heaven tonight: *Malmsteen, Yngwie & Rising Force* / Teenage bride: *Grip (1)* / Headless cross: *Black Sabbath* / She's a little angel: *Little Angels* / Let there be rock: *Onslaught* / Ready for love: *Moore, Gary* / Love has taken it's toll: *Saraya* / There she goes again: *Quireboys* / Last mile: *Cinderella* / Tonight I'm falling: *TNT* / I want out: *Helloween* / How comes it never rains: *Dogs D'Amour* / Do you like it: *Kingdom Come*.
VHS . . . . **VVD 516**
Virgin Vision / Jun '89 / Gold & Sons / TBD.

KERRANG KOMPILATION 5.

Tracks: Dive dive dive: *Dickinson, Bruce* / She's so fine: *Thunder (1)* / Now you're gone: *Whitesnake* / Holy wars..The punishment due: *Megadeth* / Heartbreaker at the end of Lonely Street: *Dread Zeppelin* / Heart and soul: *No Sweat* / Lips 'n' hips: *Electric Boys* / She's a little angel: *Little Angels* / Up all night: *Slaughter* / Love is a killer: *Vixen* / Rocking chair: *Magnum*.
■ **VHS** . . . . **MVP 99 1264 3**
PMI / Jan '91.

KERRANG LADYKILLERS.

Tracks: All fall down: *Dominique, Lisa* / First time: *Beck, Robin* / Sex as a weapon: *Benatar, Pat* / Hot girls are easy: *Cherry Bombz* / Crying: *Vixen* / Waiting for the big one: *Femme Fatale* / Cry myself to sleep at night: *Romeo's Daughter* / Back to the bullet: *Saraya* / Whiter shade of pale: *Doro* / Why call it love: *Phantom Blue* / Trouble in pardise: *Princess Pang* / I hate myself for loving you: *Jett, Joan* / Only human: *Aaron, Lee*.
■ **VHS** . . . . **MVP 9912203**
PMI / May '90.

KIDS ARE UNITED.

Tracks: Not Advised.
■ **LP** . . . . **MFN 4**
Music For Nations / Jun '83.

KINGDOM OF ROCK, THE.

Tracks: Praying to the red light: *Almighty* / Too far gone too be wasted: *DC Kicks* / Sexman: *Goat* / Hypnotised: *Hellfire Club* / Scene of the crime: *Kill City Dragons* / Young gods: *Little Angels* / Cocaine and guns: *Naughty Naughty* / Hate / Railroad: *Rattlesnake Kiss* / Englishman on holiday, An: *Thunder (1)* / Smashed and blind: *Wolfsbane* / What do they want from us: *2 Tribes* / Praying To The Light: *Almighty*.
CD. . . . . **HEDRC 102**
■ **LP** . . . . **HEDRL 102**
MC. . . . . **HEDRM 2**
Head / Jul '92 / Total / BMG.

KISS YER SKULL GOODBYE.

Tracks: Seven by seven: *Hawkwind* / Time we left: *Hawkwind* / Hard times: *Bernie Torme* / Beat: *Bernie Torme* / Take it for granted: *Atomic Rooster* / Sleepless nights: *Atomic Rooster* / Hide in the rain: *Four X* / In the fire: *Four X* / Because you lied: *McCoy, John* / Temporary threshold shift: *McCoy, John*.
MC. . . . . **MCFRC 509**
Conifer / Apr '86 / Conifer Records / Jazz Music.
■ **LP** . . . . **CFRC 509**
Conifer / Jan '87.

KNEBWORTH - THE ALBUM.

Tracks: Everybody wants to rule the world: *Tears For Fears* / Dirty water: *Status Quo* / Rockin' all over the world: *Status Quo* / Do you wanna dance: *Richard, Cliff & The Shadows* / Liar's dance: *Plant, Robert* / Wearing and tearing: *Plant, Robert & Jimmy Page* / Turn it on again (medley): *Genesis* / Sunshine of your love: *Clapton, Eric* / Money for nothing: *Dire Straits* / Saturday night's all right for fighting: *John, Elton* / Hey Jude: *McCartney, Paul* / Run like hell: *Pink Floyd* / Badman's song: *Tears For Fears* / Whatever you want: *Status Quo* / On the beach: *Richard, Cliff & The Shadows* / Hurting kind: *Plant, Robert* / Tall cool one: *Plant, Robert* / Mama: *Genesis* / Sussudio: *Collins, Phil* / Think I love you too much: *Dire Straits* / Sad songs (say so much): *John, Elton* / Coming up: *McCartney, Paul* / Comfortably numb: *Pink Floyd*.
CD. **843 921-2**
■ **LP** **843 921-1**
MC. **843 921-4**
Polydor / Aug '90 / PolyGram.

KNEBWORTH - THE EVENT 1.

Tracks: In the air tonight: *Collins, Phil* / Sussudio: *Collins, Phil* / Coming up: *McCartney, Paul* / Birthday: *McCartney, Paul* / Hey Jude: *McCartney, Paul* / Can't buy me love: *McCartney, Paul* / Change: *Tears For Fears* / Badman's song: *Tears For Fears* / Everybody wants to rule the world: *Tears For Fears* / On the beach: *Richard, Cliff & The Shadows* / Good golly Miss Molly: *Richard, Cliff & The Shadows* / Do you wanna dance: *Richard, Cliff & The Shadows* / Living doll: *Richard, Cliff & The Shadows* / We don't talk anymore: *Richard, Cliff & The Shadows*.
Laser Disc . . . . **CMPL 6006**
■ **VHS** . . . . **CMP 6006**
Castle Music Pictures / Aug '90.

KNEBWORTH - THE EVENT 2.

Tracks: Whatever you want: *Status Quo* / Rockin' all over the world: *Status Quo* / Dirty water: *Status Quo* / In the army now: *Status Quo* / Before you accuse me: *Clapton, Eric* / Tearin' us apart: *Clapton, Eric* / Solid rock: *Dire Straits* / Think I love you too much: *Dire Straits* / Money for nothing: *Dire Straits* / Sacrifice: *John, Elton* / Sad songs (say so much): *John, Elton*.
Laser Disc . . . . **CMPL 6007**
■ **VHS** . . . . **CMP 6007**
Castle Music Pictures / Aug '90.

KNEBWORTH - THE EVENT 3.

Tracks: Hurting kind (I've got my eyes on you): *Plant, Robert* / Tall cool one: *Plant, Robert* / Wearing and tearing: *Plant, Robert & Jimmy Page* / Rock 'n' roll: *Plant, Robert* / Mama: *Genesis* / Turn it on again: *Genesis* / Medley: *Genesis* / Shine on you crazy diamond: *Pink Floyd* / Run like hell: *Pink Floyd*.
Laser Disc . . . . **CMPL 6008**
■ **VHS** . . . . **CMP 6008**
Castle Music Pictures / Aug '90.

KNIGHTMARE II.

Tracks: Not Advised.
■ **LP** . . . . **IW 1020**
Iron Works (USA) / May '88.

L

LADYKILLERS.

Tracks: Not Advised.
■ **LP** . . . . **GWD 90541**
MC. . . . . **GWC 90541**
New Renaissance(USA) / Nov '87 / Pinnacle.

LAS VEGAS GRIND PART.2.

Tracks: Not Advised.
CD . . . . **EFA 11512 CD**
LP . . . . **EFA 11512**
Crypt / Mar '93 / SRD.

LAST WARRIOR, THE.

Tracks: Not Advised.
■ **LP** . . . . **OTH 10**
Metalother / Aug '88.

LEADWEIGHT.

Tracks: Inquisitor: *Raven* / Cheetah: *White Spirit* / Angel dust: *Venom* / S.S.Giro: *Axe* / Inferno: *Blitzkrieg* / Noonday: *Aragorn* / Throwing in the towel: *Fist* / Messiah: *Axis* / Down the road: *Bitches Sin* / Flying high: *Warrior* / Soldiers of war: *Satan's Empire*.
MC. . . . . **NEATC 1000**
Neat / '85 / Grapevine Distribution.

LEATHER AND LACE (The Men and Women of Rock).

Tracks: Not Advised.
CD. . . . . **DINCD 9**
LP . . . . **DINTV 9**
MC. . . . . **DINMC 9**
Dino / Jun '90 / Pinnacle.

LEATHER AND LACE - THE SECOND CHAPTER.

Tracks: Radio ga ga: *Queen* / Black velvet: *Myles, Alannah* / Road to hell: *Rea, Chris* / Rooms on fire: *Nicks, Stevie* / Hurting kind (I've got my eyes on you): *Palmer, Robert* / Edge of a broken heart: *Vixen* / Better days: *Gun (1)* / I don't want a lover: *Texas (2)* / Run to you: *Adams, Bryan* / Big love: *Fleetwood Mac* / Radar love: *Golden Earring* / Get your love: *Black Velvette* / From out of nowhere: *Faith No More* / Martha's harbour: *All About Eve* / I'm a believer: *Giant* / First time: *Beck, Robin* / Centrefold: *Geils, J. Band*.
CD. . . . . **DINCD 12**
LP . . . . **DINTV 12**
MC. . . . . **DINMC 12**
Dino / Nov '90 / Pinnacle.

LET IT ROCK.

Tracks: Rocker: *Thin Lizzy* / Soft lights, sweet music: *Liar* / Highfly: *Miles, John* / Steppin' out: *Mayall, John & The Bluesbreakers* / Backstreet luv: *Curved Air* / You can choose: *Hartley, Keef Band* / Taste and try before you buy: *Savoy Brown* / Jig a jig: *East Of Eden* / Save my love: *Black Cat Bones* / Baby please don't go: *Them* / Two sisters: *Wolf (1)* / Still as stone: *Brown, Alan* / I'm just a singer (in a rock and roll band): *Moody Blues* / Stumble: *Mayall, John & The Bluesbreakers* / Be my eyes: *Edge, Graeme Band* / I'm going home: *Ten Years After*.
■ **CD**. **8205732**
Deram / Jan '88.

LET THERE BE ROCK.

Tracks: Not Advised.
CD. . . . . **NTRCD 016**
MC. . . . . **NTRC 016**
Quality / Jun '94 / Pinnacle.

LET'S ROCK WITH SMASHEY & NICEY.

Tracks: You ain't seen nothin' yet: *Bachman-Turner Overdrive* / 2-4-6-8 Motorway: *Robinson, Tom* / Since you've been gone: *Rainbow (1)* / More than a feeling: *Boston* / Elected: *Cooper, Alice* / Here I go again (1987 remix): *Whitesnake* / Centrefold: *J.Geils Band* / Smoking in the boys room: *Brownsville Station* / Rockin' all over the world: *Status Quo* / Run, run, run: *Jo Jo Gunne* / Can't get enough: *Bad Company* / Radar love: *Golden Earring* / Black night: *Deep Purple* / Born to be wild: *Steppenwolf* / Wishing well: *Free (1)* / Rocker: *Thin Lizzy* / Black Betty: *Ram Jam* / Nutbush City Limits: *Turner, Ike & Tina* / Play that funky music: *Wild Cherry* / (Don't fear) The Reaper:

Blue Oyster Cult / God gave rock 'n' roll to you: *Argent.*
CD . . . . CDEMTV 67
■ LP . . . . EMTV 67
■ MC . . . . TCEMTV 67
EMI / Oct '92.

LITTLE BIT OF LIGHT RELIEF.
Tracks: Not Advised.
■ LP . . . . ROCK 2
Polydor / '83.

LIVE AND HEAVY.
Tracks: Smoke on the water: *Deep Purple* / Razamanaz: *Nazareth* / White line fever: *Motorhead* / Rocks off: *Def Leppard* / All night long: *Rainbow (1)* / Roll over lay down: *Status Quo* / Ain't no love in the heart of the city: *Whitesnake* / Lights out in London: *UFO* / Unchain your brain: *Gillan* / Paranoid: *Black Sabbath.*
■ LP . . . . NEL 6020
Nems / Nov '81.

LIVE FROM NEW YORK CITY (Hardcore and More).
Tracks: Sightseeing: *Adrenalin O.D.* / Destructive engagement: *False Prophets* / Yaddie ho: *Damage* / Boots of God: *Damage* / Riot: *Reverb Motherf*ckers* / Idols and dolls: *Skulls* / Chop up your momma: *Sic F*cks* / Rock or die: *Sic F*cks* / Axe to grind: *Letch patrol* / Rock 'n' roll party town: *GWAR* / Sexorcist: *Honeymoon Killers* / Copshot: *Shaved Pigs* / Action speaks louder: *Token Entry.*
VHS . . . . JE 187
Jettisoundz / May '89 / TBD / Visionary Communications.

LIVE 'N' LOUD.
Tracks: Aces high: *Iron Maiden* / Big city nights: *Scorpions* / Ain't no love in the heart of the city: *Whitesnake* / Highway star: *Deep Purple* / Backstreet symphony: *Thunder (1)* / 747 (strangers in the night): *Saxon (1)* / Wild child: *W.A.S.P.* / Whippin' boy: *Quireboys* / All over now: *Great White.*
CD . . . . CDFA 3264
■ LP . . . . FA 3264
■ MC . . . . TCFA 3264
Fame / Nov '91.

LIVE TO RIDE (18 Rock Classics).
Tracks: I want you to want me: *Cheap Trick* / Barracuda: *Heart* / Carrie: *Europe* / She's not there: *Santana (1)* / Up around the bend: *Hanoi Rocks* / Breaking the law: *Judas Priest* / Silver machine: *Saxon (1)* / Rock 'n' me: *Miller, Steve* / Show me the way: *Frampton, Peter* / I surrender: *Rainbow (1)* / Waiting for an alibi: *Thin Lizzy* / Radar love: *Golden Earring* / Closer to the heart: *Rush (1)* / Whatever you want: *Status Quo* / Victims of circumstance: *Barclay James Harvest* / Lady in black: *Uriah Heep* / This flight tonight: *Nazareth.*
CD . . . . VSOPCD 194
Connoisseur Collection / Apr '94 / Pinnacle.

LIVING LEGENDS.
Tracks: Rain / 4500 times / Rocks off / Junior's eyes / Die young / Rocker / Suicide / Satellite / Temples of Syrinx / What you're doing.
■ LP 6498 092
Vertigo / Dec '80.

LOUDER THAN WORDS.
Tracks: Freedom: *Helicon* / Woman: *Helicon* / Making plans for Nigel: *Burning Heads* / Blind: *Burning Heads* / Circus divine: *Sevenchurch* / Fleischwolf: *Fleischmann* / Holle: *Fleischmann* / Tumor: *Gunjah* / Sooner of later: *Gunjah* / Sublime dementia: *Loudblast* / Wisdom (Further on): *Loudblast* / Corporal punishment: *Crusher.*
CD . . . . N 0214-2
Noise / Apr '93 / Pinnacle.

MAGNUM FORCE ROCKFILE.
Tracks: Not Advised.
■ LP . . . . MFM 006
Magnum Force / Jul '82.

MARQUEE METAL.
Tracks: We will rock you: *Queen* / Smoke on the water: *Deep Purple* / Wishing well: *Free (1)* / Voodoo chile: *Hendrix, Jimi* / Down down: *Status Quo* / Epic: *Faith No More* / She's a little angel: *Little Angels* / Killer on the loose: *Thin Lizzy* / School's out: *Cooper, Alice* / Crazy, crazy nights: *Kiss* / Can't get enough: *Bad Company* / Ace of spades: *Motorhead* / Paranoid: *Black Sabbath* / Walk this way: *Run D.M.C. & Aerosmith* / Is there anybody there: *Scorpions* / Wizard: *Uriah Heep* / Days of no trust: *Magnum* / Living after midnight: *Judas Priest* / Free 'n' easy: *Almighty.*
CD 8454172
Double LP 8454171
MC 8454174
Marquee / Apr '91.

MARQUEE THE COLLECTION 1958-1983 - VOL.2.
Tracks: Hey Joe: *Hendrix, Jimi Experience* / Here comes the night: *Them* / Strange brew: *Cream* / Boys are back in town: *Thin Lizzy* / Fire: *Brown, Arthur* / Silver machine (Live): *Hawkwind* / Broken down angel: *Nazareth* / Delta lady: *Cocker, Joe* / Whatever you want: *Status Quo* / Love like a man: *Ten Years After* / Paranoid: *Black Sabbath* / Devil's answer: *Atomic Rooster* / I need a lover: *Cougar, Johnny* / Darlin': *Miller, Frankie (1)* / Don't bring me down: *Animals* / Natural born boogie: *Humble Pie.*
■ LP . . . . MAR 2
MC . . . . MARC 2
England / Jun '83 / Mean Records.

MASTERS OF METAL.
Tracks: Not Advised.
■ LP . . . . NE 1295
MC . . . . CE 2295
K-Tel / Feb '86 / I & B Records / C.M. Distribution / Arabesque Ltd. / Mono Distributors (Jersey) Ltd. / Prism Leisure PLC / PolyGram / Ross Records / Prism Leisure PLC.

MENTAL MANIAXE.
Tracks: Not Advised.
■ LP . . . . EBON 8
Ebony (Pinnacle) / Dec '83.

METAL BATTLE.
Tracks: Mind over metal: *Raven* / Motormount: *Anvil* / Ready to deliver: *Battleaxe* / Black funeral: *Mercyful Fate* / Laughing in the face of death: *Tank* / Leave me in hell: *Venom* / Run for your life: *Jaguar (1)* / I'd rather go wild: *Witchfynde* / Dancin': *Hellanbach* / Hunt you down: *Satan* / Racing time: *Santers.*
■ LP . . . . NEAT 1014
Neat / Jan '85.

METAL BOX, THE.
Tracks: Paranoid: *Black Sabbath* / Stakk atakk: *Wrathchild* / Bounty hunter: *Molly Hatchet* / Balls to the wall: *Accept* / Somebody's out there: *Triumph* / Ace of spades: *Motorhead* / Gimme your love: *Schenker, Michael* / Sweet danger: *Angel Witch* / Stroke: *Squier, Billy* / Cat scratch fever: *Nugent, Ted* / Whatever you want: *Status Quo* / Don't let me be misunderstood: *Moore, Gary* / Dead ringer for love: *Meat Loaf* / Don't take nothing: *Tygers Of Pan Tang* / Don't fear the reaper: *Blue Oyster Cult* / Start talking love: *Magnum* / 747 (Strangers in the night): *Saxon (1)* / Gypsy: *Uriah Heep* / Is there anybody there: *Scorpions* / Metal health: *Quiet Riot* / Up and the bend: *Hanoi Rocks* / Riding with the angels: *Samson* / Take on the world: *Judas Priest* / Born to be wild: *Steppenwolf* / Broken down angel: *Nazareth* / Freebird: *Lynyrd Skynyrd* / Ships in the night: *Be-Bop Deluxe* / Epic: *Faith No More* / Hammer horror: *Warfare* / Blitzkrieg: *Blitzkrieg* / Black night: *Deep Purple* / Bed Of nails: *Cooper, Alice* / Satellite kid: *Dogs D'Amour* / Moonlight: *Dancer 'n' Nasty* / Am I evil: *Diamond Head* / Rock the night: *Europe* / Planet girl: *Zodiac Mindwarp & The Love Reaction* / I want you to want me: *Cheap Trick* / Between a rock and a hard place: *UFO* / Who do you love: *Juicy Lucy* / Please don't touch: *Headgirl (1)* / Break the chain: *Raven* / Die hard: *Venom* / Heavy metal love: *Helix* / Race with the Devil: *Girlschool* / Insanity addicts: *Slammer* / D Generation: *Loud.*
■ LP Set . . . . TMBLP 47007
■ MC Set . . . . TMBMC 47007
■ CD Set . . . . TMBCD 47007
Knight / Apr '91.
CD . . . . NXTCD 247
Sequel / May '93 / Castle Communications / BMG / Hot Shot.

METAL CITY.
Tracks: Not Advised.
VHS 041 306 2
Polygram Music Video / Jun '86 / PolyGram.

METAL CONCUSSION.
Tracks: Malibu beach nightmare: *Hanoi Rocks* / Trapped under ice: *Metallica* / Black metal: *Venom* / War pigs: *Black Sabbath* / Motorhead: *Motorhead* / Back on the streets: *Moore, Gary* / Shake your heads: *Accept* / Open fire: *Marseille* / Won't get out alive: *Waysted* / Thunder on the tundra: *Thor* / Axe crazy: *Jaguar (1)* / Never satisfied: *Judas Priest.*
■ LP . . . . BRLP 101
MC . . . . BRC 101
Bandit / Jun '86 / Backs Distribution.

METAL EXPLOSION.
Tracks: Take it like a man / Johnny Cool / Visonary / Paper chaser / Soldier / Leo the jester / If you believe me / Extermination day.
■ MC . . . . ZCR 397
■ LP . . . . REH 397
BBC / Sep '80.

METAL FATIGUE.
Tracks: Not Advised.
■ LP . . . . EBON 1
Ebony (Pinnacle) / Dec '83.

METAL FOR MUTHAS.
Tracks: Sanctuary: *Iron Maiden* / Sledgehammer: *Sledgehammer* / Fighting for rock'n'roll: *E.F. Band* / Blues in A: *Toad The Wet Sprocket* / Captured city: *Praying Mantis* / Flight back: *Ethel The Frog* / Baphomet: *Angel Witch* / Wrathchild: *Iron Maiden* / Tomorrow or yesterday: *Samson* / Bootliggers: *Nutz.*
■ LP . . . . EMC 3318
EMI / Jan '80.
■ LP . . . . BBLP 2
Wishbone / Oct '84.

METAL FOR MUTHAS VOL.2.
Tracks: One of these days: *Trespass* / Telephone man: *Eazy Money* / Cutting loose: *Xero* / High upon high: *White Spirit* / Lady of Mars: *Dark Star (1)* / You give me candy: *Horsepower (1)* / Open heart: *Red Alert* / Chevvy: *Chevvy* / Hard lines: *Raid* / Storm child: *Trespass.*
■ LP . . . . EMC 3337
EMI / May '80.

METAL FORCES PRESENTS DEMOLITION (Scream your brains out).
Tracks: Not Advised.
■ LP . . . . CRE 103
Chain Reaction / Apr '88.

METAL HAMMER.
Tracks: Not Advised.
VHS . . . . CFV 07422
Channel 5 / Jun '88 / Channel 5 Video / P.R.O. Video / Gold & Sons.

METAL HAMMER - IRON MAIDEN/ MONSTERS OF ROCK SPECIAL.
Tracks: Not Advised.
VHS . . . . MVH 4910213
PMI / Aug '92 / EMI / Gold & Sons / TBD.

METAL HAMMER - THE VIDEO MAGAZINE (Thrash Special).
Tracks: Not Advised.
VHS . . . . MHV 4910163
PMI / Jul '92 / EMI / Gold & Sons / TBD.

METAL HAMMER, VOL. 1 (The Video Magazine).
Tracks: Not Advised.
■ VHS . . . . MHV 9913023
PMI / Sep '91.

METAL HAMMER, VOL. 2.
Tracks: Not Advised.
■ VHS . . . . MHV 9913033
PMI / Nov '91.

METAL HAMMER, VOL. 3.
Tracks: Not Advised.
■ VHS . . . . MHV 9913043
PMI / Feb '92.

METAL HAMMER, VOL. 4.
Tracks: Not Advised.
VHS . . . . MHV 9913053
PMI / May '92 / EMI / Gold & Sons / TBD.

METAL INFERNO.
Tracks: Not Advised.
■ LP . . . . KKLP 103
MC . . . . KKMC 103
Kastle Killers / Feb '85.

METAL KILLERS.
Tracks: White line fever: *Motorhead* / Blood guts and beer: *Tank* / Nothing to lose: *Girlschool* / Urban

■ DELETED

guerilla: *Hawkwind* / Now comes the storm: *Thor* / Not for sale: *Girlschool* / Run like hell: *Tank* / Beer drinkers and hell raisers: *Motorhead* / Start raisin' hell: *Thor* / Last flight: *Jaguar* (1) / Bump and grind: *Williams, Wendy O.*.

■ **LP** . . . . **RAWLP 004**
MC. . . . . **RAWTC 004**
Raw Power / Apr '86 / Pinnacle.
CD. . . . . **MATCD 264**
Castle / May '93 / BMG.
■ **MC.** . . . . **MATMC 264**
Castle / May '94.

METAL KILLERS KOLLECTION VOL 1.

Tracks: Paranoid: *Black Sabbath* / Boogie: *UFO* / Armed and ready: *Schenker, Michael* / Rocka rolla: *Judas Priest* / Ace of spades: *Motorhead* / Under the blade: *Twisted Sister* / Demolition boys: *Girlschool* / Gypsy: *Uriah Heep* / Master of the universe (live): *Hawkwind* / Fast as a shark: *Accept* / Parisienne walkways: *Moore, Gary* / Run like hell: *Tank* / Black metal: *Vonom* / Antigua: *Di'Anno* / Night of the blade: *Tokyo Blade* / Twist of the knife: *Wrathchild* / Wiped out: *Raven* / Burning in the heat of love: *Lea, Jim* / Hells bells: *Hells Bells* / Bump and grind: *Williams, Wendy O.* / Start raisin' hell: *Thor* / Thanks for the angst: *Chrome Molly* / Rock steady: *Waysted* / Am I evil: *Diamond Head*.

■ **Double LP.** . . . . **CCSLP 112**
■ **CD.** . . . . **CCSCD 112**
■ **MC.** . . . .**CCSMC 112**
Castle Collector Series / Nov '85.

METAL KILLERS KOLLECTION VOL 2.

Tracks: Tragedy (live): *Hanoi Rocks* / Let them eat metal: *Rods* / Rock six times: *Starz* / Hang 'em high: *Waysted* / Heat of the night / Eat the rich: *Tyson Dog* / Sabbath bloody sabbath: *Black Sabbath* / Boys nite out: *Teaze* / Goin' on crazy: *Smashed Gladys* / Friends of hell: *Witchfinder General* / Destroyer: *Twisted Sister* / Burn the Kings Road: *Warfare* / Restless and wild: *Accept* / Sorcerer: *Alaska* / I'll get you rockin': *Godz* / Crazy motorcycle: *Rogue Male* / Turn the hell on: *Fist* / Hot 'n' ready: *Reckless* / Break the chain: *Raven* / Heartuser: *Di'Anno* / Angeline: *Sabu* / Art and illusion: *Twelth Night* / Ready as hell: *Jim Dandy*.

■ **Double LP.** . . . . **CCSLP 134**
■ **MC.** . . . .**CCSMC 134**
Castle Collector Series / Apr '86.

METAL KILLERS KOLLECTION VOL 3.

Tracks: Bark at the moon: *Osbourne, Ozzy* / Cat scratch fever: *Nugent, Ted* / Metal health: *Quiet Riot* / Hit and run: *Magnum* / Don't let me be misunderstood: *Moore, Gary* / Bad or just no good: *Little Angels* / We are the road crew / All for one: *Raven* / Freewheel burning: *Judas Priest* / Burning: *Accept* / (Don't fear) The reaper: *Blue Oyster Cult* / Easy livin': *Uriah Heep* / Something special: *Chrome Molly* / Shnibob (part 1): *Dumpy's Rusty Nuts* / Walk this way: *Aerosmith* / I'm alive: *Helloween* / I won't dance: *Celtic Frost* / Toxic trace: *Kreator* / Boots: *Megadeth* / Breaking the silence: *Heathen* / Hole in the sky: *Black Sabbath*.

■ **Double LP.** . . . . **CCSLP 168**
■ **MC.** . . . . **CCSMC 168**
■ **CD.** . . . . **CCSCD 168**
Castle Collector Series / May '88.

METAL KILLERS VOL I.

Tracks: Not Advised.
■ **LP** . . . . **KKLP 101**
MC. . . . . **KKMC 101**
Kastle Killers / Jan '85.

METAL KILLERS VOL II.

Tracks: Not Advised.
■ **LP** . . . . **KKLP 102**
MC. . . . . **KKMC 102**
Kastle Killers / Jan '85.

METAL MACHINE.

Tracks: Not Advised.
■ **LP** . . . . **RR 90841**
Road Runner / Dec '84.

METAL MADNESS.

Tracks: Not Advised.
■ **LP** . . . . **NR 01**
MC. . . . . **NRC 01**
New Renaissance(USA) / Nov '87 / Pinnacle.

METAL MANIA.

Tracks: Heavy metal rock 'n' roll: *Rock Goddess* / This time: *UFO* / Reckless: *UFO* / I want to do everything for you: *Nazareth* / Beggar's day: *Nazareth* / Shout it out: *Warlock* / You've got: *Warlock* / Stealing: *Uriah Heep* / Only you can rock me: *UFO*.
■ **VHS** . . . . **HEN 2213**
Hendring Video / Feb '90.

METAL MASSACRE 10.

Tracks: Not Advised.
LP . . . . **ZORRO 4**
Music For Nations / May '90 / Pinnacle.
CD. . . . . **CD ZORRO 4**
Music For Nations / May '94 / Pinnacle.

METAL MASTERS.

Tracks: Not Advised.
CD. . . . . **MBSCD 411**
Castle / Jun '93 / BMG.

METAL OVER AMERICA.

Tracks: Not Advised.
■ **LP** . . . . **SKULL 8340**
Mausoleum / Mar '85.

METAL PLATED.

Tracks: Not Advised.
■ **LP** . . . . **EBON 14**
Ebony (Pinnacle) / Nov '83.

METAL PRAISE.

Tracks: Rock of ages / Jehovah Jireh / Holy, holy, holy / What a friend we have in Jesus / O come, o come Emmanuel / We exalt thee / Spirit song / I love you Lord / Life begun / He's the Lord.
CD. **7016944611**
MC. **7016944387**
Myrrh / Apr '92 / Word Records (UK) / Sony.

METAL THUNDER.

Tracks: All wrapped up in mystery: *Arch Rival* / Digital life: *Apocalypse* (1) / Don't feed the animals: *Sleazy Roze* / Sex shop: *Wolf Spider* / Queen of the world: *Rescue* / She goes on: *FN Guns* / Stay: *Graffiti* / He has a grenade: *Hammer* / Suicide: *Dirty Side*.
■ **CD** . . . .**RUMCD 002**
■ **LP** . . . . **RUMLP 002**
Rumble / Dec '90.

METAL TREASURES AND VINYL HEAVIES.

Tracks: Not Advised.
■ **LP** . . . . **ARLP 105**
■ **MC.** . . . . **ZCAR 105**
Action Replay / Aug '84.

METAL VISION.

Tracks: Not Advised.
■ **VHS** . . . . **RRV 09970**
Road Runner / Jul '90.

METAL WARRIORS.

Tracks: Not Advised.
■ **LP** . . . . **EBON 11**
Ebony (Pinnacle) / Dec '83.

METAL XS VOL 4.

Tracks: Not Advised.
VHS . . . . **MXS 004**
Fotodisk Video / Apr '91.

METAL YEARS, THE.

Tracks: Not Advised.
VHS . . . . **PVC 3020**
Palace Video / Oct '89 / Palace Video.

METALGON.

Tracks: Not Advised.
■ **LP** . . . . **A 30**
Azra (USA) / Jun '87.

METALHEAD VOL. 1.

Tracks: Not Advised.
■ **VHS** **790 397**
BMG Video / Jul '90.

METALHEAD VOL. 2.

Tracks: Not Advised.
■ **VHS** **790 451**
BMG Video / Nov '90.

METALHEAD VOL. 3.

Tracks: Not Advised.
■ **VHS** **790 496**
BMG Video / Feb '91.

METALHEAD VOL. 4.

Tracks: Not Advised.
■ **VHS** **791093**
BMG Video / May '91.

METALHEAD VOL. 5.

Tracks: Not Advised.
■ **VHS** **791.136**
BMG Video / Jul '91.

METALHEAD VOL. 6.

Tracks: Not Advised.
■ **VHS** **791158**
BMG Video / Jan '92.

METALLERGY.

Tracks: Not Advised.
■ **LP** . . . . **BRLP 102**
Bandit / Jun '86.

METALLERGY (JET).

Tracks: Not Advised.
■ **LP** . . . . **JETMP 228**
Jet / Apr '80.

MIGHTY FEEBLE.

Tracks: Not Advised.
LP . . . . **NAR 013**
New Alliance (USA) / May '93 / Pinnacle.

MILK FOR PUSSY.

Tracks: Not Advised.
CD . . . . **MQCD 9301**
Mad Queen / Jan '94 / SRD.

MOLTEN METAL.

Tracks: Not Advised.
■ **LP** . . . . **STAR 2429**
■ **MC.** . . . .**STAC 2429**
■ **CD.** . . . . **TCD 2429**
Telstar/Ronco / Aug '90.

MONSTERS OF DEATH.

Tracks: Not Advised.
CD. . . . . **RC 91902**
■ **LP** . . . . **RC 91901**
■ **MC.** . . . . **RC 91904**
Road Runner / Mar '92.

MONSTERS OF ROCK.

Tracks: Stargazer: *Rainbow* (1) / Another piece of meat: *Scorpions* / All night long: *Rainbow* (1) / Don't ya know what love is: *Touch* (1) / Loving you Sunday morning: *Scorpions* / Backs to the wall: *Saxon* (1) / I like to rock: *April Wine* / Road racin': *Riot*.
■ **LP** **2488 810**
Polydor / Dec '80.
MC. **3199 256**
Polydor / Oct '80 / PolyGram.
CD. **843 689-2**
■ **LP** **843 689-1**
■ **MC.** **843 689-4**
Polydor / Aug '90.

MONSTERS OF ROCK II.

Tracks: Not Advised.
CD . . . . **SMR 29**
Simple Machines / Jun '94 / SRD.

MONSTERS SPECIAL.

Tracks: Not Advised.
VHS . . . . **MHV 9913073**
PMI / Nov '92 / EMI / Gold & Sons / TBD.

MONUMENT TO BRITISH ROCK.

Tracks: Not Advised.
■ **LP** . . . . **EMTV 17**
EMI / May '79.

MOOSE MOLTEN METAL VOL.1.

Tracks: Not Advised.
■ **LP** . . . . **HMUSA 55**
Heavy Metal America / Nov '85.

MOOSE MOLTEN METAL VOL.2.

Tracks: Harlot's web / Black is the nite / Rise / Lonely lonely / Harlott / There for the taking / Ready to rip / Conquer or be conquered / Nytrix / Don't believe in tomorrow / Vigilants / Coming back on you / Sentinel / Rock free / Sye / You've got the power / Hateful snake / Dark of the night / Outrage / Until you bleed in.
■ **LP** . . . . **HM USA 55**
FM Records / Oct '92.

MORE THAN A FEELING.

Tracks: You're the voice: *Farnham, John* / Nothing's gonna stop us now: *Starship* / More than a feeling: *Boston* / You took the words right out of my mouth: *Meat Loaf* / Can't fight this feeling: *REO Speedwagon* / Don't sop believin: *Journey* / Rosanna: *Toto* / Satellite: *Hooters* / Final countdown: *Europe* / Broken wings: *Mr. Mister* / When I see you smile: *Bad English* / (Don't fear) The reaper: *Blue Oyster Cult* / Flame: *Cheap Trick* / So tired: *Osbourne, Ozzy* / Rock 'n' roll dreams come through: *Steinman, Jim* / Stairway to heaven: *Far Corporation*.
CD. **473045 2**
MC. **473045 4**
Columbia / Feb '93 / Sony.

MORTAR COMPILATION.
Tracks: Not Advised.
CD . . . . PPP 104
Pathological / Feb '92 / Cadillac.

MORTUARY VOL. 1.
Tracks: Not Advised.
CD . . . . SKELETON 93
Skeleton / Jun '94 / Plastic Head.

MOSCOW ROCK LABORATORY.
Tracks: Painted gentle ape: *Sailors Silence* / We are the world: *Die Schwarze Katzen* / Tanks-punks: *Naive* / We won't go to the movies: *Bakhit-Compote* / Bohemian part: *Dumb* / Birds: *Anch* / Valerka: *Handy Pepper* / Butterfly: *T.34* / TV-Pixel head: *Xmas Eve* / A-Yee's with us: *A-Yee* / Train anarchy: *Mongol Shuudan* / Tazepam: *Cramp In The Leg.*
VHS . . . . JE 225
Jettisoundz / Mar '92 / TBD / Visionary Communications.

MUSIC FOR NATIONS SINGLES ALBUM.
Tracks: Not Advised.
■ **Double LP** . . . . MFN 71
MC . . . . TMFN 71
Music For Nations / Dec '86 / Pinnacle.

NAIVE.
Tracks: Not Advised.
CD . . . . MOSH 076 CD
■ MC . . . . MOSH 076 MC
Earache / Oct '92.

NEVER MIND THE MOLLUSCS.
Tracks: Not Advised.
CD . . . . SPCD 84/255
Sub Pop / Mar '93 / RTM.

NEW ELECTRIC WARRIORS.
Tracks: Not Advised.
■ LP . . . . MOGO 4011
Logo / Sep '80.

NEW WAVE OF BRITISH HEAVY METAL (1979 Revisited).
Tracks: Not Advised.
■ **Double LP** 8463221
■ **CD Set** 8463222
■ **MC Set** 8463224
Vertigo / Jul '90.

NEW YORK HARDCORE.
Tracks: Not Advised.
MC . . . . BL 001C
Link / Jul '90 / ACD Trading Ltd.

NEW YORK THRASH.
Tracks: Not Advised.
MC . . . . A 113
Reach Out International / '83 / Reach Out Int. Records / Windsong International Ltd.

NEW ZONE HISTORY VOL.1, THE.
Tracks: Not Advised.
CD . . . . MET 003-2
Metamatic / Jul '93 / Plastic Head.

NICE ENOUGH TO EAT.
Tracks: Not Advised.
CD . . . . RRCD 143
LP . . . . RRLP 143
MC . . . . RRLC 143
Receiver / Jul '93 / Total / BMG / Grapevine Distribution.

NIGHT OF THE GUITAR.
Tracks: Dr. Brown, I presume: *Haycock, Pete* / Lucienne: *Haycock, Pete* / Hey Joe: *California, Randy* / King will come: *Wishbone Ash* / Never in my life: *West, Leslie* / Wurm: *Howe, Steve* / Ain't nothin shakin': *Lee, Alvin* / Idler: *Hunter, Steve* / Groove thing: *California, Randy* / Love me two times: *Kreiger, Bobby* / Theme from an imaginary western: *West, Leslie* / Clap medley: *Howe, Steve* / No limit: *Lee, Alvin* / Whole lotta shakin' goin' on / *Johnny B.*

Goode / Bye bye Johnny / All along the watchtower / Dizzy Miss Lizzy / Rock 'n' roll music.
CD . . . . EIRSACD 1005
■ **Double LP** . . . . EIRSDA 1005
MC . . . . EIRSAC 1005
I.R.S. (Illegal) / Apr '89 / EMI.

NIGHTMARE ON CARNABY STREET.
Tracks: Brain dead / Death by hanging / Run for your life / Never surrender / Psychoradio / Hellion / Self destruct / I can't wait / Pay for your love / Hollywood killer / Passing / Rock that makes me roll / Steal the away / Arthur Whiteside / Fall in love again.
■ **Double LP** . . . . MFN 83
MC . . . . TMFN 83
Music For Nations / Jul '88 / Pinnacle.

NO RULES.
Tracks: Time bomb city / Cold love: *Cult Maniax* / City brave: *Cult Maniax* / Poison pen letters: *Cult Maniax* / Shout and scream: *Sex Gang Children* / Time of our lives / Duty unto death / Khmer Rouge: *Destructor* / Religion: *Destructor* / Electronic church: *Destructor* / No compromise: *Blitzkrieg* / Conscience prayer: *Blitzkrieg* / No rules: *Leather Nun* / Slow death: *Leather Nun.*
■ LP . . . . CFRC 508
Conifer / Jan '87.

NOISE NEW YORK.
Tracks: Motor city: *Honeymoon Killers* / Hazed and dazed: *Honeymoon Killers* / Mind the gap: *Prong* / Daily dose: *Prong* / I don't know: *Jad Fair* / Diamonds: *Jad Fair* / Father: *Of Cabbage & Kings* / European son: *Moore, Thurston* / How do you spell relief: *Bank Of Sodom* / Rear view mirror: *Black Snakes* / I'm cheap: *Black Snakes* / I ride a white horse: *Krackhouse* / Against UFO's: *Krackhouse* / Rock 'n' roll lifestyle: *Krackhouse* / Hell cat II: *Phantom Tollbooth* / Poly ratmatazz: *Phantom Tollbooth* / Cut you loose: *Royal Trax* / Luminous dolphin: *Royal Trax* / Spider and the fly: *Needlenose* / At home: *Needlenose.*
MC . . . . A 156
Reach Out International / May '88 / Reach Out Int. Records / Windsong International Ltd.

NOISE RECORDS VIDEO COMPILATION, VOL. 1.
Tracks: Not Advised.
VHS . . . . NFV 106
Fotodisk Video / May '90.

NOISE RECORDS VIDEO COMPILATION, VOL. 2.
Tracks: Not Advised.
VHS . . . . NFV 110
Fotodisk Video / Jul '90.

NORTH AMERICAN THRASH ASSAULT.
Tracks: Not Advised.
LP . . . . BOXLP 1
Black Box / Feb '90.

NORTH AMERICAN THRASH ASSAULT VOL.2.
Tracks: Not Advised.
LP . . . . BOXLP 2
Box / Jun '90.

NORTH ATLANTIC NOISE ATTACK.
Tracks: Not Advised.
CD . . . . ACHE 17 CD
■ LP . . . . ACHE 17
Manic Ears / Apr '89.

NOTHING SHORT OF TOTAL WAR.
Tracks: Come and smash me said the boy with the magic penis: *Sonic Youth* / Bugged: *Head Of David* / Fire in Philly: *Ut* / He's on fire: *Sonic Youth* / Kerosene: *Big Black* / Magic wand: *Sonic Youth* / Dutch courage: *Rapeman* / Bulbs of passion: *Ranaldo, Lee* / Scratchy heart: *Ciccone Youth* / Evangelist: *Ut* / Snake domain: *Head Of David* / He's a whore: *Big Black* / Devils jukebox: *Big Stick* / 108: *Head Of David* / Sheikh: *AC Temple* / Just got payed today: *Rapeman* / Throne of blood: *Band Of Susans* / Little Hitlers: *Arsenal* / Jimi: *Butthole Surfers.*
CD . . . . BFFP 013CD
■ LP . . . . BFFP 013
MC . . . . BFFP 013C
Blast First / Mar '89 / RTM / Pinnacle.

NUCLEAR BLAST 100.
Tracks: Not Advised.
CD . . . . NB 100
Nuclear Blast / Feb '94 / Plastic Head.

NWOBHM COMPILATION (New Wave Of British Heavy Metal).
Tracks: Not Advised.
■ CD . . . . HMRXD 157

■ LP . . . . HMRLP 157
■ MC . . . . HMRMC 157
Heavy Metal / Dec '90.

OH NO, IT'S MORE FROM RAW.
Tracks: Not Advised.
■ LP . . . . RAWLP 2
Raw / '78.

ON THE EDGE OF DEATH.
Tracks: Not Advised.
CD 15 216
MC 79 090
Laserlight / Aug '91 / TBD / BMG / Target.

OVERTONE 3 - THE ROCK ALBUM.
Tracks: Not Advised.
■ LP . . . . OVLP 3
Overtone / Jun '84.

PATHOLOGICAL COMPILATION.
Tracks: Genital grinder: *Carcass* / John F Poodle: *Terminal Cheesecake* / Contains a disclaimer: *Coil* / Dum dum slug: *God* / Hepatic tissue fermentation: *Carcass* / Internal animosity: *Napalm Death* / Live is a dog from hell: *Godflesh* / Three pottery owls: *Stretcheads* / Head's human: *Terminal Cheesecake* / Groin death: *Stretcheads* / My own light: *Godflesh.*
CD . . . . PATH 01CD
LP . . . . PATH 01
MC . . . . PATH 01C
Pathological / Feb '90 / Cadillac.

PEEL SESSIONS: HARDCORE HOLOCAUST 1 (87-88 sessions).
Tracks: Heard it all before: *Stupids* / Dog log: *Stupids* / Sheep: *Electro Hippies* / Chickens: *Electro Hippies* / Mother: *Electro Hippies* / False profit: *Extreme Noise Terror* / Another nail in the coffin: *Extreme Noise Terror* / Carry on screaming: *Extreme Noise Terror* / Conned thru life: *Extreme Noise Terror* / Attack in the aftermath: *Bolt Thrower* / Pyschological warefare: *Bolt Thrower* / Skate bored: *Intense Degree* / Intense degree: *Intense Degree* / Daydreams: *Intense Degree* / Bursting: *Intense Degree* / Voice your opinion: *Unseen Terror* / Moral crusade: *Napalm Death* / Divine death: *M.A.D.* / Control: *M.A.D.* / Pink machine gun: *Dr. & The Crippens* / Garden centre murders: *Dr. & The Crippens* / Skin tight: *Dr. & The Crippens* / Exploitation: *Doom* / No religion: *Doom.*
■ MC . . . . SFRMC 101
Strange Fruit / Nov '88.
CD . . . . SFRCD 101
■ LP . . . . SFRLP 101
Strange Fruit / Oct '88.

POSSESSED.
Tracks: Crackhouse (more music mix): *Consolidated* / (I'm the radio) King kong: *Peace, Love and Pitbulls* / Valley song (demo version): *Mystery Machine* / I believe in you (bassnotized): *Final Cut (1)* / Tingler (Itch-E & scratch-E-mix): *Severed Heads* / Refuse to be a man: *Childman* / Dancing barefoot (Remix): *M.C. 900 FT Jesus* / I am what I see (The New Delhi remix/edit): *Single Gun Theory* / K9: *Skinny Puppy* / What you're good 4: *Brothers and Systems* / Sheila liked the rodeo: *Teargarden* / Good to be alive: *Itch.*
■ CD . . . . NET 045 CD
Nettwerk Europe / Feb '93.

POWER OF METAL.
Tracks: Roll the fire: *Conception* / And I close my eyes: *Conception* / Promiser: *Conception* / Parallel

■ DELETED

inds: *Conception* / Black & white: *Helicon* / Woen: *Helicon* / On the edge: *Rage (1)* / Nevermore: *age (1)* / From the underworld: *Rage (1)* / No return: *amma Ray* / Space eater: *Gamma Ray* / Heading r tomorrow: *Gamma Ray*.
HS . . . . **NV 0010**
loise / Jan '94 / Pinnacle.

OWER OF METAL.
racks: Intro: *Gamma Ray* / Tribute to the past: *amma Ray* / No return: *Gamma Ray* / Space eater: *amma Ray* / Changes: *Gamma Ray* / Insanity & enius: *Gamma Ray* / Last before the storm: *Gamma ay* / Heal me: *Gamma Ray* / I want out/future world: *amma Ray* / Future madhouse: *Gamma Ray* / eading for tomorrow: *Gamma Ray* / Black and hite: *Helicon* / Woman/lead out: *Helicon* / Shame n you: *Rage (1)* / Don't fear the winter: *Rage (1)* / ertain days: *Rage (1)* / Suicide: *Rage (1)* / Refuge: *age (1)* / Baby I'm your nightmare: *Rage (1)* / Down y law: *Rage (1)* / Nevermore: *Rage (1)* / Firestorm: *age (1)* / Solitary man: *Rage (1)* / Enough is nough: *Rage (1)* / Invisible horizons: *Rage (1)* / Roll ne fire: *Conception* / And I close my eyes: *Conception* / Promiser: *Conception* / Parallel minds: *onception*.
D . . . . **N 0237-2**
loise / Jan '94 / Pinnacle.

OWERTRAX.
racks: Not Advised.
■ **LP** . . . . **NEAT 1033**
leat / '88.

RECIOUS METAL.
racks: Not Advised.
D . . . . **SMD 976**
■ **LP** . . . . **SMR 976**
IC . . . . **SMC 976**
Stylus / May '89.

RIMAL SOUNDS FROM NYC.
racks: Axe to grind: *Tabb, George Experience* / iregod: *Bloodsister* / '58 black Impala: *Porno Dracula* / Time bomb: *P.M.S.* / Hippie: *Destroy All Bands* / Deans of discipline: *White Trash* / Sugar love: *Lunachicks* / Junkie business: *Waldos* / Piece of me: *Slugfest* / Salesman of death: *Bates, Norman & Showerheads* / Rock 'n' roll barroom: *Fastlane McNuggets* / 2.36: *W.O.O.* / Thirty six hours: *Holycrow* / Girl like you: *Ed Gein's Car* / L.A. woman: *Rats Of Unusual Size* / Just another scumrock song: *Traci Lord's X Lovers*.
VHS . . . . **JE 208**
Jettisoundz / Jan '91 / TBD / Visionary Communications.

PROJECTIONS OF A STAINED MIND (Scandinavian Death Metal Compilation).
Tracks: Not Advised.
CD . . . . **CBR 128CD**
LP . . . . **CBR 128**
Chicken Brain / Jan '92 / Plastic Head.

PROTECT THE INNOCENT.
Tracks: Prime mover: *Rush (1)* / Back on the streets: *Saxon (1)* / Ultimate sin: *Osbourne, Ozzy* / Gypsy road: *Cinderella* / Paranoid: *Black Sabbath* / Don't fear the reaper: *Blue Oyster Cult* / Fireball: *Deep Purple* / Start talkin' love: *Magnum* / Ace of spades: *Motorhead* / Kiss me deadly: *Ford, Lita* / Breakin' the law: *Judas Priest* / Fallin' in and out of love: *Femme Fatale* / Rhythm of love: *Scorpions* / Dream evil: *Dio* / Rock seat education: *Zodiac Mindwarp* / Get it on: *Kingdom Come* / Scream dream: *Nugent, Ted* / How come it never rains: *Dogs D'Amour* / I wanna be loved: *House Of Lords (2)* / Born to be wild: *Steppenwolf* / Na na nukklear rokket: *Wrathchild* / Rock'n'roll lady: *Dominique, Lisa* / Love overload: *Tigertailz* / Goddess: *Acid Reign* / Metal thrashing mad: *Anthrax (1)* / Fabulous disaster: *Exodus (1)* / Rattlehead: *Megadeth* / Killing hand: *Dream Theater* / Helter skelter: *Vow Wow* / Fat man: *Mammoth*.
MC . . . . **STAC 2363**
■ **CD** . . . . **TCD 2363**
■ **LP** . . . . **STAR 2363**
Telstar/Ronco / Jun '89.

PROTECT THE INNOCENT.
Tracks: Not Advised.
■ **VHS** . . . . **TVE 1001**
Telstar Video / Jul '89.

PURE DEVOTION.
Tracks: Not Advised.
CD . . . . **CDDVN 17**
LP . . . . **DVN 17**
MC . . . . **TDVN 17**
Music For Nations / Oct '92 / Pinnacle.

PURE SOFT METAL (It takes your breath away).
Tracks: Kind of magic: *Queen* / (I just) died in your arms: *Cutting Crew* / Missing you: *Waite, John* / Kyrie: *Mr. Mister* / Summer of '69: *Adams, Bryan* / Forget me not: *Bad English* / Every rose has it's thorn: *Poison* / Rosanna: *Toto* / Can't fight this feeling: *REO Speedwagon* / Take my breath away: *Berlin* / Crying: *Vixen* / Forever free: *W.A.S.P.* / Over the hills and far away: *Moore, Gary* / Modern girl: *Meat Loaf* / Play for your life: *Wasch* / Bad times: *Mammoth* / True: *Spandau Ballet* / China in your hand: *T'Pau*.
CD . . . . **SMD 996**
■ **LP** . . . . **SMR 996**
MC . . . . **SMC 996**
Stylus / Dec '89.

PURPLE RAINBOWS.
Tracks: Black night: *Deep Purple* / Speed king: *Deep Purple* / Child in time (Extra track on CD and cassette.): *Deep Purple* / Strange kind of woman: *Deep Purple* / Fireball: *Deep Purple* / Smoke on the water: *Deep Purple* / Highway star: *Deep Purple* / Woman from Tokyo (Extra track on CD and cassette.): *Deep Purple* / Perfect strangers: *Deep Purple* / Hush ('88 version): *Deep Purple* / Since you been gone: *Rainbow (1)* / I surrender: *Rainbow (1)* / Fool for your loving (original version): *Whitesnake* / Here I go again (US remix): *Whitesnake* / Night games: *Bonnet, Graham* / Rock 'n' roll children: *Dio*.
■ **LP** **845534-1**
Polygram T.V. / Jul '91.
CD **845534-2**
MC **845534-4**
Polygram T.V. / Apr '94 / PolyGram.

Q

QUIET NIGHT IN.
Tracks: Not Advised.
■ **LP** . . . . **BRON 537**
Bronze / Dec '81.

R

RADIO HELL.
Tracks: Lambs to the slaughter: *Raven* / Hold back the fire: *Raven* / Hard ride: *Raven* / Chainsaw: *Raven* / Black metal: *Venom* / Nightmare: *Venom* / Too loud for the crowd: *Venom* / Bloodlust: *Venom* / Death charge: *Warfare* / Burn down the Kings Road: *Warfare* / Ebony dreams: *Warfare* / Revolution: *Warfare*.
CD . . . . **FRSCD 009**
Raw Fruit / Dec '92 / Pinnacle.

RAGE TEAM, THE.
Tracks: Back from the grave: *Nekromantix* / We did nothing wrong: *Adolescents UK* / Am I crazy: *Mad Heads* / Jeff's head: *Pikehead* / Rude: *Grind* / Self destruct: *Plastic Bag* / Big wide world: *Strange Behaviour* / And it hurts: *Psycho Bunnies* / Drop dead: *Switchblade* / Everything's so perfect: *Dead Lillies* / Monster metal: *Nekromantix* / Mrs. Thatcher's on the dole: *Adolescents UK* / Now or never: *Mad Heads* / Individuality eagle: *Pikehead* / Paparazzi: *Grind* / Right to remain silent: *Plastic Bag* / It's alright to cry: *Strange Behaviour* / Not with you: *Psycho Bunnies* / I'm your slave: *Switchblade* / Freak show: *Dead Lillies*.
CD . . . . **RAGECD 112**
Rage / Sep '93 / Nervous Records.

RAGING DEATH.
Tracks: Not Advised.
CD . . . . **CDGRXCD 1**
LP . . . . **GRX 001**
Godley Records (USA) / Mar '90.

RATHER NASTY DREAM ON PAPPLEWICK POND.
Tracks: Not Advised.
■ **LP** . . . . **CMO 191**
RKT / Nov '89.

RAWPOWER SAMPLER.
Tracks: Parisienne walkways (live): *Moore, Gary* / Run to your mama: *Moore, Gary* / Gypsy: *Uriah Heep* / Wizard: *Uriah Heep* / In nomine satanus: *Venom* / Devils answer: *Atomic Rooster* / Walking in the park: *Colosseum* / Chase is better than the catch: *Motorhead* / Bang the drum all day: *Rundgren, Todd* / In the beginning: *Magnum*.
CD . . . . **RAWCD 1000**
Raw Power / Mar '88 / Pinnacle.

READING FESTIVAL '82.
Tracks: Not Advised.
■ **LP** . . . . **MNLP 82**
Mean / Jan '83.

RED HOT METAL (18 Rock Classics).
Tracks: Breakthru: *Queen* / Just like paradise: *Roth, David Lee* / Wild frontier: *Moore, Gary* / Bark at the moon: *Osbourne, Ozzy* / Days of no trust: *Magnum* / Up all night: *Slaughter* / Miles away: *Winger* / There she goes again: *Quireboys* / Your mama don't dance: *Poison* / Black velvet: *Myles, Alannah* / That's when I think of you: *1927* / All fired up: *Benatar, Pat* / Gimme some lovin': *Thunder (1)* / I don't need no doctor: *W.A.S.P.* / Devil and daughter: *Black Sabbath* / Love is a killer: *Vixen* / Got the time: *Anthrax (1)* / Night crawler: *Judas Priest*.
■ **CD** . . . . **CCD 21**
■ **LP** . . . . **ADD 21**
■ **MC** . . . . **ZDD 21**
Dover / Apr '91.

ROCK AID ARMENIA.
Tracks: Not Advised.
VHS . . . . **VVD 636**
Virgin Vision / Nov '89 / Gold & Sons / TBD.

ROCK ANTHEMS II.
Tracks: Walk on the wild side: *Reed, Lou* / Don't fear the reaper: *Blue Oyster Cult* / Hot blooded: *Foreigner* / Black Betty: *Ram Jam Band* / Radar Love: *Golden Earring* / School's out: *Cooper, Alice* / All along the watchtower: *Hendrix, Jimi* / Badge: *Cream* / White light, white heat: *Velvet Underground* / For your love: *Yardbirds* / Here comes the night: *Them* / Nutbush City Limits: *Turner, Ike & Tina* / Fire: *Crazy World of Arthur Brown* / Layla: *Derek & The Dominoes* / One & one is one: *Mediceine Head* / Spanish stroll / Mockingbird: *Hart, Tim & Maddy Prior* / In a broken dream: *Python Lee Jackson* / Paranoid: *Black Sabbath* / Silver machine: *Hawkwind* / Rock and roll star / American woman: *Guess Who* / We gotta get out of this place: *Animals* / Hi ho silver lining: *Beck, Jeff*.
■ **LP** . . . . **NE 1319**
MC . . . . **CE 2319**
K-Tel / Nov '86 / I & B Records / C.M. Distribution / Arabesque Ltd. / Mono Distributors (Jersey) Ltd. / Prism Leisure PLC / PolyGram / Ross Records / Prism Leisure PLC.

ROCK BALLADS.
Tracks: Not Advised.
CD . . . . **STACD 044**
Stardust / Sep '94 / Pickwick / Conifer Records.

ROCK BALLADS.
Tracks: Once in a lifetime: *Kansas* / Parisienne walkways: *Moore, Gary* / Amanda: *Boston* / Winning man: *Krokus* / On and on: *Bishop, Stephen* / Surrender: *Trixter* / Thrill is gone: *King, B.B.* / Pusher: *Trixter* / She's gone (live): *Steelheart* / Sara: *Starship* / Still believe: *Starship* / Washable ink: *Hiatt, John* / Gail live: *Cooper, Alice* / Just one precious moment: *Emergency* / Stairway to heaven: *Far Corporation*.
CD . . . . **MCD 30202**
Ariola Express / Mar '94 / BMG.

ROCK CITY NIGHTS.
Tracks: One vision: *Queen* / You give love a bad name: *Bon Jovi* / Big area: *Then Jerico* / King of emotion: *Big Country* / Red sky: *Status Quo* / Incommunicado: *Marillion* / Satisfied: *Marx, Richard* / Some like it hot: *Power Station* / Rock the night: *Europe* / Need you tonight: *INXS* / I don't want a lover: *Texas (2)* / I won't back down: *Petty, Tom* / Silent running: *Mike & The Mechanics* / Africa: *Toto* / More than a feeling: *Boston* / Go your own way: *Fleetwood Mac* / I surrender: *Rainbow (1)* / Eye of the tiger: *Survivor*.
CD **840 622-2**
■ **LP** . . . . **RCNTV 1**

■ DELETED

MC . . . . **RCNTC 1**
Polygram T.V. / Oct '89 / PolyGram.

ROCK CITY SIGHTS.
Tracks: Not Advised.
VHS . . . . **CFV 10042**
Channel 5 / Nov '89 / Channel 5 Video / P.R.O. Video / Gold & Sons.

ROCK FURY.
Tracks: Radar love: *Golden Earring* / Boys are back in town: *Thin Lizzy* / Freebird: *Lynyrd Skynyrd* / Cat scratch fever: *Nugent, Ted* / Hold your head up: *Argent* / What you're proposing: *Status Quo* / Career of evil: *Blue Oyster Cult* / Hit me with your best shot (live): *Benatar, Pat* / Funk no.48: *James Gang* / Spaceman: *Journey* / Natural born boogie: *Humble Pie*.
■ **LP** . . . . **RAWLP 002**
MC . . . . **RAWTC 002**
Raw Power / Apr '86 / Pinnacle.

ROCK GUITAR LEGENDS.
Tracks: Johnny B. Goode: *Berry, Chuck* / Albatross: *Fleetwood Mac* / Black magic woman: *Fleetwood Mac* / Badge: *Cream* / get it on: *T. Rex* / Dance on: *Shadows* / Perfidia: *Shadows* / Going home: *Shadows* / Sabre dance: *Edmunds, Dave* / I hear you knocking: *Edmunds, Dave* / Red house: *Hendrix, Jimi* / Guitar jamboree: *Spedding, Chris* / Becks's bolero: *Beck, Jeff* / I pity the fool: *Manish Boys* / Laguna sunrise: *Black Sabbath* / Tomorrow's dream: *Black Sabbath* / My baby gives it away: *Townshend, Pete & Ronnie Lane* / Lady livin alone: *Beck, Jeff* / Smoke on the water: *Deep Purple* / Memphis: *Faces (1)* / Take it off the top: *Dixie Dregs* / Dreams: *Allman Brothers Band* / Jessica: *Allman Brothers Band* / Fooled around and fell in love: *Bishop, Elvin* / Jemima surrender: *Band* / Shape I'm in: *Band* / Everything's coming our way: *Santana (1)* / Born to be a rock 'n' roll man: *Lee, Albert* / China groove: *Doobie Brothers* / Hold the line: *Toto* / Man I'll never be: *Boston* / More than a feeling: *Boston* / Emotions in motion: *Squier, Billy* / Snortin' whiskey: *Travers, Pat* / I saw the light: *Rundgren, Todd* / Two trains: *Little Feat* / Thing called love: *Raitt, Bonnie* / Down to nothin: *Dudek, Les* / Bell bottom blues: *Derek & The Dominoes* / Sweet dreams: *Buchanan, Roy* / Confessor: *Walsh, Joe* / All night long: *Rainbow (1)* / Demons: *Allman, Greg* / Very thing that makes you rich: *Cooder, Ry* / Lies: *Cale, J.J.* / Rockin' guitars: *Morse, Steve Band* / One-way ticket: *Johnston, Tom*.
■ **LP Set** . . . . **RGLLP 47001**
■ **MC Set** . . . . **RGLMC 47001**
■ **CD Set** . . . . **RGLCD 47001**
Knight / May '90.

ROCK GUITAR LEGENDS VOL. 2.
Tracks: Mercury blues: *Lindley, David* / Over and over: *Walsh, Joe* / Juke box hero: *Foreigner* / Lost in the shuffle: *Kortchmar, Danny* / Long time til' I get over you: *Little Feat* / River of tears: *Raitt, Bonnie* / Ashphalt jungle: *Felder, Don* / So wrong: *Simmons, Patrick* / Stainsby girls: *Rea, Chris* / Spirit of radio: *Rush (1)* / I can see for miles: *Who* / Cocaine: *Cale, J.J.* / Sky high: *Atlanta Rhythm Section* / Waiting for the man: *Velvet Underground* / Whisky in the jar: *Thin Lizzy* / From little things big things grow: *Edmunds, Dave* / Confidence man: *Healey, Jeff* / We can be together: *Jefferson Airplane* / Built for speed: *Stray Cats* / Roll with the changes: *REO Speedwagon* / Don't stop believing: *Journey* / Honey don't leave L.A.: *Taylor, James (1)* / Sweet potato pie: *Taylor, James (1)* / Rock 'n' roll hoochie coo: *Winter, Johnny* / East of Eden's gate: *Thorpe, Billy* / Need your love so bad: *Fleetwood Mac* / Where have you been all my life: *Nugent, Ted* / Ready for love: *Mott The Hoople* / Once bitten twice shy: *Hunter, Ian* / American girl: *Petty, Tom* / Sweet home Alabama: *Lynyrd Skynyrd* / Gotta hurry: *Yardbirds* / No particular place to go: *Berry, Chuck* / Natural born boogie: *Humble Pie* / Parisienne walkways (live): *Moore, Gary* / I'm your witch doctor: *Clapton, Eric Allstars* / Laundromat: *Gallagher, Rory* / Bleeding heart: *Hendrix, Jimi* / You won't see me anymore: *Green, Peter* / Breakdown: *Coverdale, David* / I've been born again: *Frey, Glenn* / Who do you love: *Juicy Lucy* / Paranoid: *Black Sabbath* / Rocky mountain way: *Walsh, Joe* / Drift away: *Gray, Dobie* / I came to dance: *Lofgren, Nils* / Show me the way: *Frampton, Peter* / Dear Mr. Fantasy: *Traffic*.
■ **MC Set** . . . . **RGLMC 47006**
■ **CD Set** . . . . **RGLCD 47006**
Knight / Feb '91.
CD Set . . . . **NXTCD 248**
Sequel / May '93 / Castle Communications / BMG / Hot Shot.

ROCK HARD, HARD ROCK.
Tracks: Not Advised.
CD . . . . **DCD 5369**
Disky / Jul '94 / TBD.

ROCK LEGENDS.
Tracks: Not Advised.
■ **Double LP** . . . . **SSD 8032**
■ **MC Set** . . . . **SSDC 8032**
Pickwick / Sep '80.
MC Set . . . . **STAC 2290**
■ **Double LP** . . . . **STAR 2290**
Telstar/Ronco / Oct '86.
CD Set . . . . **MBSCD 406**
Castle / Nov '93 / BMG.

ROCK LEGENDS.
Tracks: Everybody oughta make a change / Rita Mae / Lay down Sally / Rambling on my mind / Cocaine / Man smart, woman smarter / Roadrunner / Slowdown sundown / Take me to the river / Gimme some lovin'.
VHS . . . . **V 3339**
Missing In Action / Jul '92 / Gold & Sons / TBD / Video Collection.

ROCK LEGENDS (2).
Tracks: This flight tonight: *Nazareth* / N.I.B. / Sweet Lorraine: *Uriah Heep* / Silver machine (live): *Hawkwind* / Down the dustpipe: *Status Quo* / Race with the devil: *Girlschool* / Dancin': *Moore, Gary* / Kingdom of madness: *Magnum* / Overkill: *Motorhead* / Who do you love: *Juicy Lucy* / Ace of spades: *Motorhead* / Natural born boogie: *Humble Pie* / Broken down angel: *Nazareth* / Levitation: *Hawkwind* / Ice in the sun: *Status Quo* / Wizard: *Uriah Heep* / All of my life: *Magnum* / Parisienne walkways (lives): *Moore, Gary*.
CD . . . . **MCCD 045**
MC . . . . **MCTC 045**
Music Club / Sep '91 / Gold & Sons / TBD / Video Collection / C.M. Distribution.

ROCK LEGENDS 2.
Tracks: Star cycle / Pump (the pump) / Goodbye pork pie hat / Hi ho silver lining / Who's to blame / City sirens / Stairway to heaven / Tulsa time / Layla / Goodnight Irene.
VHS . . . . **V 3340**
Missing In Action / Jul '92 / Gold & Sons / TBD / Video Collection.

ROCK MACHINE.
Tracks: Not Advised.
■ **LP** . . . . **ARLP 106**
■ **MC** . . . . **ZCAR 106**
Action Replay / Nov '85.

ROCK MACHINE VOL 1.
Tracks: Beg to differ / Burning tree / Future tense / Dirty weapons / Solitary solitude / Hey kid / Paris calling / Devil wears lingerie / Maryanne / Summer / Shot in the dark (live) / Only my heart talkin' / Guilty.
CD **4669342**
MC **4669344**
■ **LP** **4669341**
Epic / Jun '90.

ROCK ME ALL NIGHT LONG.
Tracks: Not Advised.
■ **LP** . . . . **FLY 606**
Flyright / Nov '85.

ROCK OF AGES.
Tracks: Hey Joe: *Hendrix, Jimi* / Africa: *Toto* / State of independence: *Jon & Vangelis* / Broken wings: *Mr. Mister* / Take it on the run: *REO Speedwagon* / Wooden ships: *Jefferson Airplane* / Burnin' for you: *Blue Oyster Cult* / In a lifetime: *Clannad* / White room: *Cream* / You're the voice: *Farnham, John* / Dead ringer for love: *Meat Loaf* / Rock of life: *Springfield, Rick* / Talking all night: *Hall & Oates* / Dust in the wind: *Kansas* / Flame: *Cheap Trick* / Diamond dust: *Beck, Jeff* / Presence of the Lord: *Blind Faith* / More than a feeling: *Boston* / Because the night: *Smith, Patti Group*.
CD . . . . **STDCD 32**
Solitaire / Mar '90 / BMG.
MC . . . . **STDMC 32**
Masterpiece / Mar '90 / BMG.

ROCK POWER.
Tracks: This flight tonight: *Nazareth* / You ain't seen nothin' yet: *Bachman-Turner Overdrive* / Paranoid: *Black Sabbath* / Roll away the stone: *Mott The Hoople* / Rock the night: *Europe* / Whisky in the jar: *Thin Lizzy* / Dont fear the reaper: *Blue Oyster Cult* / Holding out for a hero: *Tyler, Bonnie* / You took the words right out of my mouth: *Meat Loaf* / Free me: *Uriah Heep* / Walking on sunshine: *Rockers Revenge* / who do you love: *Juicy Lucy* / Night games: *Bonnet, Graham* / Shot in the dark: *Osbourne, Ozzy* / Start talking love: *Magnum* / Please don't touch: *Headgirl (1)* / Iron fist: *Motorhead* / I want you to want me: *Cheap Trick*.
CD . . . . **PMP 103**
Pickwick / Nov '92 / Pickwick.

ROCK THE NIGHT (54 Rock And Po Classics From The 70's And 80's).
Tracks: Heat is on: *Frey, Glenn* / Fade to grey *Visage* / More than a feeling: *Boston* / Wishing (If had a photograph of you): *Flock Of Seagulls* / Swee test taboo: *Sade* / Secrets: *Sutherland Brothers* / O Sherrie: *Perry, Steve* / Loving you is sweeter tha ever: *Kamen, Nick* / Dark lady: *Cher* / Heartbea *Johnson, Don* / Rosanna: *Toto* / You are the gir *Cars* / What is love: *Jones, Howard* / Carrie: *Europe* Wide boy: *Kershaw, Nik* / Bring it on home: *Stewar Rod* / Hold on tight: *E.L.O.* / Can't fight this feeling *REO Speedwagon* / Come on Eileen: *Dexy's Mid night Runners* / Roll on down the highway: *Bach man-Turner Overdrive* / Gypsies, tramps & thieves *Cher* / All day and all of the night: *Stranglers* / Luck man: *Emerson, Lake & Palmer* / Morning dance *Spyro Gyra* / Boy from New York City: *Darts (1)* / I'm not in love: *10 CC* / Look away: *Big Country* / Africa *Toto* / Cutter: *Echo & The Bunnymen* / Hold you head up: *Argent* / Spooky: *Atlanta Rhythm Section* Born to be wild: *Steppenwolf* / Ramblin' man: *Allmar Brothers Band* / St. Elmo's fire: *Parr, John* / Stop loving you: *Toto* / 99 red balloons: *Nena* / Tota eclipse of the heart: *Tyler, Bonnie* / Parisienne walk ways: *Moore, Gary* / Gloria: *Branigan, Laura* / Cum on feel the noize: *Slade* / Bat out of hell: *Meat Loaf* Silver dagger: *Oldfield, Sally* / Like to get to know you well: *Jones, Howard* / Eloise: *Damned* / Oh no not my baby: *Stewart, Rod* / Start: *Jam* / Hold me close: *Essex, David* / Take it on the run: *REO Speed wagon* / Goody two shoes: *Adam & The Ants* / Goo gave rock 'n' roll to you: *Argent* / Sun goes down *Level 42*.
CD Set . . . . **BOXD 44**
Pickwick / Jan '94 / Pickwick.

ROCKTASTIC.
Tracks: Not Advised.
CD . . . . **CLACD 999**
Castle / Jul '94 / BMG.

RUBAIYAT.
Tracks: Hello I love you: *Cure* / House of the rising sun: *Chapman, Tracy* / Tokoloshe man: *Happy Mondays* / You're so vain: *Faster Pussycat* / Hotel California: *Gipsy Kings* / Seven and seven is: *Bragg, Billy* / Motorcycle mama: *Sugarcubes* / Born in Chicago: *Pixies* / Marquee moon: *Kronos Quartet* / You belong to me: *Baker, Anita* / I want to make it with you: *Pendergrass, Teddy* / These days: *10,000 Maniacs* / One more parade: *They Might Be Giants*.
CD **7599609402**
■ **LP** . . . . **EKT 78**
■ **MC** . . . . **EKT 78 C**
Elektra / Oct '90.

S

SATAN'S REVENGE.
Tracks: Not Advised.
■ **LP** . . . . **GWD 90536**
MC . . . . **GWC 90536**
New Renaissance(USA) / Nov '87 / Pinnacle.

SCREAM - THE COMPILATION.
Tracks: Not Advised.
■ **LP** . . . . **GHS 24177**
Geffen (USA import) / Nov '87.
■ **LP** . . . . **K 9241771**
Geffen / '88.
■ **MC** . . . . **K 9241774**
Geffen / Mar '88.

SCREAM YOUR BRAINS OUT.
Tracks: Not Advised.
■ **LP** . . . . **UNKNOWN**
Chain Reaction / Jun '88.

SERIAL KILLER VOL.1.
Tracks: Not Advised.
■ **CD** . . . . **RR 90602**
Road Runner / May '93.

SLAVES TO ROCK.
Tracks: Not Advised.
■ **LP** . . . . **IW 1018**
Iron Works (USA) / Dec '87.

SOFT METAL.
Tracks: Not Advised.
CD. SMD 862
■ LP . . . . SMR 862
MC. SMC 862
Stylus / Oct '88.

SOFT METAL - IT AIN'T HEAVY.
Tracks: Not Advised.
VHS . . . . SV 0862
Stylus Video / Sep '89 / EMI / Pinnacle / TBD / Gold &
Sons.

SOFT METAL BALLADS.
Tracks: Not Advised.
CD Set . . . . .ARC 933502
■ Double LP. . . . . .ARC 933501
MC Set . . . . .ARC 933504
Arcade / Mar '91 / Sony / Grapevine Distribution.

SOUNDS ALBUM VOL. 4, THE (The Heavy Metal Album).
Tracks: Back on the road again: REO Speedwagon /
Party: Boston / Boogie no more: Molly Hatchet /
Lady luck / Paralyzed: Nugent, Ted / Exciter: Judas
Priest / Back in the saddle: Aerosmith / Bottom of the
barrel: Marino, Frank & Mahogany Rush / Need a
girl just like you: Derringer, Rick / Too wild to tame:
Boyzz.
■ LP . . . . .CBS 554
CBS / '79.

SOUNDS ALBUM VOL. 5, THE (America Strikes Back).
Tracks: Bad motor scooter: Hagar, Sammy / Ladies
man: April Wine / Narita: Riot / High class in bor-
rowed shoes: Webster, Max / Armageddon: Prism /
White hot: Red Rider / Bad case of loving you: Hoon
Martin / Party professionals: Motels / Savoir faire:
Mink Deville / Big beat: Squier, Billy.
■ LP . . . . SS 5
Capitol / '80.

SOUTHERN ROCK.
Tracks: Ramblin' man: Allman Brothers / Dixie chick-
en: Little Feat / Hold on loosely: .38 Special / Comin'
home: Delaney & Bonnie & Friends / Cold shot:
Vaughan, Stevie Ray / Travellin' shoes: Bishop, El-
vin / Keep on smilin': Wet Willie / Black Oak Arkan-
sas: Dandy, Jim / Flirtin' with disaster: Molly Hatchet
/ Midnight rider: Allman, Greg / So in to you: Atlanta
Rhythm Section / Right place wrong time: Dr. John /
South's gonna do it again: Daniels, Charlie / Cado
queen: Grey, Dobie / Mind bender: Still Water / Tuff
enuff: Fabulous Thunderbirds / Freebird: Lynyrd
Skynyrd.
■ MC. . . . . .CCSMC 322
Castle Collector Series / Feb '92.
■ CD. . . . . .CCSCD 322
Castle Collector Series / Jan '94.

SPEED KILLS VOL. 1.
Tracks: Not Advised.
■ LP . . . . MFN 54
■ MC. . . . . TMFN 54
Music For Nations / Sep '85.

SPEED KILLS VOL. 2.
Tracks: Not Advised.
■ LP . . . . FLAG 2
MC. TFLAG 2
Under One Flag / May '86 / Pinnacle.

SPEED KILLS VOL. 3.
Tracks: Not Advised.
■ LP . . . . .FLAG 17
MC. TFLAG 17
Under One Flag / Oct '87 / Pinnacle.

SPEED KILLS VOL. 4 (Speed Kills but who's Dying?).
Tracks: Not Advised.
CD . . . . .CDFLAG 33
■ LP . . . . .FLAG 33
MC. TFLAG 33
Under One Flag / Jun '89 / Pinnacle.

SPEED KILLS VOL. 5 (Head Crushing Metal).
Tracks: Not Advised.
CD . . . . .CDFLAG 46
LP .FLAG 46
MC. TFLAG 46
Under One Flag / Oct '90 / Pinnacle.

SPEED KILLS VOL. 6.
Tracks: Not Advised.
CD . . . . .CDFLAG 69
LP .FLAG 69
MC. TFLAG 69
Music For Nations / Jul '92 / Pinnacle.

SPEED METAL HELL, VOL.3.
Tracks: Not Advised.
■ LP . . . . NRR 29
New Renaissance(USA) / Aug '87.

STADIUM ROCK.
Tracks: Caroline: Status Quo / Roll over, lay down:
Status Quo / Whatever you want: Status Quo / Rockin' all over the world: Status Quo / Don't waste my
time: Status Quo / Blind before I stop: Meat Loaf /
Modern girl: Meat Loaf / You took the words right out
of my mouth: Meat Loaf / Paradise by the dashboard
light: Meat Loaf / This flight tonight: Nazareth / Love
hurts: Nazareth / Cocaine: Nazareth / Shapes of
things: Nazareth.
■ CD. . . . . XSRCD 3001
BMG / Nov '92.

STADIUM ROCK (2).
Tracks: Honky tonk woman: Cocker, Joe / Cry me a
river: Cocker, Joe / She came through the bathroom
window. Cocker, Joe / Letter: Cocker, Joe / Delta
lady: Cocker, Joe / Girl's talk: Edmunds, Dave /
Queen of Hearts: Edmunds, Dave / Wanderer: Ed-
munds, Dave / Crawling from the wreckage: Ed-
munds, Dave / I hear you knockin': Edmunds, Dave /
I knew the bride (When she used to Rock 'N' Roll):
Edmunds, Dave / Loving is easy: Barclay James
Harvest / Mockingbird: Barclay James Harvest / Life
is for living: Barclay James Harvest / Child of the
universe: Barclay James Harvest / Hymn: Barclay
James Harvest.
■ CD. . . . . XSRCD 3002
BMG / Nov '92.

STADIUM ROCK (3).
Tracks: Ace of spades: Motorhead / Bomber: Motor-
head / Motorhead: Motorhead / Overkill: Motorhead /
No class: Motorhead / Lady in black: Uriah Heep /
Free me: Uriah Heep / Easy livin': Uriah Heep /
Gypsy: Uriah Heep / And the band played on: Saxon
(1) / 747 (Strangers in the night): Saxon (1) / Wheels
of steel: Saxon (1) / Ride like the wind: Saxon (1) /
Rock 'n' roll gypsy: Saxon (1).
■ CD. . . . . XSRCD 3003
BMG / Nov '92.

STAIRWAY TO HEAVEN/HIGHWAY TO HELL.
Tracks: My generation: Gorky Park / Holidays in the
sun: Skid Row (1) / I can't explain: Scorpions / Purple
haze: Osbourne, Ozzy / Teaser: Motley Crue / Boys
are back in town: Bon Jovi / Move over: Cinderella /
Moby Dick: Drum Madness / Medley.
■ CD. 842 093-2
■ LP 842 093-1
■ MC. 842 093-4
Vertigo / Dec '89.

STARS ON THRASH.
Tracks: Not Advised.
■ LP . . . . RR 94981
■ CD. . . . . RR 94982
Road Runner / Oct '88.

STREET SURVIVORS.
Tracks: Down to the wire / Devil in you / Love
injection / Let it ride / Never run / Walk in the woods
/ Too late / Come on / You belong to me / Triangle /
Little Caesar / Black cherry / Bang tango / NRG /
Fire / Tomorrow's child / Sphinx in Cairo / Rain on
fire / Lunatic fringe / Believe it or not.
■ LP . . . . RO 94791
Roadracer / Jul '89.

STRICTLY FOR KONNOISEURS.
Tracks: Not Advised.
■ Double LP. . . . . MFN 32
MC. TMFN 32
Music For Nations / Feb '85 / Pinnacle.

SUB POP 200.
Tracks: Not Advised.
CD . . . . TUPCD 4
Tupelo / Jul '89 / Vital Distribution.
■ LP . . . . GR 0052
Glitterhouse / Jul '89.

SURF AND SKATE RIOT.
Tracks: Not Advised.
LP . . . . MR 005
Munster Records / Apr '92 / Plastic Head.

SWEDEN'S ALTERNATIVE.
Tracks: Not Advised.
CD . . . . RA 91332
Road Runner / Aug '92 / Pinnacle.

SWEDISH METAL.
Tracks: Not Advised.
■ LP . . . . SNTF 929
Sonet / Feb '85.

SWEET RELIEF (A Benefit For Victoria Williams).
Tracks: Summer of drugs: Soul Asylum / Main road:
Williams, Lucinda / Crazy Mary: Pearl Jam / Merry
go round: Buffalo Tom / Lights: Jayhawks / Animal
wild: Shudder To Think / Tarbelly and featherfoot:
Reed, Lou / Opelousas (sweet relief): McKee, Maria
/ This moment: Sweet, Matthew / Frying pan: Lemon-
heads / Weeds: Penn, Michael / Why look at the
moon: Waterboys / Big fish: Giant Sand / Holy spirit:
Shocked, Michelle.
CD. 474199 2
LP .474199 1
MC. 474199 4
Columbia / Aug '93 / Sony.

TASTE OF ARMAGEDDON, A.
Tracks: Path of no return: Treason / Slayer: Demont /
Death right at sunset: Snyper / None so blind: First
Blood / Memories of yesterday: Arbitrator / Madman:
Metal Messiah / Violence is now: Resentment / Dogs
of war: Wreckage / Nothing room: Warpspeed /
Working factory: Purgatory.
■ LP . . . . BBSLP 003
MC. BBSMC 003
Blue Beat / Aug '89 / Pinnacle.

TERROR.
Tracks: Not Advised.
CD. E 06504CD
LP . . . . E 06504
Mental Decay / Apr '93 / SRD.

TEUTONIC INVASION PT.1.
Tracks: Pray to the Godz of wrath / Terminal breath /
Killer without a face / Soulbursting / Planed head /
Final fight / Revelation / Sphinx.
■ LP . . . . RR 9624
Rock Hard / May '87.

THATS LIVE.
Tracks: Not Advised.
■ LP . . . . METALPM 125
Razor / Jul '88.

THRASH METAL ATTACK.
Tracks: Not Advised.
■ LP . . . . NRR 27
New Renaissance(USA) / Aug '87.
MC. NRC 27
MC. NRC 29
New Renaissance(USA) / Nov '87 / Pinnacle.

THRASH METAL SPEED SPECIAL.
Tracks: Not Advised.
VHS . . . . VVD 699
Virgin Vision / May '90 / Gold & Sons / TBD.

THRASH THE WALL.
Tracks: Not Advised.
CD. RR 93932
LP . . . . RR 93931
MC. RR 93934
Road Runner / Mar '90 / Pinnacle.

THRASH TILL DEATH.
Tracks: Not Advised.
■ LP . . . . PUS 0012-17
Pusmort / Mar '88.

TIME TO ROCK.
Tracks: Jailhouse rock: Motley Crue / Bathroom
wall: Faster Pussycat / Never forgive: Raven / Here it
comes: EZO / Cumin' atcha love: Tesla / Start the fire:
Metal Church / Fighting for the world / Breakout:
Frehley, Ace / Shadow of your love / Licence to kill /
Burnt offerings: Testament.
■ CD. 241158 2
■ LP . . . . WX 113
■ MC. . . . . WX 113C
WEA / Jul '87.

TOP GEAR.
Tracks: Jessica: Allman Brothers Band / Killer
queen: Queen / Sharp dressed man: ZZ Top / You
took the words right out of my mouth: Meat Loaf /
Two princes: Spin Doctors / We don't need another

hero (Thunderdome): *Turner, Tina* / More than a feelin': *Boston* / Big log: *Plant, Robert* / Inside: *Stiltskin* / Wishing well: *Free (1)* / Roll away the stone: *Mott The Hoople* / Maggie May: *Stewart, Rod* / Tuff enuff: *Fabulous Thunderbirds* / Because the night: *Smith, Patti* / Call me: *Blondie* / Rhiannon (Will you ever win): *Fleetwood Mac* / You: *Frampton, Peter* / When tomorrow comes: *Eurythmics* / Power of love: *Lewis, Huey & The News* / Do anything you wanna do: *Eddie & The Hot Rods* / 2-4-6-8- Motorway: *Robinson, Tom* / Bad case of loving you (Doctor Doctor): *Palmer, Robert* / Boys are back in town: *Thin Lizzy* / Brown eyed girl: *Morrison, Van* / Rocky mountain way: *Walsh, Joe* / Talking back to the night: *Cocker, Joe* / Show me the way: *Frampton, Peter* / I want you to want me (Live version): *Cheap Trick* / Long train runnin': *Doobie Brothers* / American pie: *McLean, Don (1)* / Black magic woman: *Santana (1)* / Everybody wants to rule the world: *Tears For Fears* / Walk on the wild side: *Reed, Lou* / Wicked game: *Isaak, Chris* / Venus in furs: *Velvet Underground.*
CD. . . . . MOOD CD33
MC. . . . . MOOD C33
Epic / May '94 / Sony.

TOUCH OF DEATH.
Tracks: Perpetual dawn: *Fleshcrawl* / Primeval transubstantation: *Agressor* / Where The Rivers Of Madness Stream: *Cemetary* / Who Will Not Be Dead: *Seance* / Within The Silence: *Rosicrucian* / Excursion demise: *Invocator* / Solace: *Necrosanct* / Born Bizarre: *Tribulation* / Enigma: *Edge Of Sanity* / Blood And Iron: *Bathory.*
CD. . . . . BMCD 026
MC. . . . . .BMCT 026
Black Mark / Sep '92 / Plastic Head.

TRASH ON DELIVERY.
Tracks: Not Advised.
■ LP . . . . SHARP 011
Flicknife / Sep '83.
■ MC. . . . . SHARP 011C
Flicknife / Oct '90.

TRIBUTE TO ROKY ERICKSON (WHERE THE PYRAMID).
Tracks: Reverberation (doubt) / If you have ghosts / I had to tell you / She lives (in a time of her own) / Slip inside this house / You don't love me yet / I have always been here before / You're gonna miss me / It's a cold night for alligators / Fire engine / Bermuda / I walked with a zombie / Earthquake / Don't slander me / Red temple prayer (two headed dog) / Burn the flames / Postures (leave your body behind) / Nothing in return / Splash 1 (Available on MC only) / We sell soul (Available on MC only) / White faces (Available on MC only).
CD. 7599264222
■ MC. 7599264224
Sire / Feb '91.

TRIUMPH OF DEATH.
Tracks: Not Advised.
CD. . . . . TURBO 011CD
Turbo Music / Nov '92 / Plastic Head.

TWELVE COMMANDMENTS IN METAL.
Tracks: Not Advised.
MC. . . . . RR 49799
Road Runner / Oct '85 / Pinnacle.
■ LP . . . . RR 9799
Road Runner / Sep '85.

UK THRASH ASSAULT.
Tracks: Not Advised.
■ LP . . . . CFMT 1
C.F.M.T. / Nov '88.

ULTIMATE REVENGE TOUR.
Tracks: Not Advised.
VHS . . . . NEATVID 002V
Neat / '88 / Grapevine Distribution.

ULTRAMETAL.
Tracks: Not Advised.
CD. . . . . .MONITOR 1
Monitor / Jan '92 / Flexitron Ltd. / C.M. Distribution.

UNDERGROUND USA VOL.3 (Heavy Metal).
Tracks: Not Advised.
■ VHS . . . . HEN 2272
Hendring Video / Oct '90.

UNDERGROUND USA VOL.6 (Heavy metal).
Tracks: Not Advised.
■ VHS . . . . HEN 2275
Hendring Video / Nov '90.

VERY SPECIAL CHRISTMAS 2, A.
Tracks: Christmas all over again: *Petty, Tom & The Heartbreakers* / Jingle bell rock: *Travis, Randy* / Christmas song: *Vandross, Luther* / Santa Claus is coming to town: *Sinatra, Frank & Cyndi Lauper* / Birth of Christ: *Boyz II Men* / Please come home for Christmas: *Bon Jovi, Jon* / What Christmas means to me: *Young, Paul* / O Christmas tree: *Franklin, Aretha* / Rockin' around the Christmas tree: *Spector, Ronnie & Darlene Love* / White Christmas: *Bolton, Michael* / Christmas is: *Run D.M.C.* / Christmas time again: *Extreme* / Merry Christmas baby: *Raitt, Bonnie & Charles Brown* / O holy night: *Campbell, Tevin* / Sleigh ride: *Gibson, Debbie* / What child is this: *Williams, Vanessa* / Blue Christmas: *Wilson, A. & N.* / Silent night: *Wilson Phillips* / I believe in you: *O'Connor, Sinead.*
CD. 540 003-2
A&M / Dec '93 / PolyGram.

VERY SPECIAL CHRISTMAS, A.
Tracks: Santa Claus is coming to town: *Pointer Sisters* / Winter Wonderland: *Eurythmics* / Do you hear what I say: *Houston, Whitney* / Merry Christmas baby: *Springsteen, Bruce & The E Street Band* / Have yourself a merry little Christmas: *Pretenders* / I saw Mommy kissing Santa Claus: *Mellencamp, John Cougar* / Gabriel's message: *Sting* / Christmas in Hollis: *Run D.M.C.* / Christmas (baby please come home): *U2* / Santa baby: *Madonna* / Little drummer boy: *Seger, Bob & The Silver Bullet Band* / Run Rudolph run: *Adams, Bryan* / Back door Santa: *Bon Jovi* / Coventry carol: *Moyet, Alison* / Silent night: *Nicks, Stevie.*
MC. . . . . AMC 3911
■ LP . . . . AMA 3911
A&M / Nov '87.
CD. . . . . CDA 3911
A&M / Dec '93 / PolyGram.

VILE VIBES.
Tracks: Not Advised.
CD. . . . . VILE 15CD
Peaceville / Feb '90 / Vital Distribution / Pinnacle.
■ LP . . . . VILE 15
■ MC . . . . VILE 15MC
Peaceville / Jan '90.

VILE VISIONS.
Tracks: Hope's end: *Decadence Within* / Self respec: *Decadence Within* / Molten tears: *Deviated Instinct* / Dripfeeder: *Deviated Instinct* / Breeding fear: *Para dise Lost* / Paradise lost: *Paradise Lost* / Evolutio: *Axegrinder* / Requienthen: *Axegrinder* / Blind ey: *Instigators* / Eye to eye: *Instigators.*
VHS .JE 20
Jettisoundz / Mar '90 / TBD / Visiona Communications.

WE WILL ROCK YOU.
Tracks: Not Advised.
CD. DINCD 2
LP. DINTV 2
MC. . . . . DINMC 2
Dino / Sep '91 / Pinnacle.

WELCOME TO THE METAL ZONE.
Tracks: Not Advised.
■ LP . . . . MFN 4
MC. . . . . TMFN 4
Music For Nations / Apr '85 / Pinnacle.

WE'VE COME FOR YOUR DAUGHTERS (C/Z Records).
Tracks: Not Advised.
VHS . . . . .ATV 25P
Jettisoundz / Mar '93 / TBD / Visionary Communications.

WHAT THE HELL.
Tracks: Not Advised.
■ CD . . . . HELLCD 014
Hellhound / Mar '92.

WHEELS OF STEEL.
Tracks: Not Advised.
Special . . . . .CPMV 002
Cromwell Productions / Jun '92 / TBD.

WILD AND CRAZY NOISE MERCHANTS.
Tracks: Not Advised.
■ Double LP. 12009
1 In 12 / Nov '90.

WILD ONE, THE.
Tracks: Breakthru: *Queen* / Crazy crazy nights: *Kiss* / Poison: *Cooper, Alice* / Tattooed millionaire: *Dickinson, Bruce* / No more Mr. Nice Guy: *Megadeth* / Dirty love: *Thunder (1)* / Battleship chains: *Georgia Satellites* / Heaven knows: *Plant, Robert* / Hey you: *Quireboys* / Piece of me: *Skid Row (1)* / Real me: *W.A.S.P.* / Kickin' up dust: *Little Angels* / Epic: *Faith No More* / Walk this way: *Run D.M.C.* / Glamour boys: *Living Colour* / Crying: *Vixen.*
■ LP . . . . EMTV 52
■ CD . . . . CDEMTV 52
■ MC. . . . . TCEMTV 52
EMI / Jul '90.

■ DELETED

1 Thing

TOUCH.
Tracks: Not Advised.
LP . . . . **GENR 1**
Generation / Dec '91 / Grapevine Distribution.

2 Tribes

BACK TO LOVE.
Tracks: Back to love / Trap / Back in black (12" & CD single only) / Trance (12" & CD single only).
■ **12"** . . . . **PULSX 2**
■ **7"** . . . . **PULS 2**
■ **CD Single** . . . . **PULSCD 2**
■ **MC Single** . . . . **PULSMC 2**
Compulsion / May '92.

FILE UNDER ROCK.
Tracks: File under rock (Radio edit).
■ **12"** . . . .**.12 PULS 3**
■ **CD Single** . . . .**.CDPULS 3**
Chrysalis / Nov '92.

RACE AGAINST TIME.
Tracks: File under rock / Seattle / Waiting for the truth / What do they want from us / Innocent man / Groove in the right direction / Immigrant song / Trap / Money outta death / Decade.
■ **CD** . . . . **CDNOIS 3**
■ **LP** . . . . **NOIS 3**
■ **MC** . . . . **TCNOIS 3**
Chrysalis / Mar '93.

TWO TRIBES.
Tracks: What do they want from us / Innocent man / Back to love / Waiting for the truth / Decade / Billy Young / File under rock / Groove in the right direction / So long so young / Information assassin / Way of the world / Immigrant song.
■ **CD** . . . . **CCD 1940**
■ **LP** . . . . **NOIS 1**
■ **MC** . . . . **ZNOIS 1**
Compulsion / Apr '92.

WHAT DO THEY WANT US.
Tracks: What do they want from us.
■ **12"** . . . . **PULSX 1**
■ **7"** . . . . **PULS 1**
■ **CD Single** . . . . **PULSCD 1**
Compulsion / Aug '91.
■ **12"** . . . .**.12PULS 5**
■ **7"** . . . . **PULS 5**
■ **CD Single** . . . .**.CDPULS 5**
■ **MC Single** . . . .**.TCPULS 5**
Chrysalis / Feb '93.

7 Year Bitch

LORNA.
Tracks: Not Advised.
■ **7"** . . . . **CZ 045**
C/Z / Nov '92.

SICK 'EM.
Tracks: Not Advised.
CD . . . . **CZ 048CD**
■ **LP** . . . . **CZ 048**
C/Z / Oct '92.

21 Guns

SALUTE.
Tracks: Knee deep / These eyes / Walking / Marching in time / Rain / Little sister / Pays off big / Just a wish / Battered and bruised / Jungleland / Tell me / No way out.
CD **078636101729**
MC **078636101743**
RCA / Jul '92 / BMG.

24-7 Spyz

GRANDMA DYNAMITE.
Tracks: Grandma dynamite / Jimmi'z jam.
■ **12"** . . . . **LONX 246**
■ **7"** . . . .**LON 246**
London / Nov '89.

GUMBO MILLENIUM.
Tracks: John Connelly's theory / New super hero worship / Deathstyle / Dude u knew / Culo posse / Don't push me / Spyz on piano / Valdez 27 million / Don't break my heart / Heaven and hell / We got a date / Dome defenders memories.
■ **CD** **4671202**
■ **LP** **4671201**
■ **MC** **4671204**
Epic / Sep '90.

HARDER THAN YOU.
Tracks: Grandma dynamite / Juni'z jam / Sypz dope / Social plague / I must go on / Ballots not bullets / Jungle boogie / Spill my guts / Sponji reggae / Tango skin polka / Pillage / New drug.
■ **LP** **828 167 1**
■ **CD** **828 167 2**
■ **MC** **828 167 4**
London / Apr '91.

STRENGTH IN NUMBERS.
Tracks: Not Advised.
CD **7567921662**
■ **LP** **7567921661**
MC **7567921664**
Atlantic / Jul '92 / WEA.

THIS IS 24-7 SPYZ.
Tracks: Tick tick tick / Stuntman / My desire / Peace & love / Earthquake.
CD **7567918072**
MC **7567918074**
East West / Nov '91 / WEA.

.38 Special

BONE AGAINST STEEL.
Tracks: Sound of your voice / Signs of love / Last Thing I ever do / You definitely got me / Rebel to rebel / Bone Against Steel / You be the dam / I'll be the water / Jimmy Gillum / Tear it up / Don't wanna get it dirty / Burning Bridges / Can't Shake it / Treasure.
■ **CD** . . . . **CDCUS 6**
■ **LP** **CUSLP6**
■ **MC** **CUSMC6**
Charisma / '92.

CAUGHT UP IN YOU.
Tracks: Caught up in you / Fire starter.
■ **7"** . . . . **AMS 8228**
A&M / Jun '82.

FIRST TIME AROUND.
Tracks: First time around / Rockin' through the night / Fantasy girl.
■ **7"** . . . . **AMS 8155**
A&M / Aug '81.

HOLD LOOSELY.
Tracks: Hold loosely / Throw out the line.
■ **7"** . . . . **AMS 8120**
A&M / Apr '81.

IF I HAD BEEN THE ONE.
Tracks: If I had been the one / 20th century fox.
■ **7"** . . . . **AM 174**
A&M / Jan '84.

LIKE NO OTHER NIGHT.
Tracks: Like no other night.
■ **12"** . . . . **AMY 321**
■ **7"** . . . . **AM 321**
A&M / May '86.

SECOND CHANCE.
Tracks: Second chance / Coming down tonight.
■ **7"** . . . . **AM 507**
A&M / Apr '89.

SPECIAL FORCES.
Tracks: Caught up in you / Back door stranger / Back on the track / Chain lightnin' / Rough housin' / You keep running away / Breakin' loose / Take 'em out / Firestarter.
■ **LP** . . . . **AMLH 64888**
A&M / Jun '82.

STONE COLD BELIEVER.
Tracks: Stone cold believer / Rockin' into the night / Robin Hood (Only on 12" single.).
■ **12"** . . . . **AMSP 7535**
■ **7"** . . . . **AMS 7535**
A&M / Jun '80.

STRENGTH IN NUMBERS.
Tracks: Somebody like you / Like no other night / Last time / Once in a lifetime / Just a little love / Has there ever been a good goodbye / One in a million / Heart's on fire / Against the night / Never give an inch.
■ **LP** . . . . **AMA 5115**
■ **MC** . . . . **AMC 5115**
A&M / May '86.

TOUR DE FORCE.
Tracks: If I'd been the one / Back where you belong / One time for old times / See me in your eyes / Twentieth Century Fox / Long distance affair / I oughta let go / One of the lonely ones / Undercover lover.
■ **LP** . . . . **AMLX 64971**
■ **MC** . . . . **CXM 64971**
A&M / Feb '84.
CD **394 971 2**
A&M / '88 / PolyGram.

WILD EYED SOUTHERN BOYS.
Tracks: Hold on loosely / First time around / Wild eyed southern boys / Back alley Sally / Fantasy girl / Hittin' and running / Honky tonk dancer / Throw out the line / Bring it on.
■ **LP** . . . . **AMLH 64835**
A&M / Apr '81.

YOU KEEP RUNNIN' AWAY.
Tracks: You keep runnin' away / Prisoners of rock 'n' roll.
■ **7"** . . . . **AMS 8246**
A&M / Aug '82.

44 Magnum

DANGER.
Tracks: Not Advised.
■ **LP** . . . . **RR 9805**
Road Runner / Jan '85.

STREET ROCK 'N' ROLLER.
Tracks: Not Advised.
■ **LP** . . . . **RR 9816**
Road Runner / Nov '84.

1000 Homo D.J's

APATHY.
Tracks: Apathy / Better ways.
■ **12"** . . . . **WAX 032**
Wax Trax / Mar '89.

SUPERNAUT.
Tracks: Not Advised.
CD . . . . **CDDVN 5M**
MC . . . . **TDVN 5M**
Mini LP . . . . **DVN 5M**
Devotion / Feb '92 / Pinnacle.

USEFUL ADDRESSES

PERIODICALS

Kerrang!
Frequency: Weekly
Format: A4 glossy
Editor: Phil Alexander
Publisher: EMAP Metro
52-55 Carnaby Street
London
W1V 1PF
Tel: 0171-437 8050
Fax: 0171-734 2287

Metal Hammer
Frequency: Monthly
Format: A4 glossy
Editor: Kirk Blows
Publisher: Dennis Publishing
19 Bolsover Street
London
W1P 7HJ
Tel: 0171-631 1433
Fax: 0171-580 6430

RAW
Frequency: Twice monthly
Format: A4 glossy
Editor: Jon Hotten
Publisher: EMAP Metro
52-55 Carnaby Street
London
W1V 1PF
Tel: 0171-437 8050
Fax: 0171-734 2287

OTHER NATIONAL MEDIA

Headbangers Ball
Weekly satellite TV show
Producer/Presenter: Vanessa Warwick
MTV Europe
Hawley Crescent
Camden
London
NW1 8TT

Noisy Mothers
Weekly terrestrial TV show
Producer/Presenter: Ann Kirk
Presenter: Steve "Krusher" Joule
Music Box
247-257 Euston Road
London
NW1 2HY

Radio 1FM Rock Show
Weekly radio show
Presenter: Claire Sturgess
Producer: Tony Wilson
BBC Radio 1FM
Broadcasting House
London
W1A 1AA

RECORD LABELS

Alternative Tentacles
64 Mountgrove Road
London
N5 2LT
Tel: 0171-354 5455
Fax: 0171-359 2232

Earache Records
Suite 1-3 Westminster Building
Theatre Square
Nottingham
Notts
NG1 6LG
Tel: (01602) 506400
Fax: (01602) 508585

FM/Revolver/Heavy Metal Records
152 Goldthorn Hill
Penn
Wolverhampton
West Midlands
WV2 3JA
Tel: (01902) 345345
Fax: (01902) 345155

Music For Nations
333 Latimer Road
London
W10 6RA
Tel: 0181-964 9544

Neat Records
71 High Street East
Wallsend
Newcastle
Tyne & Wear
NE28 7RJ
Tel: 0191-262 4999
Fax: 0191-263 7082

Noise Records
10 Tariff Street
Manchester
M1 2FF
Tel: 0161-237 1672

Peaceville Records
PO Box 17
Dewsbury
West Yorkshire
WF12 8AA
Tel: (01924) 467929
Fax: (01924) 455120

Razor Records
1A Yeomans Row
London
SW3 2AL
Tel: 0171-584 9939

Receiver Records
2nd Floor
Twyman House
31-39 Camden Road
London
NW1 9LF
Tel: 0171-267 6899
Fax: 0171-267 6746

Road Runner Records
Suites W & T
Tech West Centre
10 Warple Way
Acton
London
W3 0UL
Tel: 0181-749 2984

Sub-Pop
1932 1st Avenue
Suite 1103
Seattle
WA 98101
U.S.A.

Vinyl Solution
231 Portobello Road
London
W11 1LT
Tel: 0171-792 9791
Fax: 0171-792 9871

MAIN DISTRIBUTORS

BMG
Bedford House
69-79 Fulham High Street
London
SW6 3JW
Tel: 0171-973 0011
Fax: 0171-973 0354